D1257866

ANIMAL PARASITES:
Their Biology and Life Cycles

SECOND EDITION

O. WILFORD OLSEN, A. B., M. A., Ph. D.

Head, Department of Zoology
Colorado State University
Fort Collins, Colorado

Illustrations by the author

Burgess Publishing Company
426 South Sixth Street • Minneapolis, Minn. 55415

Library of Congress Catalog Card Number 62-17053

DEDICATION

To my students of the past who have inspired me to learn how to teach parasitology in a more interesting and informative manner, as well as to those of the future who may rightly expect similar treatment of this fascinating subject, and to my wife, Ione Palfreyman Olsen, who encouraged me to do it for them.

PREFACE

The objective of this work is to introduce the principles of parasitism in a stimulating and readily understandable manner to students interested in the biological sciences.

The basic principles set forth are those of morphology, classification, ecology, biology, host specificity, and evolution of parasites. Pathology is treated indirectly through the graphic presentations which indicate where diseased conditions result due to the migrations of larval stages or the presence of adults. Immunity and physiology are treated in a very limited manner.

Medication of hosts for the removal of parasites is not included because it is beyond the intent of this book. Prophylactic measures to limit or avoid infection of hosts, on the other hand, become self-evident as the understanding of the biology of the parasites develops.

The selection of the parasites was done with an eye to the common North American species that illustrate the different types of life cycles, the variations within them, and the basic principles of parasitism. In some instances, the choice was limited by the information available. In most of them, however, it remained to the discretion of the author to choose from several different ones. In addition to the life cycle illustrated on each plate, those of related species are presented in the text. The total number of life cycles considered in the book therefore greatly exceeds that figured, yet each illustration serves as a type for all the related forms.

Illustrations of the parasites are free-hand reproductions by the author of drawings selected from the parasitological literature and used through the courtesy and permission of the publishers and authors. Full acknowledgment of the source of material appearing on each plate is given. The information for developing the life cycles was taken from the published accounts of many authors, as acknowledged in the selected references.

The plan followed for the presentation of each species is the same throughout the book, thus facilitating its use and comprehension of the subject and its relationships.

The book may be used as a text for a course in parasitology based on the biological principles, or in conjunction with other texts to supply additional information on life cycles.

The prototype of this book in the form of multicolored plates produced by hectograph has been used over a number of years in the author's classes in parasitology as an aid to understanding the complexities of the life cycles of protozoan and helminth parasites. The enthusiasm with which the plates have been received by the students led to the preparation of this book in the hope that it would be useful to others interested in parasitology.

The task of preparing the book was undertaken through the encouragement of colleagues in parasitology and my graduate students. To each of these persons, together with our librarians, appreciation is expressed for his or her particular support and help. An especially great debt of gratitude is acknowledged to my wife, Ione Palfreyman Olsen, for encouragement and forbearance during the seemingly endless months of preparation of the text, for help in proofreading and preparing the index, and unstinted assistance in numerous ways.

The courtesies extended by the publishers of numerous books and periodicals and by parasitologists from all over the world have made this book possible. To each of them goes an expression of warm gratitude.

Much credit is due the staff of the Burgess Publishing Company for suggestions, ideas, editing, and craftsmanship necessary to bring this work to fruition in a pleasing and artistic form.

O. Wilford Olsen
Colorado State University
Fort Collins, Colorado

PREFACE TO SECOND EDITION

The second edition of "Animal Parasites" follows the original in presenting basic morphology, classification, ecology, and detailed illustrations of life cycles of parasitic protozoans and helminths. It is designed for students in classes in parasitology and all who have occasion to seek information on the life cycles of these parasites.

Much new material has been added in order more adequately to represent typical life cycles, especially those of the Protozoa. Plates on the morphological characteristics of adult and larval forms of each major group and subgroups within them are included. These will enable students to visualize the differences among the related groups. Two plates containing diagnostic illustrations of the shells of representatives of common families of North American fresh-water and land snails have been added in order to provide students an acquaintanceship with the first intermediate hosts of digenetic trematodes. New information on life cycles and additional references have been incorporated. The illustrations are free-hand drawings selected from many sources and adapted to the style used in the book. Acknowledgment of all sources is made.

No attempts are made to include information on the subjects of physiology and immunology. Pathology caused by parasites is not discussed as such; however, the graphic life cycles indicate where much of it occurs owing to the migrations of the parasites and their locations in the cells, tissues, and organs.

Grateful acknowledgment is due Dr. William C. Marquardt, Department of Zoology, and Dr. Charles P. Hibler, Department of Pathology, College of Veterinary Medicine, Colorado State University, for their painstaking proofreading and editing of the manuscript and to Mrs. Hazel B. Kautz, departmental secretary, for proof-reading, editing, and typing.

Appreciation is expressed to the librarians of Colorado State University for their assistance in obtaining the necessary literature and to the publishers of books and journals for generously permitting use of printed material.

Finally, the author is grateful to the staff of Burgess Publishing Company for their assistance, skill, and taste in producing a book that is pleasing and artistic in appearance and usuable in its design.

O. Wilford Olsen

CONTENTS

Preface i
Preface to second edition iii

PART I. PARASITISM 1

Development of parasitism 1
Ecology of parasitism 2
Kinds of parasites 2
Properties of parasitism 3
Effects of parasitism on the evolution of the host species 5
Evolutionary effects of parasitism 6
Life cycles of parasites 6
Selected references 7

PART II. PHYLUM PROTOZOA 9

Subphylum Plasmodroma 10
Class Mastigophora 10
Order Rhizomastigina 10
Family Mastigamoebidae 10
Histomonas meleagridis 10
Order Protomonadina 11
Family Trypanosomatidae 11
Leptomonas ctenocephali 12
Crithidia gerridis 12
Herpetomonas muscarum 12
Phytomonas davidi 12
Leishmania 14, 16
Trypanosomes of mammals 17
SECTION A
I. The *lewisi* group 17
Trypanosoma lewisi 17
Trypanosoma cruzi 18
SECTION B
I. The *vivax* group 22
Trypanosoma vivax 22
II. The *congolense* group 22
Trypanosoma congolense 22
III. The *brucei-evansi* group 23
A. The *brucei* subgroup 23
Trypanosoma gambiense 23
B. The *evansi* subgroup 24
Trypansomes of birds, reptiles, amphibians, and fish 26
Leishmania 28
Leishmania donovani 28
Family Cryptobiidae 29
Cryptobia helicis 29
Trypanoplasma borrelli 31
Family Bodonidae 33
Proteromonas lacertae 33
Order Polymastigina 34
Suborder Monomonadina 36
Family Tetramitidae 36
Costia necatrix 36
Family Chilomastigidae 38
Chilomastix mesnili 38
Family Trichomonadidae 39
Tritrichomonas foetus 39
Trichomonas spp. 43
Suborder Diplomonadina 43
Family Hexamitidae 43
Hexamita spp. 43
Octomitus 46
Giardia lamblia 46
Class Sarcodina 49
Family Endamoebidae 49
Endamoeba 49
Entamoeba 49
Iodamoeba 49
Endolimax 49
Dientamoeba 49
Hydramoeba 49
Schizamoeba 50
Entamoeba histolytica 50
Class Sporozoa 52
Evolutionary development of some sporozoan parasites 56
Subclass Telosporidia 53
Order Gregarinida 53
Suborder Eugregarinina 53
TRIBE ACEPHALINA 54
Family Monocystidae 54
Monocystis lumbrici 54
Family Diplocystidae 60
Lankesteria culicis 60
Suborder Schizogregarinina 62
Family Schizocystidae 63

Schizocystis gregarinoides 63
TRIBE CEPHALINA 63
Family Gregarinidae 64
Gregarina blattarum 64
Order Coccidia 66
Suborder Eimeridia 68
Selenococcidium 68
Eimeria 68
Aggregata 68
Schellackia 68
Family Selenococcididae 68
Selenococcidium intermedium 68
Family Eimeriidae 69
Eimeria tenella 69
Family Aggregatidae 74
Aggregata eberthi 74
Family Lankesterellidae 76
Schellackia bolivari 76
Suborder Adeleidea 77
Family Adeleidae 78
Adelina cryptocerci 78
Family Hepatozoidae 82
Hepatozoon muris 83
Family Haemogregarinidae 84
Haemogregarina stepanowi 84
Karyolysis lacertae 88
Order Haemosporidia 89
Family Plasmodiidae 90
Plasmodium vivax 90
Plasmodium of birds 95
Host-parasite specificity 95
Geographic distribution 95
Morphology of parasites and their effect on blood cells 95
Family Haemoproteidae 96
Haemoproteus 98
Haemoproteus columbae 98
Leucocytozoon 101
Leucocytozoon simondi 101
Family Babesiidae 104
Babesia 104
Babesia bigemina 104
Theileria 108
Theileria parva 108
Toxoplasma 109
Toxoplasma gondii 109
Subclass Acnidosporida 114
Order Sarcosporidia 114
Sarcocystis 114
Subclass Cnidosporidia 116
Order Myxosporidia 118
Family Myxosomatidae 118
Myxosoma cerebralis 118
Family Myxobolidae 119
Myxobolus notemigoni 119
Family Myxidiidae 120
Myxidium spp. 120
Sphaeromyxa spp. 120
Family Ceratomyxidae 122
Ceratomyxia blennius 122
Order Actinomyxidia 122
Triactinomyxon ignotum 122
Order Microsporidia 122
Suborder Moncnidina 123
Family Nosematidae 123
Nosema 123
Nosema apis 123
Nosema bombycis 124
Nosema helminthorum 124
Glugea anomala 126
Glugea hertwigi 126
Suborder Dicnidina 126
Family Telomyxidae 126
Telomyxa glugeiformis 126
Order Helicosporidia 126
Helicosporidium parasiticum 126
Subphylum Ciliophora
Class Ciliata
Subclass Protociliata
Family Opalinidae
Opalina
Opalina ranarum
Order Spirotricha
Suborder Heterotricha
Family Balantidiidae
Balantidium
Balantidium coli
Subclass Euciliata
Order Holotricha
Family Holophryidae
Ichthyophthirius
Ichthyophthirius multifiliis
Family Spirostomidae
Nyctotherus
Nyctotherus cordiformis

PART III. PHYLUM PLATYHELMINTHES

General considerations 139
Class Trematoda 139
Subclass Monogenea 139
Order Monopisthocotylea 139
Family Dactylogyridae 139
Dactylogyrus vastator 139
Order Polyopisthocotylea 142
Family Polystomatidae 142
Sphyranura oligorchis 142
Polystoma nearcticum 144
Subclass Aspidobothrea 148
Family Aspidogasteridae 148
Aspidogaster conchicola 148
Subclass Digenea 149
General classification 150
General characteristics of Digenea 153
Adult flukes 53
Cercariae 53
Morphology and life history stages of Digenetic trematodes 158
Freshwater snails 162
Land snails 164
Superorder Anepitheliocystidia 167
Order Strigeatida 167
Superfamily Strigeoidea 167
Family Strigeidae 167
Cotylurus flabelliformis 168
Family Diplostomatidae 170

Uvulifer ambloplitis 171
Diplostomum baeri eucaliae 172
Alaria canis 176
Superfamily Clinostomatoidea 179
Family Clinostomatidae 179
Clinostomum complanatum 179
Superfamily Schistosomatoidea 180
Family Schistosomatidae 180
Subfamily Schistosomatinae 182
Schistosomatium douthitti 182
Subfamily Bilharziellinae 186
Trichobilharzia cameroni 186
Family Spirorchiidae 189
Spirorchis parvus 189
Family Sanguinicolidae 192
Cardicola davisi 192
Suborder Brachylaemata 194
Superfamily Brachylaemoidea 194
Family Brachylaemidae 194
Postharmostomum helicus 195
Superfamily Bucephaloidea 196
Family Bucephalidae 196
Bucephalus elegans 196
Order Echinostomida 200
Suborder Echinostomata 200
Superfamily Echinstomatoidea 200
Family Echinostomatidae 200
Echinostoma revolutum 200
Family Fasciolidae 201
Fasciola hepatica 202
Suborder Paramphistomata 206
Superfamily Paramphistomatoidea 206
Family Paramphistomatidae 206
Paramphistomum cervi 206
Stichorchis subtriquetrus 207
Family Diplodiscidae 208
Megalodiscus temperatus 208
Superfamily Notocotyloidea 214
Family Notocotylidae 214
Quinqueserialis quinqueserialis 214
Superorder Epitheliocystida 216
Order Plagiorchiida 216
Suborder Plagiorchiata 216
Superfamily Plagiorchioidea 216
Family Dicrocoeliidae 217
Dicrocoelium dendriticum 217
Family Plagiorchiidae 220
Plagiorchis muris 220
Haematoloechus medioplexus 223
Haplometrana utahensis 226
Lechriorchus primus 229
Family Prosthogonimidae 230
Prosthogonimus macrorchis 232
Superfamily Allocreadioidea 234
Family Allocreadiidae 234
Crepidostomum cooperi 234
Plagioporus sinitsini 236
Family Gorgoderidae 240
Gorgodera amplicava 240
Family Troglotrematidae 243
Paragonimus kellicotti 243
Nanophyetus salmincola 246
Order Opisthorchiida 247
Suborder Opisthorchiata 248
Superfamily Opisthorchioidea 248
Family Heterophyidae 248
Apophallus venustus 248
Family Opisthorchiidae 252
Metorchis conjunctus 252
Suborder Hemiurata 255
Superfamily Hemiuroidea 255
Family Halipegidae 255
Halipegus eccentricus 255
Class Cestoda 258
Morphological types 258
Order Caryophyllidea 262
Family Caryophyllaeidae 262
Archigetes sieboldi 262
Glaridacris catastomus 264
Order Pseudophyllidea 266
Family Dibothriocephalidae 266
Dibothriocephalus latus 266
Order Proteocephala 268
Family Proteocephalidae 269
Proteocephalus ambloplitis 269
Order Cyclophyllidea 270
Family Taeniidae 270
Taenia solium 270
Taeniarhynchus saginatus 272
Echinococcus granulosus 274
Life cycles of some common taenioid cestodes of dogs and cats 276
Families of Cyclophyllidea other than Taeniidae 280
Family Dilepididae 280
Dipylidium caninum 280
Family Davaineidae 282
Davainea proglottina 282
Raillietina 283
Raillietina (S.) cesticillus 283
Raillietina (R.) echinobothrida 283
Raillietina (R.) tetragona 283
Family Hymenolepidiidae 284
Hymenolepis carioca 284
Drepanidotaenia lanceolata 286
Hymenolepis fraterna 288
Family Anoplocephalidae 292
Moniezia expansa 292

PART IV. PHYLUM ACANTHOCEPHALA 297

Classification 298
Order Archiacanthocephala 300
Family Oligacanthocephalidae 300
Macracanthorhynchus hirudinaceus 302
Family Moniliformidae 304
Moniliformis dubius 304
Order Palaeacanthocephala 308
Family Rhadinorhynchidae 308
Leptorhynchoides thecatus 308
Order Eoacanthocephala 311
Family Neoechinorhynchidae 311
Neoechinorhynchus cylindratus 311
Resume of acanthocephalan life cycles 314

PART V. PHYLUM NEMATHELMINTHES 315

Classification 315
Morphological characteristics of nematodes 317
Reproductive systems 318
Life cycles 322
Class Secernentea 322
Order Rhabditida 322
Suborder Rhabditina 323
Superfamily Rhabditoidea 323
Family Strongyloididae 323
Strongyloides papillosa 323
Suborder Strongylina 326
Superfamily Strongyloidea 326
Family Ancylostomatidae 326
Ancylostoma caninum 326
Uncinaria lucasi 327
Family Strongylidae 332
Oesophagostomum columbianum 333
Stephanurus dentatus 334
Genus Strongylus 338
Strongylus edentatus 338
Strongylus equinus 338
Strongylus vulgaris 339
Syngamus trachea 340
Superfamily Trichostrongyloidea 344
Family Trichostrongylidae 344
Haemonchus contortus 344
Ostertagia circumcincta 345
Trichostrongylus colubriformis 346
Superfamily Metastrongyloidea 348
Family Metastrongylidae 348
Dictyocaulus filaria 348
Protostrongylus rufescens 349
Muellerius capillaris 349
Metastrongylus apri 352
Suborder Ascaridina 354
Superfamily Oxyuroidea 354
Family Oxyuridae 354
Enterobius vermicularis 354
Superfamily Ascaroidea 355
Family Heterakidae 355
Heterakis gallinae 355
Ascaridia galli 358
Family Ascaridae 360
Ascaris lumbricoides 360
Toxocara canis 361
Contracaecum 366
Contracaecum aduncum 366
Order Spirurida 368
Suborder Camallanina 369
Superfamily Dracunculoidea 369
Family Dracunculidae 369
Dracunculus medinensis 369
Suborder Spirurina 370
Superfamily Spiruroidea 372
Family Thelaziidae 372
Oxyspirura mansoni 372
Family Spiruridae 374
Habronema megastoma 374
Family Tetrameridae 376
Tetrameres crami 376
Family Ascaropidae 378
Ascarops strongylina 380
Family Physalopteridae 382
Physaloptera phrynosoma 382
Superfamily Filarioidea 385
Family Diplotriaenidae 385
Diplotriaenoides translucidus 385
Family Onchocercidae 388
Litomosoides carinii 388
Dirofilaria immitis 390
Family Dipetalonematidae 392
Genus *Foleyella* 392
Foleyella brachyoptera 394
Class Adenophorea 397
Order Enoplida 397
Suborder Enoplina 397
Superfamily Trichuroidea 397
Family Trichuridae 397
Trichuris ovis 398
Capillaria annulata 400
Capillaria hepatica 402
Capillaria plica 405
Family Trichinellidae 406
Trichinella spiralis 406
Suborder Dioctophymatina 410
Superfamily Dioctophymoidea 410
Family Dioctophymatidae 411
Dioctophyma renale 411

LIST OF PLATES

PLATE

1 *Histomonas meleagridis* 13
2 *Genera of Trypanosomatidae and Their Basic Life Cycles* 15
3 *Trypanosoma lewisi* 19
4 *Trypanosoma cruzi* 21
5 *Trypanosomes of the vivax (I), congolense (II), and brucei-evansi (III) groups* 25
6 *Trypanosoma percae* 27
7 *Leishmania donovani* 31
8 *Cryptobia helicis, Trypanoplasma borreli, Chilomastix mesnili* 33
9 *Proteromonas lacertae* 35
10 *Costia necatrix* 37
11 *Tritrichomonas foetus* 41
12 *Hexamita ovatus, H. intestinalis, H. muris, H. salmonis, Octomitis pulcher* 45
13 *Giardia agilis, G. muris, G. lamblia* 47
14 *Endamoebidae (nuclei)* 51
15 *Entamoeba histolytica* 55
16 *Summary of Evolutionary Development of Some Sporozoan Parasites* 57
17 *Monocystis lumbrici* 59
18 *Lankesteria culicis* 61
19 *Schizocystis gregarinoides* 65
20 *Gregarina blattarum* 67
21 *Selenococcidium intermedium* 71
22 *Eimeria tenella* 73
23 *Aggregata eberthi* 75
24 *Schellackia bolivari* 79
25 *Adelina cryptocerci* 81
26 *Hepatozoon muris* 85
27 *Haemogregarina stepanowi* 87
28 *Karyolysus lacertae* 91
29 *Plasmodium vivax* 93
30 *Morphological Features Used to Identify Species of Plasmodium in Birds* 97
31 *Haemoproteus columbae* 99
32 *Leucocytozoon simondi* 103
33 *Babesia bigemina* 107
34 *Theileria parva* 111
35 *Toxoplasma gondii* 113
36 *Sarcocystis tenella* 117
37 *Myxosporidian Types* 121
38 *Microsporidian Types, Nosema apis* 125
39 *Balantidium coli* 127
40 *Ichthyophthirius multifiliis* 131
41 *Nyctotherus cordiformis* 135
42 *Opalina ranarum, Zelleriella elliptica, Cepedea cantabrigensis, and Protoopalina mitotica* 137
43 *Types of Common Monogenetic Trematodes* 141
44 *Dactylogyrus vastator* 143
45 *Sphyranura oligorchis* 145
46 *Polystoma nearcticum* 147
47 *Aspidogaster conchicola* 151
48 *Morphological Types of Adult Digenetic Trematodes* 155

PLATE

49 *Cercarial Types* 157
50 *Morphology and Life History Stages of Digenetic Trematodes* 161
51 *Some Families of Common Fresh-water Snails of North America* 163
52 *Some Families of Common Land Snails of North America* 165
53 *Cotylurus flabelliformis* 169
54 *Uvulifer ambloplitis* 173
55 *Diplostomum baeri eucaliae* 175
56 *Alaria canis* 177
57 *Clinostomum complanatum* 181
58 *Schistosomatium douthitti* 183
59 *Trichobilharzia cameroni* 187
60 *Spirorchis parvus* 191
61 *Cardicola davisi* 193
62 *Postharmostomum helicus* 197
63 *Bucephalus elegans* 199
64 *Echinostoma revolutum* 203
65 *Fasciola hepatica* 205
66 *Paramphistomum cervi* 209
67 *Stichorchis subtriquetrus* 211
68 *Megalodiscus temperatus* 213
69 *Quinqueserialis quinqueserialis* 215
70 *Dicrocoelium dendriticum* 219
71 *Plagiorchis muris* 221
72 *Haematoloechus medioplexus* 225
73 *Haplometrana utahensis* 227
74 *Lechriorchis primus* 231
75 *Prosthogonimus macrorchis* 233
76 *Crepidostomum cooperi* 237
77 *Plagioporus sinitsini* 239
78 *Gorgodera amplicava* 241
79 *Paragonimus kellicotti* 245
80 *Nanophyetus salmincola* 249
81 *Apophallus venustus* 251
82 *Metorchis conjunctus* 253
83 *Halipegus eccentricus* 257
84 *Some Representative Life Cycles of Digenetic Trematodes* 259
85 *Morphological Types* 261
86 *Archigetes sieboldi* 263
87 *Glaridacris castastomus* 265
88 *Dibothriocephalus latus* 267
89 *Proteocephalus ambloplitis* 271
90 *Taenia solium* 273
91 *Taeniarhynchus saginatus* 275
92 *Echinococcus granulosus* 277
93 *Resumé of Life Cycles of Some Taenioid Cestodes of Dogs and Cats* 279
94 *Dipylidium caninum* 281
95 *Davainea proglottina* 285
96 *Rallietina (S.) cesticillus, R. (R.) echinobothrida, R. (R.) tetragona* 287
97 *Hymenolepis carioca* 289
98 *Drepanidotaenia lanceolata* 291
99 *Hymenolepis nana fraterna* 293
100 *Moniezia expansa* 295

PLATE

101 *Common Orders of Cestodes Summary of Life Cycles of Three* 296
102 *Morphological Characteristics of Acanthocephala* 301
103 *Morphological Characteristics of Acanthocephala* 303
104 *Macracanthorhynchus hirudinaceus* 305
105 *Moniliformis dubius* 307
106 *Leptorhynchoides thecatus* 309
107 *Neoechinorhynchus cylindricus* 313
108 *Basic Morphology and Stages of Development of Nematodes* 319
109 *Morphological Characteristics of Superfamilies of Nematodes* 321
110 *Strongyloides papillosus* 325
111 *Ancylostoma caninum and A. braziliensis* 329
112 *Uncinaria lucasi* 331
113 *Oesophagostomum columbianum* 335
114 *Stephanurus dentatus* 337
115 *Strongylus edentatus, S. equinus, and S. vulgaris* 341
116 *Syngamus trachea* 343
117 *Haemonchus contortus, Ostertagia circumcincta, Trichostrongylus colubriformis* 347
118 *Dictyocaulus filaria, Protostrongylus rufescens, Muellerius capillaria* 351
119 *Metastrongylus apri* 353

PLATE

120 *Enterobius vermicularis* 357
121 *Heterakis gallinae, Ascaridia galli* 359
122 *Ascaris lumbricoides* 363
123 *Toxocara canis* 365
124 *Contracaecum aduncum* 367
125 *Dracunculus medinensis* 371
126 *Oxyspirura mansoni* 373
127 *Habronema megastoma, H. microstoma, H. muscosae* 377
128 *Tetrameres crami* 379
129 *Physocephalus sexalatus, Ascarops strongylina* 381
130 *Physaloptera phrynosoma* 383
131 *Diplotriaenoides translucida* 387
132 *Litomosoides carinii* 389
133 *Dirofilaria immitis* 393
134 *Foleyella brachyoptera* 395
135 *Trichuris ovis* 399
136 *Capillaria annulata* 401
137 *Capillaria hepatica* 403
138 *Capillaria plica* 407
139 *Trichinella spiralis* 409
140 *Dicotophyma renale* 413
141 *Summary of Direct Life Cycles of Some Nematodes* 414
142 *Summary of Indirect Life Cycles of Some Nematodes* 415

PART I PARASITISM

Animal parasitism is a way of life in which one species, the *parasite*, living in or on another species, the *host*, gains its livelihood at the expense of the latter. The host furnishes both the habitat and the food for the parasites which are physiologically dependent on it for life. Moreover, the parasite always does damage in some degree to its host.

Parasitology is the study of parasitism. It includes the morphology, classification, biology, and physiology of the parasites. In addition to these, it involves the relationships between them and their hosts, as well as the reactions toward each other. Its purpose is to lead to a fuller understanding of these relationships and the results of them on both the host and the parasite.

DEVELOPMENT OF PARASITISM

As phylogenetic groups of animals appeared in the beginning of our planet, they spread throughout the world, occupying all the available ecological niches of the physical environment. Their bodies, both inside and outside, constituted new ecological biohabitats ready for occupancy by those species that possessed the potential and capability of adapting to them. Many different phylogenetic groups of animals invaded this new living habitat but few were capable of adapting to it in a large measure of success. The protozoa, the helminths, and some of the arthropods were the most successful. They constitute the important groups of parasites known today. This biotic association is one of *symbiosis* in which animals live together in varying degrees of dependency between the *host* and the *symbiont*.

SYMBIOTIC RELATIONSHIPS. Three degrees of symbiosis are generally recognized. They are *mutualism*, *commensalism*, and *parasitism*.

Mutualism constitutes one type of relationship in which the host and the symbionts are physiologically dependent upon each other and mutually beneficial. Termites and their intestinal protozoa are an example. The termites provide the habitat and the food in the form of wood (cellulose) which they cannot digest. The protozoa in the intestinal habitat, however, are capable of hydrolyzing the wood for their own and the termites' use. Ruminants and other herbivores with their rich flora of bacteria and fauna of protozoa are additional examples of mutualism wherein both the host and the symbionts are physiologically dependent on each other.

Commensalism is the condition in which the host provides the habitat and food for its symbionts which live without benefit or harm to it. The symbionts, however, are physiologically dependent on the host for their existence. The host, on the other hand, is not dependent on them. Certain of the protozoans living in the alimentary canal of man or on the bodies of hydra are examples of commensals. Other examples of commensalism appear among the marine animals, particularly sea anemones and crabs.

Parasitism is that relationship in which the symbiont is both physiologically dependent on the host for its habitat and sustenance and at the same time may be harmful to it. All of the trematodes, cestodes, acanthocephalans, and many of the protozoans and nematodes are examples of true animal parasites.

ECOLOGY OF PARASITISM

These symbiotic relationships between animals and their biotic habitats are a phase of ecology. Parasitology embodies the study of the relationships existing between the parasite and its environments, both physical and biotic. These relationships are multiple and complex, and the requirements for adaptation in each are different.

PHYSICAL ENVIRONMENT. The physical environment of parasites is similar to that of the free-living organisms. The requirements of the free-living stages of the parasites in it are much like those of the non-parasitic animals. There must be protection against desiccation and unfavorable temperatures. These are met through the development of cysts, thick coverings on the eggs, and retention of the cast cuticle of larvae. The moisture, oxygen, and temperature in the microenvironment must be adequate to assure survival and the development necessary for the parasite to infect the host. Food from the environment may or may not be necessary.

BIOTIC ENVIRONMENT. The biotic environment of parasites consists of all parts of the host's body. Each of the specific areas constitutes a microhabitat to which the parasite is adapted in a special way. It is often necessary for it to pass through several microhabitats in order to reach the definitive one. Five major biotic environments may be recognized. They are the outside of the body, the body cavities, organ systems, tissues, and cells. Examples of animals living in these environments are numerous and well known.

Fleas, lice, leeches, and monogenetic trematodes live on the outside of the body. Some of them occupy only specific areas, whereas others are distributed widely over the body.

Of the organ systems, the alimentary canal is inhabited by the greatest variety of species. Specific areas within it are occupied by certain species, as no single one is able to establish itself in all parts. Many others must enter it in order to reach definitive sites in the body. Other organ systems inhabited by parasites include the liver, lungs, and blood vessels. Examples of parasites in them are liver, lung, and blood flukes, and lung and kidney worms. Some adult filarioids live in the coelom of vertebrates. Larval trematodes, cestodes, acanthocephalans, and nematodes occur in the haemocoel of invertebrates.

Tissues are occupied by many species of parasites. Adult dracunculid and filarioid nematodes live in the subcutaneous tissues. Larval stages of trematodes, cestodes, and nematodes are found commonly in the subcutaneous and muscle tissues.

Protozoan parasites infect cells. *Eimeria* occurs in epithelial cells of the alimentary canal and the biliary ducts. *Plasmodium* is found in the erythrocytes and liver cells, *Leishmania* in the leucocytes, and *Toxoplasma* in the nerve and reticuloendothelial cells.

The stages of parasites living on or in the bodies of their hosts are confronted with new problems of survival. They must evolve by means of natural selection protective measures against the digestive processes in the stomach and intestine, and the immunological reactions of the host in all parts of the body.

KINDS OF PARASITES

The degree to which parasites are dependent on their hosts ranges from intermittent visits for food, as in the case of mosquitoes, to one of complete dependence inside the body with no free-living stage, as occurs in the plasmodia and trichinella. Several groups of parasites are recognized, depending on their relationship to the host.

Location *on* or *in* the body of the host serves as one basis for dividing parasitic animals into two groups. *Ectoparasites* live on the external surface of the body of the host or in cavities that open directly onto the surface. They include monogenetic trematodes, lice, mites, and ticks. *Endoparasites* live in the bodies of the hosts, occurring in the alimentary canal, lungs, liver and other organs, tissues, cells, and body cavity. Examples are tapeworms, digenetic trematodes, nematodes, and protozoa.

The amount of time spent *on* or *in* the host serves as temporal basis for dividing parasites into two major groups. *Temporary parasites* visit of the host for food. Having satisfied their hunger, they leave. Bloodsucking arthropods and leeches are examples. *Stationary parasites* spend a definite period of development on or in the body of the host. They may be divided into groups, according to the amount of time spent with the host. Those which remain with the host for only a part of their development and then leave to complete it and continue a non-parasitic life are known as *periodic* parasites. Botflies and mermithid nematodes represent this group. Parasites that spend their entire existence in hosts except for the times they occur free while transferring from one host to another are designated as *permanent parasites*. The trematodes, cestodes, acanthocephalans, nematodes, and protozoans are examples.

Parasites found in unusual hosts or places in normal hosts are designated by terms indicating the nature of their abnormalities. *Incidental parasites* are those which occasionally appear in unusual hosts under natural conditions. The double-pored tapeworm of dogs is found sometimes in children, or the common liver fluke of sheep occurs in dogs or cats. *Erratic* or *aberrant* parasites are individuals of a species that wander into unusual positions in the normal host. Ascarids of swine and man may wander from the intestine into the liver, body cavity, or nostrils.

All of the parasites listed in these categories are *obligate parasites*. They are unable to exist without some degree of development on or in the host. A few normally free-living animals, on the other hand, are able to exist for short periods in the bodies of other animals when accidentally introduced into them. They are spoken of as *facultative parasites*. Representatives of them are certain free-living nematodes of the genera *Rhabditis* and *Turbotrix*, and fly maggots such as those of the cheese skippers (*Piophila casei*) and some of the blowflies.

PROPERTIES OF PARASITISM

The basic properties of parasitism appear in the many adaptations necessary for the parasite to live in its biotic environment, to reproduce, and to infect new hosts. These interactions between the two living organisms give rise to both consequences and specializations for each participant, which become fixed through inheritance.

ADAPTATIONS FOR PARASITIC LIFE. The basic physiological requirements of a parasite are similar to those of free-living animals. They are habitat, food, and reproduction. The problems in achieving these requirements under the conditions of parasitism are complex, and special adaptations have evolved to meet them. Probably the one basic underlying principle characteristic of parasitism is that of adaptation. One writer has called it the hallmark of parasitism.

In order to live on or in a host, the parasite must evolve structures for adhering to it. Such adaptations appear in the tarsi of Anoplura for holding on to hairs. Monogenetic trematodes and acanthocephalans have rigid hooks for attaching to the host. Suckers for the same purpose are highly developed by trematodes and cestodes.

Living in a host necessitates means of leaving it in order to reach new ones. Parasites of the alimentary canal, lungs, liver, and reproductive system utilize the natural outlets of these organ systems as avenues of exit for cysts or eggs protected against an unfavorable environment. Those living in the blood stream and tissues generally utilize other animals or means to leave their hosts. Bloodsucking arthropods serve as the route by which malaria and related protozoans and the microfilariae of filarioid nematodes escape from the body and in which further development occurs. Dracunculid worms in the subcutaneous tissues vesiculate the epidermis, forming openings through which the female releases active larvae into the water. Others (trichinella, cestodes, and trematodes) depend on the digestive processes of predators or scavengers which serve as definitive hosts to release them from the tissues of their intermediate hosts. *Capillaria hepatica* eggs in the liver of rodents may be freed by postmortem decomposition of the host or digestion of it by another animal, after which development of them proceeds under favorable conditions in the physical environment.

Means of survival and development are essential during the interval of transfer from one definitive host to the next. This transfer involves a period of development in the soil or water, in the case of parasites having a *direct* life cycle, or development in the body of one or more intermediate hosts with those having an *indirect* cycle. In parasites with a direct life cycle, protective cysts, thick egg shells, or the retained cuticle of larvae are adaptations to protect the stages free in the soil against the hazards of desiccation and freezing. Species having an indirect life cycle may depend on some of the features listed above for protection during the time of transfer between their several hosts. But since practically all of their development takes place in the body of one or more intermediate hosts, their adaptational requirements must be adjusted to the biotic environment of the bodies of several species, often from different phyla. An example is the lancet fluke, *Dicrocoelium dendriticum,* which lives and developes successively in sheep, snails and ants.

Transmission of the infective stage of the parasite to the next host in the developmental cycle is accomplished by one of three methods. They are *passive, active,* or *inoculative.* Passive transmission occurs when the infective stages of the parasites contaminate or infect the food or water of the host and are swallowed with them. Examples are the eggs of ascarids, cysts of *Entamoeba,* and larvae of trichostrongyles. Infection of food occurs in the larval stages of trematodes, cestodes, acanthocephalans, and many nematodes. Active transfer occurs in the hookworms, and the miracidia and cercariae of trematodes. These parasites actively penetrate the bodies of their hosts upon coming in contact with them. Often responses such as thermotropic, geotropic, as in the case of hookworm larvae, or chemotropic, as occurs in miracidia toward their snail hosts, aid in bringing the host and parasite together. Inoculative transmission occurs when the infective stage of the parasite has developed in the body of a bloodsucking arthropod, as with *Plasmodium* in mosquitoes. Transfer back to the definitive host is accomplished when the arthropod inoculates the parasites into the host while feeding upon it.

Survival within the host is dependent upon the ability of the parasites to withstand the destructive action of the digestive juices and the immunological reactions of the host against them, or to reach microhabitats within the host where the required nutrients for growth and reproduction are available in adequate amounts.

The most successful parasites have evolved a biotic potential of great capacity in order to compensate for the tremendous losses of eggs or larvae, or both, incurred in the completion of their complicated life cycles. This is accomplished by an increased production of eggs, as in the ascarids and cestodes, the duplication of sex organs in segments, as in cestodes, or vegetative reproduction extending over long periods of time such as occurs in the sporocysts or rediae of trematodes and scolices in cestodes (*Echinococcus* and *Multiceps*).

SPECIFIC HOST-PARASITE RELATIONSHIPS. Parasites generally do not infect different species of animals at random under natural conditions but show varying degrees of preference for hosts and for habitats within them. Thus parasites of horses, cattle, dogs, or humans are most likely to be found in their respective hosts. Moreover, parasites of the intestine, the liver, or tissues occur with marked regularity in these sites. This condition is designated as *host specificity, organ specificity,* or *tissue specificity,* as the case may be.

SPECIFICITY OF HOST-PARASITE RELATIONSHIPS. Specificity of host-parasite relationships is determined by the success of the parasite to invade, occupy, and reproduce in certain microhabitats inside or on the outside of the bodies of hosts. The factors involved in the development of host specificity among parasites are opportunities for contact between them and their hosts, followed by entrance, adaptation, establishment, nourishment, and reproduction in them.

Opportunities for infection of the host are present only when it and the parasite come in contact with each other under favorable conditions. This occurs during periods when developmental, kinetic, or behavioral activities of the parasite and the host bring them together.

Ability to invade the host and survive in it involves the capabilities, requirements, and susceptibilities of the parasite. Structural properties of the integument may be beyond the capability of the parasite to penetrate, thereby serving as a barrier. The physiological properties of the tissues or organs may not meet the requirements of the parasite, making growth and development impossible. Susceptibility to antibodies produced by the host in response to the presence of the parasite may prove lethal to it or produce an environment unfavorable to growth and reproduction.

Chemotropic response by parasites to substances elaborated by hosts leads to host, organ, or tissue specificity. The miracidia of trematodes are attracted to their specific snail hosts by certain substances in the mucus secretions. Parasites in the body of hosts are directed to specific organs or tissues through their chemotropic responses to them. Young liver flukes, *Fasciola hepatica, Dicrocoelium dendriticum,* and *Clonorchis sinensis,* liberated from their cysts in the small intestine of the definitive host, find their way to the bile ducts, each by its own route, doubtless being directed by different stimuli originating in the liver. In cases where distribution is directed by chemotropic responses, parasites accumulate in specific hosts or tissues within them. In the absence of such responses, they occur at random in species or tissues. The cercariae of echinostome flukes encyst in a number of species of snails, and trichinella larvae may be found in the skeletal muscles of many species of mammals.

Distribution of parasites in species of hosts varies from one of extreme limitation to one of wide range, including a single species, on the one hand, and several orders, on the other, such as the trematode *Plagiorchis muris* which may develop in birds, rats, and humans.

Substances in certain organs or tissues become inimical to parasites and interfere with their development in them. After chicks become a few weeks old, the goblet cells of the mucosal lining of the intestine develop and secrete mucus which hinders the establishment and development of the larvae of *Ascaridia galli.*

The specific nutritional requirements of parasites must be satisfied if they are to succeed. These are developed through the evolutionary processes of host and parasite, resulting in host specificity.

EFFECT OF PARASITISM ON THE EVOLUTION OF THE HOST SPECIES

Parasitism may be considered as an evolutionary pressure in which the host and parasite adapt to each other through a selective process. Since parasitism has a deleterious effect on the host, it may be manifested in lowered vitality, reduced rate of reproduction, slower growth, or death of infected individuals. This can result in extinction of a species or it can lead to a change in the population through the selection of resistant species or strains. Host adaptation to parasitism develops from selective pressure resulting in strains better adapted to resist or tolerate parasitism. This is accomplished through the evolution of antibody responses on the part of the host.

EFFECT OF PARASITISM ON INDIVIDUAL HOST

The effect of parasitism on the individual host may be *injurious* or *defensive.*

Injurious effects show a wide range of severity, leading to manifested disease often resulting in the death of the host. When parasites, such as hookworms in man or trichostrongyles in cattle and sheep, affect the entire population, the effect of the disease is masked and often not recognized. The less severe effects of parasitism are kept in repair by the host and therefore are not readily detectible. The mechanisms of injury are mechanical, chemical, inflammatory, and the introduction of pathogens.

Mechanical injury involves destructive action such as perforation of an organ (ascarids, acanthocephalans), destruction of cells (coccidia, plasmodia), piercing tissues (whipworms, mosquitoes), chewing (Mallophaga), obstruction of a lumen (ascarids, cestodes), or the interference of transfer of foods across cell membranes (*Giardia*).

Chemical injury results from secretions by the parasites. Hookworms secrete substances from the cephalic glands that interfere with the blood. One of them is an anticoagulant that permits the blood to continue to flow from the wound after the worm has left the site, and another depresses haematogenesis. *Cysticercus fasciolaris* of the cat tapeworm is carcinogenic in the liver of rats.

Parasites rob the host of essential food products. Trichostrongyles and hookworms feed on blood. Moreover, the injection of the anticoagulant factor by hookworms while feeding results in a great loss of blood through bleeding into the intestine. The broad fish tapeworm, *Dibothriocephalus latus,* of man absorbs vitamin B_{12} from the tissues of the intestinal mucosa and stores it in its own body.

The introduction of pathogenic organisms such as bacteria (*Clostridium novyi*) by the common liver fluke into the liver of sheep, rickettsiae (*Neorickettsia helminthoeca*) into the tissues of the intestine by the salmon poisoning fluke of dogs, or protozoans (*Histomonas meleagridis*) through the eggs of the caecal nematode into the alimentary canal of turkeys results in a high mortality among these hosts.

Defensive reactions to invasion or attack by parasites are aspects of physiological or conscious responses by the host against them. Inflammatory responses of a general or local nature are often the first reaction to the presence of parasites. It is primarily cellular and is divided into relatively distinct but overlapping stages of 1) temporary localization and destruction of parasites, as in the case of the cercariae of blood flukes of birds that infect humans, causing papules; 2) walling off or encapsulation of the invaded area, seen in infection by the large American liver fluke, *Fascioloides magna*, of Cervidae in cattle; and 3) repair of damaged tissue, as occurs in light infections of amoebiasis. Antibodies may destroy, localize, neutralize, or interfere with the reproduction of parasites and thereby serve as secondary defenses. Conscious efforts are made by the host to avoid parasitism by fleeing, as cattle do from botflies, or bunching, in the case of sheep, as a protective measure against nose bots.

EVOLUTIONARY EFFECTS OF PARASITISM

Once parasitism has been achieved, it proceeds by its very nature to exert a definite directive influence on the evolution of the host and the parasite. In the biotic environment, the parasite is isolated in the body of the host and confronted with the dynamic defensive mechanisms of it. The host, which constitutes the environment, is attacked and injured by the parasite. Improved relations on the part of each are indicated. In order to be successful, the evolution of parasitism must be toward better adaptation between the host and parasite. Any other course would lead to the ultimate destruction of one or both.

The direct force in achieving better adaptation between parasites and hosts is natural selection. The conditions for it are excellent. Through isolation of the parasites in the host, a population of genotypes of parasites is evolved that is adapted to meet more successfully the resistive efforts of the host. By the same selective forces, strains of genotypes of host animals appear whose antibody systems have evolved to cope more adequately with the destruction caused by the parasites in them. Thus, through the processes of isolation and natural selection, populations of parasites and hosts with specific tolerances for each other have developed.

LIFE CYCLES OF PARASITES

The life cycles of parasites are complex and the physical and biological requirements for completing them are manifold and exacting. In order to surmount the many adverse conditions encountered in the course of maintaining themselves, parasites have developed a great reproductive potential together with the means of protection against physical hazards. In spite of the great odds, sufficient numbers of them succeed to assure continuity of the species.

The life cycles fall into two basic types. They are 1) the direct one with only the definitive host, and 2) the indirect one with a definitive host and one or more intermediate hosts. Parasites with a direct life cycle have a free-living phase, except for a few species, during which they develop to the infective stage. Those with an indirect life cycle usually, though not always, have a free-living stage between some of the hosts.

The Protozoa have both types of life cycles among their members. In the Sporozoa, which have both types of life cycles, there are intermediate stages such as trophozoites, merozoites, sporozoites, and gametocytes which may occur in a single host in the case of the direct type of cycle or in two hosts in the indirect type (Plate 16).

Among the Trematoda, the Monogenea and most of the Aspidogastrea have the direct type of life cycle. The stage hatching from the egg is a larva that develops directly into the adult. Others of the Aspidogastrea and all of the Digenea have an indirect life cycle involving mollusks. In the Digenea, the egg produces a miracidium whose development in a mollusk produces the sporocyst, rediae, and cercariae. The cercariae, with the exception of several families of blood flukes, encyst on objects or in other animals and develop into metacercariae which are infective to the definitive host upon entering the alimentary canal (Plate 84).

In nearly all cases, the Cestoda have one or two intermediate hosts in the life cycle. The eggs hatch into a six- or ten-hooked larva. In the Proteocephala and Pseudophyllidea, there is a procercoid and plerocercoid larval stage, usually each in a different intermediate host (Plate 101). The Cyclophyllidea have three basic types of larvae in the intermediate hosts (Plates 93, 101). They are the cysticercoid, the dithyridium, and the vesicular type. The vesicular type has such variations as the cysticercus, strobilocercus, coenurous, and hydatid.

All species of Acanthocephala have an intermediate host. An acanthor hatches from the egg in the intestine of the intermediate host and develops into an acanthella and a cysticanth in succession. Species infecting aquatic vertebrates usually have aquatic invertebrates as the intermediate host; those in terrestrial vertebrates usually have terrestrial invertebrates as the intermediaries.

The Nemathelminthes have both a direct (Plate 141) and an indirect (Plate 142) type of life cycle. The larvae pass through a series of four molts to become adults. Some of the molts take place in the egg, in the free-living phases, and others in the intermediate and definitive hosts.

While these are basic patterns on which broad principles of the parasite life cycles can be based, the individual cycles in each of them often vary greatly within the fundamental plan. Some parasites, such as the sporozoans, trypanosomes, trichinella, and filaroids, with intermediate hosts, have no free-living stages. In others, such as *Probstmyria viviparus* and *Hymenolepis nana* (Plate 99), the eggs may hatch and the larvae develop to sexual maturity without ever leaving the definitive host.

The life cycle of each parasite presents its own peculiarities. Solution of it requires a broad knowledge of the physiology, biology, and ecology of the parasite and all of the hosts involved. The elucidation of the life cycle of a parasite, or, indeed, a part of it, is a distinct challenge and a gratifying achievement.

SELECTED REFERENCES

Baer, J. G. (1951). Ecology of Animal Parasites. University of Illinois Press, Urbana, 224 pp.

Caullery, M. (1952). Parasitism and Symbiosis. Sidgewick and Jackson, Ltd., London, 340 pp.

Huff, C. G., L. O. Nolf, R. J. Porter, C. P. Read, A. G. Richards, A. J. Riker, and L. A. Stauber. (1958). An approach toward a course in the principles of parasitism, J. Parasit. 44:28.

Kudo, R. R. (1966). Protozoology. 5th ed. Charles C Thomas, Springfield, 1174 pp.

Self, J. T. (1951). The biological significance of parasitism and its evolutionary accomplishments. Bios 32:51.

Whitlock, J. H. (1958). The inheritance of resistance to trichostrongyloidosis in sheep. I. Demonstration of the validity of the phenomena. Cornell Vet. 48:127.

PART II PHYLUM PROTOZOA

Among the Protozoa are many symbiotic species living in various degrees of relationship with other animals, both invertebrates and vertebrates. Numerous species of Protozoa are parasitic, living in cells (cytozoic), tissues (histozoic), or cavities (coelozoic). Some of them are notorious as causes of serious diseases in humans, as well as in domestic and wild animals from honeybees to cattle.

The phylum Protozoa consists of an assembly of unicellular animals of varying degrees of complexity in both structure and biology. It is only reasonable, therefore, to expect that various schemes of classification have evolved. They continually trend toward greater sophistication as information becomes more precise through the use of new tools of investigation such as phase contrast and electron microscopy and through more detailed studies on life cycles.

Two basic classifications are currently in use. One is that of Kudo as set forth in his well-known text, "Protozoology." The other appears in some variation in the works of Jahn and Jahn, Hall, and Levine. More recently, Honigberg *et al.*, speaking as a committee for the Society of Protozoologists, have refined the latter scheme.

While the classification used by Levine and that proposed by the committee has the acceptance in substance of many protozoologists, there is at present a lack of information on the composition of the various taxa below the order level in the report by Honigberg *et al.* Since Kudo has included this information in his "Protozoology," his classification is followed. Parasitologists should examine the other classification for the new relationships among the Protozoa that it sets forth.

The phylum Protozoa consists of the subphyla Plasmodroma and Ciliophora. The Plasmodroma contains the class Mastigophora whose members bear flagella, the class Sarcodina whose members have pseudopodia at some stage in their development, and the class Sporozoa that are without apparent organelles of locomotion, except in the microgametes. The subphylum Ciliophora consists of the class Ciliata with cilia throughout the trophic life and the class Suctoria in which cilia in the early stages are replaced by tentacles. The class Ciliata contains a number of parasitic species.

Each class of Protozoa has one or more genera whose species parasitize humans, causing dreaded disease that results in much suffering, morbidity, and mortality. There are *Trypanosoma gambiense* and *Leishmania donovani* of the Mastigophora, causing African sleeping sickness and kala azar, respectively; *Entamoeba histolytica* of the Sarcodina, producing amoebic dysentery; *Plasmodium vivax* of the Sporozoa as an etiological agent for malaria; and *Balantidium coli* of the Ciliophora, which is least serious but still responsible for damage to the intestine. Each of these species has its counterpart in the domestic and wild animals. The species illustrated below represent some of the major ones from all of the classes except Suctoria.

SELECTED REFERENCES

Hall, R. P. (1953). Protozoology. Prentice-Hall, New York, 682 pp.

Honigberg, B. M., W. Balamuth, E. C. Bovee, J. O. Corliss, M. Gojdics, R. P. Hall, R. R. Kudo, N. D. Levine, A. R. Loeblish, Jr., J. Weiser, and D. H. Wenrich. (1964). J. Protozool. 11:7.

Jahn, T. L., and F. F. Jahn. (1949). How to Know the Protozoa. W. C. Brown, Dubuque, 234 pp.

Kudo, R. R. (1953). Protozoology. Charles C Thomas, Springfield, Ill., 966 pp.

Levine, N. D. (1961). Protozoan Parasites of Domestic Animals and of Man. Burgess Publishing Co., Minneapolis, 412 pp.

SUBPHYLUM PLASMODROMA

Of the classes of Plasmodroma, the Mastigophora bear flagella for locomotion and the Sarcodina bear pseudopods for traveling and capturing food. The Sporozoa lack organelles of locomotion as adults but are capable of gliding and amoeboid movement; microgametes bear flagella.

CLASS MASTIGOPHORA

The members of this class are both plants (subclass Phytomastigina) and animals (subclass Zoomastigina) and are characterized by the presence of one to eight flagella located at one end of the body. Generally there is a single nucleus.

Zoomastigina lack chromatophores characteristic of their plant counterparts. Organelles, in addition to flagella, such as parabasal body, axostyle, pelta, cytostome, and undulating membrane are present.

Parasitic Zoomastigina are parasites of the alimentary canal of both invertebrates and vertebrates, and of the circulatory, reproductive, and muscle systems of vertebrates.

Their life cycles are both direct and indirect. In the latter case, an invertebrate and a vertebrate are involved.

Some cause serious diseases in their hosts and are of major medical and veterinary significance. These forms have been studied most intensively and form the basis for much of the knowledge pertaining to the biology of this group of parasites.

ORDER RHIZOMASTIGINA

Members of this order have amoeboid characteristics, including pseudopodia, in addition to flagella.

FAMILY MASTIGAMOEBIDAE

The species belonging to this family have one to three flagella, sometimes four. One species, *Histomonas meleagridis*, is parasitic in gallinaceous birds.

Histomonas meleagridis (Smith, 1910) (Plate 1)

Histomonas meleagridis is a flagellate parasite of the caecum of turkeys, chickens, ruffed grouse, quail, pheasants, Hungarian partridges, and pea fowls. It produces a serious disease in turkeys, but not in chickens, known as blackhead, infectious enterohepatitis, or histomoniasis.

DESCRIPTION. It is a flagellated protozoan having different forms according to the stage of development. The trophozoites are somewhat amoeboid and with or without flagella which originate from an extranuclear body. The aflagellate stages are crowded in the liver or mucosa of the caeca and assume variable shapes due to the pressure exerted on them. Small oval bodies without flagella and surrounded by a thick membrane have been reported as resistant stages but the existence of true resistant forms is doubtful.

LIFE CYCLE. It is believed that *Histomonas meleagridis* may be transmitted from host to host by 1) direct ingestion of protozoan-bearing eggs of caecal worms (*Heterakis gallinae*) from infected birds, and 2) by ingestion of faeces of infected birds in which the trophozoites are present. While the experimental evidence for transmitting the histomonads and the disease through the faeces is weak, it has been done. Transmission through the eggs and larvae of caecal worms appears unquestionable and perhaps is the more important means, even though the protozoans have never been seen there. Both means of infection will be discussed.

Chickens serve as natural reservoirs of infection without suffering from the disease, whereas turkeys, especially poults, are very susceptible and suffer a high mortality.

Infection from ingesting the histomonads takes place under natural conditions when motile forms passed in the faeces are swallowed. They enter the intestine and go to the caeca and liver. In the caeca, the trophozoites penetrate the mucosa, entering between the cells, and transform to the vegetative stage which undergoes multiplication by binary fission, resulting in large aggregations of them with resultant lesions. The vegetative forms change into the so-called "resistant" stage which has a thick outer covering of host material. There is no encystment. Trophozoites entering the venules of the hepatic portal vein from the caeca and possibly the intestine of turkeys are transported to the liver. In this organ, they enter the parenchyma and multiply. They produce large, saucer-shaped lesions on the face of the liver of turkeys; these lesions are first dark red in color, later yellowish, and finally yellowish green.

Eggs of caecal worms from infected birds are capable of transmitting infections to healthy individuals. Having introduced the histomonads through the eggs, they are incorporated in the larvae and liberated somewhere in the alimentary canal and undergo the cycle in the caeca and liver, as described above.

Infections acquired by healthy birds kept on lots occupied previously by infected flocks are believed to originate from eggs of caecal worms that survive for long periods under favorable conditions. Earthworms may be responsible for carrying eggs into the soil where the environment for prolonged survival is good, later bringing them to the surface where they become available to the fowl.

EXERCISE ON LIFE CYCLE

Infection may be transmitted to healthy young turkey poults by 1) feeding them faeces from turkeys infected with *Histomonas meleagridis* or *Heterakis gallinae*, or 2) placing them on old turkey runs, and 3) quartering them with grown chickens. Feeding the eggs of caecal worms from chickens or turkeys is a fairly certain means of producing an infection. To demonstrate that the worm eggs convey the infection, they should be fully incubated, sterilized thoroughly to destroy any histomonads that might possibly be present on the outside, and fed to young poults. When the eggs hatch in the intestine, the causitive organism produces the lesions in the caeca and liver characteristic of the disease in about three weeks.

SELECTED REFERENCES

Becker, E. R. (1959). Protozoa. In Diseases of Poultry, 4th Ed., Iowa State University Press, Ames, p. 828.

Farr, M. M. (1956). Cornell Vet. 46:178.

Lapage, G. (1956). Veterinary Parasitology. Oliver and Boyd, London, p. 751.

Levine, N. D. (1961). Protozoan Parasites of Domestic Animals and Man. Burgess Publishing Co., Minneapolis, p. 74.

Lund, E. E. (1956). Poultry Sci. 35:900.

Smith, T., and H. W. Graybill. (1920). J. Exp. Med. 32:143.

Tyzzer, E. E. (1919). J. Med. Res. 40:1; (1926). Proc. Soc. Exp. Biol. Med. 23:708.

Tyzzer, E. E., and M. Fabyan. (1922). J. Exp. Med. 35:791.

ORDER PROTOMONADINA

This group of protozoans is characterized by the presence of one or two flagella and constitutes a heterogeneous assembly. They are mostly parasitic. Reproduction is by longitudinal fission normally, although multiple fission and budding occur.

FAMILY TRYPANOSOMATIDAE

The family Trypanosomatidae consists of six genera of monoflagellates parasitic in vertebrates and invertebrates (arthropods and leeches). Four distinct types of bodies, known as leishman, leptomonas,

EXPLANATION OF PLATE 1 ▷

A. Profile of invasive trophozoite. **B.** Section of crypt of caecum with invasive phase of amoebiform parasites. **C.** Trophozoite with food granules and extranuclear granules. **D.** Trophozoite with light areas, indicating digestion of food particles. **E.** Large vegetative forms prior to division packed in liver. **F.** Four cells in so-called "resistant" stage. **G.** Four "resistant" cells in giant cell. **H.** Groups of "resistant" cells in mucosa of caecum. **I.** Chicken host. **J.** Turkey host. **K.** Liver with characteristic saucer-shaped lesions caused by *Histomonas meleagridis.* **L, M.** Anterior and posterior ends, respectively, of male caecal worm *(Heterakis gallinae).*

1, nucleus; **2**, nucleolus; **3**, extranuclear bodies; **4**, flagella; **5**, food particles; **6**, food particles being digested; **7**, epithelial cells of caecum; **8**, trophozoite in caecal crypt; **9**, invasive trophozoites in caecal epithelium; **10**, liver parenchyma; **11**, large vegetative protozoans preparing for division; **12**, "resistant phase" of protozoans; **13**, thicker outer tissue covering laid down by host; **14**, giant cell of host; **15**, caecal mucosa.

a, "resistant stage" in caeca; **b**, "resistant stage" passed in faeces; **c, d**, "resistant phase" in faeces; **e**, "resistant stage" swallowed; **f**, trophozoite developing; **g**, flagellated trophozoite in mucosa; **h**, adult caecal worm; **i**, eggs of caecal worm presumably containing histomonads; **j, k**, egg passed in faeces; **l, m, n**, development of egg in faeces; **o**, infective egg swallowed; **p**, egg hatches in alimentary tract; **q**, larva containing protozoan; **r**, larva in caecum where it is believed to liberate pathogenic histomonads.

a′, (over head of turkey) histomonad from faeces of chickens; **b′**, histomonad swallowed; **c′**, trophozoite active in intestine; **d′**, trophozoite enters caecum; **e′**, trophozoite enters interstices between cells; **f′**, vegetative cells multiply; **g′**, mass of vegetative cells causes destruction of epithelial cells; **h′**, adhesions resulting from destruction of masses of epithelial cells; **i′**, caseous core in lumen of caeca due to reaction to protozoa; **j′**, "resistant" cells of protozoa in mucosa; **k′**, "resistant" cell passed in faeces; **l′**, "resistant" cell in faeces; **m′**, "resistant" cell in faeces a source of infection to turkeys; **n′**, trophozoites enter hepatic portal vein from intestine and caecum; **o′**, trophozoites enter liver parenchyma from capillaries; **p′**, "resistant stages" in saucer-shaped lesions in liver.

a″, *Heterakis* egg passed in faeces of chicken; **b″**, developing egg; **c″**, embryonated egg containing larva and histomonads; **d″**, infective egg swallowed by turkey; **e″**, egg hatches; **f″**, larva free in intestine goes to caeca where histomonads are liberated; **g″**, adult caecal worm; **h″**, eggs of caecal worm deposited in caeca; **i″**, eggs passed in faeces; **j″**, eggs in faeces; **k″, l″, m″**, eggs embryonate and larvae contain infective histomonads (see Plate 121).

Figures A-H adapted from Tyzzer, 1919, J. Med. Res. 40:1; K, from photograph (Fig. 11) in Richard and Kendall, 1957, Veterinary Protozoology, Oliver and Boyd, London; L, M, from Clapham, 1933, J. Helminth. 11:67.

---

crithidia, and trypanosome, occur of which two, three, or all appear in the life cycle of individual species.

MORPHOLOGY. In addition to the nucleus, the internal structure consists of a parabasal body, a blepharoplast, and an axoneme which extends to the margin of the body. When the latter continues externally, it forms a free flagellum (Plate 2, A, B). Multiplication is by binary fission.

There are two body types, one oval and aflagellate as in the leishmanias (Plate 2, A), and the other fusiform and flagellate as in the leptomonads, crithidias, and trypanosomes. The leptomonad type is distinguished by having the blepharoplast near the anterior extremity of the body and being without an undulating membrane (Plate 2, B), the crithidial type with the blepharoplast or basal granule farther back near the anterior margin of the nucleus and usually having a short undulating membrane (Plate 2, C), and the trypansomal type in which the blepharoplast is near the posterior extremity of the body with the undulating membrane extending along the entire length of the body (Plate 2, D).

CLASSIFICATION. The genera are based on the type of life cycles. These include those that are completed in a single invertebrate host (*Leptomonas, Crithidia, Herpetomonas*), in a single invertebrate host and a plant (*Phytomonas*), and in an invertebrate and vertebrate host (*Leishmania* and *Trypanosoma*) shown in Plate 2, E-J.

Leptomonas ctenocephali occurs as a leishmania and leptomonad in the gut of dog fleas. Transfer is through the leishmania in the faeces where they become resistant to desiccation (Plate 2, E).

Crithidia gerridis is in the gut of water striders. Three forms, the leishmania, leptomonad, and crithidia, are present in the gut and occur in the life cycle. Infection is by ingestion of cysts of leishmanias voided in the faeces (Plate 2, F).

Herpetomonas muscarum is parasitic in the gut of house flies and blowflies. The stages in the life cycle include leishmanial, leptomonad, crithidial, and trypanosomal forms. The leptomonad is most frequently seen. Infection of new hosts is by means of cysts voided by infected individuals (Plate 2, G).

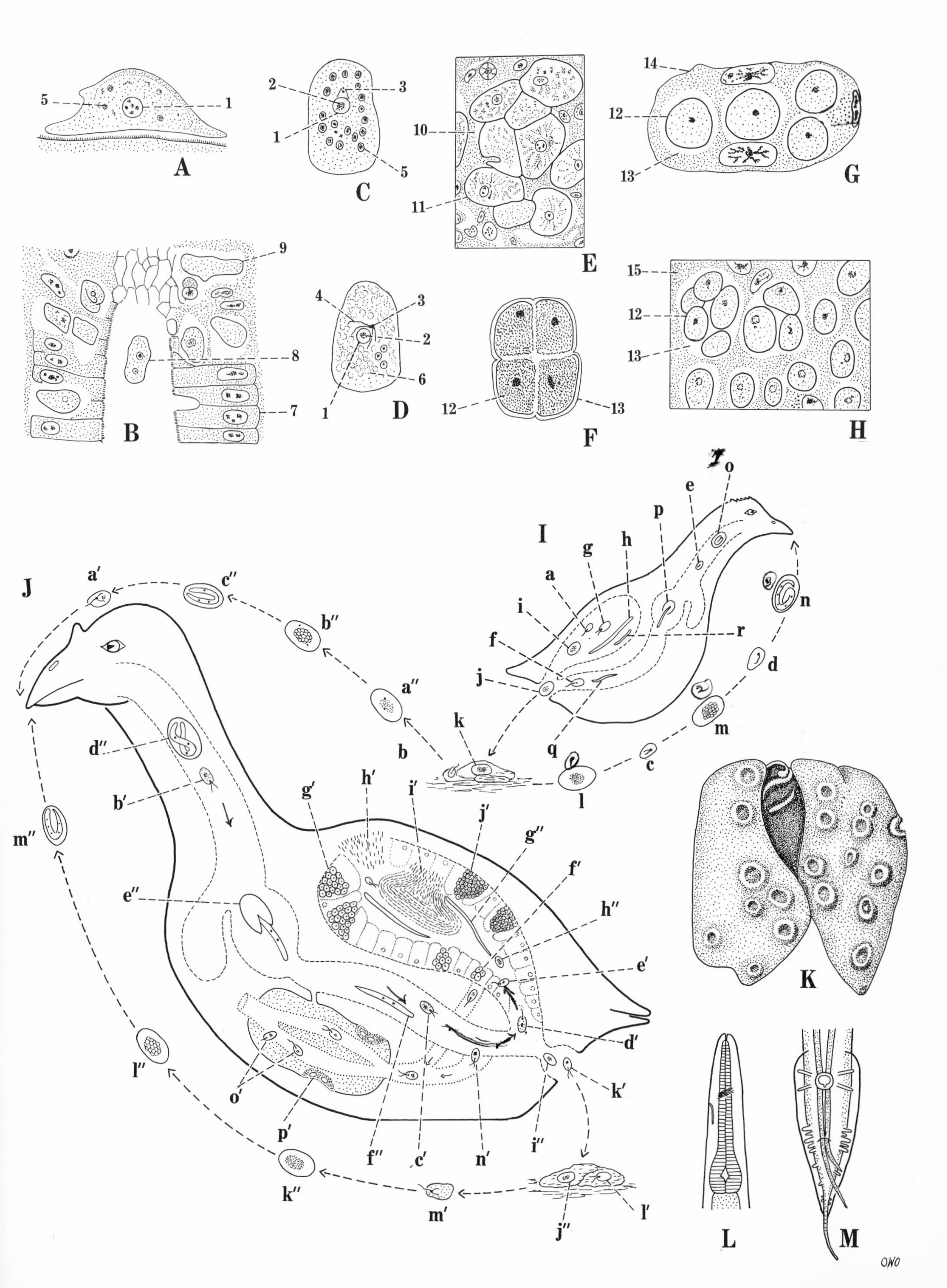
5
1
A
2
3
1
5
C
10
11
E
14
12
13
G
9
8
7
B
4
3
2
6
1
D
12
13
F
15
12
13
H
o
e
p
I
g
h
a
i
r
f
j
n
d
m
q
c
l
k
b
J
a′
c″
b″
a″
d″
b′
m″
g′
h′
i′
j′
g″
f′
h″
e″
e′
d′
k′
l″
o′
p′
f″
c′
n′
i″
k″
m′
j″
l′
K
L
M
OWO

EXPLANATION OF PLATE 2

A. *Leishmania.* **B.** *Leptomonas.* **C.** *Crithidia.* **D.** *Trypanosoma.* **E.** Life cycle of *Leptomonas ctenocephala* with leptomonad and leishmanial stages in dog flea *(Ctenocephalides canis).* **F.** Life cycle of *Crithidia gerridis* with crithidial, leptomonad and leishmanial stages. **G.** *Herpetomonas muscarum* with trypanosomal, crithidial, leptomonad, and leishmanial stages. **H.** *Phytomonas davidi* with leptomonad and leishmanial stages in the latex of milkweeds *(Euphorbia)* and in the intestine of bugs, especially *Stenocephalus agilis,* which feed on these plants; **I.** Life cycle of *Leishmania donovani* with leptomonad stage in the sand fly *(Phlebotomus)* intermediate host and leishmanial bodies in reticuloendothelial cells of humans, dogs, and other mammals. **J.** Life cycle of *Trypanosoma lewisi* with trypanosomal forms in the blood of rats, and the crithidial, leptomonad, and leishmanial forms in the intestine of fleas.

1, nucleus; **2,** parabasal body; **3,** blepharoplast; **4,** axoneme; **5,** flagellum; **6,** undulating membrane.

a, flea larva; **b,** leptomonad; **c,** leishmania; **d,** water strider; **e,** crithidia; **f,** leptomonad; **g,** leishmania; **h,** house fly; **i,** trypanosome; **j,** crithidia; **k,** leptomonad; **l,** leishmania; **m,** milkweed bug; **n,** leishmania; **o,** milkweed; **p,** leptomonad; **q,** mammalian (man and dog) hosts; **r,** leishmania; **s,** leptomonad; **t,** sand fly invertebrate host; **u,** rat host; **v,** trypanosome; **w,** crithidia; **x,** leptomonad; **y,** leishmania; **z,** flea invertebrate host.

Figures A-D adapted from Medical Protozoology and Helminthology, Naval Medical School, Bethesda, Maryland, 1955, p. 87; others original.

Phytomonas davidi, and related forms, occur in hemipteran bugs and the latex of euphorbid plants in many parts of the world. Leishmanial and leptomonad stages appear in the intestine of bugs and the latex. Encysted forms are voided with the faeces of bugs. Multiplication occurs in both hosts. Transmission between the plant and bug probably occurs through feeding, as suggested by the presence of leptomonads in the salivary glands (Plate 2, H).

Leishmania parasitizes mammals and sand flies (*Phlebotomus*). The leishmanial forms occur in the lymphoid macrophage cells of the mammalian host, whereas the leptomonads are in the gut of the sand flies. Leishmanias taken into the gut of sand flies transform into leptomonads and multiply. Upon injection into the blood stream by feeding flies, they transform into leishmanias which are ingested by the lymphoid macrophage cells where multiplication takes place (Plate 2, I).

Trypanosoma parasitizes the blood stream of all classes of vertebrates and are transmitted by leeches and a variety of bloodsucking arthropods. All four stages of the parasite (leishmanial, leptomonad, crithidial, and trypansomal) occur in the life cycle. Generally, only the trypanosomal stage occurs in the vertebrate host, except for *T. cruzi,* in which leishmanial forms also are present. Trypanosomal forms ingested by invertebrate vectors transform through the leishmanial, leptomonad, crithidial, and trypanosomal stages. The final stage is known as a metacyclic trypanosome and is infective to the vertebrate host. The metacyclic trypanosomes of some species are injected into the blood stream of the vertebrate by the feeding invertebrate host, or in other species they are voided in the faeces of the invertebrate host and infection occurs upon being swallowed and entering the blood stream from the alimentary canal of the vertebrate host (Plate 2, J).

In *T. equiperdum* of equines, the invertebrate host and the leishmanial, leptomonad, and crithidial stages have been dropped from the cycle. Because this trypanosome has only a single stage and form, it is said to be monomorphic. They occur abundantly in the mucus of the reproductive tract and less so in the blood stream. Transmission is primarily through coitus, although it is conceivable that bloodsucking flies may function as vectors by mechanical transfer.

Other species of *Trypanosoma* will be discussed later to show basic differences in their life cycles that place them in somewhat natural groups.

EXERCISE ON LIFE CYCLE

House flies, blowflies, water striders, boxelder bugs, and mosquito larvae among the insects, and Norway rats among the vertebrates, together provide a ready source of fresh leishmanial, leptomonad, crithidial, and trypanosomal stages. The common milkweed *Ascelepias syrica* is infected with the trypanosomatid *Phytomonas elmassiani,* which is transmitted by the bug *Oncopeltis fasciatus.*

PLATE 2 *Genera of Trypanosomatidae and Their Basic Life Cycles*

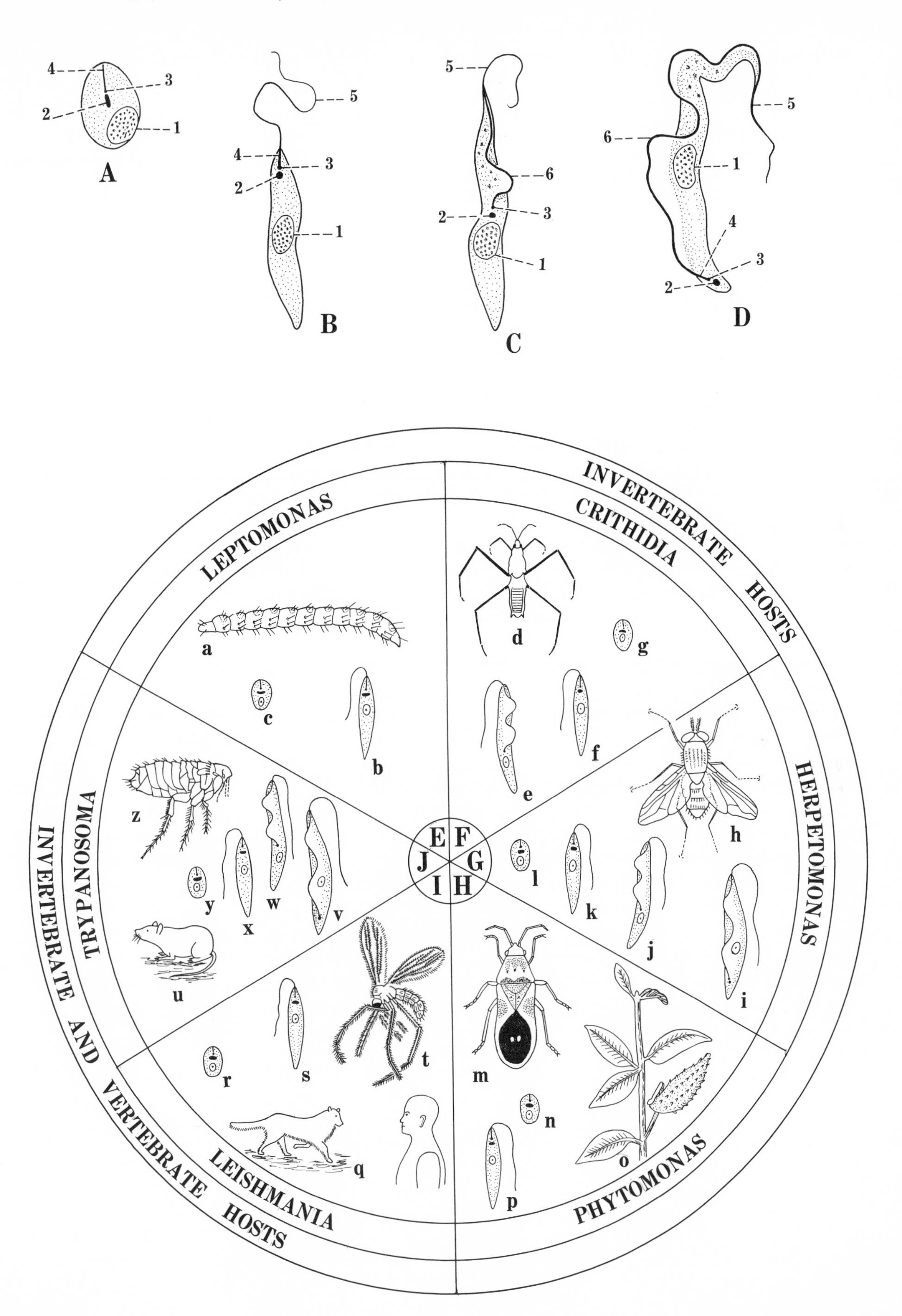

In order to find the parasites in insects, the alimentary canal should be removed to a microscope slide, teased apart in a drop of saline, covered with a cover glass, and examined, using the lowest illumination feasible. A phase contrast microscope is preferable for this purpose. Smears of infected intestines stained with Giemsa blood stain are necessary for detailed studies of the morphological features.

Trypanosomal forms of *T. lewisi* occur commonly in the blood of young Norway rats. A drop of blood examined under the microscope shows the parasites moving rapidly among the erythrocytes. A phase contrast microscope is advantageous for viewing them while still alive. Blood smears stained with Wright's or Giemsa blood stains are necessary for studying morphological details.

Experimental infections of trypanosomes may be established in the blood of young white rats by injecting two or three ml of infected blood from wild rats into the body cavity. Trypanosomes appear in the blood after one or two days, increase rapidly to a peak, and slowly decline, disappearing in about a month.

Cultures of the flagellates can be reared by standard techniques for invertebrates (Wallace) and vertebrates (Diamond and Herman).

SELECTED REFERENCES

Becker, E. R. (1923). Amer. J. Hyg. 3:202; J. Parasit. 9:141, 199.

Diamond, L. S., and C. M. Herman. (1954). J. Parasit. 40:195.

Gibbs, A. J. (1951). J. Parasit. 37:587.

Hewitt, R. (1940). J. Parasit. 26:160.

McCulloch, I. (1915). Univ. Calif. Publ. Zool. 16:1.

McGhee, R. B., and W. L. Hanson. (1964). J. Protozool. 11:555.

Wallace, F. G. (1943). J. Parasit. 29:196; (1959). J. Protozool. 6:58.

Trypanosoma

The *Trypanosoma* are parasites of the blood, lymph, tissues, or cavities of all classes of vertebrates. Because of their importance as causes of decimating diseases in man and domestic mammals, species infecting these hosts have been studied more extensively than those occurring in the other vertebrates. While trypanosomes are widespread in the world, generally speaking the pathogenic species are tropical or subtropical in distribution. One highly pathogenic and aberrant species occurs in horses in temperate climates.

Transmission is by invertebrates in which cyclic development occurs, with a few exceptions. Trypanosomes of fish, amphibians, and aquatic reptiles are transmitted by leeches, and those of terrestrial animals by bugs, fleas, tabanids, mosquitoes, and tsetse flies. Mechanical transmission through the agency of tabanids occurs in *T. evansi* and *T. equinum* of equines, which species have no developmental stages in the flies. T. *equiperdum* of equines, having no known cyclic development, is transmitted venereally.

MORPHOLOGY. The stages of the life cycle include leishmanial, leptomonad, crithidial, and trypanosomal forms, which have been described above in sufficient detail for present purposes.

BASIC LIFE CYCLE. There are two hosts, a vertebrate and a bloodsucking invertebrate, in the life cycle with specific development in each, except for *T. evansi, T. equinum,* and *T. equiperdum* in which there is but one host.

Multiplication is always by binary fission. In the vertebrate host, the final stage of development is the trypanosome. When taken into the alimentary canal of the invertebrate host, it undergoes transformation through one or more stages such as the leishmanial, leptomonad, or crithidial forms which are not infective to the vertebrate host. The final infective stage is the metacyclic trypanosome, a small form that develops either in the anterior or in the posterior part of the alimentary canal of the arthropod intermediate host.

In rat fleas, sheep keds, and reduviid bugs, the metacyclic trypanosomes of *T. lewisi, T. melophagium,* and *T. cruzi,* respectively, develop in the hindgut or posterior station, as it is called, and are expelled in the faeces. Infection of the vertebrate host is by the contaminative method in which faeces containing the metacyclic trypanosomes are swallowed or rubbed into abrasions of the skin.

In tsetse flies (*Glossina* spp.), development of the metacyclic trypanosomes takes place in the proboscis or salivary glands. This is designated as the anterior station and is where trypanosomes of the *vivax*, *congolense*, and *brucei-evansi* groups develop. Infection of the vertebrate host is through injection of the metacyclic trypanosomes by the feeding flies. This is the inoculative method of infection. A similar situation occurs between aquatic vertebrates and leeches.

Trypanosomes of mammals

The classification of the trypanosomes of mammals is based on a combination of morphological, physiological, and biological features. The parasites may be divided into two major sections based on 1) the morphology of the trypanosomes in the blood, 2) stage of multiplication in vertebrates, 3) location of development of metacyclic trypanosomes in the invertebrate host, and 4) mode of infection of vertebrate host. Subgroups of each section are recognized.

Section A

Morphologically, the posterior end of the body is pointed, the blepharoplast is subterminal, and multiplication in the vertebrate host is in the leishmanial or crithidial stages.

Biologically, the metacyclic trypanosomes develop in the rectum, or posterior station of fleas, keds, and reduviid bugs and are voided with the faeces. Transmission to the vertebrate host is by contamination wherein the metacyclic trypanosomes enter the wound made by the biting arthropod or through abrasions of the skin, or are swallowed and migrate through the intestinal mucosa into the blood.

I. The lewisi group

The members of this group are characterized by a large blepharoplast and long pointed posterior end of body.

Trypanosoma lewisi (Kent, 1880) (Plate 3)

Trypanosoma lewisi is a cosmopolitan parasite of rats.

DESCRIPTION. The body is about 25 μ long, curved, and with the posterior end sharply pointed. The nucleus lies anterior to the middle of the body; the blepharoplast is well developed and some distance from the posterior tip of the body. A weakly convoluted undulating membrane with an axoneme lies along the free margin, running in a fairly straight course. The flagellum is well developed. A curved body, eccentric nucleus, and pointed posterior end are characteristics of the species.

LIFE CYCLE. The period of multiplication of trypanosomes in the blood of rats is of short duration. Division of the individuals is incomplete, resulting in a rosette of small crithidia still attached by their posterior ends. These become detached from each other and repeat the division process, thereby greatly increasing their number. Eventually, the small crithidia transform into trypanosomes and the dividing forms disappear from the blood.

Shortly after being sucked into the stomach of fleas, the trypanosomes enter the epithelial cells. Division begins and a clump of 8 to 10 trypanosomes similar to the parent forms develop and escape into the lumen of the stomach. These may re-enter other cells of the stomach, repeating the process several times. Finally, they migrate to the hindgut and rectum, transforming first to crithidia that multiply, and eventually develop to infective metacyclic trypanosomes which are voided with the faeces.

Related species occur in several different mammals. *T. duttoni* occurs in house mice in many parts of the world. Its life cycle is similar to that of *T. lewisi*. *T. melophagium* is a parasite of sheep, with the ked, *Melophagus ovinus*, as the intermediate host in which the cyclic development of the trypanosome is similar to that of *T. lewisi*.

EXPLANATION OF PLATE 3 ⇨

A-H. Trypanosomes from blood of rat. **A.** Typical mature trypanosome. **B.** Crithidia preparing to divide. **C.** Early stage of multiple division forming crithidias. **D.** Multiple division of original trypanosome into rosette of incompletely separated crithidias. **E-F.** Free crithidia from blood. **G.** Young trypanosome. **H.** Older, fully developed trypanosome. **I.** Metacyclic trypanosome from rectum of rat flea. **J.** Rat vertebrate host. **K.** Rat flea *(Nosopsyllus fasciatus)* invertebrate host.

1, characteristic pointed posterior end of mature trypanosome; **2,** flagellum; **3,** parabasal body; **4,** blepharoplast; **5,** axoneme; **6,** undulating membrane with extension of axoneme forming border and continuing as flagellum; **7,** nucleus; **8,** parabasal body and blepharoplast combined; **9,** individual crithidia of rosette.

a, metacyclic trypanosome from faeces of flea being swallowed by rat; **b,** metacyclic trypanosome migrating through wall of oesophagus into blood vessels; **c,** transforming into a crithidia and dividing; **d,** a step further in the process of division; **e,** beginning of multiple fission forming rosette of crithidia in heart; **f,** further division of crithidias in pulmonary artery; **g,** new generation of crithidias in pulmonary vein; **h,** further multiplication of crithidias in left ventricle; **i,** recently transformed trypanosomes with long, slender posterior ends; **j,** newly formed trypanosomes infective to fleas when sucked up by them; **k,** trypanosome in foregut of flea and entering stomach; **l,** trypanosomes in stomach of flea often adhere to each other; **m,** shortened trypanosome attached to epithelium by flagellum; **n,** trypanosome entering epithelial cell; **o,** trypanosome assuming pear shape inside cell; **p-r,** pear-shaped cell enlarging and dividing to form trypanosomes; **s,** trypanosomes produced by intracellular multiplication; **t,** cell wall ruptures and trypanosomes enter lumen of stomach, some reentering cells (n) to begin a new generation; **u,** trypanosomes enter rectum; **v,** trypanosomes attach to rectal wall and undergo transformation leading to crithidias; **w,** multiplying crithidias; **x,** transformation of crithidias to metacyclic trypanosomes which fill rectum; **y,** metacyclic trypanosomes voided with faeces while fleas are feeding; **z,** infective metacyclic trypanosomes in faeces.

Protozoans adapted from Minchin and Thomson, 1915, Quart. J. Micr. Sci. 60:463.

EXERCISE ON LIFE CYCLE

A readily available source of mammalian trypanosomes for life history studies is *T. lewisi* of wild rats. A drop of blood placed on a slide and examined under a 4-mm lens of the microscope with reduced light will reveal the presence of the active parasites by the movement of the erythrocytes. Blood (3 to 5 ml) from infected rats injected into the body cavity of young white rats will initiate an infection with numerous parasites appearing in the blood after four to five days. Rosettes of dividing crithidias appear early in the course of the infection. The infection persists for about 30 days, during which it gradually declines.

Crithidias occur in the mucosal cells of the midgut and the lumen of the hindgut of fleas. Metacyclic trypanosomes are present in the hindgut and the faeces.

Natural transmission of trypanosomes by fleas from wild rats to young white rats may be accomplished by placing the insects on the latter. As the fleas feed, they deposit faeces laden with metacyclic trypanosomes. Infection of the rats takes place when the faeces are ingested as the animals cleanse themselves. Rats become infected by eating fleas harboring metacyclic trypanosomes in the rectum.

SELECTED REFERENCES

Levine, N. D. (1961). Protozoan Parasites of Domestic Animals and of Man. Burgess Publishing Co., Minneapolis, p. 43.

Minchin, E. A., and J. D. Thomson. (1915). Quart. J. Micro. Sci. (N.S.) 60:463

Wenyon, C. M. (1926). Protozoology, Vol. 1. Baillière, Tindall, and Cox, London, p. 463.

Trypanosoma cruzi Chagas, 1909 (Plate 4)

T. cruzi is a parasite primarily of the blood, reticuloendothelial cells of the blood vessels, liver, spleen, lymph glands, bone marrow, and skeletal and cardiac muscles of humans in the tropical and subtropical regions of the American continents. In addition to man, bats, opossums, armadillos,

PLATE 3 *Trypanosoma lewisi*

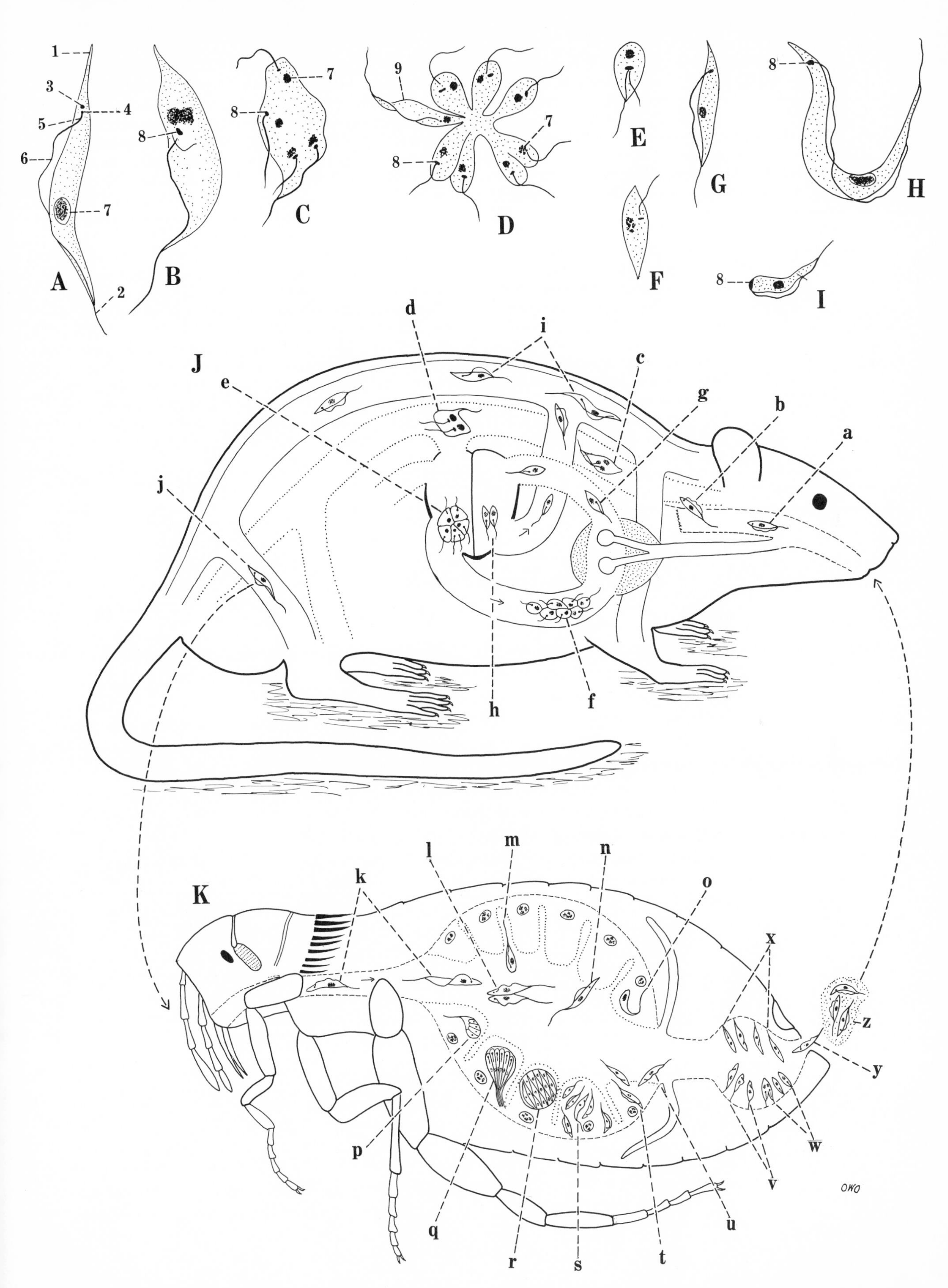

EXPLANATION OF PLATE 4 ▷

A. Typical C-shaped trypanosome from blood of vertebrate host. **B.** Reduviidae bug *(Panstrongylus megistus)* invertebrate host. **C.** Side view of head of bug. **D-I.** Some common vertebrate hosts. **D.** Humans. **E.** Bats. **F.** Opossums. **G.** Armadillos. **H.** Dogs. **I.** Cats (raccoons also serve as natural reservoirs).

1, nucleus; **2,** parabasal body; **3,** blepharoplast; **4,** axoneme; **5,** undulating membrane; **6,** free flagellum; **7,** proboscis in resting position.

a, metacyclic trypanosome that has entered blood from faeces through wound made by feeding bug; **b,** trypanosome enters macrophage cell in blood; **c,** trypanosome transforms to leishmanial stage; **d,** multiplication of leishmanias; **e,** leishmanias transform to crithidias that multiply; **f,** crithidias transform to trypanosomes which rupture cells and escape into blood; **g,** trypanosome free in blood; **h-n,** repetition of cycle depicted in a-g with appearance of trypanosomes in blood for second time (trypanosomes appear in blood periodically by repetition of reproductive cycle); **o,** trypanosomes enter skeletal muscles, as well as cardiac muscles, also reticuloendothelial cells of liver, spleen, and bone marrow; **p,** trypanosomes transform to leishmanial stage; **q,** leishmanias multiply, forming new leishmanias in cystlike bodies; **r,** leishmanias transform to crithidias; **s,** crithidias transform to trypanosomes; **t,** cyst ruptures and trypanosomes are freed; **u-x,** repetition of o-t; **y,** nests of leishmanias in heart muscle; **z,** nest of leishmanias in brain.

a′, bug invertebrate host sucking up trypanosome from blood; **b′,** trypanosome passing through oesophagus; **c′,** crithidia in stomach transformed from trypanosome; **d′,** dividing crithidia in stomach; **e′,** multiplication of crithidias in midgut; **f′,** crithidias in rectum transform to metacyclic trypanosomes; **g′,** metacyclic trypanosomes in faeces infect host through wound made by bug while feeding or by contamination of mucous membranes of lips **(h′)** or eyes **(i′)**.

Figures A, B, part of C, and those of protozoans, adapted from Medical Protozoology and Helminthology, 1955, Naval Medical School, Bethesda, Maryland, p. 92.

---

raccoons, dogs, and cats are common reservoir hosts. This parasite is of great medical importance because of its widespread prevalence and the serious nature of the disease caused by it.

DESCRIPTION. Both slender and broad trypanosomes occur in the blood, averaging 20 μ in length. The body is characteristically U- or C-shaped in stained specimens. The posterior end is pointed, the nucleus is located near the middle of the body, and the blepharoplast is subterminal and so wide that it produces a bulge on each side of the body. The undulating membrane is poorly developed, having two or three convolutions, and the flagellum is always free.

LIFE CYCLE. In the mammalian host, the trypanosomes penetrate the reticuloendothelial cells of the blood and various organs, and the skeletal and cardiac muscles, especially the latter. Having entered these cells, the trypanosomes transform to the leishmanial stage that multiplies by binary fission. These forms fill the cells, transforming to crithidias that later change to trypanosomes which burst out of the cells. The cycle is repeated over and over with trypanosomes appearing periodically in the blood at the completion of each cycle.

When sucked into the intestine of reduviid bugs (Reduviidae) of a number of genera and many species, the parasites undergo a cycle of development. Trypanosomes from the blood transform into crithidias which multiply in the stomach and intestine. These pass to the rectum, where development into metacyclic trypanosomes takes place. While feeding, the bugs habitually void faeces which contain the infective metacyclic trypanosomes. Infection of the vertebrate host occurs when the metacyclic trypanosomes in the faeces enter the body through the mucous membranes of the eyes and lips, or through abrasions on the skin or the wounds made by the feeding bugs.

SELECTED REFERENCES

Doflein, F., and E. Reichenow. (1953). Lehrbuch der Protozoenkunde. Gustav Fischer, Jena, p. 522.

Elkeles, G. (1951). J. Parasit. 37:379.

Faust, E. C., and P. F. Russell. (1957). Craig and Faust's Clinical Parasitology. Lea and Febiger, Philadelphia, p. 158.

Hoare, C. A. (1949). Medical Protozoology. Baillière, Tindall and Cox, London, p. 206.

Levine, N. D. (1961). Protozoan Parasites of Domestic Animals and of Man. Burgess Publishing Co., Minneapolis, p. 58.

Wenyon, C. M. (1926). Protozoology, Vol. 1. Baillière, Tindall, and Cox, London, p. 486.

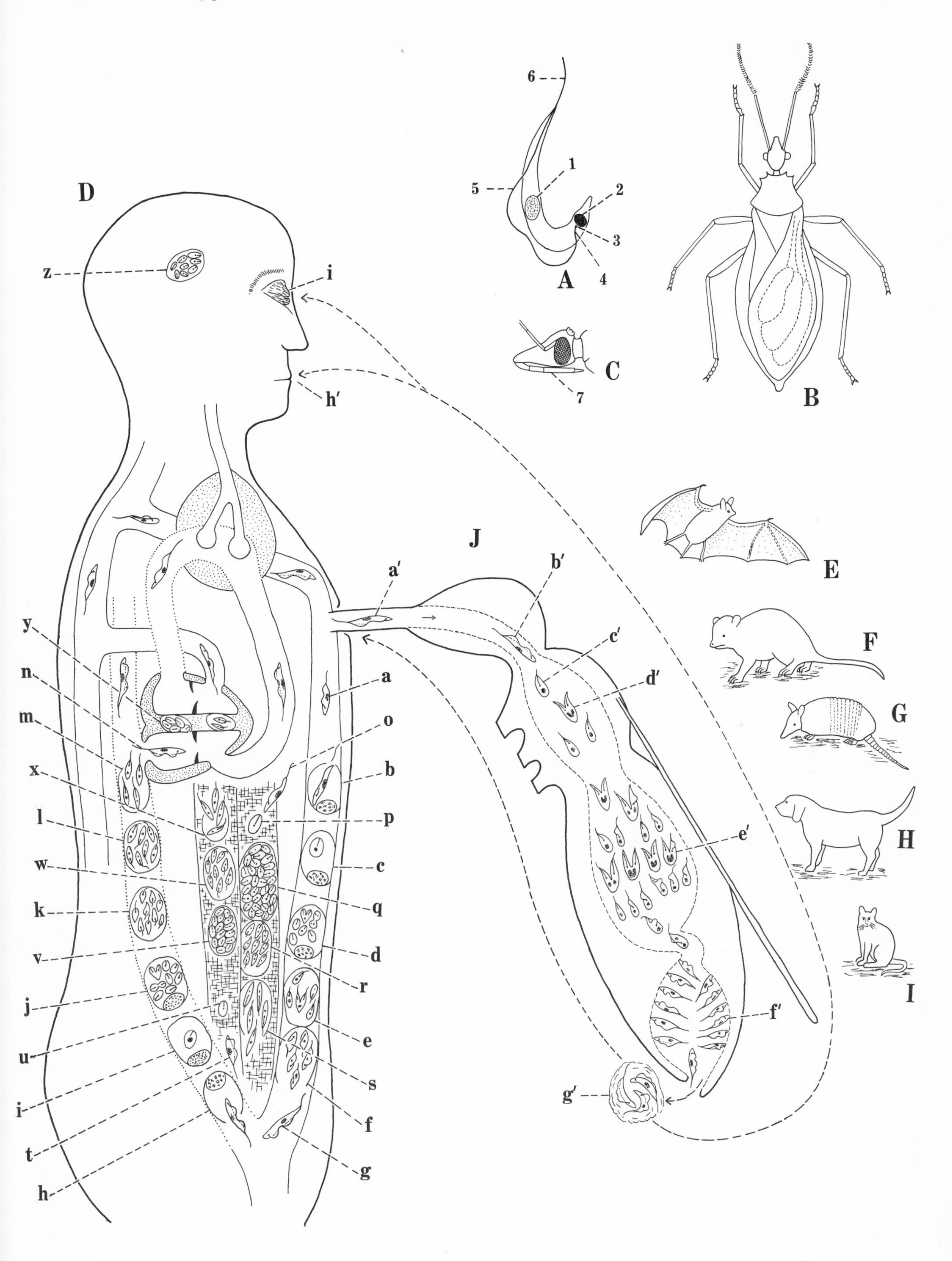
D
A
B
C
E
F
G
H
I
J
1
2
3
4
5
6
7
z
i
h′
y
n
m
x
l
w
k
v
j
u
i
t
h
a
o
b
p
c
q
d
r
e
s
f
g
a′
b′
c′
d′
e′
f′
g′

Section B

Trypanosomes of this section are characterized morphologically by a body that is blunt posteriorly, blepharoplast terminal or subterminal, and multiplication in the vertebrate host by division of the trypanosomal stage.

Biologically, the metacyclic trypanosomes develop in the proboscis or salivary glands (anterior station). Infection occurs when these forms are injected (inoculative method) by bloodsucking invertebrates.

Transmission may be mechanical when trypanosomes are carried from one host to another on the proboscis of feeding flies as in the case of *T. evansi* and *T. equinum* by tabanid flies, or by contact during coitus as occurs with *T. equiperdum* which are abundant in the mucus secretions of the genital tracts of equines.

The members of this section are divided into three basic groups, according to the manner in which cyclic development takes place in the tsetse flies.

I. The vivax group

Trypanosoma vivax Ziemann, 1905 (Plate 5, I)

T. vivax occurs in big game and domestic animals in Africa, but has been transported in domestic animals to other parts of the world, including the West Indies, and Central and South America.

DESCRIPTION. The body is 20 to 26 μ long with a blunt posterior end. A large blepharoplast, a terminal free flagellum, and an inconspicuous undulating membrane are present. They are monomorphic because the forms in the blood of the vertebrate host are structurally all alike.

LIFE CYCLE. Trypanosomes circulating in the blood of the vertebrate host are sucked up by tsetse flies (*Glossina* spp.). In the oesophagus, they transform into crithidias, multiply, and enter the salivary glands. After attaching to the walls of both the salivary glands and pharynx, further multiplication occurs. The crithidias move into the hypopharynx and transform into infective metacyclic trypanosomes. These are injected into the vertebrate host when the tsetse flies suck blood.

In the West Indies and Central and South America, where there are no tsetse flies, the trypanosomes are transmitted mechanically by other bloodsucking insects.

T. vivax causes a severe disease known as nagana in cattle, goats, and sheep, especially the last, in tropical Africa.

SELECTED REFERENCES

Doflein, F., and E. Reichenow. (1953). Lehrbuch der Protozoenkunde, 4th Ed. Gustav Fischer, Jena, p. 538.

Hoare, C. A. (1949). Handbook of Medical Protozoology. Baillière, Tindall, and Cox, London, p. 201, table 9.

Neveu-Lemaire, M. (1943). Traité de Protozoologie Médicale et Vétérinaire. Vigot Frères, Paris, p. 215.

Wenyon, C. M. (1926). Protozoology, Vol. 1. Baillière, Tindall, and Cox, London, p. 559.

II. The congolense group

Trypanosoma congolense Broden, 1904 (Plate 5, II)

T. congolense is a parasite of the blood of game and domestic animals in the tsetse fly belt of tropical Africa. It frequently causes an acute disease with serious effects on cattle.

DESCRIPTION. The body is 9 to 18 μ long (average, 14 μ). The blepharoplast is medium in size and some distance from the posterior end of the body and commonly marginal; the flagellum is absent or present as a very short one and the undulating membrane is inconspicuous. It is polymorphic, because forms in the blood of the vertebrate host may be slender with a free flagellum, or stumpy and without a free flagellum.

LIFE CYCLE. Trypanosomes arriving in the midgut of tsetse flies change from short thick forms into long slender ones as the first step in the cyclic life history. As these long forms migrate forward in the intestine, they change to equally long crithidias which later shorten and enter the salivary glands. They attach to the wall of the pharynx and multiply. This ends the second phase of development in the invertebrate. These short crithidias develop into metacyclic trypanosomes and are injected into the vertebrate host by feeding tsetse flies, where they develop into trypanosomes that multiply.

SELECTED REFERENCES

Doflein, F., and E. Reichenow. (1953). Lehrbuch der Protozoenkunde, 4th Ed. Gustav Fischer, Jena, p. 540.

Hoare, C. A. (1949). Handbook of Medical Protozoology. Baillière, Tindall, and Cox, London, p. 203, table 9.

Levine, N. D. (1961). Protozoan Parasites of Domestic Animals and of Man. Burgess Publishing Co., Minneapolis, p. 54.

Wenyon, C. M. (1926). Protozoology, Vol. 1. Baillière, Tindall, and Cox, London, p. 552.

III. The brucei-evansi group

The members of this heterogeneous group are divided into two subgroups, as indicated by the name. They are polymorphic flagellar or aflagellar trypanosomes in the vertebrate host with a well-developed undulating membrane and a small subterminal blepharoplast.

The geographic distribution of the *brucei* subgroup coincides with that of the tsetse fly vectors in Africa, whereas those members of the *evansi* subgroup which have no invertebrate vectors are cosmopolitan.

A. The brucei subgroup (Plate 5, III)

This group of trypanosomes consisting of *T. brucei*, *T. rhodesiense*, and *T. gambiense* occurs in man and a variety of African mammals. Morphologically, these species are indistinguishable from each other. Their identity is based largely on epidemiological and physiological differences.

Trypanosoma gambiense Dutton, 1902 (Plate 5, III)

T. gambiense is used to illustrate the life cycle of this group. This species, along with *T. rhodesiense*, causes a severe and often fatal disease in humans known as African sleeping sickness.

DESCRIPTION. Trypanosomes in the blood and tsetse flies are polymorphic with three forms. Size ranges from 12 to 42 μ, including flagellum. The slender forms are thin and long, the average length being 29 μ. The flagellum is long, the posterior end pointed, and the blepharoplast is some distance from the end. Intermediate forms average 23 μ long with the body of medium thickness; the flagellum is of medium length, the posterior end of the body is blunt, and the blepharoplast is subterminal. Stumpy forms are stout, 12 to 26 μ long, with an average length of 18 μ, usually there is no free flagellum, the posterior end of the body is broadly rounded, and the blepharoplast is terminal.

LIFE CYCLE. The trypanosomes in vertebrate hosts occur in the blood, lymph, and cerebrospinal fluid. Multiplication is primarily by the slender forms and goes on continuously.

In the midgut of tsetse flies, the trypanosomes transform into long slender individuals that multiply. The newly formed parasites migrate posteriorly through the opening of the free end of the peritrophic membrane, then forward between it and the midgut wall. Upon arriving at the junction of the midgut and peritrophic membrane, they continue through the fluid part of the latter into the proventriculus. Migration forward continues to the pharynx whence they turn back into the salivary glands. Here they transform into crithidias, multiply, and change into metacyclic trypanosomes that are injected into the vertebrate host when the flies feed.

EXPLANATION OF PLATE 5 ⇨

I. The *vivax* group *(Trypanosoma vivax).*

A. Big game and domestic mammals (not man) of Africa. **B.** Tsetse flies *(Glossina).*

1, labrum-epipharynx of proboscis; **2,** hypopharynx of proboscis; **3,** proventriculus; 4, midgut; **5,** peritrophic membrane; **6,** salivary gland.

a, trypanosome sucked up with blood by tsetse flies; **b,** trypanosomes have transformed to crithidias that divide in oesophagus and pharynx; **c,** crithidias enter salivary glands; **d,** crithidias attach to wall of pharynx and divide; **e,** metacyclic trypanosomes transform from crithidias, pass down hypopharynx, and are injected into vertebrate host; **f,** trypanosomes multiply as such in blood of vertebrate.

II. The *congolense* group *(Trypanosoma congolense).*

A and **B** as in *vivax* group above.

1-6, as in *vivax* group.

a, trypanosome sucked up with blood by tsetse flies; **b,** aflagellated trypanosome enters midgut; **c,** aflagellated trypanosome beginning first phase of development by elongation; **d,** elongated aflagellated trypanosome; **e,** long aflagellated trypanosome; **f,** long crithidias, beginning of second phase of development; **g,** crithidias enter salivary glands; **h,** crithidias shorten, attach to wall of pharynx, and divide; **i,** metacyclic trypanosomes derived from crithidias initiate third and final phase which is infective when injected into vertebrate; **j,** trypanosomes in blood divide.

III. The *brucei-evansi* group *(Trypanosoma brucei, T. gambiense, T. rhodesiense).*

A. Humans and African big game with the latter as reservoir host. **B.** tsetse flies.

1-6, as in *vivax* group; **7,** spinal cord; 8, brain.

a, trypanosomes sucked up with blood by tsetse flies; **b,** trypanosomes reach midgut; **c,** trypanosomes elongate, becoming slender; **d,** multiplication of trypanosomes; **e,** trypanosomes enter space between peritrophic membrane and midgut wall; **f,** trypanosomes migrate through soft proventricular portion of peritrophic membrane into proventriculus; **g,** trypanosomes continue forward, migrating into oesophagus and pharynx; **h,** trypanosomes enter salivary glands; **i,** trypanosomes change to crithidias which multiply; **j,** metacyclic trypanosomes develop from crithidias and are inoculated into vertebrate; **k,** medium-sized trypanosomes; **l,** stumpy trypanosomes; **m,** long, slender trypanosomes dividing; **n,** trypanosomes in central nervous system.

Figures A and protozoans from Medical Protozoology and Helminthology, 1955, Naval Medical School, Bethesda, Maryland, p. 89.

SELECTED REFERENCES

Doflein, F., and E. Reichenow, E. (1953). Lehrbuch der Protozoenkunde, 6th Ed. Gustav Fischer, Jena, 541.

Hoare, C. A. (1949). Medical Protozoology. Baillière, Tindall, and Cox, London, p. 174, table 9.

Levine, N. D. (1961). Protozoan Parasites of Domestic Animals and of Man. Burgess Publishing Co., Minneapolis, p. 47.

Wenyon, C. M. (1926). Protozoology, Vol. 2. Baillière, Tindall, Cox, London, p. 524.

B. *The evansi subgroup*

The species of this subgroup have dropped the insect vectors and cyclic development from their life cycles. Transmission is by mechanical means in which the trypanosomes are transferred directly from host to host on the sucking mouth parts of flies, as in the case of *T. evansi* and *T. equinum,* or contact during coitus, as occurs in *T. equiperdum.*

T. evansi is a parasite of the blood of cattle, horses, and camels in many parts of the tropical regions of the world. It causes a disease known as surra. *T. equinum* infects the blood of horses in South America and causes a surra-like disease known as *Mal de Caderas.* Both species are transmitted by tabanids, being transferred from host to host on the mouth parts of the flies.

T. equiperdum occurs in the mucus secretions of the reproductive tracts, rarely in the blood, of equines in many parts of the world, including North America. Transmission is by contact through the genital organs during coitus. It produces a fatal disease known as dourine.

T. evansi and *T. equiperdum* are so similar they cannot be separated on morphological features. *T. equinum* lacks a blepharoplast, which distinguishes it from the other two.

PLATE 5 *Trypanosomes of the vivax (I), congolense (II), and brucei-evansi (III) groups*

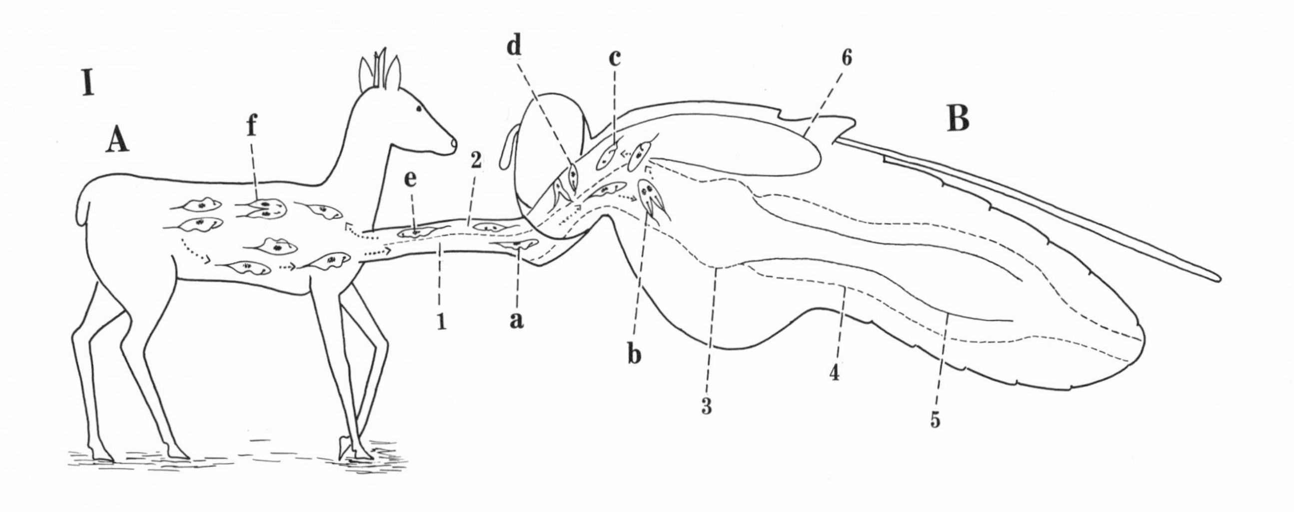

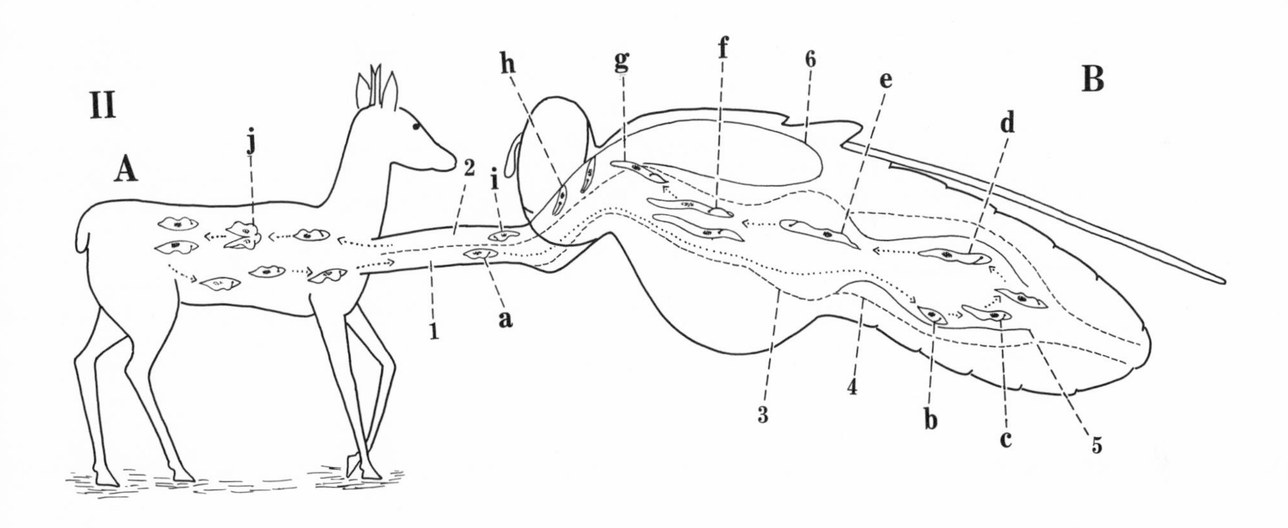

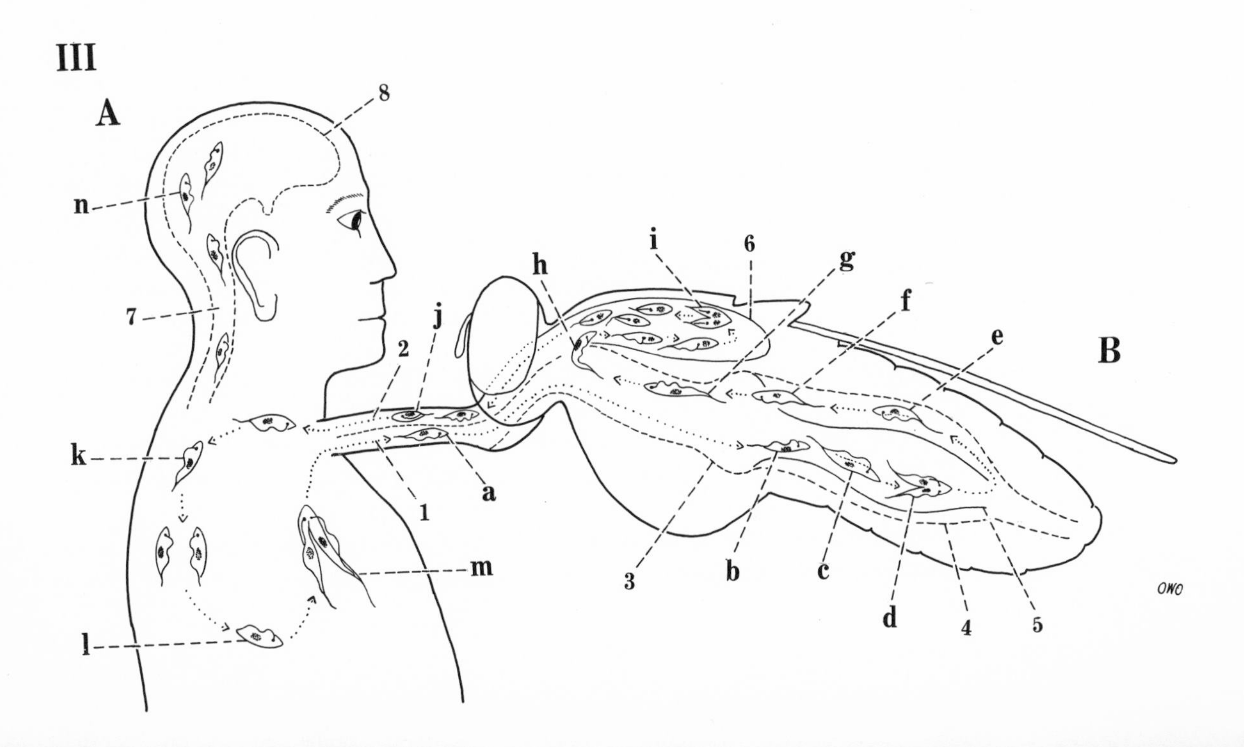

EXPLANATION OF PLATE 6

A. *Trypanosoma percae* from blood of perch. **B.** Trypanosome in process of transforming into crithidia in stomach of leech. **C.** Crithidial stage dividing. **D.** Developed crithidia. **E.** Metacyclic trypanosome. **F.** Fish vertebrate host. **G.** Leech *(Piscicola* spp.) invertebrate host.

1, nucleus; **2,** myonemes; **3,** parabasal body; **4,** blepharoplast; **5,** axoneme; **6,** undulating membrane; **7,** flagellum.

a, trypanosomes in blood; **b,** trypanosome being sucked into pharynx of leech; **c,** trypanosome in stomach; **d,** trypanosome in process of changing to crithidial stage; **e,** dividing of trypanosome and formation of crithidias; **f,** crithidial stage that multiplies; **g, h,** metacyclic trypanosomes in stomach; **i,** metacyclic trypanosome entering oesophagus; **j,** injection of metacyclic trypanosomes into blood stream; **k,** trypanosome entering blood stream; **l,** trypanosome transformed from metacyclic stage; **m,** proboscis sheath; **n,** intestine.

Figure A adapted from Minchin, 1909, Proc. Zool. Soc. London (1), Jan.-Feb. p. 2; B-E, G, from Wenyon, 1926, Protozoology, Vol. 1, Fig. 244.

SELECTED REFERENCES

Doflein, F., and E. Reichenow. (1953). Lehrbuch der Protozoenkunde, 4th Ed. Gustav Fischer, Jena, p. 550.

Hoare, C. A. (1949). Medical Protozoology. Baillière, Tindall, and Cox, London, p. 199.

Lapage, G. (1956). Veterinary Parasitology. Oliver and Boyd, London, p. 771.

Levine, N. D. (1961). Protozoan Parasites of Domestic Animals and of Man. Burgess Publishing Co., Minneapolis, p. 51.

Neveu Lemaire, M. (1943). Traité de Parasitologie Médicale et Vétérinaire. Vigot Frères, Paris, p. 193.

Trypanosomes of birds, reptiles, amphibians, and fish

The classification and biology of the trypanosomes of birds, reptiles, amphibians, and fishes are not as well understood as those of the mammals. Much work remains to be done on them.

BIRDS. Trypanosomes are common parasites of many species of birds. They may be found more often in fresh smears of bone marrow than in stained smears of blood.

The species reported from birds are numerous but the actual validity of all of them is not well established. Morphologically, they are large and have a long, pointed posterior end. The blepharoplast is a considerable distance from the hind end of the body.

The means of transmission under natural conditions are not clear. Culicine mosquitoes or hippoboscid flies are believed to be of primary importance. Mites, such as *Dermanyssus gallinae* of poultry, may be vectors.

REPTILES. Reptiles are frequently infected with large trypanosomes resembling those in birds. Insects and possibly ticks are vectors.

AMPHIBIANS. Frogs harbor large species of trypanosomes. Leeches probably serve as intermediate hosts, but the possibility of mosquitoes acting in this capacity should not be ruled out.

FISH. Trypanosomes of fish are transmitted by leeches. The pattern of cyclic development of trypanosomes of fresh-water fishes in the alimentary canal of leech vectors may be differentiated into three groups as follows: 1) trypanosomes from the blood that transform first into crithidias and later into metacyclic forms in the stomach and are injected directly into the blood stream, as in the case with *T. percae* of perch; 2) trypanosomes from the blood that a) transform into crithidias in the stomach, b) go to the intestine without further change, and c) return to the stomach where they become metacyclic trypanosomes, which d) migrate to the proboscis sheath whence they are injected into fish, as in *T. granulosum* of eels; and 3) trypanosomes that transform first into crithidial and then metacyclic stages in the stomach, following which they go directly to the proboscis sheath from where they are injected, as in *T. danilewskyi* of carp.

EXERCISE ON LIFE CYCLE

Trypanosomes of fish generally are large, being about 50 μ long. Examine a drop of fresh blood placed on a microscope slide for living trypanosomes. With reduced light, they can be seen moving

PLATE 6 *Trypanosoma percae*

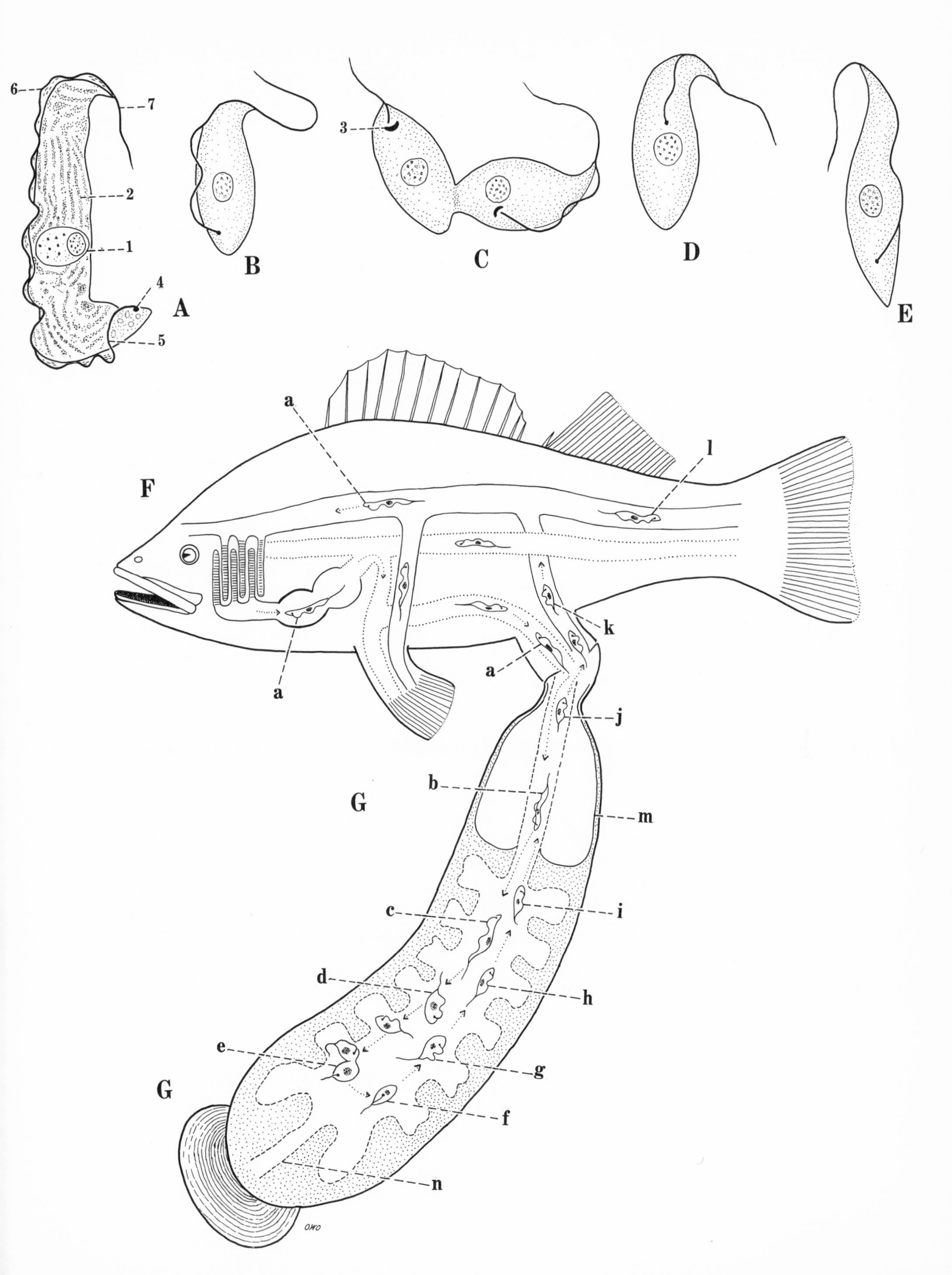

actively under the cover glass, knocking the erythrocytes about in the process. Blood smears prepared by the standard methods and stained with Wright's or Giemsa's stains provide permanent mounts for studying the details of morphology.

Examine the digestive tract and pouches of the proboscis sheath of piscicolid leeches for stages of the trypanosomes developing in them.

Having found infected fish and leeches, experiments on transmitting the trypanosomes from fish to leeches, and vice versa, can be conducted in the laboratory. Specimens of fish and leeches obtained from locations where infections do not occur are necessary for the experiments. Fish from pet shops provide uninfected specimens that may be suitable for experimental infection with species of trypanosomes found naturally infecting fish and leeches. Goldfish should be tried whenever trypanosomes are available in naturally infected cyprinids. In addition to leeches, transfers between fish may be made by injecting infected blood into uninfected fish.

SELECTED REFERENCES

Doflein, F., and E. Reichenow. (1953). Lehrbuch der Protozoenkunde, 6th Ed. Gustav Fischer, Jena, p. 560.

Minchin, E. A. (1909). Proc. Zool. Soc. London (1):2.

Stabler, R. M. (1961). J. Parasit. 47:413.

Wenyon, C. M. (1926). Protozoology, Vol. 2. Baillière, Tindall, and Cox, London, p. 599.

Leishmania

The genus *Leishmania,* as already stated, has two stages in the life cycle. They are a leishmanial form in man and other mammalian hosts and the leptomonad form in species of sand flies (*Phlebotomus*) and in cultures.

Three species of *Leishmania* are well known. They are *L. tropica,* producing cutaneous leishmaniasis; *L. braziliensis,* which causes cutaneous-mucocutaneous leishmaniasis; and *L. donovani,* causing visceral leishmaniasis. Morphologically, they are indistinguishable. Separation of the species is on the basis of clinical manifestations and serological tests. There is considerable overlapping in these differences so that it is possible that there is a complex of strains rather than distinct species, as pointed out by Garnham.

MORPHOLOGY. The leishmanias are oval bodies 2 to 3 μ long which occur in the monocytes, polymorphonuclear leucocytes, and endothelial cells. In leucocytes stained with Giemsa's or Wright's blood stain, the nucleus of the leishmania is red and the blepharoplast and parabasal body are deep red to purplish.

Leptomonads from the intestine of sand flies and cultures vary from oval to spindle-shaped, with the nucleus located somewhat centrally; length of body of large forms is 15 to 25 μ and of the small rounded forms 10 to 12 μ. The flagellum in both forms is 15 to 28 μ long.

The life cycles of all three species are basically similar. Variations occur in the species of sand flies that serve as vectors in different parts of the world. Of about a dozen species known to serve as vectors, some common ones are *Phlebotomus argentipes* in Asia, *P. papatasii* in Europe and the middle East, and *P. sergenti* in South America.

Leishmania donovani (Laveran and Mesnil, 1903) (Plate 7)

LIFE CYCLE. Leptomonads injected into the mammalian host by feeding sand flies are engulfed by the reticuloendothelial cells in which they transform into leishmanial stages and multiply rapidly by binary fission, destroying the host cells. Leishmanias liberated in the blood are engulfed by similar cells which in turn are destroyed by the multiplying parasites. Reticuloendothelial cells of the liver become infected, causing great enlargement of it. Destruction by the parasites of the phagocytic cells of the body leaves it without defense against invasion by other pathogenic organisms.

Infected macrophages ingested by sand flies are digested and the leishmanias liberated in the midgut. Division begins and the newly formed leishmanias develop into leptomonads. These multiply, filling the anterior portion of the alimentary canal. Leptomonads injected into the mammalian host by feeding sand flies initiate the leishmanial phase of the cycle.

EXERCISE ON LIFE CYCLE

No studies on the parasite are suggested.

SELECTED REFERENCES

Belding, D. L. (1952). Textbook of Clinical Parasitology, 2nd Ed. Appleton-Century-Crofts, New York, p. 201.

Chandler, A. C., and C. P. Read. (1961). Introduction to Parasitology, 10th Ed., John Wiley and Sons, New York, p. 111.

Faust, E. C., P. R. Russell, and D. R. Lincicome. (1957). Craig and Faust's Clinical Parasitology, 6th Ed., Lea and Febiger, Philadelphia, p. 112.

Garnham, P. C. C. (1965). Amer. Zool. 5:141.

Hoare, C. A. (1949). Medical Protozoology. Baillière, Tindall, and Cox, London, pp. 152, 158.

Levine, N. D. (1961). Protozoan Parasites of Domestic Animals and Man. Burgess Publishing Co., Minneapolis, pp. 65, 66.

FAMILY CHILOMASTIGIDAE

The members of this family possess a cytostomal groove with a cytoplasmic fibril extending across the anterior end and posteriorly along each side. A posteriorly directed flagellum lies in the cytostomal groove.

Chilomastix mesnili (Wenyon, 1910) (Plate 8)

This is a common inhabitant of the large intestine of humans, both as motile, flagellated trophozoites and cysts. It is cosmopolitan in distribution but more common in warm climates than in cool ones.

DESCRIPTION. Both trophozoites and cysts occur. The trophozoites are somewhat pear-shaped with a ventral groove, or cytostome, in the anterior half of the body. Three flagella extend anteriorly and a short delicate one lies in the obliquely arranged cystostomal groove, the margin of which is formed by a fibril extending around the anterior end and posteriorly along each side. Trophozoites measure 6 to 20 μ long by 3 to 10 μ wide. The nucleus is near the anterior end. The cystic forms are lemon- or pear-shaped. They are colorless, typically uninucleate, have a thick wall, and measure 7 to 10 μ long by 4 to 6 μ wide. The cytostome is visible inside the cyst (Plate, A-C).

LIFE CYCLE. The life cycle is direct, being transmitted by cysts in water and food. Multiplication of trophozoites in the intestine is by binary fission following division of the nucleus. Cysts containing two individuals have been observed. Both cysts and trophozoites appear in the faeces.

Other species have been reported from a variety of hosts. They include *C. caulleryi* from frogs, *C. bettencourti* from rats and mice, *C. cuniculi* from rabbits, *C. intestinalis* from guinea pigs, *C. caprae* from goats, and *C. gallinarum* from poultry. Monkeys of several species harbor a *Chilomastix*. Whether these various forms are different from *C. mesnili* in humans is uncertain.

EXERCISE ON LIFE CYCLE

Simple experiments on host specificity may be conducted by cross-infections, using forms from frogs to infect mice, and vice versa. Care must be taken to use parasite-free experimental animals.

SELECTED REFERENCES

Doflein, F., and E. Reichenow. (1953). Lehrbuch der Protozoenkunde. Gustav Fischer, Jena, p. 569.

Levine, N. D. (1962). Protozoan Parasites of Domestic Animals and Man. Burgess Publishing Co., Minneapolis, p. 111.

Wenyon, C. M. (1926). Protozoology. William Wood and Co., New York, p. 621.

EXPLANATION OF PLATE 7 ⇨

A. Leishmania stage. **B.** Leptomonas stage. **C.** Sand fly *(Phlebotomas)* invertebrate host. **D.** Vertebrate host.

1, nucleus; **2,** parabasal body; **3,** blepharoplast; **4,** axoneme; **5,** flagellum.

a, macrophage containing leishman bodies being swallowed by sand fly; **b,** macrophage being digested and leishman bodies released; **c,** binary division of leishman bodies; **d,** formation of leptomonad bodies; **e,** binary fission of leptomonads; **f,** multiplication of leptomonads in gut; **g,** migration of leptomonads toward proboscis; **h,** leptomonads in proboscis of feeding sand fly; **i,** leptomonad recently injected by sand fly into blood stream of vertebrate; **j,** macrophage ingesting leptomonad; **k,** leishman body from transformed leptomonad; **l,** leishman bodies divide by binary fission; **m,** two leishman bodies; **n,** multiplication of leishman bodies; **o,** macrophage completely filled with leishman bodies; **p,** macrophage ruptures, releasing leishman bodies in blood; **q,** macrophages ingest leishman bodies; **r,** infected macrophages pass through heart and into general circulation (**r, s, t, u, v**); **s, t, u,** multiplication of leishman bodies begins upon ingestion of them by macrophages; **v,** infected macrophages in general circulation available to biting sand flies; **w,** leishman bodies in reticuloendothelial cells of liver (also in spleen and bone marrow); **x,** reticuloendothelial cells rupture, releasing leishman bodies which are ingested by phagocytic cells of liver, spleen, and bone marrow where multiplication occurs with eventual destruction of the host cells.

Adapted from Medical Protozoology and Helminthology, 1955, Naval Medical School, Bethesda, Maryland, p. 89.

FAMILY CRYPTOBIIDAE

The members of this family occur in the blood and alimentary canal of fish, and in the seminal vesicles and spermatophores of mollusks.

These flagellates are similar in body shape to the trypanosomes but have two flagella. One extends anteriorly while the other is directed posteriorly and is adherent to the body, is with or without an undulating membrane, and has a free trailing portion.

Members of the genus *Cryptobia* do not have an undulating membrane, whereas those of *Trypanoplasma* do.

Cryptobia helicis Leidy, 1846 (Plate 8)

This species occurs commonly in the seminal vesicle and intestine of pulmonate land snails (*Helix aspersa, Triodopsis albolabris, T. tridentata, Anguispira alternata,* and *Monadenia fidelis*).

DESCRIPTION. The organism is typically elongate and slender, measuring 6 to 20 μ in length, with the body flattened. Some forms are short and broad. A darkly staining mass near the anterior end of the body consists of an elongate structure and two blepharoplasts. The axoneme of one blepharoplast gives rise to the anterior free flagellum, and that of the other extends backward, giving rise to the posterior flagellum which is attached to the surface of the body except for the extremity which trails freely behind. No undulating membrane is present (Plate 8, D).

LIFE CYCLE. Multiplication is by binary fission. The blepharoplasts each divide, thus making two pairs. The original axoneme and flagellum are retained by one blepharoplast and new ones are formed by the other. The kinetoplast and nucleus divides and cleavage of the organism follows, forming two new individuals.

No encysted forms have been observed. It is believed that the parasites, being in the seminal vesicle, are transferred from one snail to another during copulation.

EXERCISE ON LIFE CYCLE

While it is presumed that *Cryptobia helicis* is transmitted during copulation of the snails, it would be interesting to demonstrate whether this actually is the case and, if so, whether it is the only means of transfer of the parasite. It is the apparent absence of encysted forms that has led to this conclusion rather than actual observations.

Information on whether transmission may take place from the soil may be obtained by placing uninfected laboratory-reared snails in terrariums previously occupied by infected ones.

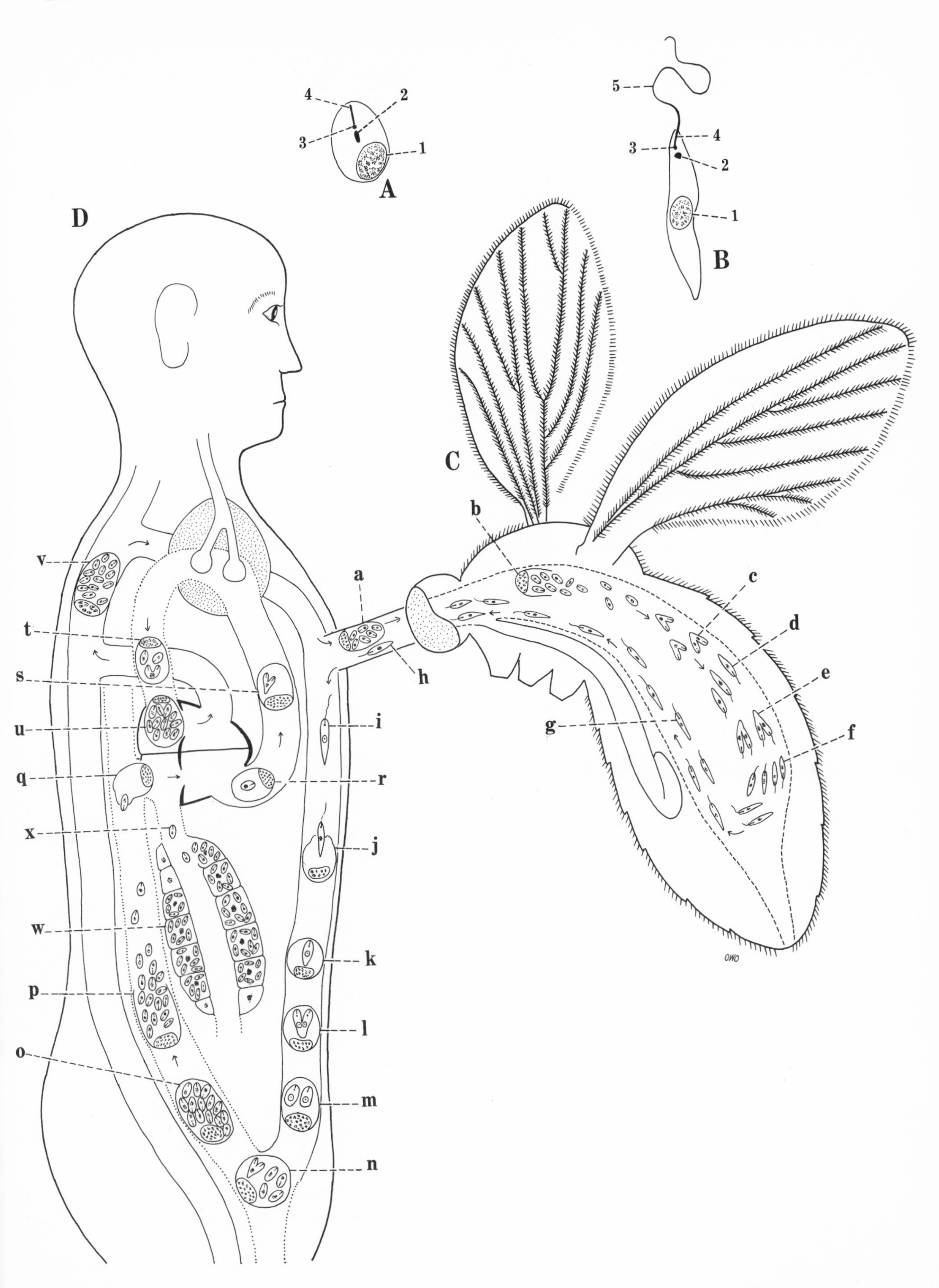
A
1
2
3
4
B
1
2
3
4
5
C
a
b
c
d
e
f
g
h
D
i
j
k
l
m
n
o
p
q
r
s
t
u
v
w
x
OWO

EXPLANATION OF PLATE 8

A-C. *Chilomastix mesnili.* **A.** Trophozoite containing food particles. **B.** Trophozoite. **C.** Cyst. **D.** *Cryptobia helicus.* **E.** *Helix* sp. **F.** *Trypanoplasma borreli.* **G.** Leech *(Piscicola* sp.*)* vector of *Trypanoplasma.*

1, blepharoplast; **2**, anterior flagella; **3**, posterior flagellum hanging in cytostome; **4**, lip of cytostome; **5**, cytostome; **6**, nucleus; **7**, food particles; **8**, cyst wall; **9**, anterior flagellum; **10**, trailing posterior flagellum; **11**, parabasal body; **12**, dividing nucleus; **13**, undulating membrane.

Figures adapted from various sources.

Uninfected sexually immature snails placed with infected sexually mature ones should suggest whether infection is via the soil. Uninfected and infected sexually mature snails placed together, in addition to the experiments mentioned above, would provide strong evidence of the mode of infection.

Trypanoplasma borreli Laveran and Mesnil, 1901 (Plate 8)

Except for the presence of an undulating membrane in species of *Trypanoplasma,* they are very similar morphologically to *Cryptobia.* Some authors consider them as being the same. Differences occur in that *Cryptobia* is in the seminal vesicles and digestive tract of snails, while *Trypanoplasma* is found only in the blood of marine and fresh-water fishes. *T. borreli* occurs in such fresh-water fish as *Catastomus* (suckers), *Cyprinus* (carp), and *Leuciscus* (rudd).

DESCRIPTION. The body if flattened, blunt anteriorly, and pointed posteriorly. It is curved, with the nucleus just behind the anterior third, and is around 20 μ long. The two blepharoplasts lie near the anterior end of the elongated parabasal body. The axoneme from one blepharoplast emerges anteriorly to form the free anterior flagellum, and that of the other passes posteriorly along the margin of an undulating membrane on the convex side of the body to the caudal end where it forms a free flagellum (Plate 8, F).

LIFE CYCLE. Multiplication in the blood of fish is by binary fission, much as described above for *Cryptobia helicis.*

Transmission among the fish is by leeches, particularly *Hemiclepsis* and *Piscicola* (Plate 8, G). Trypanoplasms ingested by the leeches divide by binary fission in the crop. After several days of division, slender forms migrate forward to the proboscis sheath, where they occur in great numbers either free or attached to the wall of the sheath by their flagella. By the time the leech is ready to feed at about 10-day intervals, all of the trypanoplasms appear to have left that part of the intestine posterior from the crop. Feeding apparently clears the leech of the trypanoplasms present in the proboscis. It becomes filled again, presumably by dividing forms from the crop. Trypanoplasms appear in the blood of fish on the seventh day after they have been injected by the leeches.

The trypanoplasms are inoculable from one species of fish to another.

EXERCISE ON LIFE CYCLE

Follow suggestion given on page 26 for trypanosomes from fish.

SELECTED REFERENCES

Cryptobia helicis

Kozloff, E. N. (1948). J. Morph. 83:253.

Kudo, R. R. (1966). Protozoology. Charles C Thomas, Springfield, Ill., p. 425.

Schindera, M. (1922). Arch. Protistenk. 48:187.

Wenyon, C. M. (1926). Protozoology. William Wood and Co., New York, p. 642.

Trypanoplasma borreli

Doflein, F., and E. Reichenow. (1953). Lehrbuch der Protozoenkunde. Gustav Fischer, Jena, p. 567.

Keysselitz, G. (1906). Arch. Protistenk. 7:1.

Mavor, J. W. (1915). J. Parasit. 2:1.

Wenyon, C. M. (1926). Protozoology. William Wood and Co., New York, p. 642.

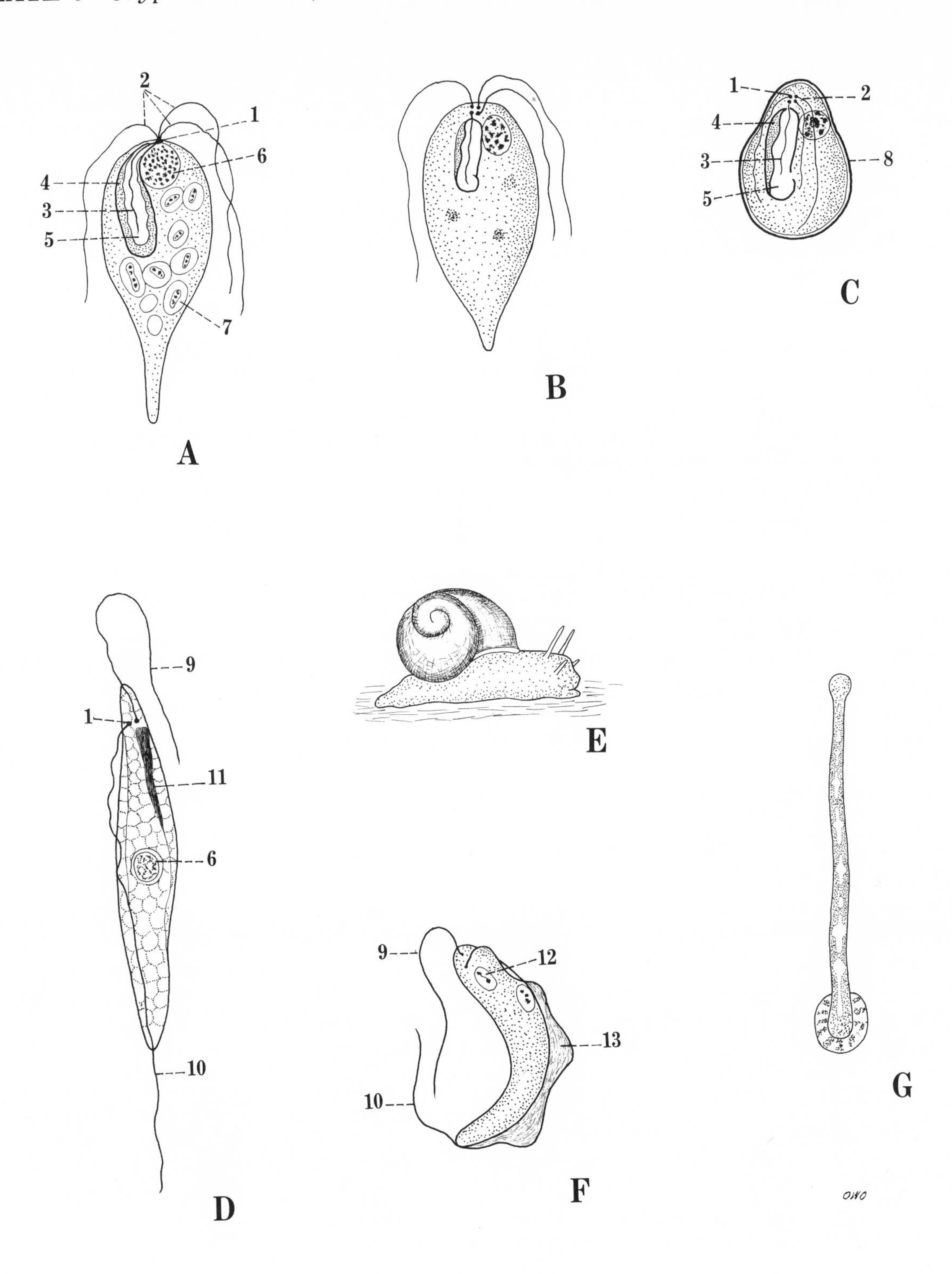
2
1
6
4
3
5
7
A
B
1
2
4
3
8
5
C
9
1
11
6
10
D
E
9
12
13
10
F
G

EXPLANATION OF PLATE 9 ▷

A. Mature flagellate, elongate form. **B.** Shortened form of mature flagellate. **C.** Dividing flagellate. **D.** Two new individuals resulting from longitudinal fission. **E.** Young flagellate from cyst. **F.** Coming together by two small flagellates. **G.** Union of two flagellates inside cyst. **H.** Complete fusion of two flagellates, union of two nuclei, and formation of vacuoles. **I.** Complete fusion of nuclei. **J.** Small uninucleate cyst with large central vacuole that crowds cytoplasm into a thin layer against cyst wall, producing a blastocystis-like appearance. **K.** Small binucleate cyst. **L.** Large multinucleate cyst. **M.** Formation of young flagellates. **N.** Fully developed and presumably infective flagellates in cyst which occurs in posterior stretch of hindgut of host. **O.** Gecko *(Tarentola mauritanica)* host. **P.** Infective cysts pass in faeces.

1, nucleus; **2**, karyosome; **3**, parabasal body; **4**, blepharoplast; **5**, axoneme or rhizoplast; **6**, chromatin ring surrounding rhizoplast; **7**, posterior or trailing flagellum; **8**, anterior flagellum; **9**, cyst wall; **10**, vacuole; **11**, thin layer of cytoplasm pressed against cyst wall by expanding vacuole; **12**, developing flagellates in large cyst; **13**, fully developed flagellates in cyst.

a, ingested cyst has ruptured and is releasing young flagellates; **b**, free flagellate just released from cyst; **c**, fully grown flagellate; **d**, dividing flagellate; **e**, two new flagellates resulting from longitudinal fission; **f**, union of two flagellates which have secreted a cyst about themselves; **g**, individuals have fused, forming a uninucleate individual with a long central vacuole; **h**, binucleate form; **i**, large multinucleated cyst; **j**, infective cyst in posterior region of hindgut which is voided with faeces (P).

Figures redrawn from various sources.

FAMILY BODONIDAE

The members of this family are characterized by two flagella at the anterior end of the body, one of which is directed anteriorly and the other posteriorly along the side of the body, often attached for a short distance, and extending beyond. Most of the species are free-living.

Proteromonas lacertae (Grassi) (Plate 9)

This parasite occurs in the colon of lizards (*Lacerta* and *Tarentola*), newts, salamanders, and axolotls, apparently throughout their geographic range.

Transmission is direct, the infective stages presumably being ingested. The parasites live in the colon where they do little if any damage.

DESCRIPTION. The fully developed parasites are elongated pyriform bodies 10 to 30 μ in length and flattened like a blade of grass. The posterior end is slender and sometimes twisted somewhat screwlike. The blunt anterior end bears two flagella. One is directed anteriorly and is three to five times as long as the body; the other trails behind and is about twice as long as the body to which it may be attached for a short distance. The nucleus, located near the anterior end of the body, has a large central karyosome. One to several parabasal bodies lie close by the nucleus. An axoneme, or rhizoplast, extends from the anterior side of the nucleus to the margin of the body where there forms a blepharoplast whence the two flagella arise. Two rings of chromatin surround the axoneme.

Cysts range from 10 to 100 μ in size. The smallest ones have one or two nuclei located near the wall and a large central vacuole. As nuclear division progresses, the cyst enlarges and the nuclei are arranged over the inside surface of the cyst, being crowded by the vacuole. Bits of cytoplasm associate with the nuclei to form small flagellates.

LIFE CYCLE. Asexual reproduction in the gut takes place by longitudinal fission, and sexual reproduction occurs in cysts following the fusion of two individuals. In dividing forms, the organisms become shortened and the nucleus divides so that each part has a blepharoplast and a rhizoplast which continue as a flagellum. The parabasal body is divided between the two nuclei.

In encysting forms, the body shortens, becoming ovoid in shape, and the flagella are lost. Two forms come together and secrete a cyst about themselves which is about 10 μ in diameter. The individuals in the cyst lose their identity and the two nuclei fuse. A large central vacuole develops and the nuclear division begins. On the first division, the two nuclei move to opposite poles of the cyst, giving it the appearance of a blastocystis. As nuclear division continues, the cyst increases in size, up

PLATE 9 *Proteromonas lacertae*

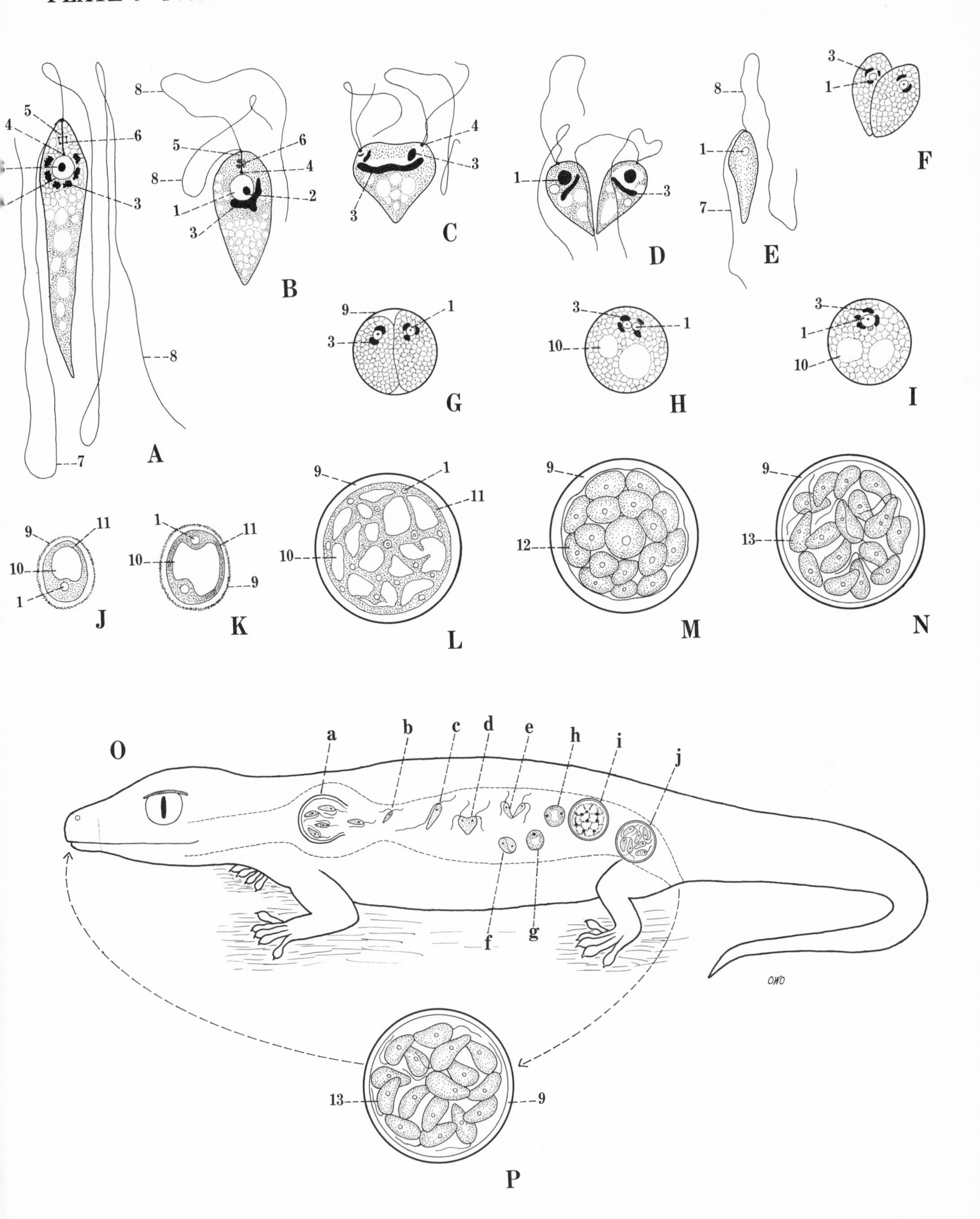

EXPLANATION OF PLATE 10 ▷

A. Sinistral view of flagellate, showing flagella, nucleus, and contractile vacuole. **B.** Ventral view, showing ventral body groove and basal granule. **C.** Dextral view, showing basal granule, cell inclusions, and anterior end of ventral groove. **D.** Dividing form, undergoing binary fission. **E.** Ventral view, showing origin of flagella. **F.** Similar view of E but from an angle. **G.** and **H.** Shapes of swimming *Costia necatrix*. **I.** Section of epidermal cells with three *Costia necatrix* attached. **J.** Section through two scales, showing flagellates attached to epidermis in scale pockets and swimming in exuded mucus.

1, anterior flagella; **2,** posterior, or trailing, flagella; **3,** ventral groove; **4,** basal body; **5,** nucleus; **6,** contractile vacuole; **7,** cell inclusions; **8,** flagellate attached to epidermal cell; **9,** epidermal cells; **10,** trailing flagella inserted into epidermal cell for attachment of flagellate to host.

a, scale; **b,** epidermis; **c,** connective tissue; **d,** epidermal pocket between scales; **e,** free-swimming flagellates; **f,** mass of mucus; **g,** flagellates swimming in exuded mucus; **h,** macrophages; **i,** flagellates in epidermal pocket.

Figures A-D and G-J redrawn from Tavolga and Nigrelli, 1947, Trans. Amer. Micr. Soc. 66:366; Figures E-F redrawn from Davis, 1946, Fish and Wildlife Serv., U. S. Dept. Int., Res. Rept. 12, p. 35.

---

to 100 μ, presumably by absorption of fluid. The cytoplasm and nuclei appear to be pressed against the cyst wall by the internal pressure of the fluid. When 32, or thereabouts, nuclei have developed, a scanty bit of cytoplasm surrounds each of the nuclei to form small flagellates which fill the cyst.

Since the cysts are in the hind part of the gut of lizards, it is presumed that they are the infective stage to other hosts which ingest them with the faeces in which they are voided. This point, however, has not been demonstrated experimentally.

EXERCISE ON LIFE CYCLE

Inasmuch as the complete life cycle has not been demonstrated experimentally, it offers an excellent opportunity to conduct investigations on the manner of infection of the hosts.

Infected hosts, as determined by recognition of the cysts in the faeces, are necessary to provide a continuous source of infective material. The other, and more difficult part, is a colony of uninfected hosts. These would of necessity be acquired by hatching them from eggs and maintaining them under conditions in which natural infection cannot occur.

When cysts are fed to uninfected animals, the development of the infection should be followed daily by postmortem examination of specimens. Other animals should be kept to determine when cysts appear in the faeces. Uninfected control animals should be maintained.

SELECTED REFERENCES

Bělař, K. (1921). Arch. Protistenk. 43:431.

Chatton, E. (1917). C. R. Soc. Biol., Paris, 80:555.

Doflein, F., and E. Reichenow. (1953). Lehrbuch der Protozoenkunde. Gustav Fischer, Jena, p. 564.

Wenyon, C. M. (1920). Parasitology 12:350; (1926). Protozoology. William Wood and Co., New York, p. 611.

FAMILY TETRAMITIDAE

Tetramitidae bear four equal or unequal flagella on the anterior end of the body, one or two of which may trail behind. They are largely free-living. Species of the genus *Costia,* however, parasitize the skin of fresh-water fish.

Costia necatrix (Henneguy, 1883) (Plate 10)

This and a related species are ectoparasites on the skin and gills of fresh-water fish in Europe and North America, possibly in many other parts of the world. *C. necatrix* causes a dermatitis in which a

PLATE 10 *Costia necatrix*

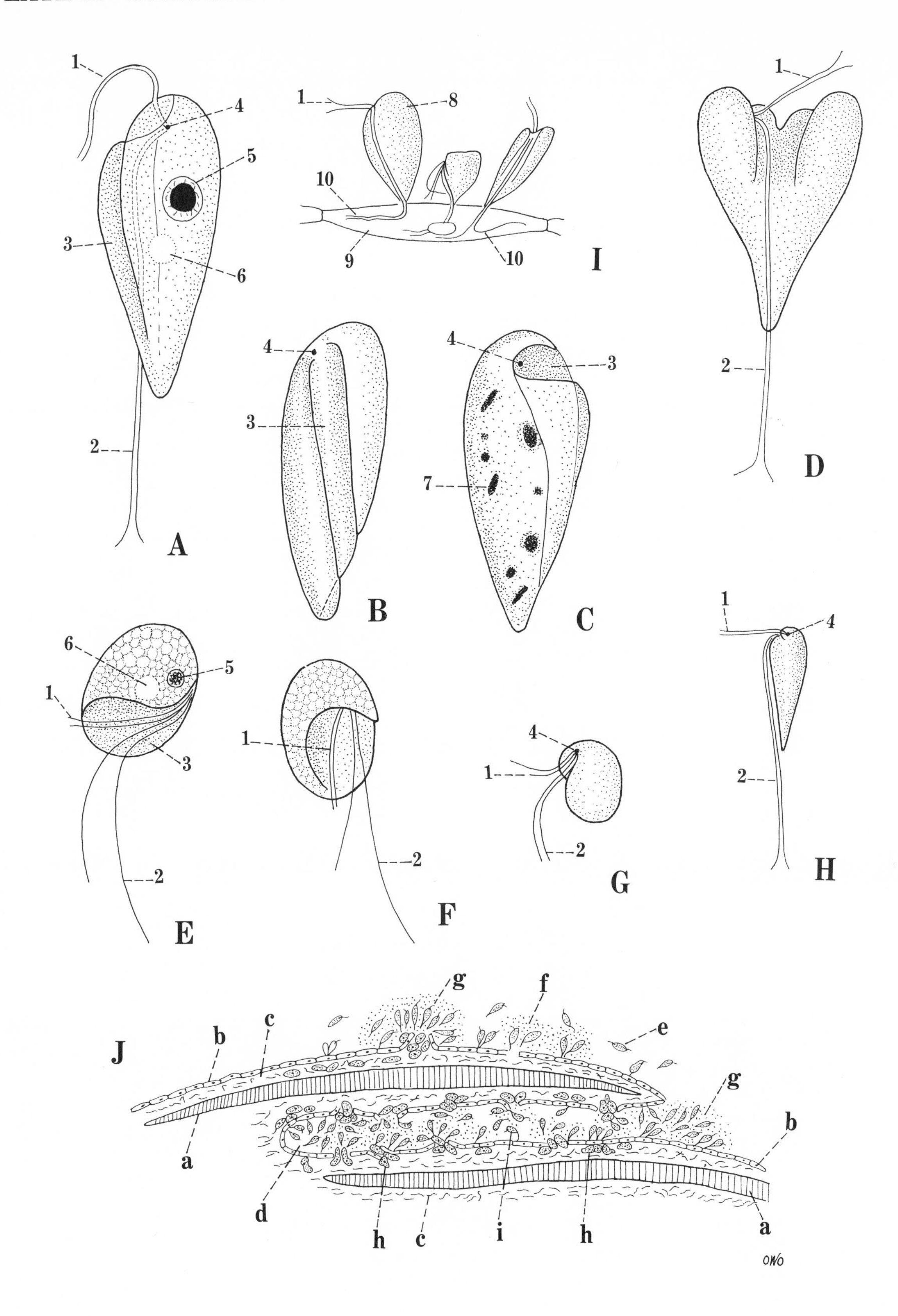

bluish or grayish film containing the parasites spreads over the body and fins. When this film is examined under a microscope, the parasites can be seen.

DESCRIPTION. These small flagellates vary from 5 to 18 μ long by 2.5 to 7.7 μ wide. The shape, likewise, is highly variable. Attached individuals are pyriform, whereas free-swimming ones are ovoid with a convex dorsal and a concave ventral side. A groove extends obliquely from the base of the flagella to the hind quarter of the body. Four flagella are attached at the anterior end of the groove in which they lie when at rest. Two flagella are shorter than the body and two are longer, ranging up to three times its length. The latter, in living specimens, appear to be adherent to the body along the ventral groove, trailing behind as free flagella which function both in swimming and in attaching to the hosts.

Structures visible inside living specimens are dark, rod-shaped or spherical granules and a contractile vacuole. The latter is located near the middle of the body or slightly posterior. It forms and empties every 5 or 10 minutes. In stained specimens, several additional bodies appear. The basal granule lies at the base of the flagella and does not seem to be connected in any way to the nucleus. The nucleus, lying slightly anterior to the contractile vacuole, contains a dark central mass surrounded by narrow clear or reticulated band.

LIFE CYCLE. Attached parasites are active, moving rather vigorously. They detach readily from the host and swim about, trailing the two long flagella. When preparing to attach to the host, the flagellates swim backwards with the long flagella extended. Upon making contact, these flagella actually penetrate the cells where they can be seen in both living and iodine-stained ones. Attached forms are pyriform in shape, free-swimming ones ovoid.

Division is by binary fission. In the case of attached forms, dividing individuals number about one in 500. Numerous specimens appear in the debris on the bottom of the pond, some swimming and some attached to fish scales. As many as 10 to 100 may be adhering to a single loose scale. Among these saprophytic forms,as many as 3 to 5 per cent of the population may be in a stage of binary fission. They are active in temperatures between 8° and 38° C.

Small resistant cysts have been reported, but in laboratory observations none has been found.

In mild infections, the parasites are attached exclusively to the cells lining the pockets between the overlapping scales. Heavy infections are manifested by a bluish or grayish film, especially around the base of the fins and tail. The gills are attacked. Up to 200 and more parasites may be attached to single scale. Heavy losses occur among severely infected fish.

There is some question whether *Costia pyriformis* Davis, 1943, described from trout might not be only a small form of *C. necatrix*.

EXERCISE ON LIFE CYCLE

Infection is common in aquarium fish, also hatchery trout. Presence of the parasite in heavily infected fish may be detected by the light bluish or grayish mucous layer at the base of the fins or caudal peduncle. Examination of a bit of the mucus on a slide by means of a high dry objective of a microscope will reveal the flagellates.

Occasionally, dividing individuals may be seen attached to scales that have been removed carefully from the fish. They are far more common, however, on detached scales on the bottom of the aquarium. Infected scales stained with iodine in 70 per cent alcohol show the ends of the posterior flagella anchored within the epidermis. Sections of skin fixed in 10 per cent formalin and stained in haematoxyln and eosin are useful for showing the parasites in the scale pockets.

Once infected fish are found, uninfected ones may be introduced into the aquarium and the course of the infection followed. Observe the gills as well as the scales for infection.

Infected fish may be freed of the parasites by immersing them in a solution of 1 part acetic acid by volume to 500 parts of water or a single treatment for 1 hour in a 1 to 4,000 solution of formalin.

SELECTED REFERENCES

Davis, H. S. (1943). J. Parasit. 29:385; (1946). Fish and Wildlife Serv., U. S. Dept. Int., Washington, Res. Rept., rev. ed., p. 35.

Moroff, T. (1904). Arch. Protistenk. 3:69.

Tavolga, W. N., and R. F. Nigrelli. (1947). Tran. Amer. Micr. Soc. 66:366.

Wenyon, C. M. (1926). Protozoology. William Wood and Co., New York, p. 305.

ORDER POLYMASTIGINA

The Polymastigina possess three to eight flagella; usually there is a stiffened rodlike axostyle extending through the body and beyond the posterior end. In the Trichomonadidae, a second rodlike structure, the costa, lies along the base of an undulating membrane. Most of the Polymastigina are inhabitants of the alimentary canal.

The order consists of three suborders, two of which will be considered. The suborder Monomonadina is characterized by having a single nucleus, and the suborder Diplomonadina, by two nuclei.

Suborder Monomonadina

FAMILY TRICHOMONADIDAE

The members of this family are pear-shaped parasites of the alimentary canal and genital tract. There are four to six flagella originating from a group of blepharoplasts lying anterior to the single large nucleus; one flagellum passes posteriorly along the free margin of an undulating membrane and may continue as a free-trailing portion. The filamentous costa arising from a blepharoplast extends posteriorly along the basal margin of the undulating membrane. The elongated parabasal body and its accompanying basal filament arise from a blepharoplast and project posteriorly alongside the nucleus. A hyaline rodlike or tubelike axostyle extends posteriorly from the blepharoplast complex through the body, projecting beyond the hind end. Chromatin dots may be present inside it. A darkly staining chromatic ring may surround the axostyle at the point where it emerges from the body. A shield-shaped pelta appears over the anterior end of the body in specimens prepared with silver stains. A cystostome may be present near the anterior end on the side opposite the undulating membrane.

The genera are characterized in part by the number of free anterior flagella. *Ditrichomonas* Duboscq and Grassé, with two anterior flagella, are of doubtful nature. Recent studies on specimens from sheep and cattle indicate that they have four flagella, hence belong to the genus *Trichomonas*. *Tritrichomonas* Kofoid from the genital tract of cattle and the alimentary canal of amphibians, *Tricercomitus* Kirby, a small form with a long trailing flagellum, and *Pseudotrypanosoma* Grassi with a long narrow parabasal body from the gut of termites, have three flagella each. *Trichomonas* Donné, the type genus, from the genital tract of humans, the mouth and alimentary canals of humans and horses, the alimentary canal of dogs, cats, pigeons, chickens, ducks, geese, reptiles, and amphibians, possesses four flagella. *Pentatrichomonas* Mesnil from the intestine of primates and *Pentatrichomonoides* Kirby from the gut of termites have five free flagella.

Tritrichomonas foetus (Riedmüller, 1928) (Plate 11)

This species is parasitic in the genital tract of male and female cattle in many parts of the world, particularly in North America, Eurasia, Japan, and South Africa. Its prevalence is high in the United States and Europe and its economic importance great since it causes abortion and sterility in cows.

DESCRIPTION. Normally, the flagellate is spindle- or pear-shaped and measures from 10 to 25 μ long with the width being about one-third to two-fifths the length. There are three anterior flagella as long as or longer than the body and a single recurrent one passing along the margin of the undulating membrane and trailing beyond as a free-trailing portion about equal in length to the anterior ones. The blepharoplasts lie at the anterior extremity of the body and are the point of origin of the flagella, costa, parabasal body, and axostyle. An undulating membrane equal in length to the body lies along the dorsal side; it has, in addition to the recurrent flagellum, an accessory filament near the free margin

EXPLANATION OF PLATE 11 ▷

A. Trophic stage of *Trichomonas vaginalis* of humans. **B.** Trophic stage of *Tritrichomonas foetus* of bovine. **C.** Trophic stage of *Tritrichomonas batrachorum* of amphibians and reptiles. **D.** dividing *T. batrachorum*. **E.** Trophic stage of *Tritrichomonas augusta* of amphibians. **F.** Early telophase of *T. augusta*. **G.** Late telophase of *T. augusta*. **H.** Mitosis completed, cytoplasm dividing in *T. augusta*. **I.** Cow showing reproductive tract with *Tritrichomonas foetus* in vagina and uterus. **J.** Bull showing reproductive tract with *T. foetus* in preputial pouch and on the glans penis. **K.** Aborted foetus with placenta. **L.** Pyrometric uterus filled with fluid and tritrichomonads from a chronically infected cow.

1, anterior flagella; **2**, trailing flagellum; **3**, undulating membrane; **4**, costa; **5**, blepharoplast; **6**, axostyle; **7**, endaxostylar chromidia; **8**, capitulum of axostyle; **9**, parabasal body; **10**, filament of parabasal body; **11**, nucleus with chromatin granules and karyosome; **12**, paradesmose; **13**, centrosome; **14**, chromosomes.

a, vulva; **b**, vagina; **c**, cervix; **d**, uterus; **e**, Fallopian tube; **f**, ovary; **g**, urinary bladder; **h**, trichomonads; **i**, anus; **j**, penis; **k**, glans penis; **l**, prepuce; **m**, scrotum; **n**, testis; **o**, vas deferens; **p**, prostate gland; **q**, retractor muscle; **r**, rumen; **s**, placenta; **t**, cotyledons; **u**, foetus outside placenta but still attached by umbilical cord.

Figures A-B, redrawn from Wenrich and Emmerson, 1933, J. Morph. 55:193; C-D, from Honigberg, 1953, J. Parasit. 39:191; E-H, from Kofoid and Swezy, 1915, Proc. Nat. Acad. Sci. U. S. A. 1:315; I-J, from Hammond *et al.*, 1956, U. S. Dept. Agr. Yrbk., p. 277; K, from photograph by B. B. Morgan; L, from Boyd, 1937, Lederle Vet. Bull. 6:3.

---

of the undulating membrane and lying parallel to the flagellum. A costa, or chromatic basal rod, extends along the base of the undulating membrane. The oval nucleus is relatively large and lies in the anterior third of the body; it contains a small karyosome. The axostyle is a stout hyaline rod with an enlarged end, the capitulum, which contains chromatin granules, and a sharp tip that extends beyond the posterior end of the body. At the point of its emergence, the axostyle is surrounded by a ring of chromatin. A cylindrical or club-shaped parabasal body lies between the nucleus and costa, terminating shortly before the posterior margin of the nucleus. A mouth, or cytostome, near the anterior end and on the ventral side, is visible in some specimens.

LIFE CYCLE. The flagellates occur first in the vagina of cattle, being introduced by infected bulls during coitus. From here, they move into the uterus which appears to be the permanent location. Disappearance of them from the vagina is due probably to an immunity that develops in the epithelium of the organ. In bulls, the parasites occur in highest numbers on the glans penis and in the adjacent part of the prepuce, with fewer in the other areas.

Multiplication is by longitudinal binary fission, beginning with the blepharoplasts and nucleus. The axostyle divides longitudinally, beginning at the anterior end. Multiple fission has been reported.

Transmission is almost entirely venereal. Infected bulls transmit the flagellates to uninfected cows. In infected females where the parasites are in the uterus, discharges from it containing the protozoans enter the vagina whence clean males servicing them become infected. Once infected, bulls remain permanently so and transmit the infection to all uninfected females with which they mate.

Infected cows commonly abort during the first to sixteenth weeks of pregnancy. Two kinds of abortion occur. In one, the foetal membranes detach from the uterine walls and are expelled together with the foetus. In the other type, a cervical seal develops and the pregnancy is terminated. The embryonic membranes and dead foetus are retained, eventually being macerated. A retained foetus results in filling of the uterus with fluid, macerated tissues, and great numbers of flagellates, a condition known as pyrometra. Progressive enlargement of the pyrometric uterus suggests, from external appearance of the cow, that the pregnancy is progressing normally. In cases in which pyrometra occurs, cows generally become sterile. Infected cows that expel the foetus re-enter oestrus and accept the bull. Such cows may conceive and bear a calf. Recurrence of oestrus at short intervals is suggestive that the cow is infected and that abortion has occurred.

The abomasum of aborted calves contains enormous numbers of the flagellates in almost pure culture.

Although transmission of the parasites is normally venereal, infections have been observed in virgin heifers. Infection might result naturally from contact between infected animals or through transfer by insects of viable flagellates from infected to noninfected individuals. House flies have been

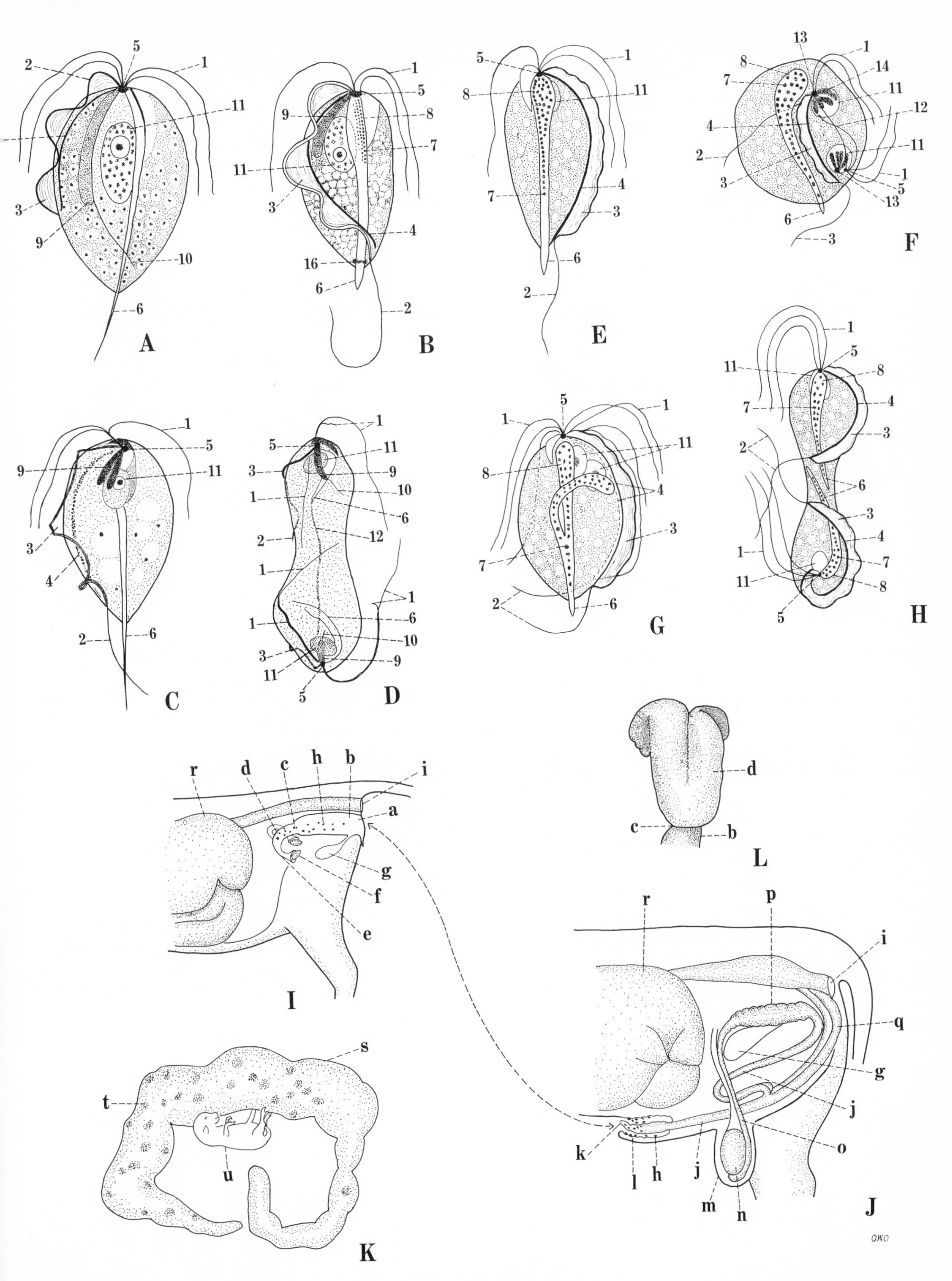
A
B
C
D
E
F
G
H
I
J
K
L

shown to ingest the tritrichomonads and regurgitate living ones within 5 minutes. They may be passed in the faeces for 8 hours, and numerous active ones remain in the intestine for longer periods. It is believed that flies feeding on vaginal exudates from infected cows might transmit the flagellates to uninfected ones. Some workers believe, however, that nonvenereal transmission is insignificant in the epizootiology of tritrichomoniasis.

Control of the disease is dependent on proper management of the breeding program. Since the sire is largely responsible for its spread and remains permanently parasitized, infected bulls should be eliminated from all breeding programs. Aborting cows that have expelled the foetus and its membranes may be freed of the parasites by withholding them from breeding for 90 days.

Other species of *Tritrichomonas* occur in the intestine or respiratory tract of a number of different kinds of animals. Levine listed the principal species in domestic animals, together with an extensive bibliography of pertinent papers.

T. muris of house mice and rats was studied extensively by Wenrich. He described the structure of the flagellate and the method of division. According to him, the blepharoplasts and nucleus divide and separate from each other, moving toward opposite ends of the cell but remaining connected by a threadlike fiber, the paradesmose. New flagella and undulating membranes develop while the nucleus is undergoing division with six chromosomes. He believed the old axostyle disappeared and new ones developed as outgrowths of the blepharoplasts. Wenyon, however, stated that the original one divided longitudinally, beginning at the capitulum and extending caudad.

T. augusta from the digestive tract of salamanders, frogs, and toads is described as having longitudinal binary fission with the axostyle dividing longitudinally, beginning at the anterior end.

EXERCISE ON LIFE CYCLE

Although life cycle studies on the trichomonads are difficult to perform, significant data on their morphology and biology may be obtained through observations on living and prepared specimens.

T. augusta and *T. batrachorum* from the recta of frogs are excellent species for study as they are common, large, and easily cultured, especially the latter species.

Specimens stained by the Giemsa method, which is easy to use, are excellent for observing morphological details.

Cultures, particularly of *T. batrachorum* made by the simple technique of Kofoid and Swezy, and of Rosenberg, yield results satisfactory for observation of the flagellates.

To prepare the culture, the rectal contents of a frog are mixed with an equal volume of 0.85 per cent NaCl solution prepared from glass-distilled water, and the pH is adjusted to 7.64 by adding a few drops of N/20 NaOH. A few drops of the mixture are placed in a cell formed by ringing a slide with Vaseline or petroleum jelly, and a cover slip is pressed in position to form an air-tight seal. The preparation should be kept in the dark at room temperature.

Directions for the preparation and use of more sophisticated media were discussed by Morgan, Wenrich, and Hibler *et al.*

Division of living flagellates may be observed. They may be fixed and stained for critical observation of progressive division as shown in Plate 11.

SELECTED REFERENCES

Doflein, F., and E. Reichenow. (1953). Lehrbuch der Protozoenkunde. Gustav Fischer, Jena, p. 594.

Gehring, K., and C. Murray. (1953). Cornell Vet. 23:335.

Hall, R. P. (1953). Protozoology. Prentic-Hall, New York, p. 188.

Hibler, C. P., D. M. Hammond, F. H. Caskey, A. E. Johnson, and P. R. Fitzgerald. (1960). J. Protozool. 7:159.

Kirby, H., Jr. (1947). J. Parasit. 33:214.

Kofoid, C. A., and O. Swezy. (1915). Proc. Nat. Acad. Sci. U. S. A. 1:315.

Kudo, R. R. (1966). Protozoology. Charles C Thomas, Springfield, Ill., p. 466.

Levine, N. D. (1961). Protozoan Parasites of Domestic Animals and of Man. Burgess Publishing Co., Minneapolis, p. 82.

Morgan, B. B. (1942). Proc. Helm. Soc. Wash. 9:17; (1944). Bovine Trichomoniasis. Burgess Publishing Co., Minneapolis, 150 pp.

Morgan, B. B., and B. A. Beach. (1942). Vet. Med. 37:459.

Rosenberg, L. E. (1936). Trans. Amer. Micr. Soc. 55:313.

Samuels, R. (1957). Trans. Amer. Micr. Soc. 76:295.

Wenrich, D. H. (1921). J. Morph. 36:119; (1945). J. Parasit. 31:375.

Wenyon, C. M. (1926). Protozoology. William Wood & Co., New York, p. 660.

Trichomonas Donné

The species of this genus have four anterior flagella and a recurrent one along the undulating membrane. There are numerous species in birds and mammals.

T. vaginalis occurs in the vagina of women and urethra of men. Transmission is through coitus. It causes inflammation of the vaginal mucous membrane and is believed to be the cause of reproductive problems in women.

T. gallinae is a frequent parasite of pigeons, occurring most commonly in the crop and that portion of the alimentary canal anterior to it. The disease is manifested by the presence of caseous masses in the pharyngeal region, as well as in the tissues. In the former area, they may be so massive as to prevent occlusion of the beak. In advanced cases, lesions appear in the liver. Carriers of the parasite appear quite normal in health.

The epizootiology of this parasite among pigeons is remarkable in its relationship to the manner in which the parent birds feed the young squabs. Birds surviving infection as squabs remain carriers with the parasites localized in the mouth, oesophagus, and crop. When the young birds are fed with the regurgitated secretions of the crop known as pigeon milk, the flagellates are transferred with it.

There are avirulent and virulent strains of the parasite. In the case of the latter, lesions appear in 7 days as small yellowish areas on the buccal mucosa. They grow rapidly, forming large caseous masses in the pharyngeal region. Fluid accumulates in the crop and the infected birds die in about 10 days.

While pigeons and doves appear to be the natural hosts of *T. gallinae,* other birds may harbor them. Hawks become infected by eating parasitized pigeons and doves, and chickens and turkeys through contamination of food and water. A number of different species of birds has been infected experimentally.

Inasmuch as the parasites are able to live for some time in water and have been recovered from contaminated drinking vessels, it is believed that these may be a source of infection among chickens and turkeys.

Some common species of trichomonads from humans include *T. hominis* from the intestine and *T. tenax* from the mouth.

SELECTED REFERENCES

Stabler, R. M. (1947). J. Parasit. 33:207.

Trussell, R. E. (1947). *Trichomonas vaginalis* and trichomoniasis. Charles C. Thomas, Springfield, Ill., 277 pp.

Suborder Diplomonadina

The principal characteristic of this group of flagellates is the duplication of the nuclei, flagella, blepharoplasts, and axostyles so that the body is bilaterally symmetrical. In this respect, they differ from all others. The bodies are pyriform with nuclei near the anterior end. They are parasites of the alimentary canal.

FAMILY HEXAMITIDAE

This is the only family of the order. The genera *Hexamita, Octomitus,* and *Giardia* are considered.

Hexamita Dujardin, 1838 (Plate 12)

The *Hexamita* are pyriform, bilaterally symmetrical animals with bodies somewhat flattened dorso-ventrally. There are eight flagella, three pairs extending anteriorly from the broadly rounded end and

EXPLANATION OF PLATE 12 ▷

A. Trophozoite of *Hexamita ovatus* from American newt. **B.** Trophozoite of *H. ovatus* dividing by binary fission. **C.** Trophozoite of *H. ovatus* undergoing multiple fission. **D.** Trophozoite of *H. intestinalis* from American newt. **E.** Trophozoite of *H. muris* from house mouse. **F.** Cyst of *H. muris*. **G.** Trophozoite of *H. salmonis*. **H.** Trophozoite of *H. salmonis* from trout dividing by binary fission. **I.** Cyst of *H. salmonis*. **J.** Section of a pyloric caecum of trout infected with intracellular stages of *H. salmonis*. **K.** Trophozoite of *Octomitus pulcher* from marmot. **L.** Anterior end of trophozoite of *O. pulcher*, showing arrangement of flagella.

1, anterior flagella; **2**, posterior flagella; **3**, basal body; **4**, nucleus; **5**, axoneme; **6**, chromatin ring; **7**, protruding portion of axoneme; **8**, cyst wall; **9**, encysted stage; **10**, circular muscle of intestine with its nuclei; **11**, epithelial cells of intestine with their nuclei; **12**, intracellular forms of *H. salmonis*.

Figures A-C, D, redrawn from Swezy, 1915, Univ. Calif. Publ. Zool. 16:71; E-F, from Doflein and Reichenow, 1953, Lehrbuch der Protozoenkunde, p. 582; G-J, from Davis, 1947, Fish and Wildlife Serv., U. S. Dept. Int., Res. Rept. 12; K-L, from Gabel, 1954, J. Morph. 94:473.

---

one posteriorly from the more pointed end. Three anterior and one posterior flagella, one nucleus, and one axoneme are in each half of the bilateral body, giving the animal the appearance of consisting of two individuals fused along their longitudinal axes. The posterior tips of the axonemes do not extend beyond the cytoplasm of the body. Cysts are formed by some species.

Parasitic forms are common in the intestine of insects and all classes of vertebrates.

Common species include *H. salmonis* (Moore) (frequently referred to as *Octomitis*) from hatchery trout, *H. ovatus* Swezy from the American newt, *H. batrachorum* Swezy from the grassfrog, *H. intestinalis* Dujardin from tadpoles of frogs, *H. meleagridis* McNeal, Hinshaw, and Kofoid from turkeys, pheasants, chukar partridges, and quail, and *H. muris* (Grassi) from rats and house mice.

LIFE CYCLE. The life cycles of these species are not well understood, as none of them has been completely worked out. It is recognized generally, however, that wherever life cycles are known, they are direct. Resistant cysts are known to occur in *H. salmonis*, *H. intestinalis*, and *H. muris*. They have been reported for *H. meleagridis* by some workers, but others deny their existence.

Two types of multiplication occur. Binary longitudinal fission, preceded by division of the nuclei, blepharoplasts, and axonemes, is common. Multiple division is seen commonly in smears of unencysted forms from the intestinal wall of newts. It consists of three divisions of the nuclei and organelles. The eight associated individuals with their 48 anterior flagella roll along somewhat like a *Volvox*. There is no evidence that multiple division takes place in encysted forms. Some workers claim to have seen schizogony in *H. meleagridis*, but this type or reproduction is considered highly unlikely on the basis of the data presented.

The life cycles of two species have been studied somewhat extensively because of their economic importance.

In *H. meleagridis* of turkeys, both flagellated and encysted forms occur. The flagellated trophozoites occur throughout the intestine, but less so in the duodenum. They form resistant cysts in the flecks of mucus in the fluid faeces. These forms are able to survive in unfavorable environmental conditions for considerable periods, depending on the nature and severity of them. Infection occurs when these resistant cysts are ingested with food, water, or soil contaminated with them. Excystation takes place in the intestine and the liberated flagellates enter the glandular crypts where growth is completed. Multiplication is by binary fission.

H. salmonis is a common parasite of hatchery trout and salmon, where it occurs in great numbers at times, especially under conditions of low sanitation. It has been thought to be a serious pathogen but experimental infections of fish failed to demonstrate disease resulting from the strain of cultured flagellates used. It seemed more likely that the large numbers of them in the intestine were the result of a weakened condition of the fish from other causes, rather than the reverse.

Flagellates in the intestine multiply by longitudinal binary fission, increasing rapidly in numbers under favorable conditions. Resistant, oval cysts are formed which are able to survive for considerable

PLATE 12 *Hexamita ovatus, H. intestinalis, H. muris, H. salmonis, Octomitis pulcher*

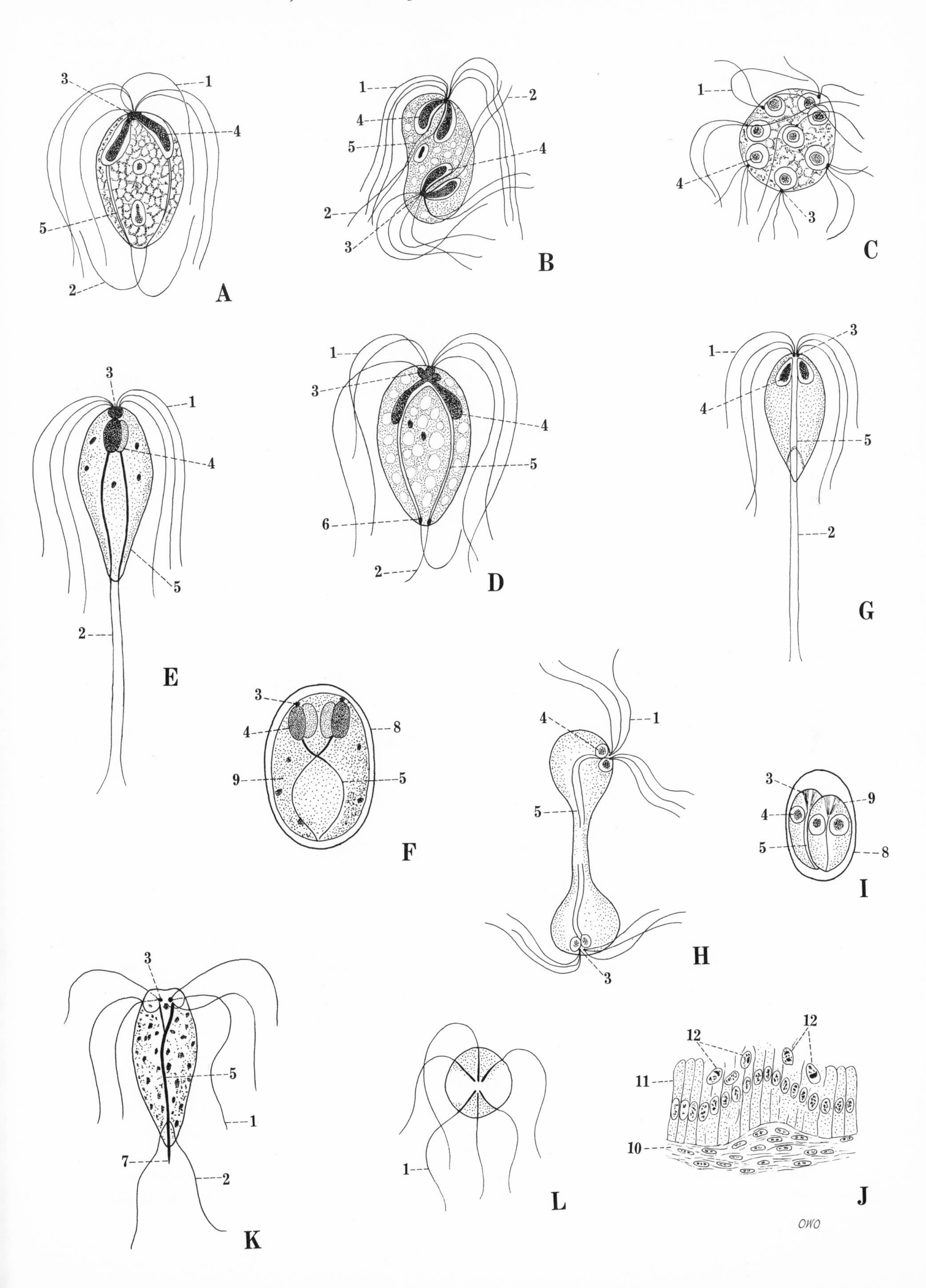

EXPLANATION OF PLATE 13 ⇨

A. Trophozoite of *Giardia agilis* from tadpole of frog, ventral view of stained specimen. **B.** Trophozoite of *Giardia muris,* ventral view of unstained individual. **C.** Ventral view of unstained *Giardia lamblia.* **D.** Ventral view of stained *Giardia lamblia.* **E.** Sinistral view of unstained *Giardia lamblia.* **F.** Recently formed unstained cyst of *Giardia lamblia.* **G.** Mature unstained cyst of *Giardia lamblia.* **H.** Stained mature cyst of *Giardia lamblia.*

1, ventral "sucker"; **2,** anterior pair of flagella; **3,** lateral pair of flagella; **4,** ventral pair of flagella; **5,** caudal pair of flagella; **6,** nucleus with endosome; **7,** axostyle; **8,** blepharoplast; **9,** chromatin mass; **10,** "sucking-disc" fibril; **11,** cyst wall.

Figures adapted from various sources.

---

periods outside the host. Shortly after formation, the organism in the cyst divides, resulting in two individuals. These cysts are probably the means by which the parasites are transmitted among the fish.

Octomitus von Prowazek, 1904 (Plate 12)

In general, this genus is very similar to *Hexamita* in body structure and conformation, differing in the nature of the axonemes. In *Octomitus* the posterior tips fuse and extend as a single pointed structure beyond the body, whereas in *Hexamita* they remain single and do not extend beyond the body. *Octomitus* is considered by some workers to be a synonym of *Hexamita,* but this difference appears to be sufficient justification for retaining them as separate genera. They are parasites of vertebrates.

O. pulcher Becker occurs in marmots in North America. Cysts have not been reported.

EXERCISE ON LIFE CYCLE

Of the hosts listed above, newts, frogs, tadpoles, and mice are likely sources of various species of *Hexamita* for experimental studies. When available, sick and dying fingerling trout from hatcheries will provide an abundance of *H. salmonis.*

Flagellates removed from the intestine with its juices and placed on slides can be viewed under the microscope. By sealing the margins of the cover slip with Vaseline, such mounts may be kept for long periods, during which encystment may be observed. Staining of the flagellates and cysts is necessary to see the details of internal structure.

H. salmonis may be cultured on a limited scale by introducing flagellates into a highly alkaline and dilute fish broth where the various growth stages occur (Moore), or a more sophisticated medium may be pre-prepared for production of large numbers of them (Uzmann and Hayduk).

SELECTED REFERENCES

Allison, L. N. (1963). Progr. Fish. Cult. 25:220.

Davis, H. S. (1947). Fish and Wildlife Serv., U. S. Dept. Int., Res. Rept. 12, 98 pp.

Doflein, F., and E. Reichenow. (1953). Lehrbuch der Protozoenkunde. Gustav Fischer, Jena, p. 582.

Gabel, J. R. (1954). J. Morph. 94:473.

Levine, N. D. (1962). Protozoan Parasites of Domestic Animals and Man. Burgess Publishing Co., Minneapolis, p. 15.

Moore, E. (1922). Trans. Amer. Fish. Soc. 52:74.

Morgan, B. B., and P. A. Hawkins. (1949). Veterinary Protozoology. Burgess Publishing Co., Minneapolis, p. 98.

Slavin, D., and J. E. Wilson. (1953). Nature 172:1179.

Swezy, O. (1915). Univ. Calif. Publ. Zool. 16:71.

Uzmann, J. R. (1963). Progr. Fish Cult. 25:141; ——— and S. H. Hayduk. (1963). Science 140:290; ——— G. J. Paulik, and S. H. Hayduk. (1965). Trans. Amer. Fish. Soc. 94:53.

Wilson, J. E., and D. Slavin. (1955). Vet. Rec. 67:236.

Giardia lamblia Stiles, 1915 (Plate 13)

This species is one of many of the genus and is the best known because of its common occurrence in the intestine of humans. It is cosmopolitan, being more common in children than in adults and in warm than cold climates. Related species occur in the intestine of many species of vertebrates.

PLATE 13 *Giardia agilis, G. muris, G. lamblia*

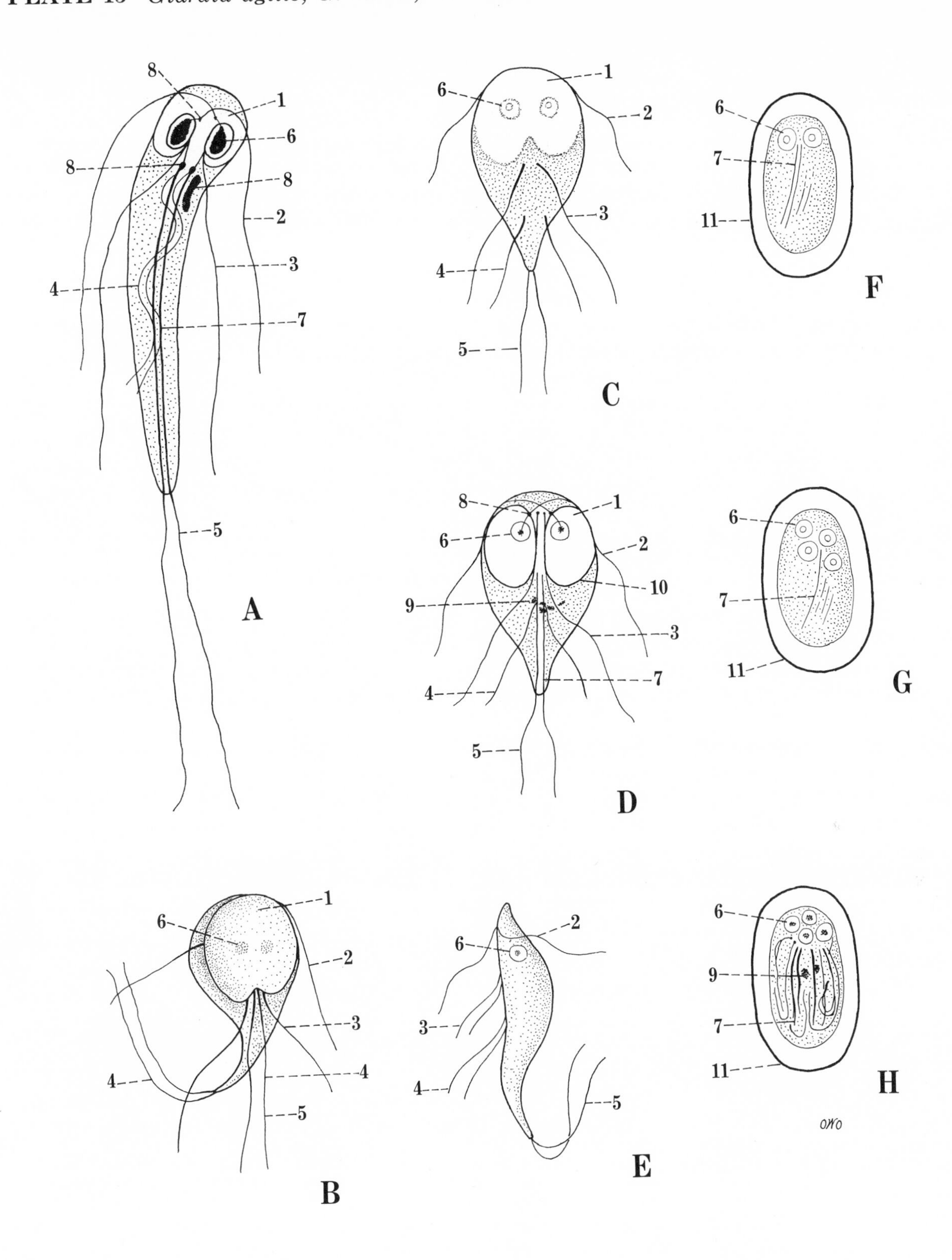

DESCRIPTION. The anterior end is broadly rounded and the posterior drawn to a point. The dorsal side is convex and the ventral concave, forming a functional sucking disc-like depression in the anterior half of the body.

The trophozoite is constant in shape, 9 to 30 μ long by 5 to 10 μ wide. The sucking disc-like ventral surface serves as an organelle of attachment on the surface of the intestinal epithelium. The axostyles extend the length of the body, remaining separate. The two nuclei are near the junction of the first and second thirds of the body. There are eight flagella in four pairs. Two originate near the anterior ends of the axostyles, cross each other and follow the anterolateral margin of the sucking "disc," becoming free; two others originate toward the anterior part of the axostyles near the nuclei, leaving the body about two thirds the distance from the anterior end; two others begin near the middle of the axostyles and two at the caudal end and extend backward as free filaments. A deeply staining median mass occurs over the axostyles.

Cysts are ovoid, measure 8 to 14 μ long by 6 to 10 μ wide, and are thin-walled. Two to four nuclei, fibrils, flagella, axostyles, and darkly staining masses are visible.

LIFE CYCLE. The trophozoites are most common in the duodenum, occurring in the crypts. Multiplication is by longitudinal binary fission, involving the nuclei, sucking disc-like ventral surface, and other parts, followed by separation of the parasite into two daughter trophozoites. The number may be so great as to virtually "line" the surface of the duodenum and adjoining part of the intestine with their bodies. Individual trophozoites rest on the cells, adhering by the sucking disc-like ventral side and waving the flagella.

EXERCISE ON LIFE CYCLE

Giardia muris from mice, *G. duodenalis* from rats, and *G. agilis* of tadpoles of frogs provide suitable material for study, depending on the facilities and material available.

In *G. duodenalis*, encystment begins in the iliocaecal region of the intestine. Cysts may be collected by breaking up faecal pellets, straining them through fine cloth, and placing the screened material in a tall cylinder of tap water where they settle to the bottom. Repeated decantation and sedimentation will remove coloring matter and fine debris. The cysts may be collected from the bottom by means of a fine pipette, placed on a slide, covered with a cover glass, and examined under high magnification. Staining with tincture of iodine will reveal internal structures.

The use of a centrifuge facilitates the collection of cysts. About 1 ml of faeces is strained and placed in a cone-shaped 15-ml centrifuge tube with normal saline. The mixture is centrifuged for 1 to 2 minutes and the supernatant fluid decanted. It is replaced by a solution of $ZnSO_4.7H_2O$ (331 gm in 1 liter of water for a specific gravity of 1.18), throughly mixed with the sediment, and centrifuged for 1 to 2 minutes. The cysts are on the surface of the fluid and may be transferred by means of a bacteriological loop to a slide for examination. For accumulating them, the supernatant fluid should be poured into 100 ml of water and this centrifuged to concentrate numerous cysts for experimental use.

Rats to be used for experimental infection must be free, or as nearly so as possible, of giardias before feeding them cysts. By keeping the cages scrupulously clean and prompt removal of faeces, the infection can be kept low, if not completely eliminated. Compare the number of cysts in the faeces prior to and after administering a large number of them. A sharp increase in the number of cysts would indicate that a new infection had been established and also give some idea of the time necessary for them to excyst, multiply, and produce cysts. Trophozoites occur in diarrheic faeces and cysts in formed ones. Trophozoites may be obtained most commonly in the small intestine of rats at a level about 10 cm anterior to the iliocaecal valve, where they occur in great numbers. Determine where excystation takes place.

Recently formed cysts have two nuclei and mature ones have four near the anterior end of the body. Fibrils representing the flagella appear in the cytoplasm.

Infection is by ingestion of mature cysts contaminating food and water, or by contact between infected and uninfected persons under unsanitary circumstances.

A number of species is known from domestic and wild animals. They include *G. agilis* Künstler from tadpoles of frogs, *G. bovis* Fanthan from cattle, *G. cati* Descheins from cats, *G. canis* Hegner from dogs, *G. caviae* Hegner from guinea pigs, *G. duodenalis* (Davaine) from rabbits, *G. equi* Fantham from horses, *G. muris* (Grassi) from rats and house mice, *G. ondatrae* Travis from muskrats, and *G. simoni* Lavier from the Norway rat and various other wild rodents.

The life cycle of each of these is basically similar to that of *G. lamblia.*

SELECTED REFERENCES

Chandler, A. C., and C. P. Read. (1961). Introduction to Parasitology. John Wiley and Sons, New York, p. 98.

Doflein, F., and E. Reichenow. (1953). Lehrbuch der Protozoenkunde. Gustav Fischer, Jena, p. 586.

Faust, E. C., and P. F. Russell. (1957). Craig and Faust's Clinical Parasitology. Lea and Febiger, Philadelphia, p. 98.

Filice, F. P. (1952). Univ. Calif. Publ. Zool. 57:53.

Grassé, P.-P. (1953). Traité de Zoologie, Vol., Fasc. 1. Masson et Cie, Paris, p. 963.

Hegner, R. W. (1922). Amer. J. Hyg. 2:442; (1923). Ibid. 3:345; (1927). Ibid. 7:433.

Kudo, R. R. (1966). Protozoology. Charles C Thomas, Springfield, Ill., p. 451.

Levine, N. D. (1962). Protozoan Parasites of Domestic Animals and of Man. Burgess Publishing Co., Minneapolis, p. 118.

Wenyon, C. M. (1926). Protozoology. William Wood and Co., New York, p. 691.

CLASS SARCODINA

The Sarcodina are amoeboid protozoans capable of forming pseudopodia for locomotion and capturing food. The outer ectoplasm is a tough hyaline layer and the inner endoplasm is granular. In some forms, young and fully developed trophozoites bear flagella, thus indicating a relationship between them and the Mastigophora.

While most of the Sarcodina are free-living, all species of the family Endamoebidae are parasites of invertebrate and vertebrate animals. The Endamoebidae belongs to the subclass Rhizopoda, order Amoebina.

FAMILY ENDAMOEBIDAE

Most of the members of the family are commensals of the alimentary canal. A few are tissue-invading forms, causing great harm to and even death of their hosts. *Entamoeba histolytica* is the tissue-invading form of humans while *E. ranarum* of frogs and *E. invadens* of snakes attack their cold-blooded hosts in a similar manner. *Hydramoeba* lives on the ectoderm of hydra.

Contractile vacuoles are absent in species living in the isotonic environment of the alimentary canal but present in *Hydramoeba* living in the hypotonic environment on hydra.

The family consists of a number of genera, seven of which are considered. They are differentiated according to the distribution of the nuclear chromatin as it appears in stained specimens.

Endamoeba Leidy is the type genus. *E. blattae* occurs in cockroaches. Other species are in termites. The chromatin granules are distributed concentrically near the periphery of the nucleus (Plate 14, A).

Entamoeba Casagrandi and Barbagallo occurs commonly in vertebrates and contains such well-known forms as the highly pathogenic *E. histolytica* of humans, *E. invadens* of snakes, and *E. ranarum* of frogs. The chromatin is located as small plaques around the inner surface of the nuclear membrane and as a small cluster of endosomal granules at or near the center of the nucleus (Plate 14, B).

Iodamoeba Dobell is found in humans and pigs. The endosome is large and surrounded by a layer of vesicles (Plate 14, C).

Endolimax Kuenen and Swellengrebel occurs in mammals, birds, reptiles, amphibians, and insects. The endosome is a large centrally located mass of irregular shape (Plate 14, D).

Dientamoeba Jepps and Dobell occurs in humans. The chromatin forms a centrally located endosome consisting of several small bodies (Plate 14, E).

Hydramoeba Reynolds and Looper parasitizes hydra. The nucleus contains a large, central, granular endosome. A layer of variously shaped chromatin material lies about midway between the endosome and the nuclear membrane (Plate 14, F).

Schizamoeba Davis is a parasite of the stomach of salmonid fishes. There is no endosome; the chromatin material is arranged in a few large plaques on the inner surface of the nuclear membrane (Plate 14, G).

Figures adapted from various sources.

SELECTED REFERENCES

Hydramoeba and *Schizamoeba*

Davis, H. S. (1926). Bull. U. S. Bur. Fish. 42, 8 pp.

Meglitsch, P. A. (1940). Ill. Biol. Monogr. 14, No. 4.

Mercier, L. (1910). Arch. Protistenk. 20:143.

Morris, S. (1936). J. Morph. 59:225.

Reynolds, B. D., and J. B. Looper. (1928). J. Parasit. 15:23.

Threlkeld, W. L. (1929). Arch. Protistenk. 68:305.

Entamoeba histolytica Schaudinn, 1903 (Plate 15)

Entamoeba histolytica is widespread throughout the world wherever unsanitary conditions exist. While more prevalent in the warm parts of the world, it extends into the temperate regions and even beyond.

Transmission of infective cysts normally is by contamination of food and pollution of drinking water with faeces from persons who as chronic carriers of the protozoans pass cysts in their faeces.

The amoebae attack and penetrate the intestinal mucosa, producing submucosal ulcers from where they get into the circulation and are carried to the liver; also, but more rarely, to the lungs and brain.

DESCRIPTION. The trophozoites are actively motile, with pseudopodia that form quickly. The ectoplasm is clear and the endoplasm granular. They range from 10 to 60 μ in size, averaging 20 to 30 μ. The nucleus is spherical, having a thick membrane lined with a single layer of fine dots of deeply staining chromatin; the nucleoplasm is unstained except for a small central karyosome and fine lines radiating from it to the dots on the membrane. The sluggish precysts are round to ovoid, smaller than the trophozoites but larger than the cysts that follow. Cysts are roundish, 5 to 20 μ in diameter, and with a smooth, refractile, unstained wall. Densely staining chromatoidal bodies with rounded ends occur in young cysts. Immature cysts have a single nucleus and mature ones have four.

LIFE CYCLE. Trophozoites are passed in diarrheic or dysenteric faeces in cases where acute amboebiasis occurs. Cysts appear in formed faeces of carriers. Upon reaching the outside and under favorable conditions of moisture, temperature, and aeration, the uninucleate cysts develop into infective quadrinucleate ones. The trophozoites die.

Food contaminated with faeces containing cysts or drinking water polluted with them are the common sources of infection. Upon being swallowed by humans, the cyst wall ruptures in the small intestine and the quadrinucleate metacystic amoeba is freed. It promptly divides into four small amoebae which enter the crypts of the large intestine and commence feeding on the mucosa. Lytic substances secreted by them dissolve the epithelial cells, which then serve as food. The amoebae grow in size and multiply by binary fission. Cysts are formed and appear in the faeces. When destruction of the epithelial cells is faster than repair, the amoebae enter the mucosa and multiply, forming colonies. Soon craterous flask-shaped ulcers are formed which extend deeper and deeper into the intestinal wall. When the broad bases of adjacent ulcers coalesce, especially at the bottom of the crypts, the overlying tissue sloughs and enlarged open ulcers appear. The ulcers are most common in the caecum and ascending colon, and in the sigmoid rectum where movement of the contents is slowest, thus giving the amoebae greater opportunity to attack the tissue. Destruction of tissue on a massive basis results in dysentery, often accompanied with blood coming from eroded vessels. Trophozoites, some containing erythrocytes, appear in the faeces at this time.

With erosion of tissue and blood vessels, amoebae enter the blood vessels of the hepatic portal system and are carried to the liver. Through the lytic action of their secretions, openings are formed in the small blood vessels and the amoebae migrate into the liver parenchyma, forming colonies. As these grow in size, large abscesses filled with necrotic fluid develop. Amoebae in them lie next to living cells around the periphery of the abscesses where they feed and continue to multiply. Individuals continuing through the liver enter the lungs, causing abscesses in a manner similar to that described

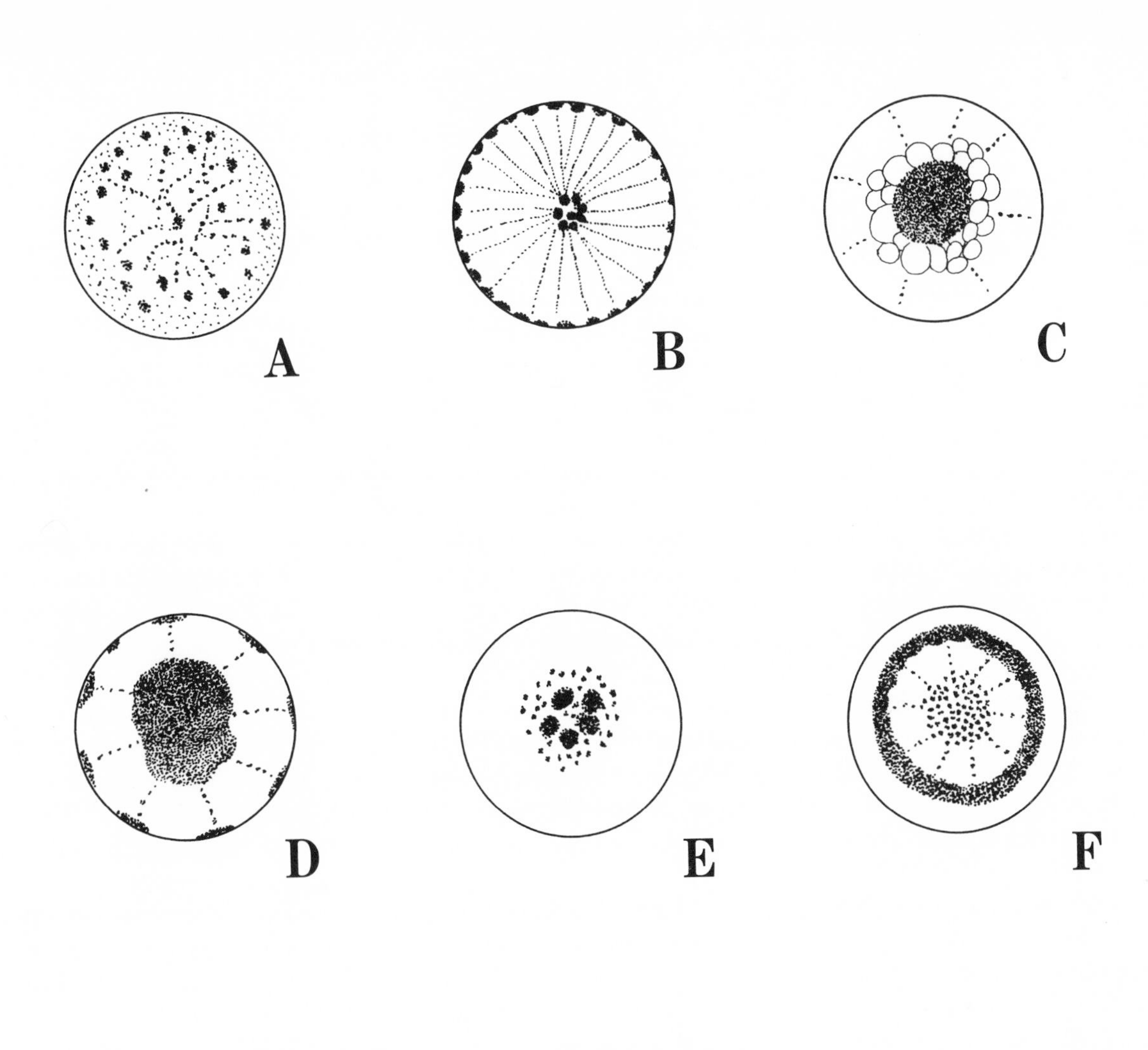
A
B
C
D
E
F

G

for the liver, or infection may be by extension of the hepatic abscess through the diaphragm and into the lungs. Amoebae carried by the blood to the brain may lodge there, likewise producing abscesses.

EXERCISE ON LIFE CYCLE

Frogs and their tadpoles the world over harbor *Entamoeba ranarum* in the colon. The vegetative stages and cysts are so similar to those of *E. histolytica* that differentiation on a morphological basis is very difficult, if not impossible. The process of excystation in both species is similar. Snakes are infected commonly with *E. invadens,* a species that resembles *E. histolytica* morphologically and pathologically. Fatal infections occur commonly in captive snakes. The life cycle of both species is similar to that of *E. histolytica. E. muris* from the caecum of mice is similar morphologically to *E. coli,* a commensal in the intestine of humans.

Stools from humans contain cysts and trophozoites of the various species of amoebae. Scrappings from around the base of the teeth often provide trophozoites of *E. gingivalis,* a species common in humans.

Finding the trophozoites and cysts of intestinal protozoa is a difficult task at best. Standardized procedures give best results which have the advantage of making it possible to compare them with studies conducted by other investigators. A few of the well-known procedures are given for class use.

Microscopic examination of smears of intestinal contents in the case of mice, snakes, or frogs, and faeces of the higher mammals, including humans, provides a simple and effective method of detecting the parasites.

A drop of Lugol's iodine solution or D'Antoni's standardized iodine solution added to the faecal emulsion on a slide makes chromatin material of cysts stand out as light-colored structures against the yellow-brown background of the cytoplasm and the mahogony brown of the glycogen masses.

Supravital staining with brilliant cresyl blue stains the living parasites. Background staining with eosin colors everything pink except the living amoebae (dead ones stain pink) which are translucent, unstained objects (Belding).

The Merthiolate-iodine-formaldehyde fixative stain (MIF) is one of the most recent and useful techniques for staining and preserving amoebae in faecal material for subsequent microscopic examination (Faust and Russell).

Methods of concentration of cysts increase the probability of finding them. Perhaps the most efficient one for protozoan cysts, as well as eggs of nematodes, is the zinc sulfate-centrifugal flotation methods developed by Faust and colleagues. For details, consult Faust et al., or Faust and Russell.

SELECTED REFERENCES

Belding, D. L. (1952). Textbook of Clinical Parasitology, 2nd Ed. Appleton-Century-Crofts, Inc., New York, pp. 74, 933, 938.

Doflein, F., and E. Reichenow. (1953). Lehrbuch der Protozoenkunde. 6th Ed. Gustav Fischer, Jena, pp. 695, 711.

Faust, E. C., J. S. D'Antoni, V. Odom, M. J. Miller, W. Sawitz, L. F. Thomen, J. Tobie, and J. F. Walker. (1938). Amer. J. Trop. Med. 18:169; ———, W. Sawitz, J. Tobie, V. Odom, C. Peres, and D. R. Lincicome. (1939). J. Parasit. 25:241; ——— and P. E. Russell. (1957). Craig and Faust's Clinical Parasitology. Lea and Febiger, Philadelphia. p. 948.

Geiman, Q. M., and H. L. Ratcliffe. (1936). Parasitology 28:208.

Goldman, M. (1964). Amer. J. Gastroent. 41:362.

Levine, N. D. (1961). Protozoan Parasites of Domestic Animals of Man. Burgess Publishing Co., Minneapolis, p. 133.

Sanders, E. (1931). Arch. Protistenk. 74:365.

CLASS SPOROZOA

All members of this class are parasitic and produce spores, as indicated by the name, that contain one to many sporozoites. In species that develop in one host, the spore membrane is thick and resistant, protecting the sporozoites while outside the host. In species with two hosts, the spore membrane is always thin and delicate, being inside an invertebrate host.

Reproduction is both sexual by gametogony (formation of gametes and fertilization) and by sporogony (multiple division) of the zygote to form sporozoites, and asexual by schizogony (multiple division) of the schizont to produce merozoites. Either sexual, or sexual and asexual, reproduction may occur in a single host, or there may be an alternation of hosts with sexual reproduction in one and asexual in the other (Plate 16).

The life cycle of these parasites appears complicated at the outset. However, they follow a pattern of development that makes comprehension of them rather easy. Basically, the three phases of development of the typical sporozoan life cycle are 1) schizogony, 2) gametogony, and 3) sporogony. Each phase is initiated by a specific stage of the parasite and culminates in the production of the succeeding one in the life cycle (text fig. 1). Each stage is different morphologically and in the process by which it produces the following one. They are the sporozoites, merozoites or gametocytes, and zygotes.

The development of each phase follows a consistent pattern. Schizogony is initiated by sporozoites entering the vertebrate host where they grow, forming large uninucleate trophozoites. Nuclear division marks the beginning of the schizont (cleaving animal) which undergoes schizogony, a process of asexual multiplication by repeated nuclear division. The end product of the schizogenous process is minute uninucleate merozoites. This is the multiplicative phase. They are capable of initiating succeeding cycles of schizogony or of transforming into gametocytes. Gametocyte formation is the beginning of gametogony, which is the sexual phase of the cycle. The gametocytes produce male and female gametes that fuse to produce zygotes which, if motile, are known as ookinetes. Sporogony, which is development of the zygote, takes place outside the body in species that have one host in their life cycle or in the body of an invertebrate in species that have two hosts. The zygote, through multifission of the nucleus, produces a variable number of sporozoites. These constitute the infective stage. The forms occurring in the sporogenous phase include the oocyst, sporoblast, and sporont, or only part of them, depending on the species.

The class is divided into three subclasses. The subclass Telosporidia possesses spores with or without a resistant membrane, containing one to many fusiform sporozoites. The subclass Acnidosporidia has spores with a resistant membrane and only a single nonfusiform sporozoite. The subclass Cnidosporidia has resistant spores composed of one (univalve), two (bivalve), or three (trivalve) parts and containing one to four polar capsules, each with a long, coiled polar filament; there are one to many sporoplasms.

Subclass Telosporidia

The spore contains one to several sporozoites. There is never a polar capsule nor polar filament.

ORDER GREGARINIDA

Gregarines are common parasites of the intestinal tract and other organs of arthropods and annelids. Most of them do not undergo schizogony but a few have a primitive type which takes place in the intestinal lumen. Sporogony also occurs in the lumen of the intestine with the formation of spores.

Suborder Eugregarinina

The members of this suborder are chiefly coelozoic parasites of arthropods. The young trophozoites enter epithelial cells of the intestine for a short time but soon return to the lumen, remaining attached to the cells until maturity, at which time they become detached and are free in the lumen of the intestine. Fully developed trophozoites (sporadins) unite in pairs and secrete a gametocyst about themselves. Following repeated nuclear division, male and female isogametes are formed. Union of the gametes produces numerous zygotes, each of which forms an oocyst. Through division of the nucleus and cytoplasm, sporozoites are formed.

Two major groups of gregarines are recognized. They are the acephaline forms without a distinct anterior organelle of attachment and the cephaline group with a well-developed one.

EXPLANATION OF PLATE 15 ▷

A. Active trophozoite. **B.** Trophozoite containing erythrocytes. **C.** Precystic stage. **D.** Young mononucleate cyst with chromatoidal bars. **E.** Binucleate cyst. **F.** Trinucleate cyst. **G.** Mature cyst with four nuclei and chromatoidal bars. **H.** Mature cyst without chromatoidal bars. **I.** Human host. **J-K.** Sections of intestine showing progression of lesions in mucosa and wall.

1, nucleus; **2,** nucleolus; **3,** linin network; **4,** chromatin granules on nuclear membrane; **5,** pseudopods; **6,** ectoplasm; **7,** endoplasm; **8,** erythrocyte; **9,** cyst wall; **10,** chromatoidal bodies; **11,** glycogen vacuole.

a, quadrinucleate cyst being swallowed; **b,** excystation of amoeba in small intestine; **c,** four metacystic trophozoites; **d,** metacystic trophozoite invading intestinal epithelium; **e,** formation of small ulcer in epithelium by amoeba; **f,** enlargement of ulcer; **g,** adjacent ulcers; **h,** fusion of adjacent ulcers, forming a large one with intervening portion being sloughed; **i,** consolidation of three ulcers form a single large one with sloughing portions; **j,** amoebae passing through intestinal wall into hepatic portal vein; **k,** amoeba entering hepatic parenchyma; **l,** hepatic ulcer; **m,** amoeba entering lung parenchyma; **n,** lung ulcer; **o,** amoeba in general circulation; **p,** amoeba entering brain; **q,** brain ulcer; **r,** cyst and trophozoite passing from intestine (trophozoite dies); **s-u,** development of cyst outside host; **s,** uninucleate cyst; **t,** binucleate cyst; **u,** infective quadrinucleate cyst.

a′, lumen of intestine; **b′-g′,** layers of intestinal wall; **b′,** mucosa with villi and crypts; **c′,** muscularis mucosae; **d′,** submucosa; **e′,** circular muscle layer; **f′,** longitudinal muscle layer; **g′,** serosa; **h′,** body cavity; **i′,** excysting quadrinucleate amoeba in lumen of intestine; **j′,** four metacyclic amoebae; **k′,** amoeba entering mucosa at tip of villus; **l′,** amoebae entering mucosa in depths of crypts; **m′,** multiplication of amoeba forming small ulcer in crypt; **n′,** ulcer at tip of villus where numerous amoebae develop and are liberated to attack other epithelial cells; **o′,** formation of numerous ulcers in depth of crypts; **p′,** individual ulcers coalesce, forming a single large one; **q′,** villi sloughing because of undermining by coalescing ulcers; **r′,** ulcer extended into muscularis mucosae and submucosal tissue; **s′,** amoebae enter blood vessels through damaged sections in deep ulcers and are carried to other parts of the body.

Adapted from Faust and Russell, 1957, Craig and Faust's Clinical Parasitology, 6th Ed., Lea and Febiger, Philadelphia, p. 189.

Tribe Acephalina

The trophozoites are not divided into distinct linear parts.

FAMILY MONOCYSTIDAE

The members of this family are common parasites of earthworms throughout the world. They live in the seminal vesicles where the sporozoites enter the sperm morulae and develop into trophozoites, absorbing the germinal cells in the process. Reproduction is completed within the seminal vesicles. Of the many species, *Monocystis lumbrici* from *Lumbricus terrestris* is one of the commonest and best known.

Monocystis lumbrici (Henle, 1845) (Plate 17)

Trophozoites live in the sperm morulae floating about in the seminal vesicles. As the trophozoites grow, they consume all but the tails of the sperms which adhere to them, giving the appearance of a covering of hair.

DESCRIPTION. Mature trophozoites are active and measure about 200 μ long by 60 to 70 μ wide. Each has a single nucleus containing one or more karyosomes. Conjugating adults come in contact with each other along the long axis of the body, round up, and secrete a two-layered cyst about 162 μ in diameter around themselves. The lower cyst wall is roughened externally and the inner one is smoother and thinner. The navicular spores measure 11 to 12 μ long by 5 to 6 μ wide. When ripe, they contain eight sporozoites.

LIFE CYCLE. The minute sporozoites in the seminal vesicles of the earthworms penetrate the sperm morulae, or mother sperm cells, and transform into trophozoites which grow at the expense of the germ cells. By the time the trophozoites have matured, the sperm morulae have been absorbed, leaving only the tails of sperms adhering to the trophozoites.

The mature trophozoites mark the end of the trophic or vegetative stage and the beginning of the reproductive phase. They are now known as sporonts or sporadins. In reality, they are gametocytes. Two of them come together, adhering along the long axis of the body, shorten, and secrete a double-layered cyst about themselves, still remaining separate individuals. The cyst may be considered as a gametocyst.

PLATE 15 *Entamoeba histolytica*

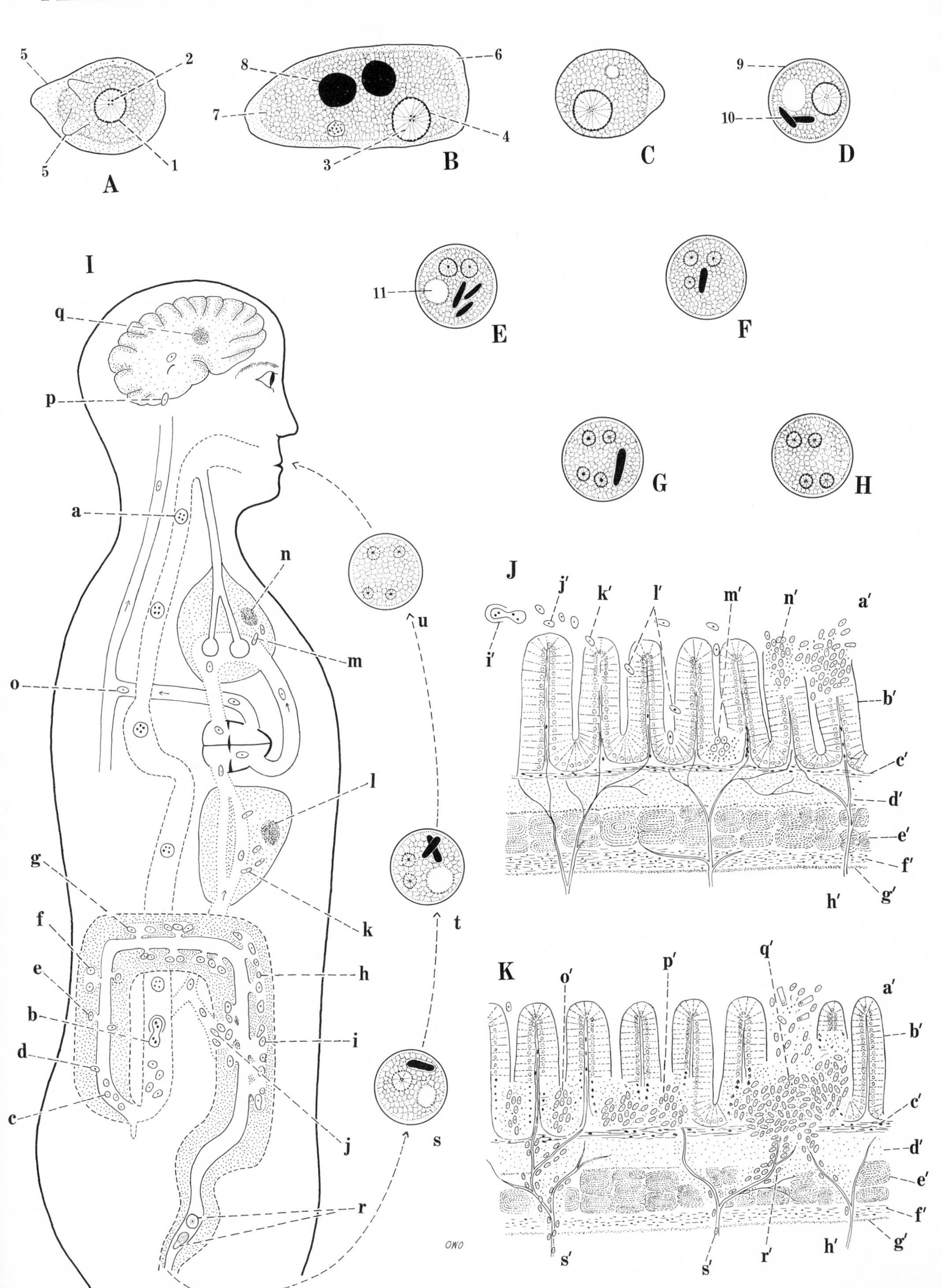

EXPLANATION OF PLATE 16 ▷

SUMMARY OF EVOLUTIONARY DEVELOPMENT OF SOME SPOROZOAN PARASITES

I. Order Gregarinida

A. Single host.

1. No schizogony; gametogony and sporogony in lumen of Malpighian tubules and hindgut of insect; infection by ingestion of sporocysts containing sporozoites. *(Lankesteria,* Plate 16, Fig. 1.)
2. Simple schizogony followed by gametogony in lumen of gut of invertebrate; infection by ingestion of sporocysts containing sporozoites. (*Schizocystis,* Plate 16, Fig. 2.)

II. Order Coccidia

A. Single host

1. Schizogony and gametogony begin in lumen of gut and are completed in epithelium of gut of lobster; gametogony in intestinal epithelium of lobster; sporogony unknown; infection presumably by ingestion of sporocysts containing sporozoites. *(Selenococcidium.)*
2. Schizogony and gametogony in intestinal epithelium; sporulation outside; infection by ingestion of sporocysts containing sporozoites. (*Eimeria,* Plate 16, Fig. 3.)

B. Two hosts

1. Schizogony submucosal in gut of crab and gametogony and sporogony submucosal in gut of cuttlefish; infection by ingestion of merozoites in crab by cuttlefish and sporozoites in cuttlefish by crabs. (*Aggregata,* Plate 16, Fig. 4.)
2. Schizogony, gametogony, and sporogony submucosal in gut of lizards; sporozoites in erythrocytes of lizards and later accumulate in intestinal epithelium of lizard mites; infection by ingestion of infected mites. (*Schellackia,* Plate 16, Fig. 5.)
3. Schizogony in hepatic cells of rat; gametocytes in leucocytes; gametogony in gut and sporogony in haemocoel of rat mites; infection by ingestion of infected mites. (*Hepatozoon,* Plate 16, Fig. 6.)
4. Schizogony and gametocytes in erythrocytes of water tortoise; gametogony and sporogony in intestine of leeches; infection by injection of sporozoites. (*Haemogregarina,* Plate 16, Fig. 7.)

III. Order Haemosporidia

A. Two hosts

1. First schizogony in liver cells, second schizogony and gametocytes in erythrocytes; gametogony in lumen of intestine and sporogony in wall of intestine of mosquitoes; infection by injection of sporozoites. (*Plasmodium,* Plate 16, Fig. 8.)
2. Schizogony in endothelial cells of lungs; gametocytes in erythrocytes of birds; gametogony in lumen of intestine and sporogony in intestinal wall of hippoboscid flies; infection by injection of sporozoites. (*Haemoproteus,* Plate 16, Fig. 9.)
3. Megaloschizonts in macrophages of intestine, spleen, heart; hepatic schizonts in macrophages of liver; gametocytes in mononuclear leucocytes; gametogony in lumen of intestine and sporogony in wall of intestine of black flies; infection by injection of sporozoites. (*Leucocytozoon,* Plate 16, Fig. 10.)

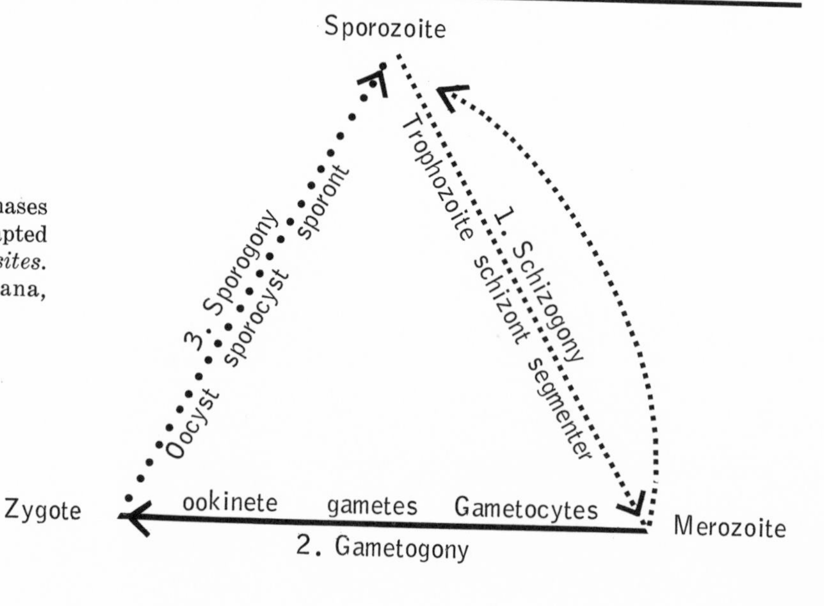

FIGURE 1. Diagram of the three phases of a typical sporozoan life cycle. Adapted from Baer, 1951, *Ecology of Parasites.* University of Illinois Press, Urbana, page 16.

PLATE 16 *Summary of Evolutionary Development of Some Sporozoan Parasites*

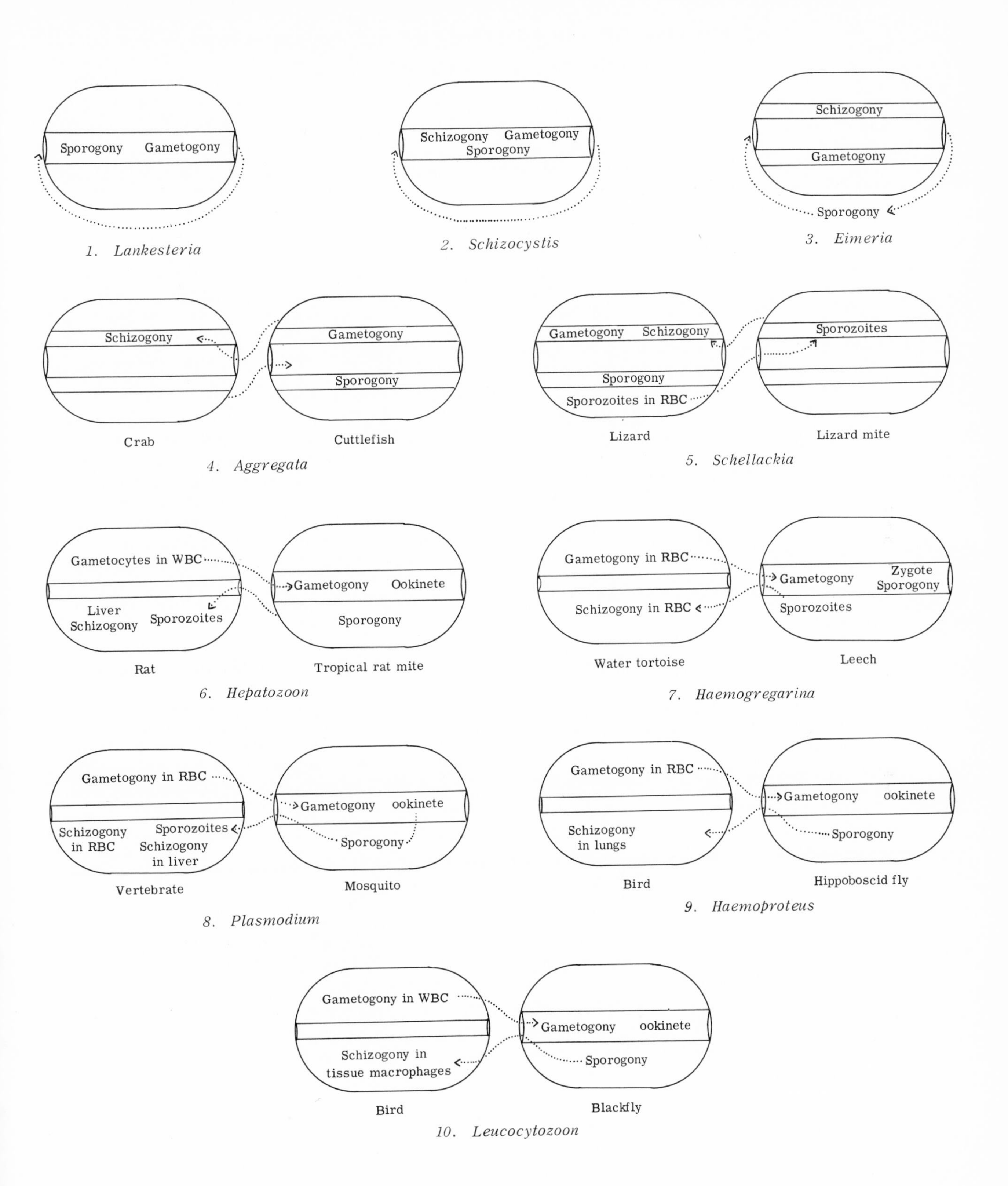

EXPLANATION OF PLATE 17 ▷

A. Sperm morula, or sperm mother cell, from seminal vesicle. **B.** Sperm mother cell containing a young trophozoite of *Monocystis.* **C.** Mature trophozoite "clothed" with the tails of spermatozoa remaining from the mature sperm cluster. **D.** Association of two mature gametocytes covered with tails of sperm cells preparatory for encystment and sporulation. **E.** Encysted mononuclear gametocytes. **F.** Segment of gametocyst, showing gametes that have formed from division of nuclei of the gametocytes and remain attached to the residual protoplasm of the gametocytes. **G.** Segment of gametocyst showing fertilization and formation of zygotes. **H.** Zygotes develop into sporocysts in gametocyst. **I.** Fully developed spore. **J.** Binucleate spore. **K.** Tetranucleate spore. **L.** Octonucleate spore. **M.** Sporulated spore containing eight sporozoites. **N.** Ruptured sporocyst liberating sporozoites. **O.** Cross-section of spore, showing arrangement of sporozoites. **P.** Earthworm *(Lumbricus terrestris),* host of *Monocystis,* showing endogenous phase of life cycle of parasite.

1, spermatogonium of mother sperm cell; **2,** cytoplasm of mother sperm cell; **3,** young trophozoite within mother sperm cell; **4,** nucleus of trophozoite; **5,** tails of sperms from destroyed mother sperm cell; **6,** conjugating gametocytes; **7,** epicyst or external layer of gametocyst; **8,** endocyst or internal layer of gametocyst; **9,** gametocyte; **10,** gamete; **11,** residual protoplasm; **12,** nucleus of residual protoplasm; **13,** gamete in residual protoplasm; **14,** fertilization and formation of zygote; **15,** fusion of nuclei and further development of zygote; **16,** complete fusion of nuclei and full development of zygote; **17,** sporoblast resulting from development of zygote; **18,** boat-shaped spore or sporocyst; **19,** sporozoite; **20,** wall of spore.

a, mature spore leaving seminal vesicle via the seminal funnel; **b,** spore leaving male genital pore to be free in soil or retained in egg cocoon; **c,** mature spore in soil; **d,** binucleate spore; **e,** tetranucleate spore; **f,** octonucleate spore; **g,** sporulated spore containing eight sporozoites; **h,** mature spore in pharynx, having been swallowed with contaminated soil by earthworm; **i,** spore in crop; **j, k,** spores in gizzard and intestine, respectively, opening and releasing sporozoites; **l,** sporozoite free in lumen of alimentary canal; **m,** sporozoite penetrating intestinal epithelium and entering capillaries of blood vessels in gut wall; **n,** sporozoites in dorsal vessel, being carried forward by blood; **o,** sporozoite in one of the hearts; **p,** testes; **q,** young sperm morula or sperm mother cell; **r,** seminal vesicle; **s,** sporozoite entering developing sperm mother cell with well-formed spermatogonia; **t,** young trophozoite in sperm mother cell; **u,** associated elongate gametocytes attached to seminal funnel; **v,** gametocytes in gametocyst; **w,** formation of gametes and fertilization with resultant zygotes; **x,** formation of mature spores which will escape via sperm funnel (a).

Figures adapted from various sources, except P, which is original.

Upon completion of the cyst, nuclear division begins in each gametocyte and continues until a great number of small nuclei is present throughout the protoplasm. These migrate to the surface of each gametocyte. Bits of cytoplasm detach from the main body and surround each nucleus, forming the gametes. A residual mass of cytoplasm remains to which the gametes are attached. At this time, the cell wall of each gametocyte disappears and the individuals become indistinguishable. The gametes show movement in the cyst. Two gametes, presumably from different gametocysts, conjugate to form a zygote in which the two nuclei fuse. Each zygote may now be considered as a sporoblast. It secretes a tough cyst about itself and assumes the typical fusiform shape.

Final development includes three successive amitotic nuclear divisions resulting in eight nuclei which take up an equatorial position in the spore. A bit of cytoplasm surrounds each to form the minute sporozoites, leaving a residuum. Numerous spores are present in each gametocyst.

Infection of earthworms apparently occurs only when the ripe spores are expelled from the seminal vesicles and subsequently ingested. Just how the spores are released from the infected worms is unknown. They may be passed through the male genital pores into the soil or into the egg cocoons. Doubtless oligochaetophagus birds and mammals play an important role in releasing them by the digestive processes and disseminating them in their faeces. Probably disintegration of dead worms in the soil is a means of freeing the spores.

Earthworms become infected by swallowing ripe spores. The route of migration of the sporozoites from the alimentary canal to the seminal vesicles is unknown. It is probable, however, that they are released from the spores in the alimentary canal, where they burrow into the intestinal wall and enter the capillaries of the circulatory system. Once inside the vascular system, they are transported via the dorsal vessel and hearts to the seminal vesicles, where they leave the capillaries. Inside the seminal vesicles, they seek out the sperm mother cells, penetrate them, and transform to trophozoites.

PLATE 17 *Monocystis lumbrici*

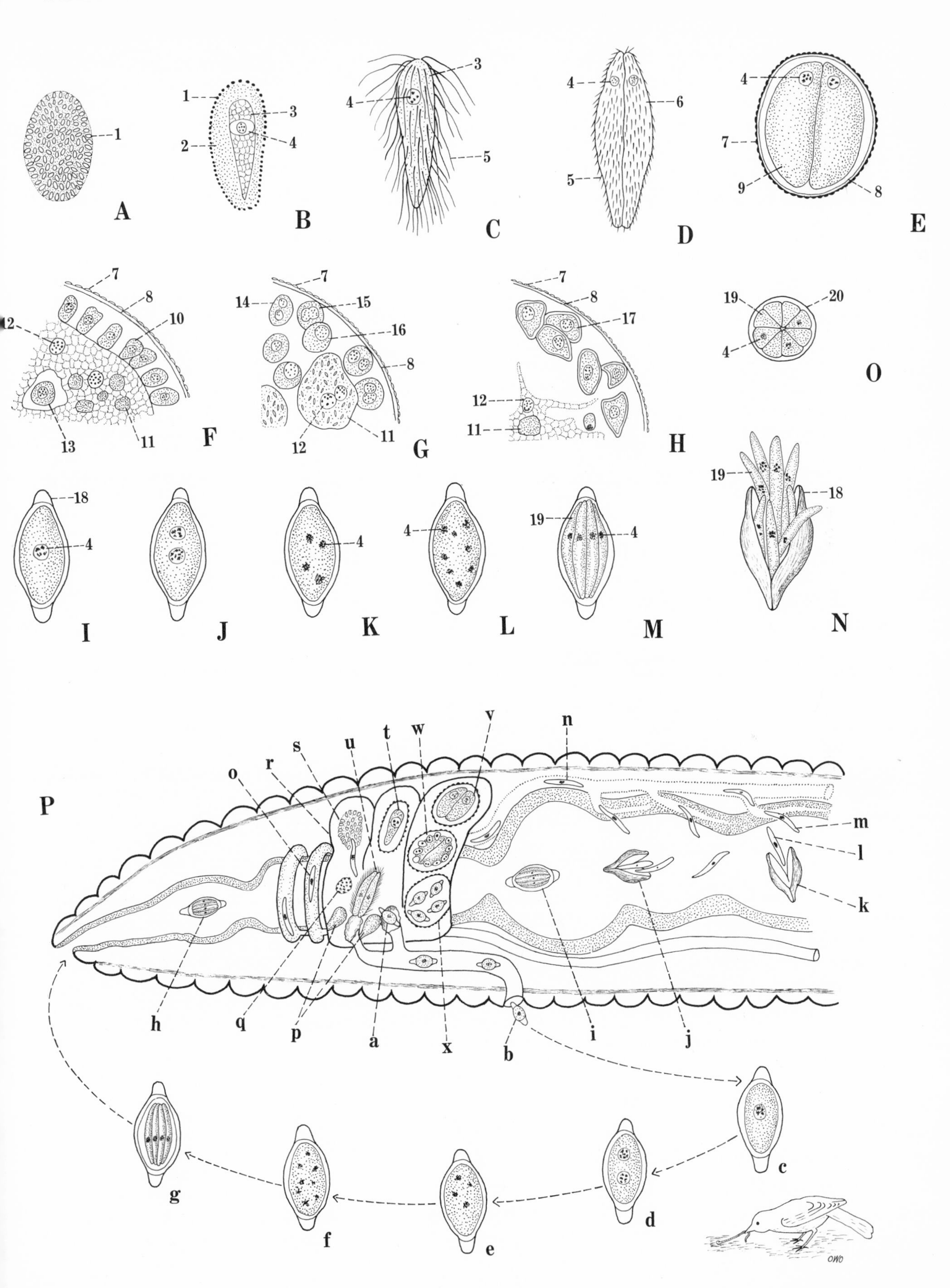

EXPLANATION OF PLATE 18 ⇨

A. Mature oocyst with eight sporozoites. **B-C.** Intracellular phases of trophozoite. **D.** Extracellular trophozoite attached and free trophozoite known as a sporadin. **E.** Mature gregarine. **F.** Larva of *Aedes* mosquito. **F'.** Midgut of larval mosquito. **G.** Pupa of mosquito. **G'.** Malpighian tubules of pupal mosquito. **H.** Adult mosquito. **H'.** Hindgut of adult mosquito.

1, wall of oocyst; **2,** sporozoites; **3,** residual mass of cytoplasm; **4,** young intracellular trophozoite; **5,** nucleus with karyosome; **6,** epithelial cell of midgut of larval mosquito; **7,** nucleus of epithelial cell; **8,** epimerite; **9,** enlarged epimerite embedded in cytoplasm of host epithelial cell; **10,** mature trophozoite in lumen of midgut but still attached to host cell by epimerite; **11,** epimerite remains embedded in host cell but detached from trophozoite; **12,** mature trophozoite, known as a sporadin, free in midgut of larva.

a, ruptured oocyst releasing sporozoites in midgut of larval mosquito; **b,** sporozoite entering epithelial cell; **c-d,** intracellular trophozoites; **e,** young extracellular trophozoite attached to epithelial cell; **f,** mature extracellular trophozoite attached to epithelial cell; **g,** detached epimerite remains embedded in epithelial cell; **h,** mature trophozoite, known as a sporadin, free in midgut goes to Malpighian tubule of pupa and becomes a gametocyte; **i,** association of two gametocytes enclosed in a gametocyst; **j-l,** division of nucleus and formation of numerous nuclei; **m,** nuclear multiplication completed; **n,** gametes formed by budding from cytoplasm; **o,** gametes formed, leaving a large residual mass of cytoplasm; **p,** conjugation of gametes which are of two kinds, based on difference in size of nuclei; **q,** zygotes (one nucleus), division of nucleus (two nuclei), division of two nuclei, and finally the formation of sporozoites in oocyst; **r,** gametocyst containing oocysts passes into hindgut and ruptures when pupa transforms into adult mosquito, releasing oocysts; **s,** ripe oocysts voided in faeces of mosquito.

Adapted from Ray, 1933, Parasitology 25:392.

EXERCISE ON LIFE CYCLE

The various stages of the parasite, such as the trophozoites, gametocytes in the gametocysts, gametes, and spores containing the sporozoites, can be demonstrated in stained sections of infected seminal vesicles. Fresh contents of the seminal vesicles examined with the aid of a microscope will reveal the various stages. Contents of the seminal vesicles spread on slides, dried, and stained with Wright's blood stain show various stages.

For experimental purposes, infective spores and uninfected earthworms are necessary. Spores may be obtained from the seminal vesicle of infected *Lumbricus terrestris*. Young, uninfected earthworms must be hatched from eggs placed in soil previously sterilized by heat to assure that natural infections may not result from it. Captive *L. terrestris* produce small numbers of lemon-shaped cocoons 5 to 7 mm long, each with several eggs only one of which hatches. Other earthworms such as the faecal earthworm, *Eisenia foetida,* is a hardy species that grows well under cultural conditions (Galtsoff *et al.*). Also, it is parasitized by gregarines of both Monocystidae and Zygocystidae.

SELECTED REFERENCES

Bhatia, B. L. (1929). Parasitology 21:120.

Cuénot, L. (1901). Arch. Biol. 17:581.

Galtsoff, P. S., F. E. Lutz, P. S. Welch, and J. G. Needham. (1959). Culture Methods for Invertebrate Animals. Dover Publications, New York, p. 195.

Hesse, E. (1909). Arch. Zool. Exp. Gen. 74:341.

Lankester, E. R. (1903). A Treatise on Zoology, Part I: Introduction and Protozoa, Fasc. 2. Adam and Charles Black, London, p. 154.

Mickel, C. E. (1925). J. Parasit. 11:135.

Troisi, R. L. (1933). Tran. Amer. Micr. Soc. 52:326.

FAMILY DIPLOCYSTIDAE

These are acephaline gregarines from the intestine of flatworms, insects, and tunicates. The trophozoites are solitary or associated in pairs during the early part of development. They produce spores that are round or oval, with eight sporozoites.

Lankesteria culicis (Ross, 1899) (Plate 18)

This gregarine occurs in the alimentary canal and Malpighian tubules of mosquitoes of the genus *Aedes* in India, South America, and Africa. Possibly it or related species has a wider distribution than now recognized.

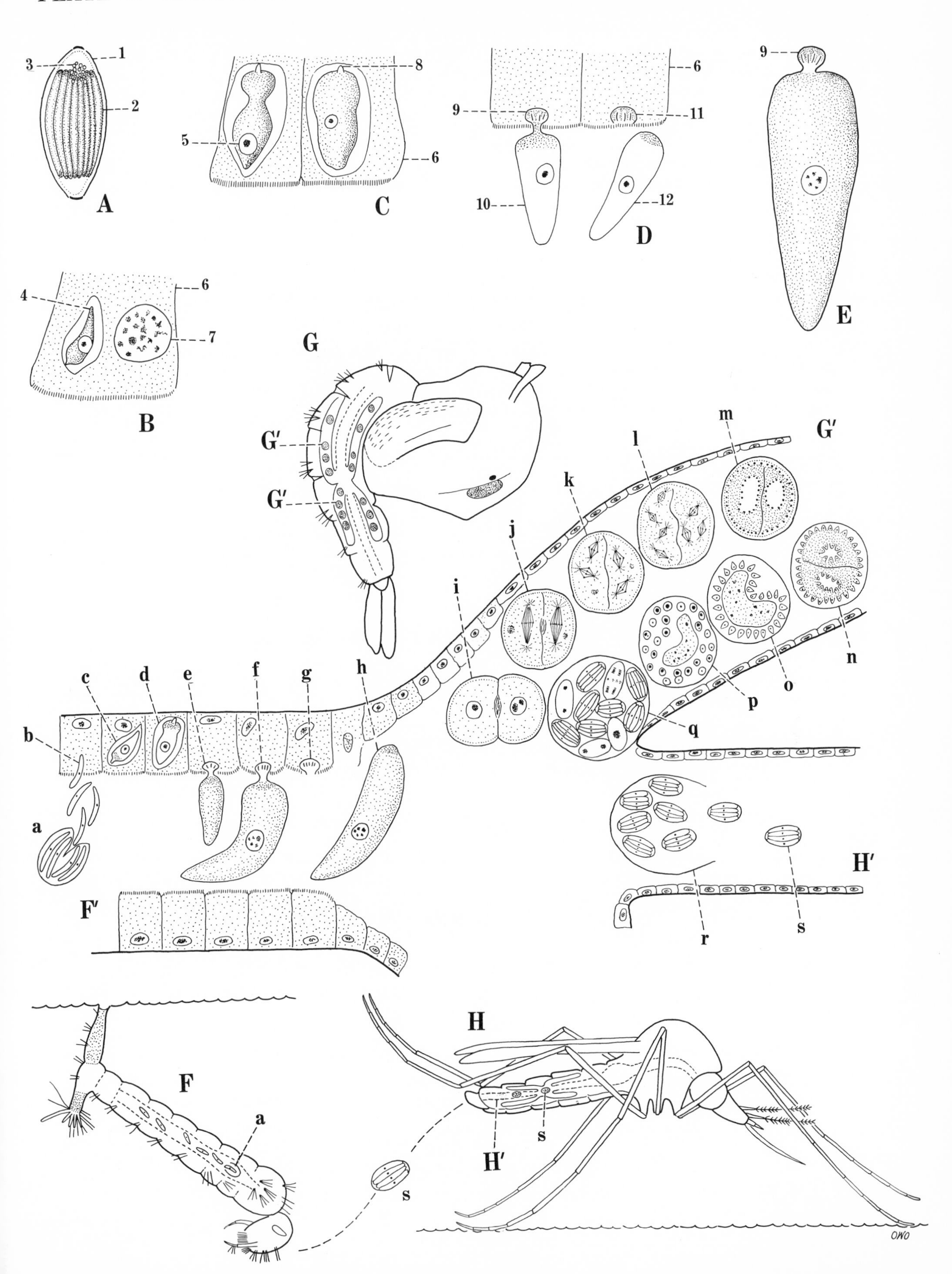
1
2
3
4
5
6
7
8
9
10
11
12
A
B
C
D
E
F
F′
G
G′
H
H′
a
b
c
d
e
f
g
h
i
j
k
l
m
n
o
p
q
r
s
OWO

Its life cycle is representative of a sporozoan in which schizogony does not occur.

DESCRIPTION. These are intracellular trophozoites with a small conical epimerite. As they grow, the body of the trophozoite becomes extracellular and is attached to the epithelial cell by an umbrella-shaped epimerite; the mature trophozoite detached from the epimerite is known as a sporadin, which is somewhat spatulate in shape and 150 to 200 μ long by 31 to 41 μ wide. Gametocysts are spherical; oocysts are oval, 10 by 6 μ, and contain eight sporozoites.

LIFE CYCLE. The life cycles of the Eugregarininida, of which *Lankesteria culicis* is a typical example, are characterized by the absence of a schizogonous phase. Both the gametogenous and sporogenous phases begin and are completed within the intestinal lumen of the same host.

Oocysts containing sporozoites voided with faeces into water by the adult mosquitoes are eaten by larval mosquitoes. Sporozoites released in the midgut enter the epithelial cells and transform into intracellular trophozoites. They soon become too large for the cells and hang free in the lumen, anchored for a short time by the epimerite that is embedded in the cytoplasm of the epithelial cell. When the stem of the epimerite breaks, the trophozoite becomes free in the lumen and is known as a sporadin.

As the mosquito larvae change to pupae, the sporadins enter the Malpighian tubules to begin the sporogenous phase. They unite in pairs, and become gametocytes enclosed in a common cyst, the gametocyst. The nucleus of each gametocyte multiplies many times and the small nuclei become arranged on the periphery of the cytoplasm. They bud off with a small amount of cytoplasm to form gametes having either large or small nuclei. Gametes with small nuclei unite with those having large nuclei to form zygotes, thus ending the gametogenous phase. Sporogony commences when the zygote begins development, leading to the formation of oval oocysts containing eight slender, spindle-shaped sporozoites each.

During metamorphosis of the pupae to adult mosquitoes, the gametocysts containing many oocysts pass from the Malpighian tubules to the hindgut. In the latter, the gametocysts rupture, releasing oocysts which are expelled with the faeces. Those falling into water infect mosquito larvae when eaten by them.

EXERCISE ON LIFE CYCLE

While *Lankesteria culicis* may not be available for study in many parts of the world, other gregarines are available from the intestine of almost any species of insect and from the seminal vesicles of earthworms, especially *Helodrilus caliginosus* from compost heaps.

Remove the intestine of the insects and examine the epithelium for intracellular trophozoites, and the lumen for extracellular trophozoites and sporadins. Gametocysts containing oocysts with sporozoites appear in the hindgut.

Smears made from the contents of the seminal vesicles of earthworms show stages of *Monocystis* or *Zygocystis*. Young trophozoites are in the blastophores of sperm morulae and older ones are free in the seminal vesicles. Gametocytes are readily recognized in gametocysts.

SELECTED REFERENCES

Ganapati, P. N., and P. Tate. (1949). Parasitology 39:291.

Kudo, R. R. (1966). Protozoology, 5th Ed. Charles C Thomas, Springfield, p. 627.

Mickel, C. E. (1925). J. Parasit. 11:135.

Ray, H. (1933). Parasitology 25:392.

Troisi, R. A. (1933). Trans. Amer. Micr. Soc. 52:326.

Wenyon, C. M. (1926). Protozoology, Vol. 2. Baillière, Tindall and Cox, London, p. 1117.

Suborder Schizogregarinina

The schizogregarines undergo schizogony, as indicated by the name, in the intestine of arthropods, annelids, and tunicates. The sporozoites develop into schizonts that either enter the intestinal epithelium or attach to it and remain hanging in the lumen. Division of the schizont is by multiple fission or budding. Fully developed merozoites pair, encyst, and undergo sexual reproduction.

The suborder consists of two families, the Ophrycystidae and Schizocystidae.

FAMILY SCHIZOCYSTIDAE

The members of this family produce two or more spores from each pair of gametocytes.

Schizocystis gregarinoides (Leger, 1909) (Plate 19)

Schizocystis gregarinoides is a parasite of the intestine of larval midges (*Ceratopogon solstitialis* and possibly other species) that develop in water or moist humus.

This species is of interest because it is one of a group that shows schizogony in its simplest form. The schizont is extracellular and therefore the merozoites develop in the lumen of the gut. Gametogony and sporogony are typically gregarine, as in *Lankesteria culicis*.

DESCRIPTION. Mature vermicular schizonts are up to 400 μ long by 15 μ wide, with the anterior end broad and bearing organelles of a sucking type for adhering to the gut. There are up to 200 nuclei. Each schizont forms into elongated clusters of merozoites equal to the number of nuclei. Gametocysts contain two gametocytes; anisogametes are round (macrogametes) or pointed (microgametes). The oocysts within the gametocysts are oval and contain eight spindle-shaped sporozoites 8 μ long.

LIFE CYCLE. Sporulated oocysts passed in the faeces of midge larvae are the source of infection of other midges when swallowed with their food. Sporozoites liberated in the intestine attach to the epithelium, where they grow into elongate trophozoites. When they reach a length of about 20 μ, the nucleus begins to divide. This is the beginning of the schizogenous phase of the life cycle. Growth continues until the schizont is about 400 μ long by about 15 μ wide and contains up to 700 nuclei. At this point in its development, the mature schizont divides into as many merozoites as there are nuclei. Some of the merozoites may attach to the intestinal epithelium and produce another generation of schizonts, whereas others develop into gametocysts, thus beginning the gametogenous phase. Two gametocytes unite and secrete a cyst known as a gametocyst about themselves.

The nucleus of each gametocyte divides a number of times and each part migrates to the surface of the cytoplasmic mass where a bit of cytoplasm surrounds it, forming isogametes of different shape. The round ones from one gametocyte are female gametes (macrogametes) and the pointed ones from the other gametocyte are male gametes (microgametes). When fully developed, pairs of isogametes fuse, forming zygotes. Each zygote secretes an oocyst wall about itself and sporogony takes place inside the gametocyst in the intestine of the midge.

The nucleus of the zygote divides three times, resulting in a total of eight. Each new nucleus is surrounded by a bit of cytoplasm and develops into a sporozoite. The gametocysts, containing the fully developed oocysts, are voided from the intestine with the faeces into the water. Larval midges become infected by eating the oocysts.

EXERCISE ON LIFE CYCLE

Remove the entire intestine of ceratopogon midge larvae and examine the wall and contents for the characteristic stages of *Schizocystis*. The sequence of the developmental stages can be ascertained from the drawings. The use of intravital stains are of value in making the gregarines more readily distinguished.

SELECTED REFERENCES

Doflein, F., and E. Reichenow. (1953). Lehrbuch der Protozoenkunde, 6th Ed. Gustav Fischer, Jena, p. 786.

Kudo, R. (1954). Protozoology, 4th Ed. Charles C Thomas, Springfield, Ill., p. 562.

Léger, L. (1909). Arch. Protistenk. 18:83.

Wenyon, C. M. (1926). Protozoology, Vol. 2. Baillière, Tindall, and Cox, London, p. 1128.

Tribe Cephalina

The body of the trophozoite is divided into two distinct linear parts by a septum. The smaller anterior part is the protomerite and the larger posterior one the deutomerite.

EXPLANATION OF PLATE 19 ▷

A. Adult vermicular schizont. **B.** Schizont in the process of segmentation and formation of merozoites. **C.** Merozoites formed. **D.** Sporulated oocyst. **E.** Larval midge, showing enlarged section of intestine.

1, holdfast organelle at anterior end; **2,** nuclei; **3,** merozoites forming from schizont; **4,** residual cytoplasm; **5,** merozoites; **6,** wall of oocyst; **7,** sporozoites.

a, ripe sporocyst in intestine; **b,** ruptured sporocyst liberating sporozoites; **c,** attachment of sporozoite to intestinal epithelium; **d,** growing schizont with two nuclei; **e,** older schizont with more nuclei; **f,** mature vermicular schizont; **g,** segmentation of schizont to form merozoites; **h,** merozoite initiating a succeeding generation of schizonts similar to **d, e, f**; **i,** merozoites initiating gametogenous phase; **j,** merozoites become gametocytes; **k,** union of gametocytes; **l,** enclosure of gametocytes in gametocyst; **m,** nuclear division in gametocytes to form gametes; **n,** formation of pointed microgametes and round macrogametes; **o,** union of micro- and macrogametes to form zygotes within gametocyst; **p,** formation of young oocysts inside gametocyst and beginning of sporogenous phase; **q,** sporulated oocyst free in intestine; **r,** sporulated oocyst passing through intestine in faeces; **s,** infective oocyst free in water.

Adapted from Léger, 1909, Arch. Protistenk. 18:83.

FAMILY GREGARINIDAE

The gregarines are parasites of the alimentary canal of arthropods, especially insects. There are many species of these simple animals parasitizing insects throughout the world. Watson and Kamm give extensive lists, together with drawings of them.

The members of the family are characterized by a simple knoblike extension of the protomerite called the epimerite, and development is always extracellular except for the epimerite which is within the cell and serves as an anchoring device. The sporonts become attached to each other in tandem, an arrangement known as syzygy. The gametocysts may or may not have sporoducts extending from them, depending on the species. Spores escape in chains through the sporoducts when they are present.

Gregarina blattarum von Siebold, 1839 (Plate 20)

This parasite is common in cockroaches (*Periplaneta americana, Blatta orientalis, Blatella germanica*), having been reported from them in many parts of the world.

DESCRIPTION. A complete trophozoite consists of three parts. They are the small anterior epimerite, which is a single hyaline knob connected by a thin strand to the protomerite for attachment to the intestinal epithelium; the larger protomerite; and the deutomerite, which is the largest and most posterior part. Gregarines free in the lumen of the gut are known as sporonts and lack the epimerite and may be single or attached to the end of another. The anterior of the biassociative sporonts is the primite and the second the satellite.

Sporonts are 450 to 500 μ long by 185 to 200 μ wide. Cysts are spherical or ovoidal, with 8 to 10 spore ducts. The spores are cylindrical to barrel-shaped with truncate ends and measure 8 to 8.5 μ long and 3.7 to 4 μ wide. Spores are extruded in chains from the spore ducts.

LIFE CYCLE. The life cycle is typically gregarine, being direct. Ripe sporocysts expelled in the faeces evaginate their sporoducts through which chains of undeveloped spores are exuded. Development of the spore proceeds through three divisions of the nucleus with the formation of eight nuclei. A fragment of cytoplasm surrounds each nucleus and forms a sporozoite. The fully developed spores containing the eight sporozoites are infective to cockroaches eating them. Upon being released from the spore in the alimentary canal of the cockroach, the sporozoites attach to the intestinal epithelium and begin development to the trophozoite. The embedded portion enlarges to form the epimerite while the free part develops into the protomerite and the deutomerite. Upon maturity, the pendent portion detaches from the epimerite and is free in the lumen of the gut. It is known as a sporadin. Two or more sporadins often attach end to end. Eventually two sporadins conjugate by attaching to each other along the long axis of the body and secrete a cyst about themselves. The nucleus of each gametocyte undergoes repeated division, forming many small nuclei scattered throughout the cytoplasm. These migrate to the surface of the cytoplasmic masses where each becomes clothed with a bit of cytoplasm to form the gametes. Union of the gametes produces zygotes which develop into spores within

PLATE 19 *Schizocystis gregarinoides*

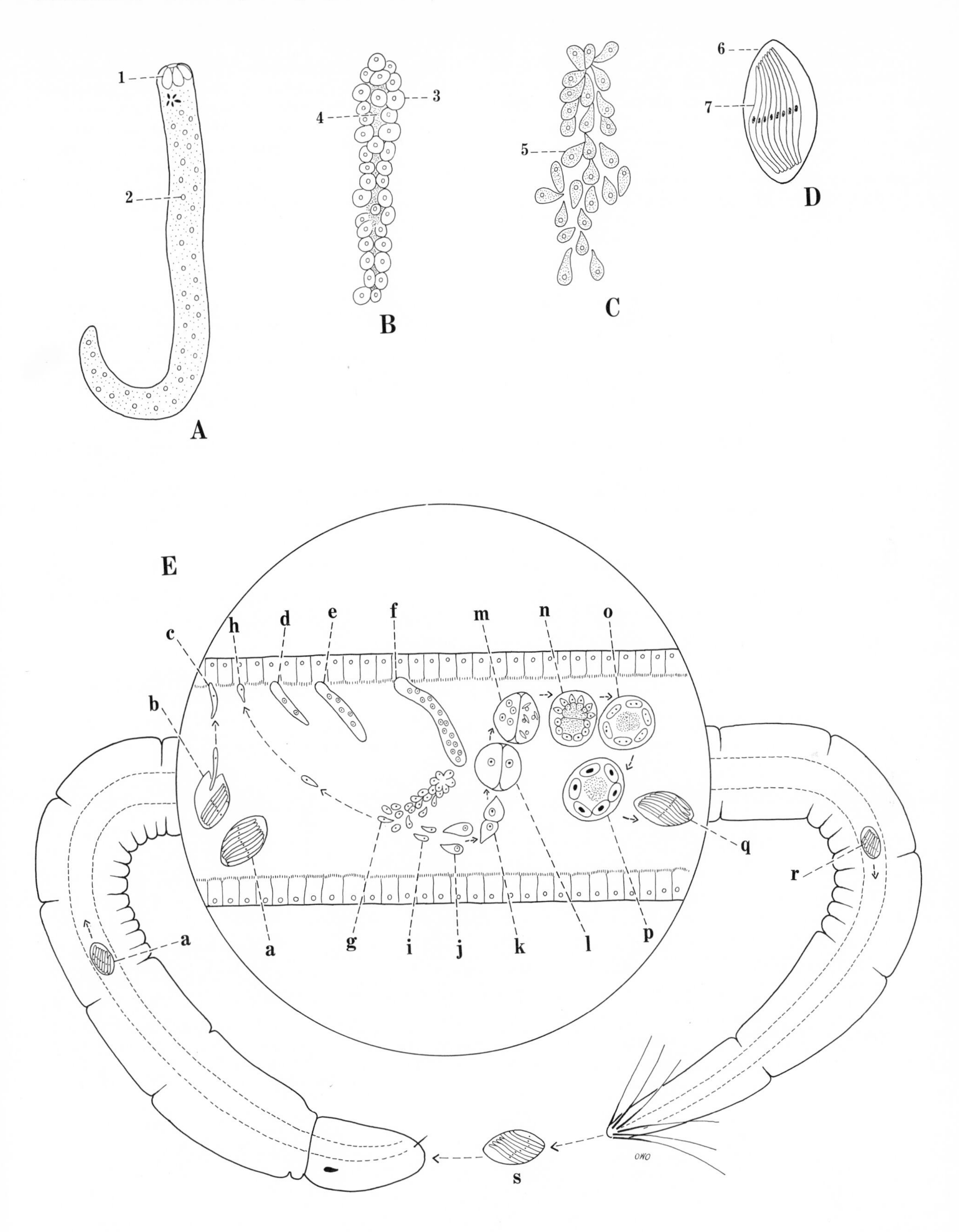

EXPLANATION OF PLATE 20 ▷

A. Two sporadins in syzygy, *i.e.*, attached end to end. **B.** Sporonts in conjugation. **C.** Conjugation of sporonts in newly secreted cyst. **D.** Cyst with gametes. **E.** Ripe cyst with sporoducts and filled with spores. **F.** Partial chains of spores. **G.** Developed spore inside mucoid covering. **H.** Sporulated spore. **I.** Sporozoite attached to epithelial cell. **J.** Growing trophozoite partially embedded in epithelial cell of gut. **K.** Older trophozoite partially embedded in gut cell, showing developing protomerite and deutomerite. **L.** *Blatta orientalis* host.

1, protomerite; **2,** deutomerite; **3,** nucleus; **4,** sporocyst wall; **5,** gametes; **6,** gelatinous wall of cyst; **7,** invaginated spore duct; **8,** evaginated spore duct; **9,** chain of spores being released; **10,** mass of spores; **11,** three spores from chain; **12,** mucoid covering; **13,** immature spore; **14,** sporozoite; **15,** epithelial cell of midgut of cockroach; **16,** striated surface of cell; **17,** sporozoite attached to epithelial cell; **18,** partially embedded trophozoite; **19,** protomerite of developing trophozoite; **20,** deutomerite.

a, sporulated spore swallowed by cockroach; **b,** spore ruptured, releasing sporozoites; **c,** free sporozoites; **d,** sporozoite attached to intestinal epithelium; **e,** developing trophozoite; **f,** fully developed trophozoite attached to epithelium by epimerite; **g,** sporadin (a detached trophozoite) free in gut; **h,** two sporadins in syzygy; **i,** two sporadins in conjugation, preparing to encyst; **j,** formation of gametes, which will be followed by fertilization and formation of spores; **k,** ripe cyst with sporoducts and containing numerous spores; **l,** ripe cyst passed in faeces of cockroach; **m,** free unsporulated spore; **n,** infective sporulated spore.

Figures adapted from various sources, except L, which is original.

---

the sporocyst. Continued development of the spore results in the formation of a thick cyst wall and a number of sporoducts through which the spores are freed.

EXERCISE ON LIFE CYCLE

Widespread distribution of cockroaches, incidence of infection, and ease of handling the hosts makes this an ideal sporozoan parasite for experimental studies.

Parasite-free roaches should be reared and kept in readiness for experimental infection. Clean sterile cages must be used.

Sporocysts collected from naturally infected cockroaches will provide spores for observing sporulation and infection of roaches. The entire process of sporulation can be observed by placing freshly extruded spores in a drop of water on a microscope slide on which the cover slip is sealed around the edges with Vaseline or petroleum jelly.

By feeding fully sporulated spores to uninfected roaches, the developing stages can be recovered by examining the contents of the alimentary canal of a series of infected insects at short intervals.

SELECTED REFERENCES

Cuénot, L. (1901). Arch. Biol. 17:581.

Kamm, M. W. (1922). Ill. Biol. Monogr. 7:1; (1922). Trans. Amer. Micr. Soc. 41:122.

Minchin, E. A. (1903). The Sporozoa in: A Treatise on Zoology (Lankester). A. and C. Black, London.

Watson, M. E. (1916). Ill. Biol. Monogr. 2(3):1.

ORDER COCCIDIA

The Coccidia are intracellular parasites mainly of the intestinal epithelium but also of the liver and blood cells. Generally those species developing in the intestinal epithelium produce thick-walled oocysts for the protection of the sporozoites during transition from one host to another. The ones developing in the liver (except *Eimeria stiedae*) and blood cells have only a thin-walled oocyst since there is no free-living stage, transmission being by bloodsucking invertebrates.

Reproduction is asexual by schizogony and sexual by sporogony. The microgametes are distinctly smaller than the macrogametes. Generally both sexual and asexual reproduction takes place in the same host, but alternate hosts occur in some genera, foreshadowing the haemosporidian type of life cycle with an alternation of hosts.

PLATE 20 *Gregarina blattarum*

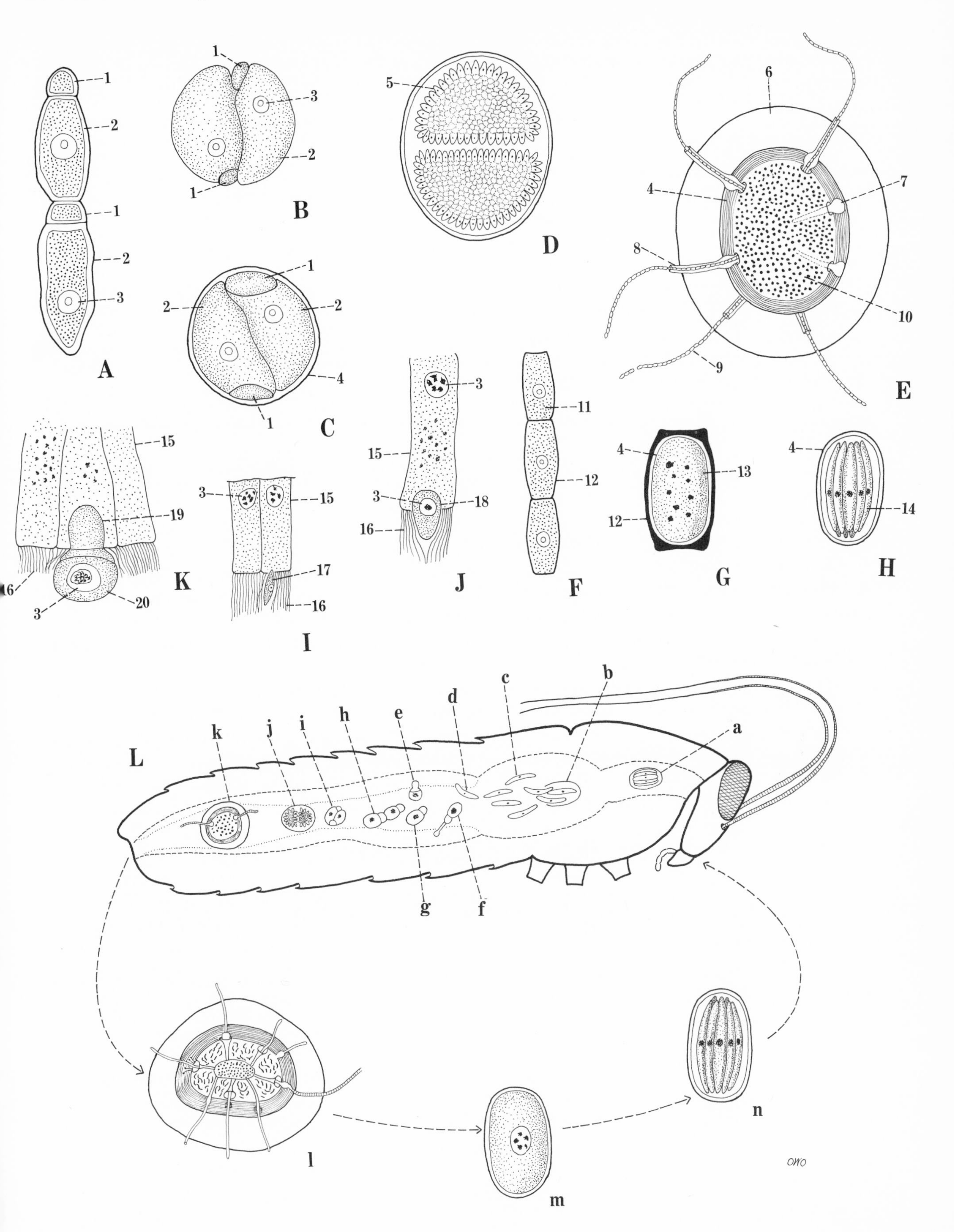

The Coccidia show a continuous evolutionary transition from the lower Gregarinida which are chiefly coelozoic to the haemogregarines which occur mainly in the blood cells. The plausible course of this evolution from the coelozoic one-host gregarines to the intracellular two-host type leading to the haemosporidians is shown by the *Selenococcidium, Eimeria, Aggregata,* and *Schellackia* of the suborder Eimeridia, and *Hepatozoon* and *Haemogregarina* of the suborder Adeleidea (Plate 16).

Suborder Eimeridia

The members of this suborder are chiefly intracellular parasites of the intestinal epithelium, although some occur in the liver and kidney cells. Both schizogenic and sporogenic development generally occur in one host, but two hosts appear in the life cycle of some genera.

The gametocytes develop separately and the microgametes are numerous minute, biflagellated, comma-shaped bodies.

Selenococcidium has a life cycle reminiscent of the gregarine *Schizocystis* in that the schizont begins development in the lumen of the intestine, but differs in that it is completed in the intestinal epithelium. Gametogony is coccidian in character, taking place in the intestinal epithelium.

Eimeria is typically coccidian in its life cycle, having an intracellular alternation of generations in the intestinal epithelium of a single host. Oocysts are thick-walled and sporulation occurs outside the host with two sporozoites contained in each of four sporocysts, making a total of eight. Infection is by swallowing sporulated oocysts.

Aggregata introduces an alternation of hosts, but it is a primitive relationship. Schizogony occurs in the intestinal epithelium of a crab and sporogony in the same cells of a cuttlefish. Infection of crabs takes place when they eat cuttlefish and of the latter when they devour crabs. The bivalved oocyst contains three free sporozoites. The appearance of an alternation of hosts points toward the haemosporidian type of life cycle.

Schellackia has a more advanced life cycle in that reproduction occurs in two organs in the vertebrate host and in having a blood sucking arthropod involved as a mechanical transport of the sporozoites. Schizogony is completed in the intestinal epithelium of lizards. Development of the microgametocytes likewise takes place in the intestinal epithelium, a coccidian trait, but that of the macrogametocytes is in the intestinal wall where the zygote is formed and the sporozoites develop in thin-walled oocysts. Upon release from the oocyst, the sporozoites enter the blood stream and penetrate erythrocytes, a haemosporidian characteristic. Infected blood cells swallowed by lizard mites are engulfed by epithelial cells of the stomach and digested, liberating the sporozoites in them. No development takes place in the mite. It serves only to collect sporozoites and as a means of transporting them to the intestine of the lizards when eaten by them. This cycle, which foreshadows that of the Haemosporidia, is advanced further by the members of the suborder Adeleidea, which is discussed in a later section.

FAMILY SELENOCOCCIDIIDAE

The schizonts are elongated vermiform bodies which together with the gametocytes are extracellular at first, but later enter the intestinal epithelium to complete their development.

Selenococcidium intermedium Léger and Duboscq, 1909 (Plate 21)

Selenococcidium is a parasite of the intestine of European lobsters. It is remarkable in that the early stages of both the schizogenous and gametogenous cycles occur in the lumen of the intestine as vermicular trophozoites, a characteristic of the gregarines. Schizogony and gametogony are completed in the epithelial cells of the intestine, similar to that which occurs in the Coccidia. Thus, this life cycle appears to be a connecting link between that of the gregarines and the coccidia. Sporogony presumably occurs outside the host, but it is unknown at present.

DESCRIPTION. Trophozoites are vermiculate bodies in the intestinal lumen where schizogony begins. The vermiculate octonucleate schizont enters the epithelial cells and produces eight merozoites; large and small vermiculate merozoites in the intestinal lumen give rise to quadrinucleate and octonucleate vermicular macro- and microgametocytes, respectively. The gametes, being of distinctly different sizes, are known as anisogametes. The microgametes are minute, elongate bodies and the macrogametes relatively large and oval or spherical in shape. Formation of gametes takes place in the intestinal epithelium. Sporogony is unknown.

LIFE CYCLE. Presumably infection of lobsters takes place when ripe oocysts thought to be free in the water are swallowed. This part of the life cycle, however, remains unknown.

The young vermiculate trophozoite in the intestine undergoes three nuclear divisions, producing an octonucleate, mature schizont. It enters the intestinal epithelium, rounds up, becomes a segmenter, and produces eight vermiform merozoites. Several cycles of schizogony of this type may take place. Finally, a generation of merozoites of two sizes but smaller than those forming the schizonts appear. The small ones develop into oval octonucleate bodies in the lumen of the intestine and produce eight vermicular microgametocytes. Upon entering the epithelial cells, they round up and the nucleus divides many times, producing as many microgametes. The large merozoites transform into quadrinucleate vermicules that produce four similar macrogametocytes in the lumen of the intestine. These enter the epithelical cells, where they round up and each one becomes a macrogamete. Fertilization occurs and a zygote is formed.

It is seen that the trophozoites, schizonts, and gametocytes develop in the lumen of the intestine, much the same as the gregarines. Completion of schizogony with the formation of merozoites, and of gametogony with the formation of gametes, takes place in the epithelial cells of the intestine, as occurs in the Coccidia. In these respects, *Selenococcidium intermedium* appears to occupy a position intermediate between the gregarines and the Coccidia, thereby bridging the gap between the extracellular development of the gregarine on the one hand, and the intracellular development of the Coccidia and Haemosporidia on the other.

EXERCISE ON LIFE CYCLE

In regions where living lobsters are available for examination, a search should be made in species off the coast of North America for *Selencoccidium intermedium* or related species. The presence of these parasites would provide an opportunity to find the oocysts and thereby complete the life cycle.

SELECTED REFERENCES

Léger, L., and O. Duboscq. (1910). Arch Zool. Exp. Gen. 40, 5. s. 5(4):187.

Minchin, E. A. (1922). An Introduction to the Study of Protozoa with Special Reference to Parasitic Forms. Edward Arnold, London, pp. 350, 351.

Wenyon, C. W. (1926). Protozoology, Vol. 2. Baillière, Tindall, and Cox, London, p. 801.

FAMILY EIMERIIDAE

The macro- and microgametes develop separately inside the host cells, the microgametes being numerous. Oocysts and schizonts are without attachment organs. Schizonts develop inside host cells, oocysts outside host body and contain one to many sporozoites.

Eimeria tenella Railliet and Lucet, 1891 (Plate 22)

The species of *Eimeria* are common sporozoan parasites of the intestinal epithelium of vertebrates and some arthropods, especially centipedes, and the epithelium of the bile ducts of rabbits. *Eimeria tenella* is a parasite of the caecal epithelium of chickens and is one of the several species of coccidia that infects these hosts throughout the world. It causes a severe disease known as caecal coccidiosis which is manifested by bloody diarrhea. Each species of *Eimeria* shows a high degree of host specificity.

A single host is involved in the life cycle. Schizogony and gametogony take place in the epithelium of the caeca. Sporogony occurs outside the body of the host. Thus an alternation of generations occurs in a single host.

DESCRIPTION. Oocysts are broadly ovoid, 29 to 19.5 μ long by 22.8 to 16.5 μ wide, average size 26.6 by 19 μ. Sporulation time is approximately 48 hours at room temperature and the prepatent period is 7 days. The schizonts and oocysts are in the caeca with the first generation of schizonts in the epithe-

EXPLANATION OF PLATE 21 ▷

A. Vermicule with eight nuclei of schizogenous phase. **B.** Vermicule forming schizont inside epithelial cell of intestine and whose merozoites will re-initiate a second schizogenous cycle. **C.** Five merozoites which will become macrogametocytes. **D.** Macrogamete. **E.** Schizont preparing to divide to form eight merozoites that will become microgametocytes. **F.** Microgametocyte with numerous microgametes. **G** Lobster host. **H.** Section of intestine of lobster showing schizogony. **I.** Section of intestine of lobster showing gametogony (sporogony unknown).

1, nucleus; **2**, merozoites; **3**, microgametes.

a-g, schizogony. **a**, large uninucleate trophozoite; **b**, quadnucleate schizont; **c**, octonucleate schizont; **d**, octonucleate schizont enters epithelial cell and assumes spherical form; **e**, vermiculate merozoites forming; **f**, fully formed vermiculate merozoites; **g**, vermiculate merozoites escaping into lumen of gut enter other cells and repeat schizogenous cycle (a-g) or initiate gametogenous cycle (h-x); **h**, small merozoite destined to form microgametes; **i**, schizont with eight nuclei that will produce eight merozoites; **j**, eight merozoites that will form microgametocytes; **k**, merozoite entering cell; **l**, young microgametocyte formed from merozoite; **m**, developing microgametocyte with many nuclei; **n**, fully developed microgametocyte with numerous microgametes; **o**, large merozoite destined to produce macrogametes; **p**, binucleate merozoite; **q**, quadrinucleate merozoite; **r**, formation of four merozoites that will develop into four macrogametocytes; **s**, merozoite entering cell; **t-u**, merozoite transforming into macrogametocyte; **v**, macrogamete; **w**, fertilization (small microgamete attached on upper side); **x**, zygote (sporogony unknown).

Adapted from Léger and Duboscq, 1910, Arch. Zool. Exp. Gen. 40, 5. s. 5(4):187.

---

lium and the second in the subepithelial layer, being highly pathogenic and producing bloody diarrheic faeces. The lesions are in the caeca but not in the intestine.

LIFE CYCLE. Infection occurs when sporulated oocysts are swallowed. The sporozoites are liberated from the oocyst and sporocysts in the intestine under the influence of the pancreatic juices and go to the caeca where they penetrate the epithelial cells in the depths of the caecal glands. They develop into the first generation of schizonts within the epithelial cells. The schizonts soon produce the first generation of small merozoites, 2 to 4 μ long by 1.5 μ wide, which are liberated in 2½ to 3 days after infection.

These merozoites, of which there are a great many, penetrate the epithelium much as do the sporozoites, and initiate the second generation with many schizonts that are larger than those of the first generation. Large groups of them occur in the submucosa. The merozoites are 16 μ long by 2 μ wide, which is much larger than those of the first generation. They are packed in great numbers in the submucosa and mature during the fourth day after infection, being released into the lumen of the caeca during the fifth day. Haemorrhage begins on the fourth day but becomes copious when the merozoites escape on the fifth day, destroying much tissue in the process.

The second generation of merozoites penetrate the epithelial cells generally producing only gametocytes, although it is thought that some may develop into a third generation of schizonts. The young gametocytes are similar at first but differentiation occurs soon. In the microgametocytes, the nucleus undergoes many divisions, resulting in the formation of tiny, biflagellated microgametes which stain dark blue with haematoxylin.

The macrogametocytes grow in size but the nucleus does not multiply. As they mature and differentiate into gametes, prominent eosinophilic granules appear in them. After fertilization and formation of the zygote, a thick cyst wall forms, presumably from the eosinophilic granules. This is the unsporulated oocyst which appears in the epithelial cells during the seventh day after infection. They escape from the host cells shortly after fertilization and appear in the faeces in great numbers for about 17 days, after which they disappear. Since the second generation of merozoites produces gametocytes, the development and elimination of them terminates the infection. Hence, *Eimeria* is a self-limiting parasite by virtue of the nature of its life cycle.

Sporogony occurs outside the host under favorable conditions of shade, moisture, and temperature. The cytoplasm soon divides into four sporoblasts. Each of these forms a covering about itself and becomes a sporocyst. The cytoplasm within each sporocyst develops into two sporozoites which constitute the infective stage.

PLATE 21 *Selenococcidium intermedium*

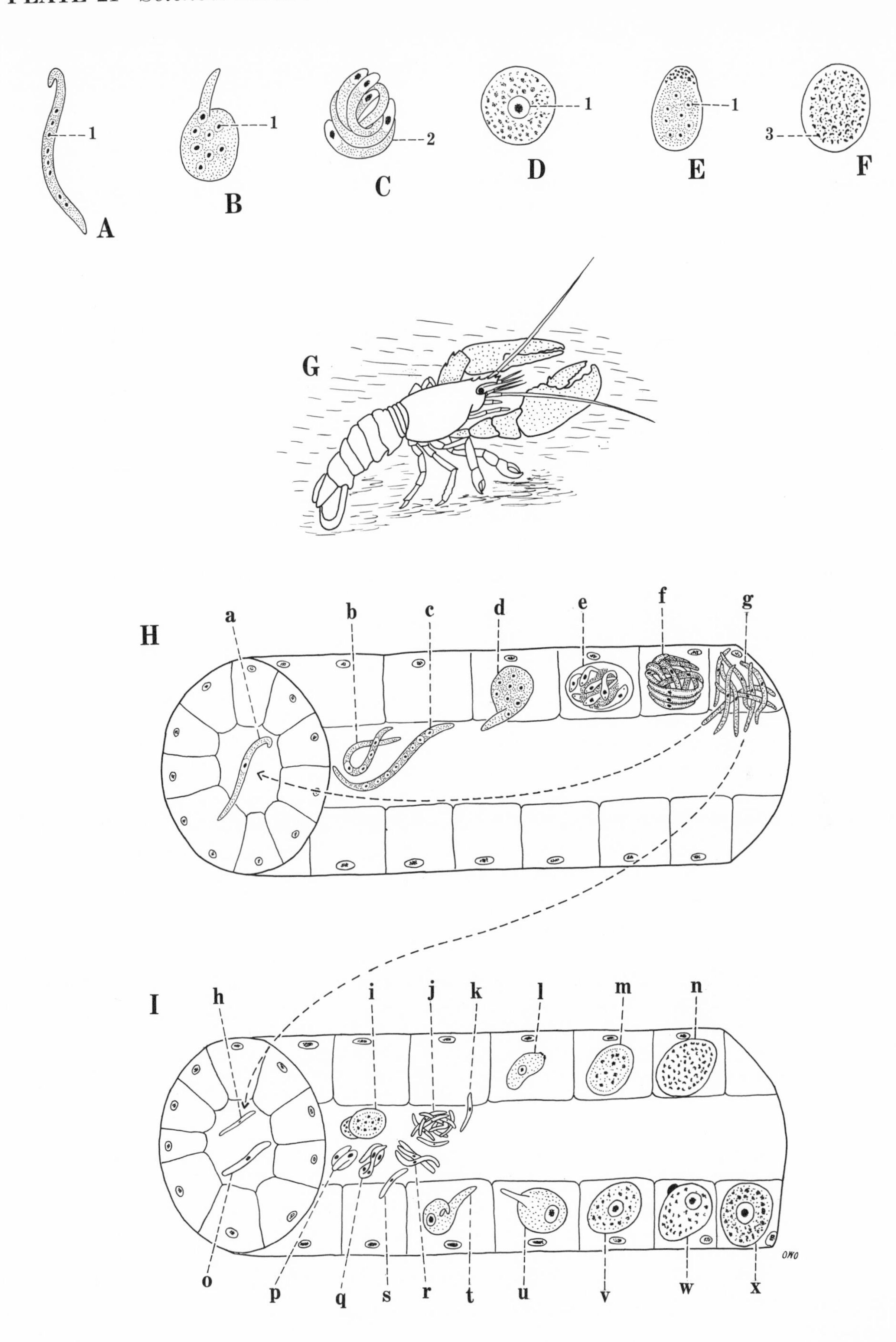

EXPLANATION OF PLATE 22 ▷

A. Unsporulated oocyst. **B.** Early stage of sporulation. **C.** Oocyst with four sporoblasts. **D.** Fully developed oocyst with eight sporozoites. **E-I.** Stages of life cycle in caecal epithelium of chick. **E.** First generation of merozoites. **F.** Second generation of merozoites. **G.** Development of micro- and macrogametocytes. **H.** Development of micro- and macrogametes, formation of zygotes, and escape of oocysts from epithelium. **I.** Chicken host.

1, oocyst wall; **2**, cytoplasm with central nucleus; **3**, dividing cytoplasm; **4**, sporoblasts; **5**, sporocyst; **6**, sporozoites; **7**, polar granule.

a-h, first generation of merozoites in caecum. **a**, epithelium of caecum; **b**, crypt of Leiberkühn; **c**, sporozoite from lumen of caecum entering crypt; **d**, sporozoite entering epithelial cell; **e**, trophozoite; **f**, schizonts; **g**, segmenter with formed merozoites; **h**, merozoites escape from segmenters into crypts and lumen; **i-o**, second generation of merozoites; **i**, mass of first generation merozoites entering crypt; **j**, mass of young trophozoites; **k**, mass of fully developed subepithelial trophozoites; **l**, schizonts; **m-o**, second generation of merozoites causing extensive destruction of tissue; **p-s**, formation of gametocytes; **p-q**, second generation of merozoites enter crypts and penetrate cells; **r**, young developing gametocytes; **s**, fully developed gametocytes; **t-x**, formation of gametes, fertilization of macrogamete, and its release from cells as an oocyst; **t**, developing microgametocyte; **u**, microgametes escaping from epithelial cell; **v**, developing macrogametocyte; **w**, fertilization of macrogamete and formation of zygote; **x**, mass of oocysts breaking out of tissue and later voided in faeces.

a′-d′, sporogony of oocyst; **a′**, unsporulated oocysts passed in faeces; **b′**, developing oocysts with sporoblasts; **c′**, sporocysts developed; **d′**, fully sporulated and infective oocyst; **e′-i′**, infection of host; **e′**, sporulated oocyst in crop; **f′**, sporocysts escape from oocyst; **g′**, sporozoites escape from sporocysts in small intestine; **h′**, sporozoites enter caeca; **i′**, sporozoites enter epithelial cells of caeca; **j′-m′**, schizogony; **j′**, trophozoites; **k′**, schizont; **l′**, segmenter; **m′**, merozoites which are the final stage of first generation that is repeated (**n′**, **j′-m′**), for second generation; **o′-t′**, gametogony of male gamete; **o′**, merozoite of second generation enters epithelial cell and initiates microgametogeny; **p′**, developing microgametocyte; **q′**, early division of nucleus; **r′**, nuclear material arranged around periphery of microgametocyte preparatory to forming microgametes; **s′**, developing microgametes; **t′**, fully developed microgametes escaping from epithelial cell; **u′-y′**, gametogony of female gamete; **u′**, second generation merozoite entering epithelial cell to develop into macrogametocyte; **v′-x′**, developing macrogametocyte (**w′-x′** shows extruded nuclear material); **y′**, macrogamete ready for fertilization; **z′**, fertilization.

a″, union of nuclei and formation of zygote; **b″**, oocyst in cell; **c″**, oocyst escapes from cell, enters lumen of caecum, and is voided with faeces.

Figures A-H adapted from Tyzzer, 1929, Amer. J. Hyg. 10:269.

Five other common species of *Eimeria* infect chickens. Similarly, sheep and calves suffer from severe and often fatal coccidiosis caused by a variety of species.

Cats, dogs, and passerine birds, particularly English sparrows (*Passer domesticus*) are infected with coccidia of the genus *Isospora*, which is characterized by having two sporocysts, each with four sporozoites. The life cycle of the species is basically similar to that of *Eimeria*.

EXERCISE ON LIFE CYCLE

Eimeria tenella, when available, provides an interesting exercise on life history studies. Oocysts usually can be obtained from the faeces of young chickens that are kept under reasonably unsanitary conditions. They may be separated from the faecal material by macerating the faeces with water, followed by allowing the oocysts to sediment for one hour in a tall container, after which the supernatant fluid containing the coloring matter and fine debris is decanted. Repeat the process until the water is clean.

The oocysts will sporulate in 24 hours at room temperature in a shallow solution of 2 per cent dichromate, which prevents an excessive growth of bacteria and fungi, or in shallow water, or if poured on filter paper that is kept moist.

Fully sporulated oocysts fed with mash to young chicks or placed in the crop by means of a tube produce an infection. Since 2½ to 3 days are required for the first generation of merozoites to develop, experimentally infected chicks should be sacrificed at intervals of 24 hours or less, and a portion of the fresh caecum fixed in one of the standard fixing agents for sectioning. These sections, stained with haematoxylin and eosin, will provide progressive stages of development of first generation schizonts.

PLATE 22 *Eimeria tenella*

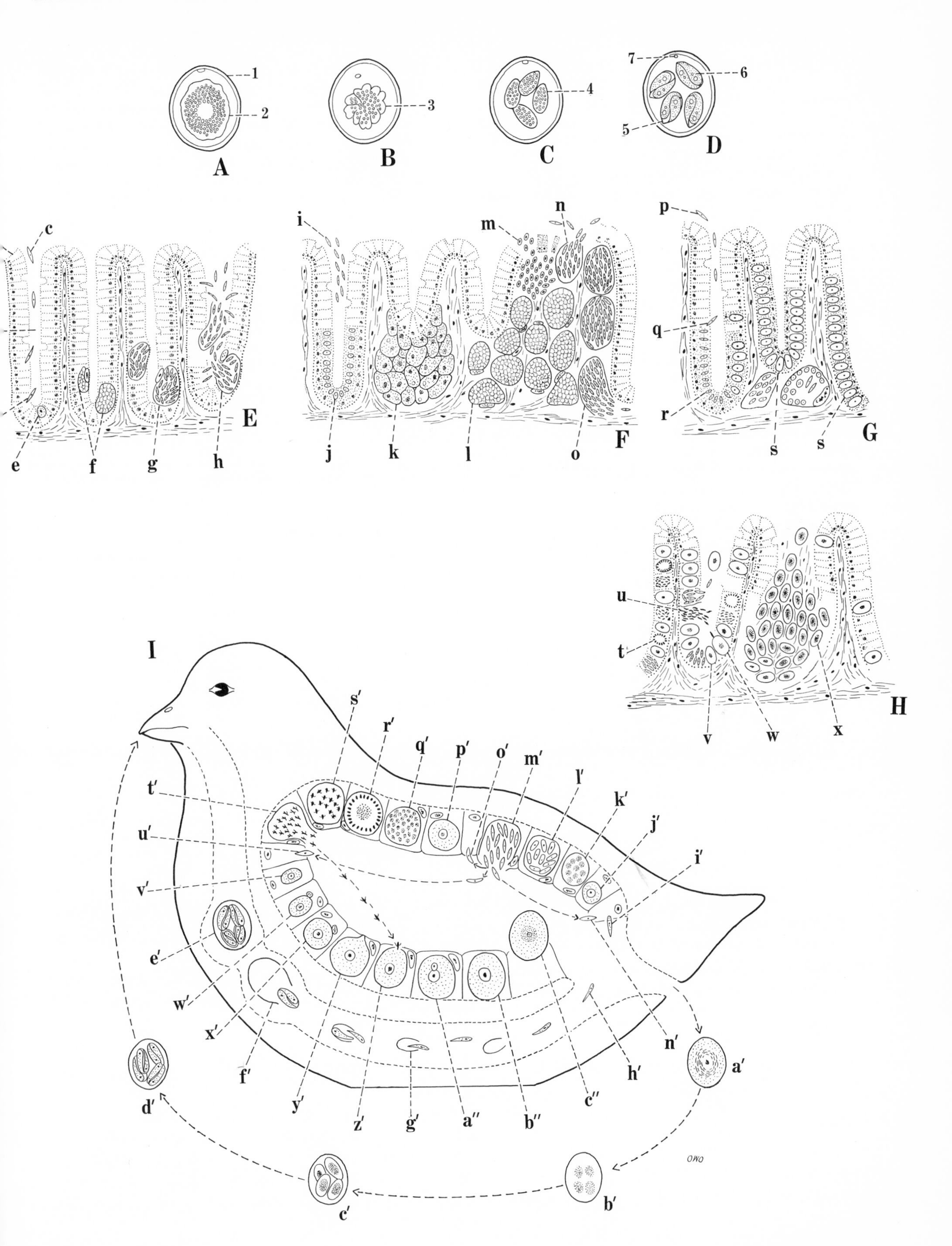

EXPLANATION OF PLATE 23

A. Mature sporocyst with full complement of three sporozoites. **B.** Sporocyst open and liberating sporozoites. **C.** Cross-section of gut of crab *(Portunus depurator)* with four schizonts containing merozoites. **D.** Mature sporocyst showing two valves and three sporozoites. **E.** Crab intermediate host becomes infected by eating sporocysts and harbors schizogenous phases of life cycle. **F.** Segment of gut of crab, showing schizogony. **G.** Infected crab harboring extra-intestinal merozoites (as in C, F) infective to definitive host. **H.** Cuttlefish definitive host *(Sepia officinalis)*. **I.** Segment of gut of cuttlefish in which gametogony and sporogony take place.

1, sporocyst; **2**, sporozoite; **3**, intestinal wall of crab; **4**, extra-intestinal cysts with merozoites; **5**, peri-intestinal tissue.

a-i, schizogony in gut of crab; **a**, segment of intestine of crab; **b**, sporocyst with two valves open and releasing the three sporozoites; **c**, sporozoites entering epithelial cell; **d**, early trophozoites in epithelial cell; **e**, young trophozoite in peri-intestinal tissue; **f**, large trophozoite with characteristic nucleus; **g**, early schizont with multiplying nuclei arranged over surface of cytoplasm (the cytoplasm may become folded or separated into individual clumps); **h**, cytomere; **i**, merozoites clustered over surface of cytomeres (this ends the schizogenous phase); **j-s**, gametogony in cuttlefish; **j**, segment of gut of cuttlefish; **k**, cytomere with merozoites which enter submucous connective tissue of gut and develop into gametocytes; **l-p**, development of microgametes; **l**, young microgametocyte in epithelial cell; **m**, older microgametocyte in submucous connective tissue; **n**, multiplication of nuclei which are precursors of microgametes; **o**, filamentous microgametes adhering to ball of residual cytoplasm; **p**, biflagellate microgamete in lumen of intestine; **q-s**, development of macrogametocyte; **q**, young macrogametocyte in epithelial cell; **r**, older macrogametocyte in submucous connective tissue; **s**, macrogamete being fertilized by microgamete; **t-v**, sporogenous phase; **t**, sporont with multiplying nuclei arranged over surface of cytoplasm; **u**, cluster of sporoblasts; **v**, individual sporocysts developed from sporoblast, each with three sporozoites which are released individually from epithelial cells into lumen or carried out in strips of necrotic intestinal epithelium discharged from the intestine.

Figures of protozoans adapted from Dobell, 1925, Parasitology 17:1.

Smears of the contents of the caeca made on the third day after infection and stained with Wright's or Giemsa's blood stains should show the first generation of minute merozoites.

Chicks sacrificed during the fourth and fifth days after infection will show the second generation of schizonts and the extensive damage done by them. Smears of caecal contents taken on the fifth day will show the large second stage merozoites mixed with erythrocytes, resulting from extensive haemorrhaging.

Sections taken between the fifth and seventh days will show the stages of development of the gametocytes and the formation of the micro- and macrogametes. Oocysts will appear in the faeces by the eighth day.

SELECTED REFERENCES

Becker, E. R. (1934). Coccidia and Coccidiosis. Monogr. No. 2, Div. Ind. Sci., Iowa State College Press, Ames, p. 29.

Becker, E. R. (1959). Protozoa. In: Diseases of Poultry, ed. by H. E. Beister et al., 4th Ed. Iowa State College Press, Ames, p. 828.

Challey, J. R., and W. C. Burns. (1959). J. Protozool. 6:238.

Levine, N. D. (1961). Protozoan Parasites of Domestic Animals and of Man. Burgess Publishing Co., Minneapolis, pp. 159, 202.

Tyzzer, E. R. (1929). Amer. J. Hyg. 10:269.

Van Dorninck, W. M., and E. R. Becker. (1957). J. Parasit. 43:40.

FAMILY AGGREGATIDAE

The parasites develop inside the hosts' cells. The oocysts normally contain many sporocysts. Schizogony occurs in one host and sporogony in another.

Aggregata eberthi (Labbé, 1895) (Plate 23)

Aggregata eberthi is a coccidian parasite of crabs and cuttlefish. Like other coccidians, there is an alternation of generations, but unlike them there is in addition an alternation of hosts. In both hosts the parasites are in the intestinal epithelium or wall. Thus two hosts appear in the life cycle of this

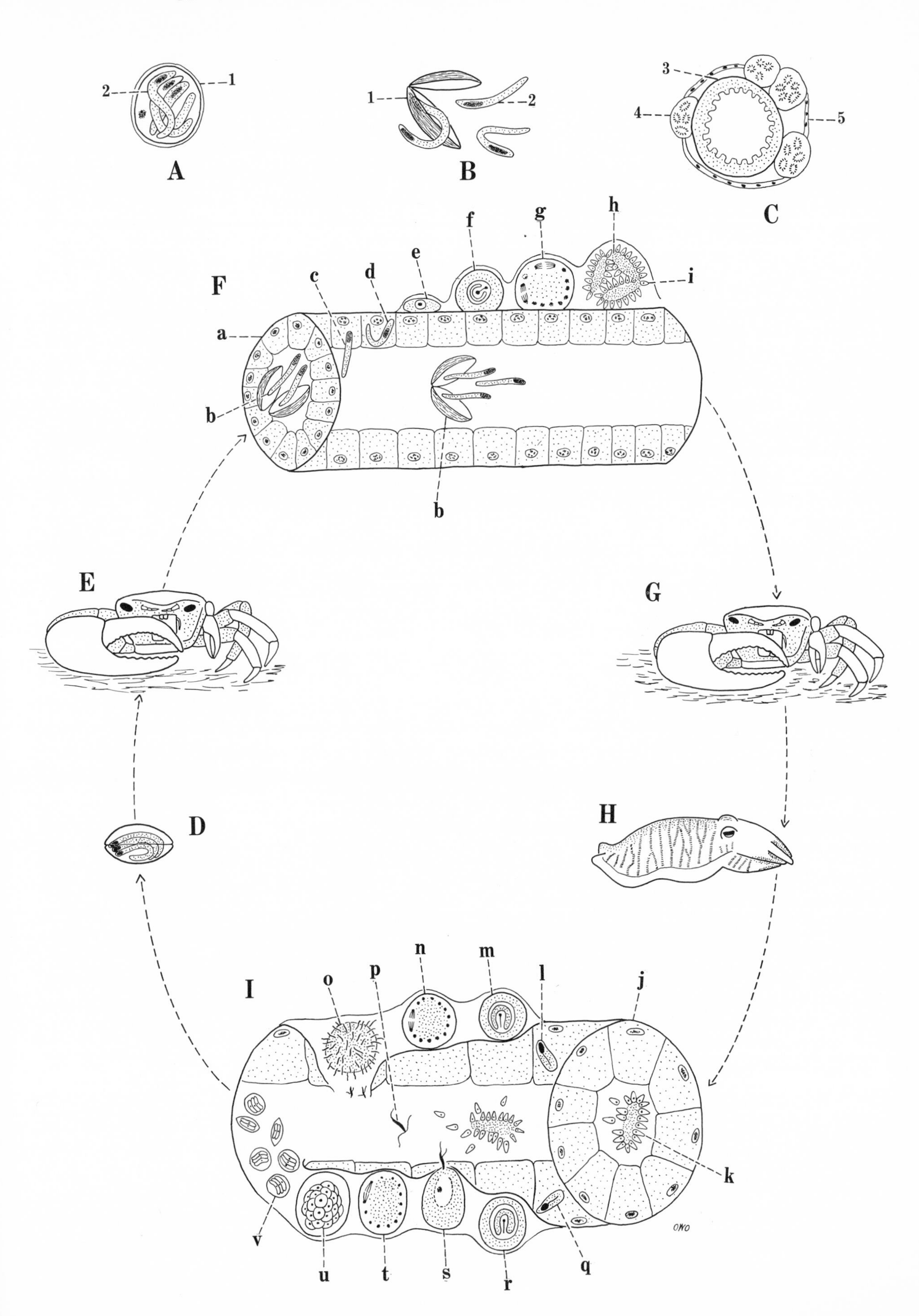
A
1
2
B
1
2
C
3
4
5
F
a
b
c
d
e
f
g
h
i
b
E
G
D
H
I
j
k
l
m
n
o
p
q
r
s
t
u
v
ONO

coccidian, in which respect it appears to be a step in the evolutionary process leading to the type of cycle characteristic of the Haemosporidia (Plate 16).

The asexual phase of the life cycle is in the peri-intestinal tissues of a crab (*Portunus depurator*), and the sexual phase in the submucous connective tissue of the intestine of cuttlefish.

DESCRIPTION. Sporocysts are hemispheric, bivalved, 8 to 9 μ in diameter, and normally with three sporozoites 10 μ long by 2 μ wide. The schizonts are in the peri-intestinal tissue of crabs and the macrogametocytes and sporocysts are in the submucosal connective tissue of the intestine of cuttlefish. The gametocytes are up to 1 mm in diameter.

LIFE CYCLE. As already pointed out, there is an alternation of hosts and of generations in the life cycle of *Aggregata eberthi*, with the crab as the intermediate host and the cuttlefish as the definitive host. Sporocysts voided in the faeces or in necrotic sloughs of intestinal epithelium of the cuttlefish, or in the intact intestine, are infective to crabs when eaten by them.

Sporozoites released from the sporocysts in the intestine of the crabs enter the epithelial cells and transform to trophozoites. These migrate into the peri-intestinal tissue and undergo schizogony, forming a single generation of merozoites which do not develop further in the crabs. There is no sexual development in the crustaceans.

When crabs are eaten by cuttlefish, the merozoites are liberated from the peri-intestinal cysts and migrate through the epithelial cells to the submucosal connective tissue where they undergo gametogony and sporogony. The epithelium becomes necrotic owing to the vast number of sporocysts in it. Large pieces are sloughed and passed from the intestine into the water. Crabs eat these, as well as the carcasses of cuttlefish or parts left by porpoises which feed on them, and become infected.

SELECTED REFERENCES

Dobell, C. (1925). Parasitology 17:1.

Levine, N. D. (1961). Protozoan Parasites of Domestic Animals and of Man. Burgess Publishing Co., Minneapolis, pp. 32, 246.

Siedlecki, M. (1898). Ann. Inst. Pasteur 12:799.

Wenyon, C. M. (1926). Protozoology, Vol. 2. Baillière, Tindall, and Cox, London, p. 869.

FAMILY LANKESTERELLIDAE

Development occurs in host cells. The oocysts are without sporocysts but contain eight or more sporozoites. Schizogony, gametogony, and sporogony take place in the vertebrate host. Sporozoites in red blood cells are ingested by mites or leeches and transferred by them without having undergone any development. The microgametes have two flagella.

Schellackia bolivari Reichenow, 1919 (Plate 24)

Schellackia bolivari is a coccidian type of parasite that completes its entire development in the intestinal epithelium, subepithelial mucosa, and blood cells of lizards (*Acanthodactylus vulgaris* and *Psammodromus hispanicus*) of the Mediterranean region of Europe and Africa. This is basically a coccidian life cycle, except for the occurrence of sporogony in the vertebrate host and the presence of the sporozoites in the blood cells.

Lizard mites, *Liponyssus saurarum*, feeding on infected lizards accumulate sporozoites in the epithelial cells of the midgut without further development of them. The mite serves merely as a collector of sporozoites and a vehicle for transporting them back to the lizards when eaten by them.

Schellackia bolivari shows an interesting evolutionary trend in its life cycle toward that of the Haemosporidia by the adoption of a mode of life in blood cells and the introduction of a haematophagous arthropod, albeit in a passive though ecologically essential role, in the life cycle. In these respects, it stands between the coccidian type of life cycle in which sporogony takes place outside the host, and the haemosporidian type in which it occurs in a bloodsucking invertebrate host through which it is transmitted (Plate 16).

DESCRIPTION. Schizonts and microgametocytes develop in the intestinal epithelium of lizards and macrogametocytes in the subepithelial connective tissue of the intestine. The spherical oocysts are 15 to 18 μ in diameter, located in the intestinal wall, and contain eight sporozoites without sporocysts.

These escape from the schizonts and enter erythrocytes in *Acanthodactylus vulgaris* and leucocytes in *Psammodromus hispanicus*. Sporozoites enter the intestinal epithelium of lizard mites when blood cells containing them are eaten but do not develop.

LIFE CYCLE. Lizards become parasitized by eating mites harboring sporozoites in the intestinal epithelium. Upon digestion of the infected mites, the sporozoites are freed in the gut of the lizard. They enter the epithelial cells of the small intestine and initiate schizogony, forming merozoites which penetrate other epithelial cells. Some of them produce another generation of schizonts. Others form gametocytes and initiate gametogony. Those that form microgametocytes develop in the intestinal epithelium along with the schizonts, eventually releasing the biflagellated microgametes. The merozoites destined to become macrogametocytes migrate to the subepithelial connective tissue, where they develop into macrogametes and are fertilized, become zygotes and thereby end the gametogenous phase of the life cycle.

Sporogony begins and is completed in the intestinal wall where the zygote is formed. When completed, there are eight sporozoites free in the thin-walled oocyst. The sporozoites are released and migrate to the blood stream where they penetrate the erythrocytes or leucocytes, depending on the species of lizard.

Lizard mites feeding on infected lacertans ingest the infected blood cells. When the parasitized corpuscles are engulfed by the amoeboid epithelial cells of the midgut, the protozoans are freed and accumulate in them without further development. Since the mites serve only to accumulate the parasites, they act as living oocysts, as it were, containing an indeterminate number of infective sporozoites.

EXERCISE ON LIFE CYCLE

Studies should be conducted on the occurrence and biology of haemococcidia in the reptiles of North America, since such observations have been neglected.

SELECTED REFERENCES

Bonorris, J. S., and G. H. Ball. (1955). J. Protozool. 2:31.

Doflein, F., and E. Reichenow. (1953). Lehrbuch der Protozoenkunde, 6th Ed. Gustav Fischer, Jena, pp. 340, 882.

Levine, N. D. (1961). Protozoan Parasites of Domestic Animals and of Man. Burgess Publishing Co., Minneapolis, pp. 32, 259.

Reichenow, E. (1920). Sitzungbs. Gesellsch. Naturf. Fr. Berlin (10) Dez. 1919, p. 440; (1921). Arch. Protistenk. 42:179.

Wenyon, C. M. (1926). Protozoology, Vol. 2. Baillière, Tindall, and Cox, London, p. 876.

Suborder Adeleina

The members of this group show relationships to the suborder Eimeridia, on the one hand, and to the order Haemosporidia, on the other.

In habitat, species of the family Adeleidae show affinities to Eimeridia by developing in the epithelium of the gut or its glands or in the body cavity of invertebrates. Species of Haemogregarinidae, on the other hand, show closer kinship to the order Haemosporidia by developing in the cells of the circulatory system of vertebrates. Moreover, bloodsucking invertebrates are involved in some way as intermediate hosts (Plate 16).

Developmentally, the Adeleidea are characterized by the formation of a large macrogametocyte and a much smaller microgametocyte which unite early in their growth, becoming enclosed in a thin-walled cyst. After the two gametocytes have united, the microgametocyte produces two to four gametes. Mature oocysts contain numerous sporocysts, each with two to many sporozoites, varying greatly with the species.

Life cycles of members of this group lead directly to the pattern of the Haemosporidia in having an alternation of both hosts and generations. This is shown particularly well by the *Hepatozoon* and *Haemogregarina* (Plate 16).

EXPLANATION OF PLATE 24 ⇨

A. Schizont from intestinal epithelium. **B.** Segmenter with fully developed merozoites. **C.** Oocyst containing sporozoites from submucosal tissue of intestine of lizard. **D.** Microgametocyte with microgametes from intestinal epithelium of lizard. **E.** Macrogamete with polar body from submucosa of intestine of lizard. **F.** Lizard *(Acanthodactylus vulgaris* and *Psammodromus hispanicus).* **G.** Lizard mite *(Liponyssus saurarum).*

1, nuclei of schizont; **2,** merozoites in schizont; **3,** sporozoites in oocyst; **4,** microgametes; **5,** residual protoplasm of microgametocyte; **6,** macrogametocyte; **7,** polar body.

a, infective mite in process of being digested; **b,** sporozoites escaping from mite in stomach of lizard; **c,** sporozoite in lumen of small intestine; **d,** sporozoite entering cell of intestinal epithelium; **e,** trophozoite; **f,** schizont; **g,** mature schizont with fully developed merozoites; **h,** merozoites enter other intestinal epithelial cells to form gametocytes; **i, j,** young microgametocytes; **k,** mature microgametocyte with microgametes; **l,** merozoite enters submucosa of intestine, where it develops into macrogametocyte; **m,** young macrogametocyte; **n,** macrogamete with polar body; **o,** zygote showing nucleus and microgamete inside; **p,** young oocyst; **q,** oocyst with sporozoites (no sporocyst); **r,** sporozoites enter hepatic portal system (and lymphatics); **s,** sporozoites enter macrophages or erythrocytes (this one is in blood vessels of liver); **t,** infected blood cell in pulmonary artery, having gone through right side of heart and entering lungs; **u,** infected blood cell in left side of heart; **v, w,** infected blood cells in dorsal aorta and general circulation; **x,** infected blood cell sucked up by mite; **y-z,** infected blood cells being phagocytized by intestinal cells.

a′, sporozoites freed in intestinal cells by digestion of blood cells accumulate in great numbers and are source of infection of lizards when eaten by them.

Protozoans adapted from Reichenow, 1921, Arch. Protistenk. 42:179.

Hepatozoon undergoes schizogony in liver cells of rats. The young gametocytes enter mononuclear leucocytes which when taken into the stomach of rat mites are liberated through the digestive processes. The gametes fuse, fertilization results, and a zygote is formed, thus completing gametogony. The motile zygote, or ookinete, migrates through the stomach wall into the haemocoel where sporogony occurs. Numerous sporocysts are formed in an oocyst. The large, thin-walled oocysts remain intact in the mite, retaining their sporocysts. Infection of rats occurs when infected mites are swallowed and digested, releasing the sporozoites in the intestine. The sporozoites enter the blood stream through the intestinal wall. Schizogony in the liver initiated by the sporozoites is suggestive of exoerythrocytic schizogony in *Plasmodium* of the Haemosporidia.

Haemogregarina closely approaches the haemosporidian type of life cycle in having schizogony in the red blood cells of the water tortoise, which is the vertebrate host, and gametogony and sporogony in the stomach of leeches, which are the invertebrate hosts. Infection of the vertebrates takes place when the sporozoites are injected by feeding leeches.

FAMILY ADELEIDAE

The Adeleidae are parasites of the gut and its appended parts, fat bodies, testes, and kidneys. The chief hosts are invertebrates, although vertebrates (mice and guinea pigs) are infected.

Adelina cryptocerci Yarwood, 1937 (Plate 25)

The members of this genus have a thick-walled oocyst, with a small number of spores. They occur in the gut or haemocoel of arthropods and oligochaetes.

A. cryptocerci occurs in the fat bodies as an intracellular parasite in the wood-eating roach (*Cryptocercus punctulatus*) living in rotten logs in Northern California, Oregon, and the eastern United States.

DESCRIPTION. Oocysts in the fat bodies are spherical, thick-walled, and measure 46 by 51 μ; they contain 5 to 21 sporocysts 10 to 12 μ in diameter, each with two sporozoites lying in close contact with the walls of the sporocyst. Sporozoites are 2 to 3 μ wide and 15 to 17 μ long and have a rounded anterior and narrow posterior end. The nucleus is a densely packed mass of chromatin located near the anterior end and appears to lack a membrane. Schizonts are of two types. One contains elongate merozoites and the other short, broad ones arranged in two groups, one at each pole and separated by a residual mass of cytoplasm. Mature gametoblasts differ greatly in size. The small microgametoblast joins laterally to the large macrogametoblast. Later in development, the microgametoblast migrates

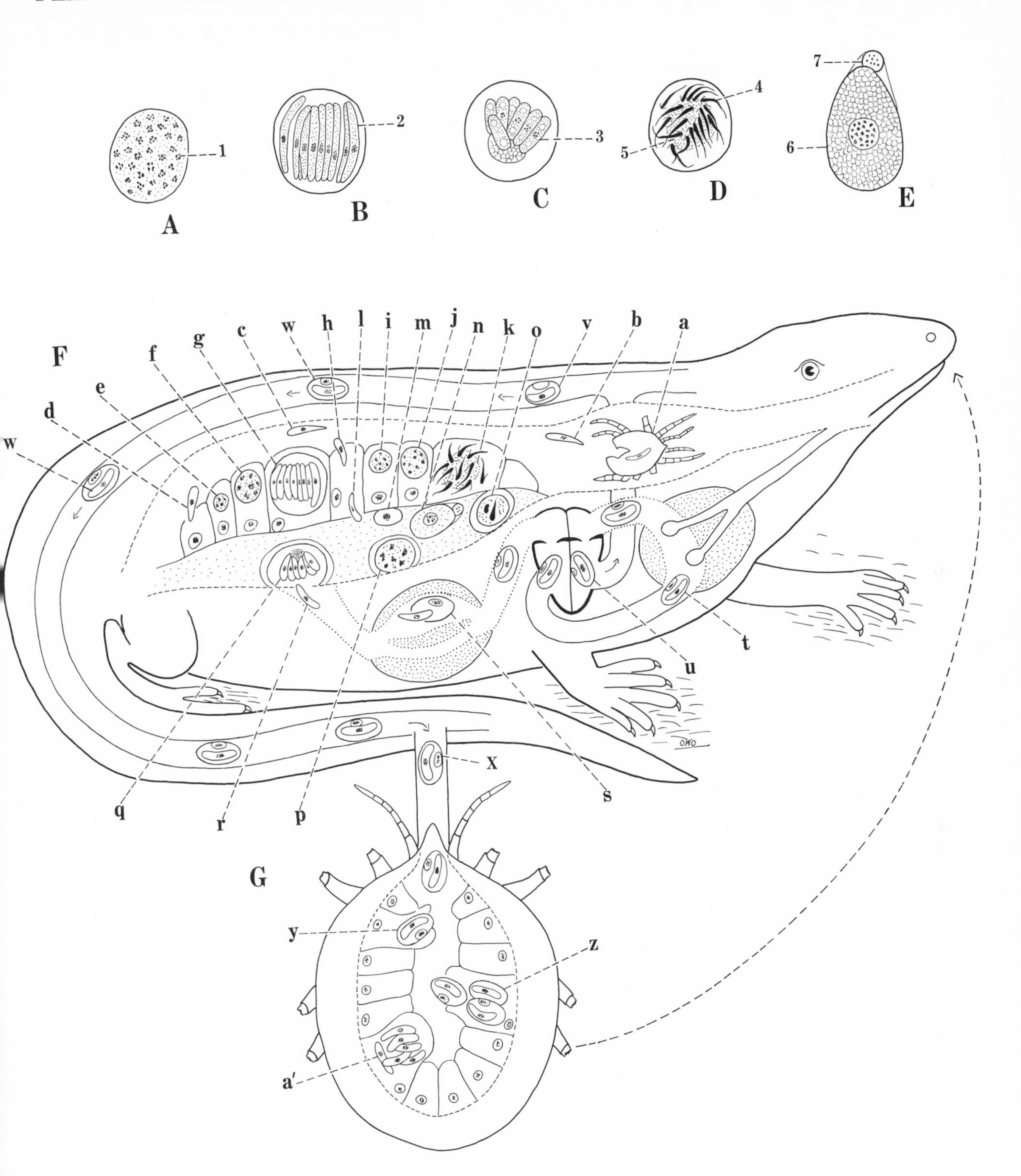
1
2
3
4
5
6
7
A
B
C
D
E
F
G
a
b
c
d
e
f
g
h
i
j
k
l
m
n
o
p
q
r
s
t
u
v
w
X
y
z
a′

EXPLANATION OF PLATE 25 ▷

A. Ripe oocyst filled with sporocysts, each with two sporozoites. **B.** Free sporozoite. **C.** Trophozoite developed from sporozoite, showing nucleus with ring of chromatin granules and central nucleolus. **D.** Schizont with four nuclei. **E.** Multinucleate schizont, showing nuclei in telophase, each with eight chromosomes. **F.** Trophozoite developed from merozoite, showing large central karyosome. **G.** Merozoites arranged like staves of a barrel. **H.** Free merozoite of first generation. **I.** Bipolar division of schizont, with short merozoites arranged at each pole (these become gametoblasts). **J.** Growing macrogametoblast. **K.** Macro- and microgametoblasts in early stage of union. **L.** Large macrogametoblast with two associated microgametoblasts. **M.** Gametoblasts enclosed in cyst; nucleus of microgametoblast undergoing division to form microgametes. **N.** Young oocyst with uninucleate sporoblasts. **O.** Older but still immature oocyst with binucleate sporoblasts which will produce two sporozoites each (see A). **P.** Wood-eating roach *(Cryptocercus punctulatus).*

1, oocyst wall; **2,** sporocyst wall; **3,** sporozoite; **4,** nucleus; **5,** dividing nucleus in telophase, showing eight chromosomes; **6,** long slender merozoites; **7,** short merozoites that will develop into gametoblasts; **8,** residual cytoplasm; **9,** macrogametoblast; **10,** microgametoblast; **11,** division of nucleus of microgametoblast in formation of microgametes; **12,** macrogamete; **13,** uninucleate sporoblasts; **14,** binucleate sporoblasts that produce sporozoites (see 3); **15,** fat body of roach.

a, ripe oocyst in stomach, acquired by eating an infected woods roach; **b,** ruptured sporocyst allowing sporozoites to escape in intestine whence they penetrate the intestinal epithelium; **c,** sporocysts free in intestine; **d,** ruptured sporocyst allowing sporozoites to escape in intestine whence they penetrate the intestinal epithelium; **e,** sporozoite entering haemocoel, having migrated through the intestinal wall; **f,** sporozoite entering fat body; **g-i,** first schizogony; **g,** young trophozoite with small anterior end; **h,** schizont with dividing nuclei; **i,** bundles of merozoites arranged in barrel-stave fashion; **j,** merozoite from first generation of schizonts entering fat body; **k,** trophozoite with narrowed anterior end and nucleus with halo of chromatin dots around nucleolus; **l,** schizont with dividing nuclei; **m,** bundles of merozoites arranged in barrel-stave fashion; **n,** merozoites escaping from schizont; **o,** merozoite entering fat body; **p-r,** third schizogony; **p,** trophozoite with narrow anterior end and with nucleolus surrounded by ring of chromatin dots; **q,** schizont with dividing nuclei; **r,** bipolar schizont with a group of small merozoites at each end, separated by a residual mass of protoplasm, will become gametocytes; **s-u,** formation of gametoblasts and their union; **s,** undifferentiated gametoblasts in fat body; **t,** male and female gametoblasts; **u,** union of male and female gametoblasts; **v,** formation of four microgametes from male gametoblast at end of female gametoblast and appearance of a second membrane to form the gametocyst; **w,** migration of one microgamete into macrogamete; **x,** union of two nuclei with appearance of eight pairs of chromosomes to form the zygote with additional membranes; **y,** reduction of number of chromosomes; **z-b′,** sporogony; **z,** division of nuclei to form sporoblasts.

a′, formation of sporoblasts; **b′,** mature oocyst with sporocysts each containing two sporozoites.

Figures A-O redrawn from Yarwood, 1937, Parasitology 29:37; P, original.

---

to one end of the fully grown macrogametoblast. The two are surrounded by a membrane and the nucleus of the former divides into four parts which become the microgametes. A zygote with eight pairs of chromosomes is formed in which reduction division occurs and the oocyst with its sporocysts is formed.

LIFE CYCLE. The life cycles of the various species of the genus appear to be similar.

Being in the haemocoel of the roaches, the ripe oocysts containing the infective sporozoites are not voided from the body as in the case of intestinal or renal forms. Infection of new hosts takes place when infected dead or incapacitated roaches are eaten by their companions.

In the alimentary canal, the sporozoites are freed, enter the epithelium of the midgut, and migrate through it into the haemocoel where they enter the fat bodies for further development. In the fat bodies, the sporozoites transform into schizonts which produce up to 40 first-generation elongate merozoites, giving the superficial appearance of barrel staves when mature. The merozoites upon release enter other fat bodies and produce a second generation of schizonts whose merozoites are similar in shape to their predecessors but somewhat longer, being 18 to 20 μ in length instead of 11 to 13 μ.

Merozoites of the second generation produce bipolar schizonts in fat bodies with small blunt merozoites arranged in a group at each end of the schizont and separated by a residual mass of cytoplasm. Each group in the schizont represents a different sex. They are known as gametoblasts because they are believed to contain the haploid number of chromosomes. They escape into the haemocoel where sexual differentiation occurs. In the young macrogametoblast, the nucleus contains a large nucleolus and is surrounded by a nuclear membrane, and the cytoplasm is vacuolated, whereas in the microgametoblast, the nucleus consists of a few granules, has no membrane, and the cytoplasm is nonvacuolated.

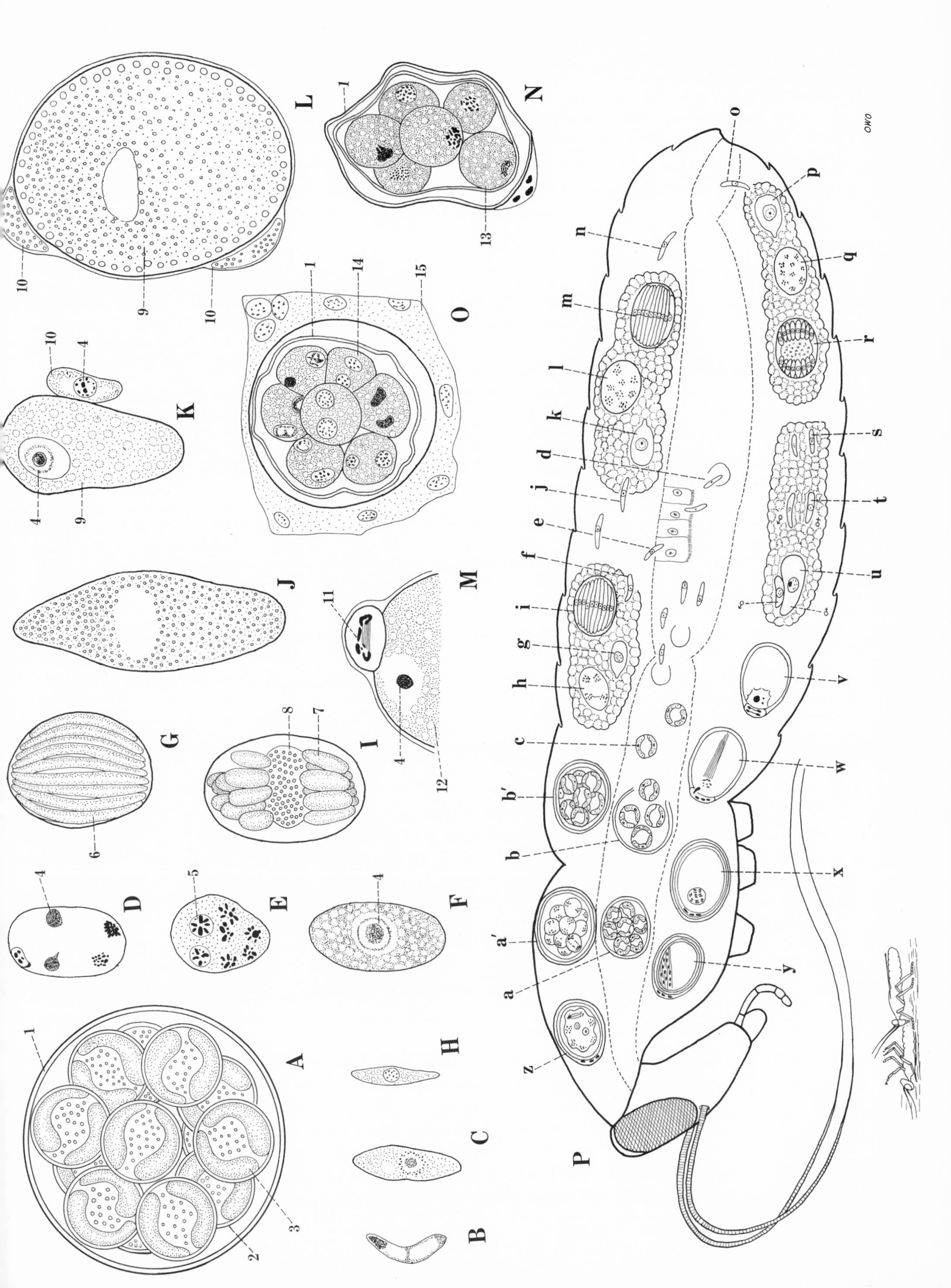

Growth of the macrogametoblast is rapid, far exceeding the microgametoblast in size. The two join laterally, the microgametoblast moves to one end of the macrogametoblast, and a membrane forms, enclosing both. The nucleus of the microgametoblast undergoes two simple divisions, resulting in four microgametes. One enters the macrogamete to form the zygote. The remaining three retain their external position. A new membrane arises over the surface of the macrogamete, enclosing the remaining microgametes and cytoplasmic residuum, thereby separating them from the zygote. Thus, a double cyst wall is formed. Later, a third membrane forms around the zygote within the cyst wall.

Eight pairs of chromatin granules appearing to be homologous to chromosomes in the micro- and macrogametes have been observed in a zygote. Subsequent stages resembling premeiotic processes occur and reduction probably takes place in the early stages of sporogony. During sporogony, the nuclei move to the surface of the sporont where division occurs. By subsequent cytoplasmic fission, the sporont divides into as many sporoblasts as there are nuclei. The nucleus of each sporoblast divides once and two sporozoites develop.

Other representatives of the Adeleidae whose life cycles are known resemble those of *Adelina*. They are 1) *Adelea ovata* Schneider from the centipede *Lithobius forficatus, A. mesnili* Pérez from the webbing clothes moth *Tineola bieseliella* and the Mediterranean flour moth *Ephestia kuehniella;* 2) *Klossia helicina* Schneider in the kidneys of land snails of the genera *Helix* and *Vitrina* and slugs of the genus *Limax;* and 3) *Orcheobius herpodellae* Schuberg and Kunze from the testes of the fresh-water leech *Herpobdella atomaria*. Additional genera and their species together with other species of *Adelina* are given by Doflein and Reichenow and by Kudo.

EXERCISE ON LIFE CYCLE

Adelina triboli of the cosmopolitan red flour beetle *Tribolium ferrugineum* is excellent for study because of the universal availability of the host.

First and second instar larvae are unlikely to be infected, but all subsequent stages harbor the oocysts. Live material may be obtained by teasing out the fat bodies in Ringer's solution and placing them on slides with the cover slips sealed by means of petroleum jelly placed along the edges and spread evenly with a hot needle. The parasites will survive for up to 24 hours in such preparations, during which time the various stages may be studied.

In order to get sporozoites to escape on slides, mature oocysts should be placed in the digestive juices of intestines dissected from beetles. Digestive enzymes from different kinds of insects should be tried, as well as artificial ones such as pepsin and trypsin. Both sporocysts and sporozoites may be liberated through mechanical pressure on the cover slip.

Means of infection have not been observed in this species but it is most likely to occur through cannibalism among the beetles. Experiments should be designed to demonstrate the means by which infection occurs. Sections of the intestine should be made to observe liberation of the sporozoites and the route taken by them in passing from it to the haemocoel. See Bhatia and Riley and Krogh for details.

SELECTED REFERENCES

Bhatia, M. L. (1937). Parasitology 29:239.

Doflein, F., and E. Reichenow. (1953). Lehrbuch der Protozoenkunde. Gustav Fischer, Jena, p. 825.

Kudo R. R. (1966). Protozoology. Charles C Thomas, Springfield, Ill., p. 701.

Riley, W. A., and L. Krogh. (1927). J. Parasit. 13:224.

Yarwood, E. A. (1937). Parasitology 29:370.

FAMILY HEPATOZOIDAE

The zygote (ookinete) is active and surrounded by a flexible membrane. The life cycle involves two hosts, a vertebrate with development of the parasite in the cells of the circulatory system, and an invertebrate with development in the digestive system. The oocysts are large and contain many sporocysts, each with 4 to 12 or more sporozoites. The microgametes are without flagella.

Hepatozoon muris (Balfour, 1905) (Plate 26)

Hepatozoon muris parasitizes the intestinal epithelium and mononuclear leucocytes of rats and the body cavity of the rat mite (*Echinolaelaps echidninus*), particularly in warm climates.

The life cycle of the haemogregarine, while retaining certain definite coccidian characteristics such as schizogony in the intestinal epithelium of the vertebrate host, approaches the haemosporidian type in the manner of gametogony and sporogony in the mite host. The route of infection of the vertebrate host is by mouth, a coccidian trait.

DESCRIPTION. Schizonts in hepatic cells are ovoid and measure up to 28 by 35 μ in size with 12 to 20 nuclei arranged in linear fashion at each extremity which form into as many vermicular merozoites. Gametocytes are in mononuclear leucocytes. Isogametes unite in the stomach of the mites, forming ookinetes that measure up to 25 by 50 μ. Sporonts in the body cavity of mites are enclosed in thin-walled cysts, and have a single large nucleus. Beginning multiplication of the nucleus transforms the sporont into an oocyst with numerous small nuclei which migrate to the surface, forming a sphere up to 250 μ in diameter with budlike projections, each with a nucleus. Sporocysts about 25 by 30 μ are formed from the buds, each producing 12 to 20 sporozoites, 14 by 5 μ, arranged in two groups, one at each end of the sporocyst.

LIFE CYCLE. Infection of rats is initiated when parasitized mites are swallowed. Sporozoites released from the mites by action of the digestive juices penetrate the intestinal epithelium and enter the blood stream. In the liver, they leave the circulation and enter hepatic cells where schizogony takes place. Schizonts are oval and produce merozoites which re-enter liver cells, producing at least three generations of schizonts, after which time the schizogenous phase is terminated. The final generation of merozoites enters mononuclear leucocytes and becomes gametocytes, thereby initiating the gametogenous phase.

When infected leucocytes are ingested by mites, the gametocytes are released by digestion of the infected blood cells. Following formation of the isogametes, two of them come together along the long axis of the body as the first step in fertilization. One grows much larger than the other, becoming pyriform in shape; this is the macrogamete, which partially surrounds the smaller spherical microgamete. Thus fertilization is completed and a pear-shaped ookinete is formed. It migrates through the intestinal wall into the body cavity to undergo sporogony. A cyst is formed about the sporont and the nucleus begins to divide. The newly formed nuclei migrate to the periphery where they are enclosed in budlike processes of protoplasm. Each one detaches from the central mass of cytoplasm to form a sporoblast. Upon secretion of a cyst about itself, each sporoblast becomes a sporocyst and the nucleus within it multiplies until there are 12 to 20 nuclei arranged in a linear fashion near each end of the sporozoite. They are arranged somewhat like fingers clasping the residual mass of cytoplasm. The sporocysts remain in the thin membranous cyst within the mite until released in the stomach of the vertebrate host by the digestive processes.

Hepatozoon canis of dogs develops in the tick *Rhipicephalus sanguineus, H. criceti* of hamsters in *Liponyssus arcuatus; H. gerbilli* of gerbils in the louse *Haematopinus stephensi; H. balfouri* of the jumping mouse *Jaculus jaculus* in the flea *Pulex cleopatra; H. pettiti* of crocodiles in the tsetse fly *Glossina palpalis; H. mesnili* of the gecko in the mosquito *Culex fatigans; H. mauritanicum* of the turtle *Testudo mauritanica* in the tick *Hyalomma aegyptium;* and *H. triatomae* of the lizard *Tupinambus teguizin* in the bug *Triatoma rubrovaria* (experimental).

EXERCISE ON LIFE CYCLE

Infected rats, either wild or white ones, harboring mites provide excellent material for observing the developmental stages of the parasite and for conducting experiments on its life cycle.

The gametocytes appear only in the leucocytes and may be seen in blood smears stained with Wright's or Giemsa's blood stain. The various stages of the schizonts may be found in smears made from the liver or sections of it.

Mites from infected rats should be dissected in saline to obtain the stages of sporogony occurring in the body cavity. Isogametes and ookinetes may be found in the stomach by direct examination of contents or by making smears of them and staining them with blood stains.

EXPLANATION OF PLATE 26

A. Section of liver of rat showing developing schizonts. **B.** Section of intestine of rat mite showing zygotes. **C.** Section of mite showing sporocysts in tissue. **D.** Rat vertebrate host. **E.** Rat mite *(Echinolaelaps echidninus)* invertebrate host.

1-4, developing schizonts in numerical order of progression; **5**, zygotes; **6**, oocyst; **7**, sporocyst filled with sporozoites; **8**, sporozoites free in oocyst.

a, infected mite being digested in stomach of rat with release of sporocysts; **b**, ruptured sporocyst freeing sporozoites; **c**, sporozoite passing through intestinal epithelium into blood vessels; **d**, sporozoite in hepatic portal vein; **e**, sporozoite passing from blood vessel into hepatic cell; **f**, early schizont; **g**, nuclei gathering near ends of schizont; **h**, mature schizont with merozoites assembled near ends; **i**, schizont ruptures, freeing merozoites; **j**, merozoites attack other hepatic cells, initiating several succeeding generations of schizonts and merozoites; **k**, after about third generation of schizonts, gametocytes are produced that enter blood stream and penetrate mononuclear leucocytes; **l**, infected leucocytes entering general circulation from heart after having passed through lungs; **m**, infected leucocyte being sucked up by mite; **n**, infected leucocytes in stomach of mite being digested with release of gametocytes; **o**, gametocytes unite; **p**, macrogamete enlarges and partially encircles microgamete; **q**, zygote; **r**, ookinete leaves stomach and enters body tissues; **s**, ookinete grows; **t**, **u**, developing sporont; **v**, nucleus multiplies and nuclei assemble over surface of sporont; **w**, budding on surface of sporont, forming sporoblasts; **x**, oocyst containing developing sporoblasts; **y**, oocysts with sporoblasts whose nuclei are dividing and arranging themselves at ends; **z**, oocyst with sporocysts each containing a number of sporozoites.

Adapted from Miller, 1908, U. S. Pub. Health Serv., Hyg. Lab. Bull. 46.

For life history studies, one must have rats free of *Hepatozoon*, as proved by parasite-free blood smears taken daily over a period of a week, and infected mites as shown by dissections. Feed infected mites collected from an infected rat to an uninfected rat and examine the blood of each daily until parasites appear in the blood of the one that received the mites. If parasites appear in both rats, the experiment should be repeated, care being taken to have uninfected rats to begin with and to keep them in cages free from mites.

SELECTED REFERENCES

Doflein, F., and E. Reichenow. (1953). Lehrbuch der Protozoenkunde. Gustav Fischer, Jena, p. 832.

Levine, N. D. (1961). Protozoan Parasites of Domestic Animals and of Man. Burgess Publishing Co., Minneapolis, pp. 31, 257.

Miller, W. W. (1908). U. S. Pub. Health Serv., Hyg. Lab. Bull. No. 46.

FAMILY HAEMOGREGARINIDAE

The zygote (ookinete) is active and surrounded by a flexible membrane. The life cycle involves two hosts, a vertebrate with development of the parasite in the cells of the circulatory system, and an invertebrate with development in the digestive system. The oocysts in the invertebrate are small and without sporocysts.

Haemogregarina stepanowi Danilewsky, 1885 (Plate 27)

Haemogregarina stepanowi is a representative of the group of the Coccidia whose schizogenous phase of the life cycle occurs in the blood cells, principally erythrocytes, of the water tortoise (*Emys orbicularis*) of Europe, and the gametogenous and sporogenous phases develop in a leech (*Placobdella catenigra*). In this respect, they are closer to the haemosporidian type of life cycle than the haemococcidian *Schellackia bolivari*. In the latter, all stages of development are completed in the single vertebrate host (lizards). The bloodsucking arthropod (mite) serves only as a passive collecting receptacle for sporozoites and a means of transmitting them mechanically from one lizard to another when it is eaten. In *Haemogregarina stepanowi*, there is a vertebrate intermediate host and an invertebrate definitive host.

DESCRIPTION. Trophozoites in the circulating erythrocytes are first U-shaped vermicular bodies with arms unequal in size that fuse to form an ovoid body. Schizonts are of two sizes; the macroschizonts that form from sporozoites in erythrocytes that lodge in bone marrow and produce 13 to 24 macromerozoites, and the microschizonts that develop from macromerozoites in erythrocytes in bone marrow

PLATE 26 *Hepatozoon muris*

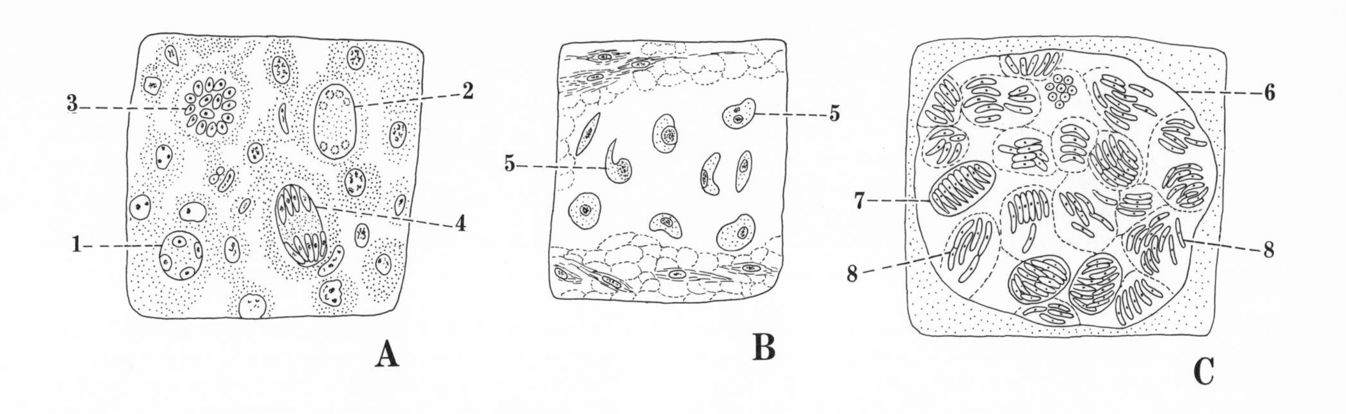

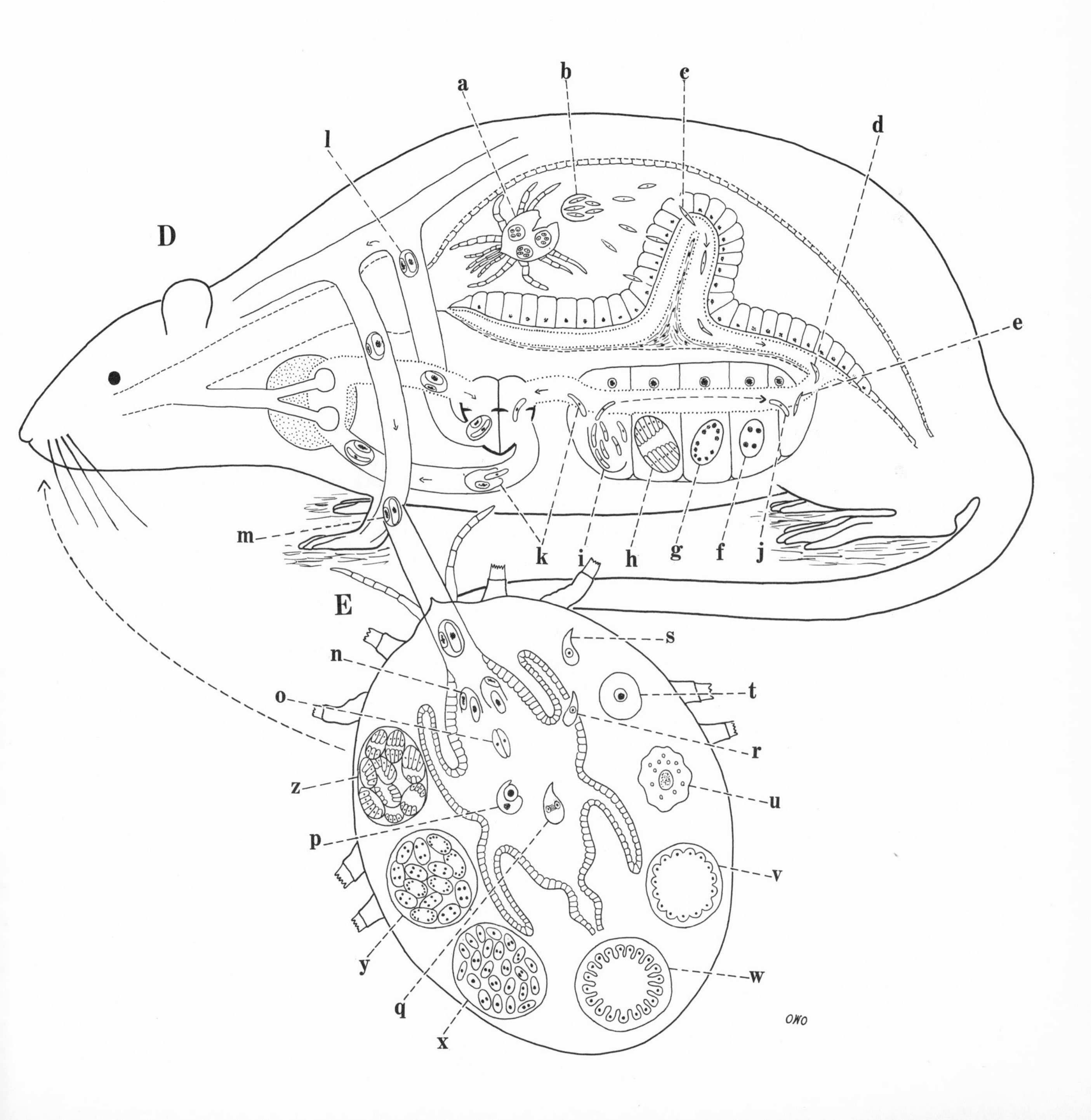

EXPLANATION OF PLATE 27 ⇨

A. U-shaped developing trophozoite. **B.** Trophozoite with arms of U fused to form ovoid body. **C.** Nucleus breaks into fragments to form schizont. **D.** Macroschizont with large merozoites of first generation. **E.** Microschizont with small merozoites of second generation. **F.** Macrogametocyte. **G.** Microgametocyte. **H.** Water tortoise *(Emys orbicularis)*, vertebrate host. **I.** Leech *(Placobdella catenigera)*, invertebrate host.

1, arms of growing trophozoite; **2**, nucleus of trophozoite; **3**, erythrocyte; **4**, nucleus of erythrocyte; **5**, small multiple nuclei; **6**, large merozoites of first generation; **7**, small merozoites of second generation; **8**, macrogametocyte; **9**, microgametocyte.

a, leech feeding on hind leg of tortoise; **b**, sporozoite injected into blood stream; **c**, sporozoite entering erythrocyte; **d**, sporozoite within erythrocyte circulated through blood stream; **e**, young trophozoite; **f**, older U-shaped trophozoite; **g**, bone marrow represented by stippled area; **h**, mature trophozoite in erythrocyte entering bone marrow; **i**, macroschizont with several nuclei; **j**, segmenter with large first generation merozoites; **k**, large merozoites escape from erythrocyte and enter blood stream (represented by unstippled area); **l**, merozoite entering erythrocyte in blood to initiate second generation of schizonts; **m, n**, U-shaped trophozoites; **o**, mature trophozoite in bone marrow (stippled area); **p**, microschizont; **q**, smaller but fewer second generation merozoites; **r**, rupture of erythrocyte and escape of merozoites into blood stream to become gametocytes; **s**, second generation merozoites free in blood initiate gametogenous cycle; **t**, merozoite entering erythrocyte to form gametocytes; **u, v**, growing gametocytes in circulation; **w**, mature microgametocyte; **x**, mature macrogametocyte in tortoise; **y**, gametocytes sucked up and swallowed by leech definitive host.

a′, b′, macro- and microgametocytes in erythrocytes in stomach of leech; **c′**, macro- and microgametocytes free in stomach; **d′**, association of micro- and macrogametocytes; **e′**, microgametocyte produces four microgametes; **f′**, fertilization of macrogamete; **g′**, zygote with fragment of microgametocyte attached; **h′, i′, j′**, growth and division of nucleus of zygote; **k′**, oocyst with eight sporozoites; **l′**, oocyst ruptures and sporozoites are released in stomach; **m′**, sporozoites enter dorsal blood vessel; **n′**, sporozoites in dorsal blood vessel; **o′**, sporozoite enters proboscis of leech; **p′**, sporozoites injected into tortoise by feeding leech, and cycle begins anew (a) in vertebrate host.

Figures of protozoans adapted from Reichenow, 1910, Arch. Protistenk. 20:251.

---

which produce six micromerozoites. Small merozoites enter erythrocytes and transform into macrogametocytes with small nuclei and microgametocytes with large nuclei and transverse bands of darkly staining material near the anterior end. Gametogony and sporogony are completed in the intestine of leeches and the sporozoites are injected by them while feeding.

LIFE CYCLE. Sporozoites injected into the blood of tortoises by feeding leeches initiate the schizogenous phase of the life cycle. The sporozoites enter erythrocytes and begin to grow, forming U-shaped vermicular trophozoites. As growth of the trophozoites continue, the arms fuse, forming larger ovoid schizonts. Erythrocytes containing these schizonts become lodged in the bone marrow, where schizogony is completed. The schizonts of this generation are of large size, known as macroschizonts, which produce 13 to 24 large merozoites. These enter other erythrocytes to form a second generation. Being smaller than the preceding ones, they are designated as microschizonts with as few as six small merozoites which are potential gametocytes. The appearance of the small merozoites ends the schizogenous phase. Upon entering erythrocytes, these small merozoites differentiate into recognizable micro- and macrogametocytes; this is the beginning of gametogony. No further development takes place in the tortoise.

When blood cells containing the gametocytes enter the intestine of leeches, they undergo the processes of gametogony and sporogony. Upon being released from the erythrocytes in the intestine of leeches, the gametocytes fuse and are enclosed in a thin membrane. The macrogametocyte becomes a large oval body and the microgametocyte a small oval one. The nucleus of the microgametocyte multiplies, forming four microgametes. Following fertilization of the macrogamete by one of these, the oocyst forms and eight sporozoites develop. When they have matured, the thin-walled oocyst ruptures, releasing the sporozoites in the intestinal lumen. They enter the circulatory system, appearing in the dorsal blood vessel. During the feeding act of the leeches, the sporozoites get into the proboscis and are injected into the tortoises.

PLATE 27 *Haemogregarina stepanowi*

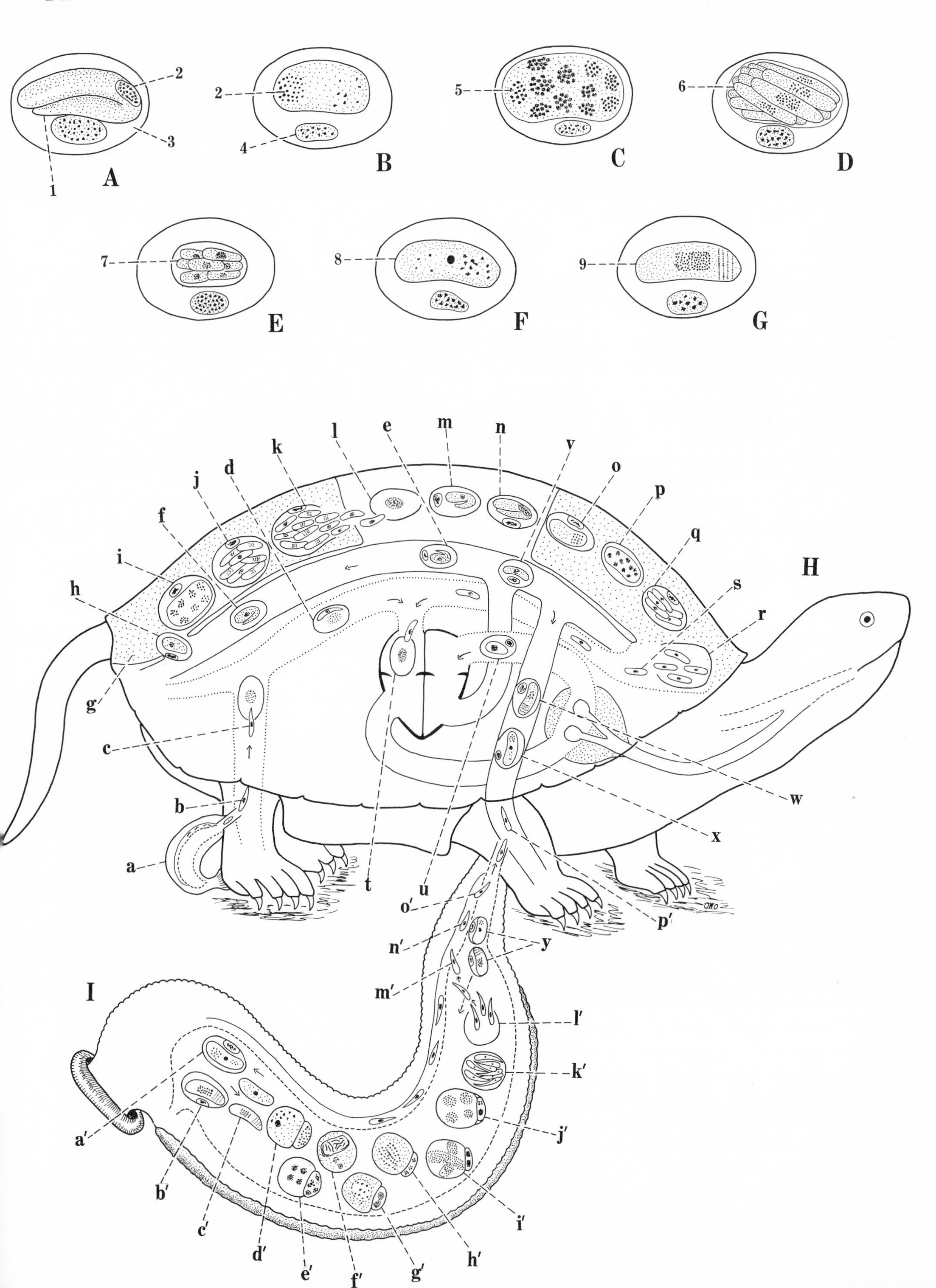

EXERCISE ON LIFE CYCLE

Haemogregarines commonly parasitize amphibians, reptiles, and birds. Trophozoites and gametocytes are in the erythrocytes of circulating blood. Schizonts with merozoites are in erythrocytes of circulating blood and the internal organs such as the liver and bone marrow. Zygotes and oocysts with sporozoites are in invertebrate definitive hosts.

Smears from circulating blood and impressions from the liver and bone marrow prepared and stained by standard procedures are satisfactory for detecting and recognizing infections of haemogregarines.

SELECTED REFERENCES

Doflein, F., and E. Reichenow. (1953). Lehrbuch der Protozoenkunde, 6th Ed. Gustav Fischer, Jena, p. 837.

Lehmann, D. J. (1959). J. Parasit. 45:198.

Osimani, J. H. (1942). J. Parasit. 28:147.

Reichenow, E. (1910). Arch. Protistenk. 20:251.

Saunders, D. C. (1955). J. Parasit. 41:171.

Wenyon, C. M. (1926). Protozoology, Vol. 2. Baillière, Tindall, and Cox, London, p. 1081.

Karyolysus lacertae Danilewsky, 1886 (Plate 28)

This blood parasite of the European wall lizard *Lacerta muralis* is used as an example of a life cycle of this genus. It infects the endothelial cells of the capillaries of the lizards and the gut epithelium and ova of lizard mites *Liponyssus saurarum* of the family Gamasidae.

DESCRIPTION. Schizonts in the endothelial cells, especially the capillaries of the liver of the lizards, contain large merozoites and a residual body that may be absorbed by their liberation. Small merozoites in second generation schizonts with a residual body represent gametocytes which penetrate erythrocytes where they fragment or displace the nucleus, hence the generic name *Karyolysus.*

Schizonts in gut epithelium of mites produce large (40 to 50 μ long), active sporokinetes that enter yolk masses of eggs of mites and migrate to the endodermal tissue of larval mites. In the latter, they produce oocysts 20 to 25 μ in diameter, containing 20 to 30 small sporozoites.

LIFE CYCLE. The life cycle of *K. lacertae* completes a sequence of progressive development in the haemogregarines in which two developmental stages in the lizard mite are necessary for completion of sporogony. The cycle may be divided into three parts as follows: 1) schizogony in lizards with eventual formation of gametocytes, 2) first sporogony in adult female mites with formation of sporokinetes, and 3) second and final sporogony in offspring of infected females with formation of sporozoites.

Beginning with lizards that have swallowed infected mites, the vermiform sporozoites are liberated from oocysts by the action of the digestive juices. The sporozoites become extremely active, burrow into the intestinal wall, enter the blood vessels, and are carried to various parts of the body. In the viscera, particularly the liver, they burrow into the endothelial cells of the capillaries. Growth begins promptly. A bandlike spindle forms and nuclear division follows. A nucleolus is associated with each nucleus. Large merozoites together with a residual body of cytoplasm develop. After absorption of the residual body, the merozoites escape into the capillaries and penetrate other endothelial cells to repeat schizogony. After a number of generations of large merozoites, one of small individuals appears. These are gametocytes which, upon being freed from the schizont, enter erythrocytes where they often damage or displace the nucleus. The macrogametocytes become recognizable by the larger nucleus and nucleolus. A tough cyst envelops the parasites. This ends the development in the lizards.

When adult female mites ingest the infected erythrocytes, the gametocytes are freed in the intestine. The micro- and macrogametocytes unite along the long axis of their bodies. They either penetrate the epithelial cells of the intestine or are phagocytized by them. Inside the cells, they shorten and the macrogametocyte grows more rapidly, becoming much larger. A thin membrane encloses both gametocytes. The nucleus of the microgametocyte divides once, forming two microgametes; the macrogametocyte transforms into a macrogamete. One microgamete enters the macrogamete and unites with the nucleus, forming the zygote. The second microgamete remains outside. As the zygote grows, a fertilization spindle forms and meiosis follows.

The oocyst forms by division of the nucleus which is the beginning of the first sporogenous phase. Upon completion of nuclear division, the cytoplasm breaks up to form large uninucleate vermiform bodies 40 to 50 μ long known as sporokinetes because they show great activity. This ends development in the intestinal cells of the gravid female mite. The next stage occurs in the larvae and nymphs.

The sporokinetes migrate from the intestinal wall of the adult female into the ovaries and then into the ova where they remain in the yolk until development of the larva begins. As soon as the endodermal tissue forms, the sporokinetes enter it, round up, and form oocysts 20 to 25 μ in diameter. At about the time nuclear division in the process of sporozoite formation is occurring, the young mite hatches. Molting of the larva into a nymph and completion of nuclear division with formation of 20 to 30 sporozoites occurs simultaneously. The sporozoites detach from the residual body in the oocyst. Formation of the sporozoites ends the second sporogenous stage of development in the offspring of the female mite.

Some of the ripe oocysts escape into the lumen of the gut through rupture of the endodermal cells and are voided with the faeces. Others remain in the gut wall. Infection of lizards takes place when either the free oocysts or infected nymphal mites are swallowed.

EXERCISE ON LIFE CYCLE

In areas where lizards are infected with *Karyolysus*, the animals should be collected together with their mite parasites for observations on the life cycle. By keeping them in cages designed to prevent the mites from escaping, a large population of the acarines may be developed for use in the studies.

The various developmental stages of the parasites in the mites can be found by sectioning a series of them collected from infected lizards. This can be done better, however, by hatching mites from eggs collected in the cages so that parasite-free ones may be available for experimental infections. Sections of engorged larval and nymphal mites at short intervals after feeding will reveal the various stages of the parasites.

The stages in the blood cells of the lizards may be found in smears stained with standard blood stains such as Wright's or Geimsa's. Those in the various organs will appear in sections.

SELECTED REFERENCES

Doflein, F., and E. Reichenow. (1953). Lehrbuch der Protozoenkunde. Gustav Fischer, Jena, p. 829.

Kudo, R. R. (1966). Protozoology. Charles C Thomas, Springfield, Ill., p. 708.

Reichenow, E. (1921). Arch. Protistenk. 42:180.

Wenyon, C. M. (1926). Protozoology. William Wood and Co., New York, p. 1095.

ORDER HAEMOSPORIDIA

The Haemosporidia are parasites of blood cells, as the name suggests, of reptiles, birds, and mammals. They have an alternation of hosts and generations. Asexual reproduction takes place in the internal organs, blood cells, reticuloendothelial cells, or combinations of them in the vertebrate host. Sexual reproduction occurs in the intestinal lumen and intestinal wall or other organs of the bloodsucking invertebrate hosts. Since there is no free-living stage, the sporozoites are not enclosed in thick-walled protective oocysts as in *Eimeria*. Transmission from host to host is through the bites of the invertebrate host.

The Haemosporidia are similar to Coccidia in many respects and probably are derived from them. Both have asexual and sexual reproduction. *Haemogregarina stepanowi*, a coccidian, has achieved an alternation of hosts with asexual development in the red blood cells instead of in the intestinal epithelium, as characteristic of the Coccidia.

Six genera from three families of Haemosporidia are considered. They are *Plasmodium vivax* of humans and some of the common species of birds from the Plasmodiidae, *Haemoproteus columbae* and

EXPLANATION OF PLATE 28 ⇨

A. Erythrocyte of lizard infected with macrogametocyte. **B.** Erythrocyte infected with microgametocyte. **C.** Microgametocyte freed from erythrocyte in gut of mite. **D.** Macrogametocyte freed from erythrocyte in gut of mite. **E.** Developing schizont. **F.** Schizont with large merozoites developed from sporozoite. **G.** Schizont with residual body and small merozoites which become gametocytes upon entering erythrocytes. **H.** Large sporokinete that develops in adult female mite, enters eggs, and gives rise to sporocysts in larvae. **I.** Sporocyst with sporozoites in larval and nymphal mites. **J.** Wall lizard showing development of parasites and final infection of erythrocytes. **K.** Infection of adult female mite, development of sporokinetes, and infection of eggs. **L.** Infection of epithelial cells of gut of larval mite and development of sporozoites. **M.** Nymphal mite containing sporocytes with sporozoites infective to lizards.

1, erythrocyte; **2**, displaced nucleus of erythrocyte, a characteristic of the action of the parasite on the red blood cells; **3**, macrogametocyte; **4**, microgametocyte; **5**, nucleus of gametocyte; **6**, nucleolus; **7**, nucleus of schizont; **8**, nucleolus; **9**, schizont originating from either a merozoite or a sporozoite; **10**, merozoites; **11**, schizont from merozoite; **12**, gametocyte; **13**, residual cytoplasmic body; **14**, reserve body of sporokinete; **15**, sporocyst; **16**, sporozoite.

a-v, infection of lizards and development of parasites in them; **a**, infected nymph being digested and sporocysts liberated; **b**, freed sporocyst; **c**, ruptured sporocyst liberating sporozoites; **d**, free sporozoites in gut lumen; **e**, sporozoite entering gut epithelial cell; **f**, sporozoite passing through gut wall and entering hepatic portal vein; **g**, sporozoite entering endothelial cells of capillaries of liver (other organs also infected); **h**, young schizont in endothelial cell; **i**, young schizont with first division nucleus; **j**, schizont with dividing nuclei; **k**, mature schizont with merozoites; **l**, ruptured schizont freeing merozoites in blood stream; **m**, merozoites entering endothelial cells to initiate new generation of merozoic schizonts; **n**, merozoite entering endothelial cell to initiate generation of gametic schizonts; **o**, young schizont; **p**, young schizont in first nuclear division; **q**, multinucleate schizont; **r**, mature schizont with gametocytes; **s**, ruptured oocyst with gametocytes being released into blood stream; **t**, gametocyte entering red blood cell; **u**, gametocyte in circulating red blood cell; **v**, infected red blood cell being ingested by mature female mite.

a′-n′, development in adult female mite; **a′**, infected erythrocytes; **b′**, gametocytes freed from erythrocytes; **c′**, gametocytes in union or syzygy; **d′**, gametocytes entering intestinal epithelial cell; **e′**, growth of micro- and macrogametocytes; **f′**, large macrogametocyte, nucleus of microgametocyte has divided once to form two microgametes; **g′**, one microgamete has entered macrogamete, fertilization spindle has formed; **h′**, zygote enlarges, one microgamete remains outside; **i′**, first nuclear division of zygote (sporont); **j′**, multinucleate sporont about to produce sporoblasts; **k′**, sporocyst with fully developed large sporokinetes; **l′**, large sporokinete free in gut lumen; **m′**, sporokinete has migrated from lumen of gut to ovary of mite and has entered egg; **n′**, egg of mite.

a″-f″, development in larval and nymphal mites; **a″**, sporokinete in tissues and gut of newly hatched larva; **b″**, sporokinete entering newly formed intestinal endoderm; **c″**, sporokinete in intestinal epithelial cell; **d″**, growth of sporokinete into young schizont; **e″**, multinucleate sporont forming sporoblasts; **f″**, sporocyst with a residual cytoplasmic body and numerous sporozoites, sporulation completed simultaneously with molting of larva to nymph.

Figures A-I redrawn from Reichenow, 1921, Arch. Protistenk. 42:180; others original.

Leucocytozoon simondi from the Haemoproteidae, and *Babesia bigemina*, *Theileria parva*, and *Toxoplasma gondii* from the Babesiidae.

FAMILY PLASMODIIDAE

The Plasmodiidae are parasites of reptiles, birds, and mammals, with schizogony in tissue or endothelial cells, and in erythrocytes. Sexual reproduction occurs in mosquitoes in which the sporozoites are formed.

Plasmodium vivax (Grassi and Feletti, 1890) (Plate 29)

Plasmodium vivax is a parasite of the liver and erythrocytes of humans, and the intestine and salivary glands of many species of anopheline mosquitoes in subtropical and tropical regions throughout the world. It is the cause of benign tertian malaria, one of the serious diseases of mankind throughout his existence. Today, vast areas of the earth are being freed of malaria by destroying the parasites in humans through medication and the mosquito hosts through spraying, thus giving hope and health to vast populations that otherwise would continue to suffer from the debilitating effects of the disease.

DESCRIPTION. Pre-erythrocytic schizonts derived from sporozoites are irregularly shaped, non-

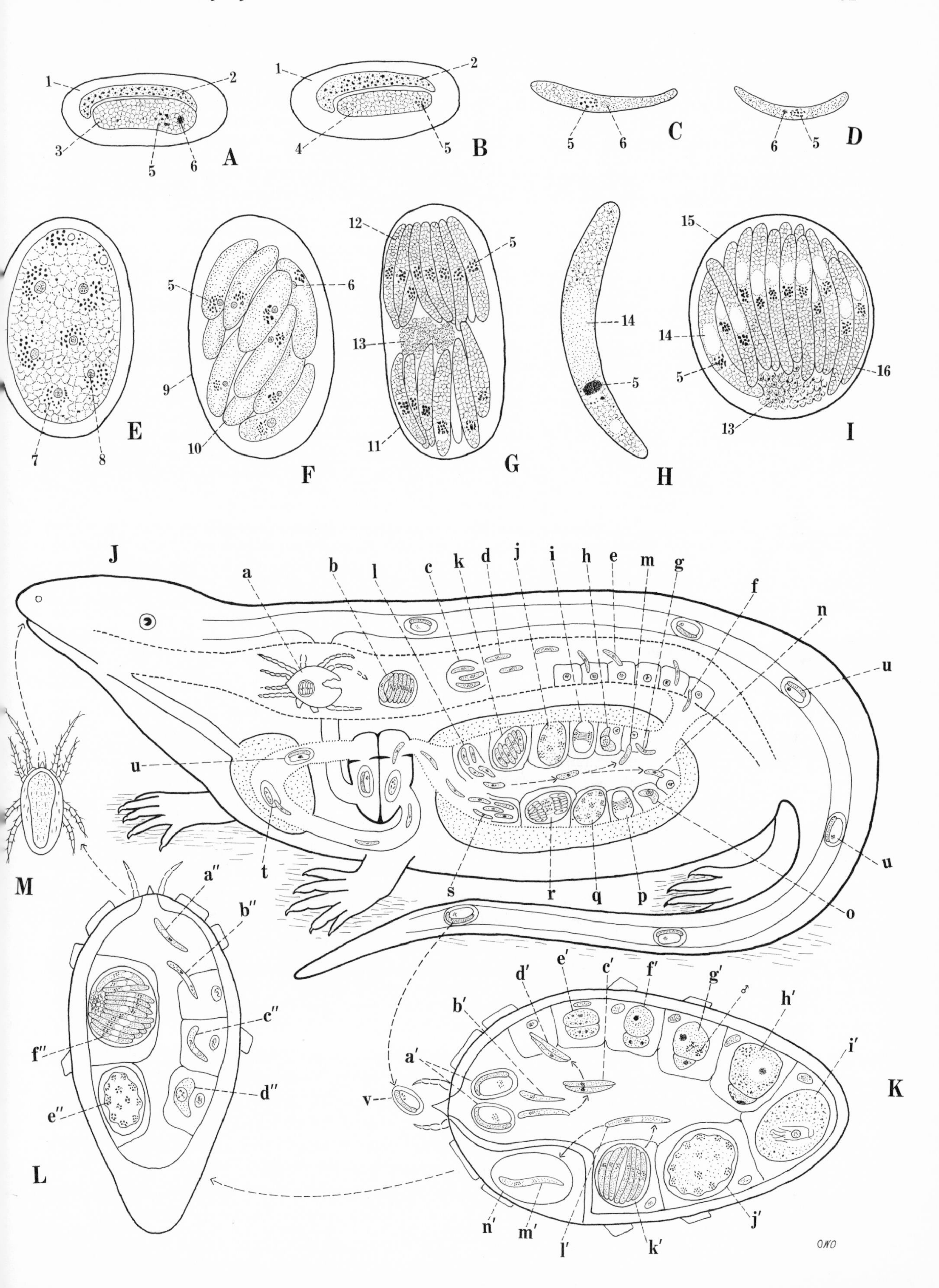
A
B
C
D
E
F
G
H
I
J
K
L
M
OWO

EXPLANATION OF PLATE 29 ▷

A. Ring stage in erythrocyte. **B-C.** Growing trophozoites. **D-E.** Young schizonts with few nuclei. **F-G.** Older schizonts with more nuclei. **H.** Segmenter with merozoites. **I.** Macrogametocyte. **J.** Microgametocyte. **K.** Anopheline mosquito host in characteristic feeding position. **L.** Human host.

1, nucleus of parasite in erythrocyte; 2, cytoplasm; 3, Schüffner's dots; 4, pigment granules; 5, merozoites.

a, gametocyte being sucked up by mosquito and entering stomach; **b**, microgametocyte; **c**, exflagellation of microgametocyte; **d**, microgamete; **e**, macrogametocyte; **f**, macrogamete; **g**, microgamete fertilizes macrogamete; **h**, zygote; **i**, ookinete; **j**, ookinete passing through intestinal epithelium; **k**, ookinete rounds up between epithelium and basement membrane to form young oocyst; **l**, growing oocyst; **m**, formation of sporoblasts; **n**, ripe oocyst with sporozoites escaping into haemocoel; **o**, sporozoites migrating through haemocoel toward salivary glands; **p**, sporozoites in cells of salivary glands; **q**, sporozoites being injected into blood by biting mosquito.

a′, sporozoites injected into blood stream; **b′**, sporozoites distributed throughout blood; **c′**, sporozoite entering hepatic cell to initiate exo-erythrocytic schizogony; **d′**, segmenter (preceding stages of trophozoites omitted); **e′**, first generation of exo-erythrocytic cryptozoites (merozoites); **f′**, cryptozoites enter other hepatic cells to produce second generation; **g′**, segmenter (trophozoite omitted); **h′**, metacryptozoites (second generation of metacryptozoites) which enter blood stream to begin erythrocytic schizogony; **i′**, metacryptozoite entering red blood cell to begin erythrocytic schizogony; **j′**, ring stage; **k′**, trophozoite stage; **l′**, **m′**, developing schizonts; **n′**, segmenter; **o′**, erythrocytic merozoites liberated 48 hours after entrance of metacryptozoites (chills and fever at the time merozoites are liberated into blood stream); **p′**, merozoites entering red blood cells to initiate second generation; **q′**, ring stage; **r′**, trophozoite; **s′**, **t′**, schizonts; **u′** segmenter; **v′**, liberation of second generation of erythrocytic merozoites (chills and fever); **w′**, merozoite entering erythrocyte; **x′-a″**, formation of microgametocyte; **b″**, merozoite entering erythrocyte; **c″-g″**, development of macrogametocyte.

Figures redrawn from various sources.

---

pigmented bodies in the liver cells. Erythrocytic forms prepared with Wright's or Giemsa's blood stain have blue cytoplasm and red nuclei. They include in the sequence of development 1) a ringlike trophozoite with a thin ring of cytoplasm and a small nucleus perched on one side; 2) a large trophozoite with enlarged, irregularly shaped cytoplasm containing a single nucleus and brownish pigment granules in an erythrocyte with numerous pink Schüffner's dots dispersed throughout its cytoplasm; 3) a schizont with two or more (up to 15 or 20) nuclei; 4) a segmenter in which a bit of the cytoplasm surrounds each nucleus to form individual merozoites, and 5) large, pigmented, oval gametocytes in which the microgametocyte is light blue and contains a large diffuse nucleus and a larger, dark blue macrogametocyte with a small, compact, deeply staining nucleus.

LIFE CYCLE. The life cycle of *Plasmodium vivax* includes an alternation of generations and hosts. The asexual part of the cycle occurs in humans and consists of three parts, the pre-erythrocytic, erythrocytic, and post-erythrocytic. The sexual part of the cycle takes place in female anopheline mosquitoes, since the males do not feed on blood.

Sporozoites injected into humans by infected mosquitoes initiate the pre-erythrocytic cycle. They quickly leave the site of entry and go rapidly by way of the blood stream to the liver, leave the capillaries, and enter the hepatic cells. Sporozoites in the liver cells transform into schizonts known as cryptozoites which undergo asexual multiplication, producing large numbers of cryptozoic merozoites. These enter other liver cells to form a second generation of schizonts known as metacryptozoites which produce the metacryptozoic merozoites about 8 days after injection of the sporozoites. This completes the pre-erythrocytic phase of the cycle and sets the stage for the beginning of the other two that follow simultaneously.

Metacryptic merozoites entering liver cells are designated as phanerozoites and are the beginning of the post-erythrocytic phase of the cycle. They transform into schizonts that normally undergo very limited schizogony, producing few merozoites which enter surrounding hepatic cells, thereby maintaining the cycle in a quiescent phase. Under certain conditions, however, schizogony becomes greatly accelerated, liberating hordes of merozoites, many of which enter the blood stream, penetrate erythrocytes, and produce relapses following periods of apparent freedom from the disease.

The erythrocytic phase of the cycle begins when metacryptozoic merozoites enter the red blood

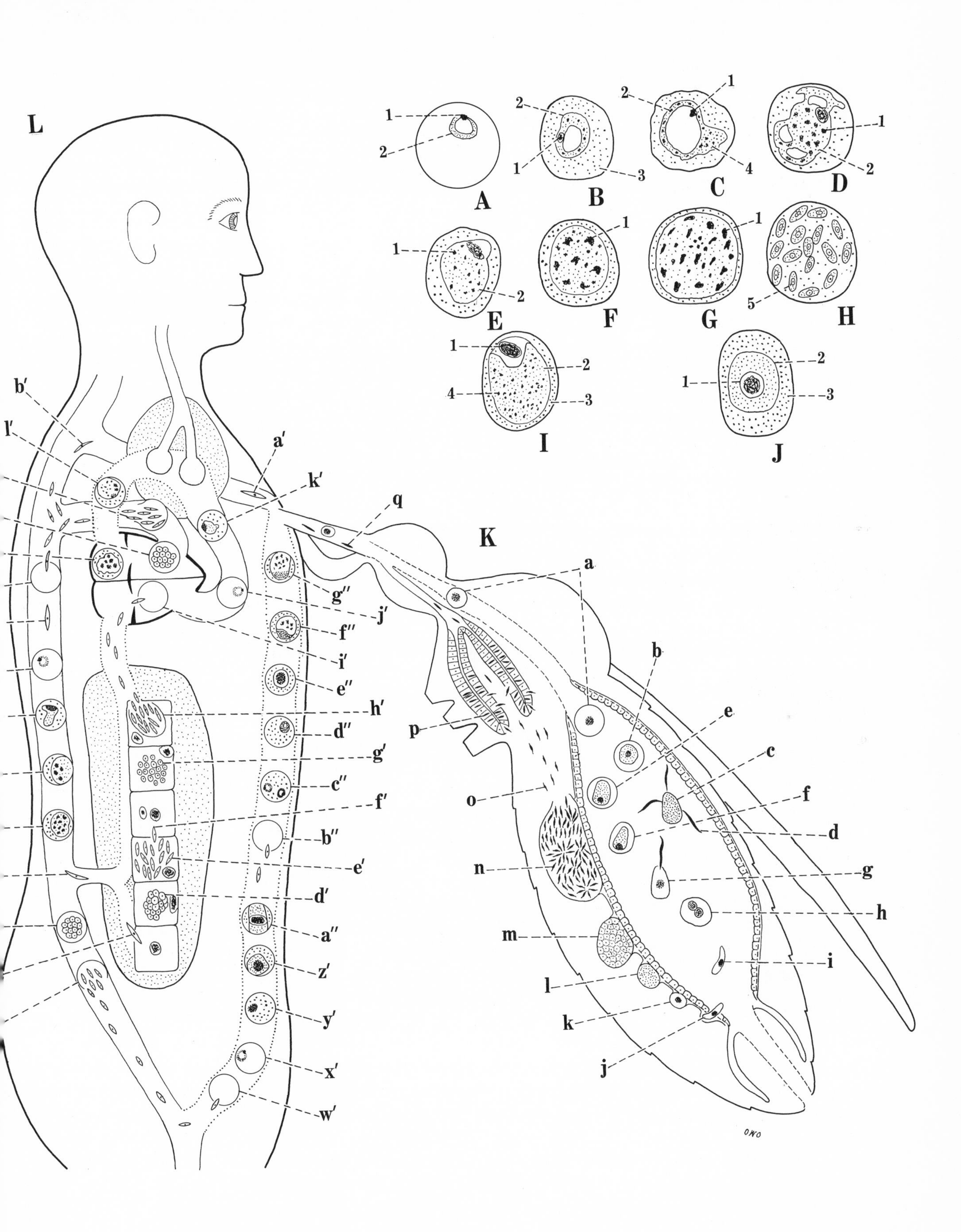
L
A
B
C
D
E
F
G
H
I
J
K
ONO

cells. They quickly transform into ring-shaped trophozoites consisting of a thin ring of cytoplasm about one-third to one-half the diameter of the host cell; a tiny nucleus perches on the margin of the ring. As growth continues, trophozoites eventually fill the entire blood cell, even causing it to enlarge. Pink granules known as Schüffner's dots appear in the cytoplasm of the host cells, and particles of brownish pigment derived from the haemoglobin appear in the parasites. The amoeboid parasites assume various shapes in the blood cells. Full grown trophozoites become schizonts when nuclear division begins, resulting eventually in 15 to 20 nuclei. Bits of cytoplasm surround each nucleus to form merozoites, and the parasite is known as a segmenter. Approximately 48 hours after the meta-cryptozoic merozoites entered the erythrocytes, the first generation of erythrocytic merozoites has been formed and liberated into the blood stream. Simultaneously with their appearance, the individual suffers the paroxysms of chills and fever characteristic of malaria. The merozoites enter other red blood cells and repeat the cycle every 48 hours. This may occur many times.

Studies utilizing the electron microscope show that the growing trophozoites ingest portions of the cytoplasm of the red blood cells of the host by a process of pinocytosis, or "cell drinking."

Not all merozoites repeat the schizogenous cycle, however, as some form gametocytes. These merozoites enter the erythrocytes in the usual manner and initiate the gametogenous, or sexual stage, by developing into micro- and macrogametocytes. No further development of them takes place in the erythrocytes.

When blood cells containing gametocytes are taken into the stomach of female anopheline mosquitoes, *Anopheles quadrimaculatus* being an especially good host, the gametes are formed. The microgametocytes produce six to eight long, slender microgametes each, one of which enters a macrogamete and fertilizes it, resulting in a zygote. This ends the gametogenous phase.

The zygotes soon become motile, vermicule-shaped ookinetes that migrate into the stomach wall, coming to rest between the epithelium and the basement membrane where they develop into oocysts. Sporogony begins promptly by repeated division of the nucleus and growth of the oocysts. Thousands of minute, slender, spindle-shaped sporozoites are formed. Upon maturity of the oocysts, they rupture, releasing the sporozoites in the body cavity of the mosquito. Large numbers of them reach the salivary glands, penetrate the cells, and migrate into the tubules. They are injected into the vertebrate host together with saliva by feeding mosquitoes.

EXERCISE ON LIFE CYCLE

In the absence of species of malaria in humans for study, one must turn to native animals for material. Several species of *Plasmodium* parasitize a large percentage of the common wild birds throughout the country. English sparrows and pigeons are especially useful because they frequently harbor *Plasmodium relictum* (*P. praecox*) which is preferred for study because its life cycle is well known.

Smears may be obtained by pricking a brachial vein or tarsal artery with a sharp needle and allowing several drops of blood to accumulate. Touch the edge of a microscope slide to the drop and quickly draw it over a clean slide, spreading the blood in a thin film. Wave the slide vigorously in the air in order to dry the blood quickly. Use standard procedures, employing Wright's or Giemsa's stains, for staining.

The different stages of erythrocytic schizogony together with the micro- and macrogametocytes may be found especially during the season when the culicine mosquito hosts are prevalent.

The exo-erythrocytic stages occur in reticuloendothelial cells of the blood vessels, especially those of the liver. Sections and smears of the liver appropriately stained are necessary to see them.

Culex pipiens, one of the most common mosquitoes, is the intermediate host. Mosquitoes allowed to feed on infected birds and kept at room temperature in a humid cage for a few days show oocysts on the stomach wall.

Blood from parasitized birds injected into susceptible unparasitized ones produces an infection. Canaries, being susceptible to *P. relictum*, are especially useful experimental animals in studies on the life cycle.

SELECTED REFERENCES

Humans

Belding, D. L. (1952). Textbook of Clinical Parasitology, 2d Ed. Appleton-Century-Crofts, Inc., New York, p. 255.

Bray, R. S. (1957). London School Trop. Med. Mem. 12, 192 pp.

Chandler, A. C., and C. P. Read. (1961). Introduction to Parasitology, 10th Ed. John Wiley and Sons, New York, p. 165.

Doflein, F., and E. Reichenow. (1953). Lehrbuch der Protozoenkunde, 6th Ed. Gustav Fischer, Jena, p. 899.

Faust, E. C., and P. F. Russell. (1957). Craig and Faust's Clinical Parasitology, 6th Ed. Lea and Febiger, Philadelphia, p. 244.

Hoare, C. A. (1949). Handbook of Medical Protozoology. Baillière, Tindall, and Cox, London, p. 218.

Levine, N. D. (1961). Protozoan Parasites of Domestic Animals and of Man. Burgess Publishing Co., Minneapolis, p. 260.

Birds

Doflein, F., and E. Reichenow. (1953). Lehrbuch der Protozoenkunde, 6th Ed. Gustav Fischer, Jena, p. 899.

Hewitt, R. (1940). Amer. J. Hyg., Monogr. Ser. No. 5.

Huff, C. G. (1934). Amer. J. Hyg. 19:123.

Levine, N. D. (1961). Protozoan Parasites of Domestic Animals and of Man. Burgess Publishing Co., Minneapolis, p. 266.

Manwell, R. D. (1940). Amer. J. Trop. Med. 20:859.

Mudrow, L., and E. Reichenow. (1940). Arch. Protistenk. 97:101.

Sergent, E. (1949). C. R. Acad. Sci. Paris 229:455.

Plasmodium of birds

Birds offer an indigenous source of *Plasmodium* for general studies in acquiring experience and knowledge of this parasite. Although infection is widespread among birds, it is not always possible to find parasitized individuals.

While blood smears are the most convenient and practical means of making surveys, they are not a highly reliable means of detecting infections. This is especially true in cases where light ones occur and only a few of the total number of erythrocytes on the slides contain parasites. Under such circumstances, identification is rendered more difficult owing to the lack of different stages for examination for specific features. Blood for making smears may be obtained easily and without danger to the birds by puncturing the tarsal artery with a very sharp fine needle. Insect pins mounted in a handle and kept sharp are excellent for this purpose. The smears should be stained as soon as possible after collection, using Wright's or Giemsa's stains. The former is less expensive and more rapid in staining, but the latter gives more critical results.

Characteristics used in the identification of the different species found in blood smears include 1) morphology, 2) age of cells parasitized, 3) host-parasite specificity, and 4) geographical distribution. The first two of these characteristics will be discussed in connection with Plate 30. The other two require separate consideration.

HOST-PARASITE SPECIFICITY. Some species are known to occur naturally only from certain hosts, such as *P. paddae* from the paddy bird or Java sparrow, *P. fallax* from an African owl, *P. oti* from the eastern screech owl, *P. polare* from cliff swallows, *P. rouxi* from Algerian sparrows, *P. vaughani* from American robins, and *P. nucleophilum* from catbirds.

The remaining well-known species, including *P. relictum, cathemerium, elongatum, hexamerium, circumflexum*, and *lophurae*, appear in a wide variety of hosts.

Another aspect of host-parasite relationship is whether canaries are susceptible to infection when parasitized blood is injected into them. This point, however, is of no significance in determining species found in blood smears collected from wild birds.

GEOGRAPHIC DISTRIBUTION. This is correlated with host-parasite specificity where the parasite is restricted to a single species of host whose geographic distribution is limited. *P. paddae* is confined to the geographic range of the Java sparrow, *P. fallax* to that of its African owl host, *P. oti* to that of the screech owl, and *P. polare* to that of cliff swallows. *P. gallinaceum* is known only from the Orient.

MORPHOLOGY OF PARASITES AND THEIR EFFECT ON BLOOD CELLS. In identifying the parasites in the erythrocytes, it is important to understand how the different species appear and affect the cells that they infect. Plate 30, redrawn from Hewitt's monograph entitled "Bird Malaria,"

EXPLANATION OF PLATE 30 ▷

I. Ring stages
- **A.** In young erythrocytes
  - **1.** *P. cathemerium, circumflexum, elongatum, nucleophilum, relictum* (Fig. 1)
- **B.** In mature erythrocytes
  - **1.** *P. lophurae;* unknown for other species (Fig. 2)

II. Difference in pigment in microgametocytes
- **A.** Round pigment granules
  - **1.** *P. relictum* (Fig. 3)
- **B.** Elongate pigment granules
  - **1.** *P. cathemerium* (Fig. 4)

III. Shape and location of young trophozoites and displacement of nucleus of host cell
- **A.** Shape of trophozoites
  - **1.** Small and elongate
    - **a.** *P. circumflexum, lophurae* (Fig. 5)
  - **2.** Small, irregular but not round or elongate
    - **a.** *P. cathemerium, gallinaceum, nucleophilum, polare, relictum* (Figs. 6, 7, 8)
- **B.** Location of trophozoites
  - **1.** Nucleus of erythrocyte in normal position
    - **a.** Free in cytoplasm
      - **(1)** Lateral to nucleus of host cell
        - **(a)** *P. circumflexum, lophurae* (Fig. 5)
      - **(2)** Terminal to nucleus
        - **(a)** *P. polare* (Fig. 7)
    - **b.** Adherent to nucleus of host cell
      - **(1)** *P. nucleophilum* (Fig. 6)
- **C.** Location of nucleus of host cell
  - **1.** Nucleus in normal position
    - **a.** *P. circumflexum, lophurae, nucleophilum, polare* (Figs. 5, 6, 7)
  - **2.** Nucleus displaced
    - **a.** *P. cathemerium, gallinaceum, relictum* (Fig. 8)

IV. Shape of gametocytes and location of nucleus of host cell
- **A.** Shape
  - **1.** Round
    - **a.** *P. cathemerium, gallinaceum, relictum* (Fig. 9)
  - **2.** Elongate
    - **a.** Thin, does not surround nucleus
      - **(1)** *P. elongatum, hexamerium, oti, polare, rouxi* (Fig. 10)
    - **b.** Thick, partially or completely encircles nucleus
      - **(1)** *P. circumflexum, lophurae* (Figs. 11, 12)
- **B.** Location of nucleus of host cell
  - **1.** Normal position
    - **a.** *P. circumflexum, elongatum, hexamerium, lophurae, oti, polare, rouxi, vaughani* (Figs. 10, 11, 12)
  - **2.** Displaced position
    - **a.** *P. cathemerium, gallinaceum, relictum* (Figs. 3, 4, 9)

V. Segmenters
- **A.** Nucleus of host cell not displaced
  - **1.** Small segmenter, characteristically with four merozoites located terminal to nucleus
    - **a.** *P. rouxi* (Fig. 15)
  - **2.** Large segmenter, partially or completely surrounding nucleus
    - **a.** *P. circumflexum, lophurae* (Fig. 16)
- **B.** Nucleus of host cell displaced
  - **1.** Segmenter small, attached to nucleus, few merozoites
    - **a.** *P. nucleophilum* (Fig. 14)
  - **2.** Segmenter large, not attached to nucleus, many merozoites
    - **a.** *P. cathemerium, gallinaceum, relictum* (Fig. 13)

---

shows these differences in an organized manner that enables the investigator quickly to place the parasites into related groups. The characteristics are based on five categories of features. They are 1) age of erythrocytes infected; 2) differences in shape of pigment granules in microgametocytes; 3) shape and position of young trophozoites in host cells and location of the nucleus of the latter; 4) shape of gametocytes and location of the nucleus of host cells; and 5) location of segmenters, number of merozoites produced, and location of nucleus of host cells.

FAMILY HAEMOPROTEIDAE

The Haemoproteidae contains two of the important and common blood parasites of birds other than *Plasmodium.* They are the genera *Haemoproteus* and *Leucocytozoon.* Schizogony occurs in the endothelial and visceral cells. Merozoites entering the blood stream penetrate circulating cells and develop to gametocytes. Sexual reproduction is completed with the formation of sporozoites in blood-sucking Diptera of the families Hippoboscidae, Simuliidae, and Ceratopogonidae in a manner similar to that of *Plasmodium* in mosquitoes.

PLATE 30 *Morphological Features Used to Identify Species of Plasmodium in Birds*

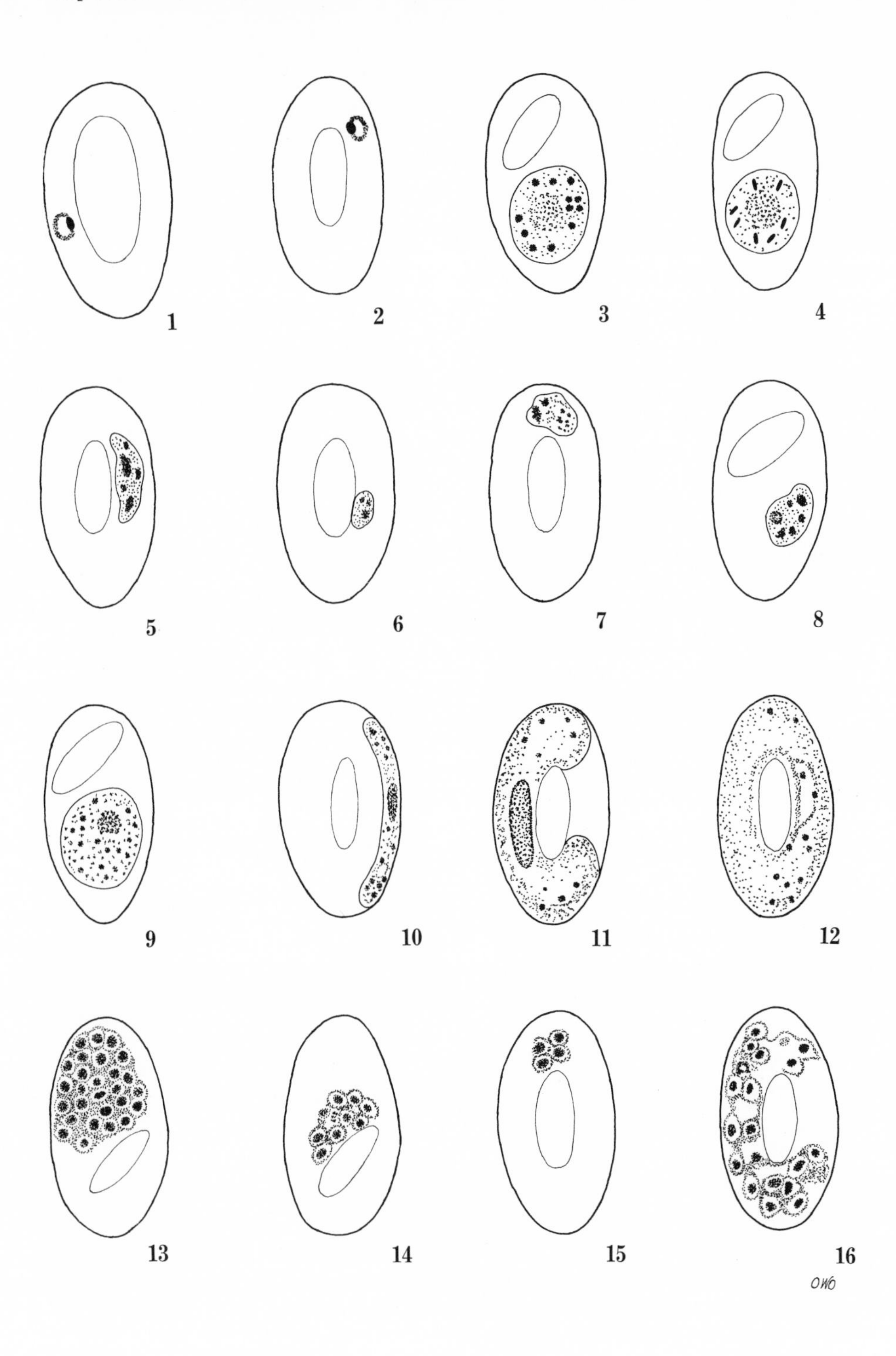

EXPLANATION OF PLATE 31

A. Mononuclear leucocyte with parasite. **B.** Erythrocyte with ring stage of gametocyte. **C-D.** Growing gametocytes. **E.** Macrogametocyte. **F.** Microgametocyte. **G.** Pigeon host. **H.** Pigeon louse fly *(Pseudolynchia maura)* invertebrate host.

1, nucleus of blood cell; **2,** young schizont; **3,** ring stage of gametocyte in erythrocyte; **4-5,** growing gametocytes; **6,** nucleus of mature macrogametocyte; **7,** nucleus of mature microgametocyte.

a-u, in pigeon; **a,** sporozoite injected into blood stream; **b,** sporozoites in blood go through heart and to lungs; **c,** sporozoite entering endothelial cell in lungs; **d,** growth of sporozoite in endothelial cell; **e-k,** schizogony in endothelial cells; **e,** formation of uninuclear cytomeres (host cell enlarges as parasite grows); **f-g,** cytomeres become multinucleate; **h,** cytomeres with large number of nuclei; **i,** great increase in number of small nuclei; **j,** formation of numerous minute merozoites in schizonts; **k,** escape of merozoites from schizonts into blood stream (this process of schizogony may be repeated); **l,** merozoite entering red blood cell; **m-u,** gametogony in erythrocytes; **m,** ring stage in erythrocyte; **n-o,** formation of macrogametocyte; **p,** merozoite entering red blood cell; **q,** ring stage; **r-s,** formation of microgametocyte; **t,** mature macrogametocyte; **u,** mature microgametocyte in general circulation.

a′-l′, in pigeon louse fly; **a′,** microgametocyte and **b′,** macrogametocyte sucked up by pigeon louse fly; **c′,** exflagellation of microgametocyte with formation of microgametes; **d′,** macrogamete being fertilized by microgamete; **e′,** zygote; **f′,** ookinete in stomach; **g′,** ookinete migrating through epithelium of stomach; **h′,** young oocyst between epithelium and basement membrane; **i′,** oocyst with sporoblasts; **j′,** ripe oocyst filled with sporozoites; **k′,** rupture of ripe oocyst and liberation of sporozoites; **l′,** migration of sporozoites into salivary glands; **m′,** injection of sporozoites into blood by feeding pigeon louse fly.

Figures adapted from Aragao, 1908, Arch. Protistenk. 12:154.

Haemoproteus Kruse, 1890

The gametocytes appear only in erythrocytes, where they lie alongside the nucleus, often partially surrounding but rarely displacing it to any extent.

Schizogony occurs in endothelial cells lining the blood vessels, particularly those of the lungs, and sporogony takes place in the intestinal wall of the insect vectors.

Haemoproteus columbae Celli and Sanfelice, 1891 (Plate 31)

Haemoproteus columbae occurs commonly in pigeons. Like *Plasmodium,* there is an alternation of generations and of hosts, involving a vertebrate and a bloodsucking arthropod. Whereas *Plasmodium* undergoes schizogony in the hepatic parenchyma and erythrocytes, *Haemoproteus* does so only in the reticuloendothelial cells, primarily of the lungs but also of the liver, spleen, and other organs. Only the gametocytes of *Haemoproteus* occur in the erythrocytes. Sporulation takes place in the hippoboscid pigeon fly, *Pseudolynchia maura,* much as *Plasmodium vivax* does in mosquitoes.

DESCRIPTION. Gametocytes are halter-shaped bodies in the erythrocytes that partially enclose the nucleus of the host cell without displacing it. The microgametocytes are 11.9 to 15.3 μ long by 2.5 to 4.3 μ wide with a large oval nucleus 2.8 by 5.8 μ in size that stains light red; the cytoplasm stains light blue. The macrogametocytes are 13.7 to 17.1 μ long by 2.8 by 2.3 μ in size with a small almost spherical nucleus 2.1 by 2.3 μ in size that stains more darkly than in the microgametocyte, as does the cytoplasm. Pigment granules are present in the cytoplasm of the gametocytes. The unpigmented schizonts are in the reticuloendothelial cells of the lungs principally but also in the liver, spleen, and other organs. Oocysts are attached to the stomach wall of the pigeon fly.

LIFE CYCLE. Sporozoites, upon being injected into the blood stream by the pigeon fly, enter the reticuloendothelial cells of the blood vessels of the lungs primarily, but other organs such as the liver, spleen, and bone marrow are involved to a lesser extent. It has been suggested that the rich supply of oxygen of the lungs may account for the higher prevalence of the parasite in them.

Schizogony begins by nuclear multiplication, resulting in approximately 20 new nuclei. Each one becomes enclosed in a separate bit of cytoplasm and develops into an individual cytomere. The nucleus of each cytomere in turn multiplies many fold, resulting in growth of the cytomeres and enlargement of the host cell containing them. Upon completion of nuclear multiplication, each newly formed nucleus combines with a bit of cytomeric cytoplasm to form a merozoite. The process requires about 4 weeks.

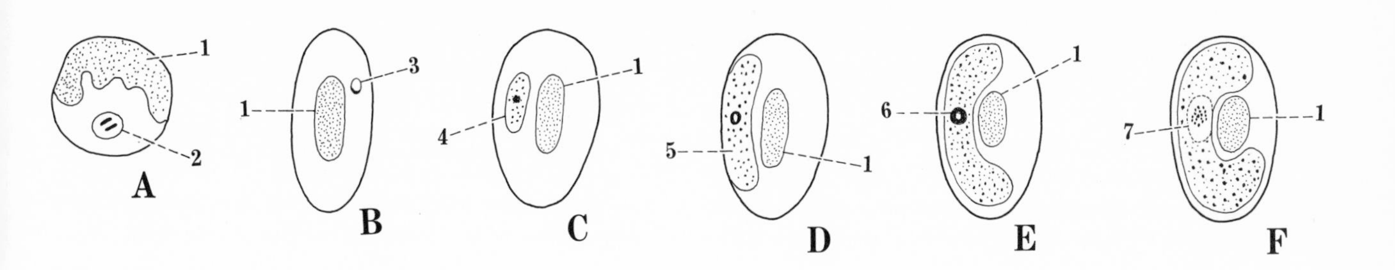
1
2
A
3
1
B
1
4
C
5
1
D
1
6
E
7
1
F

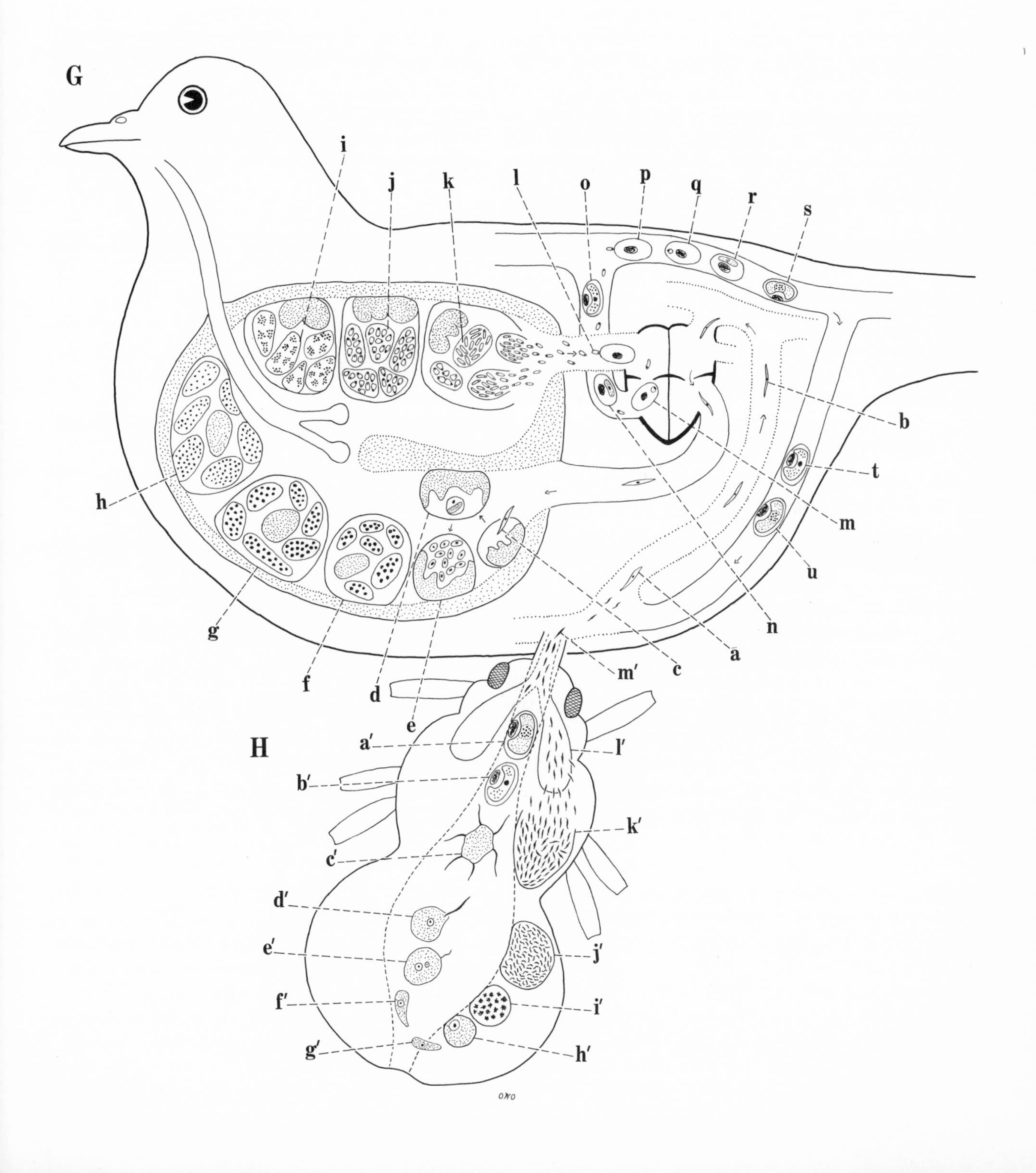
G
i
j
k
l
o
p
q
r
s
b
t
m
u
h
g
f
d
e
a
c
n
m′
H
a′
l′
b′
k′
c′
d′
e′
j′
f′
i′
g′
h′

The stretched host cell eventually ruptures, releasing the cytomeres which because of their number and size may occlude small blood vessels. Merozoites freed from them in the blood stream may either enter other endothelial cells to repeat another cycle of schizogony or penetrate erythrocytes to form gametocytes and thereby initiate the gametogenous phase of the sexual cycle.

The earliest stage of the gametocytes in the red blood cells is a minute ring similar to that seen in the plasmodia which grows rapidly into a halter-shaped body (named from the shape of stone weights known as halteridia used in broad-jumping by the ancients). No further growth takes place in the vertebrate host.

When ingested by pigeon flies, the halteridia (gametocytes) are freed from the blood cells in the midgut of the insect. A microgametocyte produces six to eight flagellar microgametes, one of which unites with a macrogamete to form a zygote, thus completing the gametogenous phase.

The zygote transforms into a vermicular ookinete that migrates through the intestinal wall, coming to rest on the outside, or possibly between the basement membrane and the epithelial cells where it develops into an oocyst. Sporogony begins with the multiplication of the nucleus, resulting in the formation of hundreds of sporozoites. Fully developed oocysts rupture 10 to 12 days after infection of the flies, releasing the sporozoites into the haemocoel. They migrate to and accumulate in the salivary glands. Infection of the vertebrate hosts occurs when sporozoites are injected into the blood stream by infected flies feeding on them.

Where known, the life cycle of other species of *Haemoproteus* are basically the same as that of *H. columbae*. *Haemoproteus lophortyx* of the California Valley quail develops in the hippoboscid fly *Lynchia hirsuta*. *Haemoproteus nettionis* from ducks and *H. canachites* from the ruffed grouse (*Bonasa umbellus* and Spruce grouse (*Canachites canadensis*), on the other hand, develop in ceratopogonid midges of the genus *Culicoides*.

EXERCISE ON LIFE CYCLE

Infected pigeons, especially squabs, provide the best source of material for experimental studies. When infected birds are found, exflagellation of the microgametocyte with formation of the flagellar microgametes may be observed on a microscope slide. Place several drops of infected blood on a slide and cover it with a cover glass. The formation of the microgametes may be observed with the aid of the 4-mm lens of a microscope.

Pigeon louse flies from lofts with infected birds will provide a source of ookinetes, sporulating oocysts, and sporozoites. Smears prepared from the intestine may show ookinetes, and those made from ripe oocysts and salivary glands will show sporozoites when stained with Wright's or Giemsa's stains.

Schizogenous stages may be obtained from smears and sections of the lungs of infected birds and stained by appropriate standard methods.

Birds free from parasites may be infected by interperitoneal injections of emulsions of lungs containing merozoites or intestines and salivary glands of infected flies. Injection of red blood cells does not produce an infection.

SELECTED REFERENCES

Adie, H. (1924). Bull. Soc. Path. Exot. 17:605.

Aragao, H. de B. (1908). Arch. Protistenk. 12:154.

Coatney, G. R. (1936). J. Parasit. 22:88.

Doflein, F., and E. Reichenow. (1953). Lehrbuch der Protozoenkunde. Gustav Fischer, Jena, p. 890.

Fallis, A. M., and G. F. Bennett. (1960). Canad. J. Zool. 38:455.

Fallis, A. M., and D. M. Wood. (1957). Canad. J. Zool. 35:425.

Herman, C. M., and B. Glading. (1942). Calif. Fish and Game 28:150.

Kudo, R. R. (1966). Protozoology, 5th Ed. Charles C Thomas, Springfield, Ill., p. 741.

Levine, N. D. (1961). Protozoan Parasites of Domestic Animals and of Man. Burgess Publishing Co., Minneapolis, p. 271.

Neveu-Lemaire, M. (1943). Traité de Protozoologie Médicale et Vétérinaire. Vigot Frères, Paris, p. 450.

O'Roke, E. E. (1930). Univ. Calif. Publ. Zool. 36:1.

Tarshis, I. B. (1955). Exp. Parasit. 4:464.

Wenyon, C. M. (1966). Protozoology, Vol. 2. Baillière, Tindall, and Cox, London, p. 885.

Leucocytozoon Danilewsky, 1890

Leucocytozoon are parasites of birds. As in *Haemoproteus,* the gametocytes occur in blood cells. They infect nonhaemoglobinous cells believed to be erythroblasts or mononuclear lymphocytes. The infected cells may be either spindle-shaped or spherical. The schizonts are in endothelial and macrophage cells of the lungs, liver, spleen, intestine, and other organs.

Leucocytozoon simondi Mathis and Léger, 1910 (Plate 32)

This sporozoan is a parasite of ducks in North America. It is the cause of a seasonal disease in young birds where the mortality may be up to 100 per cent. Infected wild ducks carry the parasites to various parts of the country. The disease occurs in ducklings only in regions where black flies (Simuliidae), the invertebrate hosts, are present.

DESCRIPTION. Macrogametocytes are oval bodies 14 to 15 μ long by 4.5 to 5.5 μ wide. The cytoplasm stains darkly and the nucleus is small, compact, and dark. Microgametocytes likewise are oval, slightly smaller than the macrogametocytes; the cytoplasm stains lightly and the nucleus is large, open, and light in color. No pigment is present. The host cell is elongated to a length of about 48 μ, spindle-shaped, and the nucleus is abnormally elongated and slender. Schizonts are of two types: 1) megaloschizonts in macrophages of the liver, spleen, intestine, heart, and lungs; and 2) small hepatic schizonts in the macrophages of the liver.

LIFE CYCLE. Sporozoites injected by simuliid flies into the blood of ducks enter cells of the macrophage system and initiate the schizogenous phase of the life cycle.

Two types of schizonts, megaloschizonts and hepatic schizonts, are recognized. Megaloschizonts develop in the macrophages of the intestine, spleen, and heart. The developmental sequence includes the trophozoite, schizont, and segmenter. The last stage attains a large size due to the great number of merozoites. These are liberated in the blood. Apparently two generations of megaloschizonts occur. The merozoites of the second generation enter mononuclear leucocytes and transform into gametocytes. Hepatic schizonts develop in the macrophages of the liver and are much smaller than the megaloschizonts. Several generations of merozoites are produced and liberated in the blood before the appearance of those capable of developing into gametocytes.

The final generation of merozoites liberated into the blood enters the mononuclear leucocytes and develops into micro- and macrogametocytes, causing the host cells to enlarge and become elongate spindle-shaped or round forms. While normally only gametocytes are seen in the blood, merozoites also are present for a short time after the appearance of the gametocytes, but they gradually disappear. This is shown by periodic injections of blood from an infected bird into noninfected ones in which gametocytes appear in decreasing numbers until finally none can be found, showing that the merozoites have disappeared from the blood of the infected bird.

When blood, liver, or spleen taken from infected ducks 9 days after being bitten by black flies is injected into uninfected ducks, both schizonts and gametocytes develop, indicating the presence of both hepatic schizonts and megaloschizonts in the donors.

Gametogony begins in ducks with the development of the gametocytes in the blood cells and is completed in the stomach of black flies, where the gametes are formed and fertilization results in a zygote.

A motile zygote, the ookinete, migrates into the stomach wall and transforms into a thin-walled oocyst in which sporulation is completed in about 2 days in optimal temperature. The ripe oocysts rupture, releasing the sporozoites into the haemocoel. They migrate into the salivary glands and are injected into the ducks by feeding black flies.

Gametocytes are very scarce in infected adult ducks during the winter. With the onset of spring, the lengthening of the daylight periods, and the beginning of the breeding season with its internal stresses, the birds relapse and gametocytes appear in the blood. The appearance of the parasites in the blood occurs at the time the black fly vectors become active, providing a supply of gametocytes for the biting flies.

Various species of black flies serve as hosts, varying according to the region and season. *Simulium venustum* is an important host in Michigan. *S. croxtoni* and *S. euryadminiculum* transmit the infection during the spring in Ontario and *S. rugglesi* during the summer.

Black flies feeding on the relapsed ducks become infected in large numbers. When these flies feed

EXPLANATION OF PLATE 32 ⇨

A. Young microgametocyte in blood cell (presumably a macrophage). **B.** Larger microgametocyte in blood cell. **C.** Mature microgametocyte in distorted blood cell. **D.** Young macrogametocyte in blood cell. **E.** Older macrogametocyte. **F.** Mature macrogametocyte. **G.** Duck vertebrate host. **H.** Black fly *(Simuliidae)* invertebrate host.

1, Young microgametocyte; **2,** host cell; **3,** nucleus of host cell varies in shape, depending on the extent of crowding by developing gametocytes; **4,** older microgametocyte; **5,** mature microgametocyte; **6,** nucleus; **7,** young macrogametocyte; **8,** older macrogametocyte; **9,** mature macrogametocyte; **10,** nucleus.

a-z, schizogony; **a,** sporozoites injected into blood by black flies; **b,** sporozoites pass through mesenteric arteries into macrophages of intestinal wall; **c,** young megaloschizont with cytomeres; **d,** older megaloschizont with well developed cytomeres; **e,** megaloschizont with merozoites that initiate a new generation of megaloschizonts some of whose merozoites become gametocytes; **f,** sporozoites entering mononuclear leucocytes in blood stream; **g, h,** sporozoite escapes from leucocyte in blood vessels of liver and enters macrophage cells; **i-r,** schizogony in liver (also spleen); **i,** trophozoite of hepatic schizont; **j,** schizont with many groups of nuclei; **k,** schizont with cytomeres; **l,** ripe schizont with merozoites; **m,** first generation of merozoites released in blood to start second generation; **n,** merozoites enter macrophage cells of liver; **o-q,** development of second generation of merozoites (as in h-m); **o,** trophozoite; **p,** schizont with many groups of nuclei; **q,** schizont with cytomeres; **r,** second generation merozoites released into blood some of which become gametocytes; **s,** megaloschizonts in endothelial cells of liver (also spleen); **t,** megaloschizont in cardiac muscle where great numbers of them occur; **u,** merozoites from megaloschizont in heart muscle released into blood; **v-z,** megaloschizogony in lungs; **v,** merozoite leaves capillaries of lungs; **w,** merozoite enters macrophages of lungs; **x,** young schizont; **y,** cytomeres formed in schizont; **z,** release of merozoites into blood stream.

a′-c′, beginning of gametogony in ducks; **a′,** merozoites enter macrophage cells and become gametocytes; **b′,** mature microgametocyte in elongated blood cell; **c′,** macrogametocyte in elongated blood cell in circulatory system of duck.

a″-l″, completion of gametogony, and beginning and completion of sporogony in black flies; **a″,** micro- and macrogametocytes in stomach of black fly; **b″,** exflagellation of microgametocyte to form microgametes; **c″,** macrogamete; **d″,** microgamete enters macrogamete and fertilization is accomplished; **e″,** zygote; **f″,** ookinete; **g″,** ookinete migrates through intestinal wall; **h″,** young oocyst; **i″,** formation of sporoblasts in oocyst; **j″,** ripe oocyst filled with sporozoites; **k″,** oocyst wall ruptures and sporozoites are freed in haemocoel; **l″,** sporozoites migrate to and penetrate salivary glands whence they are injected into vertebrate host.

Figures A-F adapted from O'Roke, 1934, Univ. Mich. School Forestry and Conserv., Bull. 4.

---

on the newly hatched duckling, intense and fatal infections develop in them. Surviving birds become immune carriers in which schizogony is at a very low level and gametocytes in the blood are extremely rare.

In the epizootiology of leucocytozoonosis, relapses in the carrier ducks with the appearance of large numbers of gametocytes in the blood, emergence of the black flies from the streams, and the appearance of susceptible ducklings all occur simultaneously, producing ideal conditions for spreading the parasites.

EXERCISE ON LIFE CYCLE

Many species of birds are parasitized by *Leucocytozoon*. The gametocytes may be found in thin smears of blood stained with Wright's or Giemsa's stains. Young birds are more likely to show infections than old ones.

Schizogenous stages appear in sections of liver, spleen, and lungs. They include large schizonts filled with cytomeres or merozoites, depending on the age of them.

Black flies allowed to feed on infected birds show fully developed oocysts on the stomach wall in 1 to 2 days.

Studies on the transmission of the parasites to uninfected birds may be done by injecting liver or spleen cells, or blood from birds in the early stages of infection. Establishment of an infection by this means is evidence of the presence of merozoites in the donor birds. Injection of blood containing only gametocytes would not produce an infection.

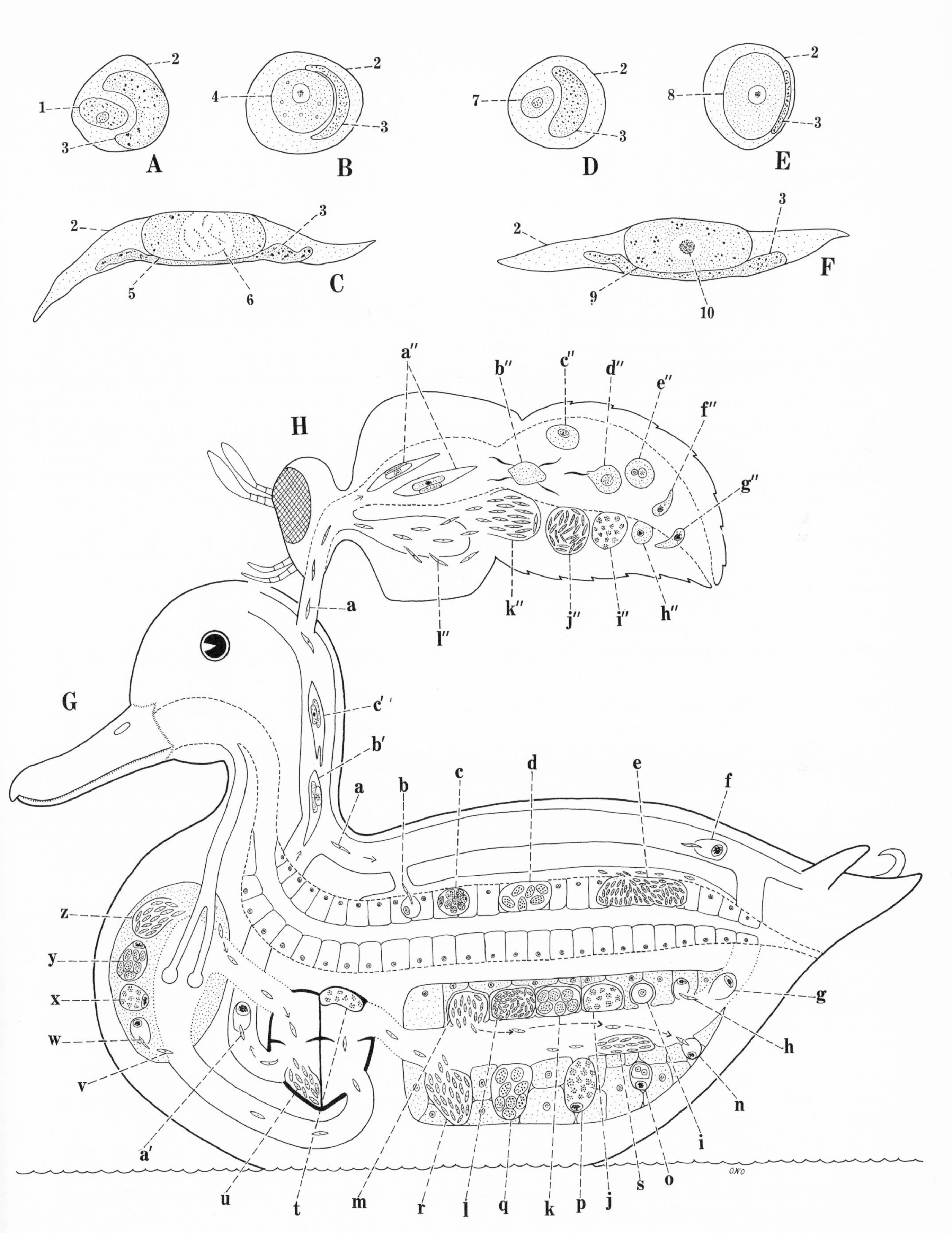
A
B
D
E
C
F
G
H
OWO

SELECTED REFERENCES

Fallis, A. M., R. C. Anderson, and G. F. Bennett. (1956). Canad. J. Zool. 34:389.

Fallis, A. M., and G. F. Bennett. (1958). Canad. J. Zool. 36:533.

Fallis, A. M., D. M. Davids, and M. A. Vickers. (1951). Canad. J. Zool. 29:305.

Huff, C. G. (1942). J. Infect. Dis. 71:18.

Levine, N. D. (1961). Protozoan Parasites of Domestic Animals and of Man. Burgess Publishing Co., Minneapolis, p. 275.

O'Roke, E. C. (1934). Univ. Mich., School of Forestry and Conserv., Bull. 4.

FAMILY BABESIIDAE

The Babesiidae are minute nonpigmented parasites of the erythrocytes of mammals. Transmission is by ticks.

Traditionally, the Babesiidae have been placed in the Sporozoa, based on the concept that sexual phases occur in their developmental cycles. Some recent workers, however, believe that sexuality does not occur. They claim, therefore, that these forms belong in a separate group. Leaving the Babesiidae in the Sporozoa, as is done here, does not in any way constitute a challenge to this point of view.

Babesia Starcovici, 1893

Species of *Babesia* occur in a variety of mammals in various parts of the world. These include rodents of many species, hares, carnivores, swine, sheep, goats, cattle, horses, and primates. Forms which may be *Babesia* are found in insectivores.

The parasites may be divided into two groups on the basis of size. Some common large species more than 3 μ long include *B. canis* (dogs), *B. caballi* (horses), *B. bigemina* (cattle), *B. motasi* (sheep), and *B. trautmani* (swine). Small species less than 3 μ long include *B. gibsoni* (dogs), *B. felis* (cats), *B. bovis* (cattle), and *B. equi* (horses).

Babesia bigemina (Babes, 1881) (Plate 33)

B. bigemina is a parasite of the erythrocytes of cattle in warm regions of the world. Its normal distribution in the United States was limited by that of its tick host (*Boophilus* (*Margaropus*) *annulatus*) which occurs in tropical and subtropical climates. Through a campaign of control, the ticks have been eradicated in the United States, thereby eliminating *Babesia* in cattle in this country.

The organism causes an acute, often fatal, disease of adult cattle known as Texas cattle fever, red water fever, or haemoglobinuria fever. The two latter names refer to the red color of the urine due to the presence of haemoglobin resulting from the massive destruction of red cells by the parasites.

DESCRIPTION. The parasites are nonpigmented organisms in the erythrocytes. Usually, they are pear-shaped but round, oval, or irregularly shaped forms appear. They are 4 μ long by 1.5 μ at the widest point. They commonly occur in pairs and are united at the pointed tips; sometimes up to four individuals are present in a single blood cell. They extend across the cell. The nucleus is small; there is a fine line of chromatin granules extending from it toward the pointed end of the parasite.

LIFE CYCLE. *Babesia bigemina* is a parasite of ticks (*Boophilus, Rhipicephalus, Haemaphysalis*) and cattle. It is transmitted to cattle by the offspring of female ticks that have fed on infected bovines.

Boophilus annulatus has but one host in its life cycle and is known as a one-host tick since all of the feeding and mating takes place on a single animal. After mating and engorging, the females drop to the ground, oviposit, and die. Larval ticks, commonly referred to as seed ticks, hatching from the eggs, climb on vegetation and attach to animals as they brush by the plants.

Parasites injected into the blood stream by the young ticks enter erythrocytes. They form first into ring-shaped and then into amoeboid trophozoites. Multiplication is by binary fission, producing two pyriform bodies which are at first attached by the pointed ends, but separate later. Upon destruction of the blood cells, they enter other erythrocytes and divide, thus continuing the cycle.

Development of the parasite in the ticks proceeds through a series of complicated stages of multiplication repeated in adult females and their young, resulting in tremendous numbers of the infective forms known as vermicules. Transmission of the parasite from the female tick to her offspring is through the eggs and is designated as transovarial.

The first report on the life cycle of *Babesia bigemina* was by Dennis. He believed the parasite to be a sporozoan in which a sexual phase appears in its life history. According to him, the isogametes in the blood of the vertebrate host conjugate in the gut lumen of engorged female ticks (*Boophilus annulatus*) to form motile zygotes. These migrate through the wall of the gut into the uterine eggs. Through a process of sporogony, the zygotes form numerous sporozoites that enter the salivary glands of larval ticks whence they are injected into the vertebrate host when these feed. He called this transovarial transmission from one generation of ticks to the next.

Regendanz and Reichenow, working on the life cycle of *Babesia canis* of dogs, could find no evidence of sexual reproduction in the tick *Dermacentor reticulatus* such as reported by Dennis. They stated that most of the forms freed from the erythrocytes in the gut of ticks died. The survivors penetrate the epithelial cells of the gut without change, grow, and divide by repeated binary fission, forming vermicules that pass into the haemolymph. These stages enter the eggs of the ticks where they divide, forming relatively few rounded forms. After hatching of the tick and its first molt to form the nymphal stage, the vermiculate bodies migrate to the cells of the salivary glands and continue development by repeated binary fission. Eventually, they enter the lumen of the salivary glands and are injected into the host by the feeding ticks. Regendanz reported that *B. bigemina* has a similar development in *Boophilus microplus*.

More recent studies by Riek on the life cycle of *Babesia bigemina* in the tick vector *Boophilus microplus* in Australia show differences from the cycles reported by Dennis and by Regendanz and Reichenow. This cycle is followed, even though all of the points are not entirely clear.

According to Riek, the trophozoites in the erythrocytes of cattle vary in shape although typically they are pyriform and paired with the pointed ends approximating each other. Generally, they are uninucleate but at times during the infection some show two nuclei, one of which stains more deeply than the other and may be extruded into the cytoplasm of the erythrocyte.

Upon ingestion of the infected blood cells by ticks, the parasites are freed by the digestive processes. Most of them show pycnotic nuclei and spikey-rayed cytoplasm. These forms are destroyed. The survivors are of three types. The most common type is 3 to 5 μ in diameter and has a large central vacuole surrounded by a thin layer of cytoplasm. The chromatin is usually arranged as a thin layer around the periphery of the parasite but it may also appear as a dot at each pole, or a single or double dot. The second and comparatively rare form has three to four separate chromatin bodies around the periphery. It divides into as many elongated spindle-shaped bodies as there are nuclei, each bearing a central nucleus and measuring 4 to 7 μ long by 1 to 2 μ wide. The third form, likewise, is spherical and has two nuclei, one of which is elongated and located at the periphery, and the other is round. The origin of this cell is uncertain but Riek suggested that it may be the result of union of the uninucleate round type mentioned first and the spindle-shaped cells arising from division of the second multinucleate type. He pointed out, however, that the true relationship of these cells in the life cycle is not entirely clear. It should be recalled that Regendanz and Reichenow did not observe this type of transformation of the trophozoites in the gut of the replete female ticks.

Toward the end of 24 hours, the developmental stages appear as blunt cigar-shaped bodies 8 to 10 μ long with a central nucleus. They penetrate the epithelial cells of the gut and develop into spherical bodies 9 to 16 μ in diameter. During the second day they undergo multiple fission of the nucleus, with the chromatin being distributed as numerous small dots throughout the cytoplasm. A ring of cytoplasm surrounds each nuclear particle, forming small nucleated bodies 3 to 6 μ in diameter. On the third day these small bodies develop into vermicules, measuring 9 to 13 μ long by 2 to 3 μ wide, which migrate from the epithelial cells of the gut into the haemolymph. After 4 days the vermicules enter the cells of the Malpighian tubules, round up, and undergo multiple fission similar to that occurring in the gut epithelium. The resultant vermicules, which are similar to their predecessors, migrate to the eggs. At first they are scattered in the yolk, but as the larval ticks develop they enter epithelial cells of the gut where multiple fission of the nucleus takes place and more vermicules are formed. Upon rupture of the infected epithelial cells, these vermicules enter the gut lumen and the haemolymph, presumably remaining there during the larval stage which is 5 to 7 days after attachment. They migrate to the salivary glands of the nymphs, round up, grow in size, and undergo multiple nuclear division. Enormous

EXPLANATION OF PLATE 33 ▷

A. Bovine host. **B.** Tangential section of adult female tick attached to host. **C.** Unembryonated egg. **D.** Embryonated egg. **E.** Larval tick attached to host. **F.** Nymphal tick attached to host.

1, chelicera; **2,** infected erythrocytes being swallowed; **3,** parasites escaping from erythrocyte in stomach; **4,** spherical multinucleate parasite developed from pyriform stage in erythrocytes; **5,** spindle-shaped stage presumably resulting from division of multinucleate sphere (4); **6,** uninucleate cell probably originating from pyriform stage in red blood cells; **7,** binucleate spherical cell believed to result from union of spindle-shaped cell (5) and uninucleate spherical cell (6); **8,** vermiform stage thought to develop from binucleate sphere (7); **9,** vermicule in intestinal epithelium; **10,** multifission of nuclear material; **11,** formation of vermicules from multifission body; **12,** rupture of cell, releasing vermicules into haemocoel; **13,** vermicule from intestinal generation in cells of Malpighian tubules; **14,** multifission of nuclear material in Malpighian tubules; **15,** rupturing Malpighian cell with release of vermicules into haemocoel; **16,** egg in ovary; **17-19,** vermicules accumulating in developing eggs in ovary, oviduct, and uterus; **20,** unparasitized mature egg; **21,** vagina; **22,** rectum; **23,** coxa; **24-28,** details of development of parasites in intestinal epithelium of adult female tick; **24,** vermicule in cell; **25,** spherical stage with nuclear material increasing in amount; **26,** multifission stage; **27,** formation of vermicules; **28,** individual vermicule free in haemocoel; **29-34,** stages of development in cells of Malpighian tubules of adult female tick; **29,** vermicule in cell; **30-31,** growth with increase in the amount of nuclear material; **32,** multifission of nuclear material; **33,** formation of vermicules in cells of Malpighian tubules; **34,** vermicule free in haemolymph; **35,** vermicules in yolk of undeveloped egg; **36,** egg shell; **37,** unhatched larva; **38,** intestine; **39-42,** growth of parasite in intestinal epithelium of unhatched larval tick; **39,** vermicule; **40,** vermicule inside cell; **41,** growth of chromatin material; **42,** multifission of chromatin; **43,** formation of vermicules; **44-48,** details of development in intestinal epithelium of unhatched larval tick; **44,** vermicule in cell; **45,** increase of chromatin material; **46,** multifission of nuclear body; **47,** fully developed stage with vermicules; **48,** free vermicule in haemolymph; **49,** vermicules in intestinal epithelium of feeding larva (E); **50,** rupture of infected cell, freeing vermicules in haemolymph; **51-59,** development in salivary glands of nymph; **51,** vermicule in haemolymph; **52,** vermicule entering salivary gland; **53,** vermicule in cell of salivary gland; **54-55,** growth of chromatin; **56,** multiple fission of nuclear material; **57,** vermicules in cells; **58,** rupture of cell with liberation of vermicules in lumen of salivary glands; **59,** vermicules being injected into vertebrate host by feeding nymph; **60-65,** details of developmental forms in salivary cells in nymphal stages; **60,** vermicule in cell; **61-62,** growth of chromatin; **63,** multifission of nuclear material; **64,** formation of short oval vermicules; **65,** details of vermicules in lumen of salivary glands which are infective to erythrocytes when injected into vertebrate host.

a, parasite injected by tick, entering erythrocyte; **b,** "ring" stage; **c,** amoeboid form; **d-e,** trophozoites in stages of binary fission; **f,** two trophozoites escaping into blood stream from destroyed erythrocyte and ready to enter other erythrocytes.

Figures adapted from various sources, including Riek, 1954, Aust. J. Agr. Res. 15:802; A, original.

---

numbers of minute pyriform bodies about 2 to 3 μ long by 1 to 2 μ wide are produced. These are injected into the host by the feeding nymphs. The parasites appear in the erythrocytes 8 to 10 days after larval attachment which is one to five days after the onset of the nymphal stage.

This complicated life cycle may be summarized in four steps as follows: 1) binary fission of trophozoites occurs in the erythrocytes of the bovine host; 2) trophozoites ingested by adult female ticks undergo growth and a process of multifission in the epithelial cells of the gut, producing vermiculate bodies that enter the cells of the Malpighian tubules and repeat multifission; vermicules from the Malpighian tubules enter and accumulate in developing eggs; 3) vermicules in the yolk migrate to the gut epithelium of the larval ticks (seed ticks), grow, undergo multifission, and are released into the haemolymph; and 4) the vermicules invade the salivary glands of newly formed nymphal ticks, grow, and divide by multifission to form vermiculate progeny that are injected into the vertebrate host by feeding nymphs and subsequent developmental stages of the ticks.

While *Babesia bigemina* is transmitted by a one-host tick in America, one-, two-, and three-host ticks serve as vectors in other parts of the world. Transovarial transmission occurs only in the one-host ticks.

Inasmuch as all stages of the one-host ticks, including the adults, remain on one animal and do all of their feeding on it, direct transmission from one host to another by them does not occur. When the gravid females drop to the ground, they die following oviposition. In the process of their develop-

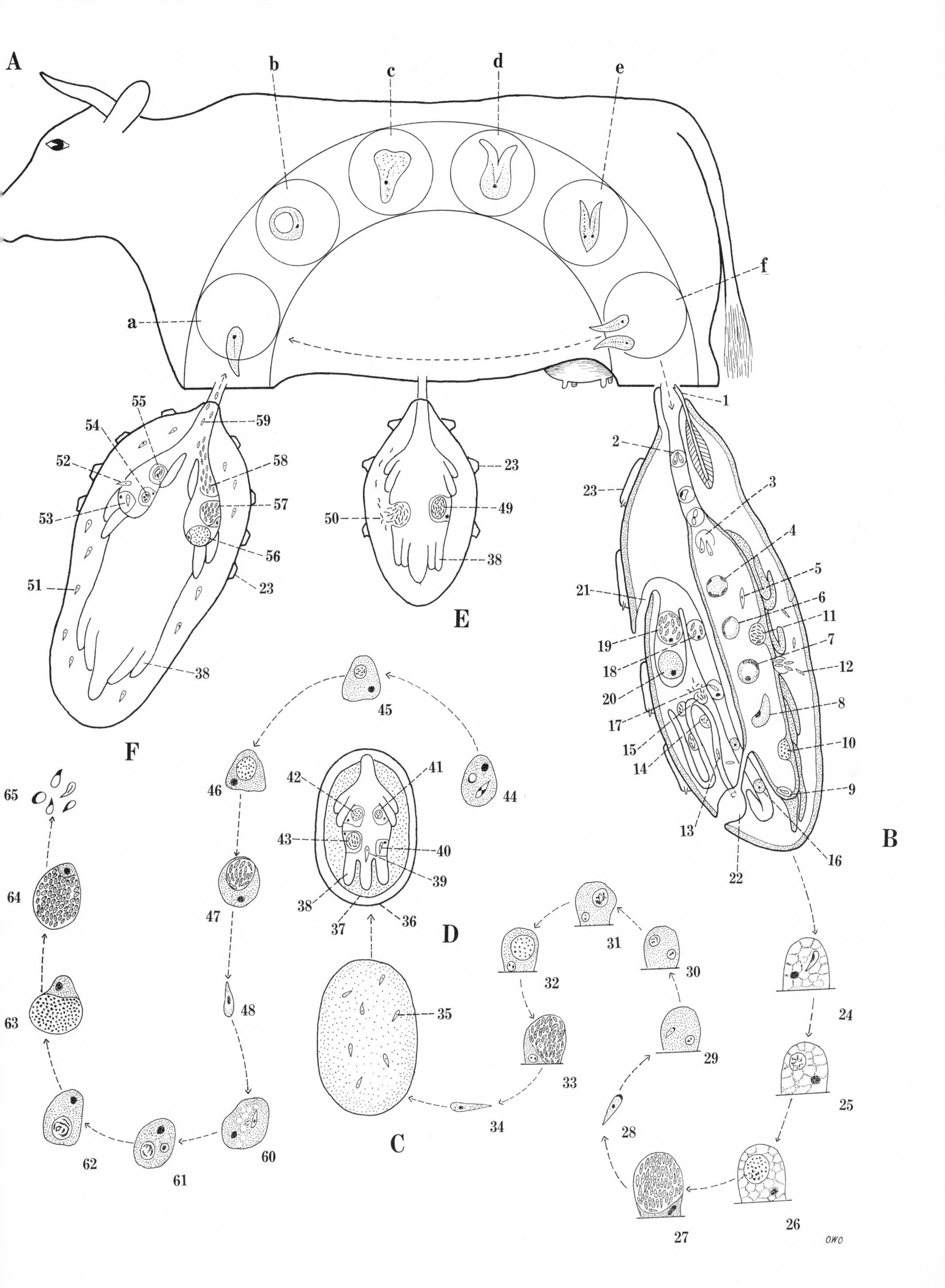
A
a
b
c
d
e
f
B
C
D
E
F
OWO

ment, the babesias go to the eggs in the female and the salivary glands of the larvae which transmit them to a new host.

In the two-host tick, the larvae and nymphs feed on a parasitized host, become infected, and drop to the ground to molt to the adult stage. The infected adults, upon re-attaching to and feeding on another animal, transmit the disease.

In the three-host ticks, each stage feeds, drops to the ground, molts, and re-attaches to feed again. Thus, infection acquired in any stage of the ticks may be transmitted by the next one.

Because of this change of animals by the two-and three-host ticks, transovarial transmission is unnecessary and, indeed, does not occur.

Other species of babesiids occurring in cattle, sheep, goats, horses, swine, primates, elephants, dogs, cats, hyenas, civets, mice, rats, and hares in various parts of the world are given by Doflein and Reichenow.

EXERCISE ON LIFE CYCLE

Where babesiids can be found in dogs or rodents, observations may be made on the growth of trophozoites in the erythrocytes. The stages in the ticks may be detected in stained smears of the organs in which the developing forms occur.

SELECTED REFERENCES

Dennis, E. W. (1930). Calif. Publ. Zool. 33:179. Ibid. 36:263.

Doflein, F., and E. Reichenow. (1953). Lehrbuch der Protozoenkunde, 6th Ed. Gustav Fischer, Jena, p. 957.

Lapage, G. (1956). Veterinary Parasitology. Oliver and Boyd, London, p. 813.

Levine, N. D. (1961). Protozoan Parasites of Domestic Animals and of Man. Burgess Publishing Co., Minneapolis, p. 275.

Regendanz, P. (1936). Zbl. Bakt. (Orig.) 137:423.

Regendanz, P., and E. Reichenow. (1933). Arch. Protistenk. 79:50.

Reichenow, E. (1935). Zbl. Bakt. (Orig.) 135:108.

Riek, R. F. (1964). Aust. J. Agr. Res. 15:802.

Theileria Bettencourt, Franca, and Borges, 1907

This genus is related to *Babesia* but the life cycle of its species is different. They are parasites of the red blood cells of cattle in South, Central, and East Africa and of deer in North America. While several species have been described on doubtful morphological features, it is more likely that only one species consisting of different strains exists.

Theileria parva (Theileria, 1904) (Plate 34)

These parasites are the cause of a disease of cattle known as African East Coast fever. Ticks serve as the vectors.

DESCRIPTION. The forms occurring in the erythrocytes appear as rings, ovals, comma-shaped bodies, or rods, the last shape predominating. Giemsa-stained smears show a small red nucleus at one end of the rod, with blue cytoplasm extending as a short blunt rod somewhat narrower than the diameter of the nucleus. They measure 0.5 to 1.0 μ wide by 1.5 to 2.0 μ long.

Actively multiplying forms occur in the endothelial cells and lymphocytes. They are known as Koch's blue bodies, appearing as irregularly shaped masses of cytoplasm with a diameter of 10 to 12 μ or more. The blue cytoplasmic masses contain varying numbers of red chromatin dots derived from a series of binary fissions of the nucleus. As growth continues, each minute nucleus becomes enclosed in a small bit of cytoplasm to form the small bodies that penetrate the erythrocytes, other lymphocytes, or endothelial cells.

LIFE CYCLE. The principal vector is the brown cattle tick *Rhipicephalus appendiculatus*. It is a three-host tick, *i.e.*, each stage (larva, nymph, and adult) feeds, drops to the ground to molt, and re-attaches to a bovine host for the next blood meal preparatory to molting or ovipositing. All of this may take place on a single animal or on several different ones. In any event, the ticks must leave the animal for each molt and to oviposit.

Ticks become infected upon ingestion of parasitized erythrocytes containing the small rod-shaped bodies. While taking their first blood meal from infected cattle, the seed or larval ticks ingest infected erythrocytes. Upon entry into the intestine, the red blood cells are digested and the parasites liberated. Having fed, the larvae drop to the ground where they molt and transform into nymphs. During this time, the parasites that survive digestion or escape phagocytosis by the intestinal cells migrate through the gut wall into the haemolymph and swim to the salivary glands, which they penetrate. In the secretory cells, they round up and the nucleus undergoes a series of binary fissions, forming numerous minute chromatin granules. Each one is surrounded by a bit of cytoplasm, forming a small, uninucleate, oval body. When the nymph attaches to the host and begins feeding, all of these bodies enter the lumen of the salivary ducts and are injected into the tissues. At the same time, other infected erythrocytes are ingested. When the nymph drops off the host and molts into an adult, the parasites migrate to the salivary glands and multiply in the same manner as described for the nymph, resulting in destruction of the glandular cells. When the adults feed, all of the parasites in the ducts of the glands are injected into the blood, leaving none in the body of the tick for transovarial transmission by the females to their progeny, since the parasites cannot develop in the absence of the glandular cells. Hence larval ticks hatching from eggs laid by the females are uninfected.

Upon injection of the infective forms from the salivary glands by feeding ticks, they enter the lymph vessels and attack the lymphocytes where they undergo a large number of divisions by binary fission, forming 100 to 250 individuals. Each nucleus is surrounded by a small amount of cytoplasm. At first they adhere as a mass giving the appearance of a blue cytoplasmic body filled with red nuclei when stained by the Giemsa method. Growth of the parasites results in rupture of the lymphocyte and liberation of them. They enter both lymphocytes and erythrocytes. Since the latter cells are the more numerous, many of them are infected. Parasites entering the lymphocytes undergo a series of binary fissions, forming the so-called Koch's blue bodies as described above. Those in the erythrocytes do not multiply. They are the stages infective to the ticks.

In this cycle, each stage of the three-host tick may acquire infection from the bovine host while taking food, except the adult whose secretory cells have been destroyed by the parasites.

SELECTED REFERENCES

Reichenow, E. (1940). Arch. Protistenk. 94:1.

Richardson, U. F., and S. B. Kendall. (1957). Veterinary Protozoology, Oliver and Boyd, London, p. 160.

Toxoplasma Nicolle and Manceaux, 1908

Toxoplasma is a worldwide parasite of birds and mammals, including humans and domestic animals. It is primarily intracellular, occurring in the reticuloendothelial cells of the lungs, liver, spleen, mononuclear leucocytes, in striated muscle cells, both cardiac and skeletal, and in cells of the central nervous system. They occur free in the blood and peritoneal exudate during acute infections.

Toxoplasma gondii Nicolle and Manceaux, 1908 (Plate 35)

The minute crescent-shaped bodies, somewhat pointed at the anterior and rounded at the posterior end, were discovered in the gondi (*Ctenodactylus gondi*), a small North African histricomorphous rodent, and named *Toxoplasma gondii.* Subsequently, similar forms were found in many different kinds of mammals and birds and numerous species named. On the basis of similarity in structure and non-specificity for hosts, as shown by the ease with which cross-infections take place, only one species, *T. gondii* is recognized.

DESCRIPTION. The parasite appears in two forms, the trophozoite which is highly proliferative and the resistant stage which constitutes the terminal form in cysts.

The trophozoite consists of a small crescent-shaped body somewhat pointed at the anterior and broadly rounded at the posterior end. The surrounding membrane is double. The size varies greatly, according to measurements given in the literature, and may represent differences in stages of development. They range from 2.5 to 12 μ long, 1 to 4 μ wide. The vesicular nucleus with a small karyosome

EXPLANATION OF PLATE 34 ▷

A. Bovine host. **B.** Tick egg. **C.** Empty egg shell. **D.** Newly hatched and unfed larval tick. **E.** Feeding larval tick with infected erythrocytes in stomach. **F.** Detached larval tick on ground that has just molted to nymphal stage, with dividing parasites in salivary glands. **G.** Feeding nymph injects all parasites into bovine host. **H.** Cleaned nymph in Figure G ingesting infected red blood cells. **I.** Detached nymph on ground molting to adult, with dividing parasites in salivary glands. **J.** Feeding infected adult tick injects parasites into bovine and becomes free of them. **K.** Clean gravid female lays eggs which hatch into uninfected larvae.

1, uninfected salivary glands; **2,** salivary glands with dividing parasites; **3,** salivary glands containing infective fusiform parasites; **4,** exhausted uninfected salivary glands; **5,** empty stomach; **6,** extended stomach of engorged tick; **7,** anus; **8,** infected erythrocytes in stomach of recently fed tick; **9,** exuvia; **10,** developing uterus; **11,** gravid uterus filled with eggs; **12,** vulva.

a, erythrocyte being parasitized; **b,** infected erythrocyte; **c,** lymphocyte; **d,** Koch's blue body in lymphocyte; **e,** Koch's blue body escaping from ruptured lymphocyte; **f,** Koch's blue body free in lymph and blood vessels; **g,** parasite entering lymphocyte; **h,** parasites in lymphocyte; **i,** parasites injected into bovine host by feeding tick; **j,** parasites leaving Koch's blue body; **k,** ingestion of erythrocytes by ticks.

Figure A original; others redrawn from Richardson and Kendall, 1957, Veterinary Protozoology, Oliver and Boyd, London, p. 162.

---

is surrounded by a double membrane and is located near the middle of the body. Some variation in shape may appear, depending on the fixative and stain used and the stage of development of the cell. A clump of small granules appears in the posterior end of cells stained with silver protein.

In whole specimens stained with silver protein and photographs taken with the electron microscope, a small circular opening, the polar ring, shows at the anterior extremity. A pointed structure projects from the polar ring in trophozoites fixed in weak formalin.

Within the anterior end of the cell is a truncated hollow cone, the conoid, whose forward end opens into the polar ring and hind end is in contact with the cytoplasm. Fourteen to 18 evenly spaced fibrils, the toxonemes, originate inside the conoid and extend caudad through the cytoplasm, enlarging as they approach the posterior end of the cell. In addition to the toxonemes, other fibrils originating on the outer surface of the conoid extend posteriorly along the inner surface of the cell membrane or perhaps within it. Both the toxonemes and fibrils may have a kinetic function.

The cyst wall of the resistant stage stains with silver and periodic acid-Schiff techniques, indicating parasite origin. Electron microscope studies of young cysts show that the wall is composed of small vesicular and membranous profiles, or projections, embedded in opaque matter that extends inward between the parasites as septa. The outer surface of the wall consists of membranous projections that blend into the endoplasm of the host cell. In older cysts, the wall is similar but due to compression is more opaque.

LIFE CYCLE. The life cycle is incompletely known. Experimental evidence shows that infective stages are passed in the faeces of infected cats and are capable of surviving under favorable conditions up to 12 months and cause infection when eaten by mice. Concepts of the way in which it takes place will be discussed below in connection with the epidemiology.

Trophozoites invade cells of all kinds, as observed in cultures of various kinds of tissue. Multiplication takes place rapidly inside the cells. As a result of the great number of parasites in them, the host cells rupture and the trophozoites are liberated. They appear free in the blood and peritoneal exudate during the early stage and acute phase of infection. Invasion of other cells takes place.

While multiplication has been considered to take place by longitudinal fission, rosette formation, and internal budding, only the last method is generally accepted at present as the means of reproduction.

Trophozoites stained with silver protein and observed as whole specimens under the light microscope or in electron microscope photographs show internal budding or endodyogeny (endo = internal, dyo = two, genesis = reproduction). In the process of reproduction, two budlike processes appear on the anterior margin of the nucleoplasm. As growth continues, they become detached, forming daughter cells similar to the parent that encloses them. As growth proceeds in an anterior direction, the daughter cells attain greater size, acquire a conoid, limiting membrane, and nucleus. Eventually the parent cell is destroyed

A
B
C
D
E
F
G
H
I
J
K

EXPLANATION OF PLATE 35

A. Trophozoite from peritoneal exudate of mouse. **B.** Trophozoites inside macrophage. **C.** Diagrammatic reconstruction of trophozoite based on electron micrographs. **D.** Cross-section of trophozoite through region of conoid. **E-P.** Process of endodyogeny or schizogony, as shown by specimens stained with silver protein. **E.** Rodlike structure from anterior end of specimen fixed in weak formalin. **F.** Undividing form, showing nature of nucleus. **G.** Apical ring or opening shown. **H-O.** Dividing stages. **H-J.** Early stages of division, daughter cells without nuclei. **K.** Each daughter cell with a nucleus. **L.** Daughter cells have grown anteriorly and show apical rings, parent nucleus not seen. **M.** Similar stage to L but parent nucleus without endosome. **N.** Daughter cells outside parent cell but still attached along entire longitudinal axis of body. **O.** Daughter cells outside parent cell, pulling apart. **P-U.** Schematic representation of process of endodyogeny of trophozoite. **P.** Parent cell in resting stage. **Q.** Formation of daughter cells as two budlike processes originating from parent nucleoplasm. **R.** Growth of daughter cells, disappearance of parent nucleoplasm, and appearance of endosome in daughter cells. **S.** Continued growth and forward extension of daughter cells and formation of complete nucleus in each. **T.** Rupture of parent cell and emergence of daughter cells. **U.** Daughter cells free from parent cell but still attached along longitudinal axis of body. **V.** Longitudinal section through two toxoplasms inside vacuole of host cell. **W.** Dividing toxoplasm in rosette formation around central mass. **X.** Life cycle, showing multiplication of trophozoites in cells and formation of cysts following development of antibodies.

1, nucleus of parent cell; **2,** nucleolus of parent cell; **3,** nucleus of daughter cell; **4,** nucleolus of daughter cell; **5,** nucleus of host cell; **6,** toxoplasms in macrophage cell; **7,** apical ring; **8,** conoid; **9,** submembranous fibril; **10,** toxonemes; **11,** mitochondrium; **12,** double outer membrane of toxoplasm; **13,** double membrane of nucleus; **14,** wall of vacuole in host cell containing parasites; **15,** vacuole in cytoplasm of parasite; **16,** Golgi complex; **17,** endoplasmic reticulum; **18,** vacuole of host cell containing parasites; **19,** residual cytoplasmic body of cell rosette; **20,** toxoplasms surrounding residual cytoplasmic body.

a-m, life cycle; **a,** rapid proliferation of parasites for a few days in host cells, often referred to as proliferative stage; **b,** entrance of parasite into host cell; **c-d,** multiplication in host cell; **e,** destruction of host cell and liberation of parasites to infect more cells (b); **f,** development of immunity resulting from cycle in proliferative phase (a); **g,** phase in life cycle when cysts are formed due to immunity in which proliferation is within cysts over a period of week; **h,** infection of host cell; **i,** formation of cyst (commonly designated as pseudocyst) of parasite origin with multiplication of cells within; **j-k,** continued multiplication of parasites in cyst inside host cell; **l,** host cell degenerates leaving cyst filled with parasites; rupture of cyst liberates parasites and leaves scar; **m,** after decline of immunity, liberated parasites through rupture of cell initiate new proliferative (a) and cystic (g) cycles.

Figures D, V, W, X redrawn from electron micrographs by Gavin, Wanko, and Jacobs, 1962, J. Protozool. 9:222; E-P and Q-U, from Goldman, Carver, and Sulzer, 1958, J. Parasit. 44:161; others original.

---

and the daughter cells are released while still attached to each other on the long axis of their bodies. The fate of the parent cell is uncertain. Budding is interpreted as a type of schizogony in which two merozoites are formed.

The presence of numerous trophozoites results in the production of antibodies which in turn appear to influence the development of the succeeding forms. These are small in size and enclosed in intracellular double-walled cysts whose inner wall, at least, is a parasite origin. The cysts are commonly in neuroglial cells but may appear elsewhere.

Cysts containing resistant forms are of two types. In one, the parasites are few in number, oval in shape, and loosely aggregated. In the other type, the organisms are numerous and tightly packed together. In each case, the cyst appears as a double wall. From the inner one, septa extend into the cyst, separating each of the organisms from its neighbor. The outer one sends membraneous projections into the cytoplasm of the host cell. The inner cyst is of parasite origin and the outer one probably results from an interaction between the parasite and the host cell. Reproduction in the resistant cysts is restricted greatly and limited to endodyogeny.

The routes of infection of new hosts is not well understood in all cases. It appears definite that intrauterine infection occurs in humans and other mammals. The fact that trophozoites are quickly destroyed by the action of digestive juices and the resistant forms survive for several hours suggests that the latter are the infective stages and that the route of entrance might be through the intestinal wall. The difficulty here is that herbivorous animals are infected as frequently as carnivorous ones. Cysts occur in both the lungs and intestine. For this reason, the contaminative method of infection

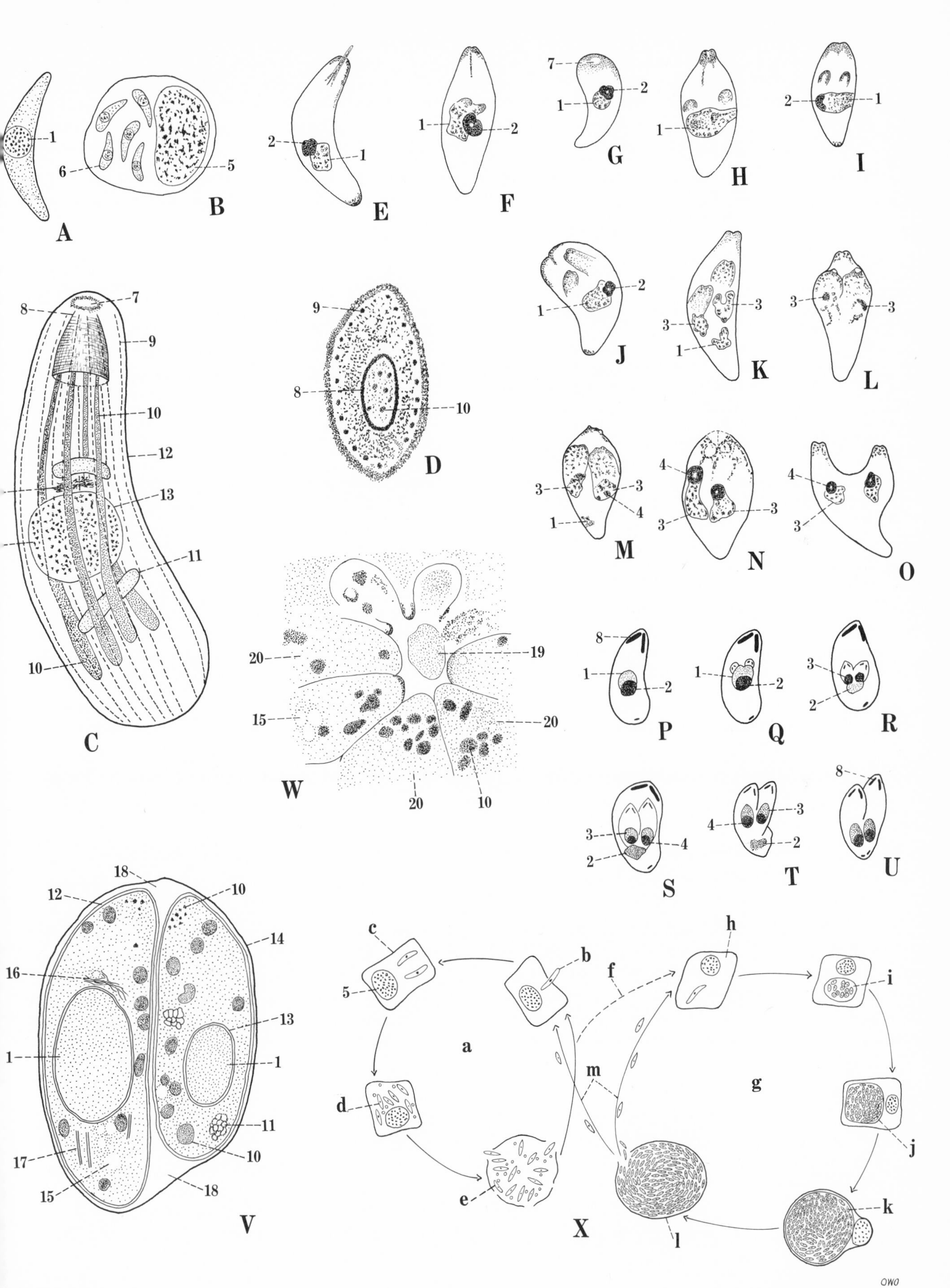
A
B
C
D
E
F
G
H
I
J
K
L
M
N
O
P
Q
R
S
T
U
V
W
X
a
b
c
d
e
f
g
h
i
j
k
l
m
OWO

needs to be explored further. The greater frequency of infection in warm, moist regions than in cold dry ones lends weight to the contaminative route.

As a pathogen, *T. gondii* produces severe disease in humans. In the congenital type contracted during the uterine existence, newborn children suffer from hydrocephalus resulting in idiocy and chorioretinitis with blindness or impaired vision. Mortality is high. Human toxoplasmosis acquired postnatally is manifested by four major types: 1) lymphadenopathy, 2) typhus-like disease, 3) cerebrospinal involvement, and 4) infection of the retina (chronic chorioretinitis). Mortality is low.

SELECTED REFERENCES

Frenkel, J. K., and L. Jacobs. (1958). A. M. A. Arch. Ophthal. 59:260.

Goldman, M., R. K. Carver, and A. J. Sulzer. (1958). J. Parasit. 42:161.

Hutchinson, W. M. (1965). Nature 206:961.

Jacobs, L. (1956). Ann. N. Y. Acad. Sci. 64:154; (1957). Public Health Rep. 72:872; (1963). Ann. Rev. Microbiol. 17:429.

Levine, N. D. (1961). Protozoan Parasites of Domestic Animals and of Man. Burgess Publishing Co., Minneapolis, p. 325.

Remington, J. S., L. Jacobs, and H. E. Kaufman. (1960). New Eng. J. Med. 262:180, 237.

Wanko, T., L. Jacobs, and M. A. Gavin. (1962). J. Protozool. 9:235.

Subclass Acnidosporida

The sporozoans in this group are simple in structure. The spores consist of a membrane and sporoplasm. They are widespread and very common parasites of the muscles of reptiles, birds, and mammals.

ORDER SARCOSPORIDIA

Sarcosporidia form compartmentalized sarcocysts of varying shape, usually oval or elongate, that contain banana-shaped bodies known as spores, sporozoites, schizozoites, trophozoites, or Rainey's corpuscles. Sarcosporidia are now believed not to be Sporozoa; however, they are treated as such here.

The sarcocysts are known as Miescher's tubes. If elongated in shape, they normally lie parallel with the muscle fibers. Calcified sarcocysts are opaque and visible to the naked eye, whereas living ones can be seen only with the aid of a microscope.

The parasites are very common in cattle, horses, sheep, and swine but probably do not occur in dogs and cats, a few reports notwithstanding. They are prevalent in the breast muscles of ducks. Usually the sarcocysts are only a few millimeters in length, but may attain the size of a walnut in sheep and a fist in horses.

Sarcocystis Lankester, 1882 (Plate 36)

While many species have been named, probably there are actually very few. Identification is based on the host in which they occur, the structure of the sarcocyst wall, and the size of the trophozoites.

The most commonly found species are *S. tenella* of sheep, *S. miescheriana* of swine, *S. muris* of mice, and *S. rileyi* of ducks, especially wild mallards. The best known species is *S. tenella* Railliet, 1886.

The genus will be treated as a group rather than selecting a single species.

DESCRIPTION. The wall of the sarcocyst is composed of two layers. The structure of the outer one falls into three basic types. In *S. muris* of mice, it is smooth throughout the development and duration of the sarcocyst. In *S. tenella* of sheep, the wall of young sarcocysts is thin at first, followed by the development of a roughened, bristle-like outer covering which is striated in appearance in sections, and which disappears as the cyst matures, being replaced by a smooth membrane. In *S. platydactyli* of geckos, the outer layer is covered permanently with thin, hollow, finger-like extensions known as cytophaneres which extend to the surrounding muscles. The inner layer extends inward, as septa, forming separate compartments within the cyst. Cells in the outer compartments are hexagonal through crowding. Growth of them results in the formation of banana-shaped trophozoites toward the center of the cyst. In mature sarcocysts, the central portion may be empty. Whether the trophozoites have escaped or been destroyed is unknown (Figs. I, M, N, O).

Mature banana-shaped trophozoites measure from 6 to 15 μ long by 2 to 4 μ wide. They are capable of flexing movements and gliding. Through use of the electron microscope and histochemistry, much has been learned regarding detailed structure and function of parts of the trophozoites. One of the results of these studies has shown that the Sarcosporidia probably are not Sporozoa, as formerly thought.

The body of the trophozoite may be divided into three parts, based on internal structure. The anterior third consists of the fibrillar section since the interior is filled with 300 to 500 minute fibrils called sarconemes (Figs. A, C). At the anterior end is a ringlike opening, the polar ring, from which fibrils originate and extend embedded in the pellicle to the posterior end of the trophozoite (Fig. B). Within the polar ring is a hollow cone-shaped structure, the conoid. Midway in the fibrillar section and on the convex side is a discoid granule. The middle third of the body is filled with large granules and is called the granular region. Dispersed among the large granules are small ones, some of which contain volutin and others, ribonucleic acid (RNA). The posterior end, or third, of the body contains the nucleus, several mitochondria, granules, and vacuoles. This region is the most active chemically. Granules in the nucleus contain RNA. The entire posterior region is positive for polysaccharides and glycogen.

LIFE CYCLE. While much work has been done on the life history of various species of Sarcosporidia, especially *S. tenella* and *S. muris*, actually it is not well understood. Scott analyzed all the literature dealing with studies, including his own, on the life cycle of various species. He concluded that while many erroneous statements occurred, a basic pattern could be seen, especially for *S. tenella* of sheep which has been studied the most intensively. The life cycle outlined below refers primarily to that of *S. tenella* and represents what is agreed generally as being feasible, based on present knowledge.

The life cycle is direct, being completed without the necessity of an intermediary, and appears to have no sexual stages in it. Trophozoites have been demonstrated in the faeces and nasal secretions of sheep. Water and food contaminated with trophozoites provide direct means of infection of sheep which swallow them. Claims are made that mice may be infected by feeding muscle tissue containing sarcocysts, but Scott raises some doubts based on what he considers inadequate controls.

Upon entering the alimentary canal, the trophozoites migrate between the epithelial cells of the intestine where they enter the lymphatics and blood vessels. They have been recovered from the blood of sheep. Upon entering the circulation, they are carried to all parts of the body to enter cardiac and skeletal muscles, especially those in the oesophagus. In the muscle cells, the trophozoites become rounded, forming "amoeboid" bodies which probably undergo repeated binary fission, forming rounded, tightly packed trophoblasts. As growth of the sarcocyst continues, folds of the internal wall extend inward as septa, forming numerous compartments filled with trophoblasts. The trophoblasts divide to produce the banana-shaped trophozoites. These, in turn, multiply by repeated binary fission, beginning at the conoid.

As the cysts mature, the septa in the internal part break down and there are no trophozoites in that region. Whether the trophozoites have been destroyed or have escaped is uncertain. Upon reaching maturity, the cysts rupture and escaping trophozoites enter the blood. Those reaching the intestine work through the wall and enter the lumen to be voided with the faeces. Apparently, they pass through linings of other cavities of the body such as the lungs, nasal passages, and mouth since trophozoites appear in nasal secretions.

On the basis of feeding experiments, it appears that trophozoites passed in the faeces require time outside the host in which further changes are necessary before they can infect sheep. Infection occurs when the mature infective trophozoites are swallowed with food and water. Based on seasonal appearance of sarcocysts in lambs, Scott believed that under certain conditions at definite times infective trophozoites are produced in the intestine which are capable of infecting sheep by way of the alimentary canal. The length of time from ingesting trophozoites until the appearance of the sarcocysts in the muscles of mice is around 6 weeks. It is uncertain for other species.

EXERCISE ON LIFE CYCLE

Sarcocysts obtained from the oesophagi of sheep, the breast muscles of ducks, or skeletal muscles

EXPLANATION OF PLATE 36 ⇨

A. Mature banana-shaped sarcosporidian cell reconstructed from electron micrographs. **B.** Anterior end of sarcosporidian cell. **C.** Cross-section through fibrillar region (anterior third of body). **D-H.** Developing stages of *Sarcocystis tenella* in muscle. **D.** Young unicellular stage. **E.** Young multinucleate stage. **F.** Cross-section of young sarcocyst, showing fibrillar outer layer and sporoblasts. **G-H.** Progressively older unicameral sarcocyst. **I.** Diagrammatic sketch of cross-section of mature sarcocyst. **J.** Diagrammatic sketch of oesophagus of sheep, showing large sarcocysts of *S. tenella* embedded in muscle. **K.** Sarcocyst of *S. miescheriana* of swine. **L.** Diagrammatic sketch of piece of breast muscle of mallard duck, showing calcified sarcocysts. **M.** Portion of sarcocyst of *S. tenella* of sheep, showing structure of wall. **N.** Portion of sarcocyst of *S. platydactyli* of gecko, showing structure of wall. **O.** Portion of sarcocyst of *S. muris* of mouse, showing smooth wall. **P.** Sheep host of *S. tenella.*

1, fibrillar region (anterior third of body) ; **2,** granular region (middle third of body) ; **3,** nuclear and mitochondrial region (posterior third of body) ; **4,** polar ring; **5,** conoid; **6,** fibril; **7,** sarconemes; **8,** granules; **9,** vacuoles; **10,** mitochondrium; **11,** nucleus with chromatin granules; **12,** nucleolus; **13,** double membrane of sarcocyst; **14,** host muscle; **15,** fibrillar outer layer of sarcocyst; **16,** sporoblasts; **17,** sporocysts; **18,** developing trophozoites; **19,** mature trophozoites in compartments of sarcocyst; **20,** envelope formed by host surrounding sarcocyst; **21,** external spongy layer of sarcocyst; **22,** internal layer extends into sarcocyst as septa, forming compartments; **23,** hollow finger-like cytophaneres of external layer of sarcocyst; **24,** smooth outer layer of sarcocyst; **25,** empty central portion of mature sarcocyst; **26,** calcified sarcocyst in breast muscle of mallard duck; **27,** connective tissue layer.

a, intact sarcocyst in wall of oesophagus; **b,** ruptured sarcocyst liberating trophozoites (black ones) ; **c,** trophozoites in venous blood; **d,** trophozoites passing through right side of heart; **e,** trophozoites passing through lungs; **f,** trophozoites entering dorsal aorta; **g,** trophozoites passing through mesenteric artery into arterioles of intestinal wall; **h,** trophozoites entering lumen of intestine; **i,** trophozoites leaving intestine with faeces; **j,** faecal pellets bearing trophozoites; **k,** trophozoites on faeces; **l,** faecal pellets contaminate forage and water with trophozoites; **m-n,** ingestion of trophozoites (clear ones) with contaminated food and water; **o,** entry of ingested trophozoites into small intestine, having passed through oesophagus and four parts of stomach; **p,** penetration of trophozoites through intestinal epithelium, entering capillaries and venules of hepatic portal system; **q,** trophozoites in hepatic portal vein; **r-s,** trophozoites passing through liver and hepatic vein; **t,** trophozoites in right auricle; **u,** trophozoites passing through capillaries of lungs; **v-w,** trophozoites passing through left auricle and ventricle; **x,** trophozoites in aortic arch; **y,** trophozoites in carotid artery; **z,** trophozoites entering wall of oesophagus to develop into sarcocysts.

Figures adapted as follows: A-C, from Ludvík, 1958, Zbl. Bakt. (Orig.) 172:330; D-E from Betegh and Dorcich, 1912, Zbl. Bakt. (Orig.) 63:387; F-H, from Bertram, 1892, Zool. Jahrb. Abt. Anat. 5:581; K, from Wasielewski, 1896, Sporozoenkunde; M, from Alexeieff, 1913, Arch. Zool. Exp. Gén. 51:521; N, from Chatton and Avel, 1923, C. R. Soc. Biol. (Paris) 89:181; O, from Prowazek; others original.

---

of mice may be used for experimental infection of mice. Faeces from infected mice or sheep may be fed to mice in attempts to produce infections. Chickens have been infected with *S. tenella.*

The sarcocysts contain a filterable endotoxin known as sarcocystin which is highly toxic to mice, rabbits, and sparrows. It acts on the central nervous system.

Feeding experiments should be conducted to produce sarcocysts and to test the toxicity of sarcocystin.

SELECTED REFERENCES

Doflein, F., and E. Reichenow. (1953). Lehrbuch der Protozoenkunde. Gustav Fischer, Jena, p. 1042.

Grassé, P. P. (1953). Traité de Zoologie, Vol. 1. Masson et Cie., Paris, p. 907.

Kudo, R. R. (1966). Protozoology. Charles C Thomas, Springfield, Ill., p. 766.

Levine, N. D. (1961). Protozoan Parasites of Domestic Animals and of Man. Burgess Publishing Co., Minneapolis, p. 317.

Ludvík, J. (1958). Zbl. Bakt. (Orig.) 172:330.

Scott, J. W. (1943). Univ. Wyo. Agr. Exp. Sta. Bull. No. 259, pp. 1-63.

Subclass Cnidosporidia

This group is characterized by having resistant spores with one to four polar capsules and one or more sporoplasms. The outer covering may consist of single piece or of two or three parts known as valves. A polar filament is coiled inside each capsule.

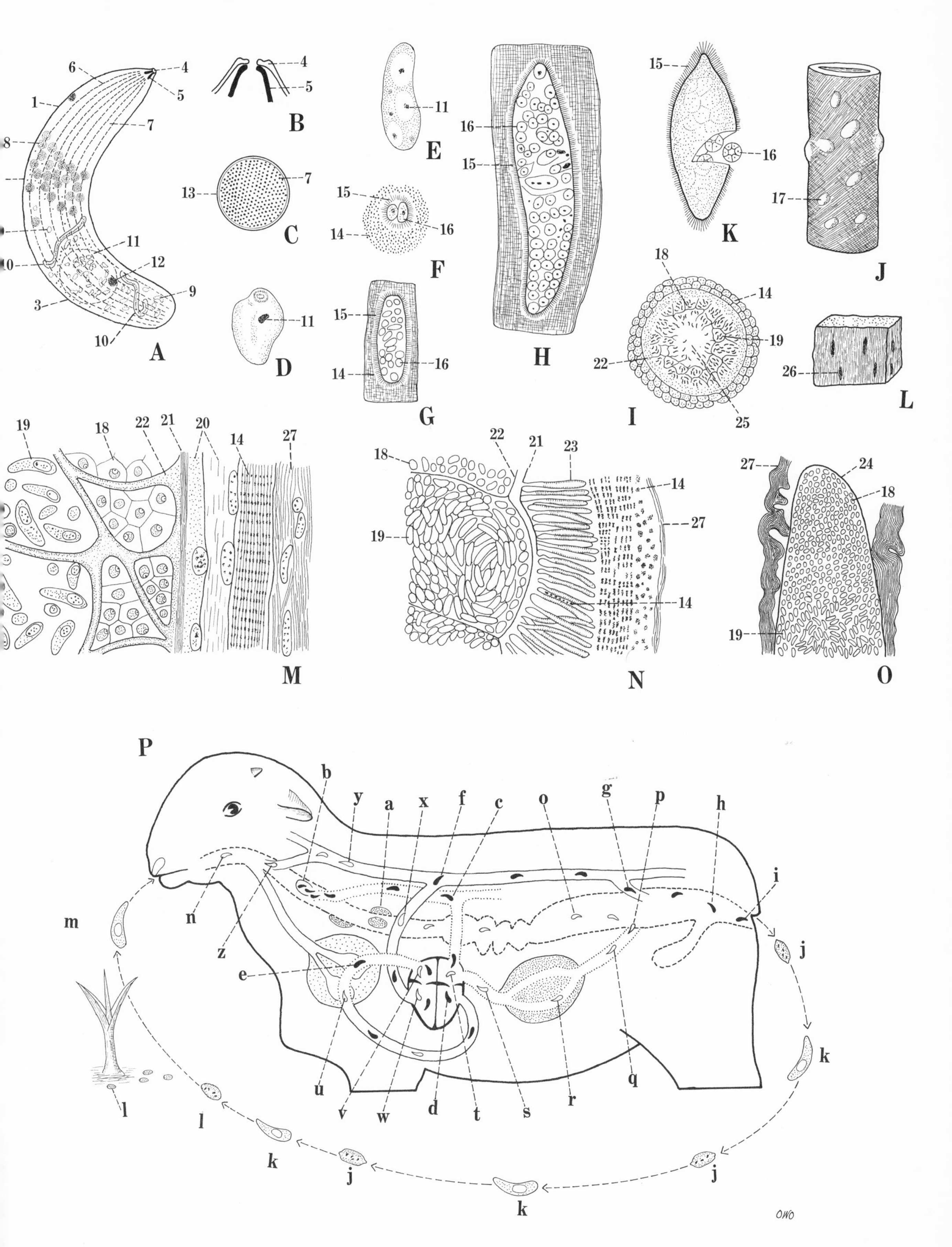
A
B
C
D
E
F
G
H
I
J
K
L
M
N
O
P
OWO

Members of this group are parasites of invertebrates and lower vertebrates, primarily fish. The life cycles are direct.

The subclass consists of the Orders Myxosporidia, Actinomyxidia, Microsporidia, and Helicosporidia. The Myxosporidia and Microsporidia are known best. The basic classification rests on the number of valves, polar capsules, and filaments.

ORDER MYXOSPORIDIA

The spore covering consists of two valves united in a distinct sutural plane and contains one to four polar capsules, each with a coiled extensible filament. The polar capsules are grouped at one end of the spore designated as anterior, or the spore may be elongated and have one capsule at each end, as in the family Myxidiidae. Representatives of the order appear on Plate 37.

In addition to the polar capsules, each spore contains a protoplasmic body known as the sporoplasm. While young, it contains two haploid nuclei which fuse to form the zygote before or after the sporoplasm escapes.

Kudo prepared a key to the genera and species of Myxosporidia in which nine families are listed. Hoffman *et al.* published a key, together with illustrations, of the species of *Myxosoma.*

The species of Myxosporidia are cosmopolitan in distribution.

BASIC LIFE CYCLE. Much diversity of opinion exists on the nature of the life cycles of these parasites. This is due to the difficulties of interpreting the stages in fixed tissues. When techniques for growing them *in vitro* are available, better understanding will be forthcoming. Only the basic aspects of the life cycle as generally accepted at present are given here.

Infection takes place when free spores are ingested. An intermediate host is unknown and believed to be unnecessary. Upon reaching the intestine, the action of the digestive juices on the spores cause them to open, allowing the sporoplasm to escape. Fertilization occurs when the two haploid nuclei of the sporoplasm fuse, either before or after its escape from the spore. The zygote penetrates the gut wall, enters the circulatory system, and is carried to various parts of the body. Upon reaching tissues, development begins and this stage of the organism is designated as a sporont, which develops into a spore.

FAMILY MYXOSOMATIDAE

The spores of this family are characterized by two or four polar capsules and a sporoplasm that does not have an iodinophilous vacuole.

Myxosoma cerebralis (Hofer, 1903) (Plate 37)

The parasite is common in Europe and has been reported in Pennsylvania and Connecticut in the United States. It parasitizes the cartilaginous parts of the skeleton of salmonid fish, particularly of the head and vertebral column from the 26th vertebra back in young trout. Infection leads to destruction of the parasitized parts, resulting in deformation. The mandible and opercula shorten, the mouth gapes, a humped back develops just behind the head, and the tail becomes twisted or bent and dark in color. The dark discoloration of the tail is due to damaged nerves that control the melanophores, allowing them to expand.

Infection causes the fish to swim in circles, thus leading to the common names of tail-chasing or whirling disease. Swimming is laborious and, after efforts to move, the fish sink to the bottom exhausted.

DESCRIPTION. Spores are circular, 6 to 10 μ in diameter, and with smooth valves. There are two polar capsules and a sporoplasm with two haploid nuclei, each with two chromosomes.

LIFE CYCLE. The life cycle has not been determined experimentally because of unsuccessful attempts to establish infection by feeding spores or infected tissue to susceptible fish. Hence, certain parts of cycle are based on assumptions (Plate 37, N-Q).

It is assumed that infection takes place when spores from the bottom of ponds are ingested by young fish at the time they begin to feed. Upon reaching the stomach or intestine, the valves of the spores open and release the sporoplasms. The haploid nuclei fuse, if they have not already done so, to form the zygotes. These penetrate the intestinal mucosa and presumably are carried in the circulatory system to various parts of the body. Those entering cartilaginous tissues, particularly of the head and posterior part of the spine, begin development.

Extremely young parasites are difficult to recognize in the cartilage. Symptoms of whirling and blacktail occur, however, as early as 35 days after newly feeding fish are placed in ponds with infected ones, but verification of infection has not been made by demonstrating parasites in histological sections.

Multinucleate trophozoites are present in cavities in the cartilage 40 days after newly feeding fish are exposed to infection in a pond with parasitized fish. At 3 months of age, amoeboid trophozoites 5 by 5 μ to 30 by 8 μ in size and with at least 18 nuclei are present in cavities measuring 300 by 100 μ in size. The smaller cavities may be only cross-sections of elongated ones.

At 4 months of age, the trophozoites have grown greatly, attaining a diameter of 1 mm. The nuclei have continued to divide and now appear in groups of 12 to 14 known as pansporoblasts, each of which will develop into two spores. The process of nuclear division is one of sporogony, beginning when the zygote enters the cartilage. Through it the nuclei for the future spores are formed. They appear in groups of at least six enclosed in a small amount of cytoplasm. Two of the nuclei form the shell, two the polar capsules, and the remaining two by a process of reduction division form two haploid nuclei with two chromosomes for the sporoplasm. The haploid nuclei may unite to form the zygote before the sporoplasm escapes from the spores, but it is thought generally to occur afterwards. Sporogony is a diploid process except for the final step in the formation of the sporoplasm where the haploid nuclei are formed.

By 8 months after infection the pansporoblasts have produced spores which fill the cavities. The spores generally remain in the cavities or "lesions," as they are called, where they occur in fish up to 3 years of age, possibly older. Some workers believe that the spores may escape from the "lesions," enter the circulation, and be carried to the intestinal wall whence they enter the lumen of the gut. The spores may escape from the host by several ways. When carried by the blood to the intestinal wall, they pass through it into the lumen and are voided with the faeces. Death and disintegration or crushing of infected fish release them. Spores have been reported from the intestine of kingfishers, presumably from infected fish eaten and digested by them. All other piscivorous animals, including fish, could serve as a rapid means of releasing and disseminating spores from infected fish eaten by them. The fact that infected fingerlings are unable to swim well makes them easy prey and thereby a selective means in favor of spreading the parasite.

Other species of *Myxosoma* include *M. catastomi* of the common sucker (*Catastomus commersoni*) which infects muscles and subcutaneous connective tissue. The spores are broadly oval and measure 13 to 15 μ long by 10 to 11.5 μ wide. Extremely severe infections occur in very young suckers in which numerous whitish pustule-like cysts appear on the skin of the head and body. Upon examination, they are filled with spores.

Myxosoma cartilaginis Hoffman, Putz, and Dunbar of blue gills (*Lepomis macrochirus*), green sunfish (*L. cyanellus*), and large mouth black bass (*Micropterus salmoides*) parasitizes the cartilaginous parts of the skeleton. Its life cycle appears similar to that of *M. cerebralis*. The symptoms of whirling and darkening of the body are lacking.

FAMILY MYXOBOLIDAE

The spores have one, two, or four polar capsules at the anterior end and a sporoplasm with an iodinophilous body. They are histozoic. *Myxobolus notemigoni* Lewis and Summerfelt of the golden shiner is representative of this family in North America.

DESCRIPTION. Fresh spores average 11.8 μ long by 8.9 μ wide. The polar capsules average 4.1 μ long by 3.3 μ wide. The outer surface of the spore valves is smooth, but small spinelike projections appear on the inner surface of the posterior end. The spores occur in aggregations of cysts 0.9 to 3 mm in diameter under the scales scattered over the body, except on the head and fins.

LIFE CYCLE. This is a monosporous species in which each sporont produces by a process of sporogony a single spore containing six nuclei. Two of these form the valves, two the polar capsules, and two, by a process of reduction division, the sporoplasm with two haploid nuclei (Plate 37, K).

Infection of fish is probably by ingestion of spores and migration of the zygote to the dermal tissue

EXPLANATION OF PLATE 37 ▷

A-B. Mature spores of *Myxosoma catastomi* Kudo from skin of catfish. **A.** Flat surface of spore. **B.** Edge or sutural view of spore. **C.** Immature spore of *M. catastomi.* **D-E.** *Ceratomyxa blennius* Noble, a disporous species from the urinary bladder of blenny. **D.** Two mature spores still in cytoplasmic mass in which they developed. **E.** Free mature spore. **F-G.** *Thelohanellus notatus* (Mavor) from the subdermal tissue of minnows (shiners and fatheads). **F.** Flat surface of spore. **G.** Sutural view. **H-I.** *Henneguyia exilis* Kudo from skin of catfish. **H.** Flat surface of spore. **I.** Sutural view of spore. **J.** *Chloromyxum trijugum* Kudo from gall bladder of crappies *(Pomoxis).* **K.** *Myxobolus notemigoni* Lewis and Summerfelt from skin of golden shiner, life cycle, and pathology. **L.** *Myxidium lieberkühnii* Bütschli from urinary bladder of pickerel *(Esox).* **M.** *M. aplodinoti* Kudo from gall bladder of sheepshead *(Aplodinotus).* **N-Q.** Life cycle of *Myxosoma cerebralis* (Hofer). **N.** Life cycle as presumed to occur. **O.** Intact cartilage containing a multinucleate sporont (see 1). **P.** Lesion caused by parasites in cartilage as it is being enclosed in bone. **Q.** Lesion containing ripe spores (see m).

1, spore wall; **2,** suture; **3,** polar capsule; **4,** polar filament; **5,** sporoplasm; **6,** haploid nuclei of sporoplasm; **7,** vacuole of iodinophilous body of sporoplasm; **8,** iodinophilous body; **9,** nuclei of polar body of immature cyst; **10,** nuclei of valves of spore.

1′-15′, life cycle *Myxobolus notemigoni* of golden shiner. **1′,** surface view of mature spore, showing two haploid nuclei of sporoplasm and vacuole left in it by iodinophilous body; **2′,** sutural view of spore, showing iodinophilous body; **3′,** zygote, called a sporont, originating from sporoplasm by union of haploid nuclei; **4′-7′,** developing sporonts; **4′,** binucleate stage; **5′,** tetranucleate stage; **6′-7′,** hexanucleate sporoblasts containing the number of nuclei necessary to form a single spore and its parts in the monosporous species; **8′,** golden shiner, showing effect of *M. notemigoni;* **9′,** section of body wall of golden shiner, showing sporonts under scale; **10′,** infection causes scales to rise; **11′,** epidermis; **12′,** scale; **13′,** cyst of parasite; **14′,** corium; **15′,** muscle.

a-b, sutural and surface views of mature spores freed from dead infected fish (n); **c,** spore being swallowed; **d,** expulsion of polar filaments under influence of digestive juices; **e,** escape of sporoplasm with haploid nuclei from spore; **f,** sporoplasm free in lumen of gut, nuclei come together; **g,** zygote forms and penetrates gut wall to enter postcaval vein; **h,** zygote reaches heart; **i,** zygote passing through capillaries of gills to dorsal aorta; **j,** zygote leaving dorsal aorta through arteries and capillaries to cartilaginous parts of skeleton; **k,** zygote in cartilage transforms into sporont; **l,** multinucleate sporont in cartilage; **m,** spores in lesions in cartilage; **n,** fish dead of whirl disease or blacktail will decompose and liberate spores; **o,** kingfishers and other piscivorous animals may release spores by digestion of infected fish and subsequently distribute spores in the faeces; **p,** intact cartilage; **q,** cartilage cell; **r,** lesion caused by parasite; **s,** multinucleate sporont; **t,** mature spores in lesions; **u,** bone; **v,** cartilaginous debris; **w,** cellular debris.

Figure A-C adapted from Kudo, 1926, Arch. Protistenk. 56:90; D-E, from Noble, 1944, Quart. Rev. Biol. 19:213; F-G, from Kudo, 1934, Ill. Biol. Monogr. 13:3; H-J, from Kudo, 1920, Ill. Biol. Monogr. 5:245; K, from Lewis and Summerfelt, 1964, J. Parasit. 50:388; N, from Hoffman, Dunbar, and Bradford, 1962, U. S. Dept. Int., Fish and Wildf. Serv., Spec. Sci. Rept., Fish. No. 427.

---

via the circulatory system. Inasmuch as the cysts are under the scales, it is likely that spores may be liberated from ruptured cysts throughout the period of infection of the shiners.

Other common genera are *Henneguyia* with two polar capsules and an elongated process on the posterior end of each valve, and *Thelohanellus* with one polar capsule. For a listing of species, with keys and figures, the reader should consult Kudo.

FAMILY MYXIDIIDAE

The valves are elongated, giving a fusiform appearance. There are two polar capsules, one at the distal end of each valve (Plate 37, K-L). An iodinophilous body is lacking.

Myxidium lieberkühni Bütschli occurs in the urinary bladder of the pike (*Esox* spp.) and is widely distributed. Spores measure 18 to 20 μ long by 5 to 6 μ wide.

M. serotinum Kudo and Sprague occurs in the gall bladder of frogs and toads in North America. Spores are 16 to 18 μ long by 9 μ wide, with two to four longitudinal and 10 to 13 transverse ridges. It is both di- and polysporous with two or several cysts developing in each pansporoblast.

Sphaeromyxa spp. occur in the gall bladder of marine fish.

The life cycles of the Myxidiidae are basically similar to those of the Myxobolidae.

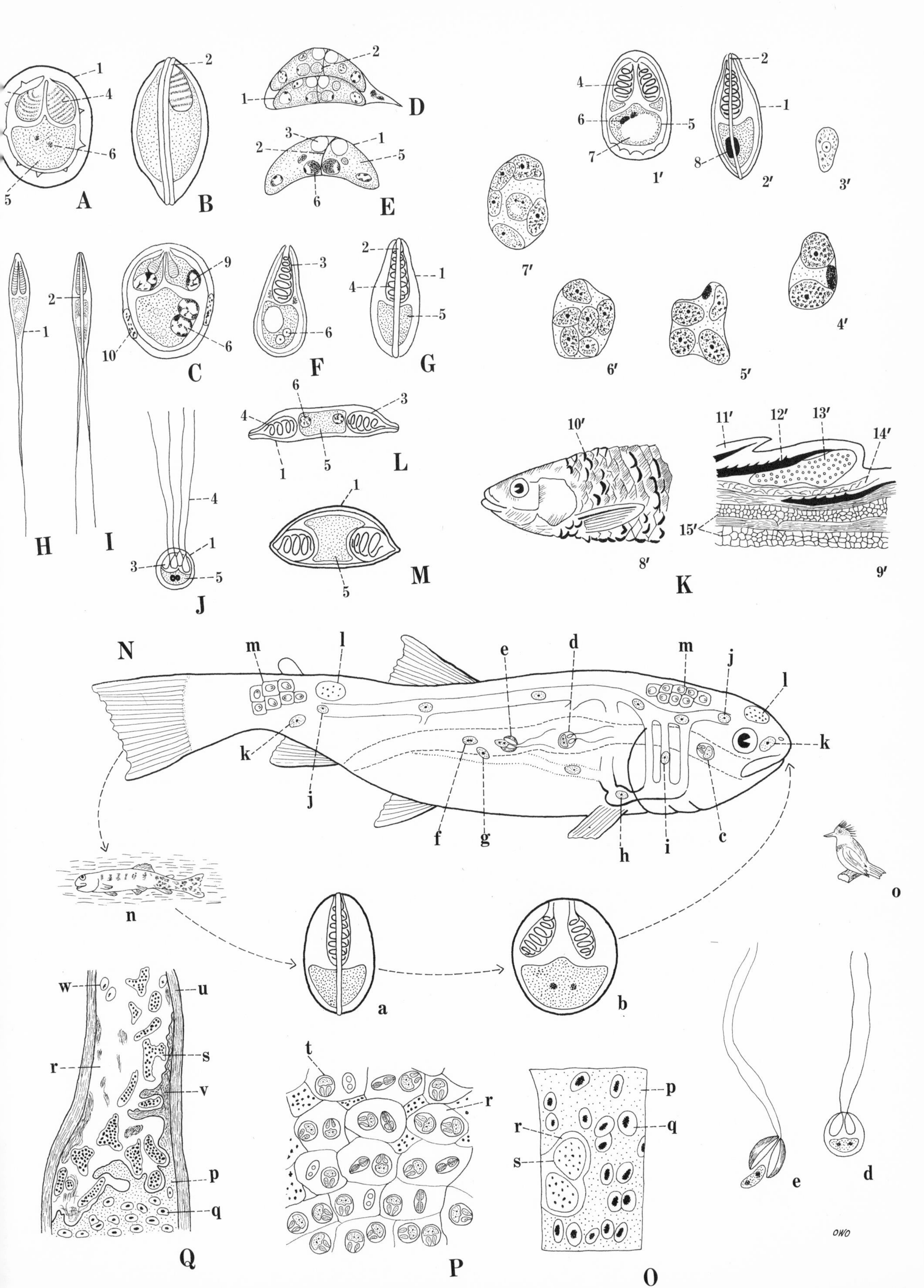
A
B
C
D
E
F
G
H
I
J
K
L
M
N
a
b
c
d
e
f
g
h
i
j
k
l
m
n
o
P
Q
O
1′
2′
3′
4′
5′
6′
7′
8′
9′
10′
11′
12′
13′
14′
15′
OWO

FAMILY CERATOMYXIDAE

The spores are markedly prolonged laterally (Plate 37, D, E). There are two polar capsules in the anterior margin with the sutural plane running between them.

Ceratomyxa blennius Noble from the gall bladder of blennies, or butterfly fish, is a disporous species in which two cysts develop in each pansporoblast (Plate 37, D). Development by sporogony proceeds as described for the other species. In addition, cytoplasmic growth with much nuclear division (nucleogony) occurs, followed by budding off of uninucleate bodies that develop into pansporoblasts to form spores.

ORDER ACTINOMYXIDIA

The members of this order infect the gut epithelium of fresh-water and marine annelids. *Triactinomyxon ignotum* infects *Tubifex tubifex,* a cosmopolitan fresh-water oligochaete. The spore bears three polar bodies and three valves. The latter are drawn out posteriorly and the ends separate to form a triradiate anchor-like structure of the whole body. Spores are contained in the anterior portion of the body.

The life cycle is not given here but an account of it was published by Mackinnon and Adam.

EXERCISE ON LIFE CYCLE

Life cycles of the Myxosporidia have not been worked out in their entirety. Infection of hosts by feeding spores or tissue infected with them has not been accomplished.

For material to work with, seek such fish as minnows, suckers, or catfish with infections in the skin or on the gills.

Since spores open in the stomach or intestine of fish, efforts should be made to get them to open in digestive juices, both natural and artificial.

Try to determine whether fertilization takes place before or after escape of the sporoplasm from the spore.

Histological sections of infected tissue will reveal the stages of sporogony, including growth of the cytoplasm, nuclear multiplication, and formation of sporoblasts, pansporoblasts, and spores.

SELECTED REFERENCES

Doflein, F., and E. Reichenow. (1953). Lehrbuch der Protozoenkunde. Gustav Fischer, Jena, p. 967.

Grassé, P. P. (1953). Traité de Zoologie, Vol. 1, Fasc. 2, Protozoaires. Masson et Cie, Paris, p. 1009.

Hoffman, G. I., C. E. Dunbar, and A. Bradford. (1962). U. S. Dept. Int., Fish and Wildl. Serv., Bur. Sport Fish. and Wildl., Spec. Sci. Rept., Fish. No. 427, 15 pp.; ———, R. E. Putz, and C. E. Dunbar. (1965). J. Protozool. 12:319.

Kudo, R. R. (1920). Ill. Biol. Monogr. 5(3/4):240; (1926). Arch. Protistenk. 56:90; (1943). J. Morph. 72:263; (1966). Protozoology. Charles C Thomas, Springfield, Ill., p. 774; ——— and V. Sprague. (1940). Rev. Med. Trop. Parasitol. Bact. Clin. Lab., Havana, 6:65.

Mackinnon, D. L., and D. I. Adam. (1924). Quart. J. Micr. Sci. 68:187.

Noble, E. R. (1943). J. Morph. 73:281; (1944). Quart. Rev. Biol. 19:213.

Schäperclaus, W. (1954). Fischkrankheiten. Akademie, Berlin, p. 379.

Wenyon, C. M. (1926). Protozoology, Vol. 1. William Wood and Co., New York, p. 716.

ORDER MICROSPORIDIA

The Microsporidia are especially numerous and widespread, occurring most frequently in arthropods, followed by fish. The minute spores are very resistant to environmental adversities, resembling bacterial spores in this respect. Their resistant properties may be responsible in a large part for the cosmopolitan distribution of them.

The covering of the spore is a single chitinous piece, not two or three as in the Myxosporidia. It contains a binucleate sporoplasm arranged as an annular mass around the inner meridian of the spore. The very long, thin, solid filament lies coiled within a relatively large vacuole.

In general, they infect specific tissues. Some infect protozoan or helminth parasites within a host. Many of the Microsporidia are host-specific. For instance, two species of mosquito larvae in a pool do not share each other's microsporidian parasites. Representatives of the order are shown on Plate 38.

There are two suborders of Microsporidia. The Monocnidina have a single filament and the Dicnidina have two, one at each end of the spore.

Suborder Monocnidina

This is the larger group based on the number of species. It consists of the families Nosematidae to which the majority of species belong, the Coccosporidae, and the Mrazekiidae.

The spores are pyriform, oval, spherical, or cylindrical in shape and contain a single filament.

FAMILY NOSEMATIDAE

This is the largest family, having seven genera. These are based on the number of spores produced by each sporont. *Nosema* has 1 spore, *Glugea* 2, *Gurleyia* 4, *Thelohania* 8, *Stempellia* 1, 2, 4, or 8, *Duboscquia* 16, and *Plistophora* variable but often more than 16. Recent writers include *Perezia* as a subgenus of *Glugea* since the basic difference between them lies in the fact that the latter causes hypertrophy of the infected cells and the former does not.

Nosema includes some well-known species of great economic importance, including those of honey bees and silkworms. Doubtless, they are also responsible for the destruction of large numbers of other kinds of insects, including mosquito larvae.

Nosema Naegli, 1857

The species of this genus are primarily parasites of insects. Each sporont develops into a single spore.

Nosema apis Zander, 1909 (Plate 38)

This species is parasitic in the intestinal epithelium of honey bees in many parts of the world. It causes a disease known by various names such as bee sickness, bee dysentery, winter losses, spring dwindling, and May sickness. The disease usually occurs late in the winter or in the spring. In epizootic form, losses may be high. Symptoms of stricken bees are marked abdominal distention, copious defaecation, sluggishness, inability to fly, and others. Such manifestations of sickness alone, however, are not reliable for an accurate diagnosis of nosemiasis because other conditions may provoke similar symptoms. The only accurate diagnosis is the demonstration of the characteristic spores. These measure 4 to 6 μ long by 2 to 4 μ wide. The filament is extremely long, measuring up to 280 μ.

LIFE CYCLE. Bees become infected by ingesting spores deposited in the hives by parasitized members of the colony. Upon reaching the proventriculus, or midgut, the spores under the influence of the digestive juices, open at one end. The long filament protrudes and is followed by the attached sporoplasm, or germ, as it is sometimes called.

The sporoplasms generally are binucleate upon emerging from the spore. The nuclei fuse and the sporoplasm begins division by binary fission, or division may begin prior to fusion. A colony of amoeboid bodies known as planonts develops in the lumen of the gut. Somehow, they pass through or circumvent the chitinous peritrophic membrane and penetrate the epithelial cells of the gut or enter between them. Some authors state that a small number of planonts pass through the intestinal wall into the haemocoel, where they remain in a quiescent stage for a short while, after which they return to the epithelial cells. Others maintain that none penetrates deeper than the basement membrane of the intestinal wall.

Upon entering the cytoplasm of the epithelial cells, the nuclear chromatin of the planonts changes in staining properties preparatory to multiplication. These bodies are now designated as meronts and are the forms that eventually produce spores. Three types of division occur. The first is by simple binary fission, whereby the meront repeatedly divides, forming a colony of separate individuals. Division begins by elongation of both the cell and nucleus. It is completed by separation of the nucleus and cleavage of the cytoplasm into two daughter meronts. The second is by multiple binary fission, producing chains of four or more meronts within the epithelial cells. Some workers state that this method of reproduction is rare; others have not observed it. The third method results in growth of the cytoplasmic mass accompanied by repeated nuclear division. The cytoplasm of the multinucleate meront concen-

EXPLANATION OF PLATE 38 ⇨

A. Diagrammatic representation of *Nosema locustae,* showing arrangement of sporoplasm in spore and attachment of polar filament to spore at one end and sporoplasm at other. **B.** *Nosema helminthorum,* diagrammatic representation, showing same features as *N. locustae.* **C.** Mature spore of *Nosema apis* of honey bees. **D.** Spore of *Nosema bombycis* of silkworms. **E.** Spore of *Telomyxa glugeiformis,* showing two polar filaments. **F-I.** Diagrammatic representation of emergence of filament and sporoplasm of *Nosema* from spore. **J.** Spore of *Nosema apis* with extremely long filament. **K-L.** Spores of *Mrazekia argoisi* before and after extrusion of polar filament. **M.** Spore of *Cocconema* with extruded filament. **N.** Mosquito larva *(Anopheles crucians)* infected with *Thelohania legeri.* **O.** Portion of ventriculus of honey bee, showing cells filled with spores of *Nosema apis.* **P.** Brain and cranial nerves of angler fish *(Lophuris piscatoris)* infected with *Nosema lophurii.* **Q.** Section of body of stickleback *(Gasterosteus)* infected with *Glugea anomala,* showing large glugea cysts. **R.** Smelt *(Osmerus),* showing numerous cysts on viscera caused by *Glugea hertwigi.* **S.** Honey bee *(Apis mellifera),* showing life cycle of *Nosema apis.*

1, spore case; **2,** sporoplasm arranged girdle-like around inner equatorial part of spore; **3,** small binucleate sporoplasm near posterior end of spore; **4,** sporoplasm freed from spore; **5,** nuclei of sporoplasm; **6,** polar filament; **7,** polar vacuole; 8, manubrium; **9,** masses of spores in body of mosquito larva; **10,** spores in epithelial cells of ventriculus (midgut) of honey bee; **11,** epithelial cell; **12,** nucleus of epithelial cell; **13,** nest, or nidi, of developing epithelial cells. **14,** basement membrane; **15,** outer muscular layer of intestinal wall; **16,** eye; **17,** brain; **18,** lobulated tumors on cranial nerves of angler fish caused by *Nosema lophurii;* **19,** cyst of *Glugea anomala* in body muscles of stickleback; **20,** intestine; **21,** cysts of *Glugea hertwigi* on viscera of smelt.

a, ingestion of ripe spores by adult bee; **b,** extrusion of polar filament; **c,** escape of binucleate sporoplasm with attached filament from spore; **d,** sporoplasm in which nuclei have fused to form zygote; **e,** beginning multiplication of sporoplasm and formation of planont; **f,** planonts resulting from multiplication of sporoplasms; **g,** planont penetrates epithelial cell and changes to a meront; **h,** meronts dividing by simple binary fission, one method of multiplication; **i,** multiplying meronts fill cell; **j,** fully developed spores fill cells, causing them to rupture; **k,** planont entering cell; **l,** chains of meronts formed by binary fission, a second method of multiplication; **m,** formation of spores; **n,** planont entering cell; **o,** meront dividing by multiple fission, a third method of reproduction; **p,** multinucleate meront that has grown in size and increased the number of nuclei; **q,** formation of sporoblasts within cytoplasmic mass of meront; **r,** formation of spores; **s,** rupture of epithelial cells and release of spores into lumen of gut; **t,** spores in lumen of gut; **u,** spores voided with faeces; **v,** infective spores in hive.

Figures A, B, F, G, H, I, redrawn from Dissanaike and Canning, 1957, Parasitology 47:92; C, from Fantham and Porter, 1912, Ann. Trop. Med. Parasit. 6:163; D, from Grassé, 1953, Traité de Zoologie, Vol. 1, Fasc. 2, p. 1045; E, J, K, L, M, N, P, Q, R, from Kudo, 1924, Ill. Biol. Monogr. 9:79; O, from White, 1919, U. S. Dept. Agr. Bull. 780.

---

trates around several nuclei, forming daughter meronts within it, or single uninucleate meronts may be budded off. In each method of merogenous division, small separate uninucleate bits of protoplasm result and are known as sporoblasts which develop into the characteristic spores.

Two views are extant on the manner in which mature spores are liberated from the cells in which they developed. In one, the cell membranes rupture, liberating the spores into the intestine. In the other, the epithelial cells are shed in the normal manner and disintegrate in the gut, freeing the spores.

The entire cycle may be completed in 4 days during warm weather. Spores are extremely durable and capable of surviving for long periods under unfavorable conditions such as occur in the bodies of decomposing dead bees, in faeces, or free in the hives.

Nosema bombycis Naegli is parasitic in the caterpillars of silk moths (*Bombyx mori*) and related species of lepidopterous larvae. Practically all tissues of the body, including the intestinal epithelium, are infected. The parasite is especially dangerous to the caterpillars of silk moths because the crowded conditions in which they are reared favor constant exposure and heavy infection. Parasitized larvae show brown spots over the body, causing a peppery appearance which suggested the name pébrine disease. In severe infections, mortality is extremely high.

Under favorable conditions the life cycle, which is basically similar to that of *N. apis,* may be completed in 4 days.

Nosema helminthorum Moniez parasitizes the cestode *Moniezia expansa* of sheep. Spores are ingested by grazing sheep. In the intestine, the sporoplasms escape and enter the parenchymous tissue of the tapeworm, where the cycle is completed. Spores are disseminated upon decomposition of pro-

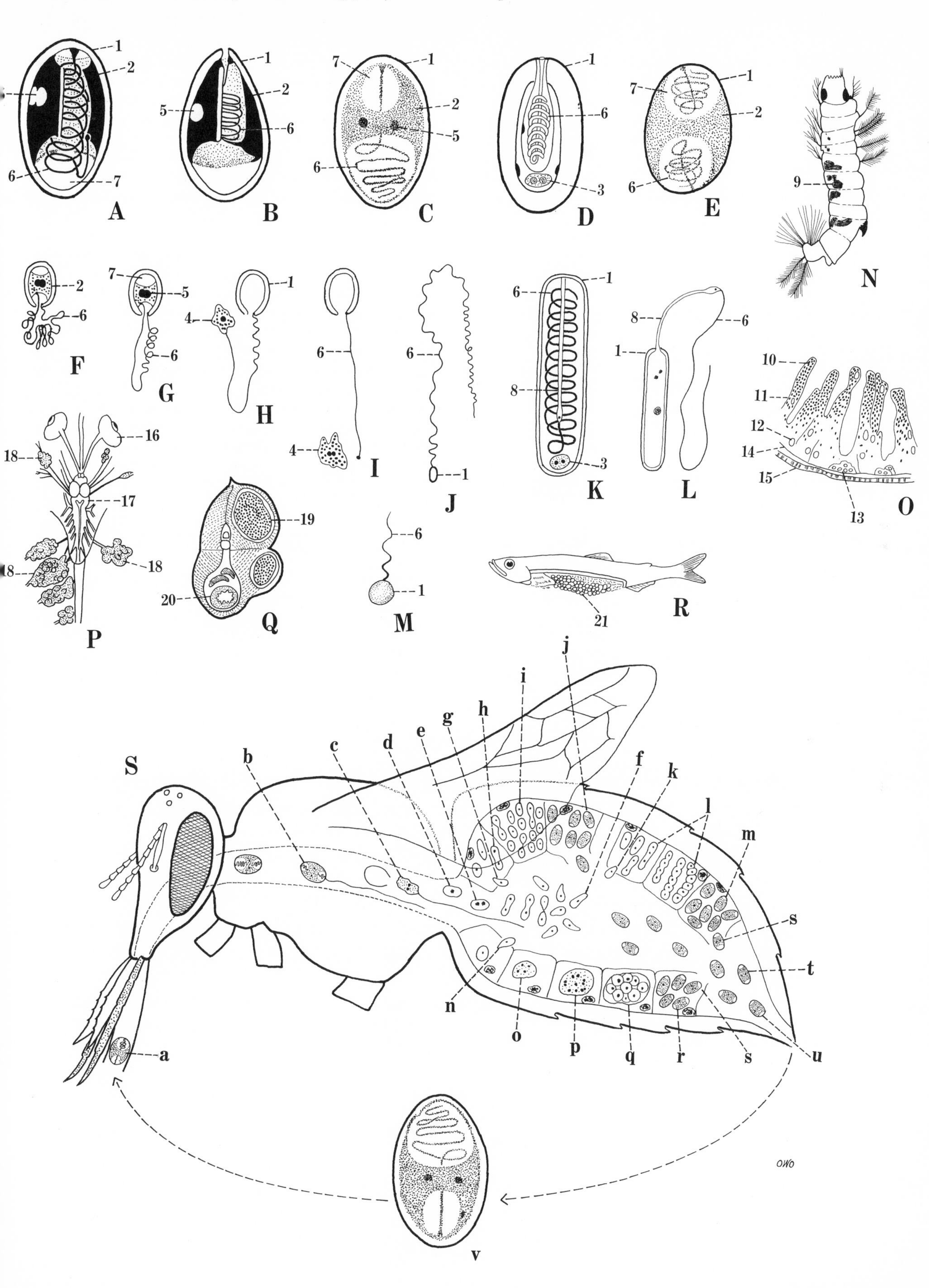
A
B
C
D
E
F
G
H
I
J
K
L
M
N
O
P
Q
R
S
a
b
c
d
e
f
g
h
i
j
k
l
m
n
o
p
q
r
s
t
u
v
OWO

EXPLANATION OF PLATE 39 ⇨

A-F. Trophic stages of four genera of Opalinidae from Amphibia. **A.** *Opalina ranarum* (multinucleate flat form). **B.** *Zelleriella elliptica* (binucleate flat form). **C.** Diagrammatic cross-section of *Opalina* and *Zelleriella*, showing flattened nature of body characteristic of these two genera. **D.** *Cepedea cantabrigensis* (multinucleate cylindrical form). **E.** *Protoopalina mitotica* (binucleate cylindrical form). **F.** Diagrammatic cross-section of *Cepedea* and *Protoopalina*, showing cylindrical shape of body characteristic of these two genera. **G.** Adult frog with vegetative stages of *Opalina ranarum* **(a-d)** in rectum, multiplying by binary fission during summer, fall, and winter. **H.** Formation of gametocytes **(e-l)** in rectum of frogs during spring concurrently with breeding activities of the amphibians. **I.** Formation of gametes and zygote **(m-s)** in the intestine of tadpoles. **J.** Development of trophic stages, beginning in tadpoles and continuing in frogs following metamorphosis.

1, cilia; **2,** nucleus.

a-d, vegetative development by binary fission in gut of frogs during summer, fall, and winter; **a,** fully developed trophic stage which is the beginning of both the vegetative and sexual cycles; **b-d,** cells undergoing vegetative binary fission and in various stages of completion; **e-k,** in frog during spring when they are undergoing breeding activities; **e-g,** division of trophic stage into gametocytes; **h-j,** formation and maturation of sexual nuclei; **k,** cyst formed around gametocyte; **l,** encysted gametocytes voided in faeces of frogs into water where they are ingested by feeding tadpoles; **m-s,** in alimentary canal of tadpole; **m,** excystation; **n,** division of cytoplasm with reduction of nuclei in each daughter cell; **o,** formation of uninucleate gametes; **p,** two gametes; **q,** fusion of gametes in fertilization; **r,** zygote; **s,** encysted zygote expelled from intestine with faeces; **s-w,** in intestine of tadpole during growth and metamorphosis; **s,** encysted zygote swallowed by tadpole; **t,** excystation of zygote in intestine of tadpole; **u,** young trophic stage; **v-w,** growth of opalinid in tadpole, followed by binary fission in rectum of metamorphosed frog.

Figure A adapted from various sources; B from Chen, 1948, J. Morph. 88:281; C and F original; D and E from Metcalf, 1923, U. S. Nat. Mus. Bull. 120.

---

glottids passed in the faeces. Many other species of helminth and protozoan parasites are infected by microsporidians.

Glugea anomala (Moniez) is a parasite of the muscles of sticklebacks (*Gasterosteus*). Large cysts, known as glugea cysts, up to 5 mm in diameter occur in the body muscles. Individual cells are greatly hypertrophied.

Glugea hertwigi Weissenberg infects the intestinal wall of smelt (*Osmerus*), producing large cysts which destroy the epithelium.

For a comprehensive discussion of Microsporidia consult Kudo.

Suborder Dicnidina

The Dicnidina contains a single family, the Telomyxidae. It is characterized by spores with a polar filament at each end.

Telomyxa glugeiformis occurs in the fat bodies of may flies (*Ephemera*). Infected nymphs are sluggish and chalky white, owing to the accumulation of spores inside. Such heavy infections are fatal. The spores are elliptical and in groups of 8, 16, or more.

EXERCISE ON LIFE CYCLE

Studies on the biology of these parasites are difficult and hardly for the beginner. Many valuable observations, however, may be made on the occurrence of them, especially in the larvae of aquatic arthropods and fish. They are best seen in histological sections where the spores and developmental stages appear inside the various tissues.

SELECTED REFERENCES

Fantham, H. B., and A. Porter. (1912). Ann. Trop. Med. Parasit. 6:163; (1914). Ibid. 8:633.

Grassé, P. P. (1953). Traité de Zoologie, Vol. 1, Fasc. 2. Masson et Cie, Paris, p. 1042.

Dissanaike, A. S. (1957). Parasitology 47:335; ——— and E. U. Canning. (1957). Ibid. 47:92.

Doflein, F., and E. Reichenow. (1953). Lehrbuch der Protozoenkunde. Gustav Fischer, Jena, p. 1004.

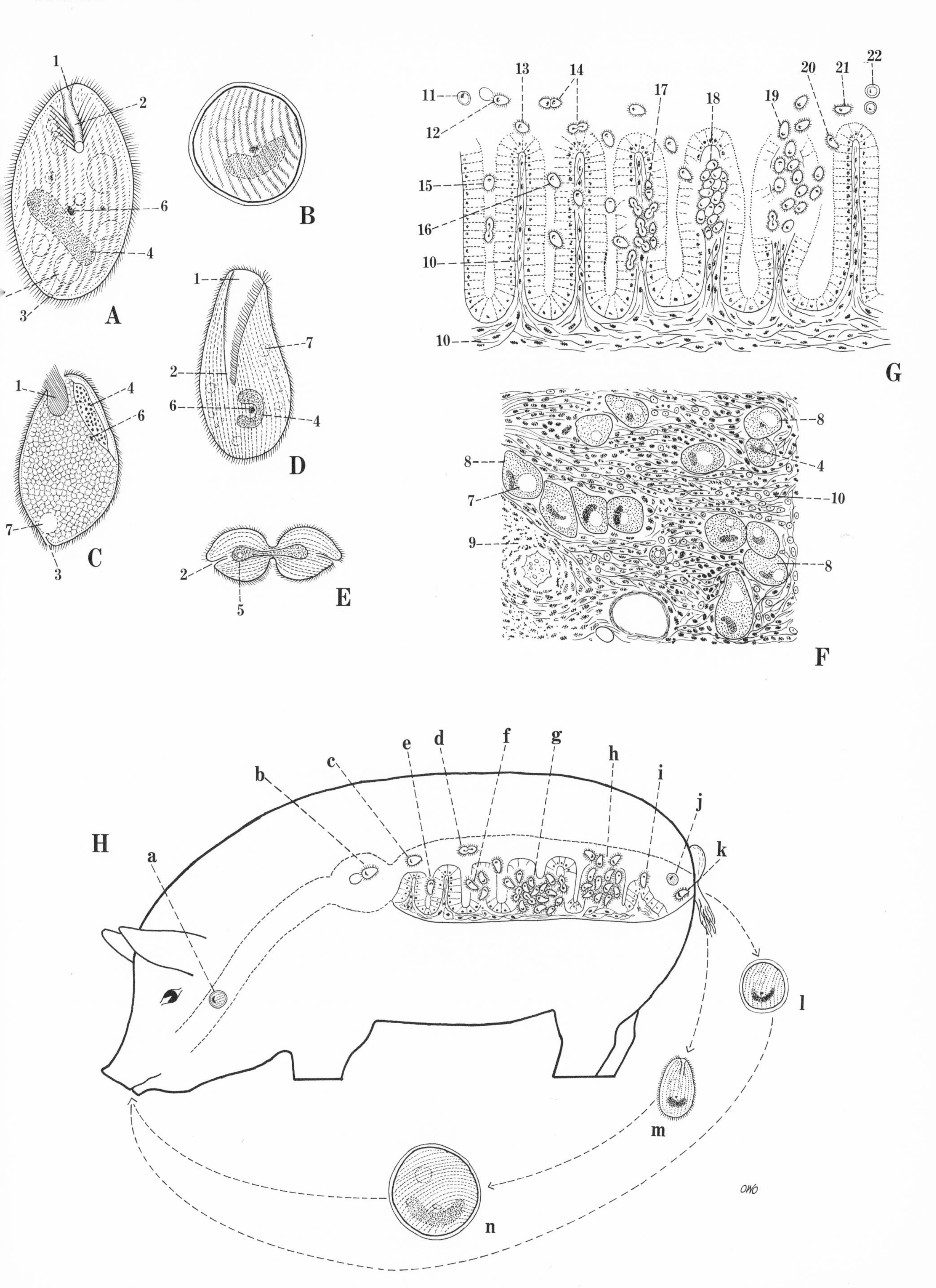
1
2
6
4
3
A
B
1
7
2
6
4
D
1
4
6
7
3
C
2
5
E
11
12
13
14
17
18
19
20
21
22
15
16
10
10
G
8
4
8
10
7
9
8
F
H
a
b
c
e
d
f
g
h
i
j
k
l
m
n
OWO

Hertig, M. (1923). J. Parasit. 9:109.
Kudo, R. R. (1920). J. Parasit. 7:84; (1924). Ill. Biol. Monogr. 9:(2/3):77; (1944). Ibid. 20:1; (1966). Protozoology. Charles C Thomas, Springfield, Ill., p. 807.
Neveu-Lemaire, M. (1943). Traité de Protozoologie Médicale et Vétérinaire. Vigot Frères, Paris, p. 335.
Sprague, V., and J. Ramsey. (1942). J. Parasit. 28:399.
Stempell, W. (1909). Arch. Protistenk. 16:281.
Wenyon, C. M. (1926). Protozoology, Vol. 1. William Wood and Co., New York, p. 734.
White, G. F. (1919). U. S. Dept. Agr., Bull. No. 780.

ORDER HELICOSPORIDIA

The Helicosporidia have a simple body consisting of a single thin membrane surrounding three uninucleate sporoplasms around which is coiled a long single filament. There is no polar capsule.

Helicosporidium parasiticum Kudo parasitizes the body cavity, fat bodies, and nervous tissue of mites and larval Diptera found in wounds of elm trees and horse chestnut trees. Little is known regarding the life cycle (see Keilin, 1921, Parasitology 13: 97).

SUBPHYLUM CILIOPHORA

The members of this phylum have cilia, cirri, or other compound ciliary structures of locomotion. They contain two kinds of nuclei, the macro- and micronucleus, of different size and function. Species of *Opalina* are an exception in which there are two to many nuclei of the same kind. For this reason, they are considered in recent classifications as being different from the other ciliated forms.

The subphylum consists of the classes Ciliata and Suctoria. Only the Ciliata contain species that are parasitic.

Class Ciliata

These protozoans are characterized by having cilia during the trophic stage.

Subclass Protociliata

These astomate forms are covered uniformly with cilia of equal length and have two to many similar nuclei. They are parasitic in the rectum of fish, amphibians, particularly anurans, and reptiles.

FAMILY OPALINIDAE

The family contains four genera.

Opalina Purkinje and Valentin is highly flattened and multinucleate; *Zelleriella* Metcalf is similarly flattened but has two nuclei. *Cepedea* Metcalf is cylindrical, being circular in cross-section, and multinucleate; while *Protoopalina* Metcalf is similar in shape but binucleate.

The opalinids are world wide in distribution, occurring mostly in the Salientia. Insofar as known, they are non-pathogenic and are considered by some workers as commensals.

Opalina ranarum Purkinje and Valentin, 1835 (Plate 42)

This is probably the best known of the many species of opalinids and will serve as an example of the life cycle of a member of the family. It is the common European form, occurring regularly in the rectum of *Rana temporaria* and *Bufo bufo,* also in turtles and salamanders. *Opalina obtrigonoidea* Metcalf is a common form in various species of North American frogs and toads (*Rana, Hyla, Bufo, Gastrophryne,* and others) throughout the continent.

DESCRIPTION. *O. ranarum* occurs in a number of shapes, the types of which carry descriptive designations. In size, they exceed 300 μ in length and appear to the naked eye as motile opalescent bodies. The cilia are arranged in parallel oblique rows and are attached to blepharoplasts lying in the endoplasm, a condition that leads some workers to consider these forms as flagellates instead of ciliates.

O. obtrigonoidea, the American representative, is similar in appearance to *O. ranarum.* It is 400 to 840 μ long, 175 to 180 μ wide, and 20 to 25 μ thick.

LIFE CYCLE. As the ciliates increase in size by osmotic assimilation of food, the nuclei enlarge and begin to divide by a modified mitosis without equatorial plates. Multiplication is by division of the body into two multinucleate individuals.

During the greater part of the year, only large forms are present in the recta of frogs. With the approach of spring, repeated division of the individual ciliates gives rise to small forms with few nuclei. These secrete a cyst 30 to 70 μ in diameter about themselves. They are voided with the rectal contents into the water, sinking to the bottom of the ponds. Newly hatched tadpoles swallowing the cysts along with food gleaned from the bottom mud become infected. The small multinucleate forms released from the cysts in the rectum are male and female gametocytes. They divide repeatedly, eventually giving rise to elongated uninucleated gametes 28 to 30 μ long with a rounded anterior and tapering posterior end. The gametes conjugate and finally fuse to form a zygote.

Opinions regarding development from this point on differ. Metcalf and Brumpt believe these zygotes develop to adults. Neresheimer and Konsuloff state that they undergo encystment, becoming multinucleate gametocytes which are expelled with the faeces into the water. When eaten by a second tadpole, the gametocytes escape from the resistant cysts in the rectum and develop into adults. The differential rate of division of the nuclei and cytoplasm results in multinucleate adults. The protozoans continue to develop in the metamorphosing tadpoles and adult frogs.

EXERCISE ON LIFE CYCLE

For study, adult ciliates should be mounted in rectal fluid on slides and the cover slip sealed with Vaseline by running a hot needle around the edge. Observe them for movement, division, and encystment.

Encysted forms should be placed in gastric and intestinal fluid of tadpoles or frogs on slides in order to observe excystation and release of the small ciliates.

SELECTED REFERENCES

Doflein, F., and E. Reichenow. (1953). Lehrbuch der Protozoenkunde. Gustav Fischer, Jena, p. 1081.

Konsuloff, S. (1922). Arch. Protistenk. 44:285.

Kudo, R. R. (1966). Protozoology. Charles C Thomas, Springfield, Ill., pp. 828, 1029.

Metcalf, M. M. (1923). Smithson. Inst., U. S. Nat. Mus. Bull. 120; (1940). Ibid. 87:465.

Neresheimer, E. (1907). Arch. Protistenk., Suppl. 1, p. 1.

Wenyon, C. M. (1926). Protozoology, Vol. 2. William Wood and Co., New York, p. 1153.

ORDER SPIROTRICHA

This order is characterized by a row of well-developed adoral membranelles that spiral clockwise into the cytostome.

SUBORDER HETEROTRICHA

The body is completely and uniformly ciliated and has a funnel-shaped peristome lined with cilia at the anterior end.

FAMILY BALANTIDIIDAE

The vestibule is near the anterior end of the body and the cytostome is at its base. Members of the family occur in the alimentary canal of invertebrates and vertebrates.

Balantidium Claparède and Lachman, 1858

The species of this genus are cosmopolitan parasites of the intestine of arthropods (insects and crustacea), fish, amphibians, and mammals, including humans and swine. Species infecting vertebrates occur in the caecum and colon.

The trophozoite is somewhat egg- or pear-shaped and as otherwise described above for the family. The macronucleus is a large sausage-shaped structure; a minute micronucleus lies beside it.

Two contractile vacuoles, one toward each end of the body, are present together with numerous food vacuoles. The cytopyge, or anus, is a permanent opening at the posterior end of the body through which the contractile vacuoles empty periodically.

EXPLANATION OF PLATE 40 ⇨

A. Fully developed *Ichthyophthirius multifiliis* from pustule of epidermis. **B.** Anterior end of fully developed ciliate. **C.** Swarmer from cyst. **D-E.** First and second divisions of encysted ciliate. **F.** Later stage of cystic multiplication. **G.** Cyst filled with swarmers, some of which are escaping into water. **H.** Section of skin of fish showing full-grown embedded ciliate. **I.** Section of tail of carp, showing ciliates developing in pustule. **J.** Infected bullhead *(Ameirus melas)*.

1, cystostome; **2,** macronucleus; **3,** longitudinal rows of cilia; **4,** vacuoles; **5,** boring or penetration apparatus; **6,** cyst; **7,** dividing of macronucleus; **8,** two daughter cells formed by first division; **9,** four daughter cells formed by second division in cyst; **10,** numerous daughter cells; **11,** swarmers; **12,** epidermis of fish skin; **13,** pigment cell in epidermis; **14,** dermis; **15,** cartilaginous skeleton of tail of carp; **16,** pustule containing ciliates; **17,** ciliate under skin.

a, pustules; **b,** ciliate escaping from pustule into water; **c,** ciliate free in water; **d,** encysted ciliate on bottom of pond in first division, showing two daughter cells; **e,** cyst with enclosed ciliate in second division with four daughter cells; **f,** cyst with many daughter cells; **g,** ruptured cyst liberating swarmers; **h,** swarmer attached to skin; **i,** swarmer partially embedded in skin.

Figures A, D, E, F, G, I redrawn from Kudo, 1953, Protozoology, p. 709; B, C, H from Schäperclaus, 1954, Fischkrankheiten, p. 334, 338.

Balantidium coli (Malmstem, 1857) (Plate 39)

This parasite occurs frequently in swine and occasionally in humans, especially persons who work around pigs. It is found also in primates and rats.

DESCRIPTION. The trophozoites measure 30 to 150 μ long by 25 to 120 μ wide. Cysts are spherical or ovoid, measuring 40 to 60 μ in diameter. The wall consists of two membranes.

LIFE CYCLE. Infection takes place by ingestion of encysted *B. coli* along with food or water contaminated with the faeces of infected animals. In the intestine, the ciliates are liberated from the cysts by the action of the digestive juices. The freed trophozoites go to the caecum and large intestine where they occur on the surface of the mucosa. They feed on bacteria and particulate matter of different kinds. During this time, they are multiplying by transverse binary fission in which cytoplasmic cleavage follows nuclear division. Conjugation apparently is rare, if at all, in the host although it takes place in *in vitro* cultures. Trophozoites carried posteriorly with the flow of intestinal contents, round up and secrete a double-walled cyst about themselves as water is absorbed from the faeces. These and unencysted trophozoites are voided with the faeces. Being resistant to drying and other adverse conditions in the soil and water, encysted forms survive long periods.

In pigs, these ciliates are usually harmless commensals. However, when lesions from various causes occur in the mucosa, they enter and multiplication takes place. Colonies of them develop, producing submucosal ulcers comparable to the ones formed by *Entamoeba histolytica*. In humans, they are regularly tissue invaders. Ulcers result from multiplication and enzymatic action of the parasites on the surrounding tissues.

As the parasites multiply and the ulcers expand, adjacent ones coalesce resulting in the formation of still larger lesions. Destruction of the cells overlaying the ulcers allows the daughter trophozoites to escape into the intestinal lumen. As the trophozoites are carried posteriorly with the flow of the intestinal contents, they begin encystment as dehydration of the faecal material proceeds. Encystment appears to be a means of protecting the ciliates after they leave the host since multiplication in cysts does not occur. In the case of trophozoites that fail to encyst in the intestine, encystment may occur outside the host.

EXERCISE ON LIFE CYCLE

Both cysts and trophozoites may be obtained from the faeces of pigs. Trophozoites may be cultured in a medium consisting of one part caecal contents of a pig mixed with nine parts of Ringer's solution. The mixture is strained through cloth or a fine copper screen and filtered through cotton in a funnel. The filtrate is a culture medium which keeps well in an ice box. When buffered to pH 8, the trophozoites live and multiply for 28 days.

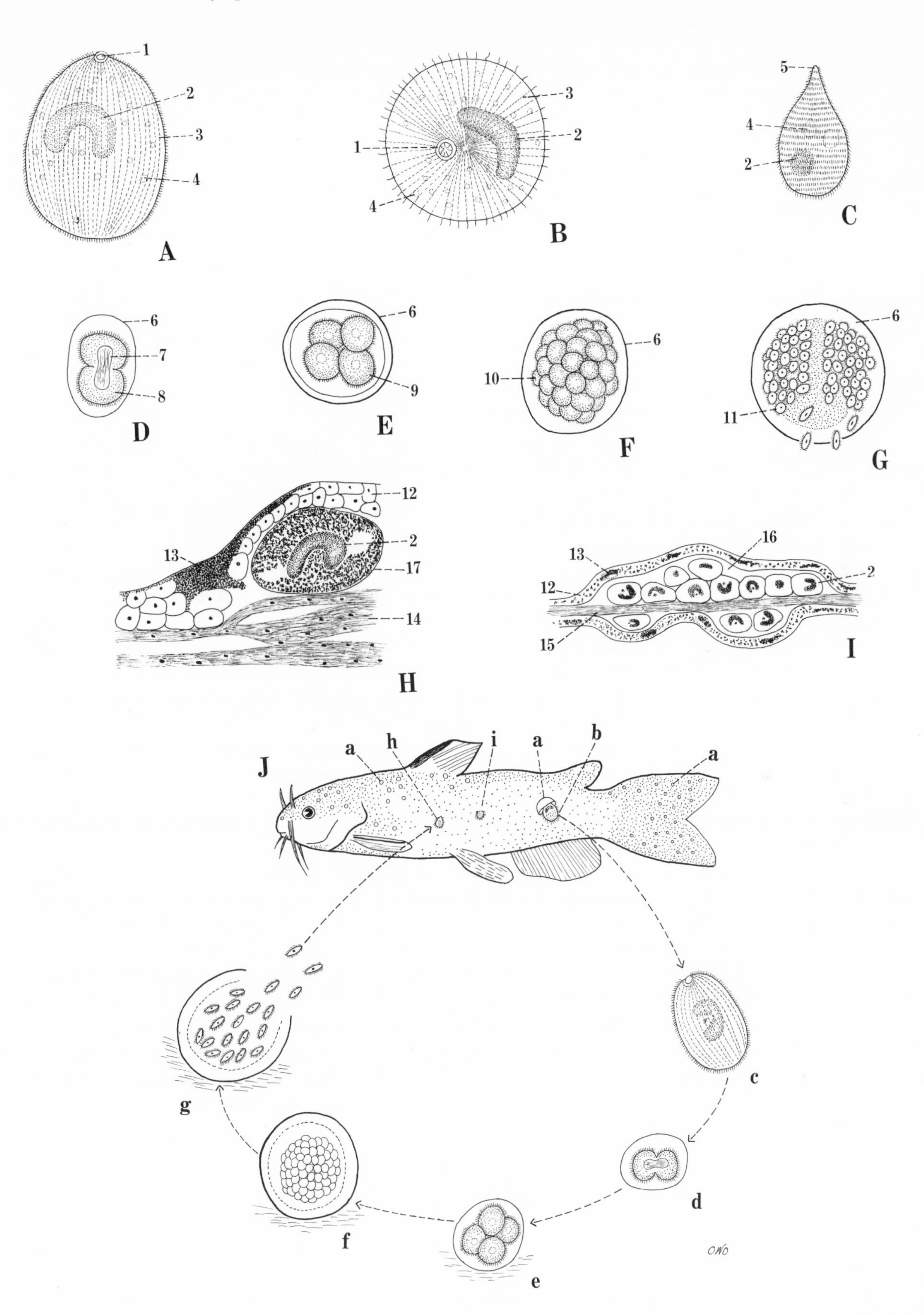
1
2
3
4
A
3
1
2
4
B
5
4
2
C
6
7
8
D
6
9
E
6
10
F
6
11
G
12
13
2
17
14
H
16
13
2
12
15
I
J
a
h
i
a
b
a
c
d
e
f
g
ONO

Subclass Euciliata

Members of this subclass are ciliated forms with a cytostome and two nuclei of different size, a macro- and micronucleus. Most species are free-living.

ORDER HOLOTRICHA

These protozoans are uniformly ciliated over the entire body, being without an adoral zone of membranelles.

FAMILY HOLOPHRYIDAE

The cytostome in the species of this family is a small circular opening at the anterior end of the body and is without specialized cilia surrounding it. At least one species is parasitic on the skin of fish.

Ichthyophthirius Fouquet, 1876

The body is ovoid with an inconspicuous vestibule and cytostome near the anterior end of the body. The large macronucleus is horseshoe-shaped.

Ichthyophthirius multifiliis Fouquet, 1876 (Plate 40)

This species attacks the skin and gills of many species of inland water fishes. It causes small greyish pustules on the body, fins, and gills. When present in large numbers, they may merge and impart a turbid appearance to the skin. The disease is known as skin disease, ichthyophthiriasis, or "ich" for short.

DESCRIPTION. Adult forms in the skin are oval and covered with numerous rows of cilia. A cytostome is formed by an unciliated ring-like structure at the anterior end. They may reach 1 mm in length. The cytoplasm contains a large horseshoe-shaped macronucleus and a small micronucleus lying in the concavity of the former. Numerous vacuoles occur throughout the cell. Adults leaving the fish encyst on the bottom of the pond, forming large gelatinous cysts with thick, clear walls. By repeated division, numerous daughter ciliates are produced within the cysts.

LIFE CYCLE. Mature ciliates are present in epidermal pustules of the skin, fins, tail, and gills of fish. Upon rupture of the pustules, the parasites are liberated and swim about feebly. Upon coming to rest on aquatic plants, snail shells or other objects on the bottom of the pond, each one secretes a thick-walled, clear, gelatinous cyst about itself. Within an hour after encystment, the mother parasite begins to divide by simple transverse division, first with two, then four, eight, and so on, until numerous daughter ciliates, or swarmers, are produced. The number may be as many as 1,000, depending on the size of the mother parasite.

The swarmers are pear-shaped, translucent, ciliated protozoans 30 to 50 μ long with a spherical nucleus and single pulsating vacuole. The pointed, unciliated anterior end serves as a boring apparatus for penetrating the skin of fish.

Within seven to eight hours after detachment of the mother parasite from the fish host in water 18 to 20° C, the swarmers have completed their development and are leaving the cysts and attaching to fish. Unattached swarmers die during the second day.

Upon attaching to a fish, the swarmers bore under the epidermis by a whirling movement. Once under the epidermis, they move about, forming galleries that are occupied by other swarmers so that a number of them occur together. These form the pustules. Division with multiplication does not occur in the epidermis.

Two to three days after attachment, a cystostome is recognizable. The boring apparatus diminishes, forming the center point of the ciliated area. Through ingestion of blood cells and nutritive substances of the skin, growing swarmers appear as opaque dark colored granules. As growth continues, the number of vacuoles in the parasites increases and the macronucleus becomes increasingly U-shaped.

EXERCISE ON LIFE CYCLE

When available, infected fish should be placed in small aquaria where cysts and swarmers may accumulate and be obtained for study.

Note the formation of the thick-walled gelatinous cyst around adult parasites freed from the pustules. This is followed by repeated binary fission within the cyst and the formation of swarmers with the unciliated pointed boring end.

Transfer swarmers to a clean aquarium containing uninfected fish and observe how long it takes for pustules to appear on them. Histological sections of the skin containing pustules should be studied to observe the effect the parasites have on it.

Observe how long it takes for an infection to produce a generally turbid condition of the skin.

SELECTED REFERENCES

Davis, H. S. (1946). U. S. Dept. Int., Fish and Wildl. Serv., Res. Rept. 12.

Doflein, F., and E. Reichenow (1953). Lehrbuch der Protozoenkunde. Gustav Fischer, Jena, p. 1115.

Kudo, R. R. (1953). Protozoology. Charles C Thomas, Springfield, Ill., p. 708.

Schäperclaus, W. (1954). Fischkrankheiten. Akademie, Berlin, p. 333.

Wenyon, C. M. (1926). Protozoology, Vol. 2. William Wood and Co., New York, p. 1187.

Balantidia obtained from frogs or cockroaches provide favorable material for studying aspects of the life cycle. A faecal medium similar to that described above for *B. coli* might be developed for studying *B. praenucleatum* from cockroaches.

In addition to swine, cockroaches, both American and Oriental, frogs and salamanders are good sources of various species of *Balantidium* for experimental studies.

SELECTED REFERENCES

Brumpt, E. (1949). Précis de Parasitologie. Masson et Cie, Paris, p. 571.

Craig, C. F. (1948). Laboratory Diagnosis of Protozoan Diseases. Lea and Febiger, Philadelphia, p. 355.

Doflein, F., and E. Reichenow. (1953). Lehrbuch der Protozoenkunde. Gustav Fischer, Jena, p. 1130.

Krascheninnikow, S., and D. H. Wenrich. (1958). J. Protozool. 5:196.

Kudo, R. R. (1966). Protozoology. Charles C Thomas, Springfield, Ill., p. 880.

Levine, N. D. (1961). Protozoan Parasites of Domestic Animals and of Man. Burgess Publishing Co., Minneapolis, p. 371.

Nelson, E. C. (1940). Amer. J. Trop. Med. 20:731.

Svensson, R. (1955). Exp. Parasit. 4:502.

Wenyon, C. M. (1926). Protozoology, Vol. 2. William Wood and Co., New York, p. 1201.

FAMILY SPIROSTOMIDAE

Members of this family are oval to kidney-shaped. Numerous species occur in the alimentary canal of invertebrates and vertebrates.

Nyctotherus Leidy, 1849

The body is somewhat flattened, oval or reniform with the dorsal surface strongly arched and the ventral concave. A groove, the peristome, begins at the anterior end, extends along the side to about midway between the ends, turns to the right and ends in the cytostome. The cytopharynx continues into the cytoplasm from the cytostome as a curved funnel-shaped tube. A row of membranelles extends through the peristome and along the right margin of the cytopharynx.

Nyctotherus cordiformis (Ehrenberg, 1838) (Plate 41)

This species occurs in the colon of frogs and is of cosmopolitan distribution. It measures 60 to 200 μ long by 40 to 140 μ wide.

LIFE CYCLE. Development consists of transverse binary fission, conjugation, and cyst formation. These modes of reproduction occur in different developmental stages of the frog host.

EXPLANATION OF PLATE 41

A. Trophozoite of *Balantidium coli.* **B.** Cyst of *B. coli.* **C.** *B. praenucleatum* from cockroaches. **D.** *B. entozoon* from frogs. **E.** Trophozoite of *B. coli* in process of transverse binary fission. **F.** Section of colon of pig, showing trophozoites of *B. coli* in mucosal layer. **G.** Diagrammatic sketch, showing stages of life cycle in colon. **H.** Swine host.

1, cytostome; **2,** cytopharynx; **3,** cytopyge, or anus; **4,** macronucleus; **5,** dividing macronucleus; **6,** micronucleus; **7,** contractile vacuole; **8,** trophozoite of *B. coli* in mucosa of intestine (section); **9,** inflammatory reaction; **10,** submucosa of intestine with its nuclei and stroma; **11,** cyst of *B. coli* entering intestine; **12,** excystation in lumen of gut; **13,** trophozoite on surface of mucosa; **14,** trophozoite dividing in lumen of intestine; **15,** trophozoite in crypts; **16,** trophozoite penetrating mucosal epithelium; **17,** multiplication of trophozoites by fission, showing destruction of tissue; **18,** nest of trophozoites, with much destruction of tissue; **19,** rupture of infected villus, releasing many daughter trophozoites into lumen of colon; **20,** some daughter trophozoites re-enter mucosal epithelium and multiply; **21,** some trophozoites are voided with faeces; **22,** most of trophozoites encyst in colon before being voided with faeces.

a, ingestion of encysted *B. coli;* **b,** excystation (occurs in stomach or small intestine); **c,** trophozoite in lumen of intestine; **d,** division of trophozoite in lumen of colon; **e,** trophozoite entering crypts of colon; **f,** trophozoite penetrating epithelial mucosa; **g,** division and colonization of trophozoites in mucosal region of colon with daughter trophozoites; **h,** rupture of villus with release of daughter trophozoites; **i,** some daughter trophozoites re-enter epithelial mucosa for further multiplication; **j,** many daughter trophozoites encyst upon being discharged from mucosa into lumen of colon; **k,** some daughter trophozoites leaving colon in an unencysted stage; **l,** cyst in faeces; **m,** trophozoites in faeces; **n,** cyst.

Figure A redrawn from Wenyon, 1926, Protozoology, Vol. 2, p. 1203; C from Kudo, 1953, Protozoology, p. 797; D from Greel, 1956, Protozoologie, p. 265; F from Brumpt, 1949, Précis de Parasitologie, p. 571; others original.

Encysted stages are formed in the colon of all stages of development of the frogs and voided with the faeces into the water. These are the infective stages.

Young, premetamorphosing tadpoles foraging on the bottom of the pond ingest the cysts which are infective to them. Excystation takes place in the small intestine. Multiplication follows by a process of transverse binary fission during the premetamorphic stage of the tadpoles.

As the ciliate prepares to divide, the body becomes shorter and broader. The macronucleus divides amitotically and the micronucleus mitotically. New cytostomal structures arise *de novo* in the posterior daughter cell. Micronuclear division occurs quickly just prior to separation of the cells.

With the appearance of the hind legs and the beginning of metamorphosis of the tadpoles, binary fission ceases and the ciliates begin to conjugate. This continues during the period of metamorphosis but is most active in tadpoles with developing hind legs. Conjugation is finished before metamorphosis of the frogs is completed.

Conjugants are smaller than normal vegetative forms. Upon coming together, the conjugating pairs adhere to each other only by the ventral side, the peristomal regions becoming tightly attached to each other. Once the two conjugants have fused, the macronuclei undergo complete fragmentation and the minute parts are dispersed throughout the cytoplasm. The micronuclei undergo three divisions. Of the four nuclei resulting from the second division, three degenerate. The remaining one is near the posterior end of the body. It divides to form two functional pronuclei.

Each migratory pronucleus moves to the anterior part of the body and crosses the cytoplasmic connection to fuse with the stationary one in the opposite cell, thereby forming the amphinucleus.

At the onset of conjugation, the original buccal organelles of each cell begin to deteriorate, eventually disappearing altogether. At the same time, new ones develop posteriorly. During conjugation, the cytopyge and contractile vacuole move laterally. They return to the normal position after the conjugants have separated. Conjugation ceases when the metamorphosing tadpoles transform into frogs.

Upon separation of the conjugants, cellular reorganization occurs. The amphinucleus moves anterior to the new cytopharynx and divides mitotically to form the new macro- and micronucleus. The fragments of the original macronucleus are completely absorbed by the cytoplasm prior to the formation of the new nuclei.

Some other common species include *N. ovalis* from cockroaches, *N. velox* from myriopods, and *N. woodi* from night lizards (*Xantusia vigilis*). Their life cycles are unknown. Since they occur in

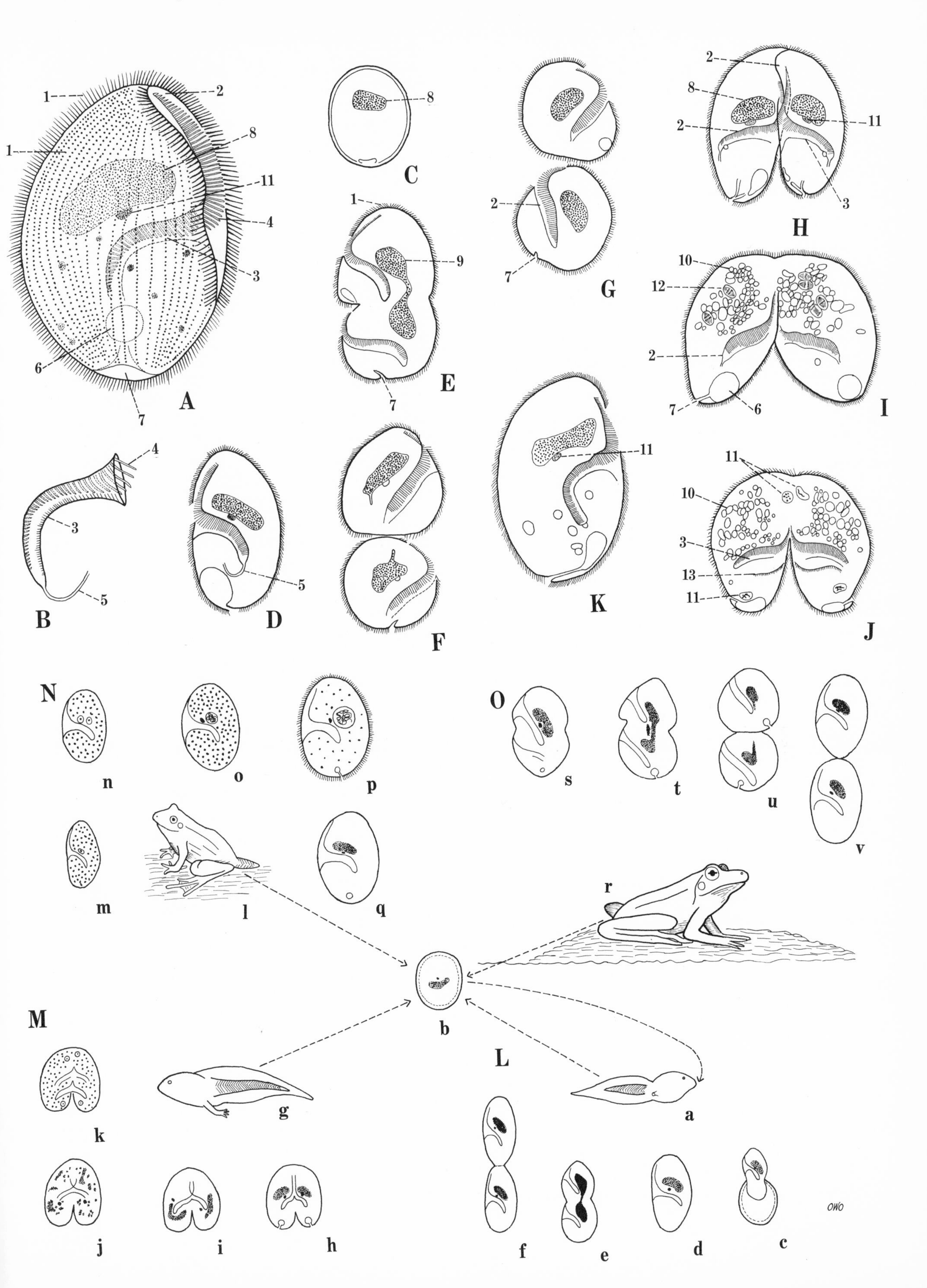
1
2
8
11
4
3
6
7
A
B
C
D
E
F
G
H
I
J
K
9
10
12
13
5
N
n
o
p
m
l
q
O
s
t
u
v
r
b
M
L
k
g
a
j
i
h
f
e
d
c
OWO

EXPLANATION OF PLATE 42 ⇨

A. Mature trophozoite. **B.** Cytopharynx. **C.** Cyst from adult frog. **D-G.** In young tadpole. **D.** Mature trophozoite from cyst. **E.** Early stage of binary fission. **F.** Advanced stage of binary fission. **G.** Completed division. **H-K.** In metamorphosing tadpole. **H.** Newly conjugated ciliates. **I.** Advanced stage of conjugation with fusion of conjugates followed by breaking up of macronucleus and division of micronuclei. **J.** Advanced stage of conjugation with formation of new ingestatory system. **K.** Fully developed exconjugate. **L.** Infection of premetamorphosing tadpoles and multiplication by transverse binary fission. **M.** Conjugation of ciliates and separation of conjugates during period of metamorphosis of tadpoles. **N.** Completion of maturation of exconjugates through formation of macro- and micronuclei which occurs in recently transformed frogs. **O.** Restoration of macro- and micronuclei through binary fission in intestine of adult frogs and the eventual formation of cyst.

1, body covering of cilia; **2**, peristome; **3**, cytopharnyx; **4**, membranelles; **5**, continuation tubule; **6**, contractile vacuole; **7**, cytopyge; **8**, macronucleus; **9**, macronucleus dividing by binary fission; **10**, fragments of macronucleus during conjugation; **11**, micronucleus; **12**, micronucleus in metaphase stage of mitosis (others in anaphase and telophase); **13**, new cytopharnyx being formed that will replace old one upon completion of conjugation.

a-f, infection of young premetamorphosing tadpoles and multiplication of ciliates in intestine; **a**, young tadpole; **b**, cyst of *Nyctotherus cordiformis;* **c**, excysting ciliate in intestine of tadpole; **d**, fully developed ciliate from cyst; **e**, multiplication of ciliate by transverse binary fission in intestine; **f**, completion of fission with formation of two individuals from one; **g-k**, metamorphosing tadpole and conjugation of ciliates in it; **g**, two-legged tadpole; **h**, early stage of conjugation with intact micro- and macronucleus; **i**, macronucleus beginning to fragment, no change in micronucleus; **j**, extensive fragmentation of macronucleus, no change in micronucleus; **k**, formation of four pronuclei (two anterior, two posterior); the migratory nuclei are exchanged and fuse with the stationary nucleus to form the amphinucleus; macronuclear material finely divided and evenly dispersed; a new buccal organelle (posterior) forms and replaces original one (anterior) which disappears; **l-q**, recently metamorphosed frog with conjugates which are found almost exclusively in this stage of host development; **l**, recently metamorphosed frog; **m**, exconjugate with amphinucleus; **n**, amphinucleus divides to form precursors of micro- and macronucleus; **o**, ciliate enlarges along with anlage of macronucleus which forms a spireme; material from former macronucleus still present as evenly dispersed fine granules; **p**, ciliate enlarges, spireme well-formed, macronuclear granules begin to disappear; **q**, macronucleus formed and located in usual position; cytophasm free of macronuclear granules; **r-v**, adult frog in which second period of binary fission in life cycle occurs followed by cyst formation; **r**, adult frog; **s**, ciliate beginning to divide; new cytostomal structure appearing; **t**, advanced division in which both nuclei are in the process of division and new ingestatory structures are well formed; **u**, division completed, ciliates preparing to separate; **v**, fully developed ciliates resulting from division; **b**, cyst expelled in faeces.

Figures C-J, a-k, m-q, s-v redrawn from Wichterman, 1937, J. Morph. 60-563, others original.

---

terrestrial, non-metamorphosing hosts, it is interesting to speculate on the difference between them and *N. cordiformis* in frogs.

EXERCISE ON LIFE CYCLE

The life cycles of species of *Nyctotherus* from terrestrial animals should be investigated to determine how they differ from that reported by Wichterman for *N. cordiformis* from frogs.

The cycle of *N. cordiformis* needs to be re-examined to determine if the stages reported follow as given.

Cultures of specimens may be obtained by simple procedures. A faecal extractor is prepared by making a constriction about 2 cm from one end of a piece of a 10-mm tube slightly shorter than a test tube. A thin plug of cotton is placed inside in contact with the upper side of the constriction which serves to retain it in place and the extractor put in the test tube. A mass of faecal material from the rectum is mixed with sterile frog-Ringer's solution (NaCl 6.5 gm, $NaHCO_2$ 0.2 gm, KCl 0.14 gm, anhydrous $CaCl_2$ 0.12 gm, NaH_2PO_4 0.01 gm, H_2O 1,000 ml) to form a volume sufficient when pipetted into the extractor to fill the test tube about 3 cm above the cotton. The test tube is plugged with cotton and let stand overnight. The extractor retains the course material but allows the solutes, fine particles, and ciliates to pass through. When the extractor is removed, the fluid in the test tube serves as the culture medium to which a small amount of rice starch is added for food. Cultures live up to three months or longer. Growth, division, and conjugation may be observed in the cultures.

PLATE 42 *Opalina ranarum, Zelleriella elliptica, Cepedea cantabrigensis, and Protoopalina mitotica*

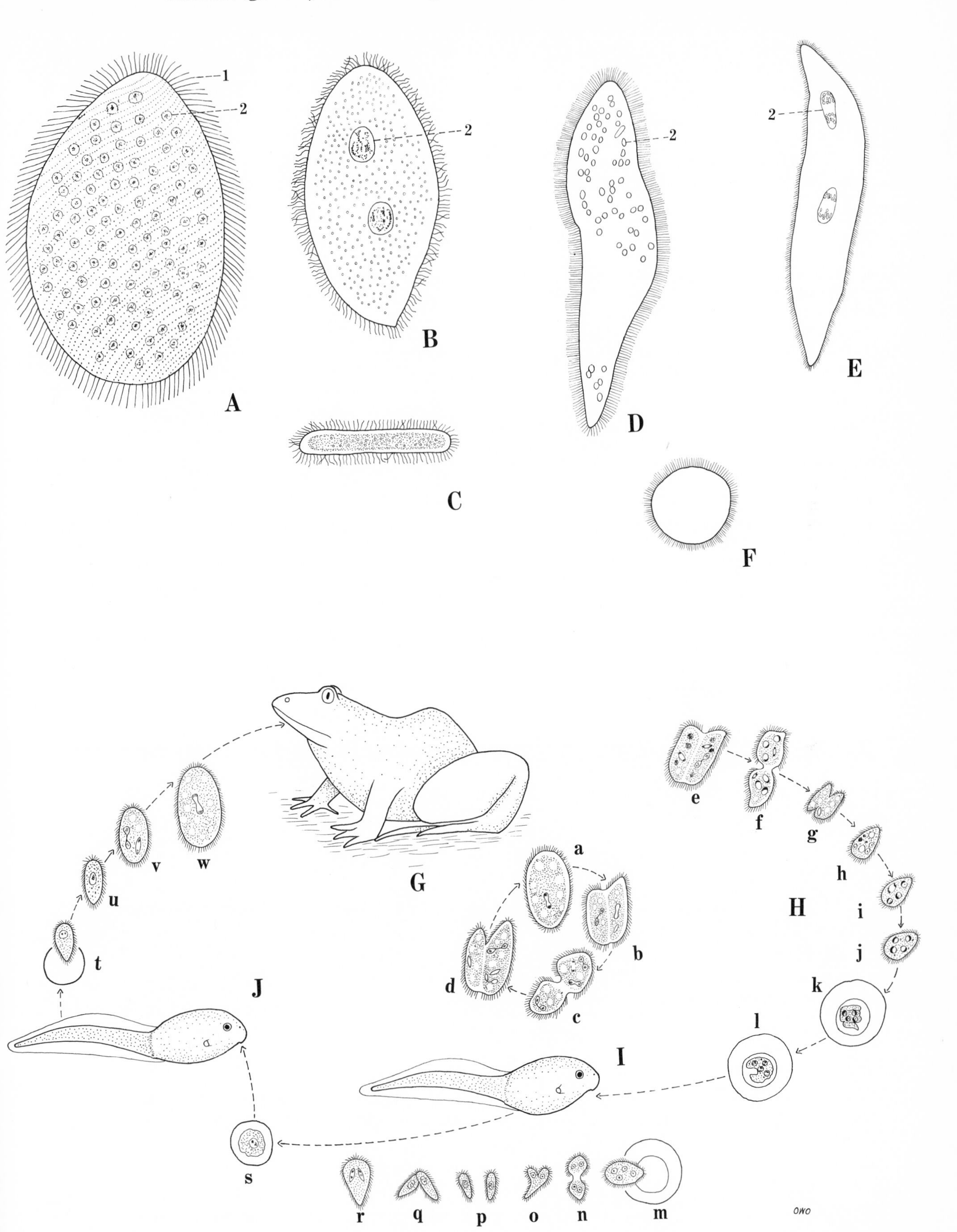

Attempts should be made to infect frogs in various stages of development by injecting ciliates from the cultures into the rectum.

Nyctotherus from terrestrial hosts should be studied in culture. Since *Nyctotherus* from frogs can be reared in cultures prepared from pig faeces (Nelson), it may be that species from various hosts may respond favorably in that medium as well as one prepared from the normal host.

SELECTED REFERENCES

Amrein, Y. U. (1952). J. Parasit. 38:266.

Doflein, F., and E. Reichenow. (1953). Lehrbuch der Protozoenkunde. Gustav Fischer, Jena, p. 1127.

Hegner, R. (1940). J. Parasit. 26:315.

Kudo, R. R. (1966). Protozoology. Charles C Thomas, Springfield, Ill., p. 967.

Nelson, E. C. (1940). Amer. J. Trop. Med. 20:731; (1943). J. Parasit. 29:292.

Wenyon, C. M. (1926). Protozoology, Vol. 2. William Wood and Co., New York, p. 1198.

Wichterman, R. (1937). J. Morph. 60:563.

PART III PHYLUM PLATYHELMINTHES

Parasitic representatives of the Platyhelminthes include the classes Trematoda and Cestoda. They are soft-bodied flat worms with an incomplete digestive tract in the Trematoda and none at all in the Cestoda. Since there is not a body cavity, the internal organs lie embedded in the spongy parenchymatous tissue. The trematodes are monozoic, *i.e.*, a single body, and the cestodes are monozoic or polyzoic, in which the body consists of a few to thousands of proglottids.

CLASS TREMATODA

The Trematoda consists of three subclasses, the Monogenea, Aspidobothrea, and Digenea.

Subclass Monogenea

The monogenetic trematodes are the most primitive of the flukes, showing relationships to free-living rhabdocoels in structure. They are parasites of cold-blooded aquatic vertebrates, especially fish. They are primarily ectoparasitic, although a few species occur in such places as the mouth, urinary bladder, and ureters. The life cycles are direct, that is, being completed without the need of an intermediate host.

The subclass consists of the orders Monopisthocotylea and Polyopisthocotylea. Some of the common representatives of each order are shown in Plate 43, together with the basic morphological characteristics of each.

ORDER MONOPISTHOCOTYLEA

The members of this order are characterized by a single organ of adhesion, usually in the form of a well-developed disc but sometimes sucker-like, located at the posterior extremity of the body. It is armed with one to three pairs of large hooks and 12 to 16 marginal hooklets. The eggs are nonoperculate. The life cycles of representatives from two families will be considered.

FAMILY DACTYLOGYRIDAE

These are small elongate, oviparous flukes on the gills of fish. They have two or more pairs of head organs, an opisthaptor (posterior sucker) with one or two pairs of large hooks, and 14 marginal hooklets.

Dactylogyrus vastator Nybelin, 1924 (Plate 44)

These flukes occur commonly on the gills of carp, where they are especially dangerous to the health of young fish.

DESCRIPTION. Adults measure 0.8 to 1.15 mm long by 0.15 to 0.25 mm wide. There are two prominent head lobes, each with a well-developed sticky gland and two pairs of eyespots in front of the pharynx. The opisthaptor is 0.12 mm in diameter and bears one pair of large hooks with bifurcate roots and seven pairs of small marginal hooklets. There is a single, oval testis and a cirrus that is 54 μ

EXPLANATION OF PLATE 43 ⇨

A. *Gyrodactylus cylindriformis* from *Umbra limi*. B. *Dactylogyrus extensus* from gills of *Cyprinus carpio*. C. *Ancyrocephalus aculeatus* from gills of *Stizostedion vitreum*. D. *Udonella caligorum* on *Gadus callarias* and *Myliobatis californicus*. E. *Benedenia girellae* from skin of *Girella nigricans*. F. *Acanthocotyle williamsi* from skin of "skate." G. *Heterocotyle minima* from gills of *Squalus acanthias*. H. *Microbothrium apiculatum* from *Squalus acanthias*. I. *Rajonchocotyloides emarginata* from gills of *Raja clavata*. J. *Polystomoides cornutum* from North American turtles. K. *Diclidophora caulolatili* from gills of *Caulolatilus princips*. L. *Neohexastoma euthynni* from gills of *Euthynnus alletteratus*. M. *Mazocraes macracanthum* from gills of a mackerel. N. *Microcotyle spinicirrus* from gills of *Aplodinotus grunniens*. O. *Octomacrum lanceatum* from gills of *Catastomus commersoni*.

1, glandular prohaptor; 2, external paired sucker-like prohaptor; 3, internal buccal suckers; 4, oral sucker; 5, mouth; 6, pharynx; 7, intestine; 8, egg; 9, first embryo; 10, second embryo; 11, ovary; 12, seminal receptacle; 13, genital pore; 14, vitellaria; 15, testis; 16, opisthaptor; 17, anchors with transverse connecting bar; 18, spines; 19, marginal hooklets; 20, sucker; 21, sickle-shaped hook in sucker; 22, opisthaptoral appendage; 23, clamps; 24, detailed view of clamp of Diclidophoridae; 25, clamp of Hexastomatidae; 26, clamp of Mazocraeidae; 27, clamp of Microcotylidae; 28, clamp of Discocotylidae; 29, haptoral hook.

Figures A, B, C redrawn from Van Cleave and Mueller, 1932, Roosevelt Wildlife Ann. 3:93; D, F, G, H, from Price, 1938, J. Wash. Acad. Sci. 28:185; E, from Hargis, 1941, J. Parasit. 41:48; I, from Price, 1939, Proc. Helm. Soc. Wash. 7:76; J, from Price, 1939, Ibid. 6:83; O, from Price, 1943, Ibid. 10:12; K, L, M, from Meserve, 1938, Allan Hancock Pacific Exped. 2:43; N, from Remeley, 1942, Trans. Amer. Micr. Soc. 61:141.

---

long. The ovary is more or less oval and located near the middle of the body. The vaginal opening is toward the right margin of the body, slightly pre-equatorial.

LIFE CYCLE. Adult flukes on the gill filaments lay unembryonated eggs that fall off the fish and sink to the bottom of the pond. They are characterized by being flattened on one side and bearing a bifurcated stalk-like structure on one end. Under summer temperatures development of the embryo is rapid, and fully formed gyrodactylid larvae appear in 2½ days. By pressing from inside the egg, the larva forces off one end of the egg shell and escapes, leaving the embryonic membrane inside.

The larvae bear a tuft of cilia on the anterior and posterior extremities and on each side near the middle of the body. There are four eyespots and a large opisthaptor bearing a pair of large hooks and 14 small hooklets. Larvae swim about actively, attaching to the skin of carp when coming in contact with them. Having attached to the fish host, they migrate over the body toward the gills, being attracted by the mucus from them.

Sexual maturity is attained about 10 days after reaching the gills. The peak of infestation on the fish is reached about the middle of July, after which the flukes begin to disappear, being gone by fall. During the last phase of oviposition, winter eggs are laid; these remain in a resting stage during the cold weather. With the arrival of spring and the warming of the water, development of the eggs begins and hatching soon takes place. Young carp especially are infested, often fatally when large numbers of flukes are present on the gill filaments. Eggs laid during the summer hatch, adding to the parasite burden of the fish.

Dactylogyrus macracanthus and *D. anchoratus* have life cycles basically similar to that of *D. vastator*. Species of *Gyrodactylus* (Gyrodactylidae), also parasites of the gills of fish, are ovoviparous. Their eggs develop and hatch within the uterus. Before birth, a second larva appears inside the first, a third inside the second, and even a fourth inside the third. After birth, the primary larva attaches to the gills of a fish and the sequence of growth and birth of the larvae contained within it ensues.

EXERCISE ON LIFE CYCLE

Eggs for experimental purposes may be obtained by two methods. Those deposited by flukes on naturally infested carp kept in small aquaria sink to the bottom and may be recovered by concentrating the sediment and recovering them from it. Adult flukes removed from the gill filaments and placed in dishes of water deposit their eggs.

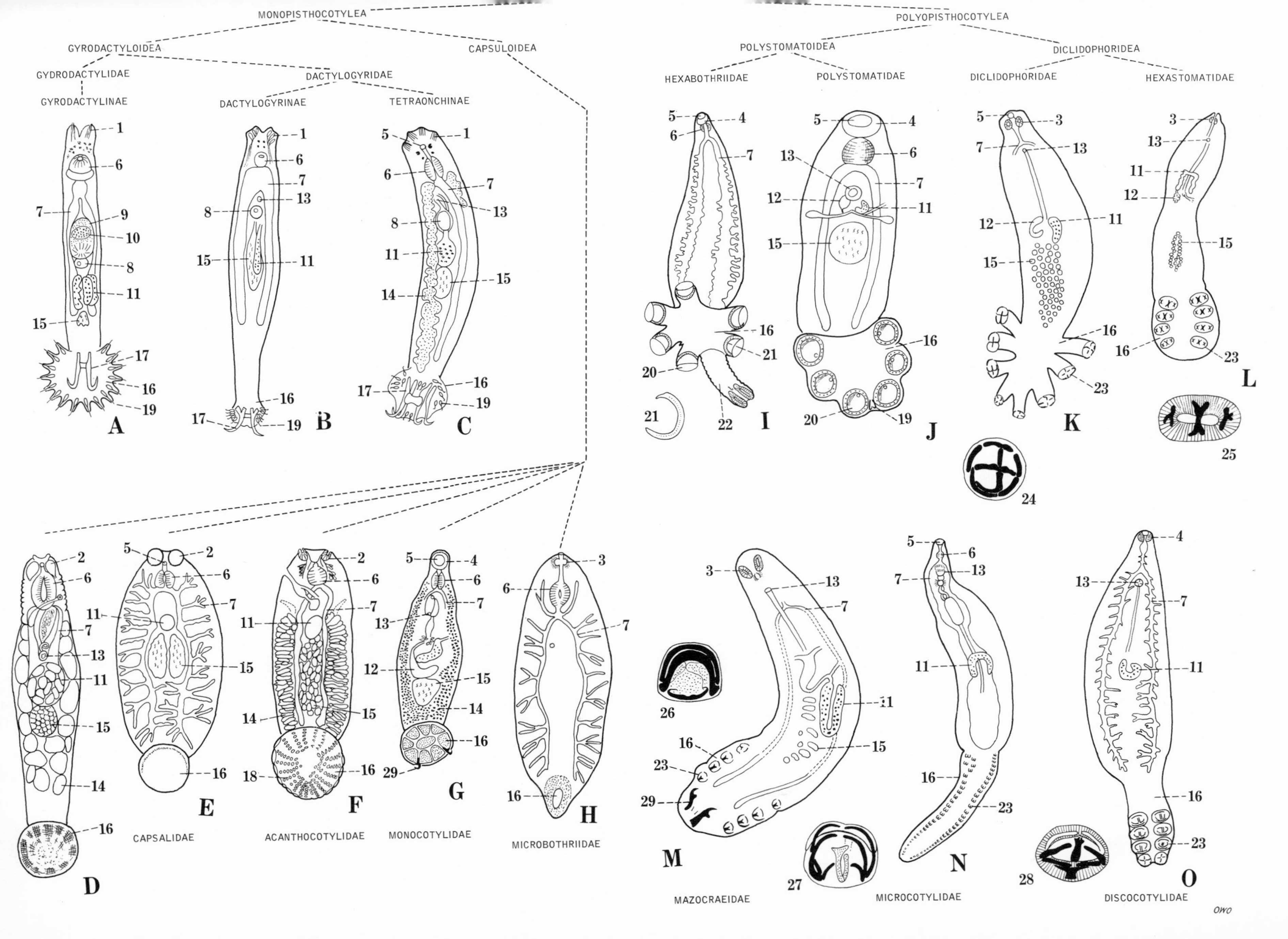
MONOPISTHOCOTYLEA
GYRODACTYLOIDEA
GYDRODACTYLIDAE
GYRODACTYLINAE
DACTYLOGYRIDAE
DACTYLOGYRINAE
TETRAONCHINAE
CAPSULOIDEA
POLYOPISTHOCOTYLEA
POLYSTOMATOIDEA
HEXABOTHRIIDAE
POLYSTOMATIDAE
DICLIDOPHORIDEA
DICLIDOPHORIDAE
HEXASTOMATIDAE
A
B
C
I
J
K
L
D
E
CAPSALIDAE
F
ACANTHOCOTYLIDAE
G
MONOCOTYLIDAE
H
MICROBOTHRIIDAE
M
MAZOCRAEIDAE
N
MICROCOTYLIDAE
O
DISCOCOTYLIDAE
OWO

EXPLANATION OF PLATE 44 ⇨

A. Adult fluke. **B.** Fully developed and recently hatched larva. **C.** Young larva having lost its cilia. **D.** Freshly laid and undeveloped egg. **E.** Partially developed embryo. **F.** Egg with fully developed larva. **G.** Larva escaping from egg. **H.** Carp *(Cyprinus carpio)* host with opercular cover removed to show gill filaments.

1, four head organs; **2,** eyespots; **3,** pharynx; **4,** cyclic intestine; **5,** testis; **6,** vas efferens; **7,** male genital pore; **8,** ovary; **9,** oviduct; **10,** genitointestinal canal; **11,** unembryonated egg in uterus; **12,** female genital opening; **13,** vitelline gland; **14,** vitelline duct; **15,** opisthaptor; **16,** anchor; **17,** transverse bar; **18,** marginal hooks; **19,** anterior tuft of cilia on a pad of cells; **20,** median tuft of cilia; **21,** caudal tuft of cilia on a pyramid of cells forming so-called tail; **22,** unembryonated egg in water; **23,** yolk material; **24,** partially developed larva; **25,** embryonic membrane; **26,** larva hatching.

a, adult fluke attached to gills of carp lays eggs; **b,** unembryonated egg falling free from gills; **c,** egg on bottom of pond; **d,** developing larva; **e,** fully developed larva in egg; **f,** hatching egg with larvae escaping into water; **g,** swimming larva comes in contact with carp; **h,** larva has shed ciliated pads and enters mucous layer; **i,** larva increases in size and continues to migrate toward gills; **j,** larger larva reaches gills and matures in about 10 days.

Figure A adapted from various sources and Figures B-G, from Gröben, 1940, Z. Parasitenk. 11:611.

Observations on the development of the eggs may be made by placing them on microscope slides and watching them through a microscope at frequent intervals for 2 to 3 days.

Observations may be made on the reaction of larvae to a small drop of mucus from the gills of carp. This experiment gives some information on how the larvae find the gills.

Infection experiments may be conducted by placing larvae in a small aquarium with goldfish. Determine how long it takes from the time of exposure of the fish to larvae until eggs appear in the aquarium.

Ascertain whether eggs laid in the fall hatch in the usual time or whether they are winter eggs and hatch the following spring. Also determine whether flukes remain on the gills over winter.

SELECTED REFERENCES

Dawes, B. (1956). The Trematoda. Cambridge University Press, London, p. 66.

Gröben, G. (1940). Z. Parasitenk. 11:611.

Hyman, L. (1951). The Invertebrates, Vol. 3. McGraw-Hill Book Co., New York, pp. 232, 239.

Kathariner, L. (1904). Zool. Jahrb. Suppl. 7:519.

Paperma, I. (1963). Bamidgeh 15:8.

Wilde, J. (1937). Z. Parasitenk. 9:203.

ORDER POLYOPISTHOCOTYLEA

The members of this order are characterized by the opisthaptor being composed of a number of suckerlets or clamps borne on a disc-like process or on the ventral surface of the posterior end of the body. They are parasites on fish, amphibians, reptiles, and sometimes in the eyes of marine mammals.

FAMILY POLYSTOMATIDAE

The species of this family are parasites of the gills, buccal and nasal cavities, pharynx, oesophagus, urinary bladder of amphibians and reptiles, and the eyes of marine mammals.

An oral sucker forms the prohaptor, while a disc bearing one to three pairs of cuplike muscular suckers forms the opisthaptor.

Sphyranura oligorchis (Alvey, 1933) (Plate 45)

This parasite infects the gills of necturus (*Necturus maculosus*) in the eastern part of the United States and possibly wherever the host occurs.

DESCRIPTION. Adult worms are 2.5 mm long. The opisthaptor consists of two large hooks 260 μ long and two large cuplike muscular suckers. In addition, there are 16 hooklets arranged with

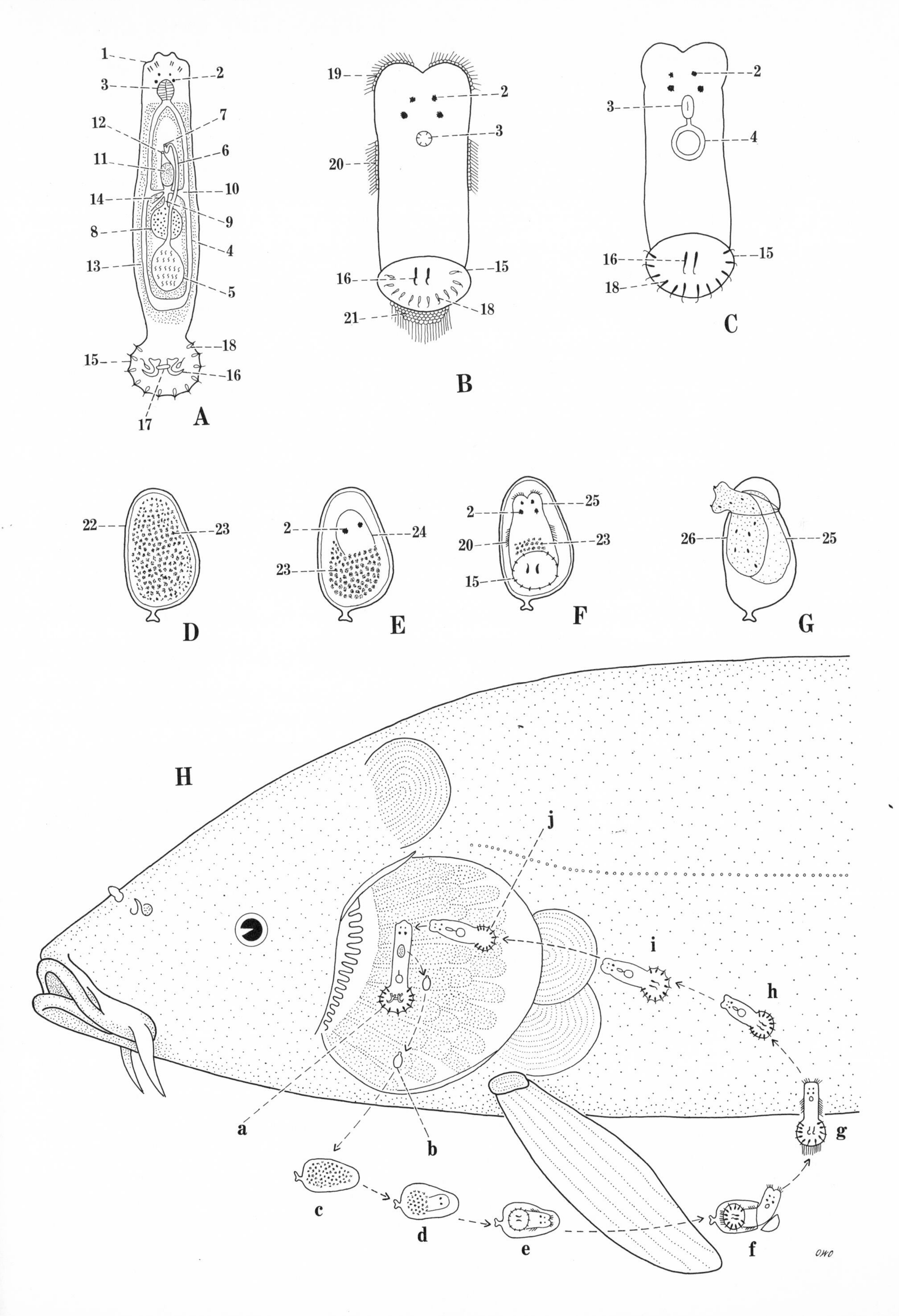
1
2
3
12
7
11
6
14
10
8
9
13
4
5
15
18
16
17
A
19
20
16
21
15
18
B
C
22
23
24
25
26
D
E
F
G
H
j
i
h
g
a
b
c
d
e
f
OHO

EXPLANATION OF PLATE 45 ⇨

A. Adult fluke. **B.** Anchor (large hook). **C.** Unembryonated egg. **D.** Egg hatching. **E.** Young larva just hatched. **F.** Slightly older larva. **G.** Larva 16 days old. **H.** Salamander *(Necturus maculatus)* host. **I.** Salamander host.

1, oral sucker (prohaptor); **2,** opisthaptor; **3,** sucker; **4,** hooklet of sucker; **5,** marginal hooklets; **6,** anchor; **7,** pharynx; **8,** intestine; **9,** testes; **10,** vas deferens; **11,** seminal vesicle; **12,** common genital pore; **13,** ovary; **14,** oviduct; **15,** genitointestinal canal; **16,** uterus; **17,** egg in uterus; **18,** excretory vesicle; **19,** shell of unembryonated egg; **20,** yolk material; **21,** larva escaping from egg; **22,** primordium of digestive tract.

a, adult worm on gills of salamander; **b,** unembryonated egg falling from gills; **c,** embryonated egg on bottom of pool; **d,** egg that has just hatched with larva free in water; **e,** newly hatched larva on skin migrating toward gills; **f,** older larva on gills; **g,** 15-day-old larva on gills continues development reaching maturity about two months after attaching to gills.

Adapted from Alvey, 1936, Parasitology 28:229.

---

seven on each side of the opisthaptor and one in each sucker. There are six testes arranged in a row one behind the other between the branches of the intestine. The ovoid ovary is located intercaecally toward the left side just anterior to the middle of the body. Vitellaria extend from near the middle of the body to the posterior end. The flukes are oviparous, producing unembryonated, operculate eggs.

LIFE CYCLE. Adult flukes on the gill filaments lay their unembryonated eggs which drop off and settle to the bottom of the pond. Development is slow at room temperature, as hatching does not occur until between the 28th and 32nd days of incubation. Newly hatched worms swim by means of the caudal disc, or creep. Larvae are very active for a few hours after hatching, then become exhausted, sink to the bottom, and die. If, however, they come in contact with a necturus during the period of activity, they attach and migrate to the gills, no growth taking place in the meantime. Once on the gills where a rich supply of blood and protection are available, development is completed in about 2 months.

EXERCISE ON LIFE CYCLE

Fertile eggs may be collected from the bottom of aquaria in which infected necturus are kept. When placed in Syracuse watch glasses for ready availability, individual eggs may be removed by means of a fine pipette, placed on a microscope slide, and studied daily by microscopic examination for progressive development and hatching.

Place uninfected necturus in an aquarium with fully developed eggs that are ready to hatch. Observe development of the flukes on the necturus at intervals of about 10 days from the time of attachment until sexual maturity.

SELECTED REFERENCES

Alvey, C. H. (1936). Parasitology 28:229.

Polystoma nearcticum (Paul, 1935) (Plate 46)

P. nearcticum occurs in the urinary bladder of tadpoles and adults of tree toads (*Hyla versicolor*) and on the gills of their tadpoles. There are two forms, the branchial form on the gills and the bladder form in the urinary bladder.

Paul considered the American flukes to be a subspecies of *P. integerrimum* from the urinary bladder of *Rana temporaria* in Europe and named it *P. integerrimum nearcticum.* Price regarded it sufficiently different to constitute a valid species and designated it *P. nearcticum* (Paul, 1935).

DESCRIPTION. The bladder forms range from 2.5 to 4.5 mm long by 0.9 to 1.5 mm wide. The cordiform caudal disc bears six muscular, cup-shaped suckers and one pair of large hooks. The testis is multilobate and the ovary comma-shaped. Eggs are unembryonated and measure 300 by 150 μ.

The branchial forms are 1.64 to 5 mm long and 0.29 to 0.76 wide. The cordiform opisthaptor

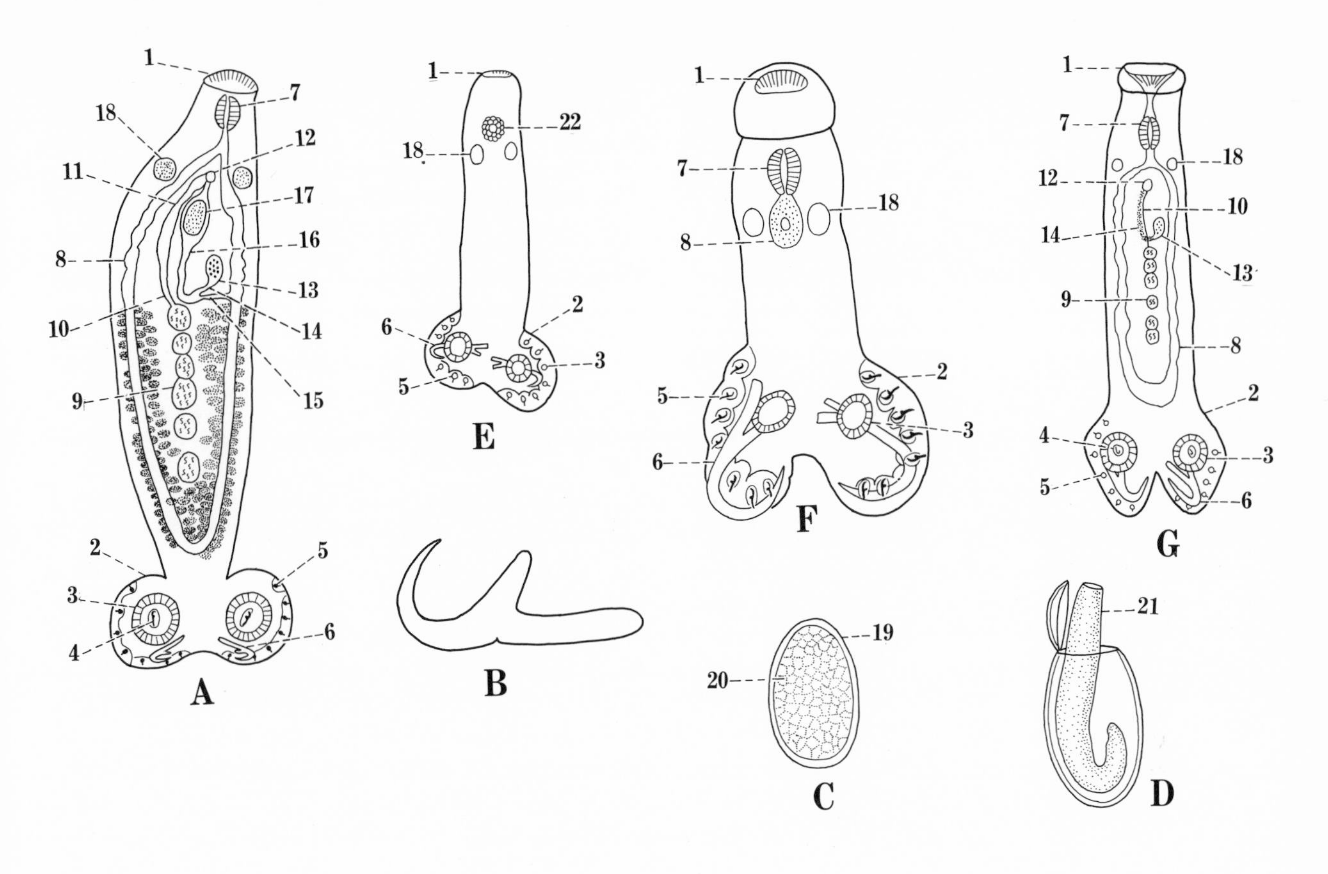
1
7
18
12
11
17
8
16
10
13
14
9
15
2
5
3
4
6
A
22
E
B
F
19
20
C
G
21
D

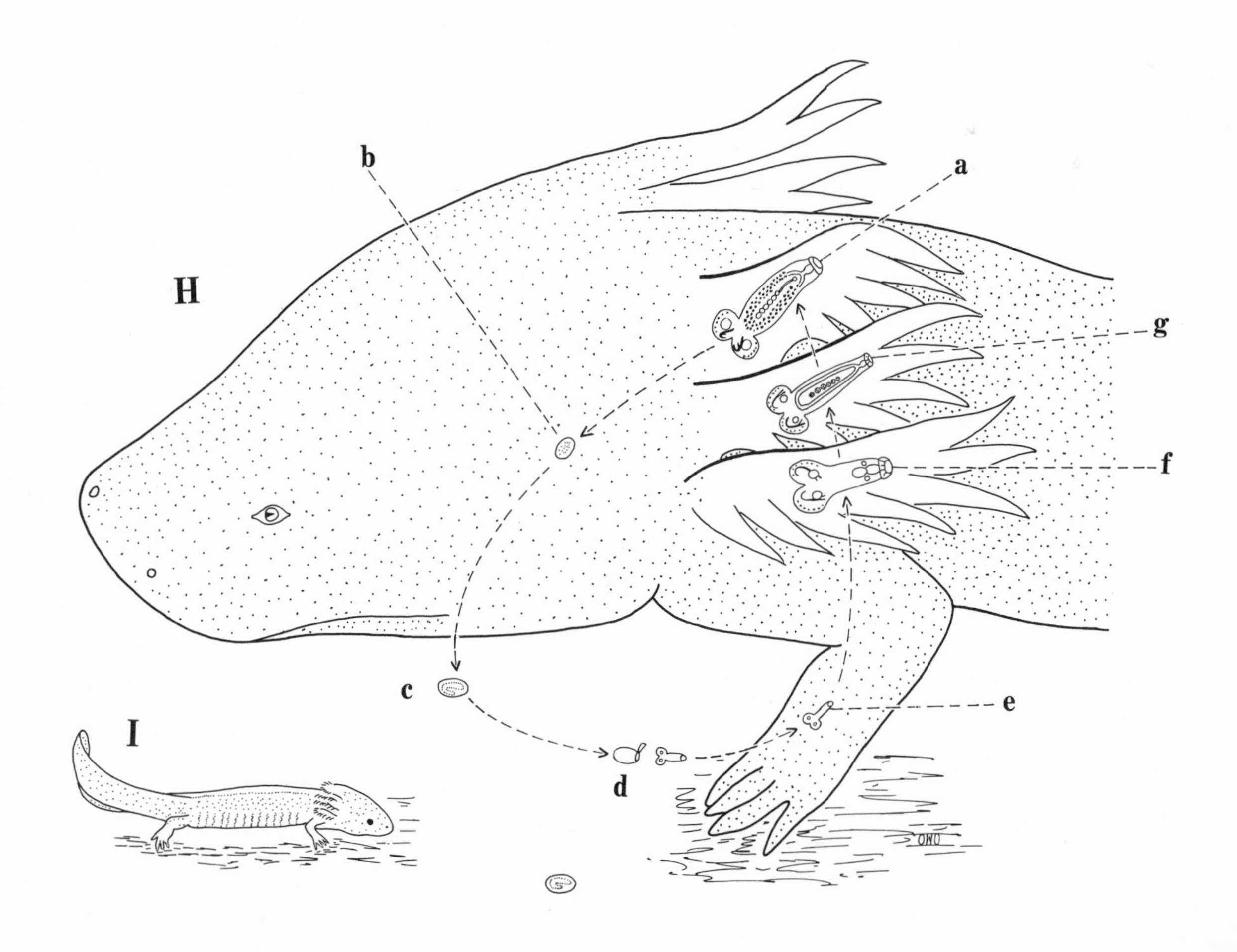
b
a
H
g
f
c
e
I
d

EXPLANATION OF PLATE 46 ▷

A. Adult bladder fluke. **B.** Adult branchial fluke. **C.** Embryonated egg of *P. intergerrimum.** **D.** Dactylogyroid type larva of *P. intergerrimum.** **E.** Adult toad *(Hyla versicolor, H. cinerea)* host of bladder generation. **F.** Tadpole of *Hyla* which is host of branchial generation. **G.** Metamorphosing *Hyla.*

1, mouth (prohaptor); **2,** opisthaptor; **3,** opisthaptoral sucker; **4,** anchors; **5,** pharynx; **6,** branched intestine; **7,** sperm; **8,** vas deferens; **9,** common genital pore; **10,** ovary; **11,** oviduct; **12,** Mehlis' gland; **13,** ootype; **14,** uterus; **15,** genitointestinal canal; **16,** vagina; **17,** vaginal duct; **18,** vitellovaginal duct; **19,** excretory pore; **20,** testis; **21,** vitelline gland; **22,** vitelline duct; **23,** eyespot; **24,** tuft of cilia; **25,** oesophageal gland; **26,** marginal hooks; **27,** excretory tubule.

a, adult fluke of bladder generation in urinary bladder of toad; **b,** unembryonated eggs laid in urinary bladder are voided with urine; **c,** development of eggs begins in water; **d,** fully developed larva; **e,** empty egg shell; **f,** gyrodactyloid larva in water enters gill chamber of tadpoles by way of spiracle, thus ending the urinary bladder generation and initiating the branchial generation; **g,** larvae attach to gills of tadpoles and mature in about 22 days; **h,** unembryonated eggs laid on gills of tadpoles are washed from gill chamber through spiracle into the water; **i,** fully developed larva, identical with those of the urinary generation; **j,** empty egg shell; **k,** gyrodactyloid larva free in water; **l,** larva enters anus of metamorphosing toad, going to urinary bladder; **m,** young flukes entering the bladder initiate the urinary bladder generation which reaches sexual maturity simultaneously with the toads.

Figures A-B adapted from Paul, 1938, J. Parasit. 24:489; C, from Zeller in Claus and Sedgwick, 1884, Elementary Textbook of Zoology. McMillan and Co., New York, Fig. 259 a; D, from Gallien, 1935, Trav. Sta. Zool. Wimereux 12:1.

---

bears six pedunculate suckers. The hooks are rudimentary when present. The testis is spherical and the ovary elongate. Eggs are indistinguishable from those of the bladder form.

LIFE CYCLE. Adult bladder forms of the flukes begin to lay eggs at the same time the toads become sexually active in the spring. The eggs are voided with the urine. In water, they are fully developed after 11 to 13 days at room temperature. Hatching occurs between the 12th and 13th days. The larvae are very active up to 20 hours, after which they slow down, sink to the bottom, and die if they do not attach to tadpoles.

Larvae that attach to the gills of tadpoles develop to sexually mature branchial flukes in 22 days. Only eggs that pass through the spiracle into the water are viable. Those that are swallowed and pass through the intestinal tract do not hatch. It is not known whether secondary infection of the gills by larvae from branchial flukes occurs.

Evidence indicates that the free-swimming larvae of the branchial flukes enter the cloaca of tadpoles by way of the anus, going to the urinary bladder as soon as it is formed. Larvae continue to enter through the anus during the process of metamorphosis of the tadpoles and young toads. At the time of atrophy of the gills during metamorphosis of the tadpoles, the branchial flukes die. Larvae entering the bladder develop into bladder forms. Inasmuch as oviposition of the flukes in the bladder coincides with that of the toads at 3 years of age, maturity of them is not attained until they, too, are 3 years old. Thus, there is an alternation of a generation of branchial flukes that requires 3 weeks to mature followed by one of bladder flukes that requires 3 years to mature. Conceivably both the branchial and bladder generations could be on and in the same tadpole. Whether this actually occurs is not known.

EXERCISE ON LIFE CYCLE

When a source of infected tree toads is available for conducting a life history study, special effort must be made to have a large supply of toad eggs on hand for providing tadpoles throughout the course of the investigation. This is accomplished by collecting an adequate number of eggs in advance of the experiment and storing them under sufficiently low temperature to allow their survival without development.

Infected toads isolated in jars partially filled with water serve as a source of fluke eggs. The eggs settle to the bottom of the container upon being voided with the urine. Collection of them should be at frequent intervals.

---

*According to Paul (1938), these stages in *P. nearcticum* are identical with those of *P. integerrimum.*

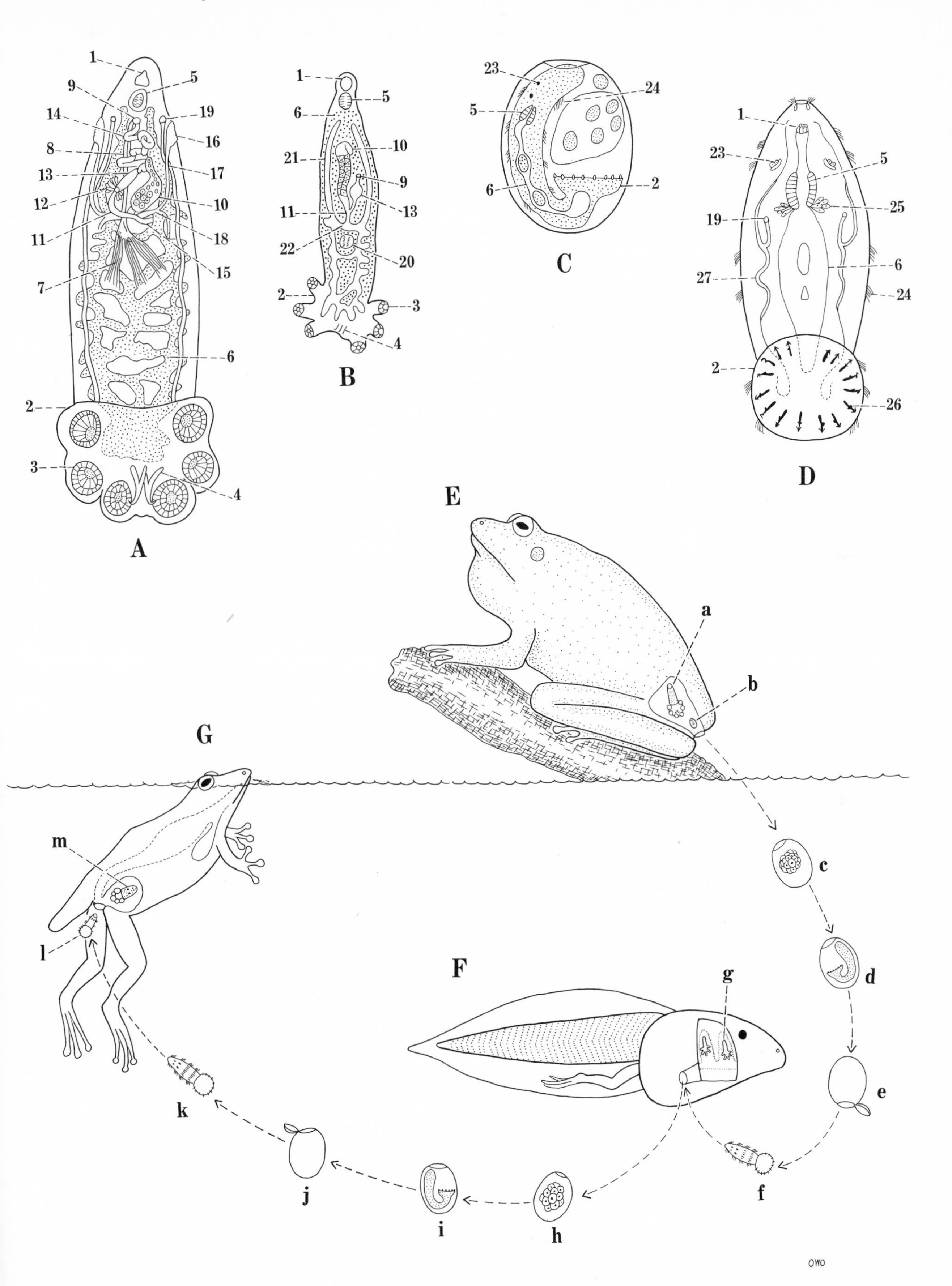
1
5
9
19
14
16
8
17
13
12
10
11
18
15
7
6
2
3
4
A
1
5
6
10
21
9
11
13
22
20
2
3
4
B
23
24
5
6
2
C
1
23
5
25
19
6
27
24
2
26
D
E
a
b
G
m
l
c
d
F
g
e
k
f
j
i
h
OWO

Development may be observed over a period of about 2 weeks at room temperature, at which time hatching begins. Fully incubated eggs or larvae placed with young gillbearing tadpoles will provide all the stages of the branchial forms over a period of 3 weeks.

Using parasite-free tadpoles, ascertain whether larvae hatching from eggs laid by branchial forms will develop into similar neotenic adults on the gills or whether they will develop only in the urinary bladder. This point has never been clarified.

Try to determine whether tadpoles become infected with bladder forms by larval flukes entering the anus, another point that needs confirmation.

SELECTED REFERENCES

Cameron, T. W. M. (1956). Parasites and Parasitism. John Wiley and Sons, New York, p. 98.

Gallien, L. (1935). Trav. Sta. Zool. Wimereux 12:1.

Paul, A. A. (1935). J. Parasit. 21:442; (1938). Ibid. 24:489.

Price, E. W. (1939). Proc. Helminth. Soc. Wash. 6:80.

Subclass Aspidobothrea

This is a small group of trematodes that parasitizes mollusks, fish, and turtles. They are characterized morphologically by the large compartmentalized adhesive organ that encompasses almost the entire ventral surface of the body. They resemble the Monogenea, on the one hand, in that none of them has asexual generations, and the Digenea, on the other hand, in that some of them have an alternation of hosts. These biological characteristics are considered justification for placing them in a position intermediate between the Monogenea and the Digenea.

The subclass consists of the families Aspidogasteridae and Stichocotylidae. The genera *Aspidogaster, Cotylaspis,* and *Cotylogaster* of the Aspidogasteridae are among the best known members of the subclass.

FAMILY ASPIDOGASTERIDAE

These are small to medium-sized trematodes with the ventral surface of the body forming a large alveolated adhesive organ; they occur commonly in fresh-water clams.

Aspidogaster conchicola von Baer, 1827 (Plate 47)

This is a cosmopolitan parasite of the pericardial and renal cavities of fresh-water clams. It is common in the family Unionidae in North America. In addition to clams, the usual hosts, it occurs also in gastropods and turtles.

DESCRIPTION. Full grown worms are 2.5 to 2.7 mm long by 1.1 to 1.2 mm wide. The large ventral portion of the body is almost entirely covered by an alveolated sucker consisting of four rows of quadrangular sucking grooves. The narrower anterior necklike portion, consisting of about one-fifth the total length of the worm, bears a terminal mouth. There is a single median testis and an ovary somewhat anterior and toward the right side. The operculate eggs are embryonated when laid and measure 128 to 130 μ long by 48 to 50 μ wide.

LIFE CYCLE. The entire life cycle occurs in a single invertebrate host. Adult worms in the pericardial or renal cavities lay eggs containing well-developed first stage larvae. Development from the earliest larval stage to the adult is one of gradual transformation.

There are four developmental stages of larvae. The first stage is unciliated, very immobile, and 130 to 150 μ long. It consists of three main body divisions set off by constrictions. They are the anterior terminal sucker, middle section, and posterior subterminal sucker followed by a blunt rudimentary taillike appendage. Each section contains primordial cells representing some future structure. The second stage is larger, being 150 to 275 μ long, has lost the constrictions, and shows considerable activity but is unable to swim. Third stage larvae are larger than the preceding one, being 880 μ long and greatly modified in shape. The oral sucker is at the end of a long necklike structure and the ventral sucker has assumed much larger proportions, foreshadowing that of the adult. Fourth stage larvae are about twice the size of the third, measuring 1.2 to 1.4 mm long. In general, the shape is similar to that of the adult. The large ventral sucker is well-developed but lacks the alveoli.

All of these stages except the first have been found in the pericardial cavity of clams. This condition led to the opinion (Williams) that the entire development might take place within a single clam. Dissemination of the eggs from the clams into the water, however, where they might hatch seems to be the more likely manner in which early development occurs. This would provide a means of dissemination of the parasite among the clams. A natural route exists for the escape of eggs from the pericardium. Eggs in it could easily enter the reno-pericardial pore, pass through the kidney and out through the kidney pore into the suprabranchial chambers of the gills. Upon being expelled by the water currents through the excurrent siphon, they would settle to the bottom of the pond where favorable conditions for hatching exist. Infection of the pelecypods might take place by drawing first stage larvae through the incurrent siphon into the suprabranchial chambers where they would be in a position to enter the renal pore and migrate through the kidney into the pericardium and develop to adults. While only the second, third, and fourth stage larvae and adults have been demonstrated in the pericardial cavity, this fact provides a basis for the postulate that the eggs are expelled into the water and hatch there. The habits, physiology, and morphology of the clams combine to provide an ideal means of infection in the manner suggested.

Adult *Aspidogaster conchicola* have been found in the digestive tract of turtles. Their presence probably resulted from the turtles eating infected clams. The interesting fact exists, however, that these worms which are normally parasites of mollusks are able to survive in the alimentary canal of a reptile. The question may be raised as to whether this is a step toward the introduction of a vertebrate host into a trematode cycle, as occurs in the subclass Digenea.

Lophotaspis vallei of the stomach of loggerhead turtles (*Caretta caretta*) appears to carry the evolution of trematodes a step further. Larval stages of the parasite occur in the flag conch (*Fasciolaria gigas*) which serves as food for the turtles. The larvae of *L. vallei* are ciliated and swim readily, as well as crawl, thus enabling them to reach the conchs. This cycle is significant in that it suggests another connecting link based on biological evidence in the evolution of the trematodes.

EXERCISE ON LIFE CYCLE

More serious studies should be conducted on the biology of this and related species of Aspidobothrea.

Infected clams placed in aquaria could be used to determine if eggs are passed from the body, as postulated above. The large size of the eggs and first stage larvae make them easy to find in the containers where infected clams are kept. If first-stage larvae can be obtained, efforts should be made to determine whether infection takes place by their being drawn into the gill chambers through the incurrent siphon. If a sufficient number of first stage larvae can be introduced into the gill chambers through the incurrent siphon, it would be possible to determine, on the basis of numbers and the stage of development, whether they were entering the pericardium via the suprabranchial chamber and kidney.

SELECTED REFERENCES

Stafford, J. (1896). Zool. Jahrb., Abt. Anat. 9:477.

Wharton, G. W. (1939). J. Parasit. 25:83.

Ward, H. B. (1918). Ward and Whipple's Fresh-Water Biology. John W. Wiley and Sons, New York, p. 380.

Williams, C. O. (1942). J. Parasit. 28:467.

Subclass Digenea

The digenetic trematodes comprise a large group of endoparasites variable in size, shape, and habitat. They are hermaphroditic except for one family in which the sexes are separate. They conform biologically in having an asexual phase of the life cycle in mollusks, usually gastropods but occasionally pelecypods, as the first intermediate host (one exception is known where a polychaete annelid replaces the molluscan intermediate host), and a sexual phase in vertebrates, the definitive host (a few exceptions

EXPLANATION OF PLATE 47

A. Adult fluke. **B.** Embryonated egg. **C.** Egg in process of hatching with first stage larva escaping. **D.** Recently hatched first stage larva. **E.** Second stage larva. **F.** Third stage larva (drawing reconstructed). **G.** Fourth stage larva. **H.** Mussel *(Anadonta grandis)* host. **I.** Turtle which may serve as a temporary host.

1, mouth sucker (surrounded by muscular tissue in larval stages) ; **2,** ventral sucker divided into alveoli in adult and late fourth stage larva but not in first, second, and third stage larvae; **3,** pharynx; **4,** intestine; **5,** testis; **6,** vas efferens; **7,** cirrus pouch; **8,** cirrus papilla; **9,** common genital pore; **10,** ovary; **11,** oviduct; **12,** Laurer's canal; **13,** descending limb of uterus; **14,** terminal portion of uterus (intervening part omitted) ; **15,** vitelline gland; **16,** transverse vitelline duct; **17,** common vitelline duct; **18,** egg shell; **19,** operculum; **20,** first stage larva; **21,** tail; **22,** groove in ventral sucker.

Two possibilities of the life cycle are given. The first is shown in **a-f** and the second in **g-l. a,** adult fluke in pericardial cavity of mussel; **b,** embryonated eggs laid in pericardium; **c,** egg hatching with first stage larva escaping; **d,** second stage larvae; **e,** third stage larva; **f,** fourth stage larva (all larvae in pericardial cavity where it is postulated that they develop to maturity, thus completing the development in a single host) ; **g,** probability that eggs may leave pericardial opening and enter kidney; **h,** egg passing through kidney into suprabranchial cavity; **i,** egg being carried from branchial cavity through excurrent siphon; **j,** egg hatching in the water; **k,** free first stage larva being drawn into branchial cavity through incurrent pore; **l,** first stage larva in position to enter renal pore and migrate through kidney to pericardial cavity; **m,** flukes liberated from infected mussels eaten by turtles may survive in the stomach of these poikilotherms which serve as a temporary second host in an otherwise simple one-host type of life cycle.

Figure A adapted from Stafford, 1896, Zool. Jahrb. Abt. Anat. 9:477; B-C, from Faust, 1927, Trans. Amer. Micr. Soc. 41:113; D-G, from Williams, 1942, J. Parasit. 28:467.

---

occur where water beetles harbor sexually mature flukes). Many species have a second intermediate host in which early development of the sexual phase takes place.

Life cycles of digenetic trematodes are complicated. The asexual phase includes eggs that produce ciliated miracidia. Continued development of this larval stage is possible only in the bodies of mollusks where it transforms into a mother sporocyst. Germinal cells within its body develop into either rediae or daughter sporocysts but never both in the same species of trematode. There may be more than one generation of rediae or sporocysts. The final product of the asexual phase in mollusks is cercariae which appear in a variety of types (Plate 49).*

With the appearance of the cercariae, the sexual phase of the life cycle is initiated but it is in an undeveloped stage. The cercariae normally escape from the molluscan host into the water. Some of them enter the definitive host directly from the water, as in the case of the blood flukes, and develop to maturity in the vascular system. The remainder encyst on objects or in the bodies of animals (second intermediate hosts), transforming into metacercariae which develop to the infective stage. Metacercariae infect the definitive host when swallowed by it. They develop to sexual maturity in organs characteristic of each particular species. The general plan of the different life cycles is shown in Plate 84.

The classification of the Digenea has been revised recently (LaRue) on the basis of whether the excretory bladder of the cercariae develops from the existing thin-walled excretory tubules (superorder Anepitheliocystida) or from mesodermal cells (superorder Epitheliocystida). This plan is followed. The basic outline of the classification is given together with the families of digenetic trematodes treated in this chapter, except where it is stated that certain groups will not be discussed.

Superorder Anepitheliocystida
  Order Strigeatida
    Suborder Strigeata
      Superfamily Strigeoidea
        Family Strigeidae

*Dawes (1956). Trematoda. Cambridge University Press; and Hyman (1951). The Invertebrates, Vol. 2, McGraw-Hill and Co., are excellent references.

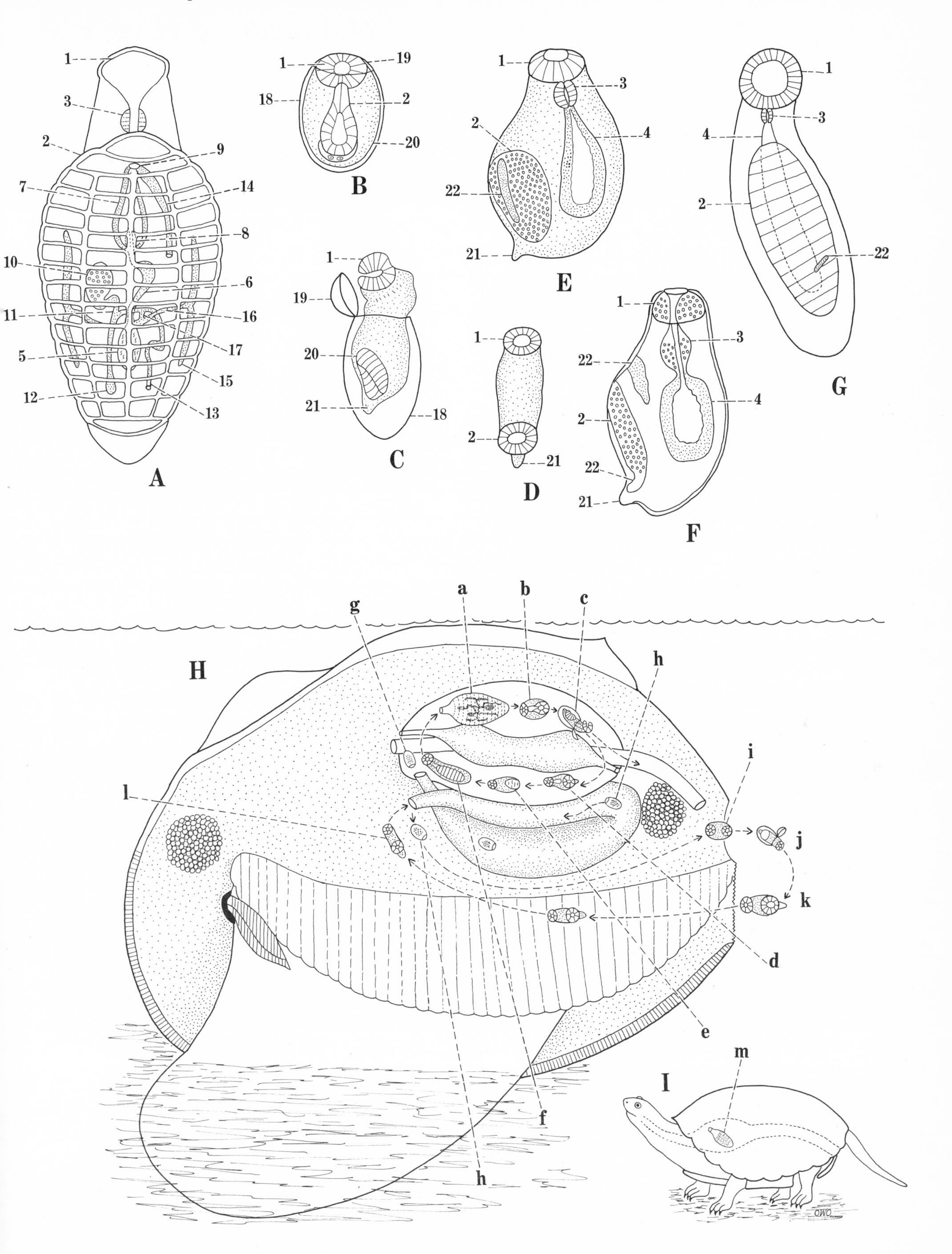
A
B
C
D
E
F
G
H
I
1
2
3
4
5
6
7
8
9
10
11
12
13
14
15
16
17
18
19
20
21
22
a
b
c
d
e
f
g
h
i
j
k
l
m
OWO

Family Diplostomatidae
Superfamily Clinostomatoidea
Family Clinostomatidae
Superfamily Schistosomatoidea
Family Schistosomatidae
Family Spirorchiidae
Family Sanguinicolidae

Suborder Azygiata
Superfamily Azygioidea
(No members discussed)
Superfamily Transversotrematoidea
(No members discussed)
Suborder Cyclocoelata
Superfamily Cyclocoeloidea
(No members discussed)
Suborder Brachylaemata
Superfamily Brachylaemoidea
Family Brachylaemidae
Superfamily Fellodistomatoidea
(No members discussed)
Superfamily Bucephaloidea
Family Bucephalidae

Order Echinostomida
Suborder Echinostomata
Superfamily Echinostomatoidea
Family Echinostomatidae
Family Fasciolidae
Suborder Paramphistomata
Superfamily Paramphistomatoidea
Family Paramphistomatidae
Family Diplodiscidae
Superfamily Notocotyloidea
Family Notocotylidae
Order Renicolida
Suborder Renicolata
Superfamily Renicoloidea
(No members discussed)

Superorder Epitheliocystida

Order Plagiorchiida
Suborder Plagiorchiata
Superfamily Plagiorchioidea
Family Dicrocoeliidae
Family Plagiorchiidae
Family Prosthogonimidae
Superfamily Allocreadioidea
Family Allocreadiidae
Family Gorgoderidae
Family Troglotrematidae

Order Opisthorchiida
  Suborder Opisthorchiata
    Superfamily Opisthorchioidea
      Family Heterophyidae
      Family Opisthorchiidae
  Suborder Hemiurata
    Superfamily Hemiuroidea
      Family Halipegidae

GENERAL CHARACTERISTICS OF DIGENEA

An understanding of some of the characteristics of the digenetic flukes is helpful for purposes of general recognition of groups and comprehension of patterns of the life cycles. A few of the basic principles are set forth in the following pages.

Adult Flukes (Plate 48)

Morphologically, adult digenetic trematodes fall into seven basic types that are easily recognized. They are 1) the gasterostomes with only a muscular oral sucker, and that on the midventral surface of the body (Plate 48, A); 2) the strigeids, or holostomes, as they are sometimes called, with a transverse equatorial constriction that divides the body into a forebody with a holdfast, or tribocytic organ, and a more or less cylindrical hindbody containing the gonads (Plate 48, B); 3) the monostomes with or without a muscular oral sucker at the anterior extremity of the body and without a ventral sucker (Plate 48, C, E); 4) the amphistomes with the oral sucker and ventral sucker at the anterior and posterior extremities of the body, respectively, with the latter much the larger (Plate 48, D); 5) the echinostomes with a spine-bearing collar around the anterior end (Plate 48, F); 6) the schistosomes with separate sexes and, in some forms, a long ventral groove, the gynaecophoric groove, in the male wherein the female is held (Plate 48, G); and 7) the distomes with the ventral sucker relatively near the oral sucker and without the characteristics that distinguish the other groups (Plate 48, H).

Cercariae (Plate 49)

Since cercariae are relatively abundant and easy to collect, they serve a as clue to the trematode fauna in a region. For recognition of the cercariae, attempts have been made to develop schemes of classification based on morphological characters. These have been concerned primarily with the number and arrangement of the suckers, presence or absence of collar spines or of stylets in the oral sucker, and morphology of the tail. Even though the shortcomings of such schemes for showing relationships among flukes are recognized, they have great practical utility for recognizing and cataloguing cercariae.

LaRue recognized two basic types of cercariae, according to the development of the excretory bladder. He noted that it develops either by fusion of the excretory tubules to form a wall of thin, flat cells (Plate 50, R) or from a mass of mesodermal cells to form a thick wall of cuboidal cells (Plate 50, S). The superorders are Anepitheliocystida and Epitheliocystida, respectively, and represent two natural groups of digenetic trematodes.

Where life history studies have been completed, they often show relationships among adult flukes previously unsuspected on the basis of body structure alone.

For convenience in recognizing cercariae commonly encountered in surveys, 13 different morphological types, as recognized by Dawes, are shown on Plate 49.

1. Amphistome cercariae (Plate 49, A): These are characterized by the ventral sucker, which is the larger, being located at the posterior end of the body. They are the largest of the cercariae, develop in rediae, are born in a relatively immature stage, and complete development in the tissues of the snail hosts. Encystment is on objects in water. There are two types: Pigmenta with stellate melanophores and Diplocotylea with abundant pigmentation in the anterior region of the body.

EXPLANATION OF PLATE 48 ⇨

A. Gasterostome *(Bucephalus elegans)*. **B.** Strigeid or holostome *(Alaria canis)*. **C.** Monostome with muscular oral sucker *(Quinqueserialis quinqueserialis)*. **D.** Amphistome *(Megalodiscus temperatus)*. **E.** Monostome without muscular sucker *(Cyclocoelium* sp.). **F.** Echinostome *(Echinostoma revolutum)*. **G.** Schistosome *(Schistosoma haemotobium)*. **H.** Distome *(Plagiorchis muris)*.

1, oral sucker; **2**, mouth without muscular sucker; **3**, ventral sucker; **4**, common genital pore; **5**, adhesive or tribocytic organ; **6**, ovary; **7**, testes; **8**, cirrus pouch.

Figures original.

---

2. Monostome cercariae (Plate 49, B): These cercariae have a muscular oral sucker at the anterior end of the body but lack a ventral sucker. They develop in rediae, are born in an immature stage, and complete development in water. Encystment is on objects in water. There are two types: Ephemera with three eyespots and Urbanensis with two.

3. Gymnocephalus cercariae (Plate 49, C, D): The cercariae of this group are without spines or stylets around the anterior end of the body or in the oral sucker, respectively. The tail is long and straight and with or without a longitudinal fin. Cercariae develop in rediae and encyst on objects in the water or in fish. Forms without a tail fin (Fig. C), such as the Fasciolidae, encyst on objects. Those with caudal fins and two eyespots (Fig. D), known also as pleurolophocercous or parapleurolophocercous cercariae, encyst in fish and are representative of the Opisthorchiidae and Heterophyidae.

4. Cystophorous cercariae (Plate 49, E): The tail has a chamber at the anterior end into which the cercariae may withdraw. It is variable in both shape and size and constitutes the morphological basis for recognizing three groups, the cystophorous cercariae, the cysticercariae, and the macrocercous cercariae.

Cystophorous cercariae have a peculiar short tail with five appendages attached, each different from the other. Development is in sporocysts in *Planorbis.* Adults are Halipegidae. Cysticercariae have a short, flat tail with a pair of large, flat, clapper-like appendages at the end. Development is in rediae in *Limnaea.* Some of these cercariae attain a length of 6 to 7 mm. They develop into Azygiidae. Macrocercous forms have a long, simple, cylindrical tail, develop in sporocysts in *Sphaerium,* and mature into Gorgoderidae.

5. Trichocercous cercariae (Plate 49, F): These are largely marine forms although a few occur in fresh water. They are characterized by having a long slender tail that bears numerous bristles, often in tufts. There are two groups, those with eyespots and those without. Some of the group develop into Allocreadiidae.

6. Echinostome cercariae (Plate 49, G): This group of cercariae is readily distinguished by the presence of a head collar bearing a ring of spines around its margin. They have a long slender tail. The cercariae develop in rediae and encyst in snails, sometimes in the species in which they developed. They are Echinostomatidae.

7. Microcercous cercariae (Plate 49, H): These are small cercariae with a minute, knoblike tail. The oral sucker bears a stylet in the anterior margin. The cercariae develop in rediae and encyst in invertebrates. They belong to the family Troglotrematidae.

8. Xiphidiocercariae (Plate 49, I, J): This group of cercariae is characterized by a stylet in the anterior margin of the oral sucker and long tails (this feature distinguishes them from the microcercous cercariae). The cercariae develop in sporocysts and encyst in invertebrates, rarely in fish, or they may encyst in sporocysts of other trematodes. Plagiorchiidae is characteristic of this group.

Four subgroups generally are recognized. They are 1) Cercariae Microcotylae, which includes small forms with ventral sucker postequatorial, tail without a fin and equal to the body in length; 2) Cercariae Virgulae with the ventral sucker smaller than the oral, tails without a fin, the excretory vesicle V-shaped, and the presence of virgula organ which is two pyriform sacs fused in the median line, with pointed ends directed forward, and located near the posterior margin of the oral sucker; 3) Cercariae Ornate includes species with a tail fin-fold; and 4) Cercariae Armate are without a virgula organ, oral and ventral suckers are unequal in size, and the excretory bladder is Y-shaped.

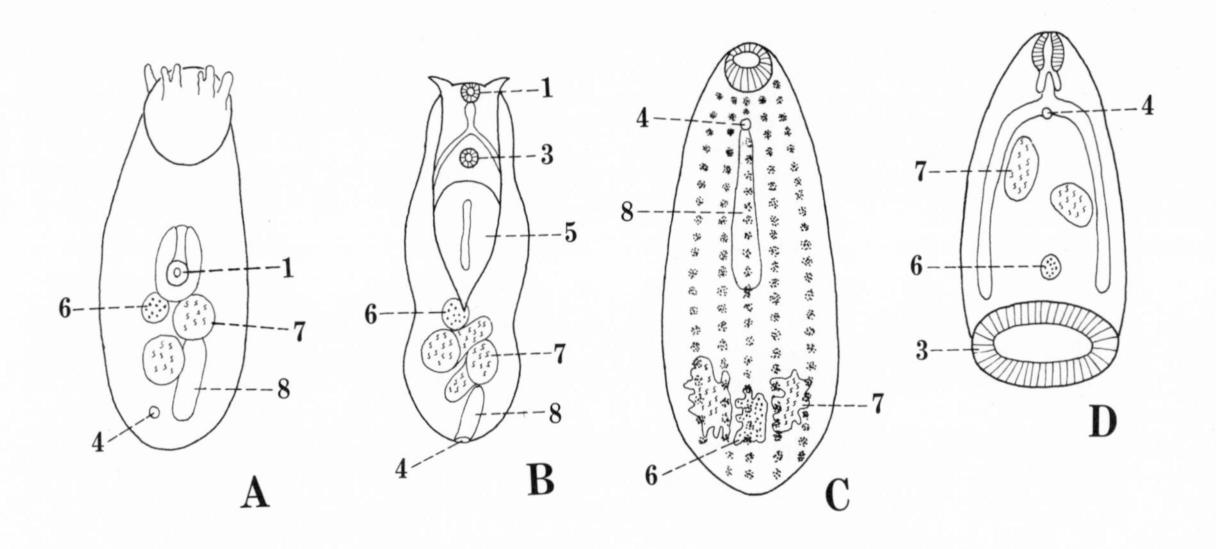
1
6
7
8
4
A
1
3
5
6
7
8
4
B
4
8
7
6
C
4
7
6
3
D

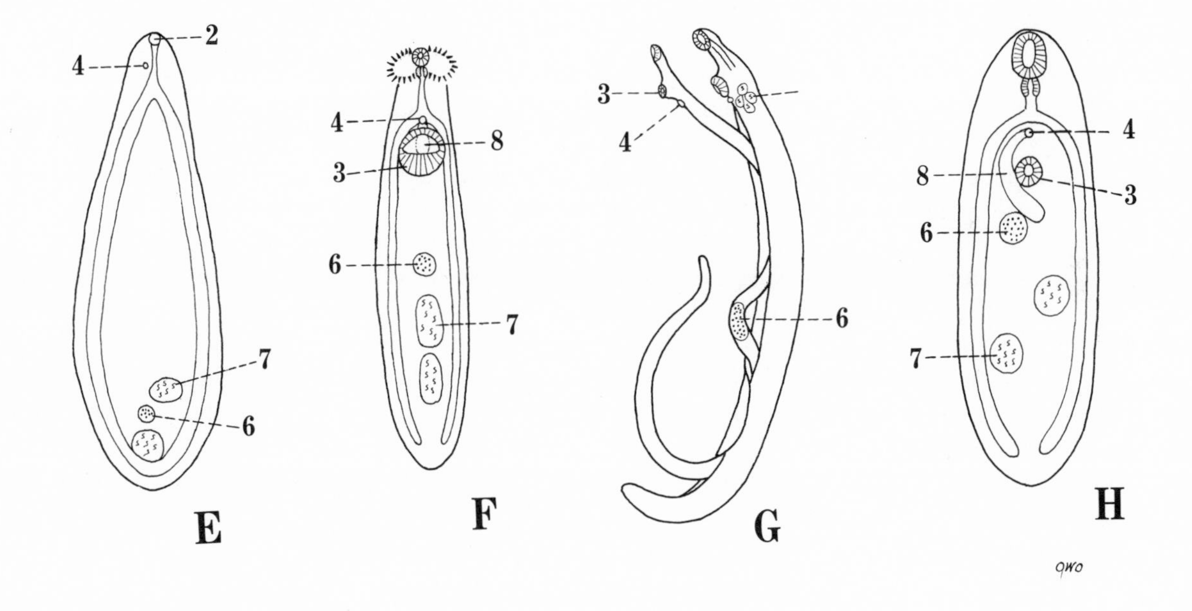
2
4
7
6
E
4
8
3
6
7
F
3
4
6
G
4
8
3
6
7
H
GWO

EXPLANATION OF PLATE 49 ⇨

A. Amphistome cercaria. **B.** Monostome cercaria. **C.** Gymnocephalus cercaria. **D.** Gymnocephalus cercaria of pleurolophocercous type. **E.** Cystophorous cercaria. **F.** Trichocercous cercaria. **G.** Echinostome cercaria. **H.** Microcercous cercaria. **I.** Xiphidiocercous cercaria. **J.** Ophthalmoxiphidiocercous cercaria. **K-O.** Furcocercous types of cercariae. **K.** Gasterostome cercaria. **L.** Lophocercous cercaria. **M.** Apharyngeate furcocercous cercaria. **N.** Pharyngeate furcocercous cercaria. **O.** Apharyngeate monostome furcocercous cercaria without oral sucker. **P.** Cotylocercous cercaria. **Q.** Rhopalocercous cercaria. **R.** Cercariaea. **S.** Rattenkönig or ratking cercariae.

Figures adapted from various sources.

---

9. Furcocercous cercariae (Plate 49, K-O): This a large and varied group of cercariae with forked tails into which the body is not retractable. Some groups develop in sporocysts and others in rediae. The cercariae may penetrate the definitive host actively without prior encystment or they may encyst in vertebrates.

Five groups are recognized on the bases of morphology and/or biology. They are: 1) *Bucephalus* group, which includes the gasterostome cercariae in which the oral sucker is on the midventral surface as in the adults. The tail lacks a stem but has two long furcae arising from a large bulbous structure. The cercariae develop in sporocysts (Fig. K). 2) Lophocercous group consists of apharyngeate, monostome cercariae. Some species have a dorsal fin extending the full length of the body. The cercariae do not encyst but penetrate the definitive host (Fig. L). 3) Apharyngeate or Ocellata group in which the cercariae lack a pharynx and bear two pigmented eyespots. They develop in sporocysts and penetrate directly through the epidermis of the definitive host without prior encystment. These cercariae are representative of the Schistosomatidae (Fig. M). 4) The pharyngeate, non-ocellate cercariae that develop in sporocysts or rediae and always penetrate a vertebrate host for encystment. The strigeids (Strigeidae, Diplostomatidae) develop in sporocysts and form tetracotyle, diplostomulum, or neascus types of metacercariae. The Clinostomatidae develop in rediae and penetrate fish for encystment (Fig. N). 5) Suckerless apharyngeate cercariae of blood flukes of the family Sanguinicolidae that parasitize fish (Fig. O).

10. Cotylocercous cercariae (Plate 49, P): These are marine species with broad, short, cuplike tails that serve as adhesive organs. They belong to the Allocreadoidea.

11. Rhopalocercous cercariae (Plate 49, Q): The tail is broad, even wider than the body. They develop in rediae in fingernail clams. *Allocreadium isosporum* is a representative in fresh-water fish.

12. Cercariaea (Plate 49, R): This group includes cercariae in which the tail is undeveloped. The Mutabile and *Helicis* groups develop in rediae, whereas the *Leucochloridium* group develops in peculiarly branched sporocysts which are banded with blue-green or brown colors. The rootlike branches are deep in the viscera of the snails and the colored saclike portion extends into the antennae, causing them to enlarge greatly. The cercariae in the sacs are infective to birds when eaten by them. They belong to the Brachylaemidae.

13. Rattenkönig or rat-king cercariae (Plate 49, S): These marine cercariae occur in writhing masses with the tips of the tails being attached to a body of protoplasm.

EXERCISE ON CERCARIAE

Cercariae are obtained by isolating snails or fingernail clams in vials of pond water overnight. Tap water may contain sufficient chlorine to kill the mollusks unless it is allowed to stand in an open container for several days.

The contents of the vials are examined by holding them toward a darkened object in a manner that light will shine through them and illuminate cercariae that might be present. They appear as minute whitish objects moving about. Their presence may be confirmed by examination under a dissecting microscope.

For studying cercariae, living specimens shed naturally by the mollusks may be observed for activity in open dishes. Internal details are seen best in specimens placed on a slide under a cover

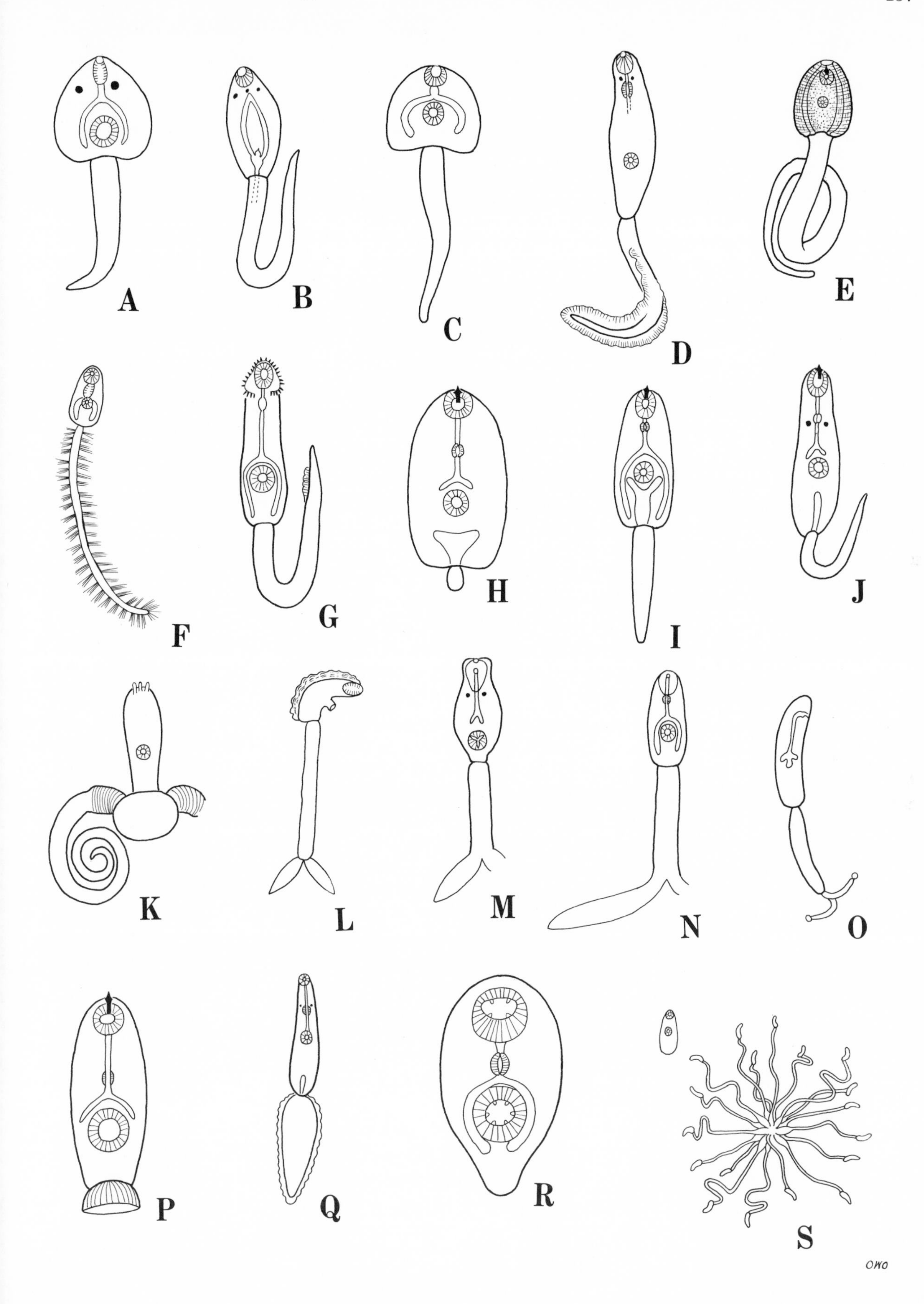
A
B
C
D
E
F
G
H
I
J
K
L
M
N
O
P
Q
R
S
OWO

slip in a very weak solution of neutral red or Nile blue and examined under a microscope. Regulation of cover slip pressure is necessary to see the flame cells, as they are clearest just before the cercariae rupture from pressure.

Expose various aquatic arthropods to cercariae to find intermediate hosts that they will penetrate. Only cercariae that have emerged naturally from the mollusks should be used, as those obtained by dissection may not be mature.

SELECTED REFERENCES

Dawes, B. (1956). The Trematoda. Cambridge University Press, New York, p. 149.

LaRue, G. R. (1957). Exp. Parasit. 6:306.

Yamaguti, S. (1958). Systema Helminthum, Vol. 1: Digenetic Trematodes of Vertebrates, Parts 1 and 2. Interscience Press, New York, 1075 pp., 106 plates.

MORPHOLOGY AND LIFE HISTORY STAGES OF DIGENETIC TREMATODES (Plate 50)

The digenetic trematodes comprise a large group of endoparasites variable in size, shape, and habitat. They conform, however, in having basic patterns of body structure and life history stages, as shown on Plate 50.

The adults are hermaphroditic, except for the blood flukes of the family Schistosomatidae, and generally similar in structure (Plate 50, A). The stages in the course of development include 1) an egg, 2) miracidium, 3) mother sporocyst, 4) daughter sporocyst or redia, 5) cercaria, and 6) metacercaria (Plate 50, B-O).

Eggs generally have a cap, or operculum, at one end (Schistosomatidae eggs are nonoperculate) and are either unembryonated or contain a fully formed miracidium when laid.

Miracidia are complex ciliated organisms that continue their development nearly always in the body of mollusks. The miracidium has penetration glands, flame cells, and associated tubules which constitute the excretory system. A mass of tissue known as germ cells provide the cellular lineage for succeeding forms appearing in the life cycle. A few miracidia are progenetic, containing later stages such as redia before they hatch, as in the case of some amphistomes and echinostomes.

Upon entering the molluscan intermediate host, the miracidia shed the ciliated covering and transform directly into a saclike body, the mother sporocyst. Germ cells within the hollow body of the mother sporocyst develop into either daughter sporocysts without mouth or intestine (Plate 50, H, I) or rediae with pharynx and simple intestine (Plate 50, J), but not both in the same species of trematode. There may be more than one generation of sporocysts or rediae.

Germ cells in the sporocysts or rediae produce cercariae (Plate 50, K). These are sexual forms and constitute the end product of asexual reproduction of the sporocysts and rediae in the molluscan intermediate host. Upon escaping from the mollusk, the cercariae are free in the water for a short time. Except for a few families, the cercariae promptly encyst on objects in the water or in the bodies of invertebrate or vertebrate animals (second intermediate hosts) and transform into metacercariae which after a variable period of development become infective to the definitive hosts (Plate 50, L). In the case of some of the blood flukes, however, the cercariae penetrate the definitive host and develop directly to adults without going through a metacercarial stage.

In the strigeids, there are three different kinds of metacercarial forms. They are 1) tetracotyles (Plate 50, M); 2) neascus (Plate 50, N); and 3) diplostomulum (Plate 50, O). In some strigeids, there is an additional stage between the cercarial and metacercarial stages known as the mesocercaria (Plate 50, P). These are in reality cercariae which upon entering the second intermediate host do not develop to the metacercarial stage. When the intermediary containing them is eaten by a definitive host, the mesocercariae migrate from the intestine via the hepatic portal vein, liver, and heart to the lungs where they transform into diplostomulae. From here, they proceed up the trachea and to the small intestine.

MOLLUSCAN INTERMEDIATE HOSTS OF DIGENETIC TREMATODES

Mollusca, especially the Gastropoda, or snails, serve as the first intermediate hosts of the digenetic trematodes. Both the land and aquatic snails are utilized. Some clams, particularly the fingernail clams, act as intermediate hosts for a small number of species.

Illustrations are given of representatives of some of the common families of North American fresh-water (Plate 51) and land snails (Plate 52) as an aid to recognizing them.

A brief classification of the class Gastropoda is included to show the major groups and their relationships.

I. Subclass Streptoneura: Visceral part of body is coiled so that the two visceral nerve commissures are twisted, as suggested by the name, into the form of a figure-8. The majority of the gastropods belong to this group.

A. Prosobranchiata: Gills located anterior to the heart. Sexes are separate. An operculum is present.

1. Fresh-water snails
   a. Amnicolidae[a,b] (Plate 51, Figs. 27-31)
      Amnicola, Cincinnatia, Pomatiopsis, Bithinia, Flumnicola
   b. Pleuroceridae
      Pleurocerca, Goniobasis
   c. Viviparidae[b] (Plate 51, Figs. 23-24)
      Viviparus, Campeloma
   d. Valvatidae (Plate 51, Fig. 32)
      Valvata

2. Brackish and salt water snails
   a. Potamidae[a]
      Pirenella
   b. Neritidae
      Neritina
   c. Littorinidae[a]
      Littorina
   d. Nassariidae[a]
      Nassarius

3. Land snails
   a. Helicinidae (Plate 52, Fig. A)
      Helicina, Hendersonia

II. Subclass Euthyneura: Visceral commissures straight, as the name states, not twisted as in the Streptoneura.

A. Order Opisthobranchiata: Gills behind heart, as given by the name, and visceral nerve commissures not twisted; hermaphroditic. Marine, living near shore.

1. Akeridae[a]
   Haminoae

B. Order Pulmonata: Mantle cavity serves as a lung, and gills are absent. Shell, when present usually is a simple, regular spire. A mass of hardened mucus may close the aperture of the shells of many species of land snails. They are nonoperculate and hermaphroditic, usually ovoviparous. Mostly fresh-water and land snails.

1. Suborder Basommatophora: With one pair of contractile tentacles with eyes at base. Shell conical, discoidal, or patelliform. Male and female genital tracts open separately.

EXPLANATION OF PLATE 50 ▷

A. Diagrammatic drawing of a typical digenetic trematode, showing parts. **B.** Egg of *Haplometrana utahensis* which is embryonated when laid and hatches only when eaten by snail host. **C-F.** Hatched miracidia. **C.** *Trichobilharzia cameroni.* **D.** *Bucephalus elegans.* **E.** *Postharmostomum helicus.* **F.** Progenetic miracidium of *Stichorchis subtriquetus,* showing redia inside. **G.** Miracidium of *Stichorchis subtriquetus* without ciliated epithelium, showing epidermal plates. **H.** Portion of branched sporocyst of *Postharmostomum helicus.* **I.** Simple saclike sporocyst of *Haplometrana utahensis.* **J.** Redia of *Echinostoma revolutum.* **K.** Cercaria of *Haplometrana utahensis.* **L.** Metacercariae of *Paragonimus kellicotti,* which is characteristic of most digenetic trematodes. **M-O.** Metacercariae of strigeid flukes. **M.** Tetracotyle. **N.** Neascus. **O.** Diplostomulum. **P.** Mesocercaria of *Alaria canis.* **Q_{1-6}.** Types of excretory bladders. **Q_1.** Short club-shaped bladder of *Macroderoides typicus.* **Q_2.** Long club-shaped bladder of *Alloglossidium corti.* **Q_3.** V-shaped bladder of Lecithodendriidae. **Q_4.** Y-shaped bladder of Styphlodorinae with collecting tubules originating from sides of arms. **Q_5.** Y-shaped bladder of *Plagiorchis* with short arms and collecting tubules originating from ends of arms. **Q_6.** Y-shaped bladder of *Haplometra cylindricea* with long arms and collecting tubules originating from ends of arms. **R_{1-5}.** Diagrammatic sketches of development of excretory bladder in a furcocercous cercaria of the Anepitheliocystida. **R_1-R_2.** Separate collecting tubules. **R_3-R_4.** Fusion of collecting tubules to form excretory bladder. **R_5.** Excretory bladder formed. **S_1-S_5.** Diagrammatic sketches of development of excretory bladder in a xiphidiocercous cercaria of the Epitheliocystida. **S_1.** Separate collecting tubules. **S_2.** Excretory tubules separate but a mass of mesodermal tissue has appeared between them. **S_3.** Excretory tubules are surrounded by mesodermal tissue. **S_4.** Mesodermal tissue forming excretory bladder. **S_5.** Excretory bladder has formed from mesodermal tissue.

1, oral sucker; **2,** ventral sucker; **3,** pre-oesophagus; **4,** pharynx; **5,** oesophagus; **6,** intestine; **7,** testis; **8,** vas efferens; **9,** vas deferens; **10,** cirrus pouch; **11,** seminal vesicle; **12,** prostate glands; **13,** ejaculatory duct; **14,** common genital pore; **15,** protruding cirrus; **16,** ovary; **17,** oviduct; **18,** Laurer's canal; **19,** seminal receptacle; **20,** Mehlis' gland; **21,** descending limb of uterus; **22,** ascending limb of uterus; **23,** metraterm; **24,** vitelline glands; **25,** lateral vitelline duct; **26,** vitelline reservoir; **27,** common vitelline duct; **28,** flame cell; **29,** capillary tubule; **30,** accessory collecting tubule; **31,** anterior collecting tubule; **32,** posterior collecting tubule; **33,** common collecting tubule; **34,** excretory bladder; **35,** excretory pore; **36,** apical gland; **37,** penetration glands; **38,** germ balls; **39,** redia; **40,** cephalic plate with bristles; **41,** spine; **42-45,** first, second, third, and fourth rows of plates, respectively; **46,** cercariae; **47,** birth pore; **48,** lateral sucker; **49,** holdfast organ; **50,** mesodermal mass from which excretory bladder arises.

Figures A-L original; M-N, from Hughes, 1929; O, from Bosma, 1934, Trans. Amer. Micr. Soc. 53:116; P, original; Q, from McMullen, 1937, J. Parasit. 23:235; R-S, from Hussey, 1941, Trans. Amer. Micr. Soc. 60:171.

---

a. Fresh-water snails

(1) Planorbidae[a,b] (Plate 51, Figs. 14-19)
Planorbis, Helisoma, etc.

(2) Lymnaeidae[a,b] (Plate 51, Figs. 7-13)
Lymnaea, Fossaria, Stagnicola, Galba, etc.

(3) Physidae[a,b] (Plate 51, Figs. 4-6)
Physa

(4) Ancylidae[a,b] (Plate 51, Figs. 21-22)
Ancylus, Ferrissia

2. Suborder Stylommatophora: Two pairs of tentacles with eyes at tips of dorsal pair, tentacles capable of being everted and inverted. Land snails with visible shells and slugs with rudimentary shells buried in tissue.

a. Land snails

1. Helicidae[a]
Helix

2. Helicellidae
Helicella, Cochlicella

3. Bradybaenidae
Bradybaena

PLATE 50 *Morphology and Life History Stages of Digenetic Trematodes*

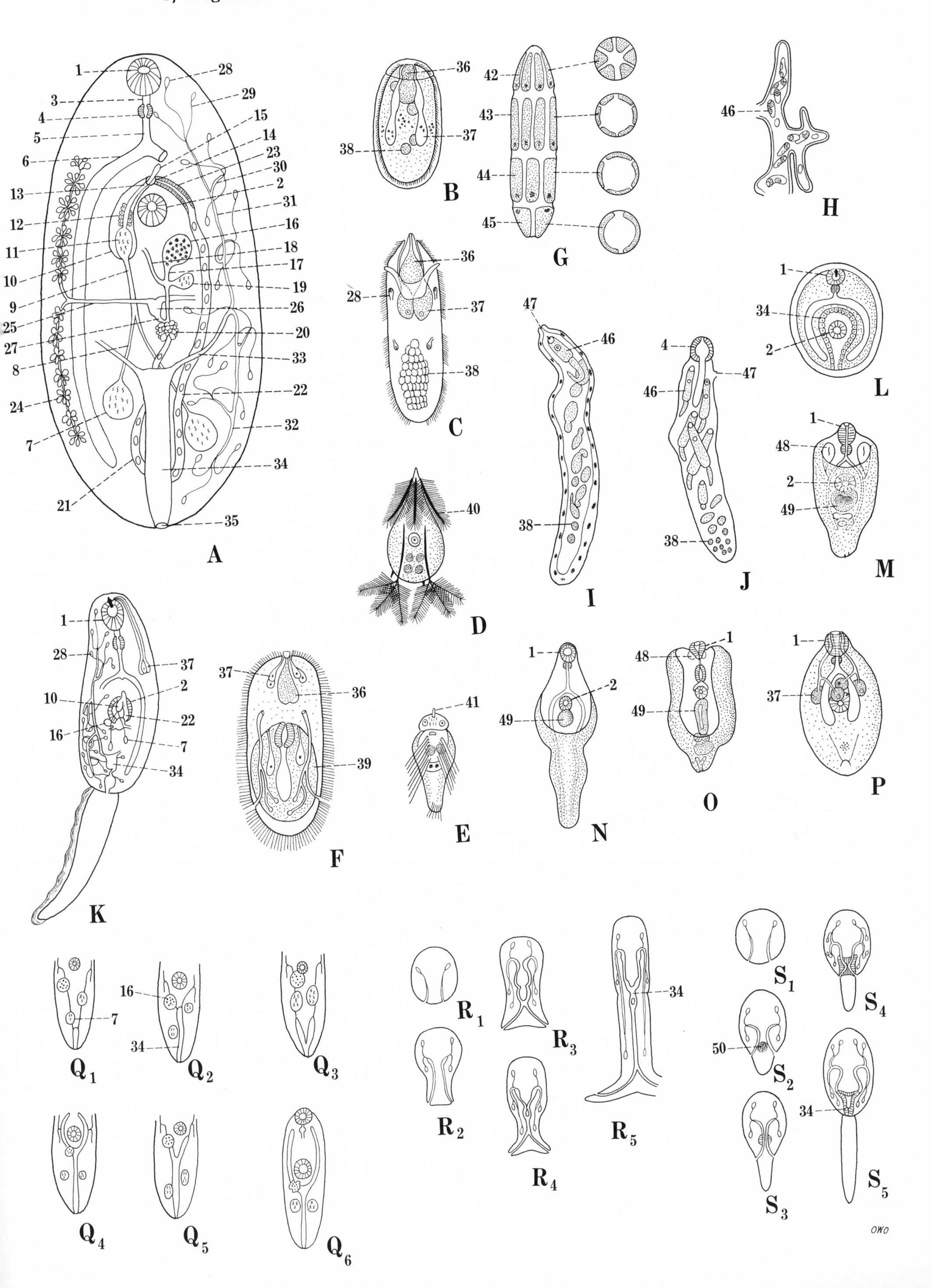

EXPLANATION OF PLATE 51 ▷

1. Diagram of spired operculate snail with dextral whorls. **2.** Diagram of spired nonoperculate snail with sinistral whorls. **3.** Diagram of discoidal snail with sinistral whorls. **4-6.** Physidae (pouch snails). **4.** *Physa sayi.* **5.** *Physa integra.* **6.** *Physa gyrina.* **7-13.** Lymnaeidae (pond snails). **7.** *Lymnaea haldemani.* **8.** *Pseudosuccinea columella.* **9.** *Fossaria modicella.* **10.** *Stagnicola caperata.* **11.** *Bulimnea megasoma.* **12.** *Lymnaea stagnalis.* **13.** *Lymnaea auricularia.* **14-19.** Planorbidae (orb or ram's horn snails). **14-14**$_a$. *Helisoma.* **15.** *Planorbula.* **16.** *Segmentina.* **17-17**$_a$. *Planorbus.* **18-18**$_a$. *Gyraulus circumstriatus.* **19.** *Gyraulus deflectus.* **20.** *Menetus exacuous.* **21-22.** Ancylidae (limpets.) **21.** *Ferrisia.* **22.** *Ancylus.* **23-24.** Viviparidae. **23.** *Viviparus.* **24.** *Campeloma.* **25-26.** Pleuroceridae (river snails). **25.** *Pleurocerca.* **26.** *Goniobasis.* **27-31.** Amnicolidae. **27.** *Cincinnatia.* **28.** *Pomatiopsis.* **29.** *Bithinia.* **30.** *Amnicola.* **31.** *Flumnicola.* **32.** Valvatidae (round-mouthed snails) *Valvata.* **33.** Ampullaridae (apple-snails). *Ampullaria.*

a, apex; **b,** spire; **c,** operculum; **d,** columella; **e,** lip; **f,** suture; **g,** umbilicus; **h,** aperture; **i,** body whorl.

Figures redrawn from various sources.

---

4. Polygyridae[a,d] (Plate 52, Figs. B, B_{1-3})
   Polygyra
5. Endodontidae[b,d] (Plate 52, Figs. E, E_1)
   Anguispira, Helicodiscus
6. Succineidae[b,d] (Plate 52, Figs. K, K_1)
   Succinea
7. Bulimulidae (Plate 52, Fig. C)
   Bulimulus
8. Cionellidae[b] (Plate 52, Figs. J, J_1)
   Cionella
9. Zonitidae[d] (Plate 52, Figs. D, D_1)
   Zonitoides

b. Slugs
1. Limacidae[b,c,d] (Plate 52, Figs. L, M)
   Limax, Deroceras
2. Philomycidae (Plate 52, Fig. N)
   Philomycus
3. Arionidae[b,c,d]
   Arion

3. Systellommatophora: Tropical slugs. Two pairs of contractile tentacles, dorsal pair with eyes at tips. Neither internal nor external shell.
   a. Veronicellidae[a,d]
      Veronicella

While space does not permit detailed descriptions of families of snails, a brief account of the shells is given as a guide to preliminary recognition of material under consideration. Critical identification of species is based on the anatomy of the soft parts, such as the presence of gills or a mantle cavity that serves as a lung, and on anatomical details of the radula and internal and external parts of the reproductive organs. Details of the parts of the shell for identification are given in Plate 51, Figures 1-3.

FRESH-WATER SNAILS

Representatives of families of fresh-water snails of North America are shown on Plate 51.

Planorbidae (orb or ram's horn snails) (Figs. 14-19): The shells are mainly discoidal. In *Planorbis,*

[a]Intermediate hosts of trematodes of humans.
[b]Intermediate hosts of trematodes of animals other than humans.
[c]Intermediate hosts of cestodes.
[d]Intermediate hosts of nematodes.

PLATE 51 *Some Families of Common Fresh-water Snails of North America*

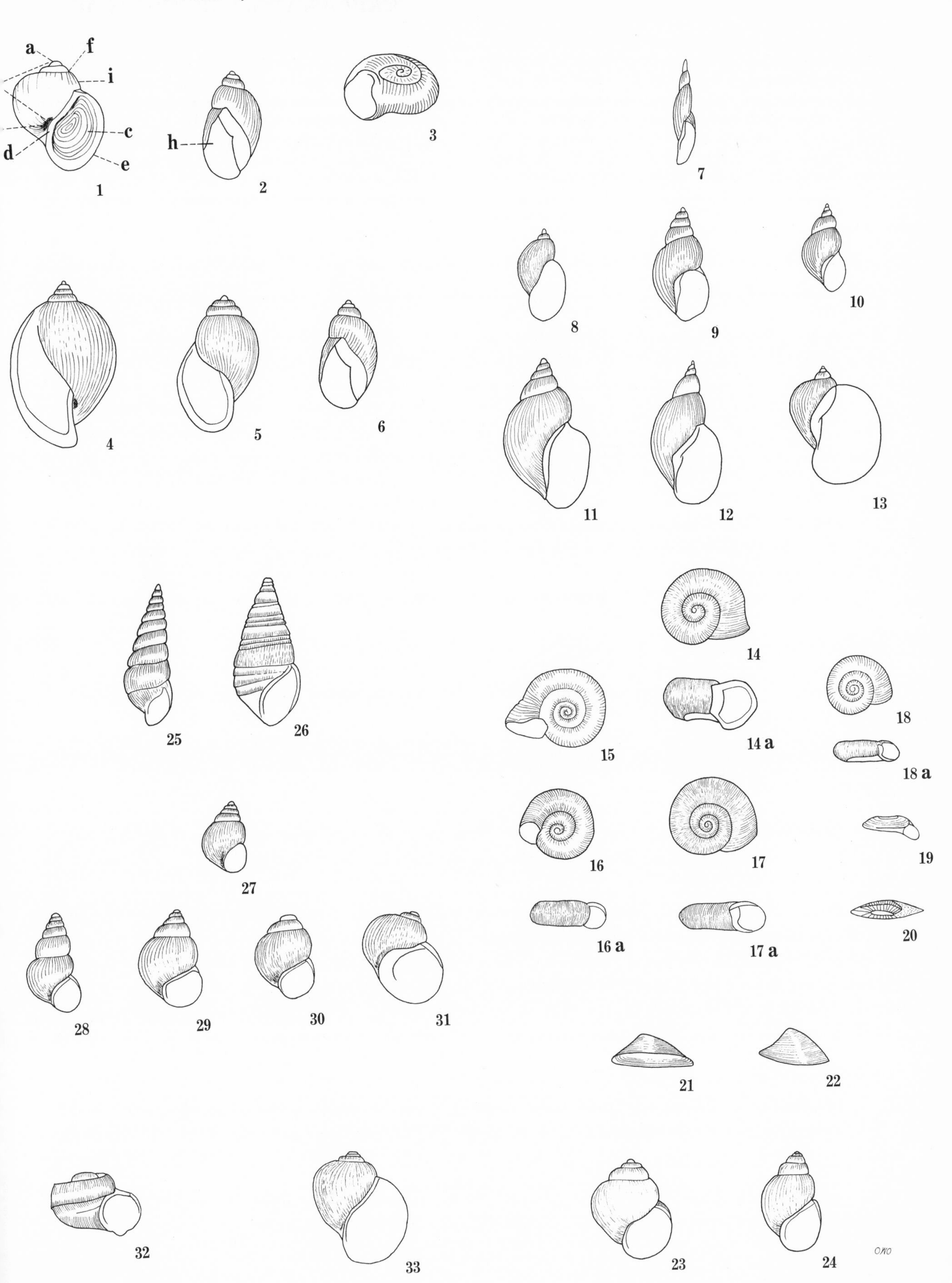

EXPLANATION OF PLATE 52

I. Order Prosobranchiata.
 A. Helicinidae *(Hendersonia occulata).*
II. Order Pulmonata.
 B. Polygyridae (B_1, *Polygyrus albolabris;* B_2, *Mesodon thryroides;* B_3, *Praticolella mobiliana).* **C.** Bulimulidae *(Bulimus dealbatus).* **D.** Zonitidae (D, D_1, *Ventrides ligerus.)* **E.** Endodonitidae (E, E_1, *Anguispira alternata).* **F.** Haplotrematidae (F, F_1, *Haplotrema concavum).* **G.** Pupillidae (G, G_1, *Gastrocopta procera).* **H.** Strobilopsidae (H, H_1, *Strobilops affinis).* **I.** Vallonidae (I, I_1, *Vallonia costata).* **J.** Cionellidae (J, J_1, *Cionella lubrica).* **K.** Succineidae (K, K_1, *Succinea retusa).* **L-M.** Limacidae (L, *Deroceras gracile;* M, *D. agreste).* **N.** Philomycidae *(Philomycus carolinianus).* **O.** Ellobiidae (O, O_1, *Carychium exiguum).*

Figures A, B, D, E, F, G, H, I, J, K, L, M, N, O redrawn from Baker, 1932, Fieldbook of Illinois Land Snails; others from various sources.

---

they are sinistral, *i.e.*, coil counterclockwise, and in the *Helisoma* they are dextral. The animals of all genera are sinistral because the genital organs are on the left side. The members of this family serve as intermediaries for many species of trematodes. Some common genera are *Planorbis, Gyraulus, Tropicorbis, Australorbis, Segmentina, Helisoma,* and *Planorbula.*

Lymnaeidae (pond snails) (Figs. 7-13): These have a dextral shell with a distinctly attenuated spire. The tentacles are flat and triangular. Size of shells varies greatly. Some common genera are *Lymnaea, Pseudosuccinea, Bulimnea, Acella, Fossaria,* and *Stagnicola.*

Ancylidae (limpets) (Figs. 21-22): The ancylids have a small caplike or patelliform shell. The animal is sinistral or dextral. Common genera are *Ferrissia* and *Ancylus.*

Physidae (pouch snails) (Figs. 4-6): The shells are spired, sinistral, thin, and have large body whorls. The aperture is large. The animal is sinistral with long, slender, cylindrical tentacles. Genera include *Physa* and *Aplexa.*

Amnicolidae (Figs. 27-31): The shell is small, dextral, conical, with four to eight whorls, and operculate. The aperture is round. Common genera include *Amnicola, Oncomelania, Pomatiopsis,* and *Bulimus* (=*Bythinia*).

Pleuroceridae (river snails) (Figs. 25-26): Pleurocerids have a shell that is thick, with whorls that have flattened sides, and a long tapering spire. They are operculate. Genera include *Goniobasis, Io, Pleurocerca,* and *Semisulcospira.*

Ampullaridae (apple snails) (Fig. 33): The shell is dextral, spired, very large, and has a big aperture. Both a gill and lung are present. The proboscis is divided into two tentacle-like structures. Genera include *Ampullaria* and *Pomacea.*

LAND SNAILS

Figures of representative families of North American land snails appear on Plate 52. The shells are dextral.

Helicinidae (Fig. A): These are operculate snails largely from tropical regions. The genera *Hendersonia* and *Helicina* occur in North America.

Polygridae (Figs. B, $B_{1\text{-}3}$): Shells are large, with a low spire, and in adult specimens the outer lip is reflected. *Polygyra* is the common genus with many species.

Helicidae: Shells are large and with five to seven whorls. The general shape is similar to *Praticolella. Oreohelex* is a common representative.

Bulimulidae (Fig. C): The shells are large, have an elongated spire, six rounded whorls, and deeply indented sutures. *Bulimus* is representative of the family.

Zonitidae (Figs. D, D_1): Members of this family have yellowish, horn-colored or clear, somewhat flattened shells with a shining surface. They range from minute (1.5 mm) to large (25 mm) in size. Genera include *Mesomphix, Ventridens, Retinella, Zonitoides, Paravitrea, Euconulus, Hawaiia,* and *Striatura.*

Strobilopsidae (Figs. H, H_1): The small shells are dome-shaped, sculptured with oblique ribs, and have 4.5 to 6 slowly enlarging whorls. *Strobilops* is the representative genus.

PLATE 52 *Some Families of Common Land Snails of North America*

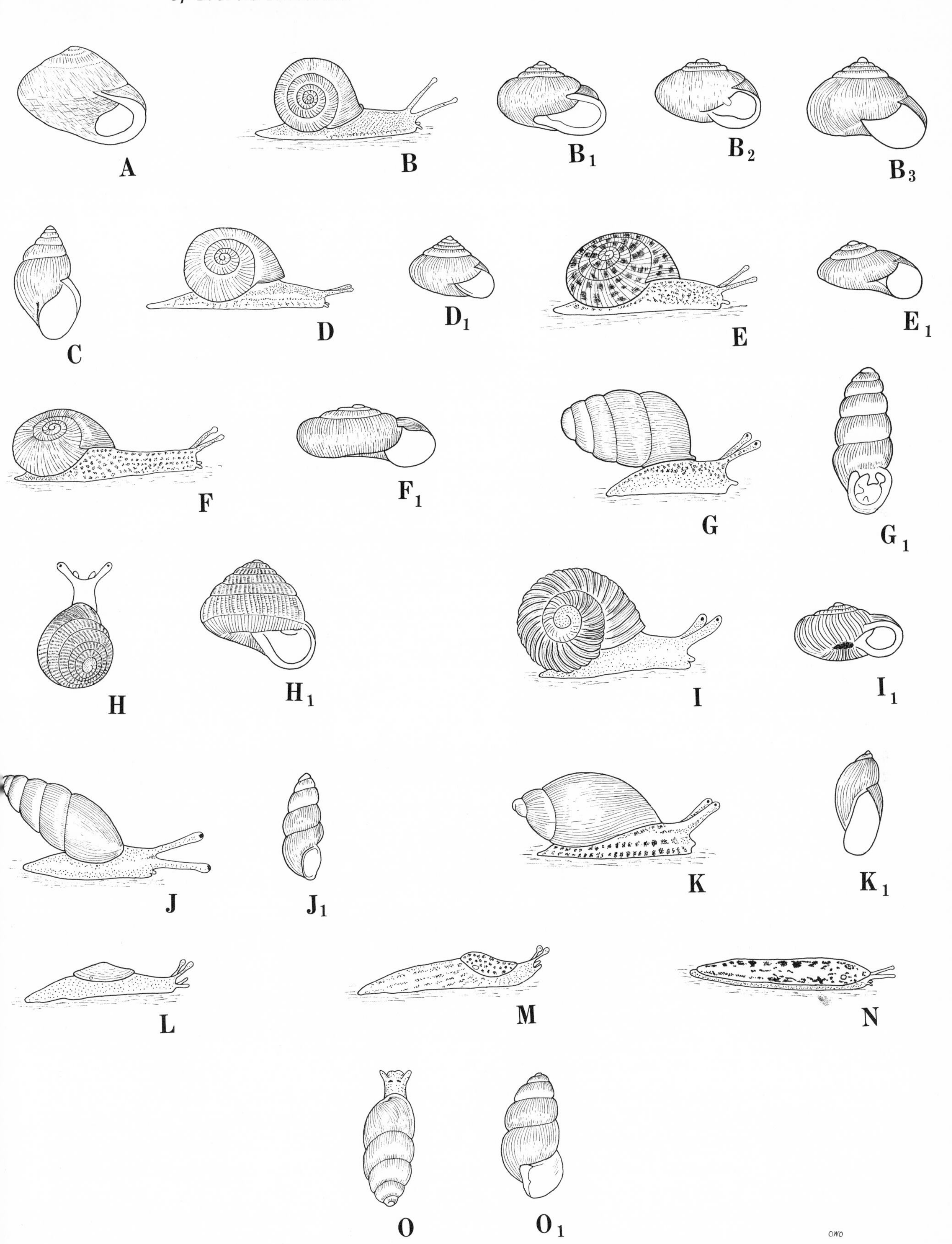

Vallonidae (Figs. I, I_1): The shells are minute (up to 2.75 mm), the spires are only slightly elevated, and provided with elevated ribs over the surface. *Vallonia* is representative of the family.

Cionellidae (Figs. J, J_1): The shell is about 6 mm long, cylindrical, smooth, shining, and horn-colored. The spire is considerably longer than the aperture. *Cionella lubrica* is the only species in North America. It is commonly listed as a member of the Cochlicopidae.

Succineidae (Figs. K, K_1): Shells are thin, amber-colored, oval, and with a very large aperture and small spire. The animal is too large for the shell. *Succinea* is the only genus.

Endodontidae (Figs. E, E_1): The shells are subconical, never smooth and shining but usually brown in color and ribbed. The lip is thin and never expanded. Size varies from minute (1.5 mm) to large (25 to 28 mm). *Anguispira, Goniodiscus, Helicodiscus,* and *Punctum* are representative of the family.

Haplotrematidae (Figs. F, F_1): The shells are large, only slightly spired, being almost discoidal, and without spotting. The lip is smooth, thin, and without protuberances. The animal is long and narrow. *Haplotrema* is the only genus.

Pupillidae (Figs. G, G_1): The shells are elongated, oval, and turreted. The outer lip is usually provided with a variable number of internally projecting teeth. The shells never exceed 5.5 mm in length. Representative genera are *Vertigo, Gastrocopta, Pupoides, Pupilla, Pupisoma,* and *Columella.*

Limacidae (Figs. L, M): These are the slugs. Contrary to the other land snails with coiled shells, the slugs have a rudimentary one completely buried in the tissue. The long, narrow body is humped toward the middle and bears a short rounded projection called the mantle, which covers the lung. A breathing pore is present on the right posterior part of the mantle. *Derocercas* is representative of the family. *Agriolimax* is a synonym. Species are about 2 inches long.

Philomycidae (Fig. N): The Philomycidae are tropical slugs with a mantle that covers three-fourths or more of the body length. The respiratory pore is on the right anterior part of the mantle. *Philomycus* and *Pallifera* are representatives of the family that occur in the United States.

Ellobiidae (Figs. O, O_1): They are largely marine forms. A few species are terrestrial. The shell is elongated. The aperture has one or more folds on the columella and frequently on the outer lip. The foot is broad and slightly indented anteriorly. It is divided ventrally by a transverse line into a short anterior and a long posterior part. *Carychium* (1.7 mm long) is representative of the family.

EXERCISE ON REARING SNAILS

It is important to have parasite-free snails in any experimental studies on the life cycles of trematodes. While the surest way of having "clean" specimens is to rear them in the laboratory where infection with flukes is precluded, it is not always easy to do so. Many aquatic snails can be reared in balanced aquaria with or without aeration. Unglazed clay pots are useful in hot climates where water in glass aquaria becomes too warm for snails to survive well.

Food consists of microflora that accumulates on the sides of the aquaria, especially on the clay containers. Dried tree leaves soaked in water to remove tannic acid is good for some snails. Fresh or boiled lettuce is good food for snails and dried powdered lettuce is excellent food for very young snails. Chopped feed used for domestic livestock provides nutritious food for snails. It is prepared by placing a few handfuls of the feed in a pail of water and allowing it to go through a fermentation process. After the water clears, the sediment provides the food that is readily eaten and does not foul the water of the aquarium. Powdered calcium or pieces of chalk may be supplied. A diet used in many laboratories where large colonies of snails are maintained consists of cerophyl (dehydrated cereal grasses), 10 gm; powdered wheat germ, 5 gm; and sodium alginate, 5 gm. It is mixed in a blender with 500 ml of water at 50° C. The viscous mixture is forced from a 2-liter suction flask by compressed air into a tray of 2 per cent $CaCl_2$ solution, where it forms a continuous strand of insoluble calcium alginate food. After washing the food in water, it can be frozen and stored until needed.

Amphibious, land, and marine snails require different procedures for rearing. Amphibious snails are reared in containers tipped so as to expose some of the soil or sand at one end above the water line.

Food and snail faeces accumulating on the bottom of the balanced aquaria may be removed by aspiration. Land snails and slugs may be reared in terrariums in which the bottom is covered with a thick layer of moist soil overlaid with moss and dead leaves. Lettuce is good food. Marine snails can be reared in trays or aquaria of aerated sea water. Satisfactory food consists of frozen shrimp, fresh yeast, baker's yeast, and calcium carbonate. Snails may be removed from the aquaria and fed in finger bowls about twice weekly. This procedure avoids contaminating the aquaria with decaying food.

For further details on rearing snails, consult Malek and Galtsoff *et al.* In addition to mollusks, the latter reference contains procedures for rearing many different kinds of invertebrates.

SELECTED REFERENCES

Baker, F. C. (1911). The Lymnaeidae of North and Middle America. Chicago Acad. Sci. Sp. Publ. No. 3, 539 pp., 58 pls.; (1928). The Fresh Water Mollusca of Wisconsin, Part I: Gastropoda. Wisc. Acad. Sci., Arts, and Letters, 507 pp., 28 pls.; (1939). Fieldbook of Illinois Land Snails. State of Ill., Nat. Hist. Surv. Div., Manual 2, 166 pp.; (1945). The Molluscan Family Planorbidae. University of Illinois Press, Urbana, 530 pp., 41 plates.

Chamberlain, R. V., and D. T. Jones. (1929). A Descriptive Catalog of the Mollusca of Utah. Bull. Univ. Utah, Vol. 19, 203 pp.

Eddy, S., and A. C. Hodson. (1957). Taxonomic Keys to the Common Animals of the North Central States, exclusive of the Parasitic Worms, Insects, and Birds. Burgess Publishing Co., Minneapolis, 141 pp.

Galtsoff, P. S., F. E. Lutz, P. S. Welch, and J. G. Needham. (1937). Culture Methods for Invertebrate Animals. Reprint Dover Publications, New York, p. 519.

Goodrich, C. (1932). The Mollusca of Michigan. Univ. Mus., Univ. Mich. Handbook, Ser. 5, 120 pp.

Henderson, J. (1936). Mollusca of Colorado, Utah, Montana, Idaho, and Wyoming. Univ. Colo. Stud. 23:81.

*Malek, E. A. (1962). Laboratory Guide and Notes for Medical Malacology. Burgess Publishing Co., Minneapolis, 154 pp.

Pennak, R. W. (1953). Fresh-water Invertebrates of the United States. Ronald Press Co., New York, p. 667.

Pilsbry, H. A. (1937-1948). Land Mollusca of North America (North of Mexico). Phil. Acad. Nat. Sci. Monogr. 1(½):1-994; 2(½):1-1113; (1940). Land Mollusca of North America. Monogr. Acad. Nat. Sci. Philadelphia, No. 5, Parts 1 and 2.

Walker, B. (1918). A Synopsis of the Classification of the Fresh-Water Mollusca of North America, North of Mexico and a Catalogue of the More Recently Described Species, with Notes. Univ. Mich. Mus. Zool., Misc. Publ. No. 6.; (1928). The Terrestrial Shell-Bearing Mollusca of Alabama. Univ. Mich. Mus. Zool., Misc. Publ. 18, 180 pp.

Ward, H. B., and G. C. Whipple (1918). Fresh-Water Biology. John Wiley and Sons, New York, p. 957; revised (1959).

*This book is excellent for all aspects of malacology as it pertains to parasitology. It has basic information on morphology, classification, keys, illustrations, and procedures. The list of references is comprehensive and organized under a variety of headings in which mollusks are related to parasitic helminths.

SUPERORDER ANEPITHELIOCYSTIDA

In this group of trematodes, the primitive thin-walled excretory bladder of the cercariae is retained and there is no stylet in the oral sucker.

ORDER STRIGEATIDA

The cercariae of this order are fork-tailed. The group contains four suborders, all of which show this gross characteristic.

Suborder Strigeata

The cercariae are fork-tailed and usually have two suckers, an oral and a ventral.

SUPERFAMILY STRIGEOIDEA

The cercariae usually have a pharynx and a long tail with a slender stem. The metacercariae are of three types, consisting of the tetracotyle, diplostomulum, and neascus. The body of the adults is divided into a forebody and a hindbody.

FAMILY STRIGEIDAE

These are parasites of the intestine of fish-, frog-, and snail-eating birds or mammals. The forebody

EXPLANATION OF PLATE 53

A. Adult fluke showing internal anatomy. **B.** Adult fluke showing external configuration. **C.** Entire mother sporocyst containing germ cells, cercariae, and tetracotyles. **D.** Cercaria. **E.** Ventral view of encysted tetracotyle (metacercaria). **F.** Lateral view of excysted tetracotyle. **G.** Duck definitive host. **H.** Snail *(Stagnicola* and *Lymnaea)* first intermediate host. **I.** Snail *(Stagnicola, Lymnaea, Physa, Helisoma)* second intermediate host.

1, forebody; **2**, hindbody; **3**, oral sucker; **4**, pharynx; **5**, oesophagus; **6**, intestine; **7**, ventral sucker; **8**, dorsal holdfast organ; **9**, ventral holdfast organ; **10**, adhesive gland; **11**, posterior testes; **12**, seminal vesicle; **13**, common genital pore; **14**, ovary; **15**, oviduct; **16**, Mehlis' gland; **17**, ascending portion of uterus; **18**, descending portion of uterus; **19**, Laurer's canal; **20**, vitelline glands; **21**, daughter sporocyst; **22**, developing cercaria; **23**, tetracotyle; **24**, penetration gland; **25**, unpigmented eyespot; **26**, flame cell; **27**, excretory bladder; **28**, collecting tubule of excretory bladder; **29**, genital primordium; **30**, tail; **31**, cyst of tetracotyle; **32**, holdfast organ; **33**, orifice of lateral sucker of tetracotyle; **34**, cleft of lateral sucker; **35**, external meatus of holdfast organ; **36**, urinary bladder; **37**, genital primordium.

a, adult fluke attached to mucosa of small intestine of duck; **b**, eggs laid in intestine; **c**, unembryonated egg passed in faeces; **d**, egg embryonates in water and hatches; **e**, miracidium attacks snails of the genera *Stagnicola, Lymnaea, Physa,* and *Helisoma;* **f**, miracidium transforms into mother sporocysts; **g**, daughter sporocyst with developing cercariae; **h**, fully developed cercaria escaping from snail intermediate host; **i**, cercaria free in water hanging in characteristic position; **j**, cercaria attacking snail second intermediate host, dropping its tail in the process; **k**, cercaria in tissues of snail; **l**, tetracotyle encysted in tissues of snail; **m**, tetracotyle encysted in redia of a different species of fluke, a case of hyperparasitism; **n**, tetracotyle encysted in the sporocyst of another species of trematode, another case of hyperparasitism; **o**, infection of definitive host occurs when snails containing tetracotyles are swallowed and released from snails by the digestive processes; **p**, encysted tetracotyle freed from snail tissues; **q**, excystation of tetracotyle in intestine of duck where it attaches to the epithelium and develops to sexual maturity after 4 days.

Figures A-B adapted from Van Haitsma, 1931, Papers Mich. Acad. Sci., Arts, Lett. 13:447; C, from Hussey, Cort, and Ameel, 1958, J. Parasit. 44:289; D, from Cort and Brooks, 1928, Trans. Amer. Micr. Soc. 47:179; E, from Hughes, 1929, Papers Mich. Acad. Sci., Arts, Lett. 10:495; F, from Faust, 1918, Ill. Biol. Monogr. 4:1.

---

of the adults is cup-shaped with the ventral sucker inside. The metacercariae are in fish, frogs, or snails.

Cotylurus flabelliformis (Faust, 1917) (Plate 53)

These are parasites of the small intestine of ducks in North America.

DESCRIPTION. Mature flukes measure 0.56 to 0.85 mm in length; the forebody is 0.2 to 0.28 mm and the hindbody 0.36 to 0.57 mm long. The oespohagus is nearly as long as the pharynx. An excretory bladder is lacking. The testes are bean-shaped and a Mehlis' gland is present. Eggs are 100 to 112 μ long by 68 to 76 μ wide.

LIFE CYCLE. Adult worms in the small intestine lay unembryonated eggs which leave the body in the faeces. Development takes place in the water where the eggs hatch in about 3 weeks and the ciliated miracidia swim about. Upon coming in contact with the snails *Lymnaea stagnalis* and *Stagnicola emarginata,* of the family Lymnaeidae, they penetrate readily and develop normally. The ciliated epithelium is shed and the miracidium transforms into a mother sporocyst. As development progresses, the germ cells within the mother sporocyst develop into daughter sporocysts which escape and migrate to the digestive gland where they grow into slender vermiform bodies. From the germ cells in the sporocysts, fork-tailed, pharyngeate cercariae develop. When fully formed, they escape from the sporocyst and eventually from the snail into the water about 6 weeks after infection.

The cercariae are active swimmers but rest after short periods of activity. Upon coming in contact with snails, they penetrate the soft tissues and migrate to the hermaphroditic gland. Further development of them to the tetracotyle stage, a type of metacercaria characteristic of Strigeidae, is dependent upon several factors. The tetracotyles develop normally and encyst in approximately 6 weeks in the tissues of the same species of snail in which they developed as cercariae, that is, in *Lymnaea stagnalis* or *Stagnicola emarginata.* If, on the other hand, they enter physid or planorbid snails, no development takes place unless these snails are infected already with some species of trematodes. In these cases, the cercariae of *C. flabelliformis* enter the sporocysts or rediae of the trematodes already present and develop into encysted tetracotyles somewhat sooner than in *Lymnaea* or *Stagnicola.* In this case, they are hyperparasites, that is, one parasite infecting another and developing in it.

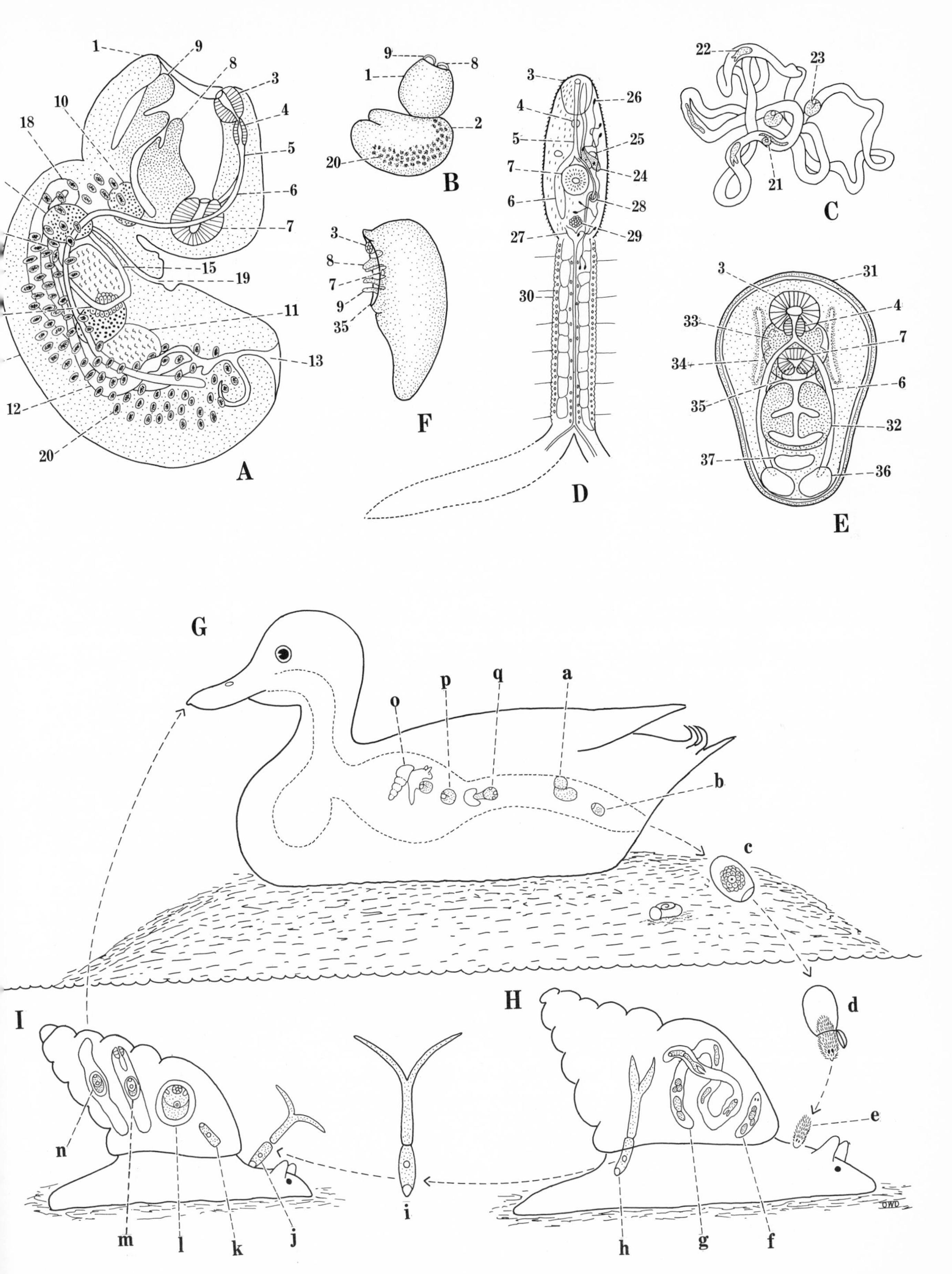
1
9
8
3
10
4
18
5
6
7
15
19
11
13
12
20
A
9
8
1
2
20
B
3
8
7
9
35
F
3
26
4
25
5
24
7
28
6
29
27
30
D
22
23
21
C
3
31
33
4
7
34
6
35
32
37
36
E
G
o
p
q
a
b
c
d
e
H
I
n
m
l
k
j
i
h
g
f
GWD

Infection of ducks takes place when snails harboring encysted tetracotyles are eaten. Sexual maturity is attained in about one week.

Life histories of some other Strigeidae that have been studied show considerable variation. Several examples illustrate this. In *Apatemon gracilis,* another parasite of ducks, the cercariae develop in the snail *Helisoma antrosa,* and the tetracotyles (metacercariae) in the leech *Herpobdella punctata.* Sexual maturity is attained after 4 days in ducks and the worms are lost after 13 days.

Apharyngostrigea pipientis develops in pigeons under experimental conditions. The first intermediate host is *Planorbula armigera* and the second is tadpoles of *Rana pipiens,* which the cercariae presumably enter by way of the branchial or intestinal epithelium. The tetracotyles develop slowly.

Strigea elegans from great horned owls and snowy owls has a more complicated life cycle in which four hosts are involved. The cercariae develop in the snail *Gyraulus parvus* and penetrate the tadpoles of *Bufo americanus, Rana sylvatica,* and *R. clamitans,* where they develop to mesocercariae. When mesocercariae are eaten by animals other than the definitive host, such as water snakes, owls, and ducks, they develop into tetracotyles that locate in the subcutaneous tissues. These animals harboring the tetracotyles are the third intermediate host in the life cycle. It is presumed that a fourth host is necessary in which adults develop from tetracotyles.

An extensive summary of the life cycles of strigeid trematodes is given by Olivier.

EXERCISE ON LIFE CYCLE

Collect specimens of *Lymnaea stagnalis, Stagnicola emarginata, Physa* spp., and *Helisoma* spp. from marshes where ducks and other animals live. Isolate specimens of them in glass jars to obtain strigeid cercariae and separate those of *Cotylurus flabelliformis.* After having determined which individuals are infected, some of them should be dissected to obtain sporocysts for study. Expose uninfected *L. stagnalis* and *S. emarginata* to cercariae of *C. flabelliformis.* Uninfected specimens may be obtained from habitats where ducks do not go. Examine exposed specimens at intervals of 4 to 5 days for a period of 3 to 4 weeks in order to follow the development and encystment of the tetracotyles in the digestive gland.

Isolate specimens of *Physa* and *Helisoma* in order to obtain individuals infected with flukes of any kind. Expose the infected specimens to the cercariae of *C. flabelliformis.* Sacrifice some individuals at intervals to 3 to 4 days for development of the tetracoytles in the sporocysts or rediae of the flukes already in them.

Feed tetracotyles to ducks and determine the length of time required for eggs to appear in the faeces and for the flukes to disappear spontaneously. The eggs may be used as a source of miracidia for infecting young *L. stagnalis* or *S. emarginata* in order to obtain the developmental stages of the mother and daughter sporocysts.

SELECTED REFERENCES

Cort, W. W., and S. T. Brooks. (1928). Trans. Amer. Micr. Soc. 47:179.

Cort, W. W., S. Brackett, and L. Olivier. (1944). J. Parasit. 30:309.

Cort, W. W., L. Olivier, and S. Brackett. (1941). J. Parasit. 27:437.

Faust, E. C. (1918). Ill. Biol. Monogr. 4:62, pl. 3.

Hoffman, G. L., and R. E. Putz. (1965). Trans. Amer. Fish. Soc. 94:143.

Hughes, R. C. (1929). Papers Mich. Acad. Sci., Arts, Lett. 10:495.

Hussey, K. L., W. W. Cort, and D. J. Ameel. (1958). J. Parasit. 44:289.

Olivier, L. (1940). J. Parasit. 26:447.

Pearson, J. C. (1959). J. Parasit. 45:155.

Stunkard, H. W., C. H. Willey, and Y. Rabinowitz. (1941). Trans. Amer. Micr. Soc. 60:485.

Van Haitsma, J. P. (1931). Papers Mich. Acad. Sci., Arts, Lett. 10:495.

FAMILY DIPLOSTOMATIDAE

The Diplostomatidae are parasites of the intestine of fish- and frog-eating birds and mammals. The body is generally divided into a fore and hind region. The forebody is spatulate or foliate in shape, the posterior cylindrical. An oral sucker and pharynx are present.

Uvulifer ambloplitis (Hughes, 1927) (Plate 54)

U. ambloplitis infects kingfishers in North America. The metacercariae, or neascus larvae, appear as small black spots in the skin of bass, rock bass, perch, and sunfish.

DESCRIPTION. Adult flukes are 1.8 to 2.3 mm long; the posterior half, or there-abouts, of the forebody forms a necklike structure. The forebody is bowl-shaped with the oral sucker inside but near the anterior margin, the ventral sucker near the center, and the holdfast organ just posterior to it. The hindbody is about 3 times the length of the forebody and about 4.5 times as long as the diameter of the small testis. Vitelline follicles extend posteriorly almost to the level of the copulatory bursa. Eggs measure 90 to 99 μ long by 56 to 66 μ wide.

LIFE CYCLE. Unembryonated eggs are passed in the droppings of kingfishers. Under favorable temperatures, they hatch in water in about three weeks. The miracidia penetrate ram's horn snails (*Helisoma trivolvis* and *H. campanulata*), shed the ciliated epithelium, and transform into mother sporocysts, which are characterized by retaining the eyespots of the miracidia. Sporocysts produced by the mother sporocyst invade the digestive gland and liver. When mature, they are about 2 mm long, have constrictions of the body and a birth pore. Cercariae appear in sporocysts in approximately 6 weeks after infection of the snails. They are filled with germ balls and cercariae; the latter are in various stages of development.

When mature, the fork-tailed cercariae escape into the water. They swim for short intervals and then rest, hanging in the water with the furcae spread and the fore part of the body folded upon itself. When coming in contact with bass, perch, and sunfish, the cercariae attach to the fish and penetrate the skin, dropping the tail in the process. Upon entering the skin, they transform into neascus-type metacercariae. These secrete a roomy hyaline cyst about themselves. By the end of the third week, the host has deposited black pigment around the cysts. They are now called black spots or black grubs. Heavy infection of the fish cause a bulging of the eyes from the socket, a condition known as popeye. Fatalities occur in fry.

Kingfishers become infected by eating fish with black spots. Development to sexual maturity in the fledgling birds requires about 27 days.

Crassiphiala bulboglossa, also of kingfishers, is closely related to *U. ambloplitis* and has a similar life cycle. It produces black spots in 11 species of fish from the families Cyprinidae, Cyprinodontidae, Esocidae, Etheostomidae, Percidae, and Umbridae. *Helisoma anceps* and *H. trivolvus* serve as the snail hosts.

A total of six species of strigeid flukes are reported to produce black spots in fish. Trout have black spots that are caused by Heterophyidae metacercariae of *Apophallus imperator* from gulls and loons and *A. brevis* from herons and mergansers.

EXERCISE ON LIFE CYCLE

Locate an area where kingfishers occur along streams or near ponds. Fish and ram's horn snails from these waters in all probability will be parasitized with strigeid larvae that cause black spots. Collect ram's horn snails from waters where infected fish occur and isolate them in small wide mouth bottles to obtain the fork-tailed cercariae.

Uninfected fish, at least those without visible black spots, should be exposed to fork-tailed cercariae from ram's horn snails. Fish should be examined at intervals of 4 to 5 days to follow the development of the metacercariae and the deposition of pigment by the host. Metacercariae can be collected readily by digesting infected fish in an artificial solution of pepsin and hydrochloric acid.

A fledgling kingfisher can be used for infection experiments without harm to it. Eggs passed in the faeces should be used for procuring miracida to be used in infecting snails. By careful planning, the entire life cycle can be demonstrated.

EXPLANATION OF PLATE 54 ⇨

A. Adult fluke. B. Miracidium. C. Mother sporocyst. D. Daughter sporocyst. E. Pharyngeate furcocercous cercaria. F. Encysted neascus (metacercaria). G. Neascus in process of excystment. H. Neascus type of metacercaria. I. Belted kingfisher *(Streptoceryle alcyon)* definitive host. J. Snail intermediate host *(Helisoma trivolvus)*. K. Fish second intermediate host *(Micropterus dolomieui)*.

1, forebody; 2, hindbody; 3, oral sucker; 4, ventral sucker; 5, holdfast organ; 6, prepharynx; 7, pharynx; 8, oesophagus; 9, intestine; 10, posterior testis; 11, vas efferentia; 12, seminal vesicle; 13, ejaculatory duct with sphincter; 14, genital cone; 15, ovary; 16, oviduct; 17, Mehlis' gland; 18, Laurer's canal; 19, proximal portion of uterus; 20, distal portion of uterus; 21, common genital pore; 22, vitelline glands; 23, part of vitelline duct; 24, apical papilla; 25, apical gland; 26, eyespot; 27, ganglion; 28, penetration gland; 29, germ cells; 30, cercaria; 31, excretory bladder; 32, tail; 33, furca; 34, metacercarial cyst.

a, adult fluke in small intestine; b, eggs laid in intestine; c, unembryonated eggs pass from intestine in faeces; d, eggs develop and hatch in water; e, miracidium free in water; f, miracidium attacks and penetrates soft tissue of snail; g, mother sporocyst; h, daughter sporocyst with germ balls and cercaria; i, free-swimming cercaria in characteristic resting position; j, cercaria attacking fish second intermediate host, dropping its tail in the process; k, encysted neascus in fish intermediate host; l, infection of definitive host occurs upon swallowing of infected fish intermediary; m, digestion of fish releases cysts from its tissues; n, cyst free in digestive tract; o, neascus released from cyst by action of digestive juices, allowing it to proceed to proper site in small intestine and develop to sexual maturity.

Adapted from Hunter and Hunter, 1935, Suppl. 24th Ann. Rept. N. Y. State Conserv. Dept. 1934, No. IX, p. 267.

SELECTED REFERENCES

Hoffman, G. L. (1956). J. Parasit. 42:435.

Hugghins, E. T. (1959). South Dakota Exp. Sta. and S. D. Dept. Game, Fish, and Parks, Bull. 484, p. 30.

Hunter, G. W., III. (1933). Parasitology 25:510.

Hunter, G. W., III. and W. S. Hunter. (1930). J. Parasit. 17:108; (1933). Ibid. 20:328; (1935). Suppl. 24th Ann. Rept. N. Y. State Conserv. Dept. 1934, No. IX, p. 267.

Krull, W. H. (1932). J. Parasit. 19:165; (1934). Copeia, No. 2, p. 69.

Diplostomum baeri eucaliae Hoffman and Hundley, 1957 (Plate 55)

This is normally a parasite of the anterior third of the small intestine of ducks in North America, and possibly many other parts of the world.

DESCRIPTION. Adult flukes reared in baby chicks are similar to those recovered from mallard ducks. They are 1.35 to 1.8 mm long and about 0.48 mm at the point of greatest width. The hindbody is 0.75 to 0.96 mm long and extends dorsoposteriorly at an angle of 65 to 80°, probably the normal position. The anterior testis is 139 by 172 μ and the posterior one 163 by 209 μ in size. Eggs measure 92 to 111 μ by 54 to 64 μ.

LIFE CYCLE. Unembryonated eggs develop and hatch in 12 days at room temperature. The miracidia penetrate the snails *Stagnicola palustris* and *S. p. elodes* in which asexual development takes place. Upon entering the tissues of these snails, the miracidia transform near the point of penetration into mother sporocysts. By the end of 3 weeks, they are fully developed and contain daughter sporocysts which escape and migrate to the liver, reaching it by the 26th day. The sporocysts have matured by the 30th day and are releasing cercariae. They emerge from the snails in small numbers throughout the day and night. In water having a temperature of 24 to 27° C, survival is up to 35 hours. Snails shedding cercariae at the onset of winter lose their infections during the course of hibernation.

Cercariae attach to and penetrate the skin of brook sticklebacks (*Eucalia inconstans*). Apparently, they enter blood vessels and are carried to the cephalic regions. They penetrate the optic lobes, optic nerves, cornea, retina, muscles, and gills, and transform into a diplostomulum type of metacercaria characterized by pseudosuckers, one on each side of the oral sucker. Two hundred or more cercariae may be fatal to fish by causing haemorrhage in the brain and viscera. The larvae reach the brain as early as 3 days after infecting the fish and are in the optic lobes after 5 days. Development appears to

PLATE 54 *Uvulifer ambloplitis*

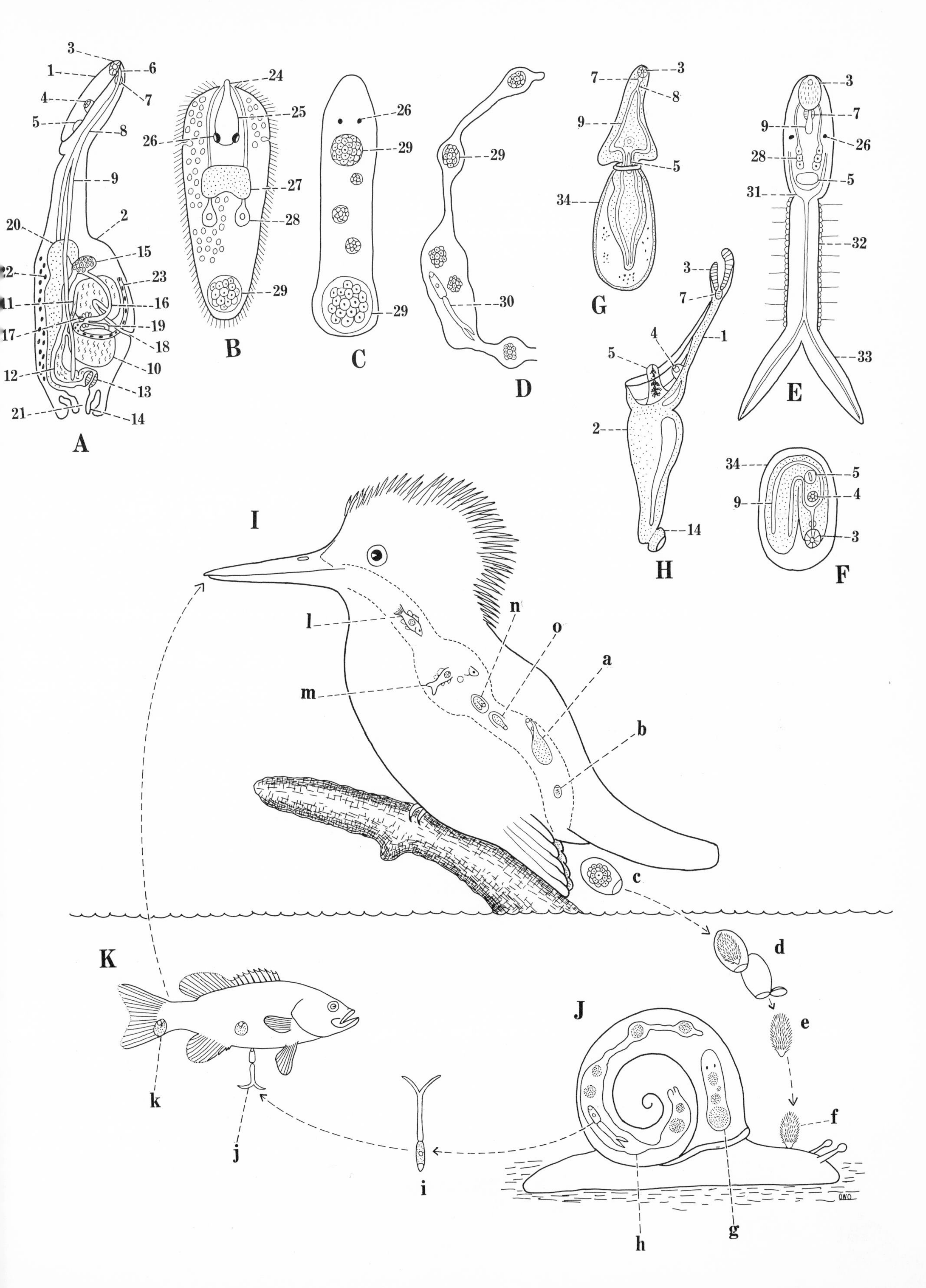

EXPLANATION OF PLATE 55 ▷

A. Ventral view of adult fluke. **B.** Sinistral view of adult fluke. **C.** Miracidium. **D.** Young mother sporocyst. **E.** Mature mother sporocyst. **F.** Mature daughter sporocyst. **G.** Pharyngeate fork-tailed cercariae. **H.** Diplostomulum 5 days old. **I.** Diplostomulum 9 days old. **J.** Dextral view of mature diplostomulum. **K.** Ventral view of mature diplostomulum. **L.** Ventral view of mature diplostomulum with pseudosuckers everted. **M.** Mallard duck definitive host. **N.** Snail *(Stagnicola* spp.) first intermediate host. **O.** Cutaway view of stickleback second intermediate host.

1, forebody; **2**, hindbody; **3**, pseudosucker; **4**, oral sucker; **5**, ventral sucker; **6**, adhesive gland; **7**, pharynx; **8**, oesophagus; **9**, intestinal crura; **10**, ovary; **11**, ootype; **12**, testis; **13**, seminal vesicle; **14**, vitelline glands; **15**, egg in uterus; **16**, genital pore; **17**, apical gland; **18**, eyespot; **19**, excretory canal; **20**, flame cell; **21**, daughter sporocysts developing in mother sporocyst; **22**, germinal mass; **23**, fully developed daughter sporocyst; **24**, birth pore; **25**, developing cercaria in daughter sporocyst; **26**, penetration glands; **27**, tail of cercaria; **28**, excretory bladder; **29**, excretory tubule of tail; **30**, furca of tail; **31**, everted pseudosucker; **32**, genital anlagen.

a, adult fluke in small intestine of definitive host; **b**, eggs laid in intestine; **c**, undeveloped eggs passed in faeces; **d**, eggs develop in water where miracidia hatch; **e**, miracidium penetrates snail intermediate host; **f**, miracidium sheds ciliated covering and transforms into young mother sporocyst; **g**, mature mother sporocyst with germ balls and developing daughter sporocyst; **h**, mature daughter sporocyst with developing cercaria; **i**, mature fork-tailed cercaria escaping from snail into water; **j**, cercaria in water hanging in characteristic position; **k**, cercaria penetrating gills of stickleback, dropping its tail in the process; **l**, cercaria in afferent branchial artery; **m**, cercaria escaping from afferent branchial artery; **n**, cercaria entering optic lobe of brain; **o**, metacercariae crowded in optic lobe; **p**, cercaria that has strayed into muscle tissues; **q**, metacercaria in olfactory lobe; **r**, metacercaria in cornea, also retina and posterior chamber; **s**, infection of duck host when infected sticklebacks are swallowed; **t**, metacercaria being freed from fish by action of digestive juices; **u**, metacercaria free in stomach; **v**, metacercaria escaping from cyst; **w**, young fluke attaches to wall of small intestine and grows to maturity in three to four days.

Adapted from Hoffman and Hundley, 1957, J. Parasit. 43:613.

---

be completed by the 11th day and the metacercariae are infective on the 13th day. Metacercariae survive in fish for 1 year and possibly more, attaining a stage of precocious development.

Ducks become infected by eating sticklebacks that harbor fully developed diplostomulae. The prepatent period for mature diplostomulae is 3 days in unfed baby chicks experimentally infected either by feeding or by injecting the metacercariae into the peritoneal cavity.

This is the only strigeid metacercaria recorded from the brain of fish in North America. Four other species are known from Europe and one from Argentina.

EXERCISE ON LIFE CYCLE

Inasmuch as *Diplostomum baeri eucaliae* has been found only in brook sticklebacks, these fish should be examined as a source of experimental material. While ducks may provide eggs of the flukes or the mature parasites, they are not always as readily obtained as the sticklebacks.

Diplostomulae from the brains of fish develop readily when administered to unfed newly hatched chicks. Determine the prepatent period.

Eggs obtained from experimentally infected chicks should be incubated and the miracidia studied. Infect *Stagnicola palustris* by placing them in a small dish with miracidia. Ascertain the course of development of the sporocysts and cercariae in the mollusks.

When cercariae appear, note the time of day when emergence from the snails occurs, their behavior in the water and toward light, and postulate the relationship of it to infection of the fish under natural conditions. Naturally infected snails should be sought in waters inhabited by ducks and sticklebacks.

Expose sticklebacks to cercariae and observe the cercariae, the effect on the behavior of the fish during the period of penetration, and later when the metacercariae are developing in the brain, the route of migration to the brain, and the process of encystment. Examine the fish carefully for damage to the brain by the diplostomulae. Sections of the brain will reveal the relationship of the larval parasites to the different parts of it and some of the pathology caused by them.

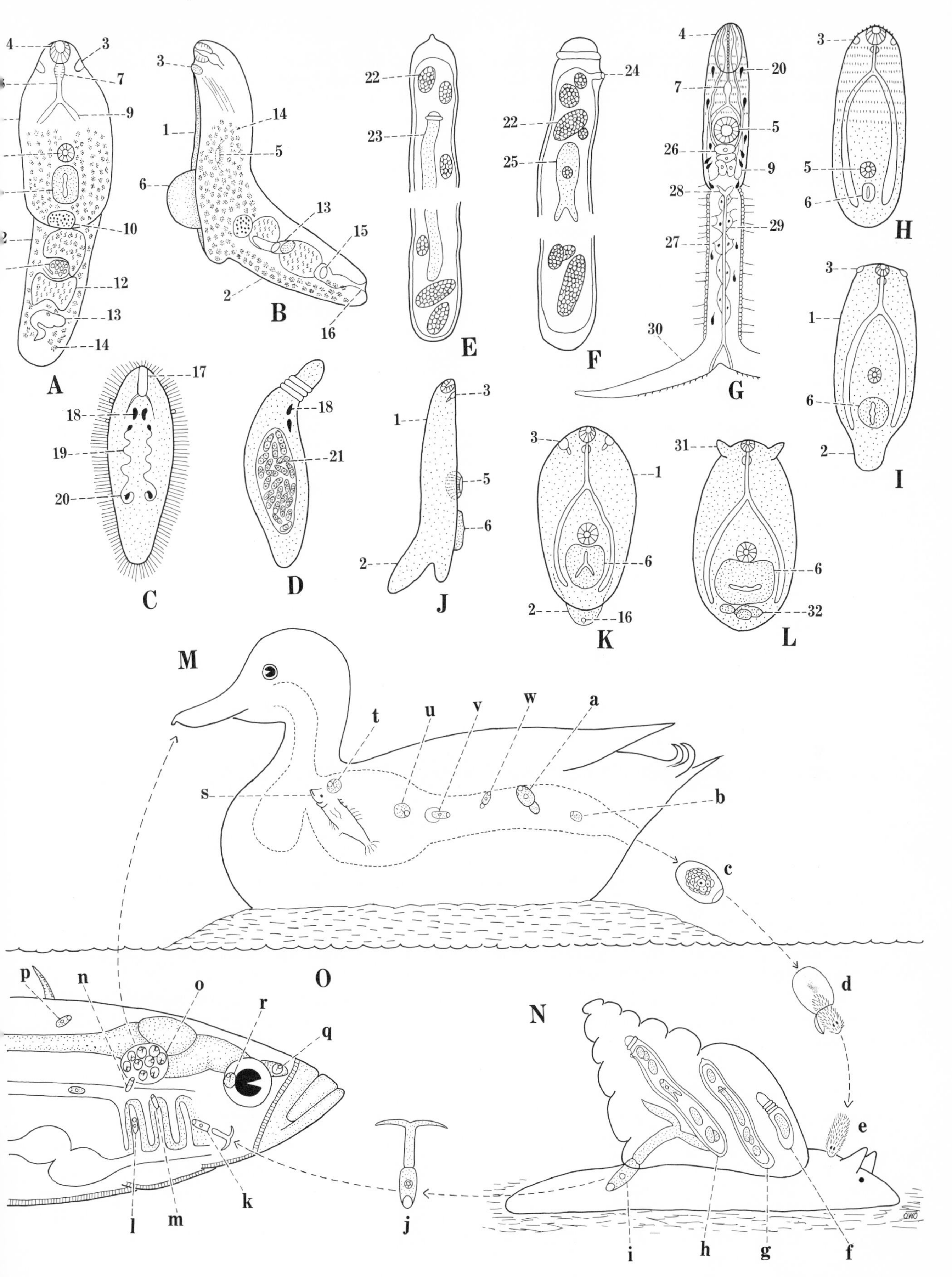
A
B
C
D
E
F
G
H
I
J
K
L
M
N
O
a
b
c
d
e
f
g
h
i
j
k
l
m
n
o
p
q
r
s
t
u
v
w

EXPLANATION OF PLATE 56 ▷

A. Ventral view of adult fluke. **B.** Miracidium. **C.** Adult mother sporocyst. **D.** Daughter sporocyst. **E.** Fork-tailed cercaria. **F.** Mesocercaria showing some internal organs. **G.** External view of mesocercaria. **H.** Diplostomulum. **I.** Fox definitive host. **J.** Planorbid snail *(Helisoma)* first intermediate host. **K.** Tadpole *(Rana, Bufo)* second intermediate host. **L.** Paratenic hosts (snakes, frogs, mice).

1, forebody; **2,** hindbody; **3,** lappet or pseudosucker; **4,** holdfast organ; **5,** oral sucker; **6,** pharynx; **7,** caecum; **8,** ventral sucker; **9,** testes; **10,** ovary; **11,** eggs in uterus; **12,** vitelline glands; **13,** common genital pore; **14,** cilia; **15,** eyespot; **16,** flame cell; **17,** germ cells; **18,** excretory opening; **19,** daughter sporocyst with germ balls or developing cercariae; **20,** birth pore; **21,** cercaria; **22,** penetration glands; **23,** duct of penetration glands; **24,** genital primordium; **25,** excretory bladder; **26,** forked tail; **27,** body spines.

a, adult fluke in small intestine; **b,** egg passing out of body in faeces; **c,** unembryonated egg; **d,** embryonated egg; **e,** egg hatching; **f,** miracidium penetrating *Helisoma* snail; **g,** young mother sporocyst; **h,** mature mother sporocyst; **i,** daughter sporocyst; **j,** cercaria free in water in characteristic resting position; **k,** cercaria penetrating tadpole, casting tail as it enters; **l,** mesocercaria; **m,** mesocercaria in snake, frog, and mouse paratenic hosts; **n,** infection of definitive host by swallowing infected tadpole second intermediate host; **o,** infection of definitive host by swallowing infected paratenic host; **p,** mesocercariae migrate through gut wall into coelom; **q,** mesocercariae enter hepatic portal vein but it has not been shown that they reach the lungs via the blood; **r,** mesocercariae pass through the diaphragm and penetrate the lungs; **s,** in the lungs the mesocercariae transform to a diplostomulum stage; **t,** diplostomula migrate up trachea; **u,** diplostomula are swallowed, go to small intestine, and develop to maturity **(a)** in 5 to 6 weeks.

Figure A adapted from LaRue and Fallis, 1936, Trans. Amer. Micr. Soc. 55:340, B-H, from Pearson, 1956, Canad. J. Res. 34:295.

SELECTED REFERENCES

Hoffman, G. L., and J. B. Hundley. (1957). J. Parasit. 43:613.

Rees, G. (1955). Parasitology 45:295.

Alaria canis LaRue and Fallis, 1937 (Plate 56)

A. canis is a parasite of Canidae in Canada. The adult flukes are in the first third of the small intestine where the eggs are laid.

DESCRIPTION. Adult worms measure 2.5 to 4.2 mm long with the forebody 1.6 to 2.6 mm and the hindbody 0.68 to 1.6 mm. The forebody has foliaceous margins that join posteriorly near the level of the body constriction. There is a conical tentacular appendage on each side of the oral sucker. The holdfast organ is oval, has a longitudinal median depression, and extends from near the ventral sucker to the level of the constriction; the posterior part is more or less covered by the foliaceous margins of the forebody. The ovary is near the level of the constriction and located toward the right. The testes are lobed, with the posterior one being much the larger. Eggs are 107 to 133 μ long by 77 to 99 μ wide and unembryonated.

LIFE CYCLE. Unembryonated eggs laid in the intestine are voided in the faeces of dogs or other canids. Development of them is rapid at room temperature, with hatching in 2 weeks. The fusiform miracidia are active swimmers. They penetrate the snails *Helisoma trivolvis, H. campanulata,* and *H. duryi,* the red ram's horn snail from Florida used in aquaria. Once inside the tissues of the snail, they shed the ciliated covering, make their way to the renal veins, and transform to mother sporocysts within 2 weeks. A birth pore is not present. They persist in this stage up to 14 months, which is the usual life span of the snail host. Presumably they produce daughter sporocysts throughout their lives. Giant sporocyst-like bodies are possibly mother sporocysts that produce cercariae instead of daughter sporocysts.

Daughter sporocysts develop from germinal cells within the mother sporocysts, escaping when fully developed in 1 to 2 weeks. They migrate to the haemocoel and over the digestive gland. They may be differentiated from mother sporocysts by the subterminal birth pore. As the mother and daughter sporocysts attain an age of about 1 year, they become yellowish in color. Cercariae are fully developed in 2 to 3 weeks after the daughter sporocysts mature. They escape one at a time, oral sucker first,

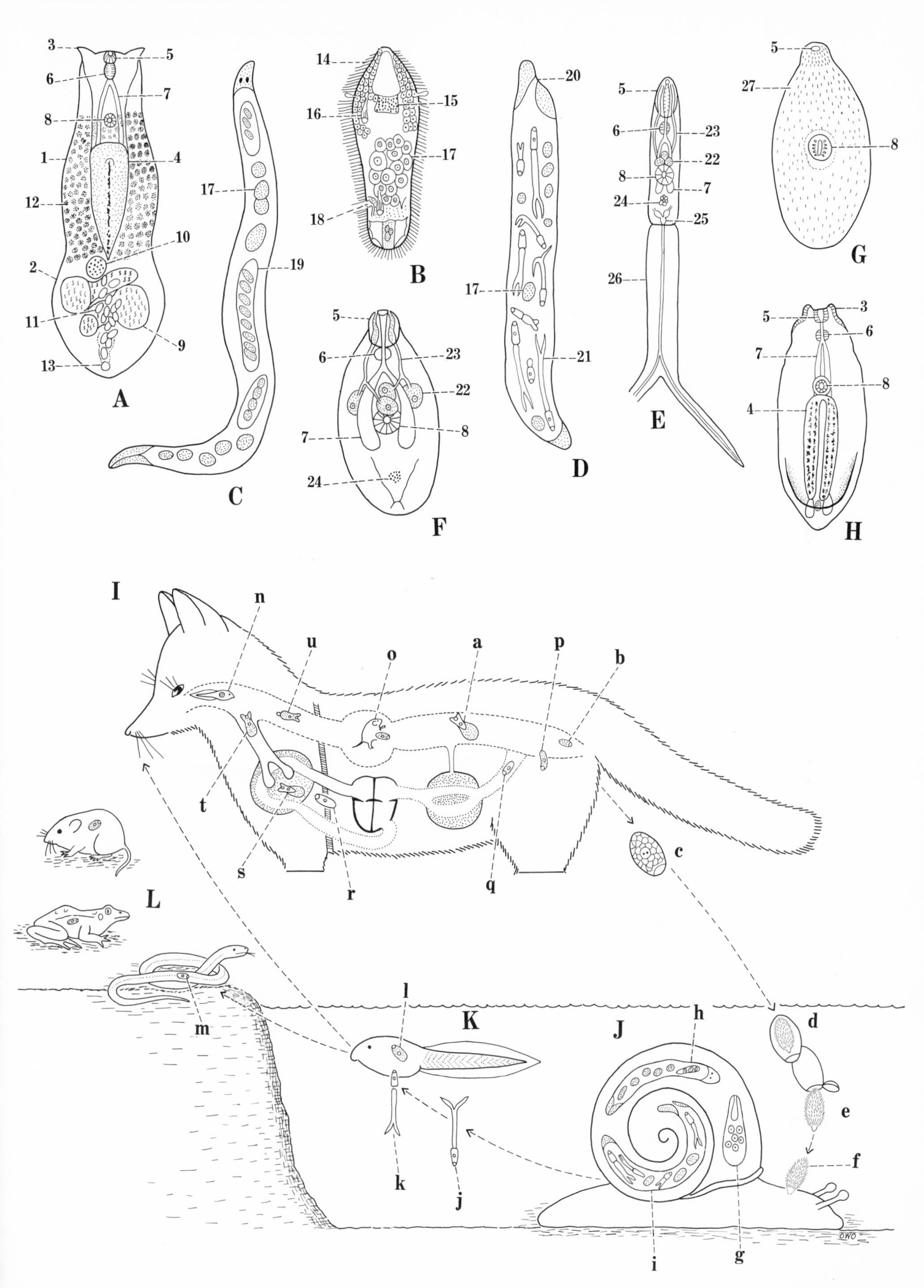
A
3
5
6
7
8
1
4
12
10
2
11
9
13
C
17
19
B
14
15
16
17
18
F
5
6
23
22
7
8
24
D
20
17
21
E
5
6
23
22
8
7
24
25
26
G
5
27
8
H
3
5
6
7
8
4
I
n
u
o
a
p
b
t
s
r
q
c
L
m
K
l
k
j
J
h
i
g
d
e
f
OWO

through the birth pore and leave the snail in intermittent bursts at intervals of several days or even weeks between 9 A.M. and 4 P.M. o'clock. They are positively phototropic, accumulating on the light side of the container. They hang in a resting position in the water, slowly sinking. These rests are interrupted regularly by swimming upward.

When tadpoles of *Rana pipiens, R. sylvatica, Pseudacris nigrita,* or *Bufo americanus* swim by, creating currents in the water, the cercariae become active and attach to them, dropping their tails as they enter the integument.

Within the body of the tadpoles, the cercariae develop into mesocercariae, an unencysted form intermediate between the cercarial and diplostomula stages. They survive metamorphosis of the tadpoles. The mesocercariae are fully developed and infective in 2 weeks after entering the second intermediate host.

Infection of the definitive host may take place by two quite different means. When infected tadpoles or frogs are eaten by canids, the mesocercariae, upon being freed from the tissues, migrate from the gut and undergo a somatic migration. They are found first in the liver and abdominal cavity. From the latter location they migrate forward, pass through the diaphragm, and into the lungs by the end of 2 to 3 weeks. Here they transform into diplostomulae in about 5 weeks. Presumably the diplostomulae migrate up the trachea where they are swallowed. Development is completed quickly in the small intestine, with eggs appearing in the faeces 34 to 37 days after ingestion of the mesocercariae.

The second method of infection involves a third host which serves as a collector of mesocercariae in its body. Water snakes, which feed on tadpoles, function especially well in this role. When infected tadpoles are eaten and digested by the snakes, as well as by frogs, mice, and possibly other animals, the mesocercariae migrate from the intestine into the tissues where they accumulate without further development. Canids eating these snakes, or other animals harboring mesocercariae, acquire large numbers of them which undergo a somatic migration in the same manner as described for those from tadpoles and frogs.

The collector, or paratenic host, serves to bridge the gap between the aquatic phase of the life cycle in tadpoles and frogs by its food habits in making the mesocercariae more readily available to the terrestrial host which normally would not eat the tadpoles because of their being in the water.

Pearson reviewed the literature on four other species of *Alaria* whose life cycles have been worked. They are essentially the same as that of *Alaria canis*. It is 1) the snail first intermediate host, 2) a vertebrate second intermediate host that harbors the mesocercariae, 3) a collector, or paratenic host, that makes the mesocercariae more readily available to the definitive host because of its habitat and food habits, and 4) the definitive host in which the diplostomulae and adults develop.

EXERCISE ON LIFE CYCLE

Eggs must be obtained from adult specimens of known species of *Alaria* as the starting point, and the cycle carried out step by step.

Incubate the eggs at room temperature to obtain miracidia. The red ram's horn snails, *Helisoma duryi,* available in pet shops, make ideal hosts for *A. canis* but not for some other species (see Pearson for a list of molluscan hosts). Expose snails to miracidia and dissect individuals at intervals of 1 to 2 days to follow the development of the sporocysts and cercariae.

Tadpoles collected from a place where they are unlikely to be infected, as demonstrated by examination of an adequate sample, or those reared from eggs in the laboratory, should be exposed to cercariae. Examine specimens at intervals of 2 to 3 days to follow the migration of the mesocercariae.

When infected tadpoles are available, feed some to dogs and begin examining the faeces after 3 weeks for eggs of flukes. If dogs are available for examination, observations should be made for mesocercariae in the body and thoracic cavities 24 hours after infection, and again 14 days later for mesocercariae and diplostomulae in the lungs.

Feed infected tadpoles to water or garter snakes, preferably specimens reared in the laboratory, to accumulate mesocercariae in the tissues. Try rats or mice to determine whether they will serve as paratenic hosts.

SELECTED REFERENCES

Bosma, N. J. (1934). Trans. Amer. Micr. Soc. 53:116.

Cuckler, A. C. (1940). Doctoral Dissertations Accepted by American Universities, No. 9, p. 69.

LaRue, G. R., and A. M. Fallis. (1936). Trans Amer. Micr. Soc. 55:340.

Odlaug, T. O. (1940). Trans Amer. Micr. Soc. 59:490.

Pearson, J. C. (1956). Canad. J. Zool. 34:295; (1957). J. Parasit. 45:155.

SUPERFAMILY CLINOSTOMATOIDEA

The members of this group are parasites of fish- and frog-eating reptiles, birds, and mammals throughout the world. The metacercariae are large and precocious, appearing in the muscles of fish and subcutaneous tissue of frogs. Caeca are long and often with lateral diverticula.

FAMILY CLINOSTOMATIDAE

One family only is recognized. The oral sucker may be surrounded by a collar-like fold. Caeca are long and with or without short lateral branches. The testes are tandem, with the ovary between them.

Clinostomum complanatum (Rudolphi, 1819) (Plate 57)

Adult flukes are in the mouth of herons, not the intestine. The large metacercariae, known as yellow grubs, are embedded subcutaneously or intramuscularly in 30 or more species of fish, yellow perch, black bass, and sunfish being among the most common hosts in North America.

DESCRIPTION. Adult worms are 3 to 8 mm long. When the oral sucker is retracted, it is surrounded by a collar-like fold of the body. The suckers are in the anterior third of the body, the acetabulum being much the larger. The caeca extend to near the posterior end of the body and have numerous short outpocketings from the level of the acetabulum caudad. The testes are tandem and lie in the middle of the postacetabular part of the body with the ovary between them and the uterus anterior to them. The eggs are large and variable in size, being 104 to 140 μ long by 66 to 73 μ wide.

LIFE CYCLE. Adult flukes lay their eggs in the mouth of the heron host. They may be washed into the water during the feeding activities when the birds dip their heads into the water to capture fish, or swallowed and voided with the droppings. Both embryonated and unembryonated eggs are laid. The developed ones hatch almost immediately upon reaching the water, while the undeveloped ones require about 19 days to hatch.

The active miracidia are covered with cilia, have three pigmented eyespots arranged in a triangular form, and contain a single germ ball. Upon coming in contact with ram's horn snails (*Helisoma campanulata* and *H. antrosum*), they burrow into them. Inside the snail intermediate host, the miracidia shed the ciliated epithelium and migrate to the digestive gland or liver. They are thin-walled, saclike creatures with three eyespots, but lack a birth pore. Inside them are several germ balls which develop into rediae.

The first generation of rediae escape from the mother sporocysts and locate in the digestive gland or liver. The digestive tract is composed of a prominent pharynx, a thin oesophagus, and a long wide gut. Each redia contains 3 to 15 developing daughter rediae. The second generation, or daughter, rediae are recognizable by the cuticular folds, masses of developing cercariae, and a birth pore in the anterior fourth of the body.

Cercariae, when fully developed, escape from the rediae and snail into the water. They are pharyngeate and brevifurcate, *i.e.*, have short furcae at the end of a short tail stem, two eyes, and a longitudinal fin over the dorsal side of the body. Upon coming in contact with fish, the cercariae attach to the skin and burrow through it. In the subcutaneous tissue and muscles, they encyst, developing in about 20 weeks into large precocious metacercariae known as yellow grubs.

When infected fish are eaten by herons, the metacercariae are released in the stomach. They migrate anteriorly through the oesophagus into the buccal cavity and attain maturity in 3 days. They live in the mouth for about 2 weeks and then are lost.

A second species, *C. attenuatum* Cort, 1913, utilizes frogs, instead of fish, as the second intermediate host. The adults are in the mouth cavity of bitterns but not herons.

EXPLANATION OF PLATE 57 ⇨

A. Adult fluke. **B.** Miracidium. **C.** Mother sporocyst. **D.** Daughter redia. **E.** Cerceria. **F.** Metacercaria. **G.** Great blue heron *(Ardea herodias)*. **H.** Snail *(Helisoma campanulata, H. antrosa)* first intermediate host. **I.** Fish *(Perca flavescens)* second intermediate host.

1, oral sucker; **2,** ventral sucker; **3,** oesophagus; **4,** intestine; **5,** testis; **6,** ovary; **7,** oviduct; **8,** uterus; **9,** vitelline glands; **10,** apical papilla; **11,** apical gland; **12,** penetration glands; **13,** large nucleated cells; **14,** germinal mass; **15,** eyespot; **16,** lateral papilla; **17,** pharynx; **18,** cercaria; **19,** prepharynx; **20,** tail; **21,** short furca; **22,** excretory tubule of tail; **23,** Mehlis' gland.

a, adult fluke in mouth of heron; **b,** unembryonated eggs laid in mouth are washed into water as heron strikes at fish and some are swallowed and expelled in faeces; **c,** eggs develop in water and hatch; **d,** free-swimming miracidium with single germ ball inside; **e,** miracidium penetrating snail intermediate host; **f,** mother sporocyst with developing mother rediae; **g,** mature mother redia with developing daughter rediae; **h,** daughter redia containing cercariae in various stages of development; **i,** cercaria resting in characteristic position in water; **j,** cercaria penetrating fish, leaving tail behind; **k,** cercaria migrating in subcutaneous tissues; **l,** metacercaria encysted in muscles of fish; **m,** heron becomes infected upon swallowing fish harboring metacercariae which are released in stomach by digestive juices; **n,** metacercaria freed from tissues; **o,** young fluke escaping from cyst migrates anteriorly through oesophagus and pharynx into oral cavity where it develops to maturity in 3 days and remains for about 2 weeks, when it is lost.

Figures A, F adapted from Cort, 1913, Trans. Amer. Micr. Soc. 32:169; B-D, G, from Hunter and Hunter, 1935, Suppl. 24th. Ann. Rept. N. Y. State Conserv. Dept., p. 267; E, from Krull, 1934, Proc. Helminth. Soc. Wash. 1:34.

EXERCISE ON LIFE CYCLE

In order to study this life cycle, herons are a necessity. Fledglings obtained from a rookery may be kept in captivity and fed fish infected with yellow grubs as a source of eggs for experimental purposes.

By lavaging the mouth of infected herons and catching the water in a pan, embryonated eggs may be obtained as required. Also they may be recovered from the faeces.

Planorbid snails (*Helisoma campanulata* and *H. antrosum*) become infected when exposed to newly hatched miracidia. Specimens should be dissected at intervals of 3 days to obtain mother sporocysts, rediae, and daughter rediae.

Cercariae obtained from experimentally infected snails, or from naturally infected ones collected in ponds with infected fish, will attack and encyst in a number of species of fish. Guppies and certain tropical fish serve as suitable hosts.

SELECTED REFERENCES

Hopkins, S. H. (1933). Trans. Amer. Micr. Soc. 52:147.

Hunter, G. W., III, and W. S. Hunter. (1934). Suppl. 23rd Ann. Rept. N. Y. State Conserv. Dept., 1933, No. VIII, p. 248; (1935). Suppl. 24th Ann. Rept. N. Y. State Conserv. Dept., No. IX, p. 273; (1935). J. Parasit. 21:186.

Hunter, G. W., III, and H. C. Dalton. (1939). Proc. Helminth. Soc. Wash. 6:73.

Krull, W. H. (1934). Proc. Helminth. Soc. Wash. 1:34.

Nigrelli, R. F. (1936). Zoologica 21:251.

Osborn, H. L. (1911). Biol. Bull. 20:350; (1912). J. Morph. 23:189.

SUPERFAMILY SCHISTOSOMATOIDEA

Members of this superfamily are the blood flukes. The adults are monoecious or dioecious, living in the blood vessels of fish, reptiles, birds, and mammals. Both the adults and cercariae are apharyngeate. The cercariae enter the definitive host directly through the skin. The eggs are non-operculated and embryonated when laid, except in the Sanguinicolidae where hatching takes place in the gills of the fish host. The cercariae are apharyngeate and brevifurcate.

FAMILY SCHISTOSOMATIDAE

This family consists of dioecious flukes parasitic in birds and mammals throughout the world. Several species are parasites of humans residing in the tropical regions.

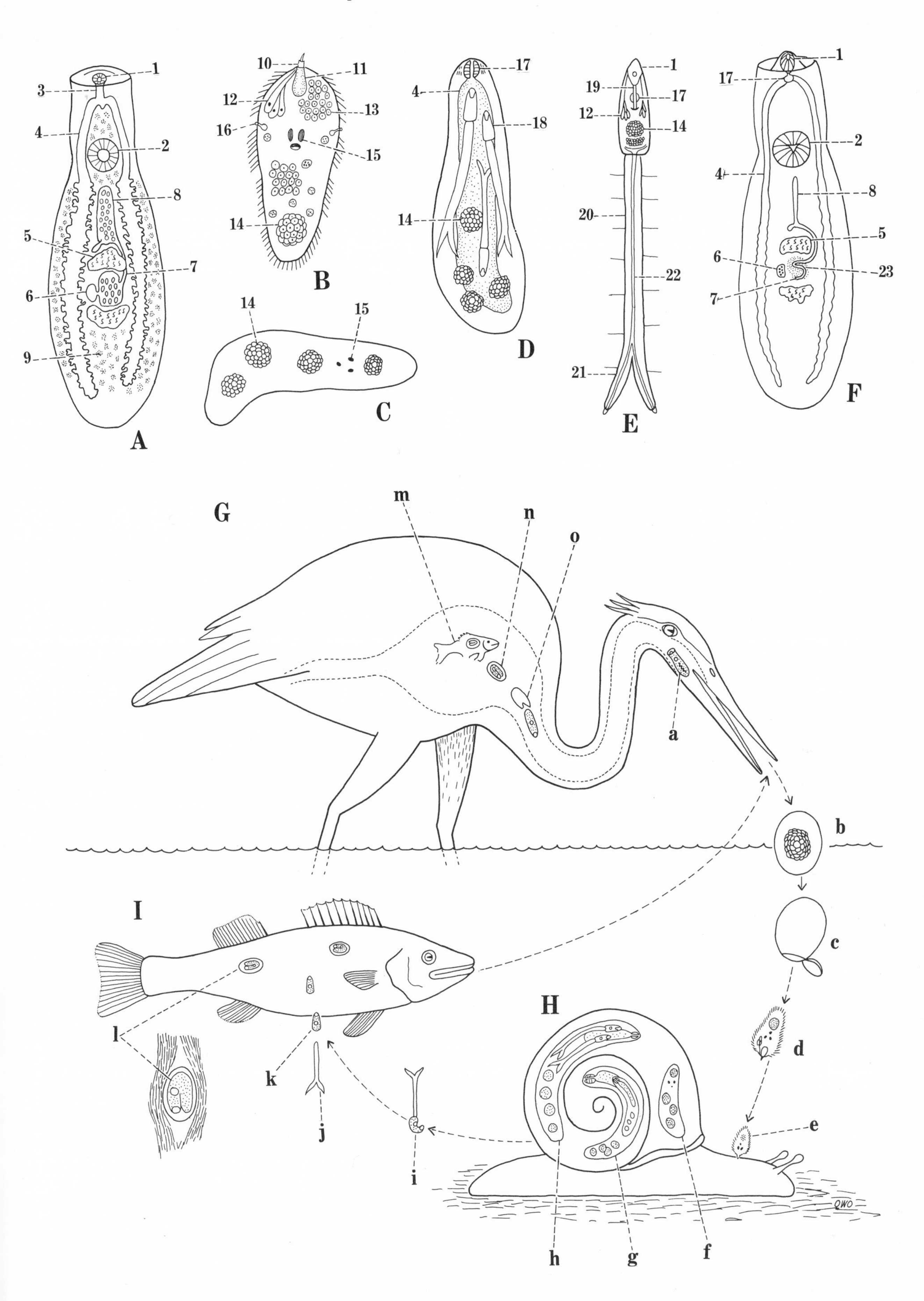
1
3
4
2
8
5
7
6
9
A
10
11
12
13
16
15
14
B
14
15
C
17
4
18
14
D
1
19
17
12
14
20
22
21
E
1
17
2
4
8
5
6
23
7
F
G
m
n
o
a
b
c
d
e
I
l
k
j
i
H
h
g
f
QWO

EXPLANATION OF PLATE 58

A. Adult male from hepatic venules. **B.** Adult female. **C.** Reproductive system of male. **D.** Reproductive system of female. **E.** Embryonated egg. **F.** Miracidium. **G.** Mother sporocyst. **H.** Daughter sporocyst. **I.** Outline of cercaria. **J.** Anterior end of cercaria, showing spination. **K.** Details of internal anatomy of cercaria taken from dorsal side. **L.** *Microtus pennsylvanicus,* definitive host of *Schistosomatium douthitti.* **M.** *Stagnicola,* one of the snail first intermediate hosts.

1, oral sucker; **2,** ventral sucker; **3,** mouth; **4,** fold of gynaecophoric groove; **5,** oesophageal glands; **6,** intestine; **7,** commissures between intestinal caeca; **8,** testes; **9,** vas deferens; **10,** cirrus pouch; **11,** genital pore; **12,** ovary; **13,** seminal receptacle; **14,** oviduct; **15,** Mehlis' gland; **16,** uterus filled with eggs; **17,** vitelline glands; **18,** common vitelline duct; **19,** unhatched egg containing miracidium; **20,** lateral papilla; **21,** ciliated dermal plates (tiers 1, 2, 3, 4); **22,** apical gland; **23,** penetration glands; **24,** brain; **25,** flame cells; **26,** germ cells; **27,** eyespots; **28,** ducts of penetration glands; **29,** genital primordium; **30,** excretory bladder; **31,** common collecting tubule; **32,** developing daughter sporocysts; **33,** developing cercaria.

a, adult flukes in copula in intestinal branches of hepatic portal vein; **b,** masses of eggs accumulating in capillaries and tissues of intestinal wall; **c,** eggs passing through intestinal wall into lumen of intestine; **d,** eggs incorporated in faecal pellets; **e,** embryonated egg free in water; **f,** egg in process of hatching; **g,** miracidium burrowing into foot of snail; **h,** miracidium shedding ciliated epithelium and beginning transformation to mother sporocyst; **i,** mother sporocyst in neck and oesophageal region, containing germ balls and developing daughter sporocysts; **j,** daughter sporocyst in digestive gland, with germ balls and developing cercariae; **k,** cercariae freed from daughter sporocyst and escaping from snail; **l,** cercariae swimming in water; **m,** cercariae in resting position attached by ventral sucker to under side of surface film of water; **n,** cercaria penetrating foot of wading meadow vole; **o-p,** cercaria or schistosomatula, migrating toward heart in lymphatic vessels; **q,** schistosomatula passing through pulmonary vein toward lungs; **r,** schistosomatula in capillaries of lungs; **s,** schistosomatula leaving capillaries for lung tissue and alveoli; **t,** schistosomatula in alveoli; **u,** adult worms in copula in lungs; **v,** masses of eggs in lungs; **w,** schistosomatula migrating from lung into pleural cavity on way to liver; **x,** schistosomatulae migrate along oesophagus and postcaval vein through pleural cavity to diaphragm, burrowing through it into peritoneal cavity; **y,** schistosomatula migrating through diaphragm into peritoneal cavity; **z,** schistosomatula in peritoneal cavity.

a′, schistosomatula penetrating liver capsule (also spleen and pancreas which are not shown); **b′,** young fluke in liver; **c′,** masses of eggs in liver; **d′,** adult flukes in copula in liver.

Figures A-K redrawn from Price, 1931, Amer. J. Hyg. 13:685; others original.

The mature males may have a longitudinal ventral groove (gynaecophoric groove) in which the more slender female is held. The caeca join to form a single terminal limb, reaching almost to the posterior extremity of the body. There are four or more testes; the ovary is oval or spirally curved and located anterior to the union of the caeca.

The cercariae of blood flukes of ducks and muskrats frequently attack people bathing or wading in water infected with them, causing a severe dermatitis which subsides after a few days. The papules resulting from the penetrating cercariae are known as swimmer's itch, water itch, or cercarial dermatitis.

Two subfamilies, the Schistosomatinae and Bilharziellinae, are recognized.

Subfamily Schistosomatinae

The Schistosomatinae include the genera *Schistosoma* of humans and *Schistosomatium* of muskrats and voles. They are characterized by males having a gynaecophoric groove and being larger than the cylindrical females. The intestinal caeca rejoin near the posterior end of the body and the testes lie anterior to that junction.

Schistosomatium douthitti (Cort, 1915) (Plate 58)

These blood flukes occur naturally in the blood vessels of the liver, mesenteries, and small intestine of field voles (*Microtus pennsylvanicus*) and muskrats (*Ondatra zibethica*) in North America.

The cercariae are capable of developing in a number of mammals such as deer mice (*Peromyscus*), house mice, and rabbits. They penetrate human skin, causing dermatitis, as does *Trichobilharzia cameroni* and the cercariae of other blood flukes of birds.

DESCRIPTION. The males vary greatly in length, being 1.9 to 6.3 mm long. The forebody of the male is flattened, occupying approximately two-fifths of the body. The hindbody forms a gynaecophoric canal by folding the sides ventrally over the female. There are 15 to 36 testes located

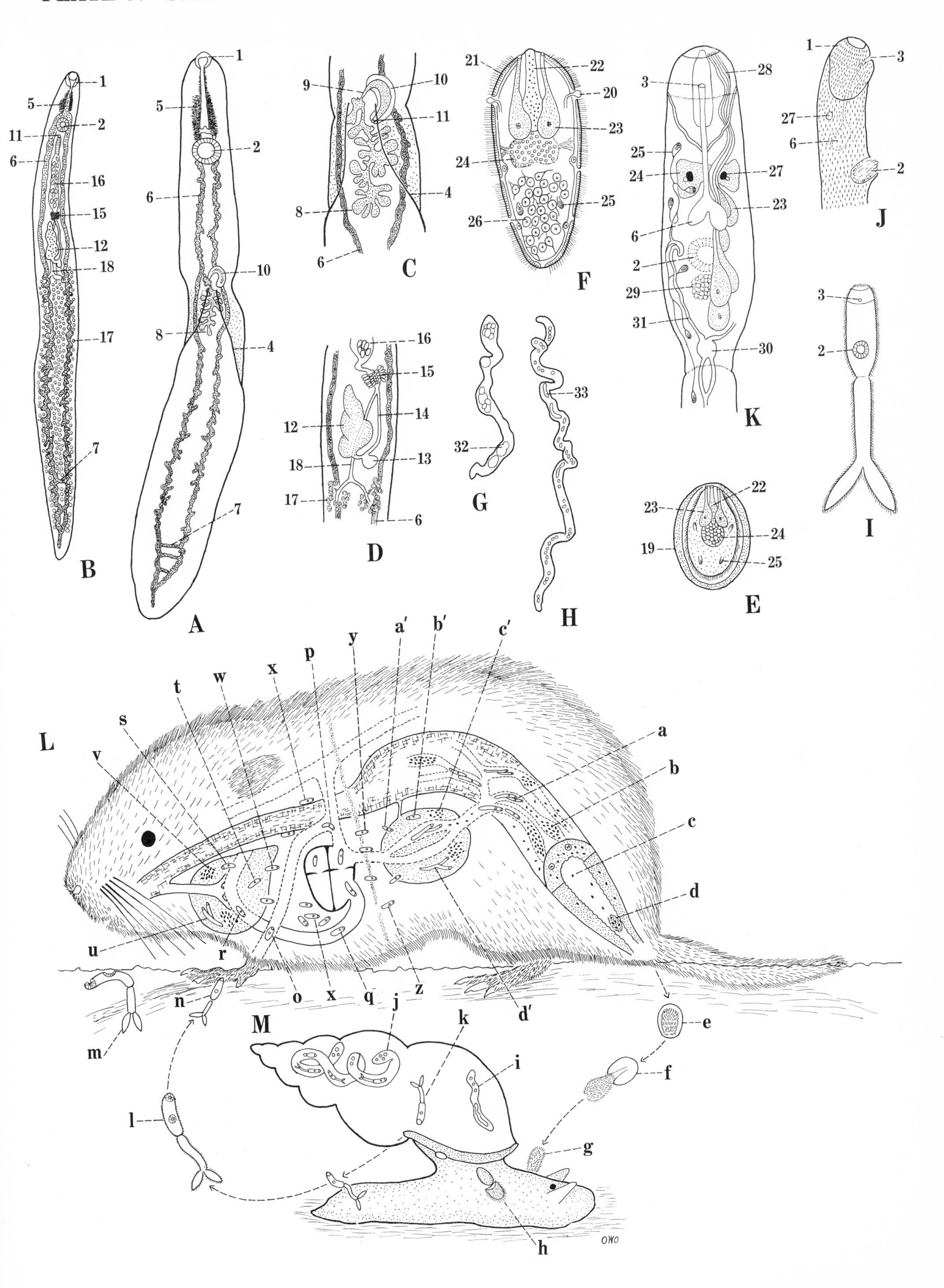

at the anterior end of the hindbody. The genital pore opens near the margin of the left gynaecophoric fold. The caeca of both sexes have many small diverticula and in each case some of them unite to form a bridge between the two caeca near their posterior union.

The females are slender and shorter than the males, being 1.1 to 5.3 mm. long. The ovary is in the anterior half of the body with the uterus extending anteriorly from it as a straight tube to the level of the caecal bifurcation. The nonoperculate eggs are unembryonated when laid.

The vitelline follicles extend from the ovary to the posterior extremity of the body, filling the intercaecal space and extending laterally.

The cercariae are apharyngeate and brevifurcate.

LIFE CYCLE. Mature flukes normally occur in the portal veins of the liver and intestine, including the caecum and mesenteric veins. Occasionally, they are in the lungs.

The females are held in the gynaecophoric groove of the males until ready to oviposit. At this time they separate from the males, migrate deeper into the blood vessels, and deposit their unembryonated eggs which accumulate in masses. As the eggs penetrate the wall of the blood vessels and intestine, development proceeds, with embryonation being completed by the time they reach the lumen of the gut. They are mixed with the intestinal contents and eventually voided with the faeces. Hatching occurs through a longitudinal slit soon after the eggs reach the water. The slit probably results from the combined pressure of absorbed water and the vigorous movements of the miracidium. Upon escaping, the miracidia swim swiftly and aimlessly through the water. Being short-lived, it is important that they find and enter a snail host soon lest they perish.

Natural snail intermediate hosts are species of Lymnaeidae, including *Lymnaea stagnalis appressa, L. stagnalis perampla, L. stagnalis lillianae, L. stagnalis jugularis, L. stagnalis sanctaemariae, L. reflexa, Stagnicola exilis, Physa gyrina elliptica,* and *P. ancillaria parkeri*. Upon coming in contact with one of these snails, the miracidia burrow through the epidermis into the tissues. Inside, they shed the ciliated epidermal plates and transform into elongated mother sporocysts in the head and neck regions.

Germ cells within the body of the mother sporocysts give rise to germ balls which develop into daughter sporocysts, usually attached to the body wall until late in their development. By 21 days after infection of the snails, young daughter sporocysts have escaped from the mother sporocysts and reached the liver by the 36th day. Daughter sporocysts mature and produce cercariae in 8 to 18 days after reaching the liver, which is damaged extensively by their activities. As the sporocysts grow, the body cavity appears in which germ balls form. When these reach a given stage of development they break apart and each fragment develops into a cercaria. It is estimated that as many as 40,000 to 60,000 cercariae may be produced from a single miracidium. All cercariae developing from a single egg produce adults of the same sex. Females in unisexual infections produce eggs in which miracidia developed, presumably parthenogenetically, as there was no evidence of any female producing spermatozoa, or the presence of them in any of the genital ducts.

Newly formed cercariae possess six pairs of penetration glands but the anterior one disappears during migration through the snails. The cercariae emerge from the snails soon after dark. At first they are somewhat quiescent. After a brief period of swimming they rise and adhere to the surface film of the water by means of the ventral sucker. When swimming, the tail lashes vigorously, causing the body to rotate. Such movement is followed by a period of rest, as if the activity tired the cercaria. Movement on the bottom is in measuring-worm fashion.

Infection of voles takes place through the feet or other lightly haired or bare parts of the body exposed to infested water by wading or swimming animals. The cercariae penetrate directly through the skin or enter by way of canals of the hair shafts, dropping their tails in the process. Inflamed papillae arise at the point of entry within 5 to 10 minutes in white mice, reaching a diameter of 4 mm after an hour. They subside and disappear by the third day. Inside the definitive host, the cercariae migrate through the lymph and blood vessels to the lungs, going by way of the right side of the heart and pulmonary artery. Arrival in the lungs is as soon as 30 minutes after exposure of the host, indicating rapid transmission such as might occur in blood vessels.

The presence of the cercariae in the pulmonary blood vessels results in great damage to them and extensive congestion of the alveoli with blood and fluid. The worms leave the blood vessels and migrate through the lung stroma for 3 or 4 days and then break into the thoracic cavity, where large numbers of them accumulate for a short time. They pass through the diaphragm, especially along the oesophagus and postcaval vein, into the peritoneal cavity. A similar route is reported for *Schistosoma haematobium*, *S. mansoni*, and *S. japonicum*, all of humans. From here, they enter the liver by burrowing through the capsule from the outside.

By the 8th to 11th days after infection, males begin to leave the liver and appear in the mesenteric veins. The females linger in the liver for a short time but soon follow the males. By the 13th day nearly all worms have left the liver and are in the mesenteric veins. Sexual maturity may occur in the lungs as early as 10 days after infection but it is later in the liver and intestinal wall. By 22 to 23 days, eggs appear in the liver parenchyma, accumulating in large masses. Their presence results in much damage, producing lesions that undergo progressive development followed by regression, becoming completely fibrous by 243 days. Eggs appear in the intestinal mucosa and submucosa of mice 34 days after infection, occurring in masses in the villi. There is a general inflammatory response, with abscesses. Eggs in the intestinal wall work through it into the lumen and are voided with the faeces.

Longevity of the worms varies, depending on the experimental hosts involved. In deer mice, males lived for 255 days and females for 468 to 484 days. In rats, females disappeared by 79 days, whereas a few males persisted for 136 days. This longevity is in contrast to the 28 years reported for *Schistosoma haematobium* in a human.

EXERCISE ON LIFE CYCLE

Schistosomatium douthitti is an ideal blood fluke for experimental studies because both the snail and mammalian hosts are readily available and easily maintained in the laboratory.

Snail hosts of choice are *Lymnaea palustris* and *L. stagnalis*. When collected from around muskrat houses in ponds, there is likelihood of finding naturally infected individuals to supply cercariae for experimental studies. They may be reared successfully in balanced aquaria of 5- to 10-gallon capacity. White enamel trays and finger bowls are useful for small numbers of snails. When kept at room temperature, the snails lay eggs from which young may be hatched for experimental infections. Aquarium plants should be provided to furnish places for the snails to attach their eggs. Tap water should be freed of chlorine by aeration in large containers before using it.

Food may be supplied as fresh green leaves of lettuce but care should be taken to remove decomposing pieces. Dried maple leaves soaked a few weeks in several changes of water before adding to the aquaria are excellent food. Vita-min, a commercial product, is very good. Powdered calcium carbonate or pieces of blackboard chalk should be added to provide calcium for maintenance of the shells.

Fluke eggs in the faeces of infected mice hatch quickly in water, providing a supply of miracidia for infection experiments. Young snails should be exposed for about 24 hours to a few miracida in shallow, wide-mouthed bottles containing a small volume of water so that they can be watched under a dissecting microscope. The incubation period in snails ranges from 37 to 52 days.

Rats and mice are good experimental definitive hosts. Exposure to cercariae may be by placing them in small jars of shallow water containing cercariae or by placing cercariae on a clipped spot of a restrained animal. Cercariae may be transferred from the surface of the container by means of a hair loop to the clipped spot. Infection is accomplished in about 30 minutes.

Migration through the host begins promptly after entering the skin. They are in the lungs in less than 1 hour after infection, the thoracic cavity in 2 to 4 days, and the liver in 8 to 10 days. By the 11th day they begin to leave the liver and migrate to the mesenteric veins, where the majority of them are by the end of 2 weeks. Sexual maturity occurs in the lungs 10 to 12 days after infection and in the liver by 16 days. Nearly all worms are mature by 20 days. These times should be confirmed by examining infected mice at appropriate periods after infection.

EXPLANATION OF PLATE 59 ⇨

A. Anterior end of adult female fluke. **B.** Anterior end of adult male. **C.** Hatched miracidium. **D.** Mature mother sporocyst. **E.** Mature daughter sporocyst. **F.** Cercaria showing certain details of internal morphology. **G.** Duck definitive host. H. Snail *(Physa gyrina)* first intermediate host. **I.** Cercaria attacking human host, causing dermatitis.

1, oral sucker; **2,** ventral sucker; **3,** oesophagus; **4,** bifurcated portion of intestine; **5,** single posterior limb of intestine; **6,** ovary; **7,** seminal receptacle; **8,** oviduct; **9,** Mehlis' gland; **10,** uterus; **11,** vulva; **12,** egg; **13,** vitelline gland; **14,** vitelline duct; **15,** testes; **16,** vas deferens; **17,** seminal receptacle; **18,** cirrus pouch; **19,** apical papilla; **20,** apical gland; **21,** ganglion; **22,** penetration glands; **23,** duct of penetration gland; **24,** flame cell; **25,** germinal mass; **26,** daughter sporocyst; **27,** birth pore; **28,** developing cercaria; **29,** tail; **30,** eyespot.

a, adult flukes in blood vessels of intestinal wall; **b,** eggs laid in blood vessels; **c,** eggs penetrate tissues, passing from blood vessels into lumen of gut; **d,** eggs mixed with faeces; **e,** embryonated eggs pass out of body with faeces; **f,** egg absorbs water; **g,** egg ruptures, releasing miracidium; **h,** miracidium penetrates snail; **i,** mature mother sporocyst with developing daughter sporocysts; **j,** mature daughter sporocyst with developing and mature cercariae; **k,** mature cercaria free in water; **l,** cercariae attack humans, causing cercarial dermatitis, but they do not develop to maturity; **m,** cercaria penetrates foot of duck, dropping tail in the process; **n,** cercaria reaches blood vessels and is carried toward the heart; **o,** cercaria approaching heart; **p,** cercaria passing through right side of heart; **q,** cercaria passes through blood vessel of lungs; **r,** cercaria having passed through left side of heart approachs dorsal aorta; **s,** cercaria in dorsal aorta; **t,** cercaria passing through anterior mesenteric artery to enter blood vessels of intestinal wall where maturity is attained; **u,** worms occur in liver on occasion.

Adapted from Wu, 1953, Canad. J. Zool. 31:351.

SELECTED REFERENCES

Batten, P. J. (1956). Amer. J. Path. 32:363; (1957). Ibid. 33:729.

Cort, W. W. (1914). J. Parasit. 1:65; (1936). Amer. J. Hyg. 23:349; ———— and S. B. Talbot. (1936). Amer. J. Hyg. 23:385; ————, D. J. Ameel, and L. Olivier. (1944). J. Parasit. 30:1; ————, D. J. Ameel, and A. Van Der Woude. (1953). Proc. Helminth. Soc. Wash. 20:43.

El-Gindy, Mohamed El Said. (1950). Microfilm Abst., Ann Arbor 10:256 (Microfilm No. A50-287).

Farley, J. (1962). Canad. J. Zool. 40:131.

Kagan, I. G., R. B. Short, and M. M. Nez. (1954). J. Parasit. 40:424; ———— and D. R. Merange. (1957). J. Infect. Dis. 100:32; (1958). Ibid. Amer. J. Trop. Med. 7:285.

Penner, L. R. (1938). J. Parasit. 24(Suppl.):26; (1939). Ibid. 25(Suppl.):8.

Price, E. W. (1929). Proc. U. S. Nat. Mus. 75(18):1.

Price, H. F. (1931). Amer. J. Hyg. 13:685.

Short, R. B. (1951). J. Parasit. 37:547; (1952). Amer. Midl. Nat. 47:1; 48:55.

Tanabe, B. (1923). J. Parasit. 9:183.

Subfamily Bilharziellinae

The males and females are similar in shape. The male lacks a gynaecophoric groove. The caecal branches unite anterior to the equator of the body and the testes are caudad from the intestinal union. Common genera of the subfamily include *Trichobilharzia* of ducks, *Bilharziella* of ducks and herons, *Dendrobilharzia* of ducks and pelicans, and *Gigantobilharzia* of gulls. *Trichobilharzia cameroni* is discussed as a representative of this subfamily.

Trichobilharzia cameroni Wu, 1953 (Plate 59)

This is a parasite of wild ducks in North America. The adults are in the peripheral blood vessels of the intestine and occasionally in the liver. The cercariae cause swimmer's itch in people who come in contact with them.

DESCRIPTION. Males measure 3.18 to 5.71 mm long. The gynaecophoral fold is well developed and thickly set with spines. The acetabulum is larger than the oral sucker. There are 80 to 110 testes arranged in a single row, beginning immediately behind the gynaecophoral fold and extending to near the tip of the intestinal caecum.

Females are 3.83 to 4.94 mm long. The caeca unite at about the equator of the seminal vesicle. The ovary is tubular, stout, and makes several loops; it measures 287 to 358 μ long. There is never more than a single uterine egg present. The vitellaria extend from just behind the seminal receptacle

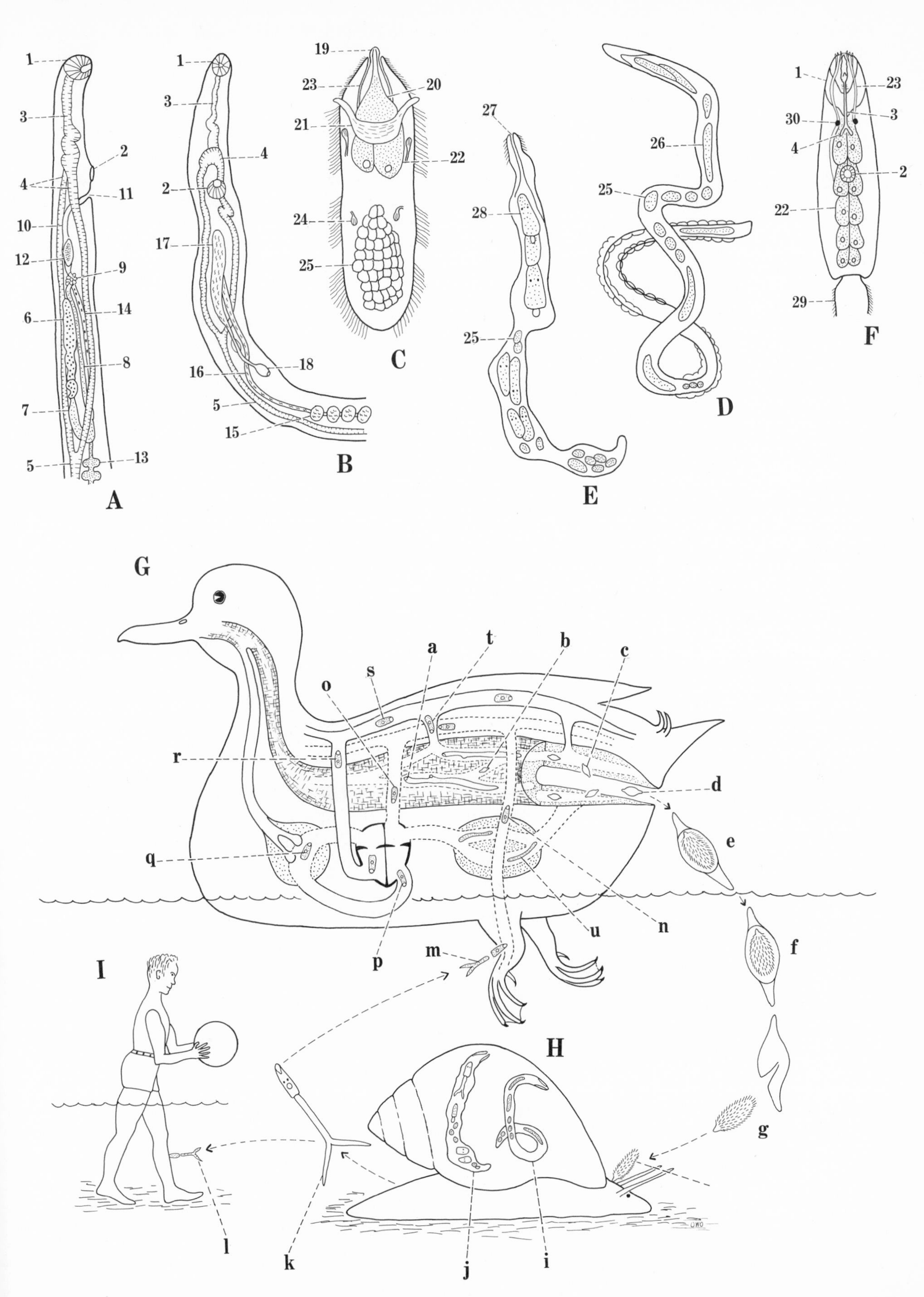
A
B
C
D
E
F
G
H
I
a
b
c
d
e
f
g
i
j
k
l
m
n
o
p
q
r
s
t
u

to the posterior end of the body. Eggs are spindle-shaped, 147 to 212 μ long by 57 to 73 μ wide, and embryonated when laid.

LIFE CYCLE. Adult flukes are in the veins of the small and large intestine of ducks. When ready to oviposit, the female leaves the gynaecophoric groove of the male where she normally rests, moves into the smaller venules, and deposits the spindle-shaped eggs. The eggs gradually work through the wall of the blood vessels and intestine into the lumen of the latter and pass in the droppings in a fully developed stage. Some eggs are carried to the liver via the hepatic portal vein. With dilution of the faeces, the eggs begin to absorb water, increasing in size until they rupture after 2 to 3 hours of exposure, releasing the miracidia which swim rapidly. They have a life span of 2 to 13 hours.

Upon coming in contact with specimens of the snail *Physa gyrina* soon after hatching, the miracidia attach to them and quickly burrow into the soft parts of the body. Ability to enter the snails gradually decreases 2 to 3 hours after hatching. Upon entering the tissues, the miracidia soon shed the ciliated epithelium and transform to mother sporocysts near the point of entry into the mantle, foot, or viscera. They migrate to the liver and grow into greatly elongated tubular mother sporocysts as soon as 1 week after infection, at which time daughter sporocysts appear in them. They contain motile daughter sporocysts, germ balls in various stages of development, and single germ cells. There is no birth pore.

Daughter sporocysts are in the liver. They differ from the mother sporocysts in being smaller and in having a terminal birth pore that is surrounded by spines during the early part of their life. Sporocysts mature and produce cercariae in about 21 days, which is 28 to 32 days after infection of the snails.

Cercariae with eyes but lacking a pharynx escape from snail hosts into the water where they alternately swim and rest. Being positively phototropic, they are attracted toward the light, a factor that brings them to the surface of the water in a favorable location to make contact with the vertebrate definitive hosts.

As ducks swim about, the active cercariae attach to their feet and, with the aid of five pairs of penetration glands, burrow through the skin into blood vessels, dropping their tails as they enter. The larval flukes are carried with the blood to the right side of the heart, through the pulmonary artery to the lungs, and back to the left side of the heart via the pulmonary vein. From here, they go out through the dorsal aorta to the various parts of the body. Those entering the mesenteric arteries reach the walls of the intestine where development to sexual maturity takes place in 12 to 14 days. Infections in ducks persist for at least 4 months, which suggests that the flukes may be carried great distances by migrating birds.

The life cycles of a number of other species of *Trichobilharzia* of ducks whose cercariae cause dermatitis in humans have been studied. They are basically the same as that of *T. cameroni*. They include *T. oregonensis* in Oregon by Macy *et al.*, *T. adamsi* in British Columbia by Edwards and Jansch, *T. physellae*, *T. ocellata*, and *T. stagnicolae* by McMullen and Beaver in Michigan, and *T. physellae* in Colorado by Hunter.

EXERCISE ON LIFE CYCLE

Physa gyrina in ponds frequented by wild ducks may be infected with *T. cameroni*. Other species of *Physa* and *Stagnicola* may harbor different species of related blood flukes of ducks or other water fowl.

Cercariae obtained from naturally infected snails and determined to be those of *Trichobilharzia* may be used for experimental infections. Canaries, pigeons, and domestic ducklings are favorable hosts, especially the last species. Submerge the feet of the experimental birds in water containing a known number of freshly emerged cercariae. Determine the number that penetrated the feet by the remainder in the container at the conclusion of the exposure.

Ascertain the prepatent period of the flukes by observing the time when eggs appear in the faeces. Some birds should be sacrificed at appropriate intervals to demonstrate the larval flukes in their lungs and the route of migration from the lungs to the mesenteric veins of the intestine. This point is not clear.

Snails to be used for experimental infections should be collected from areas where ducks do not occur, or reared for experimental infection at the time eggs appear in the faeces of the birds that were exposed to cercariae.

When eggs appear in the faeces, they should be washed free from them for hatching. Expose experimental snails of the same species from which the cercariae were obtained originally. Individuals should be dissected at intervals to determine the course of development of the mother sporocysts, daughter sporocysts, and cercariae.

In order to verify the results of the experiment, try to fulfill Koch's postulate by carrying the cycle through its entirety with experimentally reared snails and parasites.

SELECTED REFERENCES

*Cort, W. W. (1936). Amer. J. Hyg. 23:349; Talbot, S. B. (1936). Ibid. 23:372 (II); Cort and Talbot. (1936). Ibid. 23:385 (III); Cort. (1936). Ibid. 24:318 (IV); Brackett, S. (1940). Ibid. 31:49 (V); Brackett. (1940). Ibid. 31:64 (VI); Cort, D. B. McMullen, L. Olivier, and Brackett. (1940). Ibid. 32:33 (VII); Brackett. (1940). Ibid. 32:85 (VIII); McMullen and P. C. Beaver (1945). Ibid. 42:128 (IX).

Edwards, D. K., and M. E. Jansch. (1955). Canad. J. Zool. 33:182.

Macy, R. W., D. J. Moore, W. S. Price, Jr. (1955). Trans. Amer. Micr. Sci. 74:235.

Neuhaus, W. (1952). Z. Parasitenk. 15:203.

Wu, L. Y. (1953). Canad. J. Zool. 31:351.

FAMILY SPIRORCHIIDAE

The Spirorchiidae are monoecious blood flukes of turtles with the adults localized in the arteries and heart. They are lanceolate in shape, with an oral sucker, but the acetabulum may or may not be present. The oesophagus is surrounded by gland cells and the two caeca reach almost to the end of the body. There are one to many testes located intercaecally; they may be either pre- or postovarian.

Spirorchis parvus (Stunkard, 1932) (Plate 60)

S. parvus is parasitic in the arteries of the wall of the pyloric stomach and small intestine of the painted turtle *Chrysemys picta* in the central and eastern part of the United States, possibly throughout its range.

DESCRIPTION. Adult flukes are 1.07 to 2.04 mm long, very thin, transparent, and covered, at least along the margins, with sensory papillae. Needle-like spines cover the anterior end for the length of the oral sucker. There is no pharynx. The oesophagus is surrounded by gland cells. There are four to five lobed testes lying in series between the caeca, beginning near the middle of the body and extending caudad. The ovary lies at the posterior end of the seminal vesicle. Vitelline glands surround the caeca the entire length, filling the space between them except for that occupied by the gonads. The uterus is very short and usually devoid of eggs which are 54 by 38 μ and nonoperculate. The genital pore is at the level of the posterior margin of the ovary.

LIFE CYCLE. Colorless adults in the arterioles of the muscular layer of the pyloric stomach and small intestine deposit their unembryonated eggs. In cases of heavy infection, egg masses form a solid coating over large sections of the stomach and intestine of small turtles, often causing death. Two weeks are required for the eggs to work through the intestinal wall into the lumen. When voided with the faeces into water, they swell considerably, at which time the miracidia become very active. Hatching occurs in 4 to 6 days between the hours of 2 A.M. and 5 A.M. o'clock through a slit in the side of the egg, and the miracidium swims away. Survival in the water is up to 15 hours at summer temperature.

Miracidia begin to attack ram's horn snails (*Helisoma trivolvus, H. campanulata*) 30 to 60 minutes after hatching and require 10 to 60 minutes to penetrate. Only young snails become infected. The miracidia transform into mother sporocysts in the mantle of the snail. Development is completed in 18 days, at which time daughter sporocysts have developed and are ready to leave. They escape from the anterior end of the mother sporocyst and migrate through the lymph spaces of the mantle and body into

*This is a series of papers by Professor Cort and his students on the biology of some species of North American blood flukes whose cercariae produce dermatitis.

EXPLANATION OF PLATE 60 ⇨

A. Adult fluke. **B.** Embryonated egg. **C.** Miracidium. **D.** Mature mother sporocyst. **E.** Daughter sporocyst with developing cercariae. **F.** Cercaria. **G.** Turtle *(Chrysemys picta)* definitive host. **H.** Snail *(Helisoma trivolvus, H. campanulata)* intermediate host.

1, oral sucker; **2,** oesophagus, showing glandular cells; **3,** intestine; **4,** vitelline glands; **5,** testes; **6,** seminal vesicle; **7,** common genital pore; **8,** ovary; **9,** oviduct; **10,** seminal receptacle; **11,** excretory bladder; **12,** excretory pore; **13,** apical gland; **14,** penetration gland; **15,** brain; **16,** flame cell; **17,** germ cells; **18,** egg shell; **19,** eyespot; **20,** apical papilla; **21,** lateral papilla; **22,** excretory duct; **23,** developing daughter sporocysts; **24,** immature cercaria; **25,** dorsal crest; **26,** ventral sucker; **27,** genital primordium; **28,** tail; **29,** furca.

a, adult worm in arterioles of intestinal wall; **b,** eggs laid in blood vessels pass through tissues into lumen of intestine; **c,** embryonated eggs in intestinal contents; **d,** eggs passed in faeces; **e,** eggs hatch in water; **f,** miracidium penetrates snail host; **g,** mother sporocyst with developing daughter sporocyst; **h,** daughter sporocyst with cercariae; **i,** furcocercous cercaria escaping from snail; **j,** cercaria free in water; **k,** cercaria penetrating soft tissues of turtle, dropping its tail in the process; **l,** tailless cercaria in blood vessels; **m,** cercaria in precaval vein; **n,** cercaria entering right auricle of heart and passing through ventricle into pulmonary artery; **o,** cercaria in pulmonary artery; **p,** cercaria having passed through lungs enters left auricle of heart; **q,** cercaria entering dorsal aorta; **r,** cercaria passing through mesenteric artery into intestinal wall; **s,** cercaria in arteriole where it grows to maturity in about 3 months at summer temperature and passes eggs in faeces about 2 weeks later.

Adapted from Wall, 1941, Trans. Amer. Micr. Soc. 60:221.

---

the digestive gland, at which time the cercariae begin to develop. Upon reaching maturity, the cercariae, which are large, apharyngeate, distomate, and bear a longitudinal fin over the dorsal side of the body, leave the snails intermittently. Being positively phototropic, they congregate at the surface of the water where they swim and rest.

Upon coming in contact with turtles, especially young ones, they penetrate the soft membranes around the anus, eyes, between the toes, in the flanks, and in the nostrils and mouth, leaving the tail on the outside. The young flukes enter the blood vessels and are carried to the right side of the heart, through the lungs and left side of the heart, and into the general circulation, Those reaching the arterioles of the pyloric stomach and small intestine develop to sexual maturity in 3 months during the summer and eggs appear in the faeces 2 weeks later.

A second species, *S. elephantis* (Cort, 1917), also infects painted turtles. The life cycle is essentially the same as that of *S. parvus.*

EXERCISE ON LIFE CYCLE

Embryonated nonoperculate eggs appearing in the faeces of painted turtles from ponds where *Helisoma trivolvus* or *H. campanulata* appear are likely to be those of *Spirorchis.* By the same token, large, brevifurcate, nonpharyngeate cercariae with a longitudinal fin over the dorsal surface of the body obtained from these snails in ponds with painted turtles probably are those of *Spirorchis.*

When eggs are available, they should be hatched and young snails exposed to the miracidia. Dissection of the snails at intervals of 2 to 4 days is necessary to follow the development of the intramolluscan stages.

Cercariae obtained from naturally infected snails and identified as those of *Spirorchis* should be placed in a small aquarium with young painted turtles. Observe the penetration of the cercariae into the turtles and their reaction to the attack. By making dissections, verify that the larval flukes go through the lungs a few days after entrance into the turtles. Determine the migratory route from the lungs to the stomach wall.

SELECTED REFERENCES

Cort, W. W., D. J. Ameel, A. Van Der Woude. (1954). Proc. Helminth. Soc. Wash. 21:85.

Wall, L. D. (1941). Trans. Amer. Micr. Soc. 60:221; (1941). Amer. Midl. Nat. 25:402.

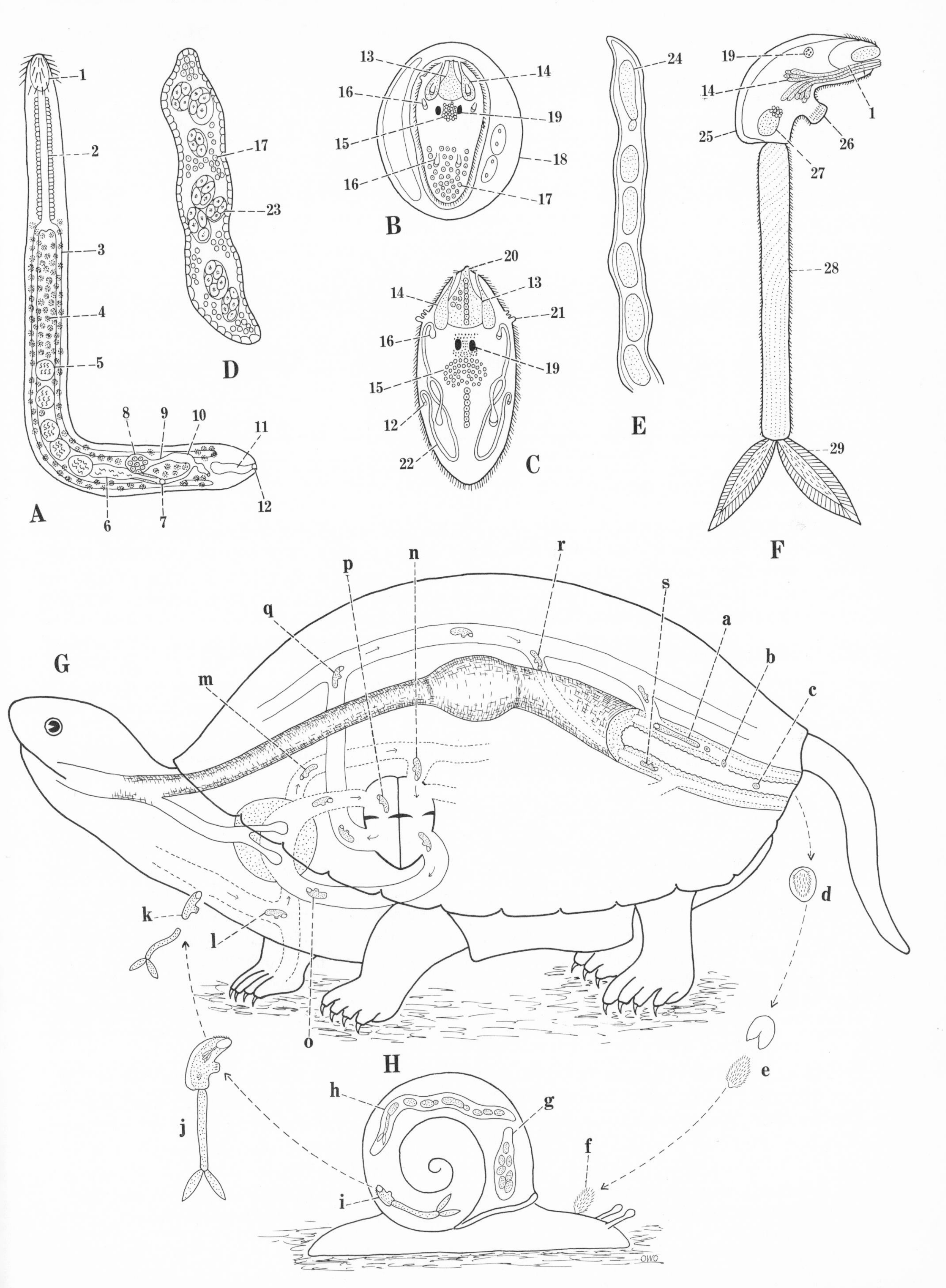
A
1
2
3
4
5
6
7
8
9
10
11
12
D
17
23
B
13
14
15
16
17
18
19
C
12
13
14
15
16
19
20
21
22
E
24
F
1
14
19
25
26
27
28
29
G
a
b
c
d
e
f
g
h
i
j
k
l
m
n
o
p
q
r
s
H
OWO

EXPLANATION OF PLATE 61

A. Adult fluke. **B.** Developing embryo in egg. **C.** Egg containing miracidium in advanced stage of development. **D.** Free-swimming miracidium. **E.** Fully developed cercaria. **F.** Gill filament of rainbow trout with adult fluke and developing eggs in it. **G.** Rainbow trout, definitive host. **H.** Snail *(Oxytrema (Goniobasis) circumlineata)* intermediate host.

1, spined anterior end; **2,** mouth; **3,** oesophagus; **4,** intestine; **5,** longitudinal rows of spines; **6,** vitelline glands which fill entire body; **7,** testis; **8,** cirrus pouch; **9,** male genital pore; **10,** ovary; **11,** ootype; **12,** single egg in ootype; **13,** female genital pore; **14,** membrane of developing miracidium; **15,** developing eyespot of miracidium; **16,** cilia of miracidium; **17,** refringent bar; **18,** eyespot; **19,** tail; **20,** furcae; **21,** spherical bodies at end of furcae; **22,** gill filament of rainbow trout; **23,** cartilaginous bar of gill filament; **24,** afferent artery of gill filament; **25,** egg developing in gill filament; **26,** adult fluke in afferent artery of gill.

a, adult fluke in afferent gill artery of rainbow trout; **b,** gill filament; **c,** efferent gill artery; **d,** dorsal aorta; **e,** developing eggs in tissue of gill filament; **f,** miracidium that has escaped from gill filament into gill chamber; **g,** free-swimming miracidium; **h,** miracidium penetrating snail intermediate host; **i,** mother sporocyst with germ balls; **j,** sporocyst with redia and germ balls; **k,** redia with furcocercous cercariae in various stages of development; **l,** free-swimming cercaria; **m,** cercaria penetrating pectoral fin has dropped tail; **n,** cercaria being carried in blood through brachial vein toward heart; **o,** cercaria in auricle; **p,** cercaria entering conus arteriosis from ventricle; **q,** cercaria entering afferent artery of gill where it matures and lays eggs.

Adapted from Wales (1958) Calif. Fish and Game 44:125.

FAMILY SANGUINICOLIDAE

This is a group of monoecious digenetic flukes that lives in the blood vessels of fish. Some workers include them in the family Aporocotylidae, claiming that Sanguinicolidae is a synonym. Others believe there are two families. The latter concept is followed herein. Species of the genus *Cardicola* have a single large testis, whereas those of *Sanguinicola* have several arranged in two regular rows. Worms in the arteries of the gills cause serious damage, often resulting in death.

Cardicola davisi (Wales, 1958) (Plate 61)

This species was described as *Sanguinicola davisi* from the gill arteries of trout on the Pacific coast of the United States. They have occurred in epizootic numbers in several hatcheries, causing severe losses through death.

DESCRIPTION. Fully developed individuals are flattened and spindle-shaped flukes, having a length of 8.5 mm and a width of 0.21 mm. There is no oral sucker, acetabulum, or pharynx. The mouth is subterminal and leads into a long, slender oesophagus that ends in an X-shaped caecum with four short, rounded lobes. The single testis is large, irregular in shape, and approximately equatorial in position; the sperm duct leads to a crooked, thick-walled cirrus sac. The bilobed ovary located at the posterior margin of the testis opens by means of a short oviduct into a gourd-shaped ootype. The genital pores open separately near the posterior end of the body with the female pore being anterior to the male pore. The entire body is filled with yolk glands. Eggs are oval, nonoperculate, and measure 63 by 35 μ.

LIFE CYCLE. The adult flukes normally reside in the main gill arteries, lying parallel with the gill cartilages. One egg is produced at a time and carried by the blood into the capillaries of the gill filaments. Here development and hatching takes place. The active miracidia work through the epithelium to the surface of the gill filaments where a lobule forms. Upon rupture of the lobule, the ciliated miracidia are liberated and swim away. They develop in the snail *Oxytrema* (*Goniobasis*) *circumlineata* and possibly other species of the genus. Infected snails contain numerous sporocysts and rediae. While experimental data are lacking on the part of the life cycle in the snails, it is presumed that the miracidia transform into mother sporocysts, followed by daughter sporocysts and cercariae. The latter are brevifurcate. Like the adult flukes, they lack suckers and a pharynx and have a caecum closely resembling that of the mature worm. Upon coming in contact with fingerling trout, they soon penetrate the tissue of the fins, dropping their tails. The cercariae are active in the blood vessels of the fins and presumably migrate through the veins to the heart and from there to the gill arteries. No information is available on the movements in the host or on the prepatent period.

PLATE 61 *Cardicola davisi*

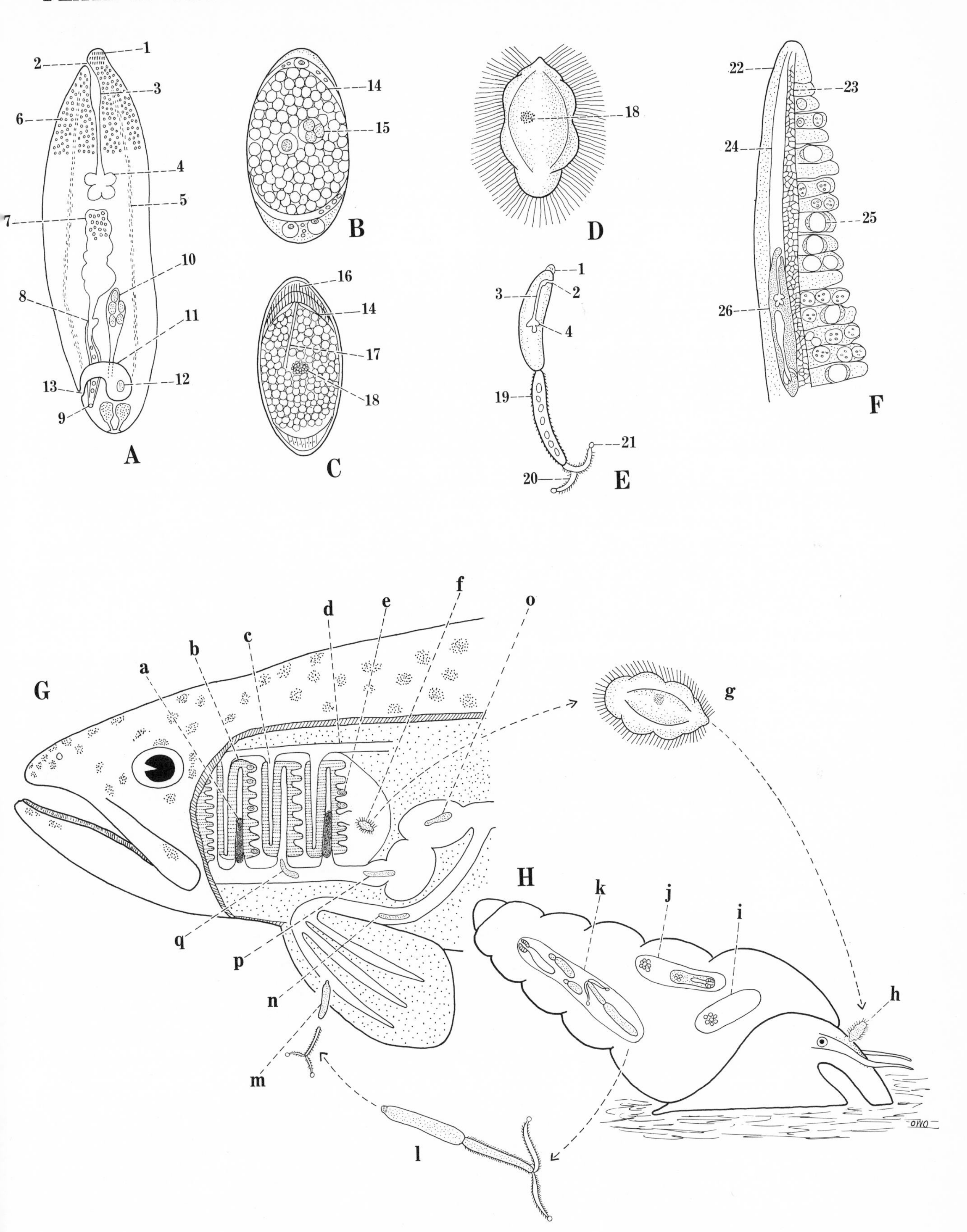

Cardicola klamathensis (Wales, 1958) is a closely related but much smaller species, occurring in trout of the same general area with *C. davisi.* They are in the efferent renal veins. The larval stages develop in the snail *Flumnicola seminalis.* The eggs are spherical and the cercariae have a longitudinal fin over the dorsal side of the body.

Sanguinicola inermis Plehn is common in the carp of Europe. The tricornered eggs hatch in the capillaries of the gills and the miracidia eventually escape into the water, where they penetrate *Lymnaea stagnalis* and *L. auricularia,* the snail hosts. The cercariae of this species and that of *C. klamathensis* are similar in that both have a dorsal fin over the body. *S. inermis* causes serious damage to young carp, often with high mortality. It has not been reported from North America.

Sanguinicola huronis of black bass and *S. occidentalis* of wall-eyed pike occur in North America, but their life cycles are not known.

EXERCISE ON LIFE CYCLE

When infections of sanguinicolid flukes are found, a study of the life cycles should be pursued to fill the present gaps in our knowledge concerning them.

Since the morphology of the cercariae is so characteristic, they can be identified with accuracy. They may be obtained from naturally infected snails in the area where the parasitized fish occur. When the species of snails are recognized, the experiments may be started by exposing them to miracidia obtained from infected fish. Also fish may be exposed to cercariae obtained from naturally infected snails.

By careful planning, the entire life cycle can be completed. Ascertain the intramolluscan development, including the stages that occur in the cycle. Likewise, follow the development in the fish host.

SELECTED REFERENCES

Fischthal, J. H. (1949). J. Parasit. 35:566.

Scheuring, L. (1922). Zool. Jahrb. Abt. Anat. 44:265.

Van Cleave, H. J., and J. F. Mueller. (1934). Bull. Roosevelt Wildlife Ann. 3:235.

Wales, H. H. (1958). Calif. Fish and Game 44:125.

Yamaguti, S. (1958). Systema Helminthum, Vol. 1. Interscience Publishers, New York, p. 364.

Suborder Brachylaemata

This suborder contains the families Brachylaemidae, Fellodistomatidae, and Bucephalidae whose adult stages are vastly different in appearance. The relationship of these flukes is shown by the distomate cercariae which develop in sporocysts and have a forked tail of moderate or small size, or no tail. The protonephridia (flame cells in the early stage of development of the cercariae) are stenostomate (with a narrow opening).

SUPERFAMILY BRACHYLAEMOIDEA

Members of the Brachylaemoidea are parasites of the cloaca of birds and caecum of mammals. They are usually elongate but sometimes oval in shape. The genital pore is located at the front margin of the anterior testis or caudad from it. The cercariae 1) develop in branching sporocysts in aquatic or terrestrial snails, 2) have a functional or rudimentary tail, or none at all, and 3) possess a V-shaped excretory bladder with long arms.

FAMILY BRACHYLAEMIDAE

The flukes of this family are parasites of the cloaca of birds and caecum of mammals. They are usually elongate and have a well-developed oral and ventral sucker and pharynx, but a very short oesophagus. The caeca extend to the posterior end of the body and the genital pore is in the posterior half of the body. The main tubules of the short excretory bladder extend to near the anterior end of the body and loop back to near the middle before dividing.

Postharmostomum helicus (Leidy, 1847) (Plate 62)

P. helicus is a natural parasite of the caecum of the white-footed mouse (*Peromyscus leucopus*) in the United States.

DESCRIPTION. The oblong body is 2.8 mm long by 1.4 mm wide, with the oral sucker somewhat larger (410 to 500 μ) than the acetabulum. The pharynx is about one-half the diameter of the oral sucker. Undulating caeca extend to the posterior end of the body. Reproductive organs are in the caudal end of the body, about equal in size, and arranged in a triangle with the ovary (right) and the anterior testis (left side) at the same level. The genital pore is median and at the level of the anterior margin of the ovary. Vitelline glands are lateral to the intestines and extend from the pharynx to the ovary. Eggs measure 29 by 18 μ.

LIFE CYCLE. Adult worms in the caecum lay eggs that are embryonated when passed in the faeces. Hatching takes place when they are eaten by the land snail *Anguispira alternata*. The miracidia migrate through the intestinal wall into the surrounding connective tissue or into the hepatic gland, where they transform into large multibranched mother sporocysts. Daughter sporocysts appear in 7 to 10 days. They localize in the hepatic gland and grow into large branched forms similar to the mother sporocysts. Some of the branches protrude from the hepatic gland into the mantle cavity. Short-tailed cercariae develop in about 12 weeks during the summer and escape through birth pores at the tips of the branches into the mantle cavity. Production of cercariae continues for longer than a year and possibly for the life of the snail. They escape from the snails via the respiratory pore and appear in the slime secreted by the host.

Snails (*Anguispira, Polygyra, Derocercas*) crawling over the slime become infected when the cercariae in it enter the pore of the primary ureter. They migrate through the ureters into the kidney and through the renal canal into the pericardial chamber. Snails containing daughter sporocysts are resistant to infection by cercariae, hence only unparasitized ones become infected as the second intermediate host. Upon reaching the pericardial chamber, the cercariae are designated as metacercariae. The short tail is lost by the end of 10 days. No encystment occurs and the infective stage is reached in about 6 months. Up to 90 per cent or more of the snails are naturally infected. Chipmunks and white-footed mice become infected by eating the snails. The metacercariae reach the caecum and begin feeding on blood as early as 6 hours after being swallowed. Sexual maturity is attained in 8 days, as indicated by the appearance of eggs in the uterus, but they do not appear in the faeces until the 19th to 20th day after infection. A minimum of 39 weeks is required for completion of the life cycle, which is longer than for other members of the family where known. Infections in mice persist for as long as 150 days and possibly longer.

Other species of Brachylaemidae, whose life cycles are known, utilize two land snails as the first and second intermediate hosts. *Brachylaemus virginianus* of opposums develops in *Polygyra thyroides; Postharmostomum gallinum* of chickens in *Eulota similaris* (sporocysts) and *Subulina octoma* (metacercariae); *Panopistus pricei* of shrews in *Zonitoides arboreus, Agriolimax agrestis,* and *Ventridens ligerus* (sporocysts and metacercariae both in a single specimen); and *Leucochloridiomorpha constantiae* of ducks in *Campeloma decisum* (sporocysts and metacercariae). *Campeloma* is a gilled aquatic snail and the others are terrestrial forms.

EXERCISE ON LIFE CYCLE

Both the cercariae and metacercariae of the several genera of the Brachylaemidae can be identified without difficulty. Land snails harboring such flukes make a good starting point for life history studies. Unencysted metacercariae found in the pericardial chamber should be fed to appropriate vertebrate hosts. Proper identification of the metacercariae will indicate the vertebrate host to which it should be fed.

When eggs become available, they should be fed to snails of the same species from which the metacercariae came in order to obtain the branching sporocysts.

If cercariae are available, uninfected snails of the same species should be exposed to them for obtaining metacercariae. Determine the development of the various stages in each snail host.

EXPLANATION OF PLATE 62

A. Adult fluke. **B.** Embryonated egg. **C.** Miracidium. **D.** Branched daughter sporocyst. **E.** Cercaria. **F.** Metacercaria. **G.** Cross-section of intestine showing cilia. **H.** Definitive host *(Peromyscus)*. **I.** Snail first intermediate host *(Anguispira alternata)*. **J.** Snail second intermediate host *(Anguispira alternata)*.

1, oral sucker; **2,** ventral sucker; **3,** pharynx; **4,** oesophagus; **5,** caecum; **6,** testes; **7,** seminal vesicle; **8,** common genital pore; **9,** ovary; **10,** oviduct; **11,** ascending arm of uterus; **12,** descending portion of uterus; **13,** vitelline gland; **14,** vitelline duct; **15,** opening of Laurer's canal; **16,** excretory bladder; **17,** arm of excretory bladder; **18,** anterior portion of body; **19,** posterior portion of body; **20,** spine; **21,** glandular structure; **22,** band of cilia; **23,** germ cell; **24,** cercaria; **25,** germinal mass; **26,** penetration glands; **27,** tubules of penetration glands; **28,** flame cell; **29,** germinal primordium; **30,** vitelline membrane; **31,** papillae of suckers; **32,** tail; **33,** intestinal wall; **34,** cilia.

a, adult worm in caecum; **b,** embryonated eggs laid in caecum; **c,** eggs voided in faeces; **d,** fully developed egg in faeces on ground; **e,** eggs eaten by land snails; **f,** eggs hatch in digestive tract where miracidum is free; **g,** miracidium passes through intestinal wall; **h,** mother sporocyst; **i,** young daughter sporocyst inside; **j,** mature daughter sporocyst containing cercariae; **k,** cercaria escaping from snail first intermediate host; **l,** mucous trail left by traveling snail; **m,** cercaria in mucous trail; **n,** cercaria entering pore of primary ureter; **o,** cercaria moving up primary ureter; **p,** kidney; **q,** cercaria passing through renopericardial canal into pericardial cavity; **r,** cercaria remain unencysted in pericardial cavity; **s,** heart; **t,** mice become infected by removing the snails from their shells and eating them; **u,** cercaria freed from pericardial cavity of snail by digestive juices; **v,** cercaria free in intestine; **w,** cercaria entering caecum where it attaches to the mucosa and grows to maturity in 8 days when eggs first appear in the uterus; they appear in the faeces of mice on the 19th to 20th day after infection. Adult flukes live longer than 140 days.

Adapted from Ulmer, 1951, Trans. Amer. Micr. Soc. 70:319.

SELECTED REFERENCES

Alicata, J. E. (1940). J. Parasit. 26:135.

Allison, L. N. (1943). Trans. Amer. Micr. Soc. 62:127.

Krull, W. H. (1935). Trans. Amer. Micr. Soc. 54:118; (1935). Parasitol. 27:93.

Reynold, B. D. (1938). Parasitology 30:320.

Ulmer, M. J. (1951). Trans. Amer. Micr. Soc. 70:189, 319.

Villella, J. B. (1954). J. Parasit. 40:470.

SUPERFAMILY BUCEPHALOIDEA

This superfamily is characterized by the mouth being on the midventral side of the body. There is a holdfast organ at the anterior end where the oral sucker normally is located. The adult worms are parasites of the gut of marine and fresh-water fishes.

The cercariae, like the adults, are gasterostomate. The stem of the tail is short and bulbous with very long, motile furcae. They develop in branched sporocysts in clams. The protonephridia are mesostomate.

FAMILY BUCEPHALIDAE

There is but a single family in this group.

Bucephalus elegans Woodhead, 1930 (Plate 63)

The adult flukes occur commonly in the caecal pouches of the rock bass (*Ambloplites rupestris*) in the Great Lakes region of North America. While a relatively large percentage of the rock bass are infected, the number of parasites per individual is small, rarely exceeding three.

DESCRIPTION. Fully developed flukes are small spiny, cylindrical forms measuring 658 μ long by 192 μ wide. A truncate anterior end bears 7 extensile appendages. The oral sucker is on the midventral surface of the body; it opens into an oesophagus directed forward which enters an oval gut that turns posteriad. The ovary and 2 testes are behind the gut. A long cirrus pouch extends posteriorly and opens through the common genital pore near the hind end of the body. The eggs average 48 μ long by 21 μ wide and have a prominent operculum.

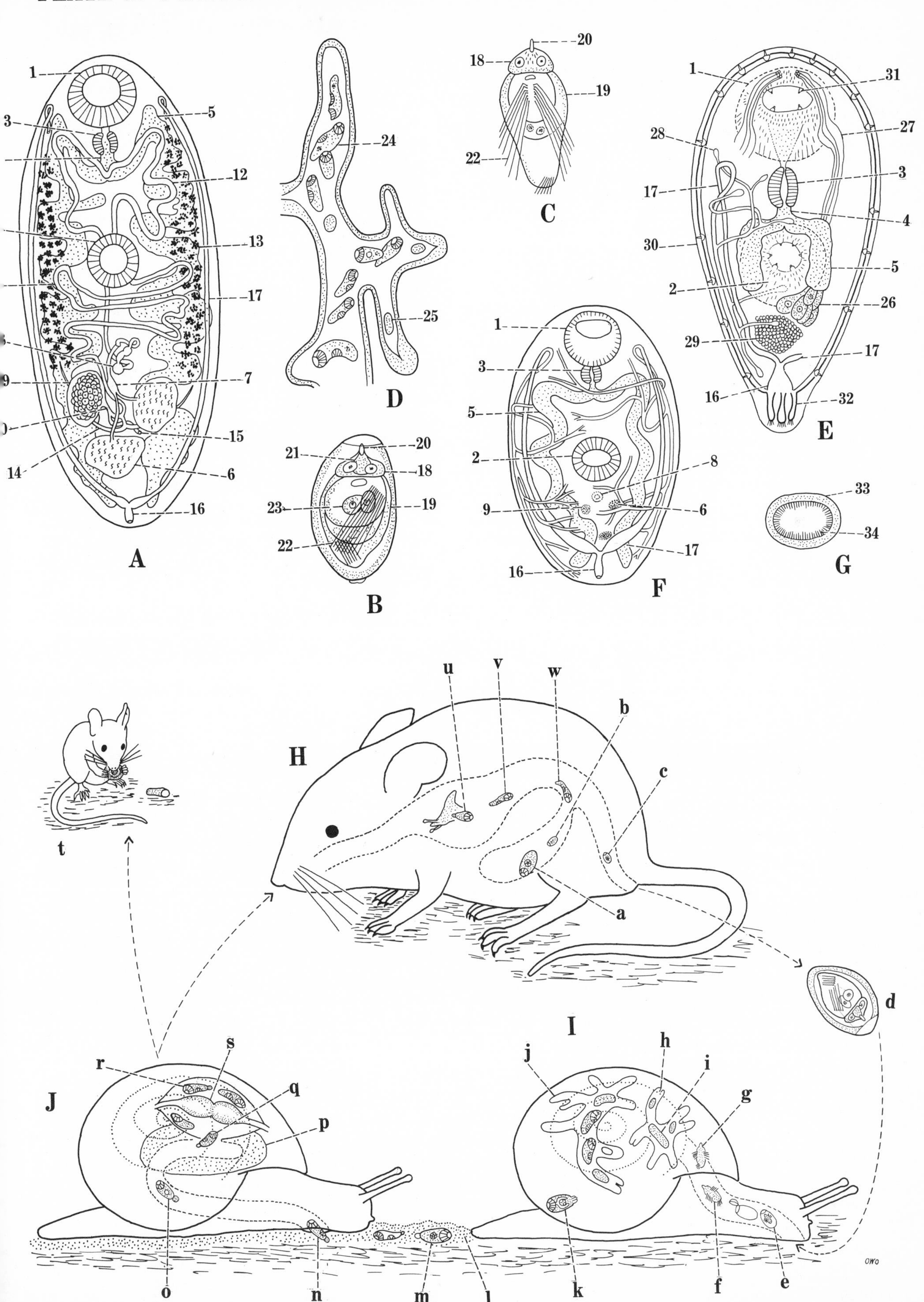

EXPLANATION OF PLATE 63

A. Adult fluke. **B.** Egg in early stages of cleavage. **C.** Miracidium. **D.** Branched sporocyst containing cercariae. **E.** Cercaria free in water. **F.** Morphology of mature cercaria. **G.** Metacercaria. **H.** Encysted metacercaria. **I.** Definitive host *(Ambloplites rupestris)*. **J.** Clam first intermediate host *(Eurynia iris)*. **K.** Fish second intermediate host *(Lepomis macrochirus)*.

1, fimbria; **2,** anterior adhesive organ; **3,** oral sucker; **4,** pharynx; **5,** oesophagus; **6,** intestine; **7,** testes; **8,** seminal vesicle; **9,** cirrus sac; **10,** cirrus extended; **11,** ovary; **12,** vitellaria; **13,** excretory vesicle; **14,** excretory pore; **15,** germ cell; **16,** yolk cell; **17,** cephalic plate; **18,** birth pore; **19,** cercaria; **20,** eyespot; **21,** vitelline gland; **22,** cirrus or perhaps anlagen of testes; **23,** bulbous tail stem; **24,** furca; **25,** subcuticular gland; **26,** genital pore; **27,** cyst.

a, small adults embedded in caecal pouches; **b,** eggs passed in faeces; **c,** partially developed egg; **d,** egg with fully developed miracidium; **e,** miracidium escaping from egg; **f,** miracidium free in water; **g,** miracidium swept into mantle cavity of clam through incurrent pore; **h,** branched sporocyst in digestive gland (preceding stages unknown); **i,** developing cercaria; **j,** ox-head cercaria ready to escape from digestive gland; **k,** cercaria free in water, having been swept from mantle cavity through excurrent pore; **l,** cercaria attacks bluegill sunfish (experimental) when disturbed by movements of water caused by swimming fish; **m,** cercaria drops tail as it penetrates fins or base of them; **n,** encysted metacercaria under skin of fin; **o,** infected bluegill or other infected fish swallowed by rock bass; **p,** encysted cercaria released from fish when latter is digested in the alimentary canal of rock bass; **q,** metacercaria escapes from cyst and migrates to the caecal pouches, where development to maturity occurs in about 30 days.

Adapted from Woodhead, 1929, Trans. Amer. Micr. Soc. 48:25; 1930, 49:1, 1931, 50:169.

LIFE CYCLE. Adult worms containing up to 200 eggs in various stages of development occur in the caecal pouches of a high percentage of the rock bass. Eggs near the genital opening contain fully formed miracidia ready to hatch upon reaching the water. Hatching takes place quickly when they reach the water. The miracidium forces the operculum from the egg, emerges, and swims rapidly away. If it strikes an object, it adheres to it, never seeming to turn away.

Infection of the rainbow clam first intermediate host (*Eurynia iris*) has not been observed. It is likely, however, that the miracidia are swept through the incurrent siphon into the branchial chamber, where they attach to the gonad and burrow into it. Up to 6 per cent of the clams from some areas are naturally infected. Branching sporocysts develop in the gonads, often completely filling them. While only a single generation has been reported, it seems probable that a mother sporocyst and daughter sporocysts occur. Early development of the cercariae in the sporocysts is rapid but the time required for reaching maturity is unknown. They emerge from the gonads into the branchial chamber. Currents of water flowing from the excurrent siphon carry them away from the clams. Upon reaching the outside, they spread the long furcae and hang with the body downward, swimming slowly.

When fish swim by, the furcae become entangled with the fins, holding the cercariae in a position that enables them to attach by the anterior holdfast and burrow into the tissues. As they work their way rapidly into the fins, the tail is discarded. Having entered the tissues, they move about, enlarging the space around them, and within an hour are enclosed in a hyaline cyst of parasitic origin.

Infection of rock bass takes place when fish harboring the cysts are eaten. Upon being released by the action of the digestive juices, the metacercariae migrate into the caecal pouches and mature in 30 days.

Woodhead reported three generations of sexual reproduction in *Bucephalus elegans*, involving sporocysts, rediae, and adults. His observations have not been confirmed nor his views accepted (Cort, Ameel, and Van der Woude).

The life cycle of *Bucephalus papillosus* Woodhead, from wall-eyed pike and pickerel, is essentially the same as that of *B. elegans*.

EXERCISE ON LIFE CYCLE

The eggs of *Bucephalus* and miracidia contained in them are so characteristic that identification of them in the faeces of fish hosts can be made with confidence. Likewise, the ox-head type of cercariae from clams (*Eurynia* and *Elliptio*) are readily recognized. With these advantages, the task of studying the life cycle is made easier.

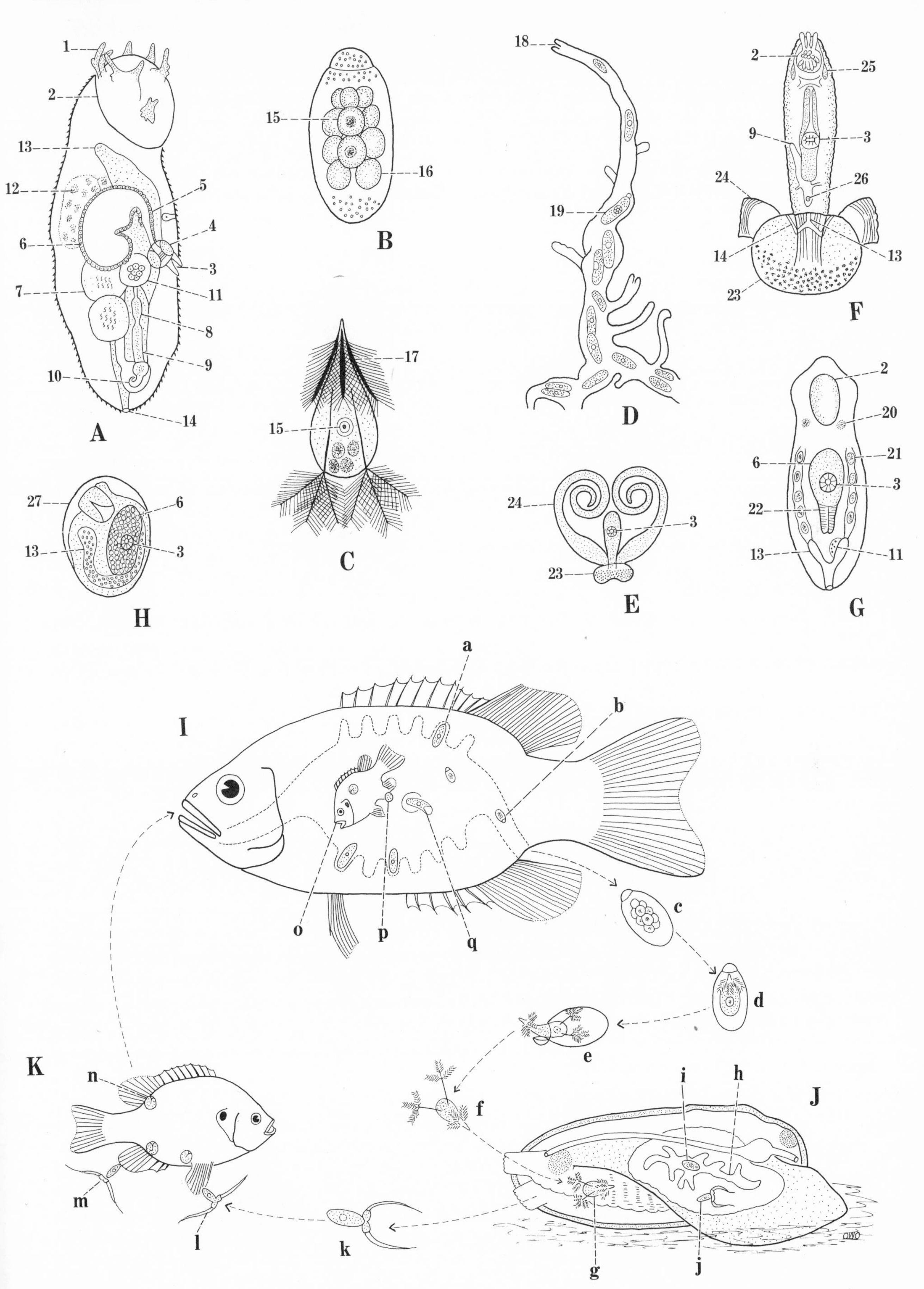
1
2
13
12
6
7
10
5
4
3
11
8
9
14
A
15
16
B
17
15
C
18
19
D
2
25
9
3
24
26
14
13
23
F
2
20
6
21
3
22
13
11
G
27
6
13
3
H
24
3
23
E
a
b
I
o
p
q
c
d
e
f
K
n
m
l
k
i
h
J
g
j

Wall-eyed pike and pickerel are frequently infected with *B. papillosus,* and rock bass with *B. elegans.* Eggs from adult worms or the faeces of infected fish provide material to observe hatching and for studying the action of miracidia. In small clams the means of infection can be followed. Determine whether one or two generations of sporocysts occur. Follow the entire intramolluscan development of the parasite. Ascertain the time required for development of the cercariae.

Using cercariae obtained from either naturally or experimentally infected clams, study the action of them in the water and the manner in which they infect the fish second intermediate host. By the use of stains, determine whether the cyst surrounding the metacercaria has the same chemical characteristic as the glandular material in the cercariae. This would provide a clue as to whether the cyst is of parasite or host origin.

By feeding encysted metacercariae to appropriate fish, determine the time required for the fluke to reach sexual maturity.

SELECTED REFERENCES

Cort, W. W., D. J. Ameel, and Anne Van der Woude. (1954) Exp. Parasit. 3:185.

Woodhead, A. E. (1929). Trans. Amer. Micr. Soc. 48:256; (1930). Ibid. 49:1; (1931). Ibid. 50:169.

ORDER ECHINOSTOMIDA

This order contains approximately two dozen families of diverse morphology. They include the fasciolids, echinostomes, paramphistomes, and certain monostomes. The relationship is shown in cercariae that develop in rediae, have large bodies, strong single tails, and numerous cystogenous glands in the epidermis.

Suborder Echinostomata

The cercariae are echinostomate, non-echinostomate, or show modifications of a collar and collar spines. They develop in collared rediae with stumplike lateral appendages. The life cycle usually requires two hosts, but three may occur in some species.

SUPERFAMILY ECHINOSTOMATOIDEA

Members of this superfamily are trematodes with a head collar bearing a row of spines.

FAMILY ECHINOSTOMATIDAE

The members of this family are more or less elongated distomate flukes. They have a distinct head collar armed with a single or double row of spines. They are parasites of the intestine and, occasionally, the bile duct or ureters of reptiles, birds, and mammals.

Echinostoma revolutum (Froelich, 1802) (Plate 64)

This fluke is among the most versatile as regards the variety of hosts it parasitizes. Adult flukes are able to develop in the ileum of 23 species of birds and nine of mammals, including man. Miracidia develop in at least four genera of snails (*Helisoma, Pseudosuccinea, Physa,* and *Stagnicola*) and 10 species in North America. The cercariae enter and develop to metacercariae in 16 species of pulmonate snails, many are the same ones in which they developed, two species of fingernail clams and seven species of tadpoles, together with catfish and bullheads. Because of its adaptability to mollusks and tadpoles as intermediate hosts and ducks as definitive hosts, this parasite is cosmopolitan.

DESCRIPTION. Adult worms vary in length from 4 to 21 mm, depending on the species of definitive host in which they develop. The number and arrangement of spines in the cephalic collar are constant. There are 37 spines arranged in three general groups; they are 1) the two corner groups of five spines each, three of which extend slightly beyond the margin of the collar and two that do not; 2) the two lateral groups, consisting of six spines each arranged in a straight row, and 3) the dorsal group consisting of 15 spines arranged in two alternating rows in which seven are in the anterior and eight in the posterior row, Eggs range in size from 91 to 145 μ long by 66 to 83 μ wide, the size being influenced by the species of host.

LIFE CYCLE. Adult worms lay an average of 2,000 to 3,000 unembryonated eggs per day which are voided in the faeces. They develop slowly in water, hatching in 18 to 30 days at room temperature.

The miracidia swim rapidly and almost constantly until they penetrate a snail or death ensues, about 18 hours after hatching. Inside the snails *Physa gyrina, Helisoma trivolvus,* and others, the miracidia transform into mother sporocysts which give rise to two generations of rediae, the second of which produces cercariae in 9 to 10 weeks after infection of the snails.

The cercariae have the 37 collar spines arranged in the same manner as in the adults; there is a membranous fin over the dorsal side of the tail. They are active swimmers and good crawlers. Upon coming in contact with snails and fingernail clams, they penetrate the soft parts and encyst. If they attach to tadpoles or silurid fishes, they creep into the cloaca and migrate up the ureters into the kidneys where encystment occurs.

Infection of the definitive hosts is accomplished when they eat mollusks, tadpoles of frogs and toads, or catfish and bullheads that harbor metacercariae. Upon being freed from the tissues of the second intermediate hosts, the metacercariae migrate to the ileum, attach to the mucosa, and develop to sexual maturity when 4 to 7 mm long, at which time individual flukes fertilize themselves. Growth continues as long as the flukes remain in the host. Eggs appear in the faeces 18 days after infection.

As a result of Beaver's extensive experimental studies on variation in pure strains of *E. revolutum,* about 15 species were declared synonyms. This is evidence for the need of studying variation in morphology as a means of delimiting the parameters of species of many of the parasites.

In cases where life cycles of other species of Echinostomatidae have been worked, they follow the general pattern shown by *E. revolutum.* In *Echinoparyphium recurvatum* of chickens and ducks, the cercariae develop in *Physa, Planorbis,* and *Lymnaea,* and encyst in *Lymnaea* and tadpoles; in *Himasthla quissetensis* of gulls, they develop in *Nassa* and encyst in *Mya* and several other marine clams; those of *Hypoderaeum conoideum,* a European species of ducks, encyst in *Planorbis* and *Limnaea;* and *Petasiger chandleri* of grebes utilizes *Helisoma* for development of the cercariae, and the gills or oesophagus of fish and tadpoles for the metacercariae.

EXERCISE ON LIFE CYCLE

Both cercariae and metacercariae of Echinostomatidae have an oral collar with spines which serves as an infallible character for identification. *Echinostoma revolutum* has 37 collar spines, *Echinoparyphium recurvatum* 45, *Himasthla quissetensis* 27, and *Petasiger chandleri* 19 to 21.

Identify any of the above genera of echinostome cercariae recovered from naturally infected snails. Following identification, expose appropriate snails, clams, tadpoles, or bullheads to the cercariae in order to obtain metacercariae. Ascertain the location of the metacercariae in the second intermediate host.

Having obtained metacercariae, feed them to some of the known definitive hosts to study the part of the life cycle in them. Eggs obtained from such infections may be hatched and snails of the same species from which the cercariae originated infected in order to get the intramolluscan stages of the parasites.

SELECTED REFERENCES

Abdel-Malek, E. T. (1953). J. Parasit. 39:152.
Beaver, P. C. (1937). Ill. Biol. Monogr. 15:1.
Johnson, J. C. (1920). Univ. Calif. Publ. Zool. 19:335.
Stunkard, H. W. (1938). Biol. Bull. 75:145.

FAMILY FASCIOLIDAE

The species of this family are parasites of mammals, commonly herbivores. They are large spiny, leaf-like, distomate flukes with the suckers close to each other. The caeca are branched or simple. The testes and ovary are dendritic. Vitellaria are profuse, lateral, and confluent posteriorly.

EXPLANATION OF PLATE 64 ⇨

A. Adult fluke, ventral view. **B.** Anterior end of fluke, showing details of collar and spines. **C.** Embryonated egg. **D.** Mother redia. **E.** Daughter redia. **F.** Cercaria. **G.** Encysted metacercaria. **H.** Duck definitive host. **I.** Muskrat definitive host. **J.** Snail *(Helisoma trivolvus* and others) first intermediate host. **K.** Frog tadpole second intermediate host. **L.** Snail *(Physa)* second intermediate host.

1, oral sucker; **2,** ventral sucker; **3,** pharynx; **4,** oesophagus; **5,** intestine; **6,** testis; **7,** cirrus pouch; **8,** common genital pore; **9,** ovary; **10,** oviduct; **11,** Mehlis' gland; **12,** uterus; **13,** excretory bladder; **14,** excretory pore; **15,** head collar; **16,** collar spines; **17,** corner spines; **18,** egg shell; **19,** operculum; **20,** miracidium; **21,** apical gland; **22,** flame cell; **23,** excretory duct; **24,** pharynx of redia; **25,** gut; **26,** daughter redia; **27,** germinal masses; **28,** birth pore; **29,** cercaria; **30,** prepharynx; **31,** tail; **32,** cyst of metacercaria.

a, adult fluke in small intestine; **b,** unembryonated eggs laid in intestine; **c, d,** egg develops and hatches in water; **e,** miracidium penetrates snails; **f,** mother sporocyst; **g,** mother redia containing daughter rediae; **h,** daughter redia containing cercariae; **i,** cercaria escaping from snail; **j,** cercaria free in water; **k,** cercaria creeping into anus of tadpole; **l,** cercaria migrates up ureters; **m,** encysted metacercariae in kidney; **n,** cercaria penetrating snail second intermediate host; **o,** metacercaria encysted in snail; **p,** ducks and other definitive hosts become infected by eating infected tadpoles or snails; **q,** metacercaria released by action of digestive juices; **r,** young fluke escapes from cyst and develops to adult stage in 15 to 19 days.

Figures A, B, F adapted from Beaver, 1937, Ill. Biol. Monogr. 15:1; C, D, E, G, from Johnson, 1920, Univ. Calif. Publ. Zool. 19:335.

Fasciola hepatica Linnaeus, 1758 (Plate 65)

This is the common liver fluke of sheep and cattle in the United States and Europe, as well as other sections of the world. It is a cause of tremendous losses to growers of these animals. In addition to rendering the livers unsuitable for human consumption, it causes losses through death, morbidity, and lowered resistance. *Clostridium novyi,* a bacillus normally dormant in healthy livers, finds the dead liver cells produced by the migrating flukes in sheep ideal for growth. The bacilli multiply rapidly and produce a toxin that is highly lethal. Sheep apparently in good health die quickly of what is called "black disease." Infected wild rabbits and hares serve as reservoir hosts in spreading and maintaining the parasites on grazed and ungrazed areas.

DESCRIPTION. Fully grown flukes reach a size of 30 mm long by 13 mm wide. They are shaped somewhat like a leaf with a narrow cephalic cone on the broad anterior end. The oral sucker is smaller than the ventral one which is at the level of the broad "shoulders." The highly dendritic intestinal caeca extend to the posterior extremity of the body. A branched ovary lies toward the right side a short distance posterior from the ventral sucker with the coils of the uterus between them. The testes are extensively branched, filling most of the body behind the ovary. Numerous vitelline glands extend backward along the sides of the body from the shoulders to the end of the body where they are confluent behind the testes. Eggs measure 130 to 150 μ long by 63 to 90 μ wide.

LIFE CYCLE. Eggs deposited in the branches of the biliary system pass through the common bile duct into the duodenum. They are carried from the body in the faeces in an unembryonated state. Those falling in water develop and hatch in 9 to 10 days at summer temperature. At lower temperatures, development is retarded. At temperatures too low for development, eggs are able to survive several years.

The miracidia are ciliated and have a proboscis-like structure at the anterior end and two semilunar eyespots. They are capable of living up to 24 hours in the water. Upon finding a suitable snail host, such as *Stagnicola bulimoides* or *Fossaria modicella* which are the common ones in the United States, they burrow into it and transform into mother sporocysts. There are two generations of rediae. The first migrates to the hepatic gland where the daughter rediae occur in great numbers. They produce cercariae in 5 to 7 weeks after the snails become infected. If the pools in which the snails live become dry, they burrow into the mud, surviving for long periods. When water reappears, they quickly emerge and, if infected, shed cercariae.

The cercariae are 250 to 350 μ long, the tail is double the length of the body, and the body wall is filled with cystogenous glands. In the water, the cercariae quickly attach to objects, particularly

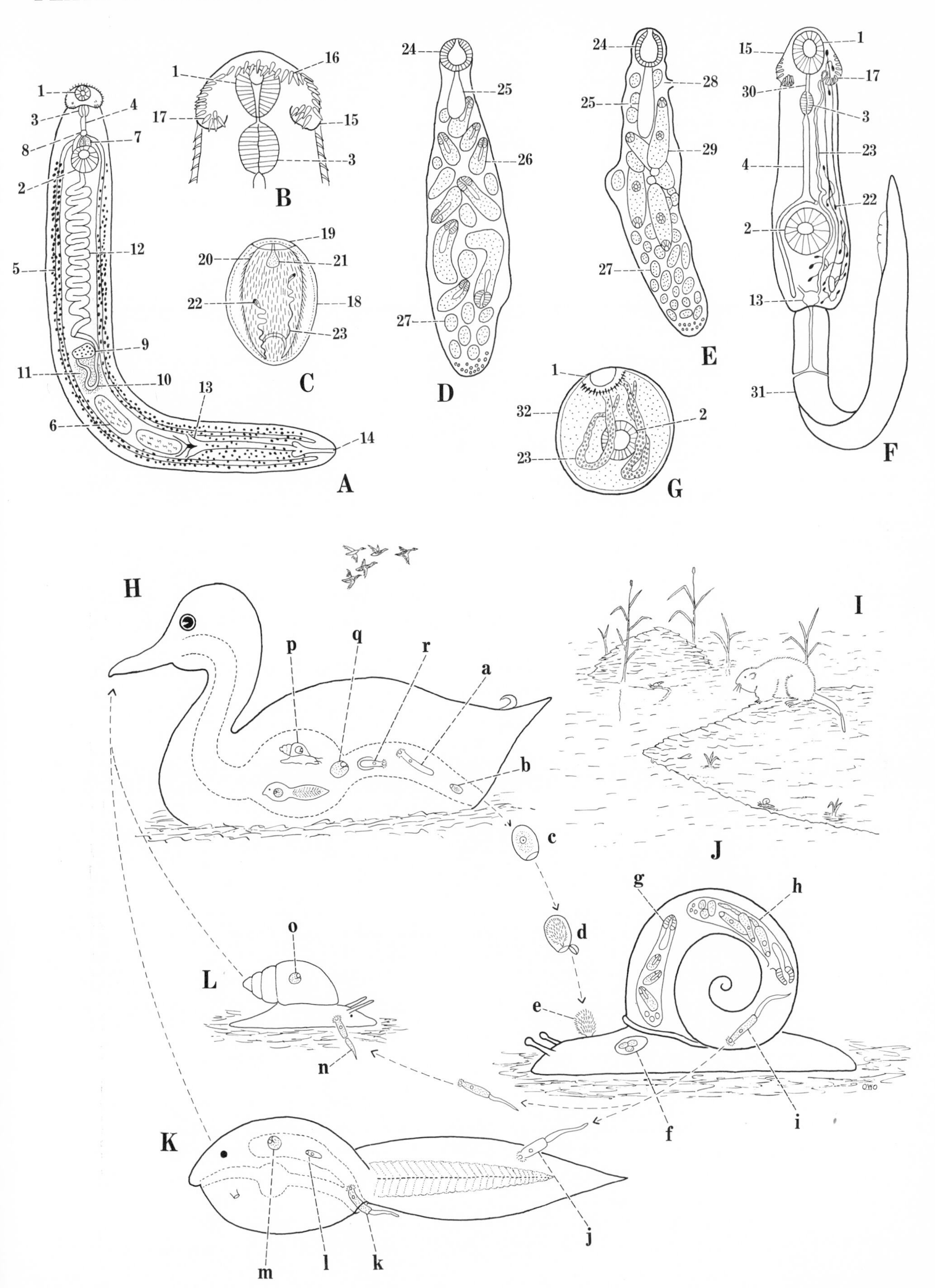

A
B
C
D
E
F
G
H
I
J
K
L
a
b
c
d
e
f
g
h
i
j
k
l
m
n
o
p
q
r

EXPLANATION OF PLATE 65

A. Adult fluke. **B.** Unembryonated egg. **C.** Miracidium. **D.** Young mother sporocyst. **E.** Mature mother sporocyst. **F.** Mature second generation redia. **G.** Cercaria. **H.** Sheep definitive host. **I.** Wild rabbits as reservoir hosts. **J.** Snail *(Stagnicola bulimoides, Fossaria modicella)* first intermediate host. **K.** Metacercaria on vegetation.

1, oral sucker; **2,** ventral sucker; **3,** pharynx; **4,** intestine; **5,** testis; **6,** vas efferens; **7,** vas deferens; **8,** cirrus pouch; **9,** common genital pore; **10,** ovary; **11,** oviduct; **12,** Mehlis' gland surrounding ootype; **13,** uterus; **14,** vitelline glands; **15,** transverse vitelline duct; **16,** operculum of unembryonated egg; **17,** apical papilla; **18,** eyespots; **19,** cilia; **20,** germ cells; **21,** germ balls; **22,** mother rediae; **23,** daughter redia; **24,** cercaria; **25,** tail; **26,** genital anlagen.

a, adult fluke in bile duct of liver, causing great hypertrophy of the ducts; **b,** unembryonated eggs leave the liver by way of the common bile duct; **c,** eggs mixed with faeces; **d,** eggs passed from body in faeces; **e,** eggs develop in water and hatch, releasing miracidia; **f,** miracidium penetrates snail; **g,** miracidium transforms into a mother sporocyst; **h,** mature mother sporocyst containing daughter rediae; **i,** first generation of daughter redia with developing rediae; **j,** second generation redia filled with germ balls and cercaria; **k,** cercaria free in water; **l,** lateral view of metacercaria encysted below water level on grass stem; **m,** surface view of submerged metacercaria; **n,** metacercaria above water due to growth of vegetation or lowering of water, or a combination of both; **o,** infection of definitive host occurs when metacercariae are swallowed with forage; **p,** young fluke escapes from metacercarial cyst in abomasum; **q,** young fluke free in intestine; **r,** flukes burrow through intestinal wall into coelom; **s,** flukes migrate to liver; **t,** flukes enter liver by penetrating capsule; **u,** young flukes migrate through liver parenchyma for a period and then enter bile ducts where maturity is attained in approximately 90 days after entering the host.

Figures adapted from various sources.

---

plants, drop their tails, and soon secrete a cyst about themselves. When encystment is completed, they are infective.

Cattle, sheep, and rabbits eating grass bearing the cysts become infected. Upon being liberated from the cysts in the duodenum, the metacercariae migrate through the intestinal wall into the coelom and to the liver, which they enter by burrowing through the capsule into the parenchyma. There is a period of growth and migration in the liver for about 2 months, after which they enter the bile ducts. Maturity is attained in another month, making a total of 3 months after entering the vertebrate host. Liver flukes have great longevity, living as long as 11 years under experimental conditions that precluded natural infection of the host.

Other well-known species of Fasciolidae include the liver flukes *Fasciola gigantica* and *Fascioloides magna* of ruminants, and *Fasciolopsis buski,* an intestinal fluke of humans and swine in the Orient. *Fasciola gigantica* replaces *F. hepatica* in some parts of the world, including Hawaii; *Fascioloides magna* is a natural parasite of Cervidae in North America which infect cattle where they occupy the same range with deer under physical conditions suitable for the snail hosts. The life cycles of these flukes are very similar to that of *F. hepatica,* except for *F. buski,* which develops in the intestine.

EXERCISE ON LIFE CYCLE

F. hepatica is an excellent subject for conducting life history studies. Its life cycle was the first worked out for a digenetic trematode, having been done independently and almost simultaneously in Germany by Leuckart in 1882 and in England by Thomas in 1883.

In areas where the flukes occur, quantities of them may be procured from the condemned livers of sheep and cattle at abattoirs. Flukes placed in a dish of water lay numerous eggs that will develop and hatch in 9 to 10 days at room temperature. Snail hosts placed with the miracidia become infected. Observe the miracidia penetrate the snails and their reactions to the attacking parasites. Place specimens of *Physa, Helisoma,* or other non-host species in a dish with miracidia and note whether they are attacked. Dissect infected snails at intervals of 2 to 3 days during the growth of the flukes in them to find and identify each of the stages.

When cercariae are shed by the snails, collect the encysted metacercariae from the side of the container or on a glass slide placed upright in the water, and feed them to rabbits. Examine the rabbits

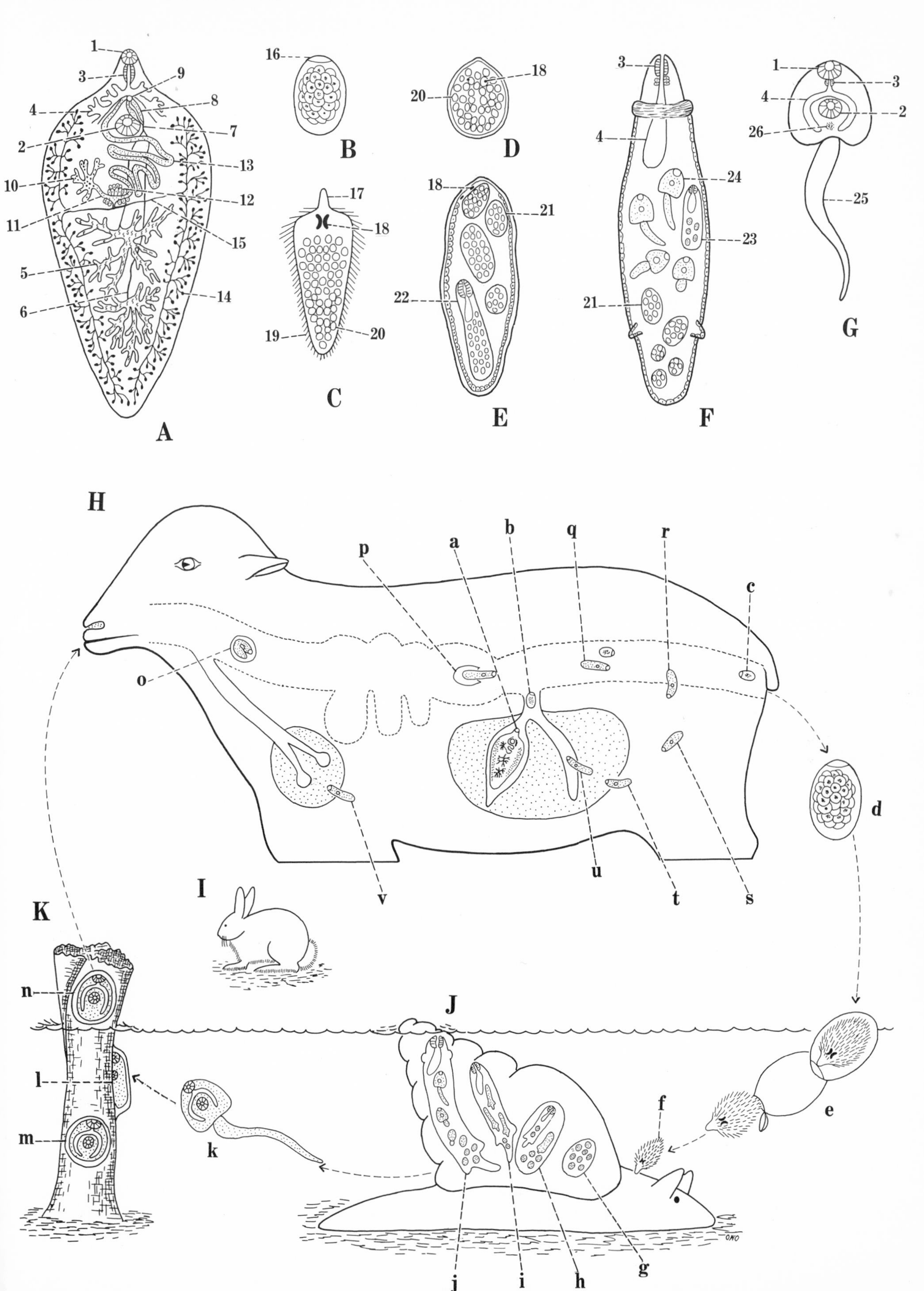
1
3
9
8
4
7
2
13
10
12
11
15
5
14
6
A
16
B
17
18
19
20
C
18
20
D
18
21
22
E
3
4
24
23
21
F
1
3
4
2
26
25
G
H
p
a
b
q
r
c
o
d
v
u
t
s
I
K
n
l
m
k
J
f
e
j
i
h
g

at intervals of 1 week after feeding the metacercariae to observe the migration and development of the flukes. Upon opening the coelom of the first rabbit, flush it with water into a pan to collect the flukes that are enroute from the intestine to the liver.

Put some metacercariae that have been washed in several changes of distilled water into the body cavity of a rabbit to demonstrate that the flukes are capable of migrating from it into the liver.

SELECTED REFERENCES

Krull, W. H., and R. S. Jackson. (1934). J. Wash. Acad. Sci. 33:79.

Olsen, O. W. (1944). J. Agr. Res. 69:389; (1947). J. Parasit. 33:36; (1948). Ibid. 34:119; (1949). Vet. Med. 44:26.

Pantelouris, E. M. (1965). The Common Liver Fluke. Pergamon Press, New York, 259 pp.

Price, E. W. (1956). Yearbook. U. S. Dept. Agriculture, p. 148.

Suborder Paramphistomata

The adult flukes are either amphistomate, *i.e.*, the oral sucker is at the anterior extremity and the ventral sucker at the posterior extremity of the body, or monostomate, in which case only the oral sucker is present and located at the anterior end.

The cercariae have the features of the adults in the number and arrangement of the suckers. Their bodies are heavily pigmented and they possess eyespots. They develop in rediae lacking a collar and the stumpy appendages on the side of the body; encystment is on objects in the water, especially vegetation.

SUPERFAMILY PARAMPHISTOMATOIDEA

These flukes, both adults and cercariae, are characterized by having a sucker at each extremity of the body.

FAMILY PARAMPHISTOMATIDAE

The members of this family are parasites of mammals, particularly herbivores. The location of the metacercariae on vegetation make them readily available to grazers and accounts for the frequency with which these parasites appear in cattle and sheep. They have thick bodies, the testes are usually near the middle of the body, and the ovary is post-testicular.

Paramphistomum cervi (Schrank, 1790) (Plate 66)

P. cervi is one of the rumen flukes of sheep, goats, cattle, deer, and other ruminants in almost all parts of the world.

DESCRIPTION. The mature worms are conical in shape and pink in color during life. They are 5 to 12 mm long. The dorsal surface is somewhat convex and the ventral concave. The oral sucker is at the anterior extremity of the body and the large ventral sucker at the posterior extremity. The testes are slightly lobed, in the posterior half of the body, and anterior to the ovary. The eggs are 114 to 176 μ long by 73 to 100 μ wide.

LIFE CYCLE. The exogenous phase of the life cycle of this species is the same as that of the common liver fluke in most respects. In North America, they develop in the same snail hosts. The cercariae are large, pigmented, and have eyespots.

When the metacercariae are freed from their cysts in the duodenum, they travel forward to the rumen. In the duodenum, they penetrate the mucosa and migrate through it, causing severe pathology, a foetid diarrhea, and frequently death. Upon reaching the abomasum, they return to the lumen and continue the migration to the rumen without further penetration of the mucosal lining. In the rumen, they attach among the villi. Sexual maturity is reached in 2 to 4 months.

Life cycles have been worked for a number of other species of Paramphistomatidae which parasitize ruminants from North America, Africa, Europe, and Australia. They are the same basically as that of *P. cervi.* No account is given, however, of a migration in the duodenal mucosa, as is said to occur in *P. cervi.*

EXERCISE ON LIFE CYCLE

Investigation on the intramolluscan phases of the life cycle should be conducted on the same basis as given for *Fasciola hepatica.* Make careful observations to determine the stages occurring in the snail and compare them with those of *F. hepatica.* The cost of sheep and calves for experimental purposes prohibit their use in most cases.

SELECTED REFERENCES

Bennett, H. J. (1936). Ill. Biol. Monogr. 14:1.

Brumpt, E. (1936). Ann. Parasit. Hum. Comp. 14:552.

Dinnik, J. A., and N. N. Dinnik. (1954). Parasitology 44:285; (1957). Ibid. 47:209.

Durie, P. H. (1953). Aust. J. Zool. 1:193; (1955). Aust. J. Agr. Res. 6:200; (1956). Ibid. 4:152.

Krull, W. H. (1934). J. Parasit. 20:173.

Olsen, O. W. (1949). Vet. Med. 44:108.

Szidat, L. (1936). Z. Parasitenk. 9:1.

Stichorchis subtriquetrus (Rudolphi, 1814) (Plate 67)

This is a parasite of beavers throughout their range.

DESCRIPTION. These are fleshy flukes with the body attenuated anteriorly and broadly rounded posteriorly. The oral sucker is large and there are two pouches within the posterior wall of it; the acetabulum is on the ventral surface of the body near but not at the posterior end of it. The cirrus sac is small and the genital sucker is distinct but not strongly developed. The testes are large and lobulated, lying anterior to the small spherical ovary. Vitelline follicles are lateral and mostly posterior to the testes. Eggs measure 118 to 154 μ long by 82 to 118 μ wide.

LIFE CYCLE. Unembryonated eggs laid in the caecum of beavers are expelled with the faeces. Development is slow but spectacular. By the end of 3 weeks a typically ciliated miracidium is formed. It contains in the posterior part of its body a single fully developed mother redia. Neither germ cells nor germ balls appear in these miracidia at this time. Hatching begins at the end of the third week. In water, the miracidia may, by contractions of the posterior portion of the body, force the mother redia forward and through a rent in the wall of the anterior end. Miracidia that attack and penetrate the mantle of the amphibious snail *Fossaria parva* in North America (it develops in *Planorbis vortex, Bithynia tentaculata, Limnaea ovata,* and *Succinea putris* in Russia) liberate the redia and then disintegrate in the tissues. By the end of the second day the mother redia has escaped from the body of the miracidium but is still in the mantle. It reaches the liver by the 17th day, perhaps somewhat earlier, at which time developing daughter rediae are present inside. Three weeks after infection, daughter rediae are present in the liver of the snail.

Cercariae are liberated about 35 days after infection of the snails. They swim about, beginning to encyst around 18 hours after becoming free in the water. Under optimal conditions, larval development in the snail requires 10 to 11 weeks.

Metacercariae encyst on submerged vegetation and are swallowed by the beavers along with their food. Upon liberation in the digestive tract, they migrate to the caecum. No data are available on the prepatent period or the length of time they remain in the host.

Helminths are reported to cause mortality among beavers in Russia, with *S. subtriquetrus* being responsible for much of the losses.

In addition to *S. subtriquetrus, Typhlocoelium cymbium,* a monostome fluke from the trachea of ducks, and *Parorchis acanthus,* an echinostome from the bursa Fabricii or rectum of herring gulls, have a well-developed mother redia inside the miracidium before it hatches from the egg.

EXERCISE ON LIFE CYCLE

In localities where carcasses of beavers are available during the trapping season, the amphistomes can be obtained readily, as they are relatively common. Eggs dissected from the uterus and washed

EXPLANATION OF PLATE 66 ⇨

A. Ventral view of adult fluke; **B.** Sinistral view of adult fluke. **C.** Free-swimming miracidium. **D.** Mother sporocyst containing mother rediae. **E.** Daughter redia (mother redia not shown). **F.** Cercaria. **G.** Bovine definitive host. **H.** Snail *(Stagnicola bulimoides)* first intermediate host. **I.** Vegetation with encysted metacercaria.

1, oral sucker; **2,** ventral sucker; **3,** oesophagus; **4,** intestine; **5,** testis; **6,** vas deferens; **7,** common genital pore; **8,** ovary; **9,** uterus; **10,** vitelline glands; **11,** Mehlis' gland; **12,** Laurer's canal; **13,** excretory bladder with excretory pore dorsal and subterminal; **14,** apical papilla; **15,** apical gland; **16,** penetration glands; **17,** germinal mass; **18,** mother redia; **19,** pharynx; **20,** gut; **21,** developing cercaria with well-formed eyespots; **22,** eyespots; **23,** excretory tubules; **24,** tail.

a, adult fluke in rumen; **b,** unembryonated eggs laid in rumen and pass out of body in faeces; **c,** unembryonated eggs must reach water to develop; **d,** developed egg hatches in water; **e,** miracidium free in water; **f,** miracidium penetrating snail; **g,** mother sporocyst containing mother rediae and germinal masses; **h,** daughter redia with developing cercariae; **i,** cercaria escaping from snail; **j,** cercaria free in water; **k,** metacercaria encysted below water line; **l,** metacercaria above water line, having reached there by growing vegetation and lowering of water, or both; **m,** host infected by swallowing metacercariae; **n,** metacercaria passes through stomachs unaffected; **o,** metacercaria excysts in duodenum; **p,** young flukes enter mucosa; **q,** young flukes migrate forward in mucosa; **r,** young flukes leave mucosa and enter intestinal lumen; **s, t,** young flukes in lumen migrate anteriorly through abomasum, omasum and reticulum to rumen where they grow to maturity in 2 to 4 months.

Figures A-B adapted from Fischoeder, 1903, Zool. Jahrb. Abt. Syst. 17:485; C-F, from Brumpt, 1936, Ann. Parasit. Hum. Comp. 14:552.

---

free of particles of tissue will develop and hatch in about 3 weeks. Observe the details of morphology of the miracidium and the mother redia contained inside. Also note how the redia is pushed forward in the miracidium and forced through the wall.

Snails collected from beaver ponds are a source of the amphistome cercariae and from them the metacercariae. Expose *Fossaria parva* to recently hatched miracidia. By means of sections, examine the mantle 48 to 60 hours after infection to see the miracidia and mother rediae.

Examination of snails at intervals of 1 week will demonstrate the mother and daughter rediae in the liver. Successful infection of *F. parva* is rather difficult, suggesting that perhaps other species of snails might serve as the natural intermediate host.

Note the morphological and behavioral characteristics of the cercariae together with the time required for them to develop in the daughter rediae.

Expose meadow voles to infection by feeding metacercariae to them. Guinea pigs also should be tried as an experimental host.

SELECTED REFERENCES

Bennet, H. J., and A. G. Humes. (1939). J. Parasit. 25:223.

FAMILY DIPLODISCIDAE

The oral sucker has a pair of posterior diverticula. The body is conical and bears a large terminal posterior sucker.

Megalodiscus temperatus (Stafford, 1905) (Plate 68)

This amphistome, formerly known as *Diplodiscus temperatus,* is a common parasite in the rectum of frogs in North America.

DESCRIPTION. Fully grown flukes measure up to 6 mm long and about 2 to 2.25 mm thick, being somewhat round. The oral sucker is well developed and bears a pair of prominent contractile posterior pouches about two-thirds the length of the sucker; the posterior sucker is terminal with a diameter about equal to that of the body. The caeca begin immediately behind the pharynx and extend to the posterior extremity of the body. The testes are in the anterior half of the body and the ovary is near the posterior end of it.

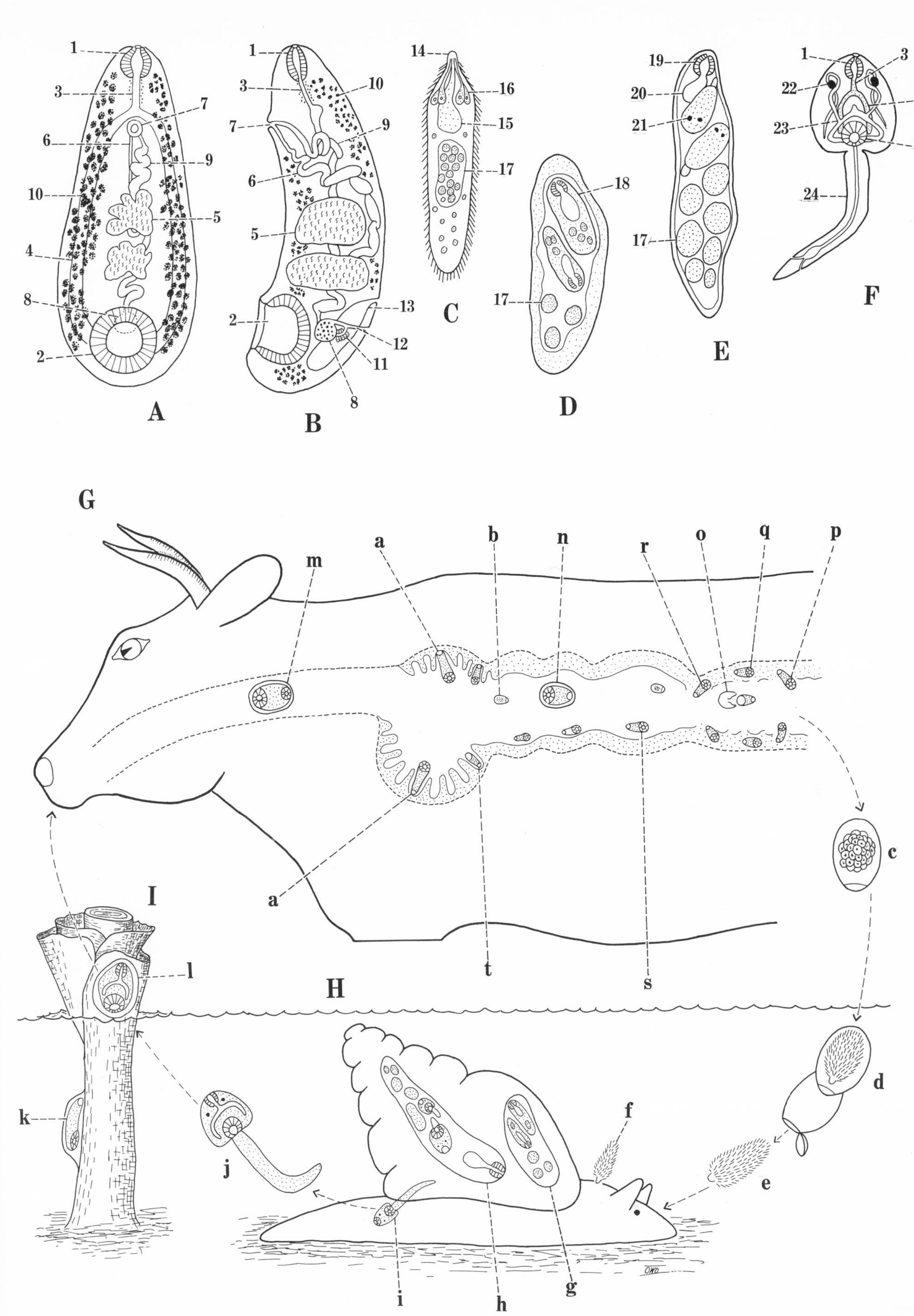

1
2
3
4
5
6
7
8
9
10
11
12
13
14
15
16
17
18
19
20
21
22
23
24
A
B
C
D
E
F
G
H
I
a
b
c
d
e
f
g
h
i
j
k
l
m
n
o
p
q
r
s
t

EXPLANATION OF PLATE 67

A. Ventral view of adult worm. **B.** Sagittal section of adult worm. **C.** Embryonated egg with miracidium containing a single redia. **D.** Miracidium. **E.** Miracidium without cilia showing dermal plates. **F.** Young mother redia just released from miracidium. **G.** Mature mother redia with daughter redia. **H.** Daughter redia with cercariae. **I.** Cercaria. **J.** Beaver *(Castor canadensis)* definitive host. **K.** Snail *(Fossaria parva)* intermediate host.

1, oral sucker; **2,** ventral sucker; **3,** oesophagus; **4,** intestine; **5,** testis; **6,** cirrus pouch; **7,** ovary; **8,** seminal receptacle; **9,** uterus; **10,** common genital pore surrounded by muscular genital sucker; **11,** vitelline glands; **12,** opening of Laurer's canal; **13,** miracidium in unhatched egg; **14,** redia inside miracidium; **15,** apical gland; **16,** penetration glands; **17,** excretory tubule; **18,** flame cell; **19,** excretory pore; **20,** redia in hatched miracidium; **21,** pharynx; **22,** gut; **23,** penetration glands; **24,** first tier of six dermal plates; **25,** second row of eight dermal plates; **26,** third row of four dermal plates; **27,** fourth row of two dermal plates; **28,** pharynx; **29,** germ balls; **30,** birth pore; **31,** young daughter redia; **32,** mature cercaria escaping through birth pore of daughter redia; **33,** cercaria; **34,** tail.

a, adult fluke in caecum of beaver; **b,** unembryonated eggs are laid in the caecum and voided in faeces; **c,** unembryonated egg free in water; **d,** egg hatching; **e,** miracidium penetrating snail; **f,** young mother redia escaping from miracidium; **g,** mature mother redia containing daughter redia and germ balls; **h,** daughter redia containing cercariae and germ balls; **i,** cercaria escaping from snail; **j,** cercaria free in water; **k,** metacercariae encysted on vegetation or other objects in water; **l,** beavers become infected by swallowing infective metacercariae with food; **m,** metacercaria escapes from cyst under influence of digestive juices and migrates to the caecum where it develops to maturity.

Figures A, B, D, H adapted from Skrjabin, 1949, Trematodes of Animals and Man, Vol. 4, Plates 57, 58 (Russian text); C, E, F, G, from Bennett and Humes, 1939, J. Parasit. 25:225.

LIFE CYCLE. Adult flukes in the rectum of frogs and tadpoles lay thin-shelled embryonated eggs which are deposited in the water with the faeces. They hatch promptly and the miracidia penetrate young snails, *Helisoma trivolvus, H. antrosum,* and *H. campanulata,* where they transform into mother sporocysts. Three generations of rediae develop in the liver. The third one produces cercariae that are released in an immature stage, and development is completed in the tissues of the snail host. Mature spermatozoa are present in the testes of the cercariae when they are shed by the snails, about 90 days after infection.

Cercariae escape daily from infected snails, the number being somewhat greater during the afternoon hours. Fewer of them appear during dull days than during bright ones. These ocellated cercariae are positively phototropic, always moving toward the light areas. They encyst on the skin of tadpoles and adult frogs, especially on the dark spots of the fore and hind legs. They attach quickly and encyst almost immediately upon making contact. In view of their positive phototropic tendencies, the question arises as to why they select the dark spots on the skin rather than the light portions. Possibly it is due to a chemotactic response. Metacercariae are attached loosely to the skin of tadpoles and become dislodged easily, whereas they adhere tenaciously to the skin of adult frogs.

Infection of adult frogs occurs normally when they ingest the sloughed stratum corneum bearing metacercariae. The larval flukes free themselves from the cysts by vigorous movements, excystment taking place in the rectum. Tadpoles become infected by eating encysted metacercariae or free cercariae. When cercariae are taken into the mouth of tadpoles, they encyst promptly and pass to the rectum, where excystment takes place. During metamorphosis of tadpoles, flukes that are not expelled migrate forward into the small intestine, appearing as far anterior as the stomach. As the intestine shortens after metamorphosis and the young frogs begin taking a protein diet, the remaining flukes return to the rectum.

Maturity of the flukes may occur as early as 27 days after infection but it usually requires 2 to 3 months. When a large number of flukes crowd the rectum, development is delayed to 3 to 4 months. Flukes remain in the frogs at least from one summer to the next and possibly longer.

EXERCISE ON LIFE CYCLE

When a source of naturally infected frogs is available for study, preparations for making the observations on the life cycle should be made in advance by obtaining a supply of frog eggs and snail eggs

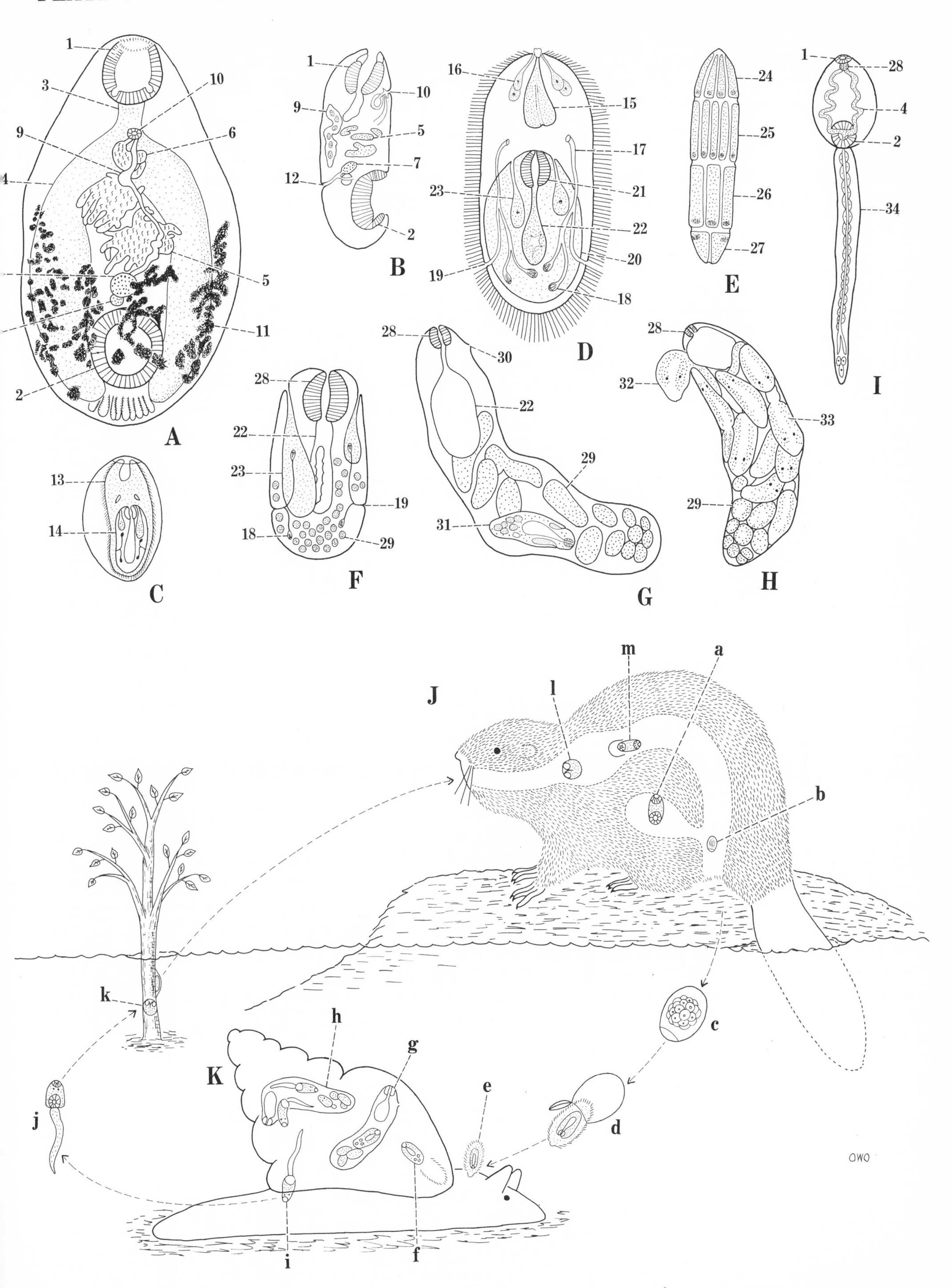
A
B
C
D
E
F
G
H
I
J
K
a
b
c
d
e
f
g
h
i
j
k
l
m
OWO

EXPLANATION OF PLATE 68 ⇨

A. Adult fluke. **B.** Miracidium. **C.** Miracidium showing epidermal plates. **D.** First generation redia. **E.** Daughter redia. **F.** Ventral view of cercaria. **G.** Dextral view of cercaria. **H.** Frog definitive host. **I.** Snail *(Helisoma trivolvus)* first intermediate host. **J.** Adult frog with encysted metacercariae on dark spots of skin. **K.** Tadpoles with metacercariae encysted on tail or eating cercariae which will encyst in mouth and be swallowed.

1, oral sucker; **2,** posterior sucker; **3,** pharyngeal pouch; **4,** pharynx; **5,** intestine; **6,** testis; **7,** vas efferens; **8,** vas deferens; **9,** common genital pore; **10,** ovary; **11,** seminal receptacle; **12,** oviduct; **13,** Laurer's canal; **14,** Mehlis' gland surrounding ootype; **15,** uterus; **16,** vitelline glands; **17,** vitelline duct; **18,** penetration glands; **19,** lateral papillae; **20,** eyespots; **21,** ganglion; **22,** germ cells; **23,** anterior row of six epidermal plates; **24,** second row of eight epidermal plates; **25,** third row of four epidermal plates; **26,** fourth row of two epidermal plates; **27,** second generation redia; **28,** developing cercariae in third generation redia; **29,** germ balls; **30,** tail; **31,** excretory tubule.

a, adult fluke in rectum; **b,** embryonated eggs laid in rectum; **c,** eggs passed in faeces; **d,** eggs in water; **e,** hatching of egg; **f,** miracidium penetrating snail host; **g,** miracidium sheds epithelial layer and transforms into mother sporocyst; **h,** mother rediae containing daughter rediae; **i,** daughter redia with cercariae; **j,** amphistome cercaria escaping from snail; **k,** cercaria free in water; **l,** cercaria attach on dark spots of skin of frogs where they encyst; **m,** cercariae attach to tadpoles; **n,** cercariae swallowed by tadpoles encyst in digestive tract; **o,** frogs become infected by eating the sloughed stratum corneum with attached metacercariae; **p,** encysted metacercaria; **q,** young flukes escape from cyst; attach to rectal wall and grow to maturity in about three months.

Figure D adapted from Herber, 1938, J. Parasit. 24:549; others from Krull and Price, 1932, Occ. Papers Mus. Zool., Univ. Mich., No. 237.

(*Helisoma trivolvus, H. antrosum, H. campanulata*). Laboratory-reared tadpoles, frogs, and snails are essential for making carefully controlled studies on the life history. The supply of experimental material may be kept in a refrigerator until needed.

Adult flukes freshly removed from the rectum of frogs and placed in a dish of water promptly shed fully embryonated eggs which hatch soon after reaching the water.

Snails 4 to 6 weeks old exposed to freshly hatched miracidia become infected with a high percentage of success. Examine these snails by making dissections and sections at intervals of 2 weeks or less to follow the development of the intramolluscan stages.

When cercariae are available, either from naturally or experimentally infected snails, place frogs in a dish of water with them. Observe encystment on the body. Place tadpoles in a dish with cercariae and note that they are ingested. Encystment occurs in the mouth almost at the moment cercariae enter it. By dissections of tadpoles, observe where excystation occurs. Likewise note what happens to parasites in tadpoles during and after metamorphosis.

Infection of adult frogs can be observed by watching for the sloughed stratum corneum that is eaten together with the encysted metacercariae that adhere tightly to it. Determine when eggs appear in the faeces.

There are other common amphistomes whose life cycles may be studied with profit when material is available. *Allassotomoides parvum* from the cloaca of snapping turtles and the urinary bladder of painted turtles and frogs develops in rediae in *Planorbis* and *Helisoma*. The cercariae encyst on vegetation, crayfish, and tadpoles. *Zygotyle lunata* of ducks develops in rediae in *Helisoma antrosum*. The cercariae encyst on objects in the water. This species is able to infect mammals in addition to ducks.

SELECTED REFERENCES

Beaver, P. C. (1929). J. Parasit. 16:13.

Herber, E. C. (1938). J. Parasit. 24:549; (1930). Ibid. 25:189.

Krull, W. H. (1933). J. Parasit. 20:109.

Krull, W. H., and H. F. Price. (1932). Occ. Papers Mus. Zool., Univ. Mich., No. 237.

Van der Woude, A. (1954). Amer. Midl. Nat. 51:172.

Willey, C. H. (1941). Zoologica 26:65.

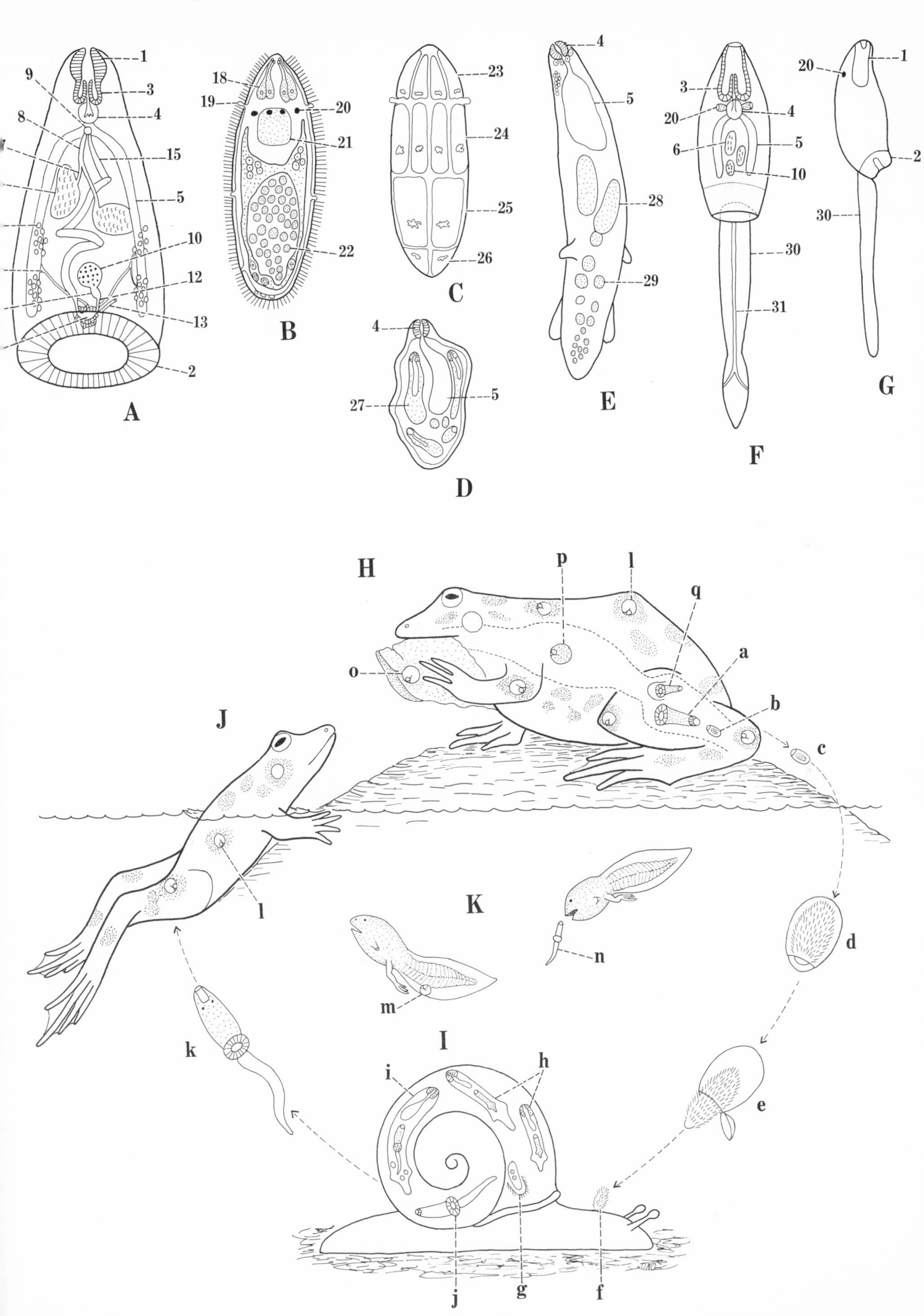
1
9
3
4
8
15
5
10
12
13
2
A
18
19
20
21
22
B
23
24
25
26
C
4
27
5
D
4
5
28
29
E
3
20
4
6
5
10
30
31
F
20
1
2
30
G
H
p
l
q
a
o
b
c
J
l
K
n
d
m
I
k
i
h
e
j
g
f

EXPLANATION OF PLATE 69 ⇨

A. Adult fluke, showing internal anatomy. **B.** Ventral surface of adult fluke, showing five rows of glands. **C.** Embryonated filamentous egg. **D.** Young mother sporocyst in mantle of snail host. **E.** Young mother sporocyst. **F.** Mother redia. **G.** Daughter redia containing cercariae. **H.** Cercaria. **I.** Encysted metacercaria. **J.** Muskrat *(Ondatra zibethica)* definitive host. **K.** Meadow vole *(Microtus pennsylvanicus)* definitive host. **L.** Snail *(Gyraulus parvus)* intermediate host.

1, oral sucker; **2,** oesophagus; **3,** intestine; **4,** testis; **5,** vas efferens; **6,** vas deferens; **7,** cirrus pouch; **8,** seminal vesicle; **9,** common genital pore; **10,** ovary; **11,** Mehlis' gland; **12,** seminal receptacle; **13,** uterus; **14,** metraterm; **15,** vitelline gland; **16,** vitelline duct; **17,** excretory pore; **18,** glands on ventral surface; **19,** embryo of egg; **20,** filament of egg; **21,** mantle of snail host; **22,** young mother sporocyst with mother rediae in mantle; **23,** mother sporocyst; **24,** mother redia; **25,** pharynx; **26,** intestine; **27,** daughter redia; **28,** germ balls; **29,** developing cercaria; **30,** eyespot; **31,** excretory bladder; **32,** excretory tubules; **33,** tail; **34,** metacercarial cyst; **35,** metacercaria.

a, adult fluke in caecum; **b,** embryonated filamentous eggs laid in caecum; **c,** eggs carried into intestine; **d,** eggs passed in faeces; **e,** embryonated egg in water; **f,** eggs eaten by snail *(Gyraulus parvus)* intermediate host; **g,** eggs hatch in intestine; **h,** miracidium passes through wall of intestine; **i,** mother sporocyst containing mother rediae; **j,** mother redia containing daughter rediae; **k,** daughter redia containing cercariae; **l,** cercaria escaping from snail; **m,** cercaria free in water; **n,** metacercaria attached to submerged vegetation; **o,** definitive host becomes infected by swallowing metacercariae on food; **p,** metacercaria in stomach; **q,** excystation of metacercaria; **r,** young fluke enters caecum, reaching maturity in 16 days.

Adapted from Herber, 1942, J. Parasit. 28:179.

SUPERFAMILY NOTOCOTYLOIDEA

This superfamily consists of monostome flukes in fish, reptiles, birds, and mammals. The oral sucker is well developed and located at the anterior end of the body. There is no pharynx and the caeca terminate near the posterior extremity of the body. The testes and ovary are near the caudal end of the body. Eggs are small and each end bears a long polar filament. The cercariae are monostomate, ocellated, and have very long tails.

FAMILY NOTOCOTYLIDAE

Notocotylidae are small flukes in the gut and caeca of birds and mammals. The cirrus pouch is well developed. The shell gland complex is anterior to the ovary. Vitelline follicles are lateral to the caeca, and anterior, lateral, or dorsal to the testes. The uterus is coiled transversely between the caeca and is filled with eggs. The excretory bladder is short, with two long arms that unite anteriorly.

Quinqueserialis quinqueserialis Barker and Laughlin, 1911 (Plate 69)

This monostome is a parasite of the caecum of muskrats (*Ondatra zibethica*), meadow voles (*Microtus pennsylvanicus*), and jumping mice (*Zapus hudsonius*) in the United States and Canada.

DESCRIPTION. Fully grown flukes are oval in shape and 2.9 mm long by 0.93 mm wide. The ventral surface bears five longitudinal rows of ventrals glands with 14 to 16 in the middle row and 16 to 19 in the others. The intestinal caeca arise near the oral sucker and extend to near the posterior end of the body as irregular tubes. The two lobed testes lie at the same level outside the caeca near their ends, and the lobed ovary is located intercaecally between them. The uterus appears as a series of close transverse loops between the ootype and the base of the long cirrus pouch which equals about one-third the length of the body. There are 12 to 17 groups of extracaecal vitelline follicles extending from the base of the cirrus pouch to the anterior margin of the testes.

LIFE CYCLE. Adult worms in the caeca lay their embryonated filamentous eggs which are mingled with the caecal contents and gradually passed from the body in the faeces. They do not hatch until eaten by the snail *Gyraulus parvus*. The miracidia penetrate the gut wall of the snail host, shed the cilia, and transform into saclike mother sporocysts containing four mother rediae in the tissue surrounding the intestine. They force their way through the body wall of the mother sporocyst and migrate to the liver, entering it 4 days later, or 19 days after infection. Daughter rediae develop rapidly and are free in the liver by the 20th day after infection. Within 3 days,.23 following infection, partially developed cercariae are present in the daughter rediae. They emerge through the birth pore in an undeveloped

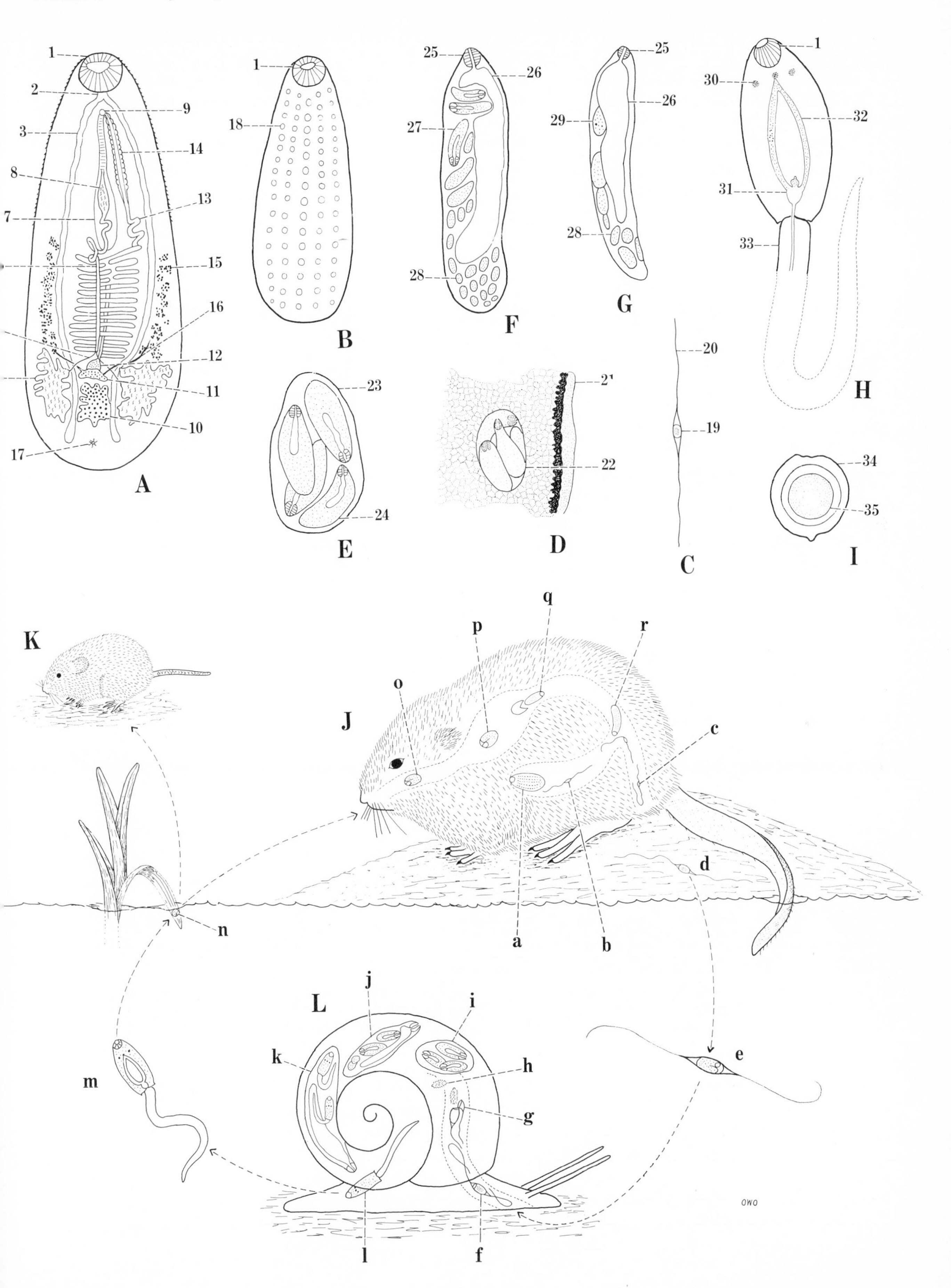
1
2
3
8
7
9
14
13
15
16
12
11
10
17
A
1
18
B
25
26
27
28
F
25
26
29
28
G
1
30
32
31
33
H
23
24
E
21
22
D
20
19
C
34
35
I
K
J
o
p
q
r
c
a
b
d
n
L
j
i
k
h
g
l
f
m
e
OWO

stage, requiring 3 days in the liver to reach maturity, thus making a total of 26 days from infection of the snails to the shedding of mature cercariae. Emergence from the snails is periodic, being between 9 and 11 o'clock in the forenoons. The tail of the cercaria is about twice the length of the body and there are three eyespots in a transverse row. When the cercariae strike an object, they attach to it and encystment is completed in 3 to 5 minutes, at which time they are infective.

Muskrats and voles feeding on vegetation in the water or on that which has emerged from it swallow the encysted flukes. Metacercariae released from the cysts go to the caecum and mature in 16 days.

Notocotylus stagnicolae Herber, 1942 is closely related to *Q. quinqueserialis* and has a life cycle very similar to it. The snail intermediate host is *Stagnicola emarginata.* They are natural parasites of willets, but chickens, ducks, and mergansers may be infected experimentally. The mother sporocyst contains but one redia in contrast to four in *Q. quinqueserialis. Notocotylus urbanensis* is a parasite of muskrats and ducks whose cercariae develop in *Stagnicola emarginata* and *Physa parkeri. Nudacotyle novicia* Barker, 1961, is a parasite of meadow voles and muskrats. *Cercaria marilli* occurring in rediae in the snail *Pomatiopsis lapidaria* forms metacercaria that develop into *N. novicia* when fed to voles and muskrats.

EXERCISE ON LIFE CYCLE

Wherever muskrat carcasses are available during the trapping season, a good supply of *Q. quinqueserialis* will be assured. Filamentous eggs teased from the flukes, which will be dead if obtained from frozen carcasses, will contain fully developed and living miracidia. They are infective to *Gyraulus parvus* when eaten by them. Feed eggs to a large number of snails, preferably laboratory-reared ones, and dissect and section them at intervals of 1 day from the time of feeding to obtain the larval stages. Examine the mantle, the tissues surrounding the intestine, and the digestive gland (liver) for the various stages. Note how rapidly the cercariae encyst when freed from the snails, a function of the numerous cystogenous glands in the body wall. Feed metacercariae to baby chicks, ducklings, and voles to obtain adult flukes.

The life cycle may begin with cercariae from naturally infected snails instead of eggs which may not be available at a suitable time.

SELECTED REFERENCES

Ameel, D. J. (1944). J. Parasit. 30:257.

Herber, E. C. (1940). J. Parasit. 26 (Suppl.):35; (1942). Ibid. 28:179.

Luttermoser, G. Q. (1935). J. Parasit. 21:456.

SUPERORDER EPITHELIOCYSTIDA

In this group of trematodes, the primitive excretory bladder of the cercariae is first surrounded by and later replaced by a layer of mesodermal cells, forming a thick epithelial wall. Caudal excretory vessels may be present or absent. The cercariae are typically distomate in form.

ORDER PLAGIORCHIIDA

The cercariae lack the caudal excretory vessels in all stages of development but a stylet may or may not be present. The adults are parasites of all classes of vertebrates.

Suborder Plagiorchiata

The cercariae are pharyngeate and have a horizontal stylet. They encyst in invertebrates, chiefly arthropods.

SUPERFAMILY PLAGIORCHIOIDEA

The principal characteristic of this superfamily is the union of the main collecting canals of the excretory system to the anterior extremity, or near it, of the arms of the Y-shaped excretory bladder.

FAMILY DICROCOELIIDAE

The Dicrocoeliidae are parasites of the liver, gall bladder, pancreas, and intestine of amphibians, reptiles, birds, and mammals. The best known member of the family is the lancet fluke in the bile ducts of sheep.

The members of the family are medium-sized flukes with the oral sucker subterminal and the acetabulum in the anterior half of the body. A pharynx, short oesophagus, and simple caeca of variable length are present. Testes are arranged variously but usually in the hind part of the body; the ovary is post-testicular.

Dicrocoelium dendriticum (Rudolphi, 1819) (Plate 70)

This species occurs in the bile ducts of sheep, goats, cattle, pigs, deer, elk, rabbits, and marmots. It is common in Europe and Asia, and limited in distribution in North America and Australasia.

DESCRIPTION. Grown flukes range from 6 to 10 mm long by 1.5 to 2.5 mm wide. The body is elongate with the widest part near the middle. The oral sucker is slightly smaller than the ventral and both are in the anterior third of the body. The large testes lie one behind the other immediately posterior to the ventral sucker. The small ovary is immediately behind the posterior testis. Loops of the uterus fill that part of the body behind the ovary. The vitellaria occupy the middle third of the lateral part of the body. The operculate eggs, which are embryonated when laid, measure 36 to 45 μ long by 22 to 30 μ wide.

LIFE CYCLE. Eggs laid in the bile ducts pass through the common bile duct into the intestine and are voided with the faeces. Hatching does not occur until they are eaten by land snails. In the United States, *Cionella lubrica* is the first intermediate host. Since a number of different species of terrestrial snails other than *C. lubrica* are known to serve as intermediate hosts of this fluke in Europe, it might be expected that several species may act in this capacity in North America. As yet none has been found, although some have been exposed to experimental infection with negative results.

Upon hatching, the miracidia migrate through the gut wall to the digestive gland where they transform into mother sporocysts. These give rise to many daughter sporocysts with a birth pore that produce stylet-bearing cercariae. Development of the cercariae is slow, requiring somewhere around 3 months. Upon reaching maturity, they migrate from the digestive gland into the respiratory chamber. As the cercariae accumulate in the respiratory chamber, the snails somehow are stimulated to secrete sufficient mucus to surround the cercariae in it. When a drop in temperature occurs, the mucus together with the enclosed cercariae is expelled explosively through the respiratory pore. This is the slimeball in which the cercariae find an aquatic environment to bridge the gap between the terrestrial snail and the second invertebrate intermediate host. The outer surface of the slime mass dries, becoming a tough membrane that retards loss of water from within. Only a very few slimeballs are produced by each snail during its life but they may contain up to nearly 500 cercariae each. Slimeballs and egg masses of the snails have a remarkable resemblance. Under conditions of too much moisture, the slimeballs soon liquefy, leaving the cercariae to die.

Ants (*Formica fusca*) foraging over leaves and sticks where the snails live find the slimeballs and carry them to their nests. Whether the adult ants eat the slimeballs and cercariae or feed them to larval ants, or both, is unknown. Up to 35 per cent of the adult ants in endemic areas are naturally infected with metacercariae. When eaten by ants, the cercariae migrate through the gut wall and encyst in the gaster. More than 100 encysted metacercariae may occur in a single ant!

Infection of vertebrate hosts occurs when infected ants are swallowed with the forage. The metacercariae are released from the cysts in the duodenum by the action of the pancreatic juice. Being attracted by the bile, the very active young flukes enter the common bile duct and migrate to the liver, reaching it within an hour after the metacercariae are swallowed. Flukes are sexually mature in 6 to 7 weeks in lambs, and eggs appear in the faeces about 4 weeks later.

In view of the high incidence of natural infection of ants, large numbers of flukes may be expected in the definitive hosts. Up to 7,000 have been found in the gall bladder of a single sheep and 50,000 in a liver. All the sheep in endemic areas may be infected. Damage to the liver is extensive. Rabbits and marmots, which are definitive hosts, serve to intensify the infection in local areas. Deer in their wider

EXPLANATION OF PLATE 70 ▷

A. Adult trematode. **B.** Sporocyst containing cercariae. **C.** Dorsal view of cercariae showing mucous glands. **D.** Ventral view of cercaria showing developing organs. **E.** Excysted metacercaria. **F.** Empty egg with operculum open. **G.** Definitive hosts (sheep, cattle, deer, cottontail rabbits, marmots). **H.** Snail *(Cionella lubrica)* first intermediate host. **I.** Ant *(Formica fusca)* second intermediate host.

1, oral sucker; **2,** ventral sucker; **3,** pharynx; **4,** oesophagus; **5,** intestine; **6,** testis; **7,** cirrus pouch; **8,** common genital pore; **9,** ovary; **10,** uterus; **11,** vitelline gland; **12,** Mehlis' gland; **13,** Laurer's canal; **14,** excretory bladder; **15,** birth pore; **16,** cercaria; **17,** germ ball; **18,** spine; **19,** mucous glands; **20,** tail; **21,** openings of mucous glands; **22,** glands; **23,** genital primordium; **24,** operculum.

a, adult fluke in hypertrophied bile duct; **b,** embryonated eggs laid in bile ducts pass through common bile duct into intestine; **c,** eggs mixed with faeces voided from body; **d,** embryonated eggs on soil; **e,** eggs hatch in intestine of snail; **f,** miracidium passes through intestinal wall; **g,** mother sporocyst with developing daughter sporocyst; **h,** daughter sporocyst with cercariae and germ balls; **i,** cercaria escaping from snail; **j,** slimeball containing cercariae; **k,** ants eating slimeballs swallow cercariae; **l,** cercariae migrate through intestinal wall into haemocoel; **m,** metacercaria encysted in gaster; **n,** definitive host becomes infected upon swallowing infected ant; **o,** upon digestion of ants, metacercariae are released; **p,** metacercaria free in duodenum; **q,** through action of the pancreatic juice, young fluke escapes from cyst and enters common bile duct; **r,** young fluke in bile duct matures in 11 to 12 weeks after entering liver.

Figures A, B, D adapted from Neuhaus, 1938, Z. Parasitenk. 10:476; C, from Neuhaus, 1936, Z. Parasitenk. 8:431; E, from Krull and Mapes, 1953, Cornell Vet. 43:389; F, from Mapes, 1951, Cornell Vet. 41:382.

---

movements disseminate it. Shipment of infected sheep to other areas gives the flukes an opportunity to leap great distances and become established because of the universality of the snail and ant intermediate hosts.

Life cycles of other dicrocoeliids, where known, are similar to that of *D. dendriticum* in principle.

A species of *Lyperosomum* from the liver of grackles and meadow larks develops in the land snails *Polygyra texasiana* and *Practicollela berlandierana* which produce slimeballs. The second intermediate host is unknown (Denton). *Lyperosomum monenteron* is a common parasite in the liver of robins. Its life cycle is unknown.

Brachylecithum americanum, a parasite of boattail and purple grackles, meadow larks, and blue jays, develops in sporocysts in *Polygyra texasiana* and *Practicollela berlandierana* in 64 days and daughter sporocysts are present between the 64th and 70th days. Slimeballs containing up to 300 cercariae are expelled from the respiratory pore. Larval chrysomelid beetles serve as the second intermediate host (Denton).

Conspicuum icteridorum from the gall bladder of purple grackles develops sporocysts in the land snail *Zonitoides arboreus.* Isopods (*Oniscus asellus* and *Armadillidium quadrifons*) serve as the second intermediate host. Metacercariae fed to grackles reach the gall bladder in 16 hours and mature in 12 weeks (Patten). *C. macrorchis* of the eastern crow develops in the snail *Bulimulus alternatus mariae,* according to Denton and Byrd. The remainder of the cycle is unknown.

Eurytrema procyonis occurs in the pancreas of raccoons. Its ova produce mother sporocysts in the common garden snail *Mesodon thyroides* in 70 days and daughter sporocysts in 141 days. Slimeballs expelled by the snails accumulate in grapelike clusters, adhering to the mollusk as it crawls about (Denton).

EXERCISE ON LIFE CYCLE

While *Dicrocoelium dendriticum* is too limited in its distribution at this time to be useful for life history studies, the dicrocoeliid trematodes of birds and raccoons offer excellent opportunities.

A good starting point is the examination of land snails for natural infection. Stylet-bearing cercariae in them are a clue that the flukes are dicrocoeliids. The definitive hosts should be sought among the vertebrates, particularly icterids, in the same areas with the snails.

Eggs should be teased from the flukes found in the vertebrate hosts and fed to hungry snails of the species in which natural infections were found. Dissections of experimentally infected snails should be made at short intervals to recover the different generations of sporocysts.

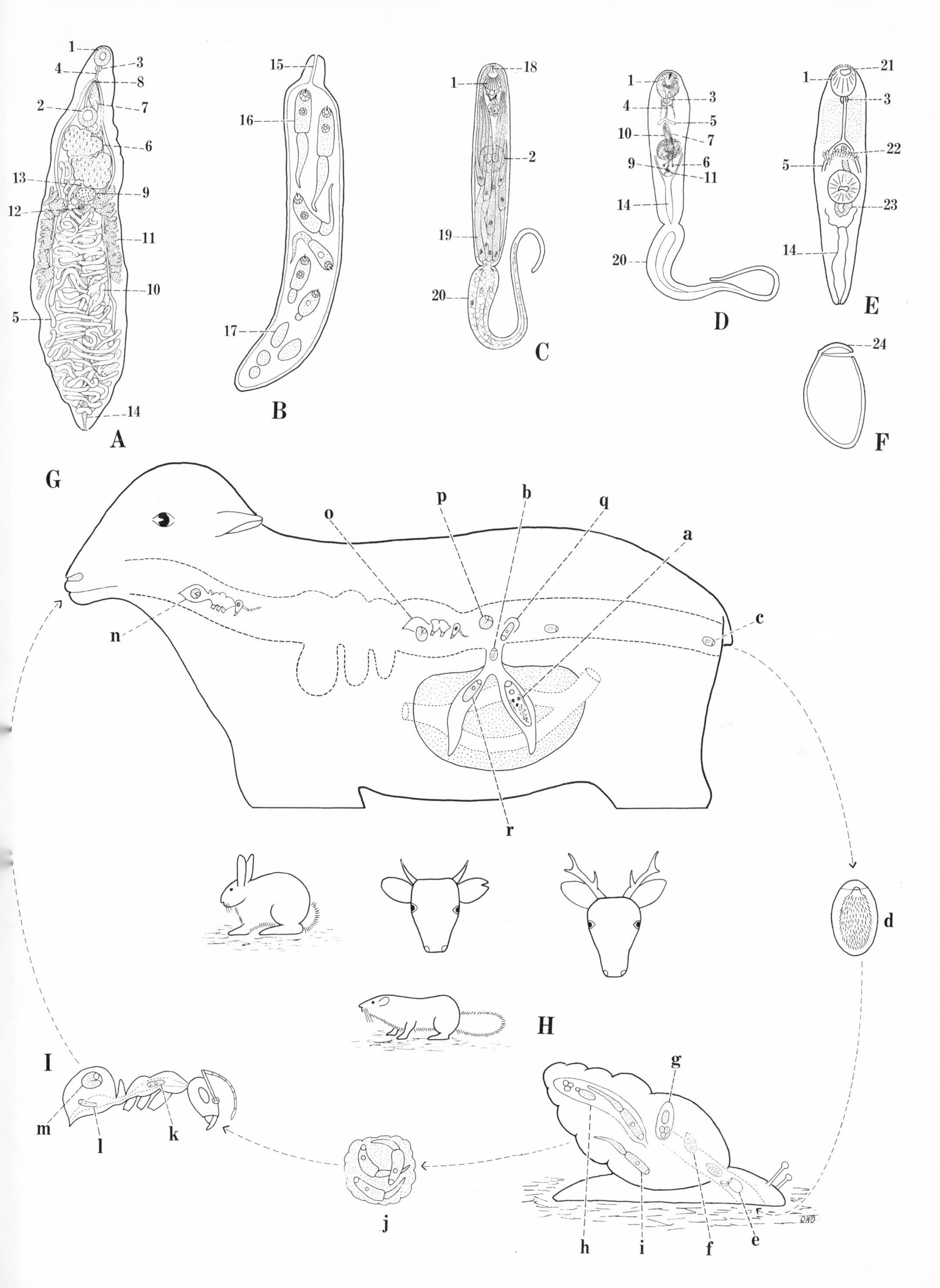
1
3
4
8
2
7
6
13
9
12
11
10
5
14
A
15
16
17
B
18
1
2
19
20
C
1
3
4
5
10
7
9
6
11
14
20
D
1
21
3
22
5
23
14
E
24
F
G
o
p
b
q
a
n
c
r
d
H
I
m
l
k
j
g
h
i
f
e

EXPLANATION OF PLATE 71 ▷

A. Adult fluke from mouse (experimental infection). **B.** Mother sporocyst attached to intestine of snail host. **C.** Daughter sporocyst. **D.** Cercaria. **E.** Encysted metacercaria. **F.** Herring gull *(Larus argentatus)* definitive host. **G.** Robin *(Turdus migratorius)* definitive host. **H.** Spotted sandpiper *(Actitis macularia)* definitive host. **I.** Nighthawk *(Chordeiles minor)* definitive host. **J.** Snail *(Lymnaea emarginata)* first intermediate host. **K.** Chironomidae larva second intermediate host. **L.** Adult Chironomidae in flight.

1, oral sucker; **2,** ventral sucker; **3,** pharynx; **4,** testis; **5,** cirrus pouch; **6,** seminal vesicle; **7,** ovary; **8,** Mehlis' gland; **9,** descending limb of uterus; **10,** ascending limb of uterus; **11,** metraterm; **12,** common genital pore; **13,** intestine of snail; **14,** mother sporocyst; **15,** cercaria; **16,** stylet; **17,** penetration glands; **18,** thick-walled, Y-shaped excretory bladder; **19,** tail; **20,** metacercarial cyst.

a, adult worm in small intestine of definitive host; **b,** partially embryonated egg passed in faeces; **c,** egg completes embryonation in water; **d,** mother sporocyst attached to intestine (a suggestion that the eggs hatch in the intestine of the snail, but this has not been observed); **e,** daughter sporocyst containing cercariae; **f,** daughter sporocyst containing encysted metacercariae; **g,** cercaria free in water; **h,** cercaria penetrating chironomid larva; **i,** metacercaria in chironomid larva; **j,** definitive hosts become infected by eating snails or chironomids harboring metacercariae; **k,** encysted metacercaria freed from snail host; **l,** metacercaria escapes from cyst, attaches to intestinal wall and matures in 7 to 9 days.

Figures A, C, D, E adapted from McMullen, 1937, J. Parasit. 23:235; B, from Cort and Olivier, 1943, J. Parasit. 29:91.

When slimeballs are produced by the snails, they should be fed to arthropods suspected of serving as intermediate hosts due to their prevalence in the area with the naturally infected snails. Exposed arthropods should be dissected to determine the course of development in them.

Observe the habits and development of the snails. Procedures for rearing them are given in detail by Krull and in the papers on *D. dendriticum* by Krull and Mapes.

SELECTED REFERENCES

Denton, J. F. (1941). J. Parasit. (Suppl.) 27:13; (1944). Ibid. 30:277; (1945). Ibid. 31:131.

Hohorst, W. (1962). Z. Parasitenk. 22:105.

Krull, W. H. (1937). Culture Methods for Invertebrate Animals. Comstock Publishing Co., Ithaca, p. 526; (1956). Cornell Vet. 45:511; (1958). Ibid. 48:17.

Krull, W. H., and C. R. Mapes. (1952). Cornell Vet. 42:253, 277, 339, 464, 603; (1953). Ibid. 43:199, 389.

Mapes, C. R., and W. H. Krull. (1951). Cornell Vet. 41:382, 433.

Patten, J. A. (1952). J. Parasit. 38:165.

FAMILY PLAGIORCHIIDAE

The members of this family of flukes are parasites of all classes of vertebrates. They are variable in shape, size, and the location and arrangement of the reproductive organs. The cuticle is usually spined. Constant characters in them are 1) the genital pore is between the suckers, 2) the ovary is pretesticular, and 3) the descending and ascending limbs of the uterus pass between the testes. A Y-shaped excretory bladder is typical.

Plagiorchis muris Tanabe, 1922 (Plate 71)

This parasite occurs in the small intestine of rats, dogs, herring gulls, robins, sandpipers, and night hawks over a wide geographic range.

DESCRIPTION. Adult worms average 2.67 mm long by 0.52 mm wide. The caeca extend to the posterior extremity of the body. A long C-shaped cirrus pouch extends posteriorly from the genital pore around the ventral sucker and caudad to the ovary. The testes are obliquely arranged in the third quarter of the body. The ovary is between the ventral sucker and anterior testis, lying to the right of midventral line.

The uterus is long, sinuous, and extends to the posterior extremity of the body with both the descending and ascending limbs passing between the testes. It terminates as a metraterm. The excretory bladder is Y-shaped. Eggs measure 38 μ long by 19 μ wide.

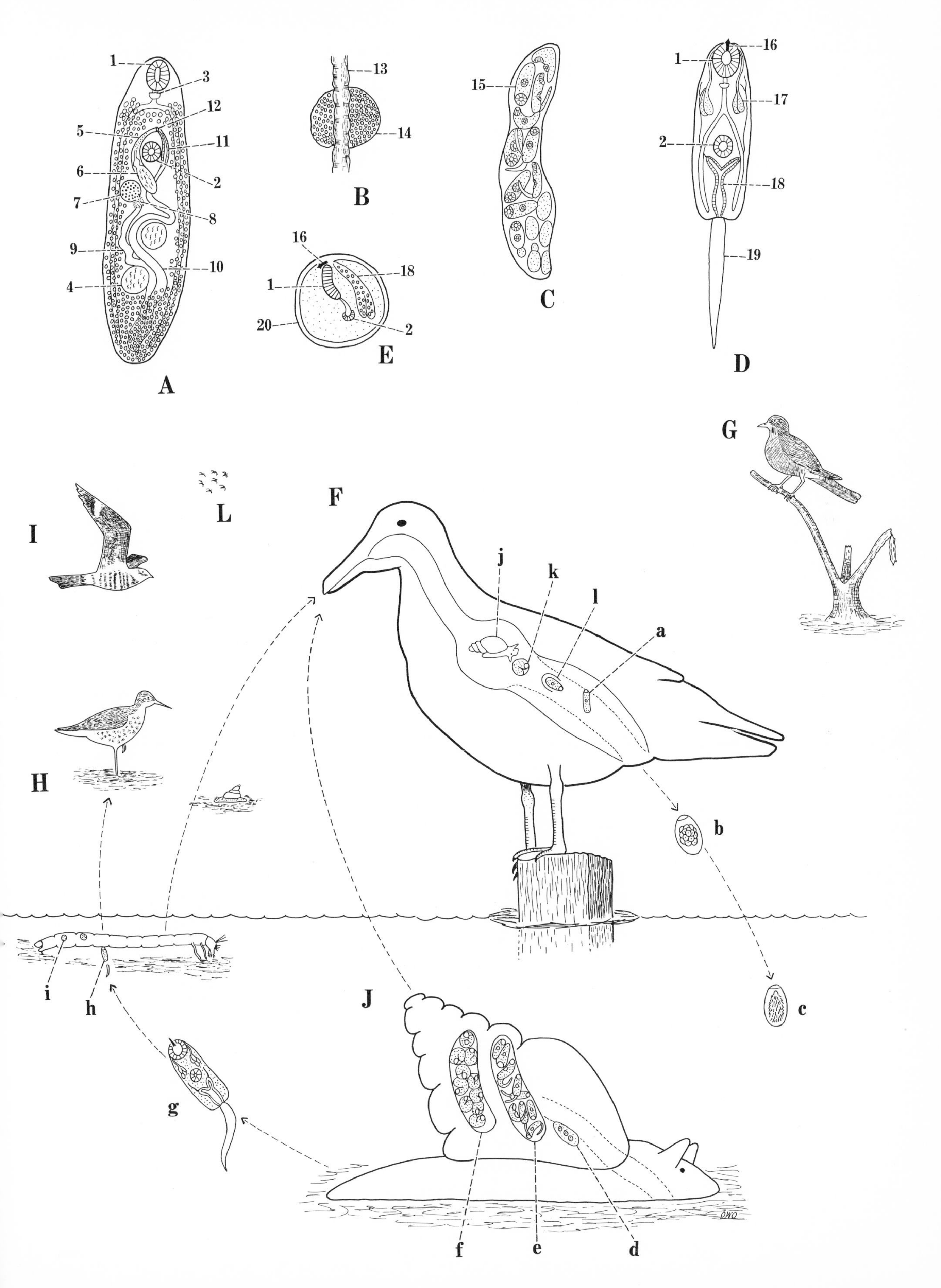
1
3
12
5
11
6
2
7
8
9
10
4
A
13
14
B
16
18
1
20
2
E
15
C
16
1
17
2
18
19
D
G
L
F
I
j
k
l
a
H
b
i
h
J
c
g
f
e
d

LIFE CYCLE. Eggs in the morula stage are laid in the intestine and voided with the faeces. Development in water requires about 24 days. No information is available on hatching of the eggs and penetration of the miracidia into the snail intermediate host. Mother sporocysts being attached to the intestine of the snails suggests that hatching may occur after the eggs are eaten. Daughter sporocysts escape from the mother sporocysts and migrate to the liver.

Cercariae, upon reaching maturity in the daughter sporocyst, bear a well-developed stylet in the anterior margin of the oral sucker and have a thick-walled, Y-shaped excretory bladder. In the process of development, they follow one of two courses. Some of them appear to be precocious and encyst within the mother sporocyst where they develop. Others escape and leave the snail to penetrate chironomid larvae (also fresh-water shrimp in Japan) and encyst. One week after encystment the metacercariae are infective to a considerable number of avian and mammalian hosts, including humans, mice, and rats.

Infection occurs when encysted metacercariae in chironomids, either larval or adult forms, or in snails, are ingested by susceptible hosts. When the metacercariae are released from the snail or insect intermediary in the intestine of the definitive host, development to maturity is completed in 7 to 9 days. Infections persist about 1 month.

The life cycles of several other species of *Plagiorchis* have been worked in part but not completely. There appear to be three types of life cycles among the few known. They are 1) encystment of the cercariae in larval insects and small crustacea, 2) encystment directly of precocious cercariae within the sporocyst in which they developed, and 3) encystment in tadpoles in which the metacercariae are progenetic, developing fertile eggs within 30 days.

Cercariae encysting in insect larvae and crustacea include *P. micracanthus* from *Lymnaea emarginata*, according to McMullen, *P. jaenschi* from *Limnaea lessoni* by Johnston and Angel, *P. maculosus* from *Radix auricularia* reported by Strenzski, *P. megalorchis* from *Limnaea pereger* worked by Rees, *P. arcuatus* from *Bithynia tentaculata* confirmed by Paskaskaya, and *P. parorchis* from *Lymnaea stagnalis* found by Macy.

Precocious cercariae from *Lymnaea emarginata* that encyst in the daughter sporocysts are *P. muris* and *P. proximus*, according to McMullen.

Cercariae developing in *Planorbis planorbis* encyst in tadpoles and develop into progenetic metacercariae that produce eggs in the cysts in 30 days (Buttner).

EXERCISE ON LIFE CYCLE

Naturally infected *Lymnaea emarginata* over wide areas of this country produce xiphidiocercariae of one or more of several species of *Plagiorchis*. Common species being *P. muris* of mice, *P. macracanthus* of bats, and *P. proximus* of muskrats and voles.

When infected lymnaeid snails shedding xiphidiocercariae are found, the cercariae should be placed in dishes with chironomid, caddis fly, and mosquito larvae and *Daphnia* to afford them an opportunity to encyst. Note the development of the metacercariae in the insect or crustacean. Examine the infected snails to determine whether metacercariae are present in the daughter sporocyst. Only *P. muris* and *P. proximus* are known to encyst in the sporocysts.

Since species of *Plagiorchis* are capable of developing in a rather wide range of hosts, mice, rats, and baby chicks are likely to serve as definitive hosts for experimental infection by feeding metacercariae to them. Observe the droppings of experimentally infected hosts for eggs, noting the length of the prepatent period.

Recover eggs from the faeces and incubate them. Determine whether they hatch in water and penetrate snails or hatch only when eaten by snails. This point has not been determined for the American species.

When the adult worms have been recovered from the experimental hosts, they should be fixed, stained, and identified.

SELECTED REFERENCES

Buttner, A. (1951). Ann. Parasit. Hum. Comp. 26:19.

Cort, W. W., and L. Olivier. (1941). J. Parasit. Suppl. 27:6; (1943) Ibid. 29:81.

Cort, W. W., and D. J. Ameel. (1944). J. Parasit. 30:37.

Johnston, T. H., and L. M. Angel. (1951). Trans. Roy. Soc. S. Australia. 74:49.

Macy, R. W. (1956). J. Parasit. 42(4/2):28.

McMullen, D. B. (1937). J. Parasit. 23:235.

Okabe, K. and H. Shibue. (1952). Jap. J. Med. Sci. Biol. 5:257.

Paskalskaya, M. Y. (1954). Dokl. Akad. Nauk SSSR 97:561; (1955). Veterinariia 32:37.

Strenzke, K. (1952). Z. Parasitenk. 15:369.

Rees, G. (1952). Parasitology 42:92.

Haematoloechus medioplexus Stafford, 1902 (Plate 72)

H. medioplexus is one of the common lung flukes of adult *Rana pipiens* and *Bufo americanus* in North America. Many species of lung flukes occur in different species of frogs and toads in this and other countries.

DESCRIPTION. They are flattened worms that are up to 8 mm long and 1.2 mm wide. The acetabulum is near the junction of the first and second thirds of the body and about one-fourth to one-fifth the size of the oral sucker. The cuticle is densely spined. The gonads occupy a little more than the middle third of the body. The testes are large oval bodies which are much bigger than the elongate ovary. A large seminal receptacle partially overlaps the smaller ovary from the dorsal side. The limbs of the uterus pass between the testes and fill the posttesticular part of the body. A common genital pore is located at the bifurcation of the caeca. The vitellaria are arranged in groups which extend from about one-half the distance between the anterior tip of the body and ovary to behind the posterior testis. The dark brown eggs measure 22 to 29 μ long by 13 to 17 μ wide. For figures and descriptions of the different species of lung flukes of North American frogs see Cort.

LIFE CYCLE. Adult flukes in the cavity of the lungs deposit fully embryonated eggs. They are carried from the lungs up the bronchioles and through the glottis by ciliary action of the lung and bronchiole cells. Upon passing through the glottis, they are swallowed and eventually voided with the faeces, sinking to the bottom of the pond. Although fully embryonated, hatching does not occur until they are swallowed by the snail *Planorbula armigera*. In lakes where the biotic and physical conditions are favorable for the snail hosts, a large percentage of them are infected with these flukes. After a short time in the stomach, the eggs pass to the intestine and hatch in 15 to 20 minutes. Egg shells and some miracidia are passed in the faeces, but these miracidia soon die. Eggs hatch in the intestine of other species of snails, but the miracidia do not develop in them. This indicates that nonspecific digestive enzymes are capable of causing the eggs to hatch. Miracidia in *Planorbula armigera* migrate through the intestinal wall.

Mother sporocysts have not been observed. Those in the hepatic gland probably are daughter sporocysts. They mature and produce cercariae in 65 days. Up to 300 cercariae may be shed per night by a single heavily infected snail. In such heavily infected snails, the liver appears to be completely destroyed. Cercariae recently escaped from the snails swim actively at summer temperatures but they are sluggish and settle to the bottom in cold water. They survive up to 30 hours.

Naiads of the dragon fly *Sympetrum obtrusum* are the second intermediate host. They respire by drawing water into and expelling it from the branchial basket by way of the anus. Cercariae swimming in the vicinity of the anus of naiads on warm days are swept into the branchial basket by the inhalent currents. Naiads show signs of great annoyance from the presence of the cercariae and attempt to expel them. Upon coming in contact with the wall and gills of the branchial basket, they quickly pass through the chitin into the tissue of the lamellae or wall of the respiratory organ and encyst in thin transparent cysts. Metacercariae are found nowhere else. Naturally only naiads can become infected, but not before the second stage. The metacercariae are infective in 6 days after encystment and the maximum size is reached in 14 to 20 days. When the naiads metamorphose to adults, the metacercariae remain in the remnant of the branchial basket in the posterior tip of the abdomen. Adults may harbor more than 200 metacercariae from natural exposure.

Parasitism of frogs occurs through eating infected naiadal and adult dragon flies. Soft tenerals

EXPLANATION OF PLATE 72

A. Dorsal view of adult fluke. **B.** Ventral view of anterior end of adult. **C.** Embryonated egg. **D.** Miracidium showing epidermal plates. **E.** Miracidium showing anterior and posterior plates together with internal anatomy. **F.** Mature daughter sporocyst. **G.** Cercaria. **H.** Lateral view of tail of cercaria, showing fin-like membrane. **I.** Encysted metacercaria. **J.** Encysted metacercaria in gill lamella of dragon fly *(Sympetrum* sp.). **K.** Excysted metacercaria. **L.** Frog definitive host *(Rana pipiens).* **M.** Snail intermediate host *(Planorbula armigera).* **N.** Naiad of dragon fly *(Sympetrum* sp.). **O.** Teneral of *Sympetrum* sp.

1, oral sucker; **2**, ventral sucker; **3**, pharynx; **4**, intestinal crura; **5**, testis; **6**, cirrus pouch; **7**, ovary; **8**, seminal receptacle; **9**, descending limb of uterus; **10**, ascending limb of uterus; **11**, vitelline glands; **12**, common collecting ducts of vitelline glands; **13**, common genital pore; **14**, posterior epidermal plates of miracidium; **15**, anterior epidermal plates; **16**, penetration gland; **17**, flame cell; **18**, germ cell; **19**, cercaria; **20**, developing cercariae; **21**, germ balls; **22**, stylet; **23**, penetration gland; **24**, excretory bladder; **25**, common collecting tubule; **26**, anterior collecting tubule; **27**, tail; **28**, fin of tail; **29**, cyst of metacercaria; **30**, metacercaria; **31**, gill lamella; **32**, trachea; **33**, tracheoles of gill.

a, adult worm in lung; **b**, egg deposited in lung is carried up bronchi into pharynx and then swallowed; **c**, embryonated egg passing through intestine to appear in faeces; **d**, embryonated egg in water; **e**, unhatched eggs swallowed by snail intermediate host, *Planorbula armigera;* **f**, eggs hatch in intestine of snail; **g**, miracidium passing through wall of intestine; **h**, mother sporocyst; **i**, mature daughter sporocyst with germ balls, and cercariae in various stages of development; **j**, cercaria that has escaped from sporocyst; **k**, cercaria free in water; **l**, cercaria swept into gill basket of naiad of dragon fly through respiratory current attaches to gill lamella, drops the tail, penetrates, and encysts; **m**, metacercaria in gill lamella; **n**, metacercaria retained through metamorphosis of naiad to teneral; **o**, dragon fly naiads or adults digested in stomach of frog, releasing metacercariae; **p**, metacercaria released from cyst by action of digestive juices; **q**, metacercaria migrates up oesophagus and enters bronchi, finally arriving in the lungs and developing to maturity in 37 days.

Figures A, B adapted from deFreitas and Lent, 1939, Livro de Homenagem, p. 246; C, F, from Krull, 1930, J. Parasit. 16:207; D, E, G, H, J, K, from Krull, 1931, Trans. Amer. Micr. Soc. 50:215; I, constructed from Krull, 1930, J. Parasit. 16:207 and 1931, Trans. Amer. Micr. Soc. 50:215.

---

resting on stems of vegetation are easily captured and eaten by the frogs. Upon being released from the dragon flies and cysts (metacercariae excyst in artificial gastric juice in 45 seconds), the young flukes migrate forward through the oesophagus, pass through the glottis, and enter the lungs by way of the bronchi. They appear to move against the current created by the ciliated epithelium of the bronchi. The flukes mature in 37 days during the summer. They remain in the frogs up to 15 months. After that, they are discarded and new ones take their place. Up to 75 flukes occur in individual naturally infected frogs.

The life cycles of several other species of *Haematoloechus* have been studied. *H. parviplexus* occurs in the green frog (*Rana clamitans*) and develops in *Gyraulus parvus* and *Sympetrum rubicundum* and *S. obtrusum*. *H. longiplexus* of bullfrogs (*Rana catesbiana*) occurs as metacercariae in damsel flies (*Lestes vigilax*). The snail host is not known. *H. complexus* from the green frog develops in *Pseudosuccinea columella* and dragon flies (*Tetragoneuria cynosura*), and damsel flies (*Chromagrion conditum, Enallagma divagans, Lestes vigilax, Argis* sp.)

EXERCISE ON LIFE CYCLE

In habitats where frogs, Odonata, and snails are present, species of *Haematoloechus* are likely to occur.

Dissection of frogs from the area will show whether the flukes are present; usually a high percentage of them are infected. Flukes placed in water shed embryonated eggs which may be fed to snails. Observe the faeces expelled by snails shortly after eating eggs and note the empty shells and miracidia entangled in them. For careful experimental studies, laboratory-reared snails should be used. Dissect naturally and experimentally infected snails for a study of the sequence of development of sporocysts.

Cercariae shed by *Planorbula armigera, Gyraulus parvus,* or *Pseudosuccinea columella* that have the

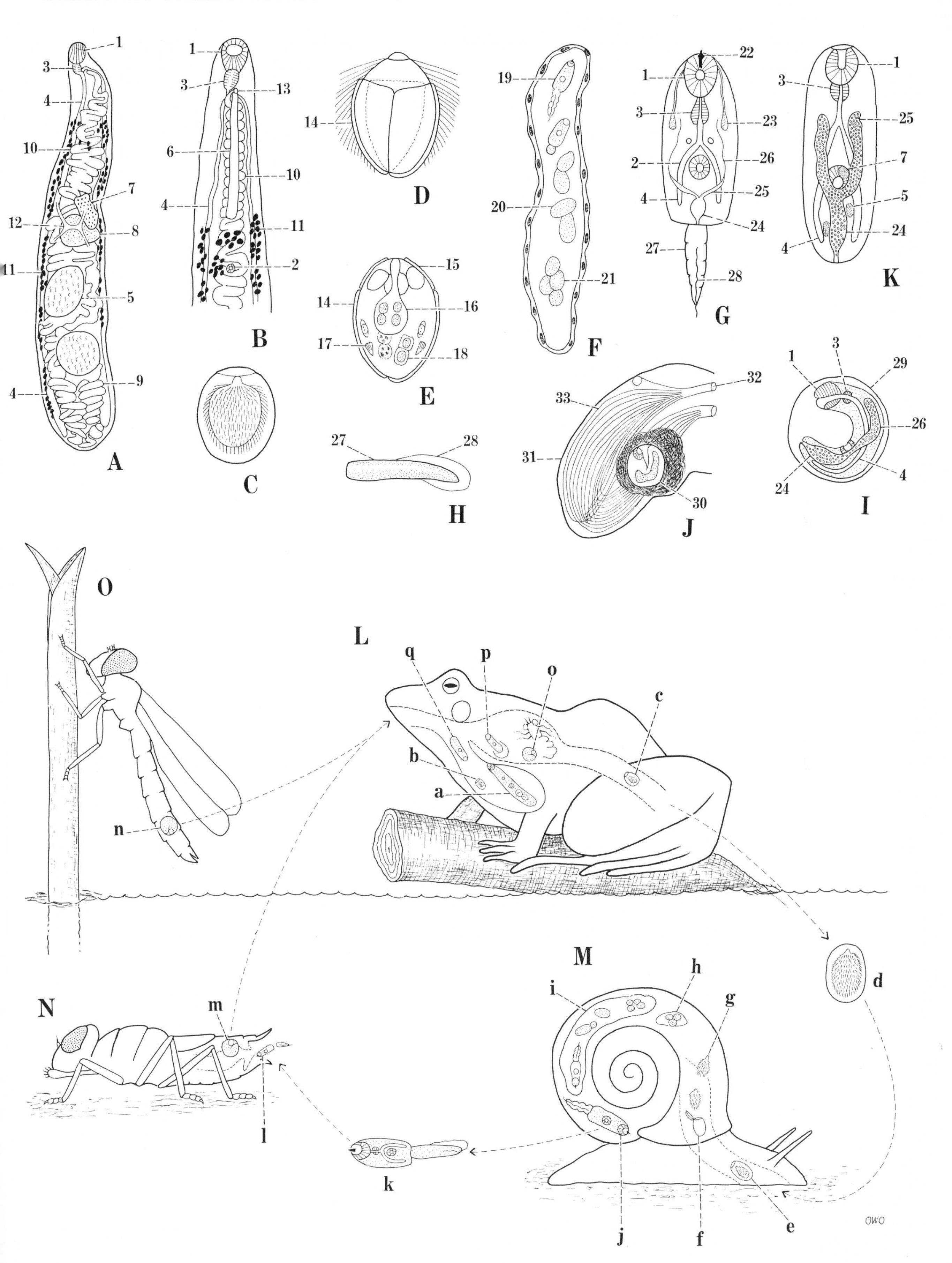
A
B
C
D
E
F
G
H
I
J
K
L
M
N
O
a
b
c
d
e
f
g
h
i
j
k
l
m
n
o
p
q
OWO

EXPLANATION OF PLATE 73 ▷

A. Adult fluke. **B.** Embryonated egg. **C.** Mother sporocyst (?). **D.** Mature daughter sporocyst. **E.** Xiphidiocercaria. **F.** Cercaria in section of web of toes of frog. **G.** Metacercaria attached to shed stratum corneum. **H.** Adult frog definitive host *(Rana pretiosa)*. **I.** Snail intermediate host *(Physella utahensis)*. **J.** Frog second intermediate host *(Rana pretiosa)*.

1, oral sucker; **2**, ventral sucker; **3**, pharynx; **4**, oesophagus; **5**, intestine; **6**, testis; **7**, cirrus pouch; **8**, common genital pore; **9**, ovary; **10**, oviduct; **11**, seminal receptacle; **12**, uterus; **13**, vitelline glands; **14**, miracidium; **15**, apical gland; **16**, penetration gland; **17**, germ cell; **18**, birth pore; **19**, cercaria; **20**, spine of oral sucker; **21**, penetration glands; **22**, flame cell; **23**, capillary tubule; **24**, anterior collecting tubule; **25**, posterior collecting tubule; **26**, excretory bladder; **27**, lateral vitelline ducts; **28**, finfold on tail; **29**, section of web of hind foot of frog; **30**, epidermis; **31**, dermis with pigment; **32**, section of cercaria; **33**, shed cuticle of frog; **34**, metacercaria; **35**, cyst of metacercaria.

a, adult fluke in small intestine; **b**, embryonated egg passing through intestine; **c**, embryonated egg in water; **d**, egg swallowed by snail intermediate host; **e**, egg hatching in intestine of snail; **f**, miracidium passing through intestinal wall; **g**, mother sporocyst; **h**, daughter sporocyst with cercariae and germ balls; **i**, cercaria escaping from snail; **j-k**, cercariae swimming free in water; **l**, cercaria penetrating skin of frog, casting its tail in the process; **m**, metacercaria encysted on stratum corneum; **n**, metacercaria on cast stratum corneum being swallowed by the frog which sheds it; **o**, metacercaria being released from stratum corneum by digestive juices; **p**, metacercaria escaping from its cyst in the intestine to develop to sexual maturity in about 50 days.

Adapted from Olsen, 1937, J. Parasit. 23:13.

---

characteristics of those of *Haematoloechus* should be placed in small dishes with appropriate species of dragon fly or damsel fly naiads. If the cercariae are retained in the branchial basket, with encystment, the probability is that the species is one of *Haematoloechus*. Dissect dragon fly and damsel fly naiads and examine the wall of the branchial basket for metacercariae in flattened cysts of thin hyaline material. The young flukes have a pronounced Y-shaped excretory bladder with long broad arms.

Feed a large number of encysted metacercariae at intervals of 2 days for 2 weeks to a frog that has been kept in the laboratory for a month in order to allow any worms that might have been acquired naturally to have matured. Sacrifice it a few hours after the last feeding and examine the intestine, stomach, oesophagus, bronchi, and lungs separately to determine the route of migration and development of the young flukes.

SELECTED REFERENCES

Cort, W. W. (1915). Trans. Amer. Micr. Soc. 34:203.

Krull, W. H. (1930). J. Parasit. 16:207; (1931). Trans. Amer. Micr. Soc. 50:215; (1932). Zool. Anz. 99:231; (1933). Z. Parasitenk. 6:192; (1934). Trans. Amer. Micr. Soc. 53:196.

Haplometrana utahensis Olsen, 1937 (Plate 73)

This is a parasite of the small intestine of the western frog, *Rana pretiosa,* in the Great Basin region of Utah and possibly over its entire range west of the Rocky Mountains in the United States.

DESCRIPTION. The length of mature worms is about 5 mm, with the sides parallel and the ends rounded. The oral sucker is subterminal and the acetabulum is in the second fifth of the body. Caeca extend to near the posterior extremity of the body. Testes are in the middle fifth of the body, intercaecal, subspherical, and arranged obliquely. The ovary is on the left side between the acetabulum and anterior testis. The common genital pore is near the anterior margin of the acetabulum. Vitellaria extend from the level of the ovary into the middle of the fourth fifth of the body.

Waitz believes that this species is a synonym of *H. intestinalis* Lucker, 1931, from the same host in Washington and Idaho. His conclusion is based on a study of specimens of Lucker, Olsen, and his own from Idaho. While he presents evidence that supports his contentions on some points, that given on others or disregarded for some, however, is in need of further investigations before it can be accepted with full confidence.

LIFE CYCLE. Fully embryonated eggs passed in the faeces do not hatch until eaten by the snail intermediate host (*Physa utahensis, Physa ampullacea, P. gyrina*). The miracidia appear in the

PLATE 73 *Haplometrana utahensis*

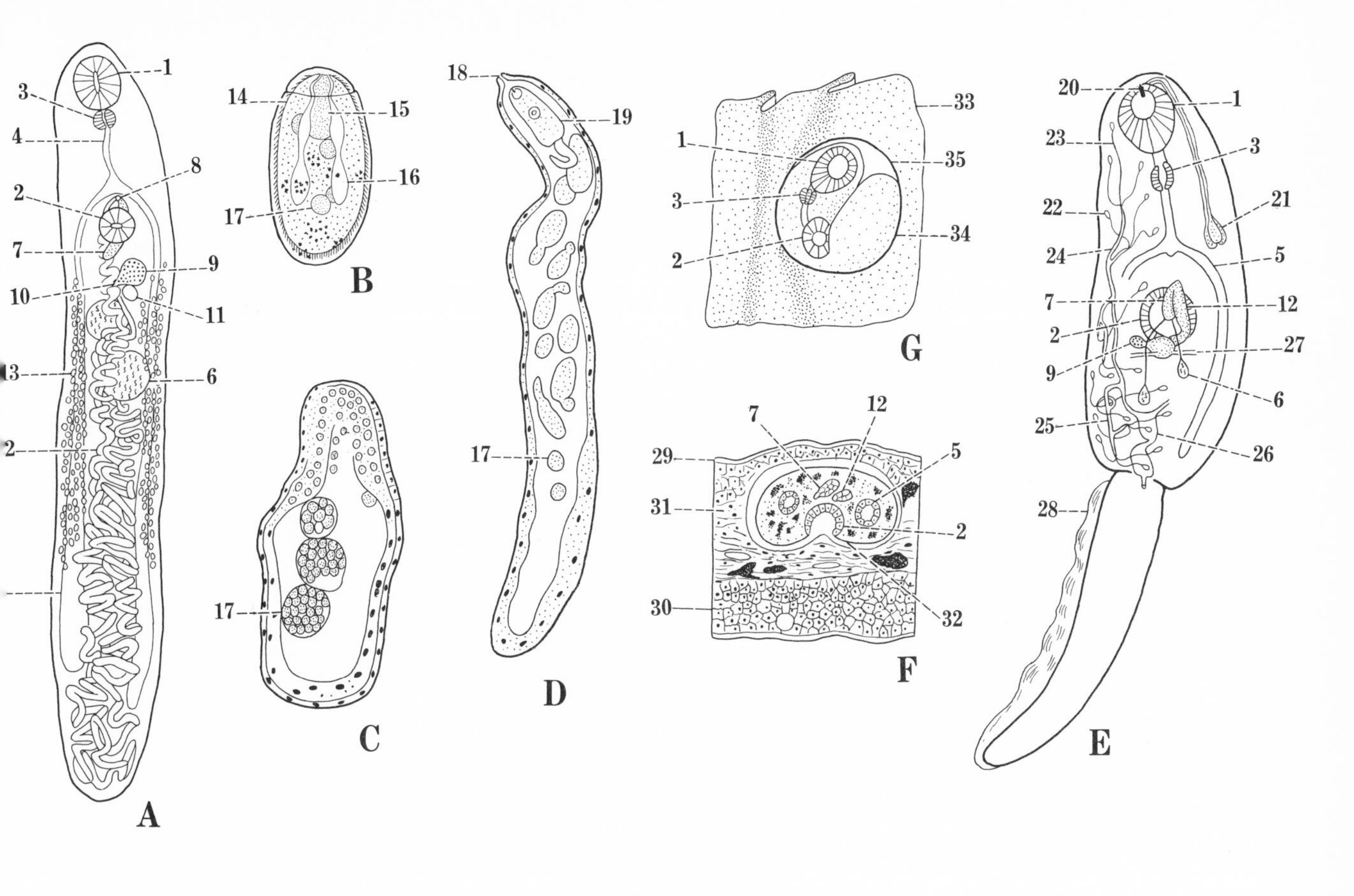

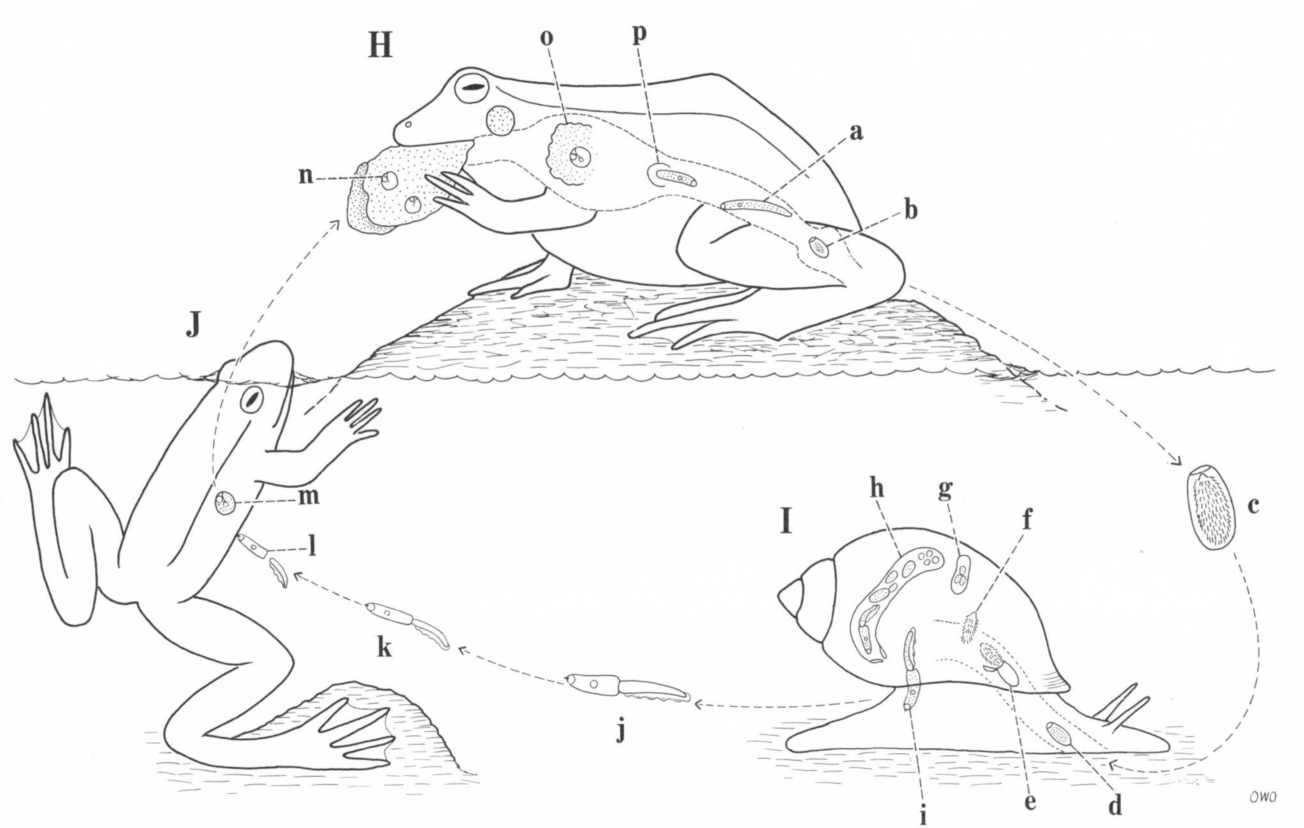

small intestine 75 minutes after the eggs are ingested. They migrate through the gut wall. Small sporocysts near the gut are thought to be mother sporocysts but the identity of them is not certain. Schell has found them for *H. intestinalis* in close association with the intestinal wall.

One month after infection of the snails, the youngest daughter sporocysts are nearest to the intestine and the older ones are further from it. In long established infections, the liver is heavily parasitized with mature daughter sporocysts entwined about each other in the host tissues.

Xiphidiocercariae appear during the 7th week following infection of the host. They escape from the sporocysts through a terminal birth pore. There is no periodicity and up to 200 cercariae appear in a span of 24 hours. They swim aimlessly, displaying no tropisms toward or against light.

Upon coming in contact with the frog definitive host, the cercariae quickly attach and crawl rapidly over them for a short time before penetrating the epidermis, which requires about 10 minutes. Once within the epidermis, large passages are formed through which they migrate some distance before secreting a delicate cyst about themselves. The cercariae do not enter the dermis but remain in the epidermis and between it and the stratum corneum.

Infectivity of the metacercariae is attained as early as 13 hours after encystment. When the epidermis is shed, the encysted metacercariae remain attached. Inasmuch as the frogs eat the skin as it is shed, they swallow the adherent metacercariae, thus becoming infected. Hence this parasite has the unique life cycle in which the same frog may serve as both the second intermediate and definitive hosts. Upon being released from the cysts, the young flukes develop to sexual maturity in 50 days at room temperature, as indicated by small numbers of eggs in the uterus.

Schell, doing intensive studies on *H. intestinalis,* which he believes includes *H. utahensis,* followed the development of mother and daughter sporocysts in laboratory-reared *Physa gyrina* and *P. ampullacea.* He found that the eggs hatch in the stomach and the weakly swimming miracidia penetrate the epithelium of the snail's digestive tract, coming to rest between it and the basement membrane. Here they shed the cilia and transform to mother sporocysts. Daughter sporocysts appear by the 9th day and production of them ceases by the 18th day. They were mature with developing cercariae by the 27th day after infection of the snails. Cercariae emerged naturally on the 34th day. The daughter sporocysts from each mother sporocyst are held together in a mass by a surrounding membrane called the paletot, which, presumably, originates from the host tissues. The daughter sporocysts do not invade the snail tissues. The cercariae have a club-shaped excretory bladder which is different from that described for *H. utahensis.* On the basis of the cercarial anatomy of *H. intestinalis,* Schell assigned this genus to the plagiorchioid family Macroderoididae.

Glypthelmins pennsylvaniensis has a similar life cycle in that its cercariae encyst in the skin of frogs. The metacercariae are shed with stratum corneum which the frogs eat, becoming infected with their own flukes.

EXERCISE ON LIFE CYCLE

In localities where *Rana pretiosa* infected with *Haplometrana* are available, the life cycle may be studied without difficulty. Adult worms placed in a dish of water lay embryonated eggs. Examine them for such details as can be seen through the brown shell and then hatch them in the stomach juices of snails (Schell).

Feed eggs to species of Physidae found in this area, preferably young ones taken from localities where frogs do not occur, or better still, to laboratory-reared specimens. Examine infected snails daily to find the mother sporocysts, and to follow the development of the daughter sporocysts and cercariae.

When cercariae appear, place some of them together with a piece of the web from the hind foot of a frog in a small dish of water. Watch them penetrate the epidermis. After they have disappeared into it, place the piece of web in a fixative and prepare sections for observing the course of movements of the cercariae and their encystment in the epidermis.

Expose frogs in a small aquarium to numerous cercariae. Later, observe the shedding of the stratum corneum and the ingestion of it, together with the metacercariae. Note the development of the flukes in the frogs and the attainment of sexual maturity as demonstrated by the appearance of eggs in the faeces.

SELECTED REFERENCES

Cheng, G. C. (1961). J. Parasit. 47:469.
Lucker, J. F. (1931). Proc. U. S. Nat. Mus. 79:1.
Olsen, O. W. (1937). J. Parasit. 23:13.
Schell, S. C. (1961). J. Parasit. 47:493.
Waitz, J. A. (1959). J. Parasit. 45:385.

Lechriorchis primus (Stafford, 1905) (Plate 74)

L. primus is a parasite of the lungs of snakes of the genera *Thamnophis* and *Natrix* in North America.

DESCRIPTION. Adult flukes are 5.5 mm long by 1.4 mm wide and have a spiny cuticle. The oral sucker is smaller than the ventral one and is located near the hind portion of the anterior half of the body. A short prepharynx, pharynx, oesophagus, and intestinal caeca are present. The common genital pore is at the posterior margin of the intestinal bifurcation and the cirrus pouch is 1 mm long, extending to near the middle of the ventral sucker. The oval testes are slightly oblique and are near the front end of the posterior half of the body. The small ovary is to the right of the midline and at the posterior margin of the ventral sucker. The vitellaria extend from between the anterior sucker and the acetabulum to the middle of the testes. The limbs of the uterus pass between the testes and reach to near the posterior end of the body. In fully matured flukes, it fills almost the entire body caudad from the oral sucker. Eggs measure 52 to 55 μ long by 26 to 29 μ wide.

LIFE CYCLE. Adult worms in the lungs of water snakes and garter snakes lay fully embryonated eggs in brown shells. They are carried up the trachea by the ciliary action of the epithelial cells and swallowed, to be passed later in the droppings of the snake hosts. Hatching does not occur until the eggs are eaten by the snail hosts, which are *Physa parkeri* and *P. gyrina*. The miracidia escape from the eggs under the influence of the gastric juice in the stomach of the snails within an hour after being ingested. After migrating through the stomach wall, the miracidia attach to the outer side of it or the first part of the intestine. When the miracidia are 2 weeks old, young daughter sporocysts are present, and at 3 weeks they escape through the birth pore and migrate to the liver. Five weeks after infection, cercariae have reached maturity and are escaping from the daughter sporocysts via a birth pore. They enter the lymph spaces of the liver and migrate through lymph channels to the outside for a period of about 2 hours just after dark in the evenings.

The stylet-bearing cercariae with a Y-shaped excretory bladder are distributed at random through the water, having no definite tropisms toward lightness or darkness. Upon coming in contact with tadpoles of frogs of several species, the cercariae penetrate the skin, migrate into the connective tissue between the muscle bundles, and encyst promptly in thin hyaline cysts. Cercariae that encyst in small perch, sunfish, and larval *Triturus* soon die. Metacercariae in frog tadpoles are infective almost immediately following encystment. After a week, the cysts become brown in color and are laminated. They persist during metamorphosis and appear in the muscles of frogs.

Snakes become parasitized by eating infected tadpoles and frogs. Excystment takes place in the stomach and the young flukes migrate to the small intestine. Growth in the intestine is slow during the first 2 months. The flukes remain dormant during the first winter when the snakes are in hibernation. With the advent of spring and resumption of activity by the snakes, the young flukes begin to grow and migrate via the stomach and oesophagus to the lungs. By the end of 10 months after infection, most of them have reached the lungs. Growth is rapid and eggs appear but presumably they are not fertilized until after the second winter in the snakes, at which time the flukes become mature. It is not known how long they live. Infections usually are light.

The life cycles of several related species from snakes have been worked. They are basically the same as that of *Lechriorchis primus*. *L. tygarti* (Talbot), and *Zeugorchis eurinus* (Talbot), both from the lungs of garter snakes, have a cycle similar to that of *L. primus*.*Dasymetra villicaeca* Byrd from the intestine of *Natrix* develops in *Physa halei* and tadpoles of several species of frogs. *Ochetosoma aniurum* (Leidy) of the mouth, oesophagus, and lungs of *Natrix, Heterodon,* and *Lampropeltis* develops in *Physa halei* and tadpoles of frogs.

EXPLANATION OF PLATE 74

A. Dorsal view of adult fluke (experimental). **B.** Miracidium. **C.** Young mother sporocyst. **D.** Fully developed mother sporocyst. **E.** Daughter sporocyst. **F.** Cercaria. **G.** Encysted metacercaria. **H.** Snake definitive host *(Thamnophis sirtalis)*. **I.** Snail first intermediate host *(Physa gyrina* or *P. parkeri)*. **J.** Tadpole second intermediate host *(Rana clamitans, R. pipiens)*.

1, oral sucker; **2**, ventral sucker; **3**, pharynx; **4**, oesophagus; **5**, intestine; **6**, testis; **7**, cirrus pouch; **8**, seminal vesicle; **9**, ovary; **10**, oviduct surrounded by Mehlis' gland and with Laurer's canal extending free; **11**, uterus; **12**, metraterm; **13**, vitelline glands; **14**, excretory bladder; **15**, apical papillae; **16**, apical gland; **17**, penetration gland; **18**, germ cell; **19**, flame cell; **20**, excretory duct; **21**, birth pore; **22**, daughter sporocyst; **23**, cercaria; **24**, stylet; **25**, tail; **26**, anterior collecting excretory tubule (bilateral); **27**, common excretory collecting tube; **28**, posterior excretory collecting tubule; **29**, accessory collecting tubule; **30**, capillary tubule; **31**, penetration glands (bilateral); **32**, cyst of metacercaria; **33**, metacercaria.

a, adult fluke in lung; **b**, eggs laid in lungs; **c**, eggs carried up trachea by ciliary action of epithelial cells, enter oesophagus, and are swallowed; **d**, eggs continue on through intestine and are voided in faeces; **e**, eggs fully embryonated when laid but do not hatch in water; **f**, eggs swallowed by snail intermediate host; **g**, eggs hatch in intestine of snail; **h**, miracidium migrates through intestinal wall; **i**, young mother sporocyst; **j**, mature mother sporocyst; **k**, daughter sporocyst; **l**, cercaria escaping from snail; **m**, cercaria free in water; **n**, cercaria penetrating tadpole and casting tail at the same time; **o**, encysted metacercaria; **p**, tadpole swallowed by snake is digested, releasing encysted metacercaria; **q**, metacercaria escaping from cyst; **r**, metacercaria free from cyst; **s**, metacercariae migrate into small intestine where they remain several months, growing slightly; **t**, young flukes migrate up oesophagus; **u**, flukes enter trachea from oesophagus; **v**, flukes migrate down trachea to lungs where they develop to maturity at about 2 years of age.

Adapted from Talbot, 1933, Parasitology 25:518.

EXERCISE ON LIFE CYCLE

Because of the long time required to complete the life cycle, it is not convenient to conduct the entirety of it. Some aspects of the cycle, however, are both interesting and informative.

Eggs of these flukes from water snakes and garter snakes may be identified tentatively by being embryonated, brown in color, and with a large single yolk cell at the end opposite from the operculum. Uterine eggs measure 48 to 50 μ long by 23 to 25 μ wide.

Eggs fed to young *Physa parkeri* and *P. gyrina* hatch in the stomach and produce cercariae in 5 weeks. Hatching can be induced by placing eggs in gastric juice from any of a number of species of snails. Tadpoles of frogs should be exposed to cercariae from experimental or natural infections of snails. Note metacercariae in the muscles and how the wall of the cyst changes in color and structure after one week. Metacercariae placed in gastric juice from snake hosts quickly excyst, an indication that excystation occurs in the stomach.

After feeding infected tadpoles to snakes, note that the young flukes go to the small intestine for a long sojourn.

SELECTED REFERENCES

Byrd, E. E. (1935). Trans. Amer. Micr. Soc. 54:196.

Cort, W. W., D. J. Ameel, and A. Van der Woude. (1952). J. Parasit. 28:187.

Price, E. W. (1936). Proc. Helminth. Soc. Wash. 3:32.

Talbot, S. B. (1933). Parasitology 25:518.

FAMILY PROSTHOGONIMIDAE

The Prosthogonimidae are parasites of the bursa Fabricii, the oviduct, and rarely the intestine of a large number of species of birds in many parts of Europe, Asia, Africa, and North and South America.

They are relatively small, flattened, and transparent distomes somewhat narrowed anteriorly and broadly rounded posteriorly. The testes are symmetrical and postacetabular. A lobed ovary lies between the acetabulum and testes. The uterine loops pass between the testes and fill the posttesticular portion of the body. The genital pores open separately or together on the anterior margin of the body near the oral sucker. The vitellaria are sparse, grapelike clusters in the lateral fields.

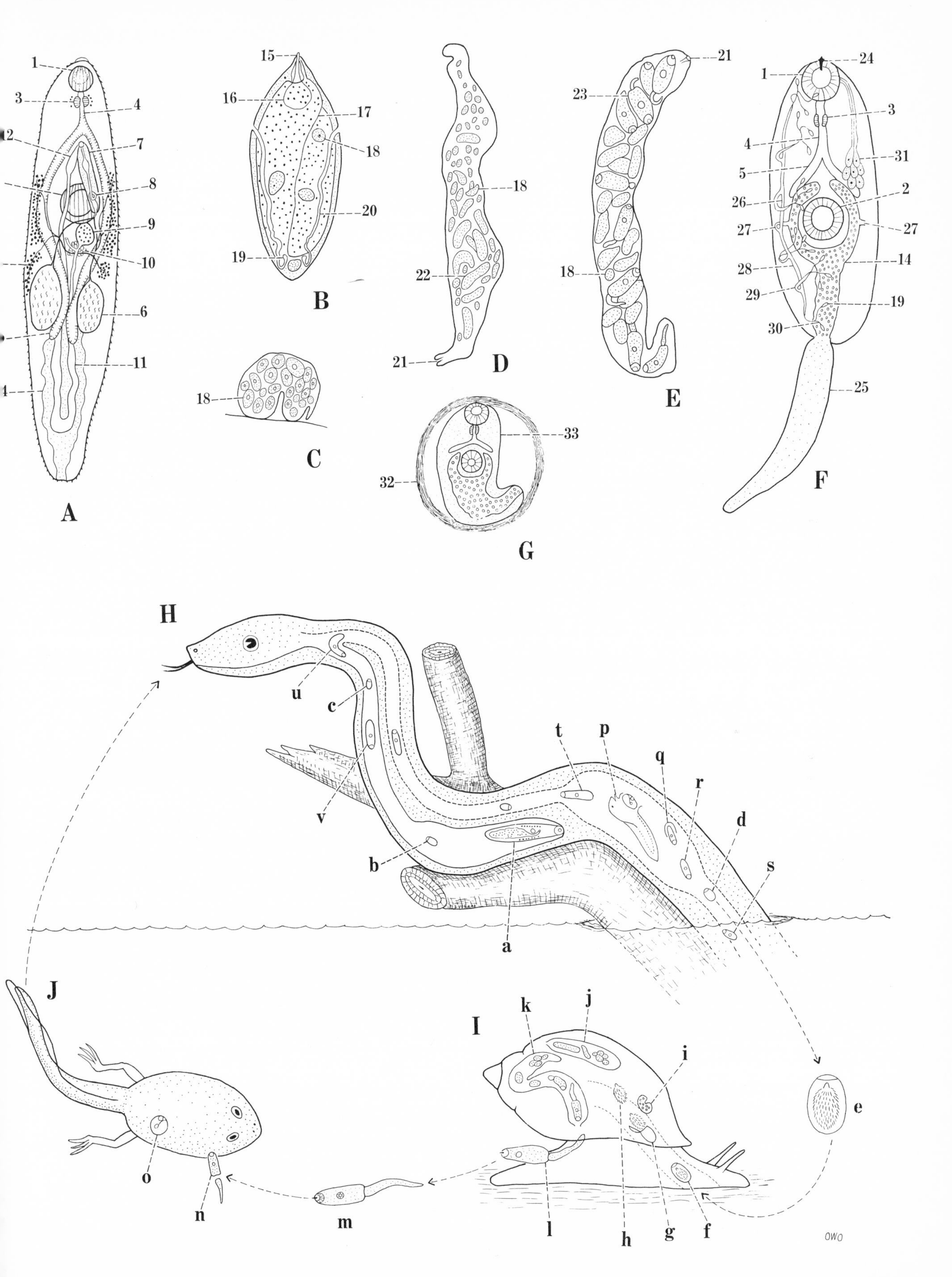
A
B
C
D
E
F
G
H
I
J
1
2
3
4
5
6
7
8
9
10
11
12
14
15
16
17
18
19
20
21
22
23
24
25
26
27
28
29
30
31
32
33
a
b
c
d
e
f
g
h
i
j
k
l
m
n
o
p
q
r
s
t
u
v
OWO

EXPLANATION OF PLATE 75 ▷

A. Adult fluke. **B.** Daughter sporocyst. **C.** Cercaria. **D.** Encysted metacercaria. **E.** Excysted metacercaria. **F.** Chicken definitive host. **G.** Ring-necked pheasant and duck definitive hosts. **H.** Snail *(Amnicola limnosa)* first intermediate host. **I.** Dragon fly naiads *(Leucorrhina, Tetragoneuria, Epicordulia, Gomphus, Mesothemis)* second intermediate host. **J.** Dragon fly imago.

1, oral sucker; **2**, ventral sucker; **3**, pharynx; **4**, oesophagus; **5**, intestine; **6**, testis; **7**, vas efferens; **8**, cirrus pouch; **9**, seminal vesicle; **10**, common genital pore; **11**, ovary; **12**, uterus; **13**, vitelline gland; **14**, vitelline duct; **15**, developing cercaria; **16**, spine of oral sucker; **17**, penetration glands; **18**, body of excretory bladder; **19**, arms of excretory bladder; **20**, tail; **21**, cyst wall of metacercaria.

a, adult fluke in oviduct; **b**, embryonated eggs laid in oviduct; **c**, eggs reach cloaca; **d**, eggs pass from body in faeces; **e**, egg in water; **f**, eggs hatch when swallowed by snail intermediate host (this has not been observed but probably is the only place where it occurs); **g**, miracidium passes through intestinal wall; **h**, daughter sporocyst bearing cercariae and germ balls (mother sporocyst not seen); **i**, cercaria escaping from snail; **j**, free cercaria being drawn into rectal chamber of naiad; **k**, cercaria drops tail and burrows through rectal wall into haemocoel; **l**, metacercaria in haemocoel; **m**, when naiad transforms into imago, metacercariae persist in body; **n**, definitive host becomes infected by eating naiads or imagoes with cysts in their bodies; **o**, digestion of dragon fly releases encysted metacercaria; **p**, metacercaria free in digestive tract; **q**, young fluke escapes from cyst with aid of digestive juices; **r**, young flukes leave intestine and enter bursa Fabricii, where some develop to maturity while others migrate up the oviducts of laying birds and develop to maturity.

Adapted from Macy, 1934, Univ. Minn. Agr. Exp. St. Tech. Bull. 98.

Prosthogonimus macrorchis Macy, 1934 (Plate 75)

This oviduct fluke occurs in chickens, ducks, pheasants, English sparrows, and crows that live near or on lakes of the Great Lakes region of North America. Being in the oviducts of laying birds, they commonly occur inside eggs. They are considered to be the cause of marked decline in egg production if not complete cessation of it.

DESCRIPTION. The flattened pyriform and transparent body is 7.56 mm long by 5.26 mm wide with the cuticle spined. The ventral sucker is near the junction of the anterior and middle thirds of the body. The ratio of size of the suckers is 1:1.7, with the ventral one being the larger. Large symmetrically placed testes occupy the middle third of the body. The length of the cirrus pouch is about twice the diameter of the oral sucker and lies lateral to it, opening at anterior extremity of the body. A multilobed ovary lies between the ventral sucker and testes. The ascending and descending limbs of the uterus pass between the testes and fill the posttesticular portion of the body. Vitelline glands are arranged in eight to nine lateral clusters between the anterior margin of the ventral sucker and posterior margin of the testes. Eggs average 28 μ long by 16 μ wide.

LIFE CYCLE. Flukes in the oviducts or bursa Fabricii lay eggs that are expelled through the anus into the water. Hatching has not been observed, although the eggs are embryonated when laid. Upon reaching the water, they gradually sink to the bottom where they remain until swallowed by *Amnicola limnosa porata*, the snail intermediate host. Snails crawling over the bottom of the lake are in a favorable position to find the eggs. Since hatching does not take place in water, it must occur in the gut of the snail. Mother sporocysts have not been seen but simple saclike daughter sporocysts in the digestive gland produce small cercariae bearing a stylet and a relatively short tail. These are expelled from the snail into the water. They are feeble swimmers.

As the cercariae swim by the posterior end of dragon fly naiads of the genera *Leucorrhina, Tetragoneura, Epicordulia, Gomphus,* and *Mesothemis,* they are drawn through the anus by the respiratory currents into the branchial basket. They attach to the wall of the rectum and the gill filaments and burrow into the body cavity. Encystment takes place primarily in the muscles of the body wall, particularly those on the ventral side toward the posterior end of the abdomen. Exposure of the naiads is during the summer in which they hatch and the following spring before they emerge from the water to molt and fly away. Development of the metacercariae is slow, requiring up to 70 days before the characteristic thick-walled, striated cysts are formed.

Ducks appear to be the normal hosts but chickens, pheasants, English sparrows, and crows become infected. Infections follow when parasitized dragon fly naiads or adults are eaten. Naiads living in lakes are available to ducks at all times except when the water is frozen. As the young dragon flies

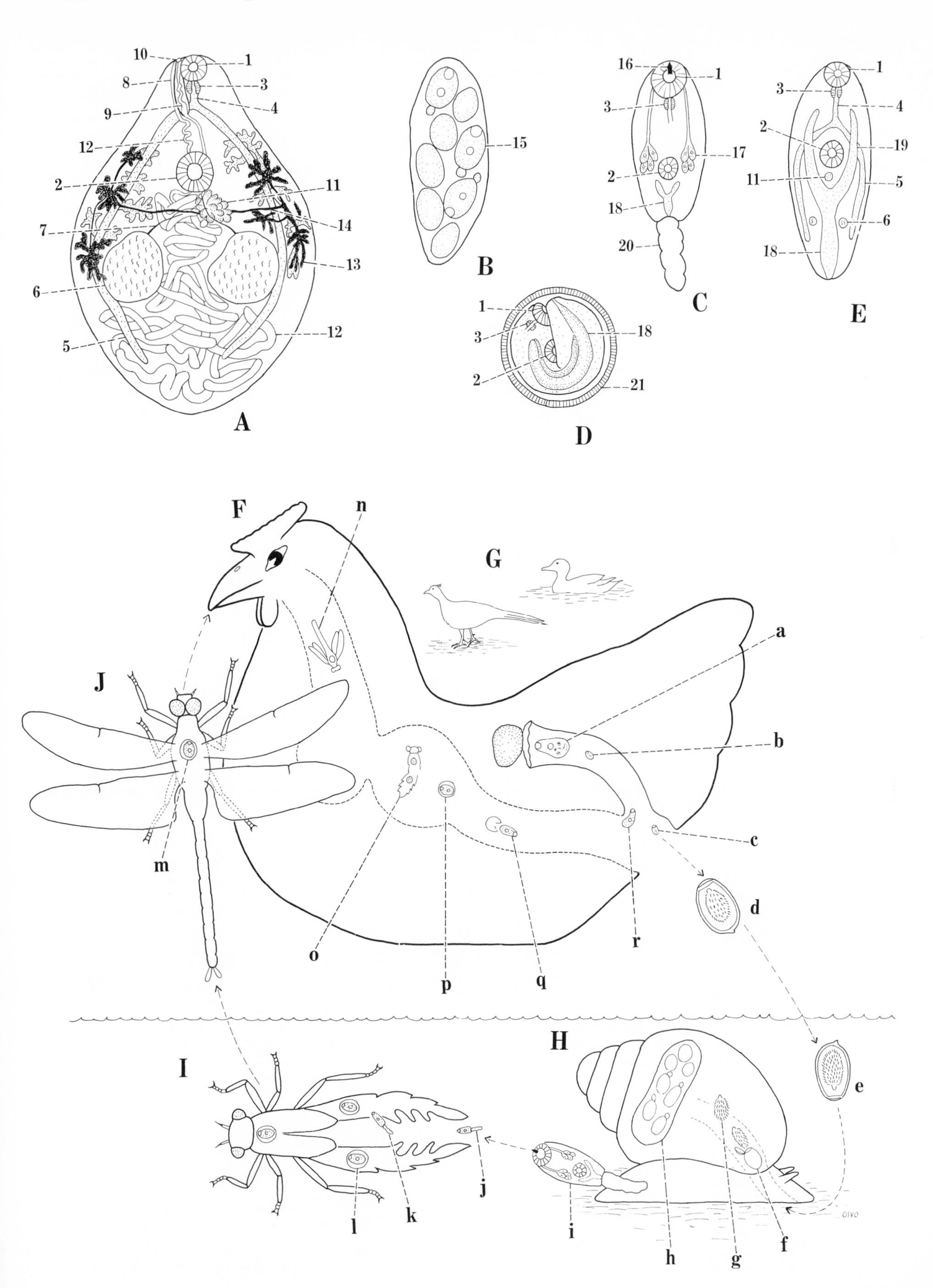
10
1
8
3
9
4
12
2
11
7
14
6
13
5
12
A
15
B
16
1
3
17
2
18
20
C
1
3
18
2
21
D
1
3
4
2
19
11
5
6
18
E
F
n
G
a
J
b
c
m
d
r
o
p
q
H
I
e
j
k
l
i
h
g
f

prepare to molt to adults, they climb out of the water onto vegetation. In this position, they are easy prey to all birds. Although adult dragon flies are swift fliers, they too may be caught, especially when resting during the cool early morning hours when birds are feeding.

When the metacercariae are released from the dragon flies as the latter are digested, they migrate to the bursa Fabricii or, if the bird is laying eggs, into the oviducts. In non-laying birds, residence of the flukes in them is correlated with the existence of the bursa Fabricii. When it atrophies, the infection is lost. Development of the flukes in chickens requires about 1 week and they are lost in 3 to 6 weeks. Development in ducks is slower, taking 3 weeks and the flukes are retained up to 18 weeks.

EXERCISE ON LIFE CYCLE

Since approximately 32 species of *Prosthogonimus* are known to occur in as many species of birds from seven orders, the likelihood of finding infected snails is fairly good during surveys for cercariae. The identity of the cercariae may be suspected by their small size, stylet, short tail, thick-walled Y-shaped excretory bladder, and origin from saclike sporocysts in *Amnicola.*

When found, such cercariae should be placed in dishes with dragon fly naiads of the species available in the pond. Observe them being drawn into the rectum. Note whether they are retained in the rectum or expelled. In the latter case, either the host is not the right one or the cercariae are not those of *Prosthogonimus.*

Dissection of dragon fly naiads from lakes where infected snails originate should reveal metacercariae with the characteristic striated, thick-walled cyst.

When metacercariae are available, they should be fed to baby chicks to get the adult worms in the bursa Fabricii. Eggs obtained from experimental infections should be fed to young *Amnicola,* preferably laboratory-reared specimens, to study the development of the intramolluscan stages. Eggs placed in the open stomach or gut of the snail host may hatch under the action of the digestive juices and the miracidia be available for study. Sections should be made of snails that have eaten eggs to study hatching and movements of the miracidia. Eggs should be studied to obtain information on the morphology of the miracidia.

SELECTED REFERENCES

Heidegger, E. (1937). Arch. Wissensch. Prakt. Tierheilkund. 72:224.

Macy, R. W. (1934). Trans. Amer. Micr. Soc. 53:30; (1934). Univ. Minn. Agr. Exp. St., Tech. Bull. 98, 71 pp.; (1939). J. Parasit. 25:281.

SUPERFAMILY ALLOCREADIOIDEA

The cercariae of this superfamily developing in rediae or sporocysts in snails or clams are of various types (ophthalmoxiphidiocercariae, microcercous, rhopalocercous, ophthalmotrichocercous, tailless, or muscular tails with lateral and ventral fins). Encystment is in arthropods chiefly, rarely in vertebrates.

FAMILY ALLOCREADIIDAE

These are parasites of fishes, principally of the digestive tract. It is a large family containing many subfamilies, genera, and species. They are small- to medium-sized flukes, having well-developed suckers with the acetabulum located ventrally. The caeca are tubular. The testes are in the posterior half of the body with the ovary between them and the acetabulum. The uterus is usually pretesticular. The excretory bladder is tubular or saccular.

Crepidostomum cooperi Hopkins, 1931 (Plate 76)

This species occurs in the pyloric caeca of a number of species of fish, including sunfish, bass, bullheads, catfish, and trout.

DESCRIPTION. Adult worms are elongate forms measuring up to 1.5 mm in length. The oral sucker bears six large papillae and the acetabulum is near or somewhat anterior to the middle of the body. The genital pore is between the anterior margin of the acetabulum and bifurcation of the intestine. A long slender cirrus sac containing a seminal vesicle twice its length extends from the genital pore to the anterior margin of the ovary. The testes are tandem in the posterior half of the body, with a pear-shaped ovary and the seminal receptacle between the anterior one and the acetabulum. The uterus is anterior to the testes and contains few eggs, ranging in size from 50 to 75 μ long by 30 to 55 μ wide. Vitelline glands extend from about midway between the pharynx and acetabulum to near the caudal end of the body. The excretory bladder is saclike and extends forward to between the anterior and posterior margins of the front testis.

LIFE CYCLE. Unembryonated eggs laid by adult worms in the alimentary canal do not begin to develop until they have been deposited in the water with the faeces. Development is completed at summer temperature in 7 days and hatching begins by the 10th day.

Miracidia penetrate fingernail clams (*Musculium transversum, Pisidium subtruncatum, P. compressum, P. adbitum, P. llijeborgi, P. nitidum*). Infections in them may run as high as 67 per cent in some locations. The miracidia penetrate between the inner and outer layers of gills and the mantle where they transform. Presumably they change into mother sporocysts but this point is not clear, as only rediae have been seen. Two generations of rediae occur. Some rediae contain only daughter rediae and others either cercariae only or both cercariae and rediae. Large rediae are in the liver. The situation concerning the rediae is not fully understood. The length of time required for the intramolluscan phase to develop is unknown.

The ophthalmoxiphidiocercariae are active swimmers, responding positively toward bright light. They attack and penetrate the nymphs of may flies (*Hexagenia limbata, H. recurvata, Polymitarcys* sp.), including up to 95 per cent of *H. limbata* during the summer in some areas. Upon entering the nymphs, the cercariae go to the muscles, usually those of the gill-bearing filaments. At first, the cyst is thin and hyaline, being of parasite origin, but by the fourth day it is surrounded by a layer of orange-brown material deposited by the host. The metacercariae are fully formed in 2 to 3 weeks. In old metacercariae, the internal organs appear in a well-developed stage, and numerous sperms are produced but no eggs have been seen in this species.

When infected may fly nymphs are eaten by susceptible fish, the metacercariae escape from the cysts and develop to maturity in 3 to 4 weeks.

Other species of *Crepidostomum* have life cycles very similar to that of *C. cooperi*. The molluscan hosts are fingernail clams. The invertebrate hosts are *Hexagenia* nymphs for *C. isostomum*. The cercariae of *C. cornutum* encyst in the vicinity of the reproductive organs of crayfish; they are particularly abundant in the females, where up to 80 per cent may be infected. The metacercariae are progenetic, having fully developed eggs which are deposited in the cysts. Adults occur in a variety of fishes in North America. *C. farionis* of trout develops in *Pisidium* sp. and may fly nymphs (*Ephemera* sp.) in lakes at high altitudes.

Megalogonia ictaluri from catfish has a life cycle similar to that of *C. cooperi*, except that the metacercariae are in the gills of *Hexagenia* and possibly other may fly nymphs.

Allocreadium ictaluri, an Allocreadiidae from catfish, develops in rediae in the snail *Pleurocerca acuta*. The cercariae, which are biocellate and do not have a stylet, encyst in unionid clams. In Europe, *Allocreadium angusticolle*, a parasite of eels and Miller's Thumb, develops in the snail *Neritina fluviatilis* and the metacercariae are in gammarids (*Gammarus pulex* and *Asellus aquaticus*).

EXERCISE ON LIFE CYCLE

With *Crepidostomum* being a very common parasite of fish in many types of habitats, it provides excellent material for studies on the life cycle of an allocreadiid trematode. When related forms are present, they can be studied, using somewhat similar approaches.

Adult flukes obtained from the pyloric caeca of fish provide a source of eggs for hatching and infection of fingernail clams. Study the development and morphology of the miracidia.

Expose fingernail clams to miracidia. Special effort should be directed toward finding the very earliest stages. Determine whether the miracidia transform into mother sporocysts, since they have not been reported.

Biocellate, stylet-bearing cercariae issuing from rediae in fingernail clams should be placed in dishes

EXPLANATION OF PLATE 76 ⇨

A. Adult fluke, ventral view. **B.** Sagittal section of adult fluke. **C.** Embryonated egg. **D.** Miracidium. **E.** Mother redia containing daughter rediae. **F.** Cercaria. **G.** Fish (trout and other fish) definitive host. **H.** Fingernail clam *(Pisidium* and *Musculium)* first intermediate host. **I.** Burrowing may fly *(Hexagenia)* nymph second intermediate host. **J.** Adult may flies retain metacercariae during metamorphosis.

1, papillae around oral sucker; **2**, oral sucker; **3**, ventral sucker; **4**, pharynx; **5**, oesophagus; **6**, intestine; **7**, testis; **8**, cirrus pouch; **9**, common genital pore; **10**, ovary; **11**, eggs in uterus; **12**, vitelline gland; **13**, embryonated egg; **14**, miracidium; **15**, apical gland; **16**, eyespots; **17**, flame cell; **18**, germinal masses; **19**, pharynx of mother redia; **20**, daughter redia; **21**, stylet of oral sucker; **22**, lateral and dorsal views of stylet from oral sucker; **23**, prepharynx; **24**, penetration glands; **25**, ducts of penetration glands; **26**, posterior collecting tubule of excretory system (there is an anterior collecting tubule); **27**, common collecting tubule; **28**, excretory bladder.

a, adult fluke in small intestine of fish; **b**, unembryonated eggs laid in intestine; **c**, egg developing in water; **d**, egg hatching; **e**, miracidium penetrating clam; **f**, mother redia with daughter rediae; **g**, daughter redia with cercariae (some rediae may contain both rediae and cercariae); **h**, cercaria free in water; **i**, cercaria penetrating abdomen of burrowing may fly; **j**, metacercariae in may fly nymph are retained throughout the life of the insect, including the adult stage; **k**, fish become infected by eating may flies; **l**, metacercaria released from may fly in stomach of fish; **m**, young fluke escapes from metacercarial cyst in intestine and develops to maturity.

Adapted from Hopkins, 1937, Ill. Biol. Monogr. 13:1.

---

with may fly nymphs, particularly those of the burrowing may fly (*Hexagenia*). Other genera, such as occur in the habitat, may be the second intermediate host. Crayfish are the hosts of some species, as are gammarids for others. Note the location of the cysts and the nature of the cyst wall. Ascertain whether the flukes are progenetic, *i.e.*, producing eggs while still encysted.

Feed may fly nymphs, or other forms containing metacercariae, to fish to complete the life cycle. Determine the time required for development to the adult stage.

SELECTED REFERENCES

Abernathy, C. (1937). Trans. Amer. Micr. Soc. 56:206.
Ameel, D. J. (1937). J. Parasit. 23:218.
Choquette, L. P. E. (1954). Canad. J. Zool. 32:375.
Crawford, W. W. (1943). J. Parasit. 29:379.
Henderson, H. E. (1938). Trans. Amer. Micr. Soc. 57:165.
Hopkins, S. H. (1937). Ill. Biol. Monogr. 13:1.
Mathias, P. (1937). C. R. Acad. Sci. Paris 205:626.
Seitner, P. B. (1951). J. Parasit. 37:223

Plagioporus sinitsini Mueller, 1934 (Plate 77)

This allocreadiid fluke is a common parasite of the gall bladder of cyprinid and catastomid fishes in North America.

DESCRIPTION. Adult worms reach a length of 0.67 to 1.5 mm. The acetabulum is near the center of the body and much larger than the oral sucker. The prepharynx is short, the pharynx is followed by a short oesophagus, and the caeca are large, reaching to the level of the posterior testis. Testes located in the last quarter of the body are subequal in size, and obliquely arranged. The ovary is dextral and at the level of the anterior margin of the forward testis. The cirrus pouch is large, sigmoid, oblique in position, and extends to the middle of the acetabulum. The genital pore is displaced toward the left side of the body at a level between the pharynx and intestinal bifurcation. The vitellaria are lateral and extend from the pharynx to near the posterior end of the body. The eggs are few in number and large in size, measuring 67 to 75 μ long by 41 to 48 μ wide. A subterminal nodule is present on the anopercular end.

LIFE CYCLE. The eggs are in the two-to four-cell stage when laid. They pass through the ductus choledochus into the intestine and are voided with the faeces. Development is completed and hatching occurs 12 to 20 days after oviposition when they are kept at room temperature.

The miracidia have 19 epidermal plates arranged in four tiers, an arrangement unique to this group of flukes. They swim actively for 24 hours. Upon coming in contact with the operculate snail *Goniobasis*

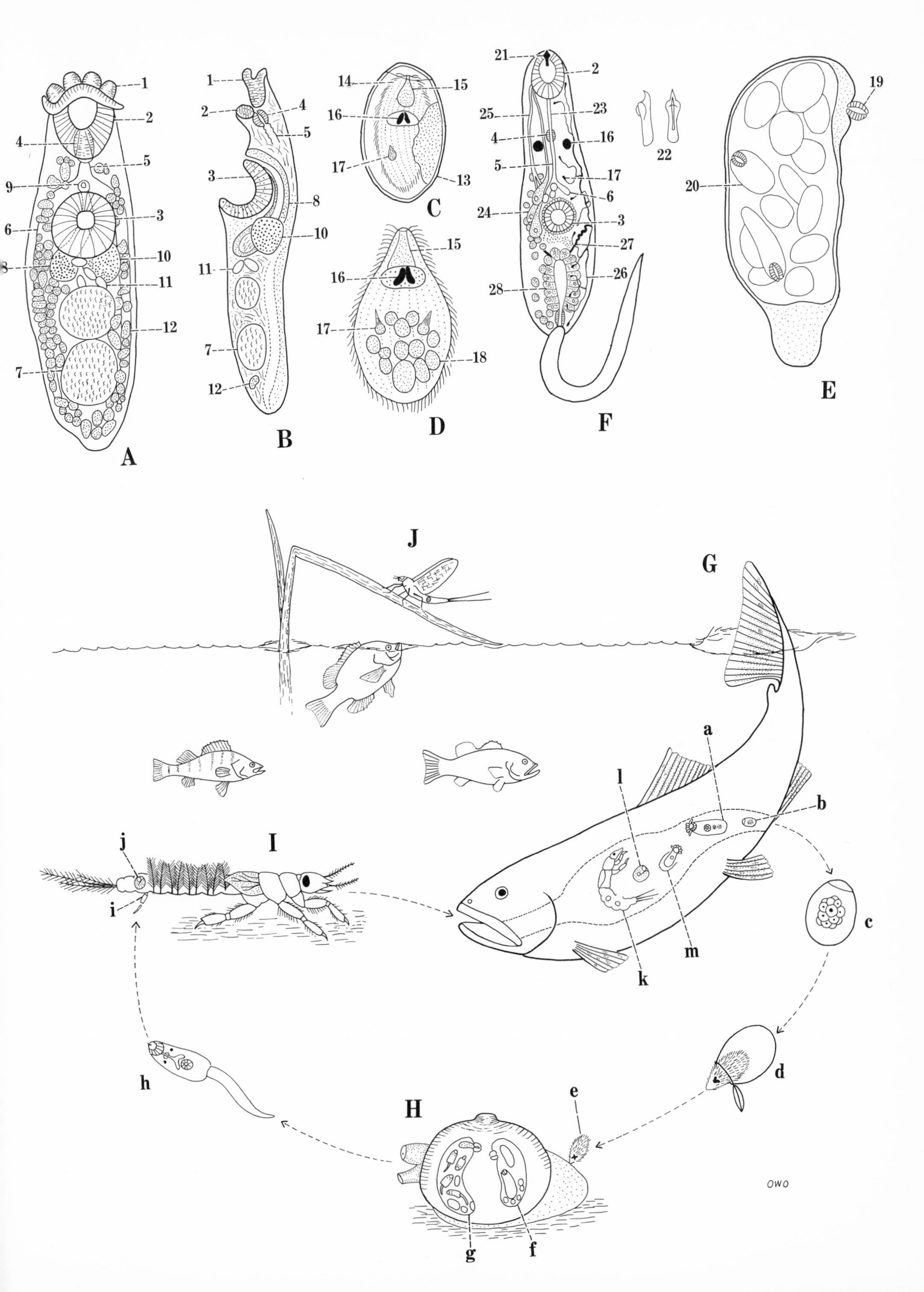
1
2
4
5
9
3
6
8
10
11
12
7
A
B
14
15
16
17
13
C
D
18
21
25
23
24
26
27
28
F
22
19
20
E
J
G
a
b
l
j
I
i
c
k
m
d
h
e
H
g
f
OWO

EXPLANATION OF PLATE 77 ⇨

A. Dorsal view of adult worm. **B.** Embryonated egg. **C.** Miracidium. **D.** Miracidium showing arrangement of dermal plates. **E.** Miracidium showing variation in arrangement of dermal plates. **F.** Daughter sporocyst from rectum of snail with enclosed cercariae and metacercariae. **G.** Cercaria. **H.** Metacercaria. **I.** Body of snail intermediate host *(Goniobasis livescens)* showing mass of sporocysts in rectum. **J.** Fish *(Notropis cornutus)* definitive host. **K.** Snail *(Goniobasis livescens)* first and second intermediate host.

1, oral sucker; **2,** ventral sucker; **3,** pharynx; **4,** oesophagus; **5,** intestine; **6,** testis; **7,** vas efferens; **8,** vas deferens; **9,** cirrus pouch; **10,** seminal vesicle; **11,** ovary; **12,** seminal receptacle; **13,** oviduct with Laurer's canal nearby to left; **14,** Mehlis' gland; **15,** proximal portion of uterus; **16,** distal portion of uterus (intervening loops left out); **17,** common genital pore far to the left of the midline; **18,** vitelline glands; **19,** vitelline duct; **20,** excretory bladder; **21,** miracidium in egg; **22,** penetration glands; **23,** flame cell; **24,** apical papilla; **25,** glandular structure; **26,** excretory tubule; **27,** excretory pore; **28,** first tier of six dermal plates; **29,** second tier of seven dermal plates; **30,** third tier of four dermal plates; **31,** fourth tier of two dermal plates; **32,** birth pore; **33,** cercaria; **34,** metacercaria; **35,** prepharynx; **36,** genital primordia; **37,** tail; **38,** early stage of cyst; **39,** sensory papillae of oral sucker; **40,** sensory papillae of ventral sucker; **41,** Laurer's canal; **42,** common excretory canal; **43,** dermal papilla; **44,** stomach; **45,** small intestine; **46,** rectum filled with sporocysts; **47,** liver.

a, adult fluke in gall bladder; **b,** unembryonated eggs laid in gall bladder; **c,** eggs pass into water with faeces; **d,** developing egg in water; **e,** fully embryonated egg; **f,** egg hatches in water in 12 to 20 days; **g,** experimental infection of snail host with cercaria not successful but presumably they penetrate soft tissues; inside the snail they probably transform into mother sporocysts; **h,** stomach of snail; **i,** mother sporocyst with daughter sporocyst in liver; **j,** daughter sporocyst with cotylocercous cercaria in liver; **k,** small intestine; **l,** rectum filled with daughter sporocysts; **m,** mature daughter sporocyst containing metacercariae escaping through anus of snail; **n,** colored daughter sporocyst with encysted metacercariae free on bottom of pool; **o,** fish definitive host becomes infected when it swallows mature daughter sporocysts containing metacercariae; **p,** metacercaria escapes from cyst through action of digestive juices; **q,** metacercaria enters common bile duct and migrates up it to gall bladder where maturity is attained in 15 to 30 days.

Adapted from Dobrovolny, 1939, Trans. Amer. Micr. Soc. 58:121.

---

livescens of the family Pleuroceratidae, they penetrate them. Early stages of development in the snail are unknown. There are two generations of sporocysts in the liver. The first, probably the mother sporocyst, produces sporocysts. The second gives rise to unarmed cotylocercous cercariae which never leave them, apparently having lost the ability to swim. Large cercariae creep about inside the daughter sporocysts where they encyst. A thin cyst is secreted about each cercaria and the tail is slowly absorbed so that mature metacercariae are tailless.

Mature sporocysts containing metacercariae are abundant in the rectum of the snails but they may be found on rare occasions in the lymph spaces below the liver, indicating their former association with that organ. How they reach the rectum from the liver is unknown. Sporocysts with infective metacercariae emerge through the anus of the snail into the water, where they are active for about 24 hours.

Small fish such as minnows (*Nocomis biguttatus, Notropis cornutus, Lebistes reticulatus*), and fingerling suckers (*Catastomus commersoni*) readily eat the sporocysts containing the metacercariae, becoming infected as a result. At least 10 species of cyprinids in Michigan are naturally infected. The worms are free in the intestine of the fish 4 to 6 hours after the sporocysts are swallowed and in the gall bladder in 25 hours. Mature flukes with eggs appear 15 to 30 days after the fish eat the sporocysts containing metacercariae.

The life cycle of *Plagioporus lepomis* differs from that of *P. sinitsini* in which the cercariae escape from the sporocysts in the snail, *Goniobasis liviscens,* and encyst in the amphipod *Hyalella knickerbockeri.* Fish become infected by eating parasitized crustaceans.

EXERCISE ON LIFE CYCLE

Eggs obtained from adult worms collected from the gall bladder of fish may be incubated to observe development and hatching. Note the unique number and arrangement of the epidermal plates.

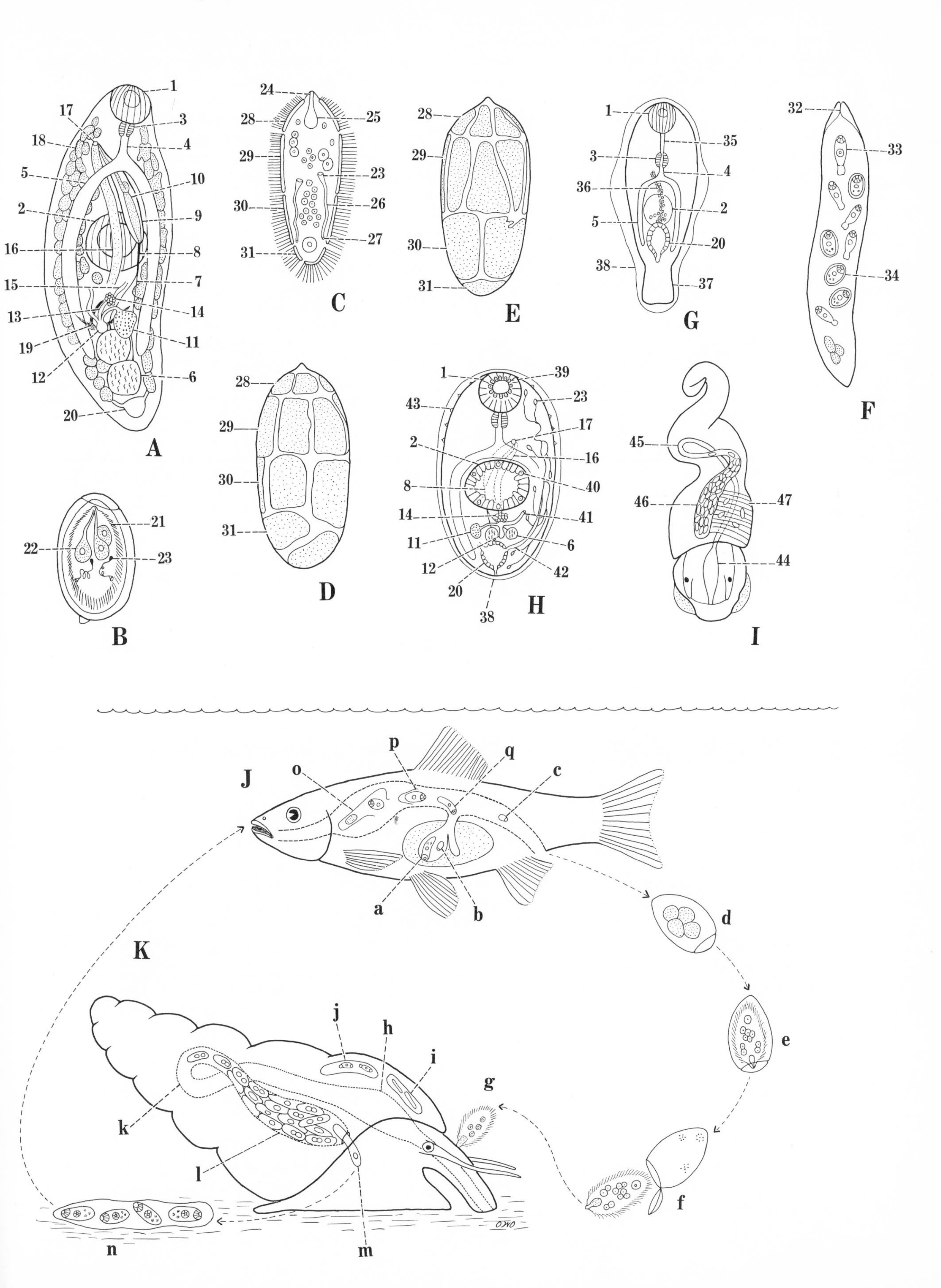
A
B
C
D
E
F
G
H
I
J
K
a
b
c
d
e
f
g
h
i
j
k
l
m
n
o
p
q

EXPLANATION OF PLATE 78 ⇨

A. Adult fluke. **B.** Embryonated egg. **C.** Miracidium. **D.** Mother sporocyst. **E.** Daughter sporocyst. **F.** Anterior portion of cercarial tail showing chamber with cercaria enclosed. **G.** Excysted metacercaria. **H.** Frog *(Rana* spp.*)* definitive host. **I.** Clam *(Musculium partumeium)* first intermediate host. **J.** Snail *(Physa)* second intermediate host. **K.** Snail *(Helisoma)* second intermediate host. **L.** Tadpole *(Rana* spp.*)* second intermediate host (salamander larvae, *Ambystoma maculatum,* become infected). **M.** Crayfish *(Cambarus* sp.*)* second intermediate host.

1, oral sucker; **2,** ventral sucker; **3,** oesophagus; **4,** intestine; **5,** testis; **6,** seminal vesicle; **7,** common genital pore; **8,** ovary; **9,** uterus; **10,** vitelline gland; **11,** embryonated egg; **12,** miracidium; **13,** apical gland; **14,** penetration glands; **15,** flame cell; **16,** germ cells; **17,** germinal mass destined to form daughter sporocyst; **18,** birth pore; **19,** germinal masses; **20,** cercaria escaping through birth pore of daughter sporocyst; **21,** tail of cercaria; **22,** chamber walls of cavity forming anterior portion of cercarial tail; **23,** cercaria detached from stem of tail; **24,** excretory bladder; **25,** point of attachment of cercaria to its tail; **26,** vas efferens; **27,** excretory pore.

a, adult fluke in urinary bladder; **b,** embryonated eggs deposited in urinary bladder; **c,** eggs expelled with urine into water hatch quickly; **d,** swimming miracidium drawn through incurrent siphon into gill chamber of clam penetrates tissues; **e,** mother sporocyst in gills; **f,** daughter sporocyst giving birth to fully developed cercariae; **g,** cercariae freed from sporocysts make their way through the tissues into the gill chamber; **h,** cercariae escape from clam through excurrent siphon; **i,** cercariae are swallowed by snails, tadpoles, and crayfish; **j,** cercariae pass into intestinal wall; **k,** encysted metacercariae in intestinal wall; **l,** frogs acquire the parasites by eating infected intermediate host; **m,** metacercariae released when intermediate hosts are digested; **n,** young fluke released from cyst by action of digestive juices migrates to urinary bladder; **o,** flukes travel up ureters to kidneys or up oviducts and return to urinary bladder in two weeks where they develop to maturity in 21 to 60 days.

Adapted from Goodchild, 1948, J. Parasit. 34:407.

Expose small *Goniobasis livescens* to infection by miracidia and determine if it can be accomplished experimentally and, if successful, try to ascertain the early developmental stages of the parasite. Observe adult snails collected from areas where infected fish occur for the appearance of the colorful sporocysts containing the cotylocercous cercariae and encysted metacercariae. Also dissect infected snails to locate the two generations of sporocysts and present evidence that both generations do occur. Note the route of exit through the snail of sporocysts containing metacercariae.

Feed sporocysts containing metacercariae that have escaped from the snails to small cyprinids and follow the development of the parasites in them.

SELECTED REFERENCES

Dobrovolny, C. G. (1939). Trans. Amer. Micr. Soc. 58:121; (1939). J. Parasit. 25:461.

FAMILY GORGODERIDAE

The members of this family are parasites of the urogenital system of fish, amphibians, and reptiles. The body of some species is divided into a narrow anterior and a broad posterior portion. The suckers are well developed, with the ventral one much the larger and projecting prominently from the ventral side of the body. The testes are two or more in number. The ovary lies between the testes and the ventral sucker. Vitellaria consist of two compact or lobed glands located behind the ventral sucker and between the caeca.

Gorgodera amplicava Looss, 1899 (Plate 78)

G. amplicava is known to parasitize the urogenital system of most anurans and one urodele in North America.

DESCRIPTION. The body is 3 to 5 mm long with the anterior portion smaller in proportion than the posterior, being about one-third as long and thicker than one-fourth as wide. The ventral sucker is 2.5 to 3.0 times larger than the oral sucker. There are nine testes, with five in a row on the same side as the ovary and four on the other. The ovary lies on the left side between the testes and

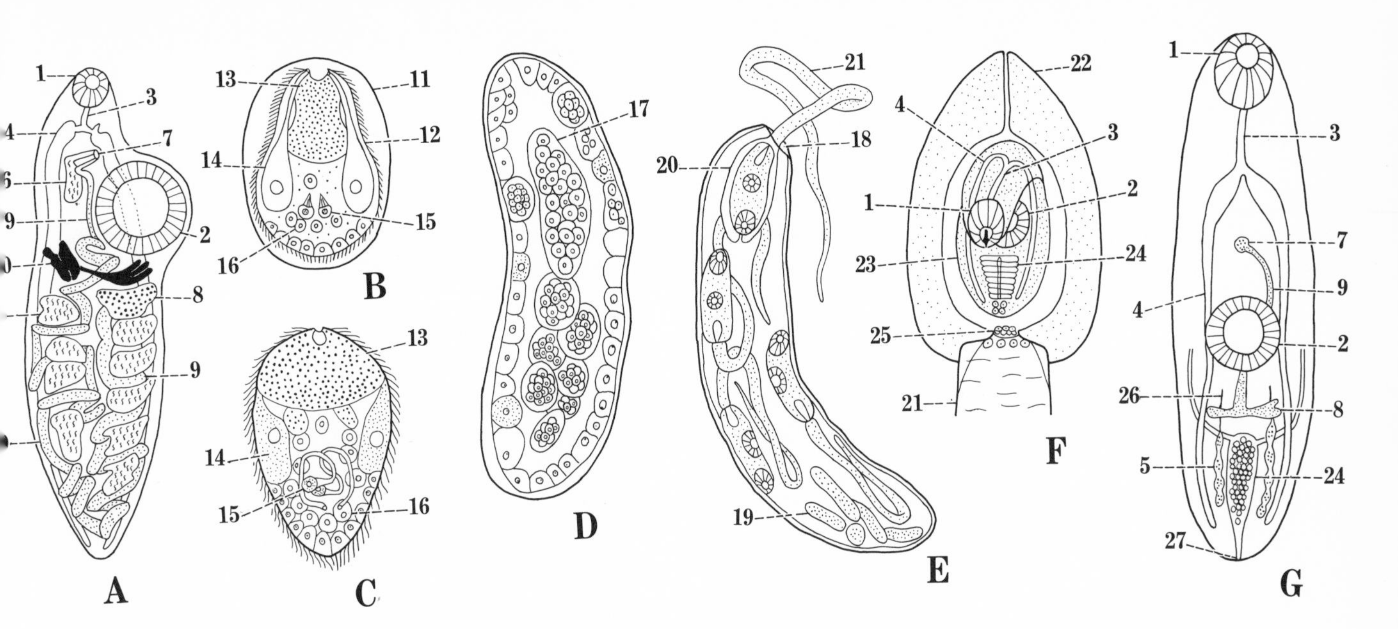

A
B
C
D
E
F
G

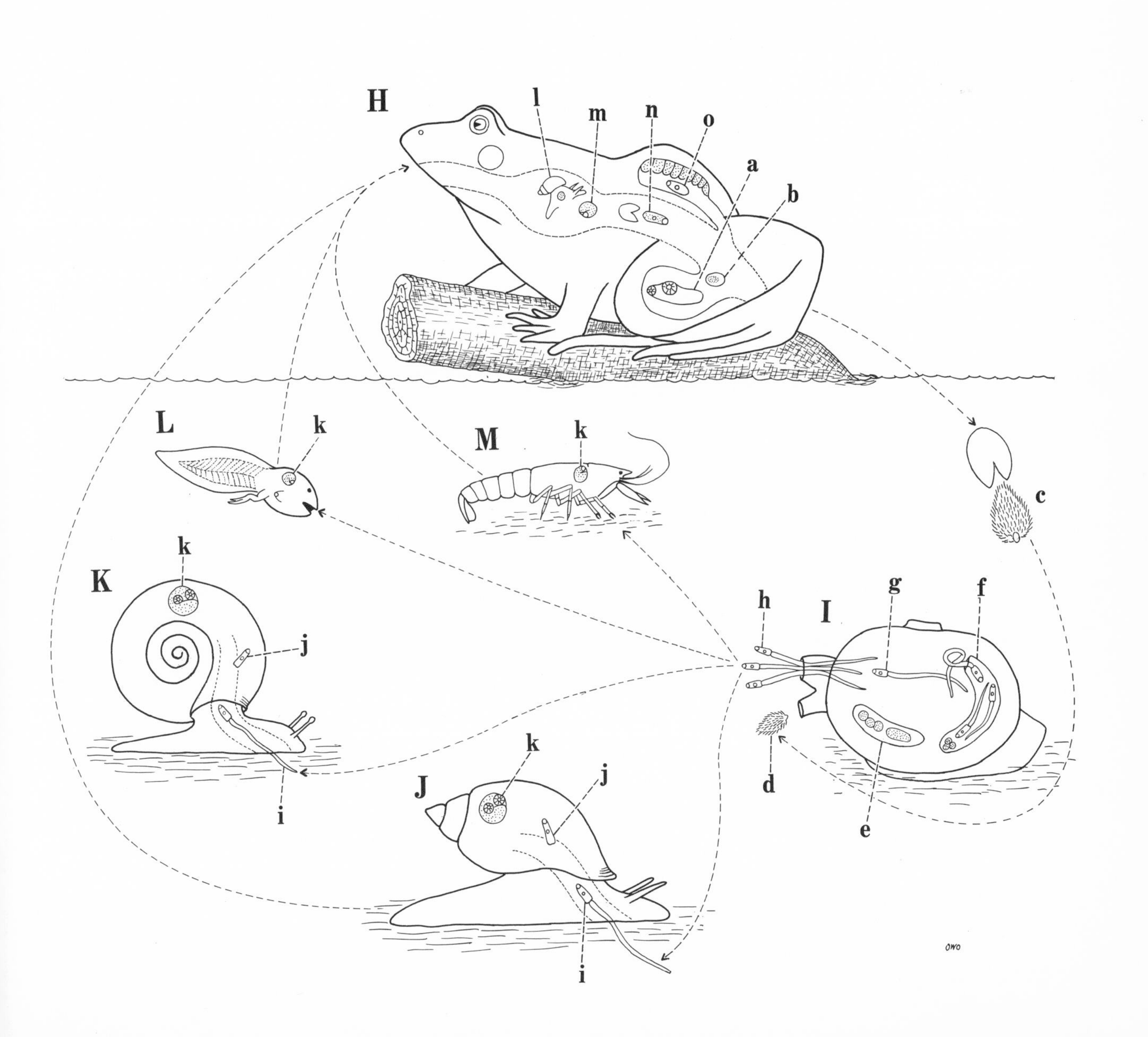

H
I
J
K
L
M

the posterior margin of the ventral sucker. The vitelline gland consists of two groups of follicles between the ventral sucker and ovary. The eggs are fully developed when laid.

LIFE CYCLE. Adult worms in the urinary bladder lay fully embryonated non-operculate eggs. They are voided with the urine and hatch almost immediately or up to 1 day after reaching the water.

The miracidia are deliberate swimmers, living up to 72 hours in the water, after which death ensues if they have not entered *Musculium partumeium,* a fingernail clam, which serves as the only first intermediate host in this country. The miracidia do not seek the clams but are drawn into the mantle cavity through the incurrent siphon by the current of water flowing into it. When in contact with the gills, they attach and penetrate within 10 minutes.

Upon entering the gills, the miracidia transform to mother sporocysts. Growth is slow. Small germ balls developing in the wall are shed into the central cavity and slowly develop into a single generation of daughter sporocysts after 40 to 50 days.

Daughter sporocysts are located ventrally between the inner and outer gill lamellae of the clams and appear as large entangled masses wholly embedded in the gill tissue. Up to 16 fully developed cystocercous cercariae may be present in a single daughter sporocyst. They escape singly through a terminal birth pore. The cercariae are 12 to 17.4 mm long. They consist of an almost structureless tail with a deep chamber at one end in which the young fluke is enclosed. The stylet-bearing larval fluke itself is spindle-shaped and 0.6 to 0.78 mm long by 0.195 to 0.235 mm wide.

Cercariae are liberated from the gills of the clams during the late afternoon and early evening, being expelled through the excurrent pore into the water. The tail is smooth and glistening when first expelled but soon becomes sticky and adheres to objects in the water. The wriggling cercariae attract tadpoles of frogs, larvae of salamanders (*Ambystoma maculatum*), snails (*Physa halei, P. parkeri, Lymnaea traskii, Helisoma trivolvis, H. antrosa, Pseudosuccinea columella*) and crayfish (*Cambarus* sp.) which eat them. The young distomes emerge from the anterior chamber of the tail in the mouth, stomach, and intestine of these second intermediate hosts. They creep over the surface of the intestine for 10 or 15 minutes, after which they burrow into the wall and encyst within it. The metacercariae are infective to frogs after they have been in tadpoles approximately 24 hours. Dragon fly larvae do not become infected even though they eat the cercariae.

Frogs become parasitized when they swallow infected second intermediate hosts. Upon digestion of the hosts in the stomach, the metacercarial cysts are liberated. Excystment may occur in the stomach but more often in the small intestine. The larval flukes migrate posteriorly through the intestine, arriving in the cloaca in 8 hours or less. They seek out the openings of the excretory and reproductive ducts and migrate up them, remaining about 2 weeks. After this time, they return to the urinary bladder where changes leading to the adult worms take place. Some flukes become sexually mature in 21 days and all of them are fully developed by the end of 2 months.

Other species of Gorgoderinae, whose life cycles have been worked, have a pattern similar to that of *Gorgodera amplicava.* The first intermediate host is a clam and the second an anamniotic vertebrate.

Gorgoderina attenuata from frogs (*Rana*) and newts (*Triturus viridiscens*) develop in sporocysts in *Sphaerium occidentalis.* The cercariae encyst in tadpoles when eaten by them (Rankin).

Phyllodistomum solidum from the urinary bladder of the dusky salamander (*Desmognathus fuscus*) develops in sporocysts in the fingernail clam *Pisidium abditum.* Odonatan naiads (*Ischnura verticalis, Argia* sp., *Enallagma* sp., *Libellula* sp.) serve as the second intermediate hosts. The metacercariae encyst in the thoracic haemocoel (Goodchild).

EXERCISE ON LIFE CYCLE

Fully embryonated eggs may be obtained from infected frogs by grasping them behind the front legs and squeezing quickly. They react by struggling and forcefully emit urine which may be caught in a container. Note that the eggs are nonoperculate. Study the miracidia inside the eggs. With a micropipette, transfer some of the eggs from the urine to water and note the rapidity with which they hatch. Determine the point of dilution of the urine with water at which eggs will hatch.

Put a specimen of *Musculium partumeium* in a small dish of water together with miracidia. Note whether they react to the mollusk. By means of a micropipette, place some miracidia in the current of water going into the inhalent siphon and observe how they are carried by it. Pipette miracidia onto the gills of an open clam and observe their reaction and penetration into the tissue. After they have completely entered the gills, fix them for sectioning to observe the location and condition of the miracidia.

Cercariae from naturally infected clams may be used for study. Find the daughter sporocysts by dissecting the mollusks. Watch the cercariae escape through the birth pore. Place fully developed cercariae in separate dishes with snails, tadpoles, and small crayfish and observe them being eaten. Dissect specimens of each species of intermediate host shortly after they have eaten the cercariae to observe the migration into the intestinal wall and encystment.

Feed several heavily infected tadpoles or snails to each of a dozen uninfected mature frogs. Examine the alimentary canal, ureters with associated ducts, kidneys, and urinary bladder of four frogs at intervals of 2 hours, beginning 6 hours after giving the metacercariae to them. Note the course of migration before the flukes enter the urinary bladder the first time. Examine one of the remaining eight frogs every third day to determine migrations in the body prior to returning to the urinary bladder where final development to maturity takes place.

SELECTED REFERENCES

Cort, W. W. (1912). Trans. Amer. Micr. Soc. 31:151.

Goodchild, C. G. (1943). Biol. Bull. 84:59; (1948). J. Parasit. 34:407.

Krull, W. H. (1935). Papers Mich. Acad. Sci., Arts and Lett. 20:697.

Rankin, J. S. (1939). Amer. Midl. Nat. 21:476.

FAMILY TROGLOTREMATIDAE

The Troglotrematidae are small to medium-sized fleshy flukes with spinous cuticle and dense vitellaria. They are parasites of the intestine, lungs, nasal cavities, frontal sinuses, and subcutaneous tissues in birds and mammals in many parts of the world.

Paragonimus kellicotti Ward, 1908 (Plate 79)

This parasite occurs as pairs in cysts in the lungs of cats, dogs, pigs, muskrats, rats (experimental), wildcats, and mink from North America. On the basis of the frequency of natural infections, mink are believed to be the natural host.

DESCRIPTION. The adult flukes have thick oval-shaped bodies 7 to 12 mm long, 4 to 6 mm wide, and 3 to 5 mm thick. They are covered with scalelike spines. The ventral sucker is slightly anterior to the middle of the body. Unbranched caeca extend to near the posterior end of the body. The two testes are irregularly lobed, slightly oblique, and in the posterior third of the body. There is no cirrus pouch, but a prostate gland is present. The ovary is lobed, larger than the testes, and on the right side near the level of the ventral sucker. The genital pore is at the posterior margin of the ventral sucker. Extensive vitelline glands fill the lateral fields for almost the full length of the body. Eggs measure 75 to 118 μ long by 48 to 65 μ wide.

LIFE CYCLE. Adult flukes in cysts in the lungs of the definitive hosts lay unembryonated eggs which are transported up the trachea, into the pharynx, and swallowed. They are voided in the faeces. Development at summer temperatures requires at least 2 weeks, at the end of which some hatch. Others are very retarded in development and do not hatch for at least 4 months.

The miracidia are very active just prior to hatching time. Their movements probably aid in forcing off the operculum. In swimming about, they come in contact with *Pomatiopsis lapidaria, P. cincinnatiensis,* and *Oncomelania nosophora,* the snails which serve as the first intermediate hosts. They penetrate the head and neck of the young snails; old ones are refractory.

Upon entering the snail hosts, the miracidia accumulate around the oesophagus, stomach, and intestine where they transform into inactive saclike mother sporocysts. They mature in 2 weeks and

EXPLANATION OF PLATE 79 ⇨

A. Adult fluke. **B.** Miracidium. **C.** Mature mother sporocyst. **D.** Mother redia. **E.** Daughter redia. **F.** Cercaria. **G.** Encysted metacercaria. **H.** Mink *(Mustela vison)* definitive host. **I.** Snail *(Pomatiopsis lapidaria)* first intermediate host. **J.** Crayfish *(Cambarus* spp.*)* second intermediate host.

1, oral sucker; **2,** ventral sucker; **3,** pharynx; **4,** intestine; **5,** testis; **6,** vas efferens; **7,** common genital pore; **8,** ovary; **9,** oviduct; **10,** uterus; **11,** vitelline glands; **12,** vitelline duct; **13,** excretory bladder; **14,** apical papilla; **15,** lateral papilla; **16,** flame cell; **17,** excretory tubule; **18,** anterior and first row of six epidermal plates; **19,** second row of six epidermal plates; **20,** third row of three epidermal plates; **21,** fourth and last row of a single epidermal plate; **22,** mother redia; **23,** daughter redia; **24,** cercaria; **25,** oral spine; **26,** prepharynx; **27,** penetration glands; **28,** ducts of penetration glands; **29,** common collecting tubule of excretory system; **30,** cyst of metacercaria; **31,** encysted metacercaria.

a, two adult flukes in cyst in lungs; **b,** unembryonated eggs laid in cysts pass up trachea and are swallowed; **c,** eggs mixed with faeces; **d,** eggs leave body in faeces; **e,** eggs develop in water where hatching occurs; **f,** miracidium free in water; **g,** miracidium penetrates snail intermediate host; **h,** mature mother sporocyst with mother rediae inside; **i,** mother redia with daughter rediae; **j,** daughter redia with cercariae; **k,** cercaria free in water; **l,** cercaria penetrates soft parts of crayfish and migrates to heart; **m,** metacercaria encysts on heart of crayfish; **n,** definitive host acquires parasites by eating infected crayfish; **o,** metacercaria is freed from crayfish when latter is digested; **p,** metacercaria free in digestive tract; **q,** young fluke escapes from metacercarial cyst in intestine; **r,** young fluke passes through intestinal wall into coelom; **s,** fluke migrates forward in coelom; **t,** young fluke migrates through diaphragm into pleural cavity; **u,** flukes burrow into lungs where cysts connecting with the air ducts are formed and development proceeds to maturity.

Figure A somewhat schematic from several sources; B-G, from Ameel, 1934, Amer. J. Hyg. 19:279.

---

begin producing short, stumpy mother rediae, each with a well-developed collar-like thickening around the anterior end.

The mother rediae escape from the sporocysts about 29 days after infection of the snails. They come to rest in the lymph channels adjacent to the liver and develop to maturity in approximately 34 days, *i.e.*, 63 days after infection. The number of daughter rediae present at one time is small, averaging about 12 per individual.

Upon escaping from the mother rediae, the daughter rediae migrate into the lymph system of the liver. They are fully developed and contain mature cercariae as soon as 15 days later, or 78 days after infection of the snails. In some snails, however, development may be delayed another 2 weeks. There is an average of around 22 cercariae per daughter rediae at any one time.

The cercariae are spiny, microcercous, stylet-bearing forms that emerge in the late afternoon and early evening, a time that coincides with the activity of the crayfish hosts. The cercariae enter crayfish (*Cambarus propinquis, C. robustus, C. virilis, C. diogenes, C. rusticus*), penetrating the soft membranous chitin between the segments. All parts of the crayfish are vulnerable to them during ecdysis. Upon entering the body, the cercariae go to the cardiac region, arriving within 12 hours.

Encystment takes place on the outside of the heart. The metacercariae generally are aligned in a transverse band extending over the dorsal side of the heart between the two ostia. A thin cyst appears around each fluke by the fifth day and they are infective by the 46th day. On the average, there are 20 to 30 cysts per crayfish but 147 have been reported. Old cysts are thick-walled, hyaline, and have a reddish color.

Infection of the definitive hosts occurs when they eat parasitized crayfish. The metacercariae are freed from their cysts in the small intestine and the young flukes migrate through the intestinal wall into the peritoneal cavity as early as 5 hours after being swallowed. They travel forward to the diaphragm and burrow through it into the pleural cavity by 96 hours at the earliest, but a few are still in the abdominal cavity 259 days later. Some reach the lungs in 14 days after entering the host. The flukes usually occur as pairs in lung cysts; occasionally there may be more per cyst. In small mammals, the cysts appear as nodules projecting above the surface of the lungs, whereas in large mammals they may be deep below the surface. Sexual maturity is attained in 22 to 24 weeks. Infection in cats persists at least 27 months, and perhaps longer.

PLATE 79 *Paragonimus kellicotti*

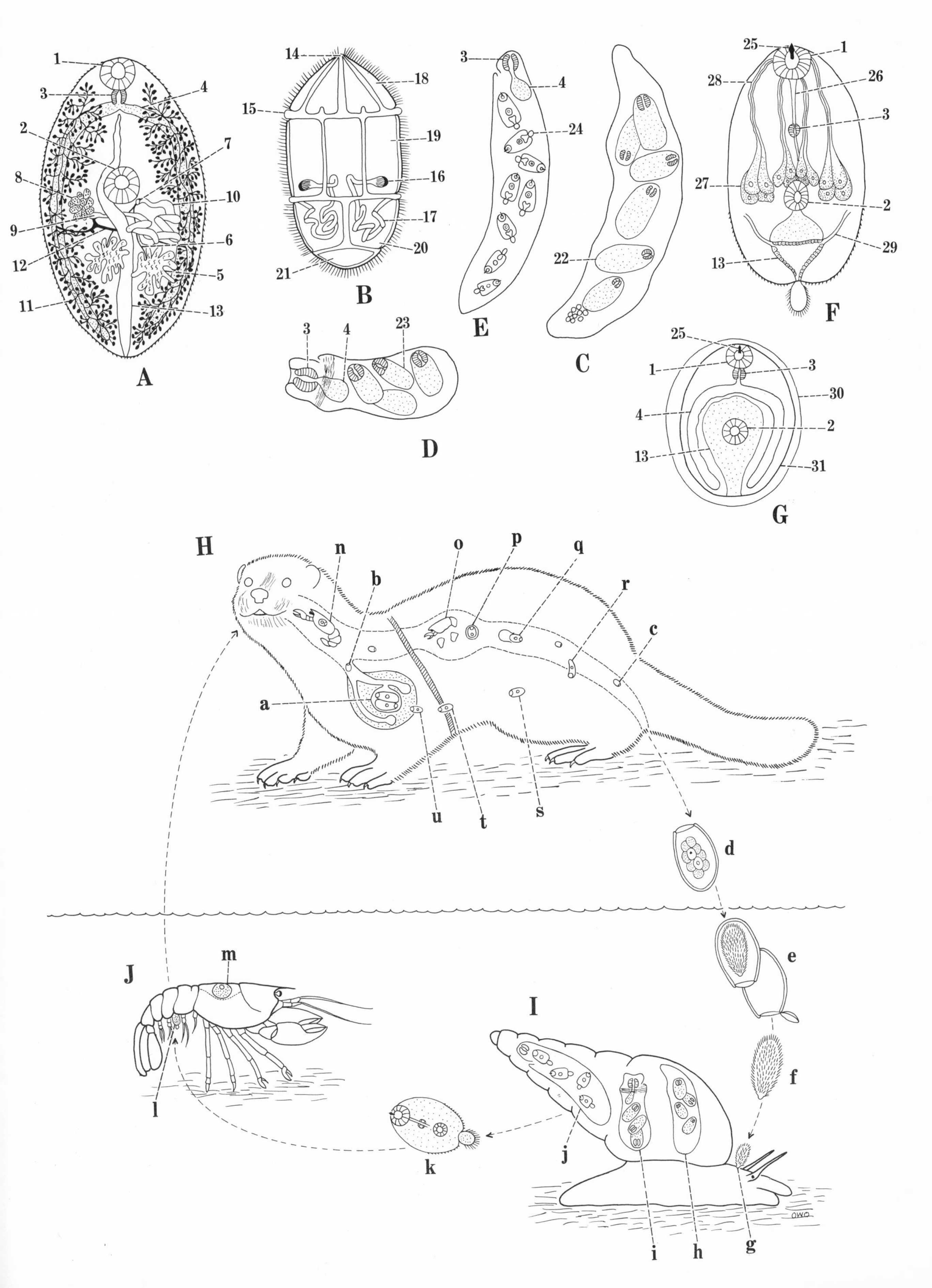

Paragonimus westermani, the oriental lung fluke which some workers believe to be conspecific with *P. kellicotti*, infects man as well as a number of domestic and wild animals. It is a fluke of great medical importance in oriental countries because of the frequency with which it occurs and the extent of the pathology it produces in humans. Its life cycle is very similar to that of *P. kellicotti*, except crabs in addition to crayfish serve as intermediate hosts.

EXERCISE ON LIFE CYCLE

The quickest and easiest way to determine whether *Paragonimus kellicotti* occurs in a region is to examine the hearts of crayfish for the metacercariae whose location and morphology are characteristic.

Upon finding a source of metacercariae, infection experiments with white rats or cats may be conducted. Using rats, feed at least half a dozen of them simultaneously with upward of 25 metacercariae each. Examine one rat after 6 hours to check for flukes in the small intestine and the peritoneal cavity. After 96 to 125 hours, examine a second one for flukes in both the peritoneal and pleural cavities. Sixteen days after infection, examine the lungs and body cavities of a third rat for flukes. If none appear in the lungs at this time, examine a fourth one. Keep the two remaining ones to determine the prepatent period by means of faecal examinations for the appearance of eggs.

Examine *Pomatiopsis lapidaria* from the same area where the infected crayfish originated for natural infections with sporocysts, rediae, and cercariae. Note the different sizes of the two generations of rediae. Observe the spiny microcercous cercariae. Expose small crayfish to the cercariae. Examine infected individuals at 1-hour intervals for a period of 8 hours after infection to determine when the metacercariae reach the pericardial cavity. Sacrifice one of the remaining individuals daily for the next 14 days to ascertain when encystment occurs.

If eggs are available, incubate them at room temperature and note when hatching occurs. Expose young *Pomatiopsis lapidaria* to miracidia in order to follow the intramolluscan development. Find the sporocysts around the oesophagus, stomach, and intestine, and the rediae in the liver. Note the time when cercariae appear. Carcasses of wild mink when available should be examined for eggs to be used in infecting snails.

SELECTED REFERENCES

Ameel, D. J. (1932). J. Parasit. 18:264; (1934). Amer. J. Hyg. 19:279.

Ameel, D. J., W. W. Cort, and A. Van der Woude. (1951). J. Parasit. 37:395.

Basch, P. F. (1959). J. Parasit. 45:273.

Chen, P. D. (1937). Trans. Amer. Micr. Soc. 56:208.

Woodhead, A. E. (1954). Trans. Amer. Micr. Soc. 73:16.

Yokogawa, M., H. Yoshimura, M. Sano, T. Okura, and M. Tsuji. (1962). J. Parasit. 48:525.

Nanophyetus salmincola Chapin, 1927 (Plate 80)

N. salmincola is a parasite of the small intestine of dogs, foxes, coyotes, raccoons, lynx, and mink in the Pacific northwest of the United States. A similar form, *N. schikhobalowi*, has been reported from humans in eastern Siberia. In the United States, it transmits *Neorickettsia helminthoeca* to dogs which is the cause of a highly fatal malady in them. Coyotes and foxes also succumb to the disease but mink appear to be immune.

DESCRIPTION. Adult flukes are 0.9 to 2.5 mm long by 0.3 to 0.5 mm wide. The suckers are nearly equal in size with the ventral one near the middle of the body or slightly anterior. The pharynx and oesophagus are about equal in length and the caeca extend near or to the posterior margin of the testes. The testes are large oval bodies arranged symmetrically at the sides in the posterior half of the body. A large cirrus pouch is located to the right of the midline and behind or somewhat dorsal to the ventral sucker; it contains a large seminal vesicle divided by a constriction into two subequal parts. The round ovary is considerably smaller than the oral sucker and located near or adjacent to it on the left of the midline. The common genital pore is median and near the posterior margin of the ventral sucker. Vitellaria consist of irregular follicles scattered over the dorsal part of the body except that portion cephalad from the caecal bifurcation. Eggs measure 82 to 97 μ long by 38 to 55 μ wide.

LIFE CYCLE. Unembryonated eggs are passed in the faeces. They develop slowly, requiring a minimum of 85 days at room temperature; many take 185 to 200 days to hatch.

Newly hatched miracidia swim at random, not being attracted to snails. However, upon coming in contact with the snail intermediate host (*Oxytrema silicula*), they burrow into them. The immediate development of the miracidia upon entering the snails is unknown. At least no sporocysts have been observed. Only rediae are known. They are small in size, taper posteriorly, and contain a few small germ balls; medium-sized ones have only a few cercariae inside; and large mature individuals are filled with 74 to 76 cercariae. They are liberated intermittently, often by the thousands, in long strands of mucus where they live up to 48 hours. Small fish may even become entangled in the mucus threads.

The cercariae show no reactions upon coming close to fish. If, however, they touch the fish at any point, they attach and quickly penetrate, entrance being completed in 30 seconds to 2 minutes. They soon enter the blood vessels and are carried to all the organs of the body, including the cornea and retina. In addition to salmonid fish, many other species are susceptible to and parasitized by *N. salmincola*.

Being transported to all the internal organs where encystment occurs, the cercariae cause high mortality in small fish. If the cyst ruptures, the flukes are able to re-encyst, indicating that the cyst is of parasite origin. Metacercariae over 10 days of age are infective. When fish harboring them are eaten by mammalian hosts, the young flukes are released in the intestine and grow to maturity in 6 to 7 days.

Because of the high incidence of infection of snails, it is believed that mink and raccoons, which eat fish and defaecate in the water, are the most common natural definitive hosts.

Sellacotyle mustelae Wallace, a closely related minute form, occurs in the small intestine of mink. The cercariae develop in rediae in *Campeloma rufum* and encyst in fish, mainly bullheads (*Ameiurus melas*). The metacercariae are infective after 8 days and develop to maturity in mink by the fifth day.

EXERCISE ON LIFE CYCLE

The characteristic cercariae are easily recognized by their short tails, stylet, and large mucous gland on the ventral side near the posterior end of the body. Observe the strands of mucus emitted by the snail with the cercariae entangled in them.

Expose small fish to a large number of cercariae and observe their reaction to the infection. When the fish die, fix them and section various organs and part of the musculature to ascertain the location of the cercariae. In fish less heavily exposed, observe the metacercariae and distribution of them in the body.

Six days and again 10 days after infection, feed metacercariae to hamsters in order to determine first, the approximate time required for the metacercariae to attain infectivity, and second, the prepatent period of the flukes.

Place eggs in a bottle of water and observe them weekly for a period of 6 to 7 months to follow the rate of development and time required for hatching.

Expose small snails to miracidia and search for sporocysts; also observe development of the rediae and cercariae.

SELECTED REFERENCES

Bennington, E., and I. Pratt. (1960). J. Parasit. 46:91.
Chapin, E. A. (1926). N. Amer. Vet. 7(4):36.
Philip, C. B. (1955). J. Parasit. 41:125.
Wallace, F. G. (1935). J. Parasit. 21:143.
Witenberg, G. (1932). J. Parasit. 18:258.

ORDER OPISTHORCHIIDA

The cercariae of this order have caudal excretory vessels during development. An oral stylet is never present.

EXPLANATION OF PLATE 80 ⇨

A. Adult fluke. **B.** Mother redia. **C.** Daughter redia. **D.** Lateral view of cercaria. **E.** Encysted metacercaria. **F.** Excysted metacercaria. **G.** Dog definitive host. **H.** Snail *(Oxytrema silicula)* first intermediate host. **I.** Fish *(Salvelinus salmo, Onchorhynchus* and others) second intermediate host.

1, oral sucker; **2,** ventral sucker; **3,** prepharynx; **4,** pharynx; **5,** oesophagus; **6,** intestine; **7,** testes; **8,** vas efferens; **9,** vas deferens; **10,** seminal vesicle; **11,** common genital pore; **12,** ovary; **13,** oviduct; **14,** uterus; **15,** egg in uterus; **16,** Laurer's canal; **17,** vitelline glands; **18,** vitelline duct; **19,** common vitelline duct; **20,** developing daughter redia; **21,** birth pore; **22,** cercaria; **23,** germinal masses; **24,** oral spine; **25,** penetration glands; **26,** genital anlagen; **27,** excretory bladder; **28,** mucous gland; **29,** tail; **30,** cyst of metacercaria; **31,** metacercaria; **32,** ruptured cyst of metacercaria.

a, adult fluke embedded in wall of small intestine; **b,** unembryonated eggs laid in intestine; **c,** eggs pass from body in faeces; **d,** eggs develop in water and hatch; **e,** miracidium free in water; **f,** miracidium penetrates snail; **g,** mother sporocyst presumably occurs but has not been reported; **h,** mother redia; **i,** daughter redia; **j,** cercaria having escaped from daughter redia is free in tissues of snail; **k,** cercaria free in water; **l,** cercaria attaches to salmonid fish, entering muscular tissue; **m,** encysted metacercaria in fish; **n,** dog becomes infected by eating fish carrying metacercariae; **o,** digestion of fish releases metacercaria; **p,** young fluke escapes from metacercarial cyst and attaches to the wall of the intestine where maturity is attained in 5 to 6 days.

Adapted from Bennington, 1951, M. S. Thesis, Oregon State Univ., and Bennington and Pratt, 1960, J. Parasit. 46:91.

Suborder Opisthorchiata

These are medium- to small-sized flukes with weakly developed musculature. They lack a cirrus pouch and the testes are behind the ovary. A seminal receptacle is present.

The primary pores of the V-shaped or globular excretory bladder of the cercaria open on the lateral margins of the tail near its base. The tail is pleuro- or parapleuro-lophocercous, *i.e.,* bearing a finlike membrane. Encystment is in the lower vertebrates, chiefly fish.

SUPERFAMILY OPISTHORCHIOIDEA

The general description is the same as for the suborder. The eggs are small, thick-shelled, and operculate.

FAMILY HETEROPHYIDAE

The species of this family are small to minute, ovoid or pyriform distomes having weak suckers with the ventral one often in a genital sinus. The cuticle is covered with large scales. A genital sucker (gonotyl) or sinus is present and near the acetabulum. The loops of the uterus lie in front of the testes. The vitellaria are lateral.

Apophallus venustus (Ransom, 1920) (Plate 81)

These small flukes are parasites in the ileum of dogs, cats, raccoons, and great blue herons in eastern Canada and the northeastern section of the United States.

DESCRIPTION. Mature specimens have elongated oval to pyriform bodies 0.95 to 1.4 mm long by 0.25 to 0.55 mm wide. The anterior half of the body is covered with scale-like spines and the hind fourth is smooth. The ventral sucker is slightly smaller than the oral one and is situated at the posterior margin of the genital sinus near the middle of the body. The pharynx and oesophagus combined are about one-fourth the length of the body, and the caeca reach to the posterior extremity of it.

The testes are arranged obliquely in the posterior half of the body and a large S-shaped seminal vesicle opens into the genital sinus. The ovary is partially overlapped by the seminal vesicle. A large transverse seminal receptacle lies just posterior from the ovary. Vitelline glands extend laterally from the intestinal bifurcation to the posterior end of the body. The excretory bladder is Y-shaped with the stem extending between the testes. Eggs measure 26 to 32 μ long by 18 to 22 μ wide.

LIFE CYCLE. Fully embryonated eggs are passed in the fæces but they do not hatch until eaten by the fresh-water snail *Goniobasis livescens.* The miracidia migrate through the intestinal wall into

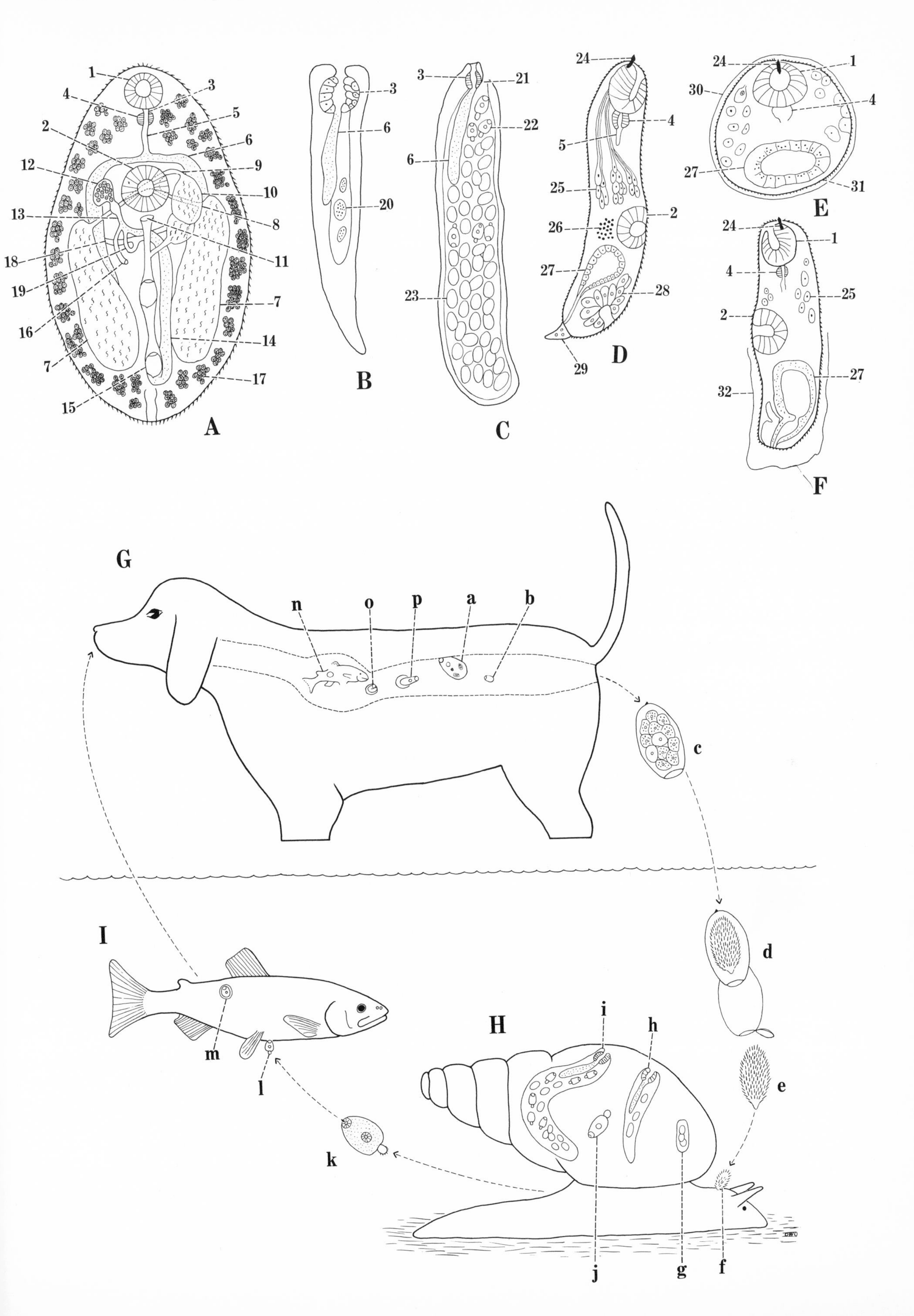
A
B
C
D
E
F
G
H
I
n
o
p
a
b
c
d
e
f
g
h
i
j
k
l
m

EXPLANATION OF PLATE 81 ▷

A. Adult fluke. **B.** Embryonated egg. **C.** Mother redia. **D.** Young daughter redia. **E.** Sinistral view of cercaria. **F.** Ventral view of cercaria without tail. **G.** Encysted metacercaria. **H.** Heron *(Ardea herodias)* definitive host. **I.** Cats, together with dogs and raccoons serve as definitive hosts. **J.** Snail *(Goniobasis livescens)* first intermediate host. **K.** Bullheads *(Ameiurus melas)* are the second intermediate host.

1, oral sucker; **2,** ventral sucker; **3,** pharynx; **4,** oesophagus; **5,** intestine; **6,** testis; **7,** vas efferens; **8,** vas deferens; **9,** seminal vesicle; **10,** common genital pore; **11,** ovary; **12,** seminal receptacle; **13,** uterus; **14,** vitelline glands; **15,** vitelline duct; **16,** vitelline reservoir; **17,** miracidium; **18,** germ cells; **19,** cercaria in redia; **20,** eyespots; **21,** genital anlagen; **22,** tail; **23,** prepharynx; **24,** penetration glands; **25,** ducts of penetration glands; **26,** dorsal membranous tail fin; **27,** ventral membranous tail fin; **28,** excretory bladder.

a, adult fluke embedded in mucosa of intestine; **b,** embryonated eggs laid; **c,** eggs pass out of intestine in faeces; **d,** eggs drop in water but do not hatch; **e,** embryonated eggs eaten by snails; **f,** eggs hatch in intestine and miracidium migrates through intestinal wall; **g,** mother sporocyst presumably forms, producing mother redia; **h,** mother redia containing daughter redia; **i,** daughter redia with cercaria; **j,** cercaria escaping from snail host; **k,** cercaria free in water; **l,** cercaria penetrating bullhead host, casting its tail in the process; **m,** metacercariae encysted in muscles, reaching infectivity in about 4 weeks; **n,** infection of definitive hosts occurs when they ingest infected fish; **o,** digestion of fish host releases metacercariae; **p,** young fluke escapes from cyst and penetrates intestinal mucosa, developing to maturity in about 1 week.

Adapted from Cameron, 1936, Canad. J. Res. D. 14:59.

---

the tissues. Although mother sporocysts have not been seen, they do occur in other members of the family and on that basis they are presumed to be present in this species.

Small rediae filled with spherical cells appear about 16 days after infection of the snails. Large ones containing long-tailed cercariae appear later. Possibly these are mother and daughter rediae, respectively, although their identity is not certain.

The cercarial tails are about 1½ times the length of the body and bear a complete dorsal and a partial ventral membranous fin. There are two eyespots and a rudimentary ventral sucker. Sixteen large glands practically fill the body. The cercariae are fully developed when shed daily by the snails between the hours of 8 and 10 P.M. o'clock. While they lash about rapidly in the water, progress is largely in an up and down direction. When they come in contact with fish of about a dozen common species (bullheads, catfish, garpike, common suckers, carp, dace, pickerel, pike, small-mouth bass, sunfish, bowfins), they quickly penetrate the fins, enter the blood vessels, and go to the muscles where encystment occurs. An adventitious cyst formed by the fish surrounds that secreted earlier by the parasites. The metacercariae grow slowly, becoming infective in about 4 weeks.

Infection of the definitive host takes place when fish harboring metacercariae in their flesh are eaten, developing to maturity in 7 days. The flukes are lost from the host in a few months.

Apophallus imperator encysts in trout in Quebec. It develops in experimentally infected cats and pigeons. The other hosts are unknown. Presumably its life cycle is similar to that of *A. venustus.*

Cryptocotyle lingua is a common heterophyiid trematode of gulls, terns, cormorants, kittiwakes, murres, loons, bitterns, grebes, herons, and other fish-eating birds, as well as cats, rats, and guinea pigs under experimental conditions. Cercariae develop in rediae in the marine snail *Littorina littorea* and encyst in the skin of cunners. Birds and mammals become infected by eating parasitized fish.

Heterophyes heterophyes, another member of the family, is well known because it parasitizes humans in the Near and Far East where raw fish are eaten. Metacercariae are common in mullets from brackish water. Eggs deposited among the villi of the small intestine of vertebrate hosts work into the wall and enter the blood vessels. Upon reaching the coronary circulation of the heart, their presence results in serious damage to that organ.

EXERCISE ON LIFE CYCLE

When adult flukes are available from cats or herons, eggs may be obtained for infecting *Goniobasis livescens.* Infect a sufficient number of small snails to examine one or two daily for several weeks to follow

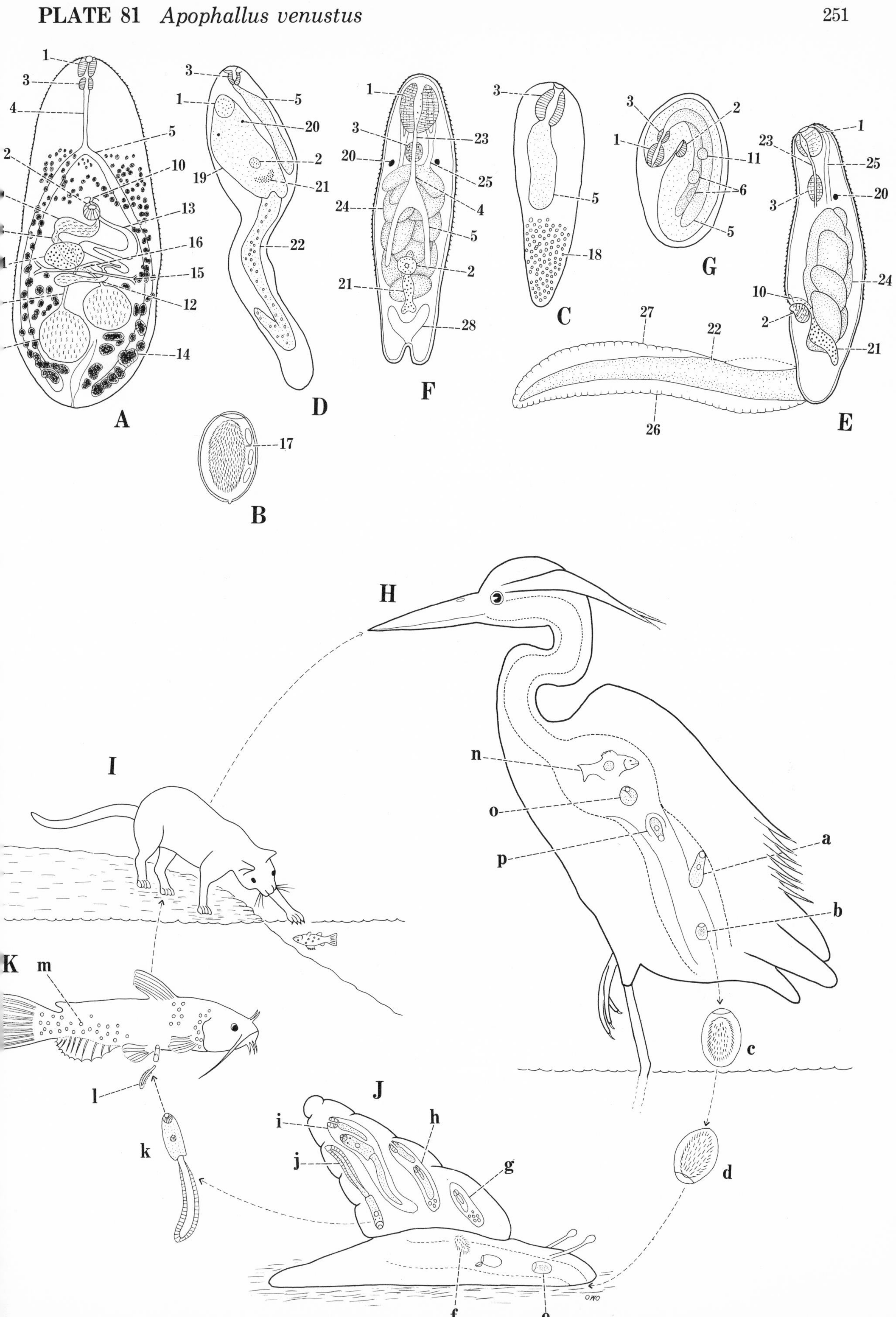
A
B
C
D
E
F
G
H
I
J
K
a
b
c
d
e
f
g
h
i
j
k
l
m
n
o
p

EXPLANATION OF PLATE 82 ⇨

A. Adult fluke. **B.** Mother sporocyst. **C.** Mother redia. **D.** Daughter redia. **E.** Pleurolophocercous cercaria. **F.** Encysted metacercaria. **G.** Dog definitive host. **H.** Mink and fox definitive hosts. **I.** Human definitive hosts. **J.** Snail *(Amnicola limosa porata)* first intermediate host. **K.** Fish *(Catastomus commersoni)* second intermediate host.

1, oral sucker; **2,** ventral sucker; **3,** pharynx; **4,** intestine; **5,** testes; **6,** ovary; **7,** seminal receptacle; **8,** uterus filled with eggs; **9,** vitellaria; **10,** developing mother rediae; **11,** gut; **12,** germinal masses; **13,** developing cercariae; **14,** eyespots; **15,** prepharynx; **16,** penetration glands; **17,** excretory bladder; 18, hairlike process; **19,** tail; **20,** finfold; **21,** encysted metacercaria; **22,** inner cyst; **23,** outer cyst.

a, adult fluke in bile ducts of liver; **b,** embryonated eggs laid in bile ducts pass out of body with faeces; **c,** eggs in water do not hatch; **d,** eggs hatch in intestine of amnicolid snail when eaten; **e,** young mother sporocyst; **f,** mature mother sporocyst filled with developing rediae; **g,** mother redia containing embryonic daughter rediae; **h,** daughter redia with developing cercariae; **i,** cercaria escaping from snail; **j,** cercaria free in water; **k,** cercaria penetrating sucker, casting its tail in the process; **l,** metacercariae encysted in musculature; **m,** infection of dog takes place when suckers containing viable metacercariae are eaten; **n,** digestion of fish releases metacercariae from muscles; **o,** pancreatic juices dissolve outer cyst and young fluke ruptures inner cyst to escape; **p,** young flukes enter liver by migrating through common bile duct, maturing in about 28 days.

Adapted from Cameron, 1944, Canad. J. Res. 22:6.

---

the complete development of the parasite, namely, the mother sporocyst, the mother and daughter rediae, and cercariae.

If naturally infected snails occur in the area, they may be used to conduct experimental infections of bullheads. The pleurolophocercous cercariae are characteristic and strongly suggest the identity of the general group of flukes. Fish, especially bullheads, from the same area should already be naturally infected. By grinding some of the fish and allowing them to be digested in artificial gastric juice, metacercariae may be obtained for study and feeding experiments.

By feeding infected bullheads to cats, the prepatent period can be determined and adult flukes obtained for study.

SELECTED REFERENCES

Cameron, T. W. M. (1936). Canad. J. Res. D. 14:59; (1937). Ibid. 15:38, 275.

Faust, E. C., and P. R. Russel. (1957). Craig and Faust's Clinical Parasitology, 6th Ed. Lea and Febiger, Philadelphia, p. 587.

Lyster, L. L. (1940). Canad. J. Res. 18:106.

Stunkard, H. W. (1930). J. Morph. Physiol. 50:143.

FAMILY OPISTHORCHIIDAE

These are parasites of the gall bladder and bile ducts of all classes of vertebrates in many parts of the world. They generally are medium-sized and weakly muscled flukes, but some are very long, with poorly developed suckers. A cirrus pouch is usually absent and the tubular seminal vesicle is free in the parenchyma. The many-coiled uterus winds between the ovary and genital pore which is just preacetabular. The excretory bladder is Y-shaped.

Metorchis conjunctus (Cobbold, 1860) (Plate 82)

M. conjunctus occurs in the liver of dogs, foxes, cats, raccons, mink, muskrats, and occasionally humans in North America, particularly in the eastern half of Canada.

DESCRIPTION. There is great variation in the dimensions of this species, depending on the host in which it developed; larger flukes occur in the larger hosts. Adults range from 1 to 6.6 mm long by 0.59 to 2.6 mm wide. The suckers are about equal in diameter, which is roughly equal to the length of the pharynx. The genital pore lies at the anterior margin of the acetabulum. Voluminous caeca extend almost to the posterior extremity of the body. The lobed or entire testes are tandem or slightly oblique, and lie in the third quarter of the body. There is no cirrus pouch and the seminal vesicle is an enlarge-

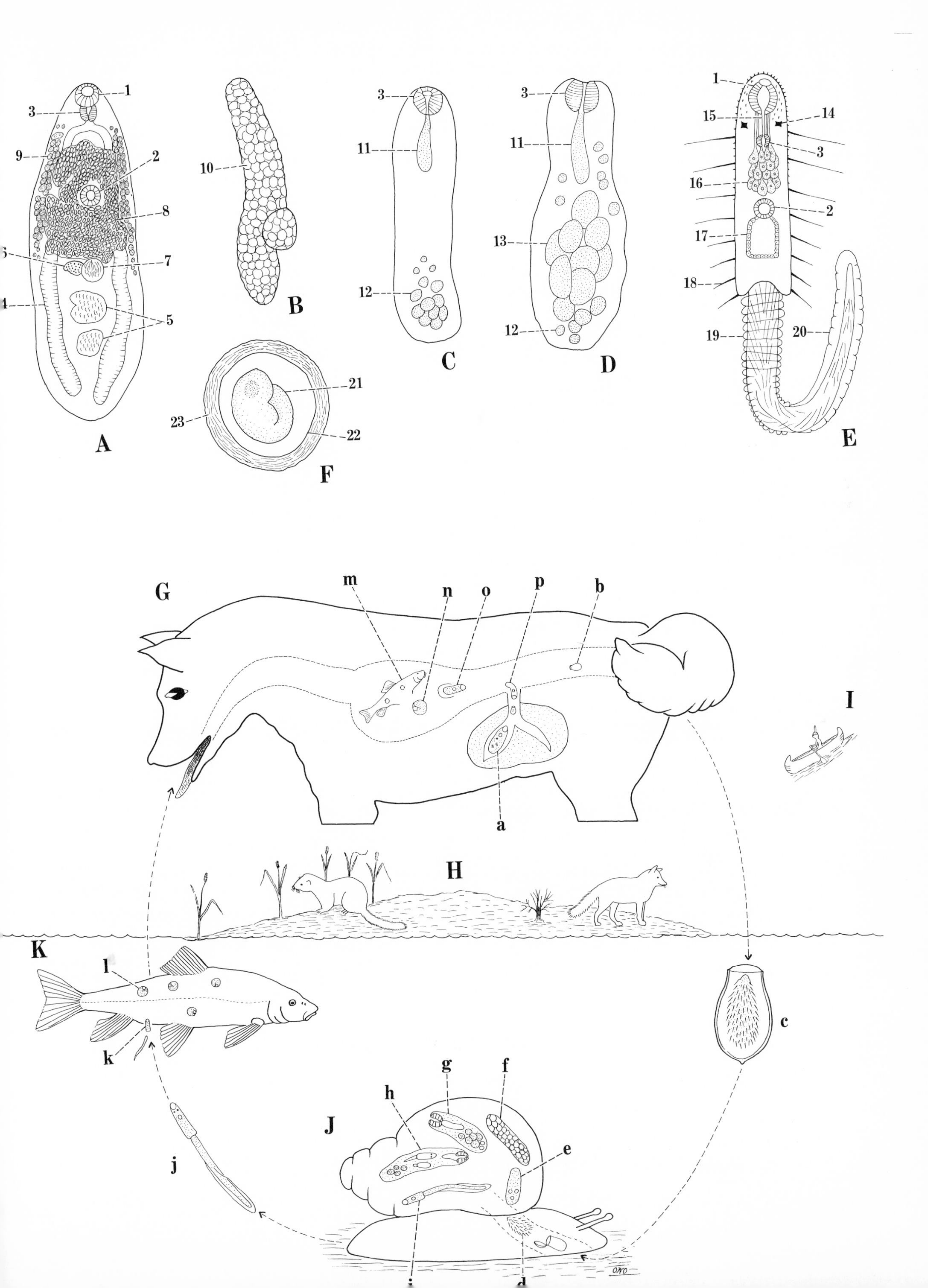

1
3
9
2
8
6
7
4
5
A
10
B
3
11
12
C
3
11
13
12
D
1
15
14
3
16
2
17
18
19
20
E
23
21
22
F
G
m
n
o
p
b
a
I
H
K
l
k
c
g
f
h
J
e
j
OKO

ment of the vas deferens. The ovary is a spherical, oval, or trilobed body located a short distance in front of the anterior testis and partially overlaid by a seminal receptacle larger than it in size. The uterus occupies nearly all the intercaecal space anterior to the ovary. Vitelline glands are lateral, never crossing the middle line of the body, and extend from the intestinal bifurcation to the ovary. Eggs measure 22 to 32 μ long by 11 to 18 μ wide.

LIFE CYCLE. Embryonated eggs laid in the bile ducts or gall bladder enter the intestine and are voided with the faeces. Hatching occurs in the intestine of the snail *Amnicola limosa porata.* The sparsely ciliated miracidia penetrate the gut wall, enter the liver, and transform into mother sporocysts. There is one generation of rediae and it produces typical pleurolophocercous cercariae. The anterior half of the cercarial body is covered with minute spines and the posterior half bears eight pairs of long, protoplasmic, hairlike processes. Upon reaching the water, they exhibit positive heliotropism and are able to survive 60 to 75 hours.

When contact is made with the common sucker (*Catastomus commersoni*), the cercariae burrow into them, encysting in the lateral muscles from the level of the dorsal fin to the tail. The metacercariae are enclosed in a double cyst. They are able to survive freezing in the fish.

Definitive hosts infect themselves by eating suckers that harbor viable metacercariae. These are freed in the stomach as the fish are digested. The outer cyst is dissolved in the pancreatic juices and the fluke escapes from the inner one, presumably as a result of muscular activity rather than from the effect of digestion. The young flukes migrate through the ductus choledochus to the liver where development proceeds to maturity. Eggs appear in the faeces in 28 days. The flukes are known to live 5 years in cats but how long beyond this time is unknown. Sledge dogs commonly become infected from frozen suckers fed to them as the main item of food. Young dogs frequently die as a result of infection. Since canine hepatitis and *Metorchis conjunctus* have been found associated in dogs, these flukes have been suggested as transport hosts.

Species of *Metorchis* (*M. intermedius, M. orientalis, M. taiwanensis, M. xanthosoma*) of ducks have a similar life cycle, with fish as the second intermediate host. *Opisthorchis tonkae* from muskrats encyst in the shiner *Notropis delicious.* Another species of this family is *Clonorchis sinensis,* the Oriental liver fluke which is of great public health importance in many parts of Asia. The cercariae encyst in cyprinid fish and people become infected by eating them raw.

These cycles are representative of those species of the family known to have pleurolophocercous cercariae that develop in rediae and the metacercariae encyst in fish.

EXERCISE ON LIFE CYCLE

If pleurolophocercous cercariae are obtained from naturally infected snails, they should be identified and allowed to encyst in fish similar to those found in the same habitat. When infected fish are fed to a variety of hosts such as ducks, rats, guinea pigs, and cats, it is likely that adult worms will be obtained from some of them.

Eggs recovered from any of these hosts can be used in experiments to infect snails and study the development of the intramolluscan stages.

If only adult opisthorchiids are obtained from a vertebrate host, eggs dissected from them or obtained from the gall bladder or faeces of the host should be fed to common snails, preferably species of genera known to serve as the intermediate host. In the event eggs are available, an entire life cycle may be worked out by careful planning. If the adult flukes are present in an area, the other stages are likely to be there.

SELECTED REFERENCES

Cameron, T. W. M. (1944). Canad. J. Res. 22:6.

Dollfus, R. P., and A. Buttner. (1953). Ann. Parasit. Hum. Comp. 28:450.

Faust, E. C., and P. F. Russell. (1957). Craig and Faust's Clinical Parasitology, 6th Ed. Lea and Febiger, Philadelphia, p. 580.

Heinemann, E. (1937). Z. Parasitenk. 9:237.

Monogeau, N. (1961). Canad. Vet. J. 2:33.

Wallace, F. G., and L. R. Penner. (1939). J. Parasit. 25:437.

Suborder Hemiurata

The cercariae are of the cystophorous type or a modified form of it. They have a saclike or cylindrical excretory bladder with the main collecting tubules fused anteriorly. The eggs are small, often with a filament opposite the operculum, and contain a nonciliated spinose miracidium with large spines on the anterior end. The cercariae develop in rediae and encyst in copepods and ostracods.

SUPERFAMILY HEMIUROIDEA

These flukes are elongate, nonspinous, and with the suckers widely separated. The testes are in the posterior part of the body and anterior to the ovary. The vitellaria are sparse.

FAMILY HALIPEGIDAE

The Halipegidae occur under the tongue and in the Eustachian tubules of frogs. Vitellaria are divided into two compact masses located at the posterior extremity of the body.

Halipegus eccentricus Thomas, 1939 (Plate 83)

This is a comparatively rare fluke of the Eustachian tubes of adult frogs in Michigan. Other species occur in Massachusetts, California, Colorado, Oregon, Canada, and Mexico, as well as other parts of the world.

DESCRIPTION. Fully grown worms are 6 to 6.5 mm long by 1.8 mm wide, the body being almost cylindrical. The oral sucker is subterminal and the ventral one near the middle of the body or caudad from it. The oesophagus is extremely short and the caeca extend to the posterior end of the body. The testes are extracaecal and obliquely arranged in the last third of the body. The ovary is median in position and posterior to the testes, being very near the caudal end of the body. The few vitelline glands, which consist of four to five follicles each, are between the ovary and the hind end of the body. Eggs measure 67 μ long by 27 μ wide; the opercular end is broad while the other terminates as a long filament.

LIFE CYCLE. Adult flukes deep in the Eustachian tubes lay fully embryonated eggs which work downward through the canal into the mouth, are swallowed, and eventually voided with the faeces.

Hatching takes place in the intestine of snails (*Physa gyrina, P. sayii, P. parkeri, Helisoma trivolvus*). The nonciliated miracidia have a spiny cuticle and eight large penshaped spines at the anterior end. They burrow through the intestinal wall by means of the spines, and possibly with the aid cf histolytic secretions.

Once inside the tissue of the snail, the miracidia slowly change into mother sporocysts about which little is known. They produce three to eight rediae characterized by punctate orange-yellow bands within a month after entering the snail hosts.

Only a single generation of redia has been reported. In about 1 month, they produce cercariae that are enclosed within a bulbous tail. The bulblike structure is complicated in morphology. It contains the elongated and somewhat coiled cercaria with a long fluted excretory appendage attached to the posterior end. There are two long ribbon-like appendages between which is a conical delivery tube.

Cercariae lying on the bottom of the pond thrust out the excretory tubule whose movement appears to attract cyclops (*Cyclops vulgaris, Mesocyclops obsoletus*). The crustaceans attack and ingest the cercariae. Upon entering the intestine, the cercarial body detaches from the bulbous cystlike structure and begins migrating posteriorly along the gut. It soon burrows through the wall into the haemocoel.

Within the body cavity of the cyclops, the cercaria transforms into a quite different type of unencysted metacercaria. It is cylindrical with the oral sucker terminal and the ventral sucker near the posterior end. A tuft of villi evert from the excretory bladder. They become infective within 2 to 3 weeks.

Infection of the frogs takes place when the tadpoles eat infected cyclops. Upon being freed from the cyclops in the stomach the flukes remain in the cardiac end of it until metamorphosis. During this time, the villi of the excretory bladder are inverted. As the tadpoles transform into frogs, the flukes migrate up the oesophagus into the mouth, and finally into the Eustachian tubes of fully developed frogs where maturity is attained.

EXPLANATION OF PLATE 83 ⇨

A. Ventral view of adult worm. **B.** Embryonated egg. **C.** Free miracidium. **D.** Young mother sporocyst. **E.** Young redia. **F.** Cystophorous cercaria recently escaped from snail. **G.** Cercaria with excretory tubule extended. **H.** Metacercaria from cyclops. **I.** Frog intermediate host. **J.** Snail *(Physa)* intermediate host. **K.** Cyclops second intermediate host. **L.** Tadpole definitive host.

1, oral sucker; **2,** ventral sucker; **3,** pharynx; **4,** intestine; **5,** testis; **6,** ovary; **7,** vitelline glands; **8,** uterus; **9,** spines; **10,** apical gland; **11,** penetration glands; **12,** germ cells; **13,** spined cuticle; **14,** gut; **15,** germinal masses; **16,** orange-yellow colored band; **17,** bulbous portion of tail; **18,** cercaria; **19,** excretory appendage; **20,** excretory bladder; **21,** delivery tube; **22,** streamers; **23,** developed excretory bladder; **24,** everted villi of excretory bladder.

a, adult fluke in Eustachian tube; **b,** embryonated eggs pass down Eustachian tube into pharynx; **c,** eggs pass down intestine; **d,** eggs enter water in faeces; **e,** eggs hatch only when eaten by snail host; **f,** miracidium migrates through wall of intestine; **g,** spined cuticle is cast off; **h,** mother sporocyst; **i,** banded redia with developing cercariae; **j,** cystophorous cercaria escaping from snail; **k,** cercaria with everted excretory tubule free in water; **l,** when eaten by cyclops, cercaria detaches from tail and passes through intestinal wall into haemocoel; **m,** metacercaria in haemocoel; **n,** tadpole becomes infected by eating cyclops; metacercariae remain in stomach without further development until tadpole metamorphoses into adult at which time they migrate into the Eustachian tubes and develop to maturity.

Adapted from Thomas, 1939, J. Parasit. 25:207.

The life cycle of *Halipegus occidualis* is similar in most respects to that of *H. eccentricus. Helisoma antrosa* is the snail intermediate host, and *Cyclops vernalis, C. serrulatus,* and the ostracod *Cypridopsis vidua* have been infected experimentally as the second intermediate hosts. Metacercariae have been found in mature dragon flies (*Libellula incesta*). Presumably dragon fly naiads become infected by eating cyclops harboring metacercariae which transfer to them, continuing on through metamorphosis. Hence frogs could become infected by eating dragon flies as naiads, tenerals, or mature individuals. Frogs have been infected experimentally by placing metacercariae in the mouth.

Halipegus amherstensis produces sluggish sporocysts and rediae in the digestive gland of *Physa gyrina*. The metacercariae develop in *Cyclops viridus.* Adult flukes were found in the stomach of tadpoles, and the mouth and Eustachian tubes of frogs (*Rana catesbiana* and *R. clamitans*) in Massachusetts.

EXERCISE ON LIFE CYCLE

Cystophorous cercariae obtained in surveys of snails for cercariae in ponds where frogs occur may be suspected as being those of *Halipegus.*

Feed the cercariae to species of *Cyclops* known to serve as intermediate hosts for these flukes. Movement of the cercariae in the gut, their penetration into the haemocoel, and development into the metacercariae can be observed in living specimens.

Flukes in the Eustachian tubes of frogs can be detected by holding them toward the light. Infected frogs serve as a source of eggs for study and infecting species of *Physa* or *Helisoma* to observe development of the sporocyst, rediae, and cercariae.

Feed metacercariae to tadpoles and note the location and stage of development in the alimentary canal before, during, and after metamorphosis. Place some free metacercariae in the mouth of an adult frog and observe what happens to them.

SELECTED REFERENCES

Ameel, D. J., W. W. Cort, and A. Van der Woude. (1949). J. Parasit. 35:569.

Krull, W. H. (1935). Amer. Midl. Nat. 16:129.

Macy, R. W., and W. R. Demott. (1957). J. Parasit. 43:680.

Rankin, Jr., J. S. (1944). Trans. Amer. Micr. Soc. 63:149.

Thomas, L. J. (1934). J. Parasit. 20:285; (1939). Ibid. 25:207.

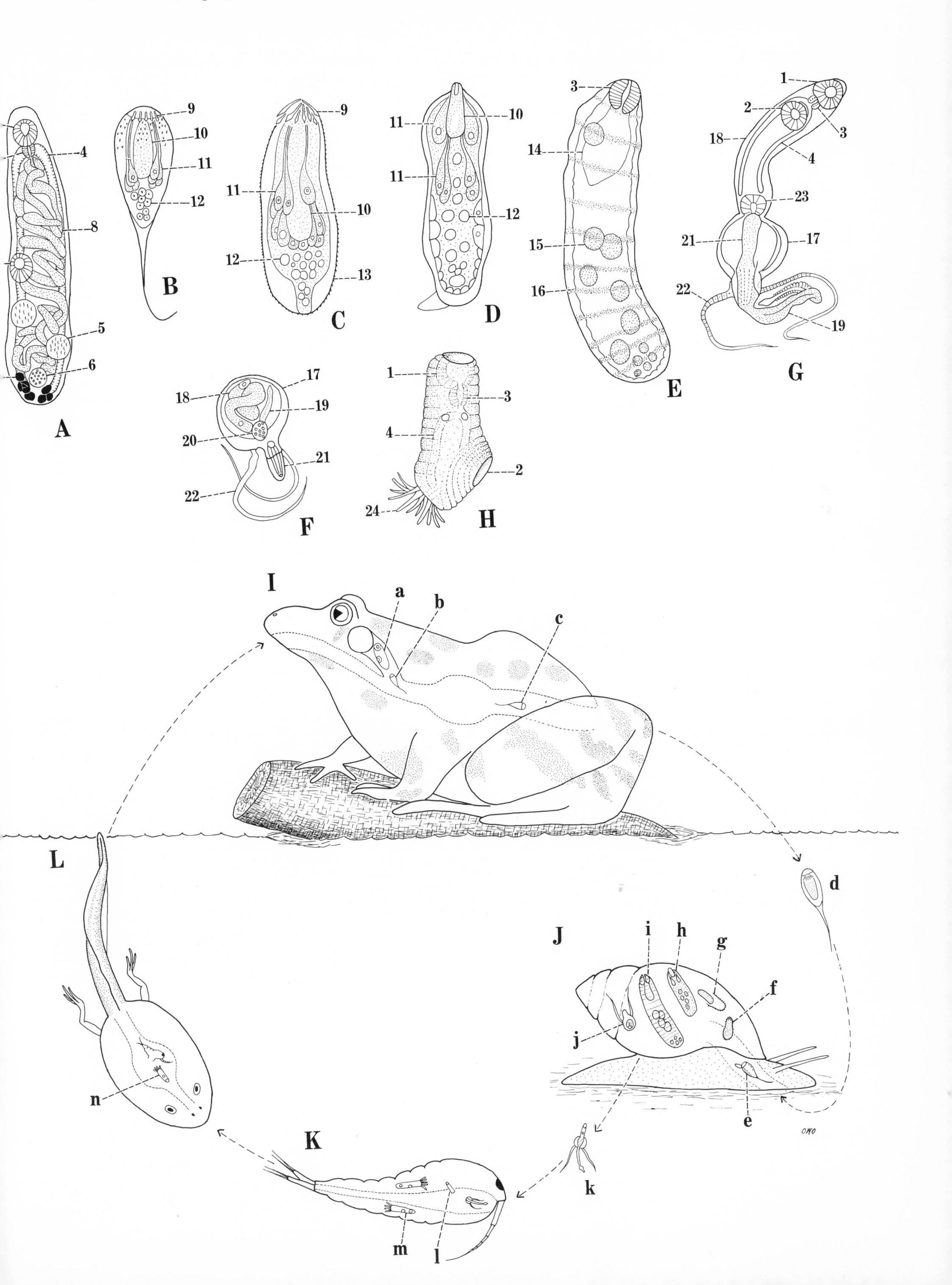
A
B
C
D
E
F
G
H
I
J
K
L
a
b
c
d
e
f
g
h
i
j
k
l
m
n

CLASS CESTODA

The cestodes are flat worms parasitic in fresh-water oliogochaetes and all classes of vertebrates, both aquatic and terrestrial. In some forms, the body consists of a single segment and is designated as monozoic, while in others, the body, or strobilus, is a chain of segments called proglottids, and are referred to as polyzoic forms. There is no digestive tract. For the most part, the adult cestodes are parasites of the digestive tract or liver.

About a dozen orders of cestodes are recognized. Of these, four occur in selachians. The remainder are found in fresh-water and terrestrial hosts and are the ones most frequently seen.

Common species of cestodes from four orders parasitizing fresh-water and terrestrial vertebrates have been chosen to depict the basic patterns of morphology and life cycles. These include the orders Caryophyllidea from oligochaete annelids and fish, Pseudophyllidea from all classes of vertebrates, Proteocephala from fish mainly, and Cyclophyllidea from birds and mammals. The basic life cycles of the Pseudophyllidea, Proteocephala, and Cyclophyllidea are presented in Plate 101.

Morphological Types (Plate 85)

The four common orders of cestodes found in fresh-water and terrestrial hosts have morphological features characteristic of each of them.

The Caryophyllidea (Figs. A-G) are monozoic. The sexual stages are considered as progenetic larval forms. The operculate eggs are unembryonated when laid.

In the genus *Archigetes* (Figs. A-C), the sexual stage is in the coelom of aquatic annelids. It resembles the tailed procercoid of the Pseudophyllidea. The life cycle is direct.

In *Caryophyllaeus* (Figs. D-G) and related genera, the sexual stage is in the intestine of catastomid fish. It resembles a plerocercoid of the Pseudophyllidea. Aquatic annelids serve as the first intermediate host, harboring the procercoid.

The Pseudophyllidea (Figs. H-N) and remaining orders are polyzoic. Members of this order are parasites of fish, amphibians, reptiles, birds, and mammals. Size varies greatly, ranging from small to large, even exceeding 40 feet in length.

The scolex is variable in shape but always bears a pair of longitudinal slits or bothria (Figs. H, N).

The proglottids are wider than long, with the genital openings on the midventral surface. A uterine pore is present, opening separately from but near those of the male and female organs. The gravid uterus is a long tube filled with eggs and folded into loops in the center of the proglottid between the ovary and uterine pore. The operculate eggs are unembryonated when laid.

The testes and vitelline follicles are numerous, small bodies scattered throughout the proglottid except for the space occupied by the ovary and uterus. The vitelline follicles are in a layer toward the ventral side of the proglottid and the testes in a layer toward the dorsal side.

The eggs are laid separately and the embryos hatching from them are ciliated hexacanths known as coracidia. The other larval stages are a procercoid in entomostraca and a plerocercoid in fish.

The Proteocephala (Figs. O-S) are parasites of fish primarily; a few species occur in amphibians and reptiles. They are different from the other polyzoic cestodes considered in having the vitelline follicles arranged in longitudinal bands along each lateral margin of the proglottids.

The cirrus pouch and vagina open in a common atrium located on the lateral margin of the proglottid. A uterine pore is lacking.

The unarmed scolex bears four muscular in-cupped suckers. A fifth sucker, or remnant of one, appears at the apex of the scolex.

The gravid uterus is a large saclike structure filling the intervitelline space. Uterine eggs contain fully developed, unciliated hexacanth larvae. Eggs are released when proglottids voided from the intestine disintegrate in the water. Procercoids occur in entomostracea and plerocercoids in the same crustaceans or in fish, varying according to the species of tapeworm.

The Cyclophyllidea (Figs. T-L′) include the largest number of families of polyzoic cestodes of any of the orders.

The scolex bears four in-cupped muscular suckers and in most species an armed rostellum.

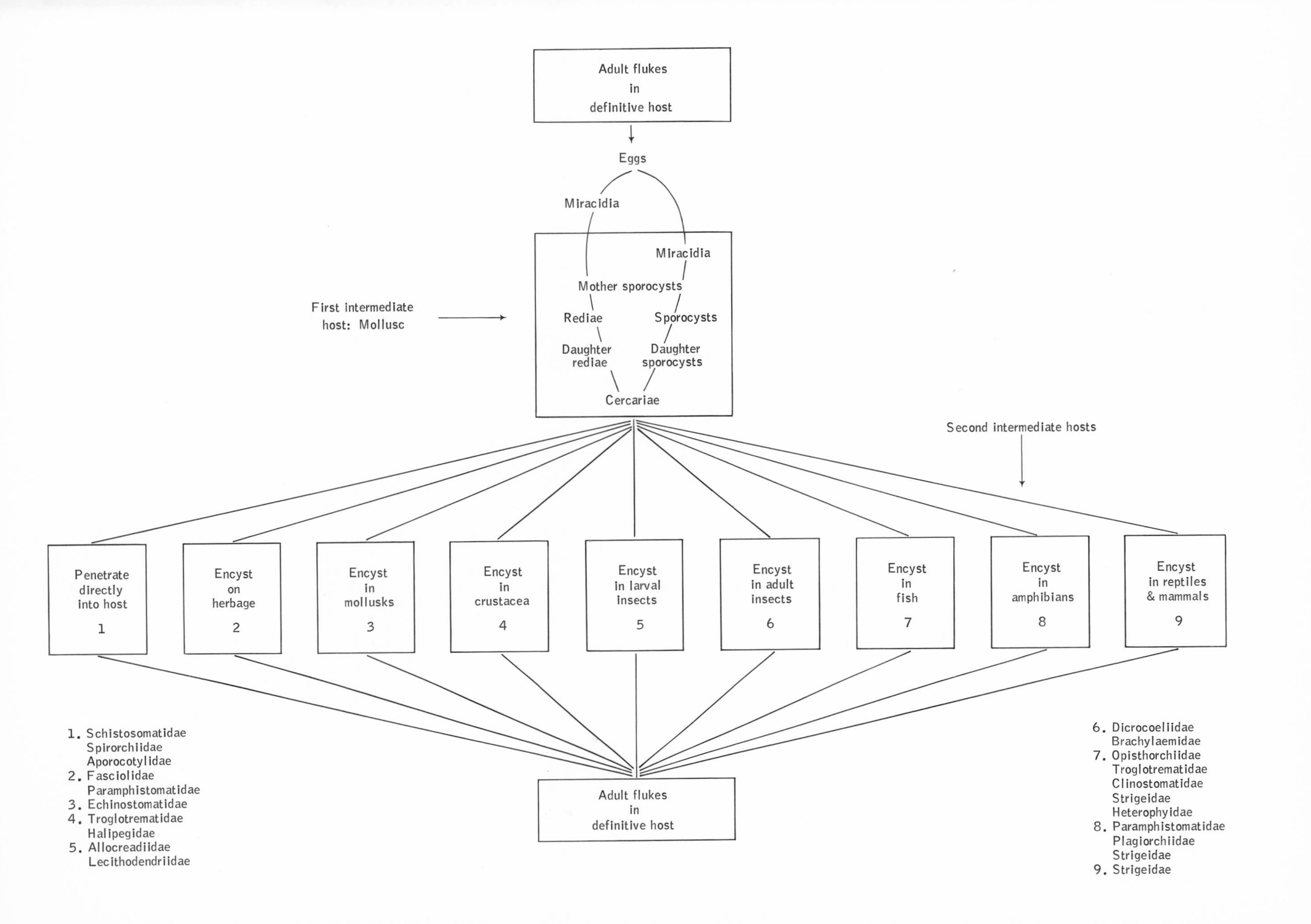
Adult flukes
in
definitive host
Eggs
Miracidia
Miracidia
Mother sporocysts
Rediae
Sporocysts
Daughter rediae
Daughter sporocysts
Cercariae
First intermediate host: Mollusc
Second intermediate hosts
Penetrate directly into host
1
Encyst on herbage
2
Encyst in mollusks
3
Encyst in crustacea
4
Encyst in larval insects
5
Encyst in adult insects
6
Encyst in fish
7
Encyst in amphibians
8
Encyst in reptiles & mammals
9
Adult flukes
in
definitive host
1. Schistosomatidae
Spirorchiidae
Aporocotylidae
2. Fasciolidae
Paramphistomatidae
3. Echinostomatidae
4. Troglotrematidae
Halipegidae
5. Allocreadiidae
Lecithodendriidae
6. Dicrocoeliidae
Brachylaemidae
7. Opisthorchiidae
Troglotrematidae
Clinostomatidae
Strigeidae
Heterophyidae
8. Paramphistomatidae
Plagiorchiidae
Strigeidae
9. Strigeidae

EXPLANATION OF PLATE 85

A-G. *Caryophyllidea.* **A-C.** *Archigetes sieboldi.* **A.** Procercoid-like adult. **B.** Embryonated operculate egg. **C.** Hexacanth larva. **D-G.** *Glaridacris catastomus.* **D-E.** Anterior and posterior ends of plerocercoid-like monozoic adult cestode. **F.** Unembryonated operculate egg. **G.** Procercoid.

H-N. *Pseudophyllidea.* **H.** Scolex of *Dibothriocephalus latus,* a polyzoic cestode, with two bothria. **I.** Mature proglottid. **J.** Gravid proglottid. **K.** Undeveloped operculate egg. **L.** Coracidium. **M.** Procercoid. **N.** Plerocercoid.

O-S. *Proteocephala.* **O.** Scolex of *Proteocephalus ambloplitis.* **P.** Mature proglottid. **Q.** Hexacanth embryo. **R.** Procercoid. **S.** Plerocercoid.

T-L′. *Cyclophyllidea.* **T-B′.** Taenioid cestodes. **T.** Scolex of hooked forms *(Taenia, Hydatigera, Multiceps, Echinococcus).* **U.** Scolex of nonhooked form *(Taeniarhynchus).* **V.** Mature proglottid. **W.** Gravid proglottid *(Taenia solium).* **X.** Taenioid egg. **Y-B′.** Different kinds of larval forms. **Y.** Cysticercus *(Taenia, Taeniarhynchus).* **Z.** Strobilocercus *(Hydatigera).* **A′.** Coenurus *(Multiceps).* **B′.** Hydatid *(Echinococcus).*

C′-K′. Non-taenoid cestodes. **C′-F′.** Types of proglottids. **C′.** *Hymenolepis* with single lateral genital pore and single set of reproductive organs. **D′-E′.** *Mesocestoides* with midventral genital pore. **D′.** Mature proglottid. **E′.** Gravid proglottid with paruterine organ, a specialized type of uterus. **F′.** *Dipylidium* with double genital pores and reproductive organs *(Anoplocephala* and *Thysanosoma* also have double sets of reproductive organs and double pores). **G′-I′.** Types of eggs. **G′.** Normal or common type represented by *Hymenolepis.* **H′.** Pyriform type of Anoplocephalidae. **I′.** Packet type of *Dipylidium;* the fringed tapeworm, *Thysanosoma,* produces a similar type. **J′-K′.** Larval types. **J′.** Tailed cysticercoid. **K′.** Nontailed cysticercoid. **L′.** Cross-section of proglottid of a cestode, showing structure.

1, adhesive organ; **2**, bothrium; **3**, sucker; **4**, apical sucker; **5**, rostellum; **6**, oncospheral hooks; **7**, tail or cercomer; **8**, common genital pore; **9**, cirrus pouch; **10**, testes; **11**, ovary; **12**, uterus; **13**, paruterine organ (gravid uterus); **14**, vitellaria; **15**, vagina; **16**, dorsal excretory or osmoregulatory canal; **17**, ventral excretory canal; **18**, cortex; **19**, medulla; **20**, circular muscles; **21**, internal longitudinal muscles; **22**, transverse muscles; **23**, external longitudinal muscles; **24**, cortical cells; **25**, cuticle; **26**, brood capsule; **27**, scolex.

Figures adapted from various sources.

The genital ducts open into a common atrium located on the side of body. In some species, a double set of reproductive organs is present, in which case an atrium is located on each side of the proglottid.

As a group, they are readily recognized from all others by the compact vitelline gland lying immediately caudad from the ovary. For convenience in consideration, they may be separated into two groups, the Taeniidae, or taenioid cestodes, and the remaining families, or non-taenioid cestodes.

The taenioid cestodes (Figs. T-B′) are characterized by several features, both morphological and biological. Most of these worms are large, muscular forms with an armed rostellum. The gravid uterus consists of a median stem with lateral branches. The eggs have thick shells, which in optical section appear to be striated. The larval stages consist of four kinds of bladders filled with fluid. They are 1) a cysticercus with a single invaginated scolex, 2) a strobilocercus in which the bladder is small and there is a long everted strobilus bearing an evaginated scolex, 3) a coenurus which is a single bladder containing numerous scolices attached to the inside of the wall, and 4) a hydatid consisting of a large capsule containing many smaller ones called brood capsules, each being attached by a slender stalk to the germinal layer of the mother cyst. The brood capsules produce scolices by a budding process from the wall. The larval stages of taenioid cestodes always develop in mammals that have swallowed eggs.

The non-taenioid cestodes (Figs. C′-L′) comprise an assembly of families varying in structural details but having a common type of larval form known as a cysticercoid. Its body consists of tissue rather than the fluid-filled, thin-walled bladder of the taenioid cestodes, and contains a retracted scolex. It develops in invertebrates and fish but not in mammals. In addition to the cysticercoid, there are other kinds of larvae. Members of the family Mesocestoididae have a larval form known as a tetrathyridium and those of the Paruterinidae have a plerocercoid.

The eggs vary but never have the thick, striated shell characteristic of the Taeniidae. The majority of the eggs are simple, oval, and thin-shelled. Those of the Anoplocephalidae have an inner membrane, with two finger-like processes, that encloses the embryo and is called a pyriform apparatus.

The scolex usually bears an armed rostellum but in some families (Anoplocephalidae, Mesocestoididae) it is absent.

The gravid uterus may be a network of tubules, may be saclike, may break up into small bits

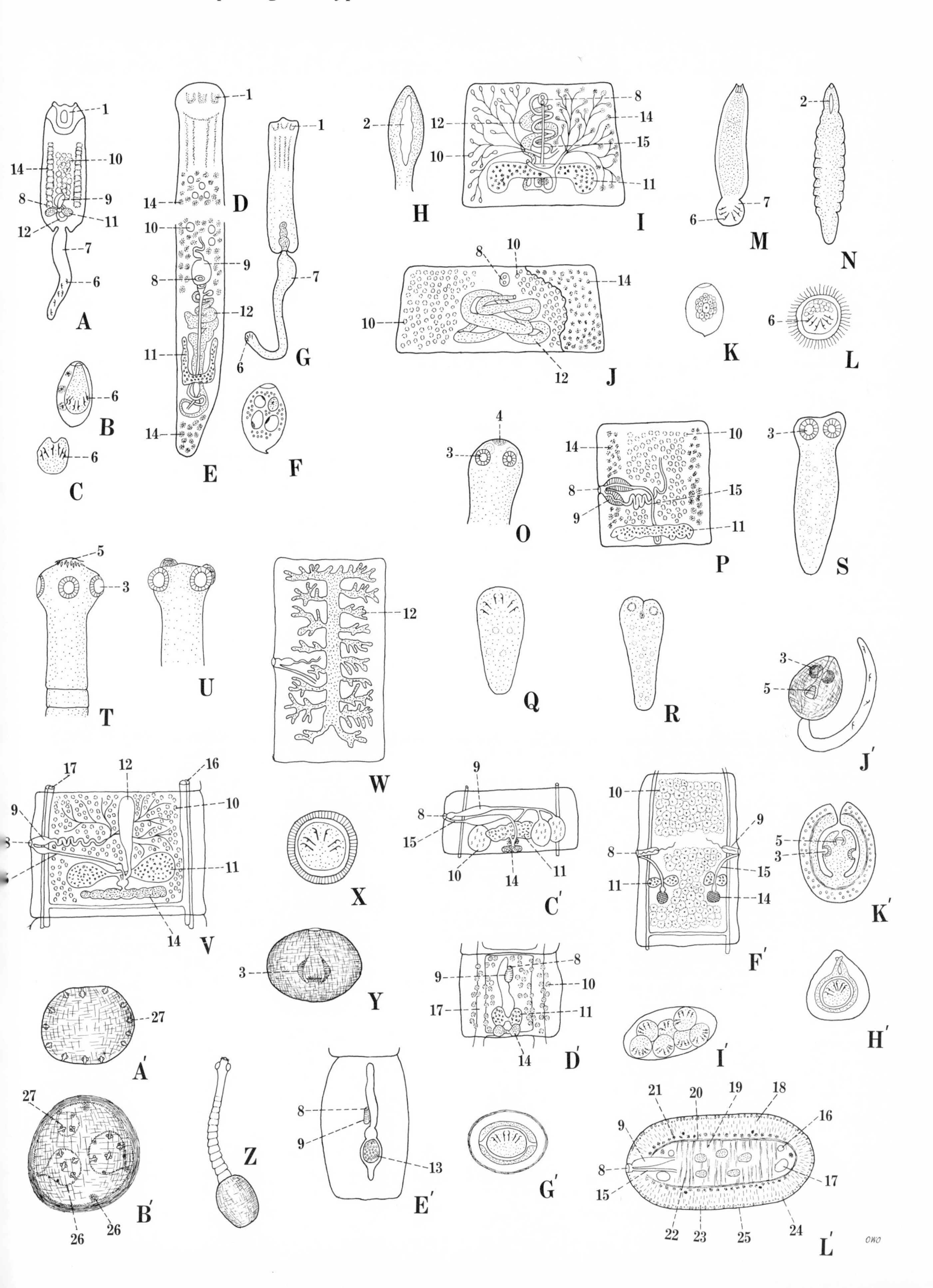
A
B
C
D
E
F
G
H
I
J
K
L
M
N
O
P
Q
R
S
T
U
V
W
X
Y
Z
A′
B′
C′
D′
E′
F′
G′
H′
I′
J′
K′
L′

EXPLANATION OF PLATE 86 ⇨

A. Ventral view of sexually mature nongravid worm. **B.** Ventral view of gravid worm. **C.** Lateral view of gravid worm. **D.** *Limnodrilus hoffmeisteri* with three fully developed worms. **E.** Embryonated egg. **F.** Hatched oncosphere. **G.** Cross-section through scolex. **H.** *Limnodrilus* with *Archigetes* escaping through slit in body wall. **I.** Infection of *Limnodrilus*.

1, bothrium or loculus; **2**, common genital pore; **3**, cirrus pouch; **4**, testes; **5**, ovary; **6**, uterus; **7**, vitelline glands; **8**, tail with hooks of oncosphere; **9**, gravid uterus; **10**, *Limnodrilus* or *Tubifex;* **11**, intestine of oligochaete; **12**, three *Archigetes* in coelom; **13**, egg shell; **14**, operculum; **15**, oncosphere; **16**, vitelline cells; **17**, hooks of oncosphere.

a, sexually mature *Archigetes* escaping from coelom of oligochaete through break in body wall; **b**, recently escaped worm alive on ooze; **c**, dead and decomposing worm liberates eggs in the ooze on the bottom of the pond; **d**, free unembryonated egg; **e**, embryonated egg; **f**, oligochaete swallows eggs; **g**, **h**, eggs pass through intestine; **i**, shell of egg that has hatched in posterior part of intestine; **j**, oncosphere in intestinal lumen; **k**, oncosphere passing through intestinal wall into coelom; **l**, developing oncosphere; **m**, young procercoid continues traveling anteriorly; **n**, well-developed procercoid approaching region of gonads; **o**, gravid neotenic procercoids associated with gonads.

Adapted from Wisňiewski, 1930, Mem. Acad. Polo. Sci. et Lett., Cracovie, Cl. Sci. Math. et Nat. s. B: Sci. Nat. 2:1.

---

forming packets containing one to several eggs each, or may form a paruterine organ in which it becomes surrounded by a thick fibrous layer (Paruterinidae, Mesocestoididae).

ORDER CARYOPHYLLIDEA

The Caryophyllidea are small monozoic cestodes parasitic in aquatic annelids and fish the world over. Two genera (*Archigetes* and *Glaridacris*) of the family Caryophyllaeidae are considered because their life cycles are known and show a gradation in which the sexually developed stages are believed to be neotenic larvae corresponding to the larvae of the Pseudophyllidea.

FAMILY CARYOPHYLLAEIDAE

These are monozoic, elongated cestodes having a scolex with frilled margins or one to three pairs of suctorial grooves.

Archigetes sieboldi Leuckart, 1878 (Plate 86)

The life cycle of this worm is direct. The sexually developed stage occurs in the coelom of aquatic oligochaetes, primarily *Limnodrilus hoffmeisteri* and less commonly in *Tubifex tubifex*.

DESCRIPTION. These are small, 2.5 to 6 mm long, monozoic cestodes which parasitize the coelom of Tubificidae, especially *Limnodrilus hoffmeisteri* as neotenic procercoids. A dorsal and ventral shallow bothrium is present on the scolex. The tail bears six embryonic hooks located near the posterior end. There are numerous testes anterior from the cirrus pouch and bounded laterally by the vitellaria. The gravid uterus fills the posterior half of the body. The operculate eggs are undeveloped in the body of the worm. Embryonation takes place in water and the oncospheres are unciliated.

LIFE CYCLE. The sexually mature worms escape from the coelom of the annelid hosts through a rent in the body wall. The eggs are liberated upon death and disintegration of the worms, with embryonation occurring in the water. Annelids become infected by swallowing the developed eggs that hatch in the posterior portion of the intestine. The unciliated oncospheres migrate through the intestinal wall into the coelom. They gradually move anteriorly, developing as they go to the region of the gonads where maturity is attained. The sexually mature stage is believed to be a neotenic procercoid, corresponding to the procercoid of pseudophyllidean cestodes, as described later for *Dibothriocephalus latus*.

EXERCISE ON LIFE CYCLE

Oligochaetes may be obtained from ponds or gently flowing streams whose bottoms are covered with rich organic ooze. Infected individuals can be recognized by the bulging body wall. *Archigetes*

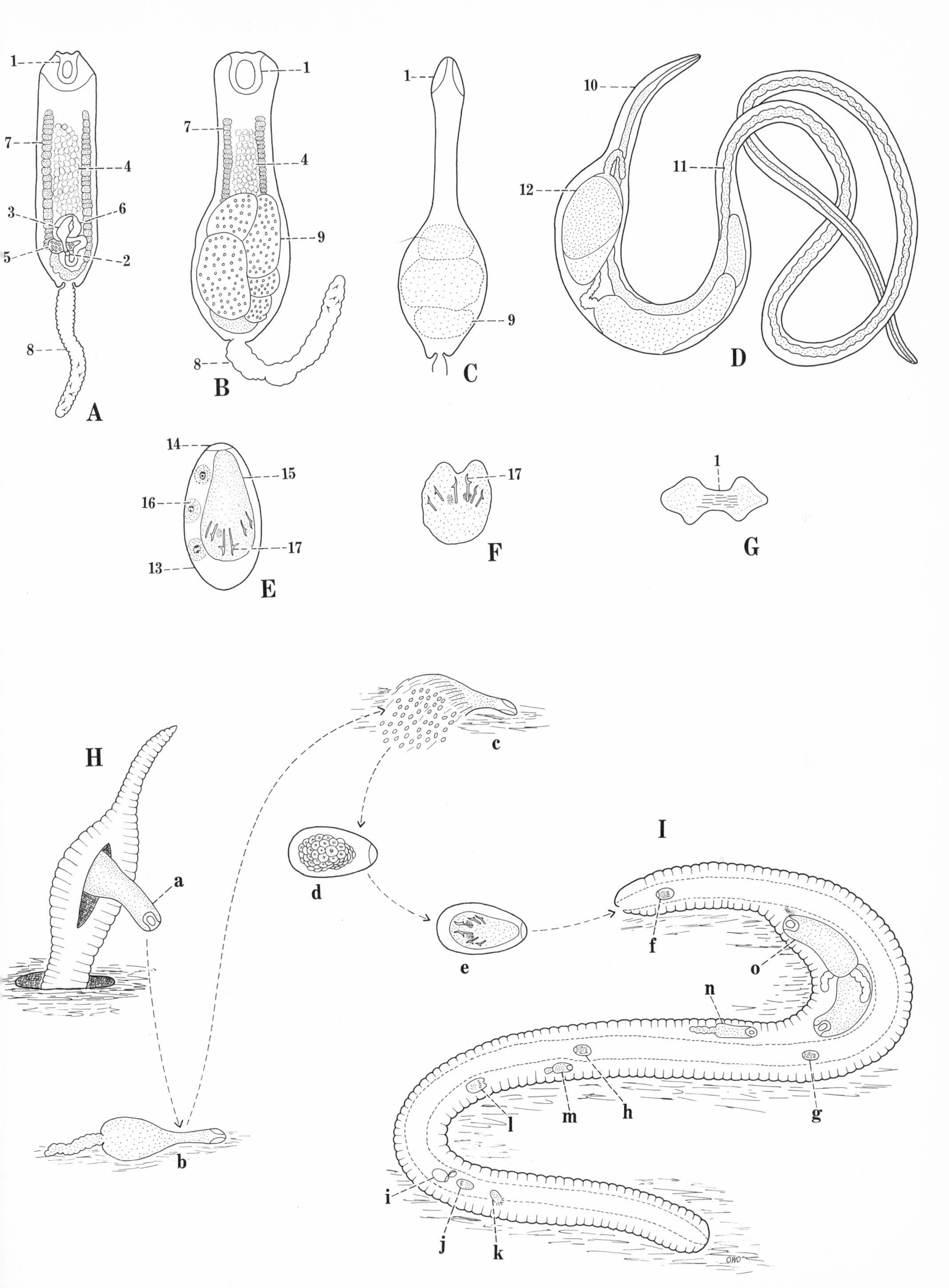
1
2
3
4
5
6
7
8
9
10
11
12
13
14
15
16
17
A
B
C
D
E
F
G
H
I
a
b
c
d
e
f
g
h
i
j
k
l
m
n
o
OWO

EXPLANATION OF PLATE 87 ⇨

A. Anterior end of adult. **B.** Posterior portion of adult worm. **C.** Unembryonated egg. **D.** Fully embryonated egg. **E.** Large and small hooks of embryo. **F.** Fully developed embryo from annelid. **G.** Young worm from intestine of sucker. **H.** Sucker *(Catastomus commersoni)* definitive host. **I.** *Limnodrilus udekemianus*, the intermediate host.

1, loculus or sucker; **2,** opening of male reproductive system; **3,** cirrus pouch; **4,** seminal vesicle; **5,** sperm duct; **6,** testes; **7,** opening of female reproductive system; **8,** vagina; **9,** ovary; **10,** oviduct and Mehlis' gland; **11,** uterus; **12,** vitelline glands; **13,** internal longitudinal muscles; **14,** operculum; **15,** germ cells of egg; **16,** yolk granules; **17,** embryo; **18,** cercomer with larval hooks at tip.

a, adult worm in intestine of sucker; **b,** eggs pass out of intestine with faeces; **c,** unembryonated egg in water or mud; **d,** embryonated egg; **e,** eggs eaten by aquatic annelids; **f,** eggs hatch in intestine; **g,** larvae pass through wall of intestine into coelom; **h,** fully developed and infective larvae; **i,** annelid digested in stomach of sucker; **j,** larval cestode freed from annelid; **k,** larvae shed cercomer and grow to adult monozoic cestodes in the intestine of suckers.

Adapted from McCrae, 1960, Dissertation, Colorado State University.

---

and *Cryptobothrius,* related genera, may be recognized by being sexually mature individuals filled with undeveloped operculated eggs and thereby differentiated from the sexually immature procercoids of *Glaridacris, Caryophalleus,* and related genera occurring in annelids and which parasitize suckers.

Eggs obtained by dissecting gravid worms and permitted to embryonate in water in a glass container at room temperature are infective to oligochaetes of the genera *Limnodrilus* and *Tubifex.*

Oligochaetes to be infected should be kept in the laboratory several weeks in order to allow any natural infections to mature and be recognized. Infected worms should be discarded. Expose uninfected annelids by placing eggs in the dish of water with them, either mixed with the ooze or free in a clean container. After they have eaten the eggs, dissect them at intervals of 1 or 2 days to observe the growth and migration of the parasites. Note how long it takes for the worms to reach sexual maturity at room temperature. Observe the procercoid characteristic of *Archigetes.*

SELECTED REFERENCES

Wisniewski, L. W. (1930). Mém. Acad. Polo. Sci. et Lett. Cracovie, Math. et. Nat. s. B:Sci. Nat. 2:1.

Calentine, R. L. (1964). J. Parasit. 50:454.

Glaridacris catastomus Cooper, 1920 (Plate 87)

Glaridacris catastomus parasitizes the stomach and small intestine of suckers (*Catastomus commersoni* and related forms) in North America.

DESCRIPTION. They measure up to 25 mm long and are somewhat cylindrical in cross-section. The scolex is short, broad, and chisel-shaped, with three sucker-like depressions of each side. The testes are few and not completely surrounded by the vitellaria. The ovary is lobular and H-shaped. The vitelline glands are in both the anterior and posterior parts of the body. The eggs have a boss on the anopercular end and are undeveloped when laid.

LIFE CYCLE. Eggs voided with the faeces develop upon reaching the water. Hatching takes place in the intestine of the fresh-water annelid *Limnodrilus udekemianus* and the six-hooked, unciliated embryos burrow through the intestinal wall into the coelomic cavity where they develop into tailed procercoids. Infection of fish occurs when infected annelids are eaten and the procercoids develop into neotenic plerocercoids.

EXERCISE ON LIFE CYCLE

Aquatic annelids of the genus *Limnodrilus* in waters where suckers occur are infected commonly with *Glaridacris* and related forms. Infected annelids generally can be recognized readily by the bulge of the body wall caused by the larval cestodes in the coelom. After they have been examined inside the annelid, they may be dissected for further study.

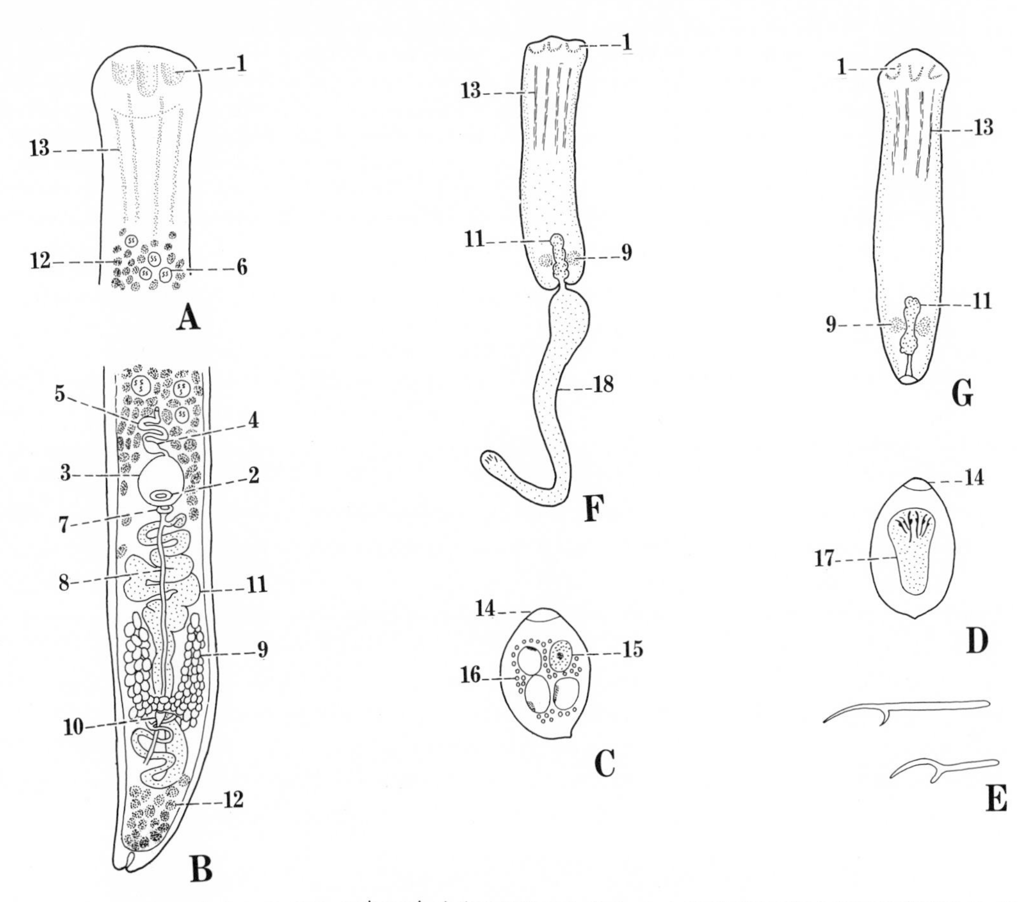
A
B
C
D
E
F
G
1
2
3
4
5
6
7
8
9
10
11
12
13
14
15
16
17
18

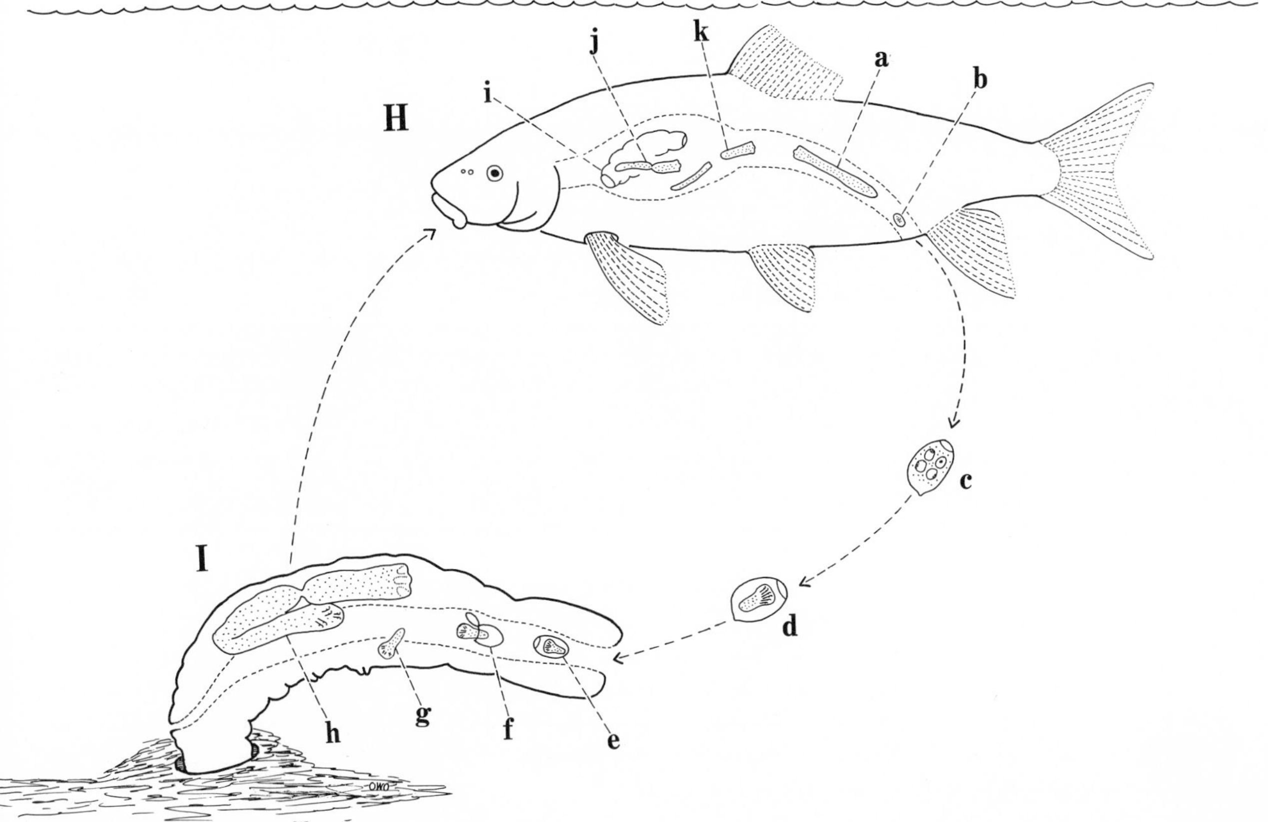
H
I
a
b
c
d
e
f
g
h
i
j
k

EXPLANATION OF PLATE 88

A. Scolex of adult worm. **B.** Cross-section of scolex. **C.** Mature proglottid. **D.** Ripe proglottid. **E.** Procercoid. **F.** Plerocercoid. **G.** Definitive host. **H.** Copepod first intermediate host. **I.** Walleyed pike *(Stizostedion vitreum)* second intermediate host.

1, bothrium; **2,** common genital atrium; **3,** male genital pore; **4,** female genital pore; **5,** uterine pore; **6,** bilobed ovary; **7,** Mehlis' gland surrounding ootype; **8,** vitelline duct; **9,** proximal portion of vagina; **10,** oviduct; **11,** vitelline glands; **12,** vagina; **13,** vas deferens; **14,** testes; **15,** uterus; **16,** cercomer with onco-spheral hooks.

a, adult in intestine of definitive host; **b,** egg passing out of intestine with faeces; **c,** unembryonated egg; **d,** embryonated egg; **e,** hatched egg; **f,** ciliated six-hooked coracidium free in water; **g,** coracidium eaten by crustacean first intermediate host; **h,** coracidium sheds ciliated covering; **i,** coracidium migrates through intestinal wall into haemocoel; **j,** procercoid; **k,** infected crustacean is swallowed by fish second intermediate host and the procercoid is liberated by the digestive enzymes; **l,** procercoid passes through intestinal wall into coelom and finally into muscles of fish where development continues to infective stage; **m,** plerocercoid in muscles; **n,** infection of definitive host occurs when infected fish are eaten; **o,** plerocercoids are liberated and develop to adults.

Figures adapted from various sources.

Adult worms removed from the intestine of fish and placed in a dish of tap water shed eggs which when incubated at room temperature develop to six-hooked larvae. Aquatic annelids placed in the dishes with the embryonated eggs ingest them and become infected. Hatching in the gut and development in the coelom may be followed by dissecting infected annelids at appropriate intervals.

Suckers may be infected by allowing them to eat annelids that have been infected experimentally. Fingerlings kept in balanced aquaria are the preferred size because of the difficulty of keeping larger fish alive sufficiently long to complete the experiments.

Suckers may be reared in the laboratory by stripping eggs and milt from adult fish and placing them together in an aquarium in which the water is constantly aerated. Dog biscuits provide suitable food for rearing the fish.

SELECTED REFERENCES

McCrae, R. C. (1960). Dissertation, Colorado State University.

ORDER PSEUDOPHYLLIDEA

The pseudophyllideans are polyzoic cestodes, occurring in the intestine of all the classes of vertebrates over the world, especially the piscivorous species. They range in size from small to over 10 mm in length, being among the largest of the cestodes.

FAMILY DIBOTHRIOCEPHALIDAE

The scolex bears a dorsal and ventral groove, followed by a neck and distinctly segmented body. The genital openings are on the midventral surface of the proglottids. Both the testes and the vitellaria are scattered throughout the proglottids, and the tubular gravid uterus loops into a rosette shape.

Dibothriocephalus latus (Linnaeus, 1758) (Plate 88)

This is a member of the family Dibothriocephalidae and is commonly known as the broad fish tapeworm of humans. It has been selected as a typical representative of this order for study of the life history. It parasitizes man and other fish-eating mammals such as dogs and bears. While worldwide in distribution, it is more prevalent in the northern hemisphere than elsewhere.

DESCRIPTION. Fresh worms are white to ivory in color and up to 10 m long. The scolex is almond-shaped, with two elongated grooves. Proglottids are wider than long. There is a separate uterine and genital pore on the midventral surface of each segment. Testes and vitelline glands are scattered throughout the proglottid. Coils of the gravid uterus form a centrally located rosette. The eggs are operculate and undeveloped when laid.

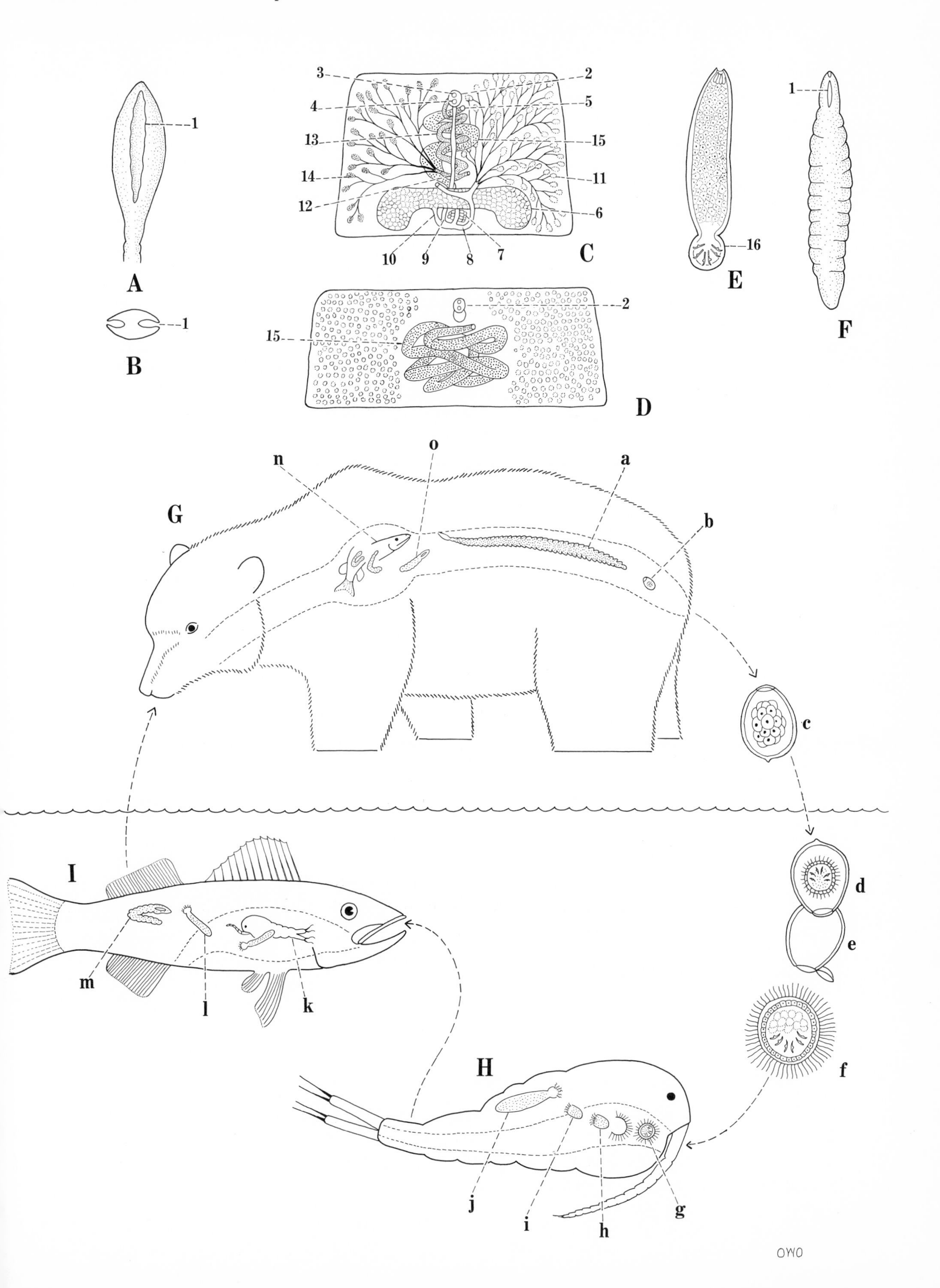
A
B
C
D
E
F
G
H
I
1
2
3
4
5
6
7
8
9
10
11
12
13
14
15
16
a
b
c
d
e
f
g
h
i
j
k
l
m
n
o
OWO

LIFE CYCLE. Eggs laid singly in the intestine of the definitive host incubate when discharged with faeces into the water. A ciliated, six-hooked coracidium hatches and swims about rather slowly. When eaten by crustacea of the genera *Cyclops* and *Diaptomus*, the coracidium sheds the ciliated epithelium in the intestine and migrates to the haemocoel where it develops into a procercoid. When fresh-water fish, including pike, perch, trout, and salmon, as a few representatives, ingest infected crustacea, the procercoids migrate from the intestine to the muscles where they develop into plerocercoids. If small fish infected with plerocercoids are eaten by large ones, the larval tapeworms migrate to the muscles again and re-encyst. Once encysted in the muscles of fish, either directly from the crustacean host or from infected fish, they develop to the infective stage for the definitive host.

Infection of mammalian hosts occurs when fish harboring plerocercoids are eaten. Upon being released from the muscle tissue in the intestine by the digestive processes, the parasites attach to the intestinal wall and develop to maturity in 5 to 6 weeks.

In cases where the life cycles of other pseudophyllidean cestodes are known, they are basically the same as that of *D. latus*. The ciliated coracidium produces a procercoid in entomostraca and a plerocercoid develops in fish usually, or in some species in amphibians.

If plerocercoids are swallowed by vertebrates unsuitable for their development, they migrate from the intestine to various parts of the body where they remain without further growth. Such a plerocercoid is known as a sparganum. It is capable of developing into an adult worm in an appropriate definitive host.

EXERCISE ON LIFE CYCLE

Eggs of *D. latus* are difficult to obtain in most localities but those of related pseudophyllidean cestodes of fish, amphibians, birds, or mammals may be obtained without too much difficulty. When available, they should be incubated in dishes of tap water at room temperature. Immediately upon hatching, place species of *Cyclops* and *Diaptomus* in the dish with them. Observe the crustacea with the aid of a dissecting microscope to ascertain whether they ingest the coracidia. Dissect procercoids from the crustacea and study them. Infected crustacea may be fed to small fishes in an effort to obtain plerocercoids. If successful, appropriate definitive hosts may be infected by feeding the fish to them. Also dissect plerocercoids from the muscles of the fish for study.

SELECTED REFERENCES

Cameron, T. W. M. (1945). Canad. J. Comp. Med. 9:245, 283, 302.

Janicki, C., and F. Rosen. (1918). Bull. Soc. Neuchâteloise, Sci. Nat. (1916-1917), 42:19.

Mueller, J. F. (1937). Proc. Helminth. Soc. Wash. 4:68; (1938). Amer. J. Trop. Med. 18:41, 302.

ORDER PROTEOCEPHALA

This group of cestodes is parasitic in fish almost exclusively. The great majority of cestodes of fresh-water fishes are species of the genus *Proteocephalus*. The adults are located in the small intestine. They are worldwide in distribution.

FAMILY PROTEOCEPHALIDAE

The scolex bears four in-cupped muscular suckers and sometimes a fifth apical one. The genital pores are lateral and the vitellaria are in two lateral bands, one on each side of the proglottid. The gravid uterus is saccular.

Proteocephalus ambloplitis Leidy, 1887 (Plate 89)

P. ambloplitis is a parasite of bass (*Micropterus dolomieui, Huro salmoides*), yellow perch (*Perca flavescens*), bowfins (*Amia calva*), and other fresh-water fish. Due to the pathology caused by the plerocercoids to the gonads of bass, especially the females, reproduction in infected fish is curtailed if not completely eliminated.

DESCRIPTION. The scolex has four in-cupped muscular suckers and a vestigial apical sucker. The genital pore is lateral. The ejaculatory duct consists of a large number of coils, and the testes are enclosed laterally by the vitellaria and posteriorly by the ovary. The vagina is surrounded by a very large sphincter near the genital pore. The vitellaria are arranged in lateral bands extending from the anterior to the posterior ends of the proglottid. The gravid uterus has 15 to 20 lobes on each side and is filled with somewhat dumbbell-shaped eggs which are fully embryonated.

LIFE CYCLE. As the cestodes mature in the definitive hosts, the terminal proglottids become gravid or "ripe" and detach from the strobilus. They pass from the intestine with the faeces. Upon absorbing water, they rupture and release large numbers of eggs, each containing a fully developed oncosphere. Eggs eaten by copepods (*Cyclops, Eucyclops*) hatch in the intestine and the nonciliated oncospheres migrate into the haemocoel where they develop into procercoids, bearing suckers characteristic of the adult. When infected copepods are eaten by fry of bass or pumpkinseed sunfish, which serve as the second intermediate hosts, the procercoids migrate through the intestinal wall into the coelom and transform into plerocercoids, the next larval stage and the one that is infective to the definitive hosts. Infection of the fish definitive host with adult cestodes takes place when fish containing fully developed plerocercoids are eaten.

If, on the other hand, fry harboring immature plerocercoids are eaten by larger fish, the parasites are unable to develop to sexual maturity even though they are in the intestine of a favorable host. Instead, they migrate to the coelom again, frequently entering the gonads, where development of the plerocercoid stage is completed. Infected gonads are destroyed by the parasites, resulting in sterile fish. These plerocercoids are capable of development to sexually mature tapeworms if eaten by bass or other appropriate hosts.

The life cycles of several additional species of *Proteocephala* have been worked. In the cases of *Ophiotaenia perspicua* from snakes, and *Proteocephalus pinguis* and *Corallobothrium parvum* from fish, the life history is similar to that of *P. ambloplitis*, wherein the procercoids are in copepods and the plerocercoids in fish. In *P. tumidicollis* from trout, the life cycle differs in that both the procercoids and plerocercoids develop in succession in a single copepod.

EXERCISE ON LIFE CYCLE

Adult cestodes of *Proteocephalus ambloplitis* and related species are readily available almost wherever bass and yellow perch occur. Likewise the copepod intermediate hosts (*Cyclops vulgaris* and *Eucyclops agilis*) are ubiquitous.

Place eggs of the cestodes in glass dishes containing pond water, a sprig of water plant, and copepods. Observe the crustaceans eat the eggs. Examine the intestinal contents of the copepods for oncospheres shortly after they have eaten the eggs, and the body cavity 4 to 5 hours later for young procercoids.

Allow fry of bass, perch, or pumpkinseed sunfish to eat the infected copepods. Examine the liver, mesenteries, and gonads of fish after 5, 10, and 15 days for plerocercoids. At the end of this time, infect hungry yearling bass or yellow perch by allowing them to eat fry containing young or fully developed plerocercoids and observe the course of development of each age group. Examine the intestine, liver, mesenteries, and gonads of the yearling bass at 3, 30, 60, and 90 days, if possible to keep them that long, for various stages and location of the parasites. It may be impractical or impossible to have yearling bass for the final step in the life cycle.

Species of *Proteocephalus* other than *P. ambloplitis* may be available for study. The life cycle would be studied in the manner described above with possible variations in the species of copepods and fish.

SELECTED REFERENCES

Hugghins, E. J. (1959). S. Dak. Agr. Expt. Sta. and S. Dak. Dept. Game, Fish, and Parks, Bull. 489.

Hunter, G. W., III. (1928). J. Parasit. 14:229; (1929). Parasitology 21:487.

Hunter, G. W., III, and W. S. Hunter. (1929). 16th Ann. Rept. N. Y. State Conserv. Dept. (1928), Suppl., p. 198.

Larsh, J. E., Jr. (1941). J. Parasit. 27:221.

Meyer, M. C. (1954). Maine Dept. Inland Fish and Game Fish. Res. and Manag. Div. Bull. 1.

Thomas, L. J. (1934). J. Parasit. 20:291.

EXPLANATION OF PLATE 89 ▷

A. Scolex. **B.** Mature proglottid. **C.** Gravid proglottid. **D.** Young procercoid. **E.** Older procercoid. **F.** Plerocercoid from lumen of intestine of fish. **G.** Plerocercoid encysted on mesenteries of fish. **H.** Bass *(Micropterus)* definitive host. **H'.** Rock bass *(Amblo-plites)* definitive host. **H''.** Bowfin *(Amia)* definitive host. **I.** Crustacean *(Cyclops, Eucyclops, Macrocyclops)* first intermediate host. **J.** Bass fingerling or fry intermediate host. **K.** Mature bass paratenic host.

1, scolex of mature cestode; **2,** sucker; **3,** rudiment of apical sucker; **4,** common genital pore; **5,** cirrus pouch; **6,** vas deferens; **7,** testes; **8,** vagina with strong terminal sphincter; **9,** ovary; **10,** vitellaria; **11,** gravid uterus; **12,** hooks of oncosphere on procercoid; **13,** cyst wall of plerocercoid.

a, adult cestode in intestine; **b,** gravid proglottid shed from terminus of strobilus; **c,** gravid proglottid free in water ruptures and releases embryonated eggs; **d,** embryonated eggs free in water; **e,** embryonated egg held by crustacean for eating; **f,** oncosphere escapes from egg shell in intestine; **g,** oncosphere migrates through gut wall into haemocoel; **h,** procercoid in haemocoel; **i,** procercoid liberated from cyclops by digestive processes in stomach of bass fry will migrate through intestinal wall into coelom and encyst; **j,** encysted plerocercoid attaches to mesenteries or enters gonads (one of two courses follow from this point, depending on whether the fry have procercoids in the digestive tract from recently digested cyclops, or underdeveloped plerocercoids in the coelom when eaten by large bass, or other hosts); **k,** procercoid released from intestine of fry penetrates wall of intestine of bass to continue development in coelom; **l,** immature plerocercoid from body cavity of fry passing through intestinal wall into coelom to continue development as a plerocercoid; **m,** plerocercoid in coelom; **n,** plerocercoid in gonads; **o,** infection of definitive host with adult cestodes takes place when fish harboring fully developed plerocercoids **(J, K)** are eaten; **p,** fully developed plerocercoid free in digestive tract; **q,** plerocercoid attaches in crypts of small intestine and develops to maturity; **r,** infected gonads.

Adapted from Hunter and Hunter, 1929, 16th Ann. Rept. N. Y. State Conserv. Dept. Suppl., p. 198.

ORDER CYCLOPHYLLIDEA

The cyclophyllidean cestodes are common parasites of birds and mammals throughout the world. Most species are inhabitants of the small intestine as adults, although a few occur in the bile ducts. They are characterized as sucker-bearing tapeworms with one or two compact vitelline glands located posterior to the ovary.

Generally an intermediate host is involved in the life history of these parasites although at least one species may complete its cycle with or without the succor of an intermediary. Two basic types of life cycles are known. The species of Taeniidae utilize mammals as intermediate hosts and the larval stage is a vesicular cysticercus, strobilocercus, coenurus, or hydatid cyst. In the other families, the larvae develop in invertebrates or vertebrates and are nonvesicular cysticercoids, tetrathyridia, or plerocercoids.

For convenience of discussion, the cyclophyllidean cestodes are divided into two groups: 1) the Family Taeniidae, and 2) other families.

FAMILY TAENIIDAE

Five genera of this family are common parasites as adults of humans, dogs, and cats. They include *Taenia, Taeniarhynchus, Hydatigera, Multiceps,* and *Echinococcus.* The larval stages occur in humans, cattle, sheep, swine, deer, rabbits, hares, and rats.

DESCRIPTION. They are small to large muscular cestodes with distinct segmentation. The scolex bears four muscular in-cupped suckers, and may have a double or single crown of rostellar hooks, or none. The genital pore is lateral and irregularly alternate. The gravid uterus consists of a medium stem and lateral branches filled with embryonated eggs having thick, striated shells. The larva developing from the oncosphere in a mammalian intermediate host is a cysticercus, strobilocercus, coenurus, or hydatid.

Taenia solium Linnaeus, 1758 (Plate 90)

Taenia solium is known as the pork tapeworm of humans. It is usually present in people as the adult worm and in swine as the larval cysticercus, but cysticerci also may appear in humans infected

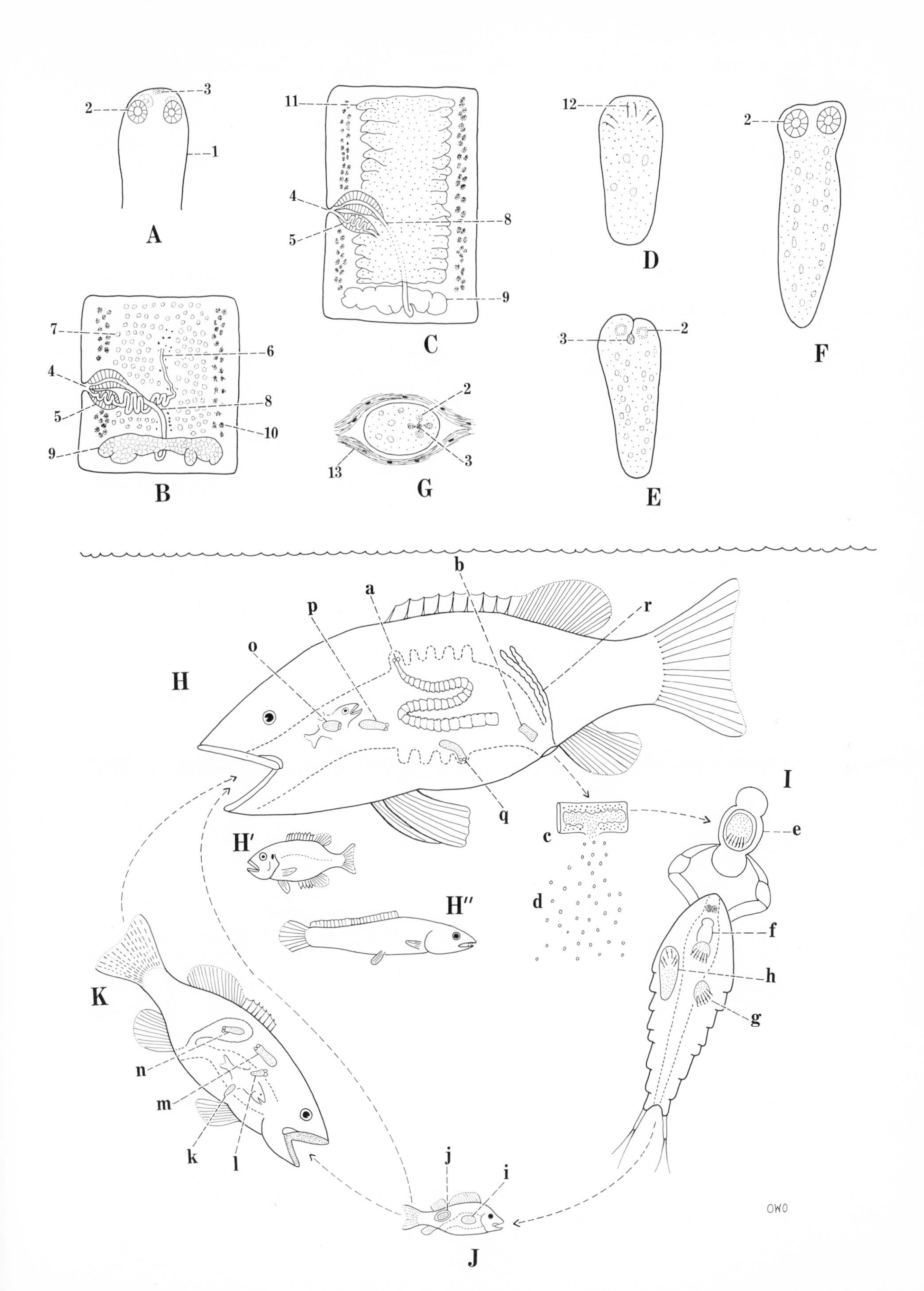

A
B
C
D
E
F
G
H
H′
H″
I
J
K
1
2
3
4
5
6
7
8
9
10
11
12
13
a
b
c
d
e
f
g
h
i
j
k
l
m
n
o
p
q
r
OWO

EXPLANATION OF PLATE 90 ⇨

A. Scolex and neck. **B.** Large and small rostellar hooks. **C.** Mature proglottid. **D.** Gravid proglottid. **E.** Egg. **F.** Invaginated cysticercus. **G.** Evaginated cysticercus. **H.** Human definitive host. **I.** Swine intermediate host.

1, scolex; **2,** sucker; **3,** armed rostellum; **4,** large rostellar hook; **5,** small rostellar hook; **6,** common genital pore; **7,** cirrus pouch; **8,** sperm duct; **9,** testes; **10,** vagina; **11,** seminal receptacle; **12,** ovary with accessory median lobe; **13,** oviduct; **14,** vitelline gland; **15,** Mehlis' gland; **16,** immature uterus; **17,** longitudinal excretory canal; **18,** lateral branch of gravid uterus; **19,** striated shell of egg; **20,** oncosphere or hexacanth; **21,** bladder of cysticercus.

a, adult cestode in intestine of human; **b,** detached gravid proglottid; **c,** proglottid rupturing to release eggs; **d,** eggs free; **e,** eggs swallowed by swine; **f,** eggs hatch; **g,** oncospheres penetrate intestinal wall and enter hepatic portal vein; **h,** oncospheres passing through liver; **i,** oncospheres in right side of heart; **j,** oncospheres in lungs; **k,** oncospheres in left side of heart; **l,** oncospheres enter general circulation; **m,** oncospheres entering skeletal muscles; **n,** cysticercus in skeletal and cardiac muscles; **o,** cysticercus in ham; **p,** cysticerci in sausages; **q,** infection of human by swallowing cysticerci in infected pork; **r,** cysticerci in piece of pork; **s,** cysticercus released from meat has evaginated; **t,** gravid proglottid carried to stomach by reverse peristalsis where eggs are released; **u,** eggs in intestine hatch; **v,** oncospheres in intestine; **w,** oncospheres in hepatic portal vein; **x,** oncospheres in right side of heart; **y,** oncospheres in lungs; **z,** oncospheres in general circulation.

a′, oncospheres leaving blood vessel in brain; **b′,** cysticerci in brain; **c′,** cysticerci in skeletal muscles (also in eyes).

Figures adapted from various sources.

---

with adult worms. Wherever pork is eaten in a cured or inadequately cooked condition and where human faeces are left for pigs to eat, these worms normally are prevalent.

DESCRIPTION. Fully developed worms are up to 7 m long and with less than 1,000 proglottids. There is a double crown of 22 to 32 rostellar hooks consisting of two sizes, measuring 160 to 180 μ and 110 to 140 μ long. The testes number 150 to 200 and are scattered throughout the proglottid. The ovary has two large lateral lobes and a median accessory one. The gravid uterus has 7 to 13 lateral branches on each side.

LIFE CYCLE. The gravid proglottids are detached in the intestine of humans and eliminated from the body in the faeces. In the air, they rupture and release the embryonated eggs. When swallowed by swine, the eggs hatch in the intestine. The oncospheres penetrate the intestinal wall, enter the hepatic portal vein, and are carried through the liver, heart, and lungs into the general circulation. They leave the blood vessels and develop into cysticerci in the skeletal and cardiac muscles. Infection of humans occurs when viable cysticerci are swallowed with pork insufficiently cooked to kill them.

When gravid proglottids are carried into the stomach of humans parasitized with the worms from the small intestine by reverse peristalsis, the eggs are released, hatch, and the oncospheres enter the circulation. They migrate through the human body and undergo development in the muscles as in swine which swallow them. Cysticerci developing in vital organs such as the brain and eyes cause serious results. This is autoinfection and occurs only in this species of Taeniidae.

Other common species of the genus are adult parasites in dogs and related carnivores such as wolves, coyotes, and foxes. The cysticerci of *T. ovis* are in the muscles of sheep, *T. krabbei* in the muscles of deer, *T. pisiformis* in the mesenteries of rabbits and hares, and *T. hydatigera* in the mesenteries of deer, elk, and sheep.

SELECTED REFERENCES

Faust, E. C., and P. F. Russell. (1957). Craig and Faust's Clinical Parasitology, 6th Ed. Lea and Febiger, Philadelphia, p. 639.

Lapage, G. (1956). Mönnig's Veterinary Helminthology and Entomology, 4th Ed. The Williams and Wilkins Co., Baltimore, p. 117.

Taeniarhynchus saginatus (Goeze, 1782) (Plate 91)

This is the beef tapeworm of humans, commonly designated as *Taenia saginata.* It is the largest of the taenioid cestodes and is prevalent wherever beef is eaten and human sanitation is lax, leaving faeces available for cattle to eat or used to fertilize pastures.

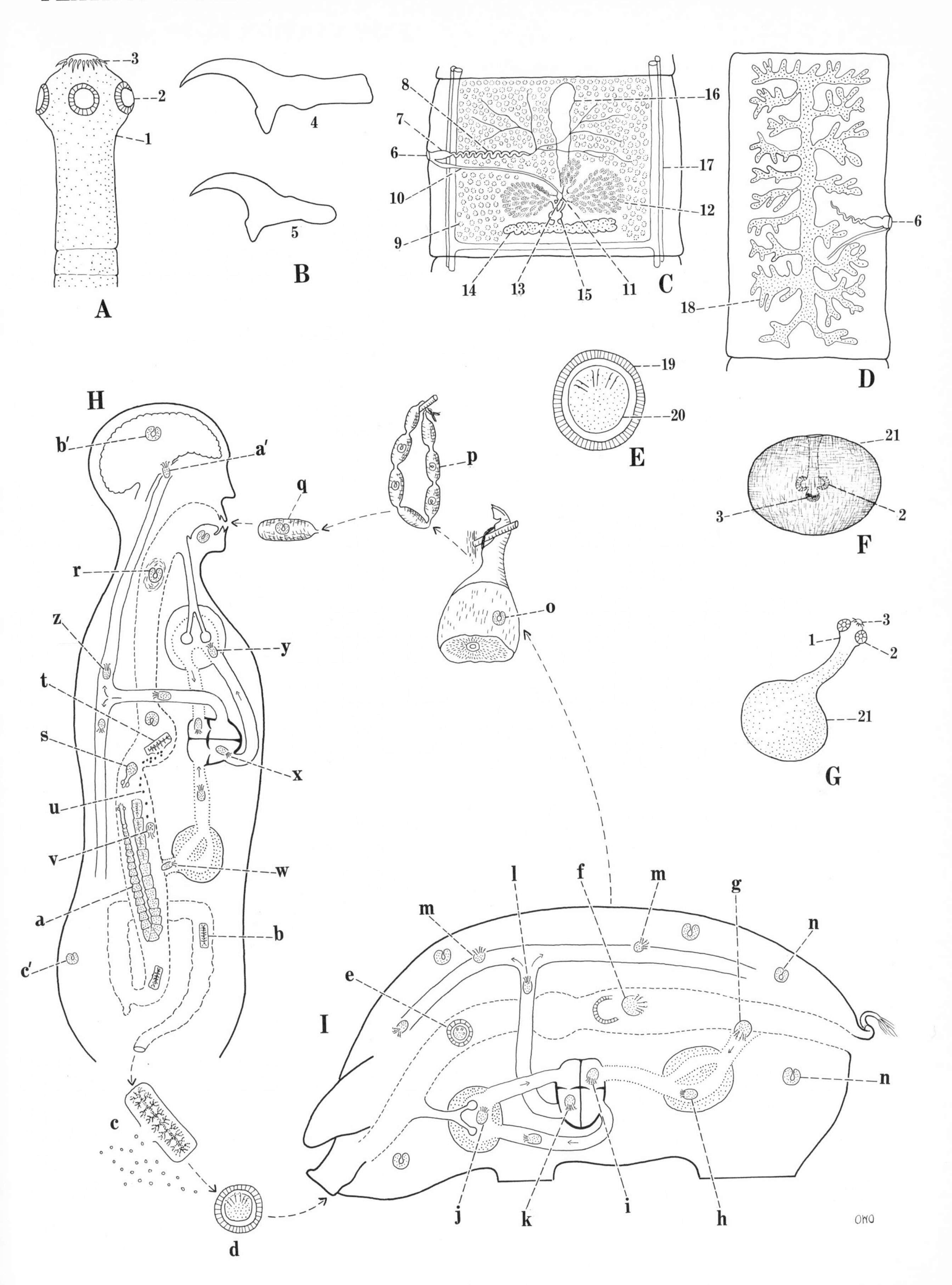

A
B
C
D
E
F
G
H
I
OWO

EXPLANATION OF PLATE 91 ▷

A. Scolex and neck. **B.** Mature proglottid. **C.** Gravid proglottid. **D.** Egg. **E.** Invaginated cysticercus. **F.** Evaginated cysticercus **G.** Human definitive host. **H.** Bovine intermediate host.

1, scolex; **2,** suckers; **3,** common genital pore; **4,** cirrus pouch; **5,** sperm duct; **6,** testes; **7,** vaginal sphincter; **8,** vagina; **9,** ovary; **10,** oviduct; **11,** uterus; **12,** vitelline gland; **13,** ventral longitudinal excretory canal; **14,** dorsal longitudinal excretory canal; **15,** transverse excretory canal; **16,** striated egg shell; **17,** oncosphere; **18,** bladder of cysticercus.

a, adult cestode in small intestine; **b,** gravid proglottid passing out of intestine; **c,** ruptured proglottid liberating eggs; **d,** eggs and proglottids mixed with hay; **e,** eggs on grass; **f,** infection of bovine by swallowing eggs; **g,** eggs hatch in small intestine; **h,** oncospheres enter hepatic portal vein; **i,** oncospheres pass through liver; **j,** oncospheres pass through heart; **k,** oncospheres pass through lungs; **l, m,** oncospheres enter general circulation; **n,** cysticercus in skeletal muscles; **o,** live cysticercus in inadequately cooked beef; **p,** infection of definitive host; **q,** cysticercus being freed from flesh in stomach; **r,** cysticercus evaginates in small intestine, attaches to intestinal mucosa, and grows to adult cestode.

Figures adapted from various sources.

DESCRIPTION. Adult worms are up to 25 m long (average, 4 to 5), with 1,000 to 2,000 proglottids. The rostellum and hooks are lacking and the ovary is without an accessory lobe. There are 300 to 400 testes per proglottid. When gravid, the uterus has 15 to 20 lateral branches on each side.

LIFE CYCLE. The life history of this species is similar to that of *Taenia solium* except that cattle instead of swine serve as the intermediate host and autoinfection does not occur in the definitive host.

SELECTED REFERENCES

Faust, E. C., and P. F. Russell. (1957). Craig and Faust's Clinical Parasitology, 6th Ed. Lea and Febiger, Philadelphia, p. 646.

Echinococcus granulosus (Batsch, 1786) (Plate 92)

Echinococcus granulosus is the smallest taenioid cestode, consisting of three to five proglottids and measuring up to 6 mm long. The adult worms live in the small intestine of dogs, wolves, coyotes, and foxes. They are cosmopolitan. The larval stage (hydatid cyst) occurs in humans, cattle, sheep, swine, deer, moose, kangaroos, and other large herbivorous mammals.

DESCRIPTION. The body consists of the scolex and usually one each of an immature, mature, and gravid proglottid. The rostellum is armed with 28 to 50 (average 30 to 36) hooks of characteristic shape and two sizes, the large ones being 40 to 49 μ long and the small ones 30 to 42 μ. The larval stage in the intermediate hosts is a hydatid cyst.

LIFE CYCLE. Eggs passed by dogs hatch when swallowed by one of the intermediate hosts. Like the other species of taenioid cestodes, the oncospheres enter the hepatic portal vein. They lodge in the liver and lungs most commonly where development of the hydatid cyst takes place. Some oncospheres continue through the lungs and reach other parts of the body, the marrow cavity of the long bones being a common site.

Infection of the definitive hosts occurs when hydatid cysts containing mature scolices are swallowed. The heads are released from the cyst and attach to the mucosa of the small intestine, growing to adult cestodes in six to seven weeks.

Echinococcus multilocularis Leuckart, 1863, recently found in North America, occurs as adults in foxes and hydatids in microtine rodents. Morphologically, it differs from *E. granulosus* in having fewer testes and the genital pore distinctly anterior to the middle of the proglottid.

PLATE 91 *Taeniarhynchus saginatus*

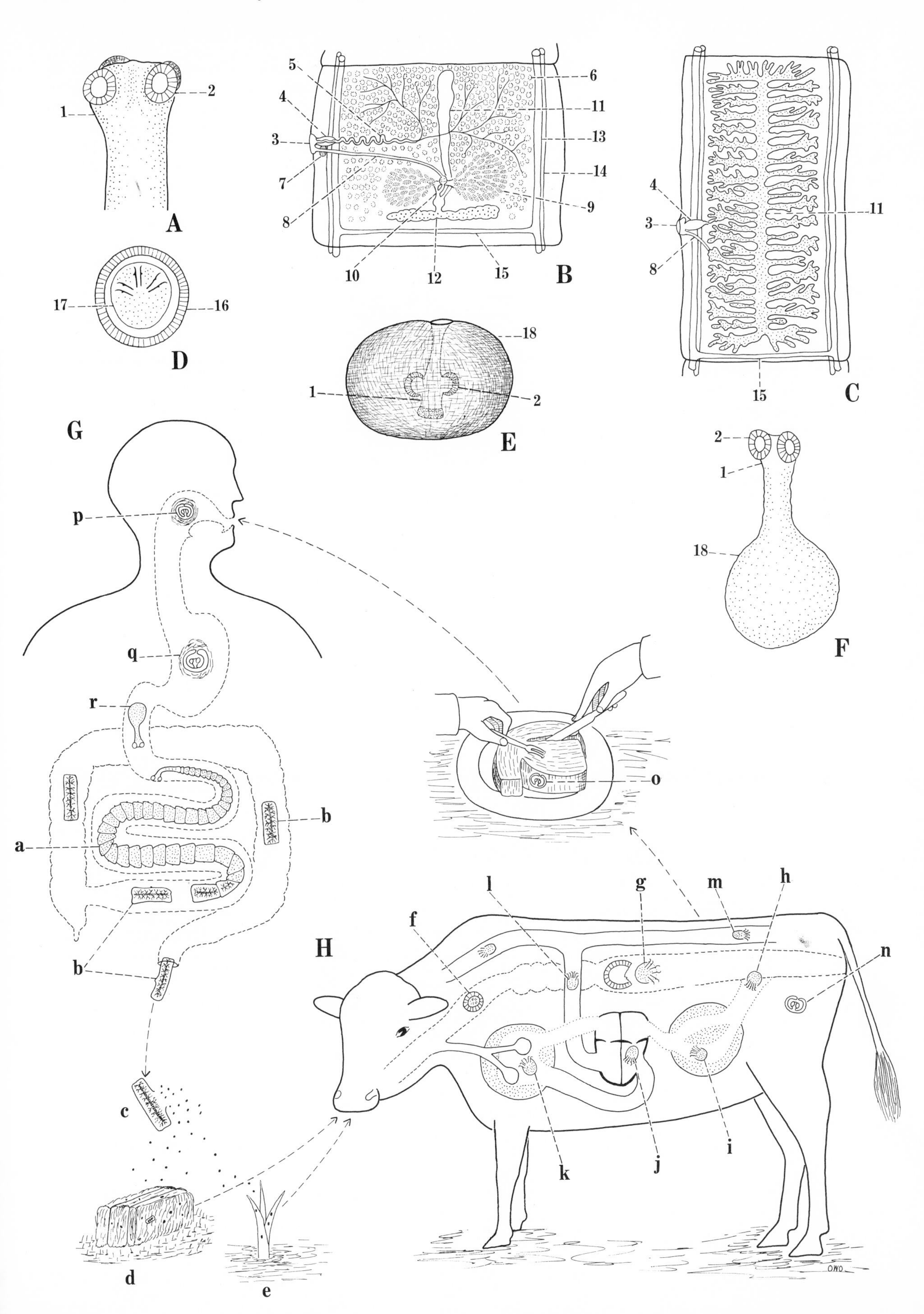

EXPLANATION OF PLATE 92 ⇨

A. Adult cestode. **B.** Rostellar hooks. **C.** Segment of hydatid cyst. **D.** Invaginated scolex from hydatid cyst. **E.** Evaginated scolex. **F.** Dog definitive host. **G.** Sheep intermediate host.

1, scolex; **2,** armed rostellum; **3,** suckers; **4,** immature proglottid; **5,** mature proglottid; **6,** common genital pore; **7,** cirrus pouch; **8,** testes; **9,** vagina; **10,** uterus; **11,** ovary; **12,** Mehlis' gland; **13,** vitelline gland; **14,** gravid proglottid; **15,** large rostellar hook; **16,** small rostellar hook; **17,** laminated wall of hydatid cyst; **18,** germinal layer of mother cyst; **19,** brood capsules in which scolices will develop; **20,** germinal epithelium extruding to outside through rupture in cyst wall; **21,** brood capsule; **22,** developing scolex; **23,** brood capsule; **24,** daughter capsule with developing scolices; **25,** fully developed scolex in brood capsule; **26,** stalk of brood capsule.

a, adult cestode in small intestine; **b,** eggs passed out in faeces; **c,** characteristic taenioid type of egg; **d,** infection of intermediate host; **e,** eggs hatch in small intestine; **f,** oncospheres enter hepatic portal vein; **g,** oncospheres enter liver parenchyma from blood vessels; **h,** hydatid cyst; **i, j,** some oncospheres continue through liver and right side of heart; **k,** oncospheres leave pulmonary circulation to enter parenchyma of lungs; **l,** hydatid; **m,** oncospheres pass through lungs and left side of heart; **n,** oncospheres in general circulation; **o,** hydatids in other organs such as brain and marrow of hollow bones; **p,** cyst wall; **q,** brood capsule with scolices; **r,** exogenous cyst that originated from germinal epithelium of mother cyst; **s,** strip of germinal epithelium free in mother cyst; **t,** infection of definitive host occurs when hydatids are eaten and digested, releasing scolices; **u,** scolices released in intestine evert and attach to intestinal mucosa, maturing in 6 to 7 weeks.

Figures A and B original; C, adapted in part from Chandler, 1955, Introduction of Parasitology, 9th Ed., John Wiley and Sons, New York, p. 359; D, E, from Belding, 1952, Textbook of Clinical Parasitology, 2nd Ed., Appleton-Century-Crofts, Inc., New York, p. 586.

SELECTED REFERENCES

Faust, E. C., and P. F. Russell. (1957). Craig and Faust's Clinical Parasitology, 6th Ed. Lea and Febiger, Philadelphia, p. 654.

Gemmel, M. A. (1957). Aust. Vet. J. 33:8, 217; (1958). Ibid. 34:269; (1959). Ibid. 35:396, 450, 505; (1960). Ibid. 36:73.

Lapage, G. (1956). Mönnig's Veterinary Helminthology and Entomology, 4th Ed. Williams and Wilkins Co., Baltimore, p. 129.

Leiby, P. D., and O. W. Olsen. (1964). Science 145:-1066.

Magath, T. B. (1954). J. Amer. Vet. Med. Assoc. 125:-411.

Rausch, R. (1956). Amer. J. Trop. Med. 5:1086.

LIFE CYCLES OF SOME COMMON TAENIOID CESTODES OF DOGS AND CATS

Several species of taenioid cestodes occur commonly as adults in canines and felines. The life cycles (Plate 93) are basically the same as those species discussed for man.

The eggs of the taenioid cestodes are so similar as to be virtually indistinguishable. The species of adult cestodes, with the exception of *Echinococcus,* are difficult to identify. Larval stages, on the other hand, form four distinct groups. *Taenia* produces a cysticercus which has a single scolex invaginated in a vesicular bladder; *Hydatigera* has an evaginated larva with a single scolex followed by a series of immature proglottids, and terminated posteriorly by a small vesicular bladder; *Multiceps* is distinguished by a single vesicular bladder containing many invaginated scolices; and *Echinococcus* produces a complicated larva, the hydatid cyst, consisting of a tough external laminated wall lined with a thin layer of germinal epithelium which produces brood capsules and daughter cysts which in turn produce scolices from their own germinal epithelium.

The cysticerci of *T. pisiformis* and *T. hydatigena* occur in the visceral cavity of lagomorphs and large herbivores, respectively. Those of *T. ovis* and *T. krabbei* are in the musculature of sheep and cervids, respectively, causing a condition of the meat commonly known as measles.

Adults of *Hydatigera taeniaeformis* are in the intestine of cats. The larval stage is a strobilocercus that develops in the liver of rodents, chiefly rats and mice.

Multiceps multiceps and *M. serialis* are parasites of the intestine of canines. The larval stage is

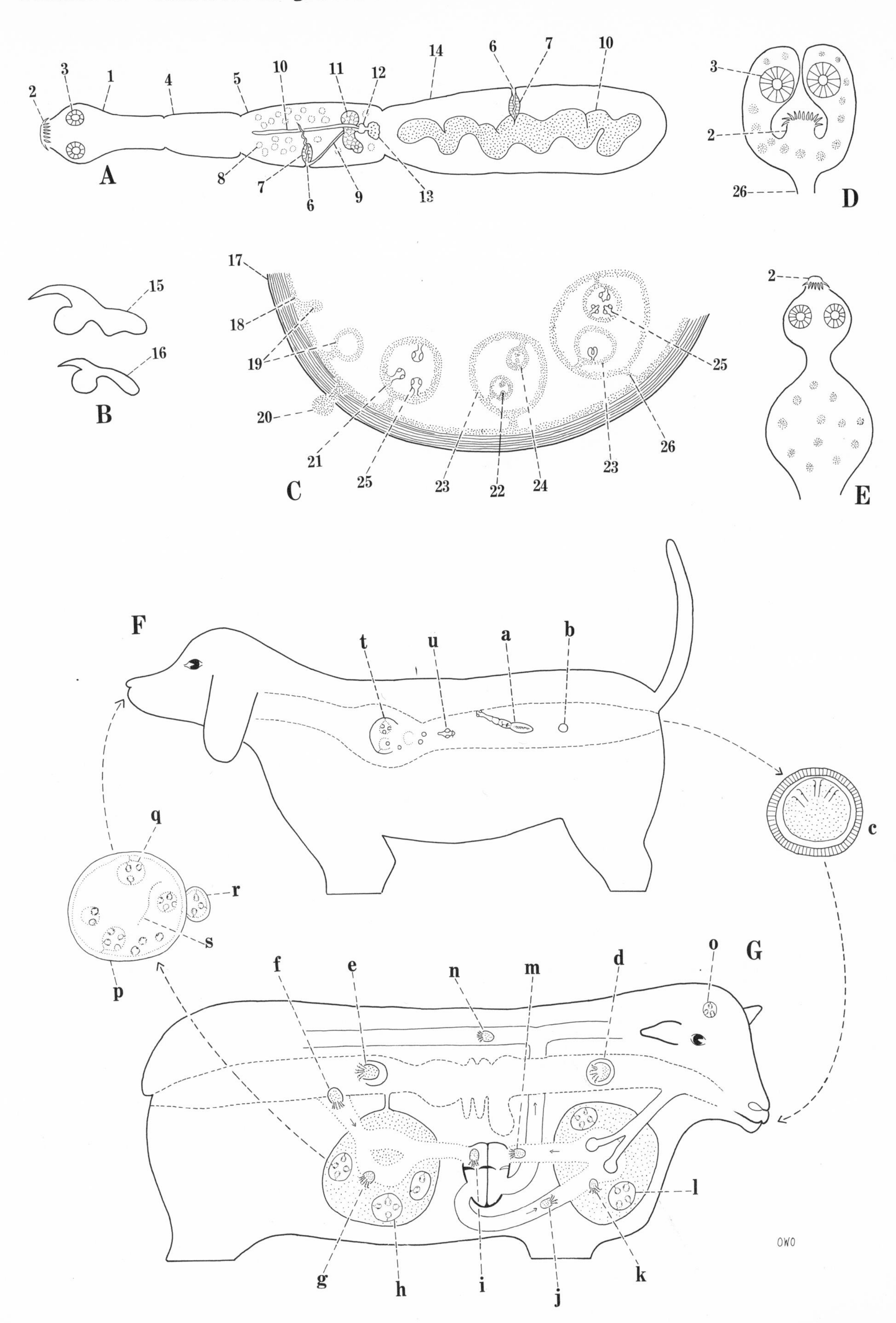
A
B
C
D
E
F
G
1
2
3
4
5
6
7
8
9
10
11
12
13
14
15
16
17
18
19
20
21
22
23
24
25
26
a
b
c
d
e
f
g
h
i
j
k
l
m
n
o
p
q
r
s
t
u
OWO

EXPLANATION OF PLATE 93 ▷

I. Definitive hosts
   A. Dogs and related Canidae.
   B. Cats and related Felidae.

II. Adult worms and eggs
   1. Dogs. *Taenia hydatigena, T. pisiformis, T. ovis, T. krabbei, Multiceps multiceps, M. seralis.*
      Cats. *Hydatigera taeniaeformis.*
   2. Dogs. *Echinococcus granulosus.*
   3. Embryonated taenioid egg.

III. Larval types
   a. Cysticercus. *Taenia.*
   b. Coenurus. *Multiceps.*
   c. Hydatid. *Echinococcus.*
   d. Strobilocercus. *Hydatigera.*

IV. Intermediate hosts
   Rabbits and hares. *a, Taenia pisiformis; b, Multiceps serialis.*
   Sheep. *a, Taenia hydatigena; b, Multiceps multiceps; c, Echinococcus granulosus*
   Swine. *a, Taenia hydatigena, c, Echinococcus granulosus.*
   Deer and other cervids. *a, Taenia hydatigena, T. Krabbei; c, Echinococcus granulosus.*
   Humans. *c, Echinococcus granulosus.**
   Rats. *d, Hydatigera taeniaeformis.*

*While larvae develop in man, normally he does not function in transmitting the parasite to dogs.

---

a coenurus in the central nervous systems of ovines and intermuscular connective tissue and abdominal cavity of lagomorphs, respectively. Coenuri of both species have been found in humans.

Hydatids of *Echinococcus granulosus* occur primarily in ruminants, whereas those of *E. multilocularis* are found in rodents, chiefly microtines. Hydatids of both species infect humans.

EXERCISE ON LIFE CYCLE

Material for the study of life cycles of several species of taenioid cestodes may be obtained readily from veterinary hospitals where dogs and cats are treated for the removal of tapeworms. These include *Taenia pisiformis* and *Multiceps serialis* from dogs, and *Hydatigera taeniaeformis* from cats.

Large numbers of eggs dissected from gravid proglottids should be fed to appropriate intermediate hosts, *i.e.*, eggs of *Taenia pisiformis* and *Multiceps serialis* to rabbits, and those of *Hydatigera taeniaeformis* to rats or mice.

Hatching takes place in the small intestine. The larval stages begin development in the liver. Only *H. taeniaeformis* remains in it; the others drop into the body cavity to complete their growth.

About a week after ingesting eggs, the larvae appear in the liver as small pearly bodies without hooks. In 3 weeks, they have attained a length of approximately 1 cm. On the 30th day, the larvae of *T. pisiformis* and *M. serialis* drop into the body cavity to complete their development. They are capable of infecting the definitive host several weeks later if eaten by it.

Dogs and cats may be infected by feeding the larval stages to them. Experimental animals should be wormed to assure freedom from the cestodes by natural infection prior to feeding the larval stages. Development of the worms to sexual maturity will be recognized when gravid proglottids appear in the faeces.

PLATE 93 *Resumé of Life Cycles of Some Taenioid Cestodes of Dogs and Cats*

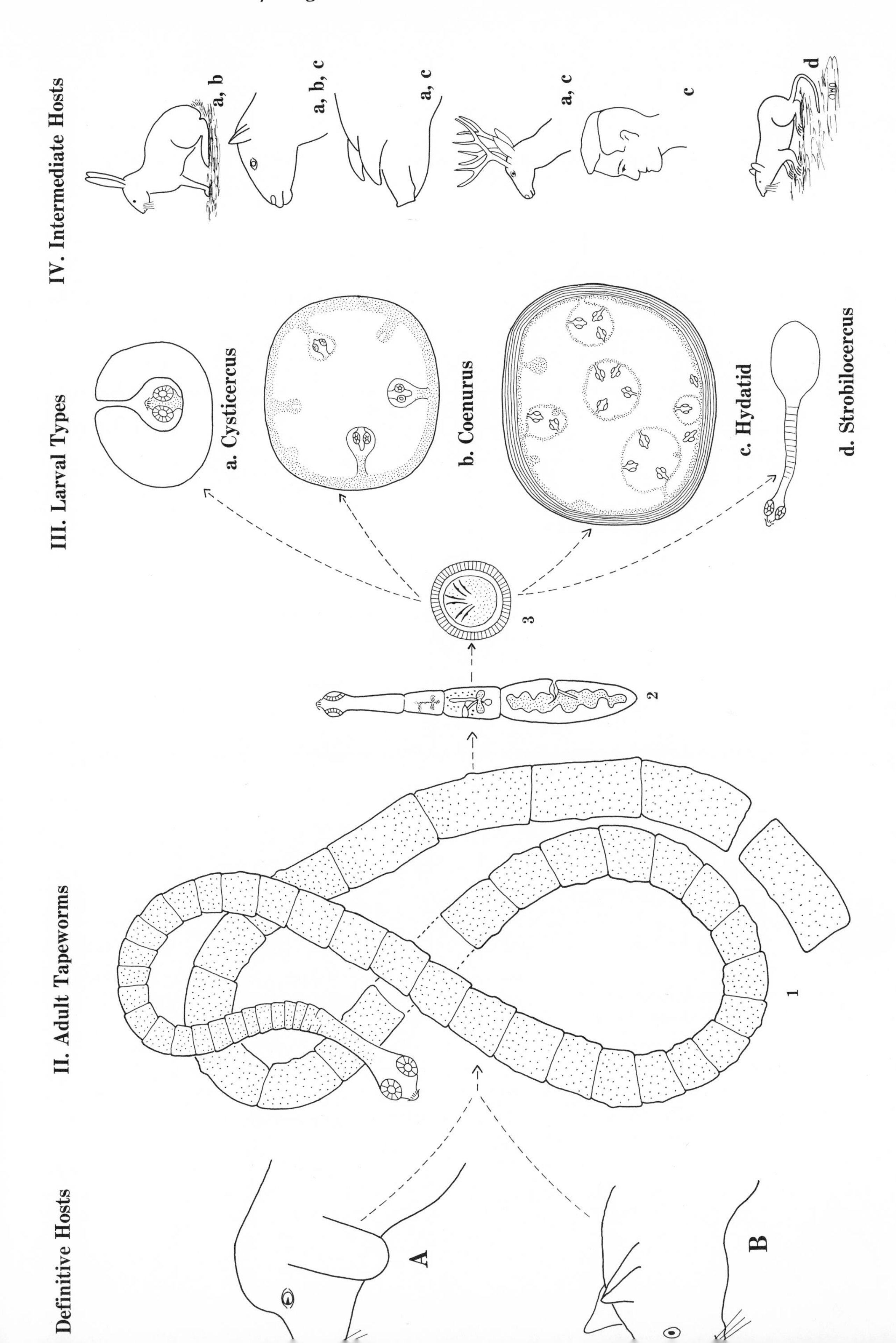

EXPLANATION OF PLATE 94 ▷

A. Adult cestode. **B.** Scolex. **C.** Rose thorn-shaped rostellar hook. **D.** Mature proglottid. **E.** Gravid proglottid. **F.** Individual egg. **G.** Capsule with eggs. **H.** Tailed cysticercoid. **I.** Dog definitive host. **J.** Flea larva intermediate host. **K.** Flea pupa. **L.** Adult flea. **M.** Adult biting louse intermediary.

1, scolex; **2,** immature proglottids; **3,** mature proglottids; **4,** gravid proglottids; **5,** rostellum; **6,** sucker; **7,** common genital pore; **8,** cirrus pouch; **9,** vas deferens; **10,** testes; **11,** vagina; **12,** ovary; **13,** vitelline gland; **14,** longitudinal excretory canal; **15,** egg capsules containing eggs; **16,** egg shell; **17,** oncosphere; **18,** egg capsule; **19,** eggs; **20,** cysticercoid; **21,** tail with some oncospheral hooks still attached.

a, adult cestode in small intestine; **b,** gravid proglottid detached from strobilus; **c,** gravid proglottid outside body; **d,** egg; **e,** egg hatching in intestine of flea larva; **f,** oncosphere migrating through intestinal wall into haemocoel; **g,** oncosphere grows only slightly in larval flea; **h,** developing cysticercoids in pupal flea; **i,** cysticercoids attain full development in imago when it begins to feed on blood from vertebrate host; **j,** eggs hatch in gut of adult biting louse; **k,** oncospheres migrate from gut into body cavity; **l,** fully developed cysticercoid; **m,** cysticercoids released from insect hosts in stomach of dog; **n,** cysticercoids migrate to small intestine, attach to the mucosa, and develop to maturity in 3 to 4 weeks.

Figures A, C, E, G original; B, D, F, adapted from Faust and Russell, 1957, Craig and Faust's Clinical Parasitology, 6th Ed., Lea and Febiger, Philadelphia, p. 632; H, adapted from various sources.

SELECTED REFERENCES

Lapage, G. (1957). Mönnig's Veterinary Helminthology and Entomology, 4th Ed. Williams and Wilkins Co., Baltimore, p. 113.

Morgan, B. B., and P. A. Hawkins. (1949). Veterinary Helminthology. Burgess Publishing Co., Minneapolis, p. 218.

FAMILIES OF CYCLOPHYLLIDEA OTHER THAN TAENIIDAE

Only about a dozen well-known families of this order, other than Taeniidae, are recognized. They are common parasites of birds and mammals. Only the life cycles of species occurring in domestic and a few species of game animals have been studied to any extent.

The infective larvae are most commonly cysticercoids or some variation of them in which the scolex is invaginated in a solid rather than a vesicular body, as in the Taeniidae. A plerocercoid-type larva occurs in the family Paruterinidae and a tetrathyridium-type in the Mesocestoididae. While invertebrates commonly serve as the intermediate hosts, vertebrates also function in this role.

FAMILY DILEPIDIDAE

A common parasite of this family is *Dipylidium caninum,* the double-pored tapeworm of dogs and cats. It is prevalent in all parts of the world where fleas and biting lice infest these mammals. Infections in dogs can be diagnosed macroscopically by the occurrence on the faeces of the active reddish-yellow gravid proglottids, which are about the size and shape of a cucumber seed.

Dipylidium caninum (Linnaeus, 1758) (Plate 94)

D. caninum occurs in the small intestine of dogs, foxes, and cats. It is found occasionally in humans, especially children.

DESCRIPTION. Adult worms attain a length of 50 cm. The scolex bears an elongated rostellum armed with four to seven rows of rose thorn-shaped hooks. Mature and gravid proglottids resemble cucumber seeds in size and shape. There are two sets of reproductive organs, each opening in a common genital pore on the lateral margin of the proglottid. Testes are numerous and fill the space between the excretory canals. The ovaries and vitelline glands are in separate clusters with the latter posterior. Several eggs occur in individual rust-colored capsules.

LIFE CYCLE. Gravid proglottids voided with the faeces, or leaving the host spontaneously, disseminate the egg capsules. These may be on the hair of the hosts or in their beds. Biting lice, *Trichodectes canis,* or larvae of the dog flea, *Ctenocephalides canis,* or the cat flea, *C. felis,* eating the

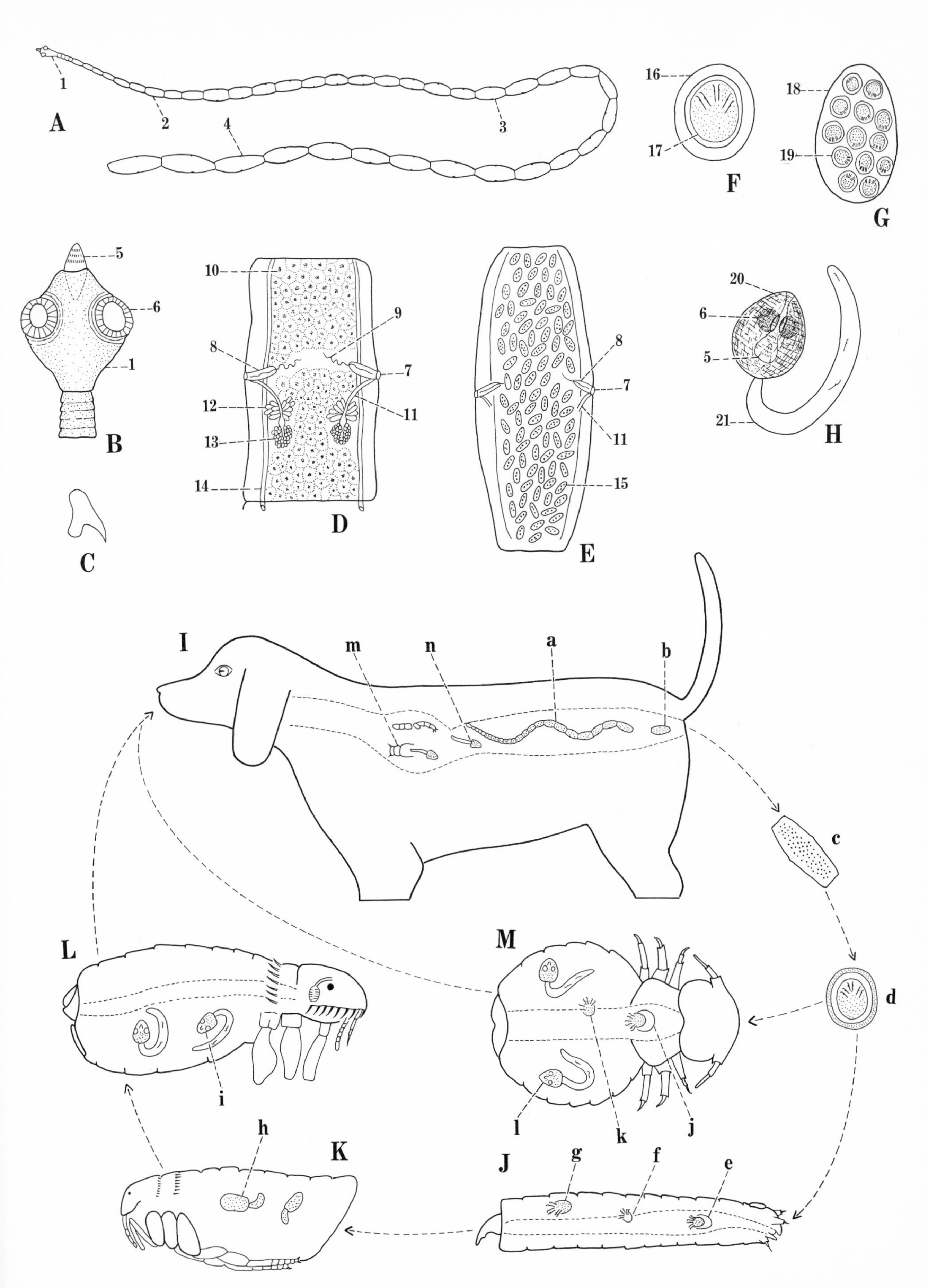
1
2
3
4
A
16
17
F
18
19
G
5
6
1
B
C
10
9
8
7
12
11
13
14
D
8
7
11
15
E
20
6
5
21
H
I
m
n
a
b
c
d
L
i
M
l
k
j
h
K
J
g
f
e

eggs, become infected. They hatch in the digestive tract of the insects and the oncospheres migrate into the body cavity. In biting lice, they develop quickly to the infective tailed cysticercoids. Growth in fleas, however, is more prolonged and development is associated with the stages of metamorphosis of the insect host. Oncospheres develop very little in the larval flea, considerable growth takes place during the pupal stage, and final development is completed in adult fleas when the latter begin to take blood meals.

Infection of the definitive host is accomplished when adult fleas or biting lice are swallowed. The cysticercoids develop directly to adult cestodes in 3 to 4 weeks. Infection of children takes place in the same manner.

EXERCISE ON LIFE CYCLE

Flea eggs may be obtained by putting an infested dog or cat in a cage under which a pan is placed to catch eggs that drop from the hair. Eggs placed in Petri dishes containing fine moist sand hatch successfully at room temperature. The larvae feed well on dog discuits and dried blood.

Flea larvae intended for infection are isolated in suitable dishes and starved for 24 hours. Gravid proglottids are teased apart in a small amount of saline to free the egg capsules. Sufficient dried and powdered blood is added to the eggs to form a soft paste which the flea larvae readily eat. After they have ingested the eggs, the larvae must be kept on the moist sand until they become adults. Little development of the oncospheres occurs in the larvae, but considerable takes place in the pupae, and is completed when the adult fleas begin feeding on the host. Dissection of larvae, pupae, and adults should be made to observe the development of the cysticercoids.

If dogs or cats are to be fed experimentally infected fleas, they should be treated first to remove any tapeworms that might be present in the intestine from natural infections.

Another common Dilepididae readily available and useful for life history studies is *Choanotaenia infundibulum* of chickens. Eggs from gravid proglottids develop into cysticercoids when fed to house flies, beetles, and grasshoppers. Infected arthropod intermediate hosts fed to young chicks produce adult cestodes. For details on procedure and specific intermediate hosts, read the paper by Horsfall and Jones.

SELECTED REFERENCES

Horsfall, M. W., and M. F. Jones. (1937). J. Parasit. 23:435.

Vernard, C. E. (1938). Ann. N. Y. Acad. Sci. 37:273.

Zimmermann, H. R. (1937). Z. Parasitenk. 9:717.

FAMILY DAVAINEIDAE

Members of this family are parasites of the intestine of birds and mammals throughout the world. Some of them cause serious damage to poultry.

They are small- to medium-sized cestodes. The rostellum is rectractable and armed with two to three rows of minute hammer-shaped hooks, and the margins of the suckers likewise may bear tiny hooks. The gravid uterus breaks up into egg capsules which contain one to several eggs each, depending on the species.

Davainea proglottina (Davaine, 1860) (Plate 95)

This minute cestode occurs in the duodenum of chickens, other gallinaceous birds, and pigeons in all parts of the world.

DESCRIPTION. The mature worms may be 0.5 to 3 mm long, with up to six proglottids. The rostellum is armed with 80 to 94 hooks 7 to 8 μ long, and the suckers with a few rows of minute thorn-shaped hooks along the margins. The genital pores are regularly alternating and located on the anterior corner of the proglottid. Eggs are distributed singly in capsules throughout the parenchyma of the ripe proglottid.

LIFE CYCLE. Eggs released from motile proglottids expelled with the faeces hatch when eaten by slugs (*Limax, Arion, Cepaea, Milax, and Agriolimax*) and land snails (*Polygyra* and *Zonitoides*). The newly hatched oncospheres migrate from the intestine to the tissues where development into infective cysticercoids requires 3 to 4 weeks during the summer. Fowls acquire the cestodes by eating infected mollusks. Development in chickens to sexual maturity is attained in about 2 weeks.

SELECTED REFERENCES

Abdous, A. H. (1958). Canad. J. Comp. Med. 22:338.

Wetzel, R. (1932). Arch. Wissensch. Prakt. Tierheilk. 65:595.

Raillietina Fuhrmann, 1920

The species of this genus are parasites of the small intestine of birds and mammals. At least three of them are of common occurrence in poultry and of cosmopolitan distribution.

In cases where the life cycles are known, ants and many species of beetles of the families Tenebrionidae, Scarabaeidae, and Carabidae serve as intermediate hosts. House flies also are intermediaries for some species, becoming infected as adults rather than as maggots.

Raillietina (*Skrjabinia*) *cesticillus* (Molin, 1858) (Plate 96, A-F)

This cestode is very common throughout the world, owing, probably, to the occurrence simultaneously of chickens and many species of intermediate hosts in the same area. They include house flies (Muscidae), ground beetles (Carabidae), dung beetles (Scarabaeidae), and meal worms (Tenebrionidae).

DESCRIPTION. They are usually about 4 cm long but may be up to 13 cm. The scolex is large and bears a broad rostellum armed with 400 to 500 small hooks. The suckers are small and unarmed. There is no distinct neck. Genital apertures are irregularly alternating. Egg capsules scattered throughout the parenchyma contain a single egg.

LIFE CYCLE. Ripe, or gravid, proglottids passed in the faeces liberate their embryonated eggs. When these are eaten by house flies (*Musca domestica*), or numerous species of beetles, they hatch in the intestine and the oncospheres migrate into the body cavity. They soon develop to infective cysticercoids. Birds become parasitized by eating the infected insects.

Raillietina (*Raillietina*) *echinobothrida* (Megnin, 1880) (Plate 96, G-K)

Like the preceding species, this one is a cosmopolitan parasite of the small intestine of chickens.

DESCRIPTION. The body length is up to 25 cm. The small rostellum is armed with about 200 small hooks arranged in two rows and the suckers have 8 to 10 rows of minute hooks. The genital pores usually are unilateral. The uterus fragments into capsules, each containing several eggs.

LIFE CYCLE. Egg capsules released from free proglottids hatch when eaten by ants (*Tetramorium* and *Pheidole*). Cysticercoids in the body cavity are infective to chickens.

Raillietina (*Raillietina*) *tetragona* (Molin, 1858) (Plate 96, L-O)

This is another cosmopolitan parasite of the small intestine of chickens, pigeons, and guinea fowls.

DESCRIPTION. The length of the strobilus is up to 25 cm. The tiny rostellum is armed with about 100 minute hooks and the suckers with 8 to 10 rows of them. The genital pores are unilateral. Egg capsules contain 6 to 12 ova each.

LIFE CYCLE. The cysticercoids develop in house flies and ants (*Tetramorium* and *Pheidole*).

Raillietina (*R.*) *loeweni* of black-tailed jackrabbits utilizes harvest ants (*Pheidole sitarches campestris*) and *P. bicarinata* as intermediate hosts in Kansas.

EXERCISE ON LIFE CYCLE

A plentiful supply of representatives of the Davaineidae for experimental studies can be obtained from establishments where farm-raised poultry is processed for market.

Eggs dissected from the proglottids should be placed in a glass dish with the respective intermediate host. These must be collected from localities where fowls have not been in order that natural infections

EXPLANATION OF PLATE 95 ⇨

A. Entire adult cestode. **B.** Scolex. **C.** Mature proglottid. **D.** Ripe proglottid. **E.** Hammer-shaped hook from rostellum. **F.** Thorn-shaped hook from suckers. **G.** Hatched oncosphere or hexacanth. **H.** Invaginated cysticercoid. **I.** Chicken definitive host. **J.** Slug *(Arion, Limax, Agriolimax, Milax)* intermediate host.

1, scolex; **2,** spiny sucker; **3,** rostellum; **4,** rostellar hooks; **5,** immature proglottid; **6,** mature proglottid; **7,** gravid proglottid; **8,** common genital pore; **9,** cirrus pouch; **10,** cirrus; **11,** vas deferens; **12,** testes; **13,** vagina; **14,** seminal receptacle; **15,** ovary; **16,** vitelline gland; **17,** embryonated eggs in uterus; **18,** hammer-shaped hook from rostellum; **19,** thorn-shaped hook from suckers; **20,** hooks of oncosphere; **21,** cells of developing embryo; **22,** wall of cysticercoid.

a, adult cestode in small intestine; **b,** gravid proglottid detaches from strobilus and passes to outside with faeces; **c,** gravid proglottid; **d,** gravid proglottid in faeces; **e,** slugs feeding on faeces eat eggs; **f,** embryonated egg in intestine of slug; **g,** oncosphere escapes from egg; **h,** oncosphere migrates through intestinal wall and grows into cysticercoid; **i,** cysticercoid embedded in body tissues; **j,** definitive host becomes infected by eating slugs that harbor cysticercoids; **k,** cysticercoids released from slug by digestive processes; **l,** cysticercoid everts scolex, attaches to wall of intestine, and grows to maturity (a) in 14 days.

Figures E, F, G from Wetzel, 1932, Arch. Wissensch. Prakt. Tierheilk. 65:595; others from various sources.

---

are not present to complicate the experiments, or they should be reared under controlled conditions in the laboratory.

The eggs hatch shortly after reaching the intestine of the intermediate hosts. Hence the gut of the intermediary should be examined within 1 to 2 hours after the eggs have been eaten, at which time the oncospheres will appear free in the intestinal lumen or be penetrating the epithelium. Mature cysticercoids appear in the tissues of snails and slugs or the body cavity of arthropods in 2 weeks during the warm summer. They may be found by dissecting the intermediate hosts that have eaten eggs.

Baby chicks fed infected mollusks or insects, depending on the species of cestode, pass gravid proglottids in their faeces in about 2 weeks.

SELECTED REFERENCES

Ackert, J. E., and W. M. Reid. (1936). Trans. Amer. Micr. Soc. 55:97.

Bartel, M. H. (1965). J. Parasit. 51:800.

Enigk, K., and Sticinsky, E. (1959). Z. Parasitenk. 19:278.

Horsfall, M. W. (1938). J. Parasit. 24:409.

Jones, M. F. (1930). J. Parasit. 16:158; (1931). Ibid. 17:234.

Reid, W. M., Ackert, J. E., and A. A. Case. (1938). Trans. Amer. Micr. Soc. 57:65.

Wetzel, R. (1932). Arch. Wissensch. Prakt. Tierheilk. 65:595; (1938). Zeitschr. Hyg. Zool. Schädelingsbekämpf. 30:84.

FAMILY HYMENOLEPIDIIDAE

The members of this family parasitize birds and mammals. Both aquatic and terrestrial species serve as definitive hosts. The cestodes occur as a vast array of species throughout the world. Some of them are important parasites of poultry, and related species occur in mice and men.

Only species of the genus *Hymenolepis* will be considered as representatives of this large family. They include one species each from terrestrial and aquatic birds, and one from mice. Those from the birds have a conventional type of life cycle with an arthropod intermediate host, whereas the one from mice deviates from conventionality in that infection may be direct or through an arthropod.

Hymenolepis carioca (Magellaes, 1808) (Plate 97)

This is one of the commonest cestodes of chickens in the United States.

DESCRIPTION. The threadlike body is 3 to 8 cm long and bears a scolex with an unarmed rostellum, but the suckers are armed with minute hooks. The genital pores are anterior to the middle of the proglottids and located on the lateral margin. The length of the cirrus pouch equals about half the width of the proglottid and is preceded by a large seminal vesicle. There are three testes arranged in a triangle. Eggs are enclosed in three membranes.

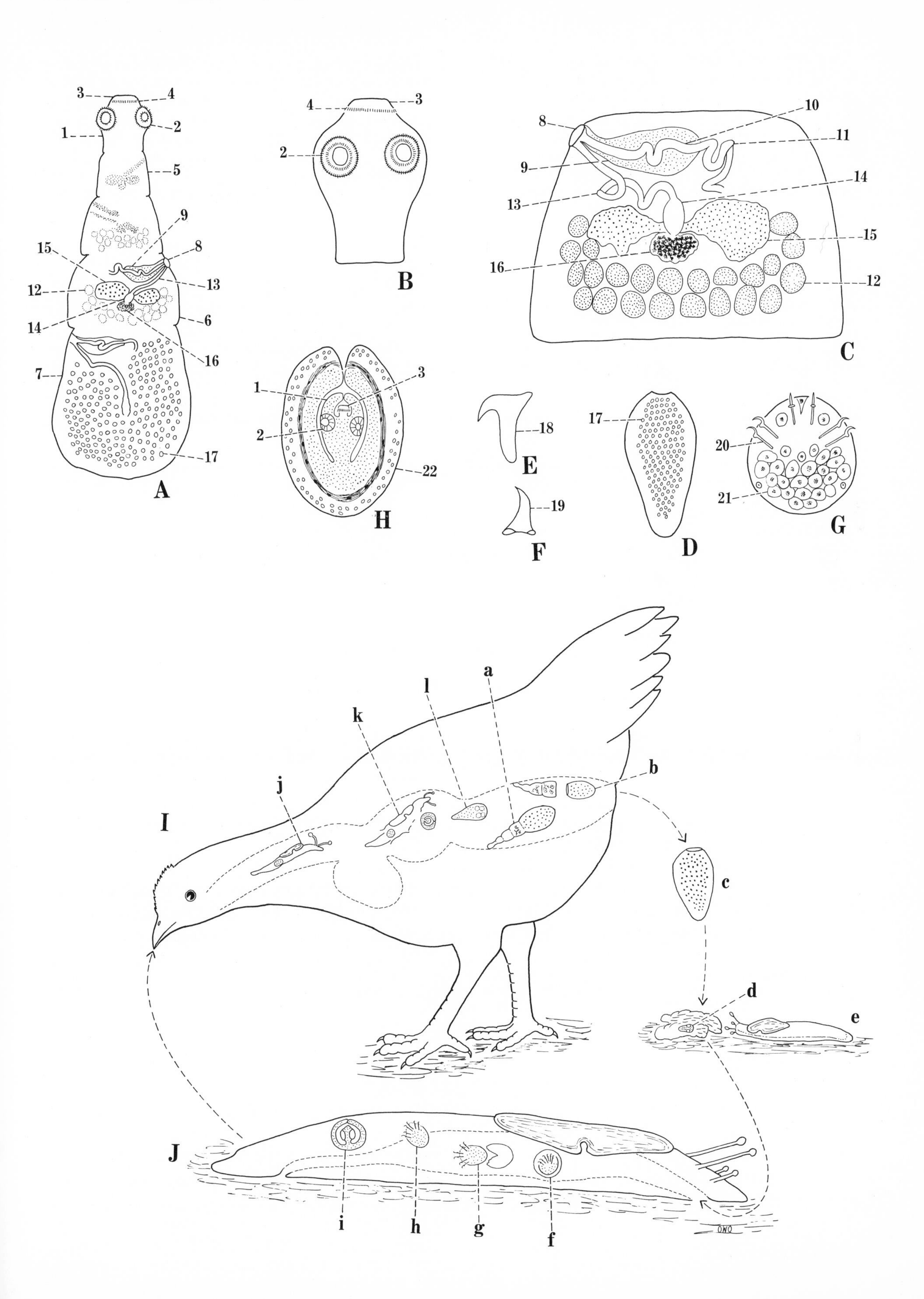

A
B
C
D
E
F
G
H
I
J
a
b
c
d
e
f
g
h
i
j
k
l
1
2
3
4
5
6
7
8
9
10
11
12
13
14
15
16
17
18
19
20
21
22

EXPLANATION OF PLATE 96

A-F. *Raillietina (S.) cesticillus.* **A.** Scolex. **B.** Hook from rostellum. **C.** Mature proglottid. **D.** Gravid proglottid. **E.** Egg with oncosphere. **F.** Invaginated cysticercoid. **G-K.** *R. (R.) echinobothrida.* **G.** Scolex. **H.** Hooks from rostellum. **I.** Mature proglottid. **J.** Gravid proglottid. **K.** Invaginated cysticercoid (cysticercoids of *R. (R.) echinobothridia* and *R. (R.) tetragona* are similar). **L-O.** *R. (R.) tetragona.* **L.** Scolex. **M.** Hooks from rostellum. **N.** Mature proglottid. **O.** Ripe proglottid. **P.** Fowl definitive host. **Q.** Ground beetle intermediate host. **R.** Ant intermediate host. **S.** Dung beetles (Scarabaeidae), along with ground beetles (Carabidae), and house flies are intermediate hosts.

1, scolex; **2**, sucker; **3**, rostellum with hooks; **4**, genital pore; **5**, cirrus pouch; **6**, vas deferens; **7**, testes; **8**, vagina; **9**, ovary; **10**, vitelline gland; **11**, uterine pouch or egg capsule; **12**, egg shell; **13**, oncosphere; **14**, body of cysticercoid.

a, adult cestode in small intestine; **b**, detached gravid proglottids; **c**, free ripe proglottid; **d**, egg; **e**, motile proglottid in faeces discharges egg capsules; **f**, eggs hatch in intestine of intermediate hosts; **g**, oncosphere migrates from lumen of intestine to body cavity of intermediate hosts; **h**, cysticercoid; **i**, infection of definitive host by eating infected intermediate hosts; **j**, cysticercoids released from intermediate hosts by digestive processes; **k**, cysticercoid evaginates and attaches to mucosa of small intestine, and develops to maturity.

Figure E adapted from Reid, Ackert, and Case, 1938, Trans. Amer. Micr. Soc. 57:65; F, from Ackert and Reid, 1936, Ibid., 55:97; K, from Horsfall, 1938, J. Parasit. 24:409; all others from Ransom, 1904, 21st Ann. Rept., U. S. Dept. Agric., p. 268.

LIFE CYCLE. Eggs passed in faeces hatch when eaten by beetles (*Apodius, Choeridium, Geotrupes, Ontophagus, Hister, Anisotarsus*). The oncospheres migrate from the intestine into the body cavity and develop into cysticercoids. Infection of the definitive host occurs when it eats beetles containing fully developed cysticercoids.

This life cycle is typical of hymenolepid cestodes occurring in terrestrial animals. The intermediate hosts are terrestrial invertebrates.

Stable flies have been reported as intermediate hosts on the basis of feeding experiments, but inasmuch as cysticercoids were not demonstrated their role as intermediaries needs confirmation.

EXERCISE ON LIFE CYCLE

Adult cestodes can be obtained from almost any place where chickens that have been kept on the ground are slaughtered and dressed. Obtain gravid proglottids and feed them to dung beetles (*Hister* or *Anisotarsus*) obtained from localities where chickens have not been kept to assure that they are not infected naturally.

Dissect some of the infected beetles on alternate days for about 3 weeks to observe the migration and progressive development of the cysticercoids.

At the end of 3 weeks, feed some of the infected beetles to young chicks that have been kept in insect-proof pens to avoid natural infection. Examine the faeces for eggs or gravid segments which should appear about 3 weeks after infected beetles have been eaten. Control chicks should be kept.

The report of Guberlet that stable flies serve as intermediate hosts should be reexamined.

SELECTED REFERENCES

Cram, E. B., and M. F. Jones. (1929). N. Amer. Vet. 10:49.

Guberlet, J. E. (1919). J. Parasit. 6:35.

Jones, M. F. (1929). J. Agr. Res. 38:629; (1929). J. Parasit. 15:223; (1932). Ibid. 18:307.

Drepanidotaenia lanceolata (Block, 1782) (Plate 98)

These are large Hymenolepidiidae from the small intestine of ducks and geese throughout the world.

DESCRIPTION. The body is lance-shaped, 3 to 13 cm long, with proglottids very narrow anteriorly and 5 to 18 mm wide posteriorly. The scolex is small, the rostellum armed with eight hooks,

PLATE 96 *Rallietina (S.) cesticillus, R. (R.) echinobothrida, R. (R.) tetragona*

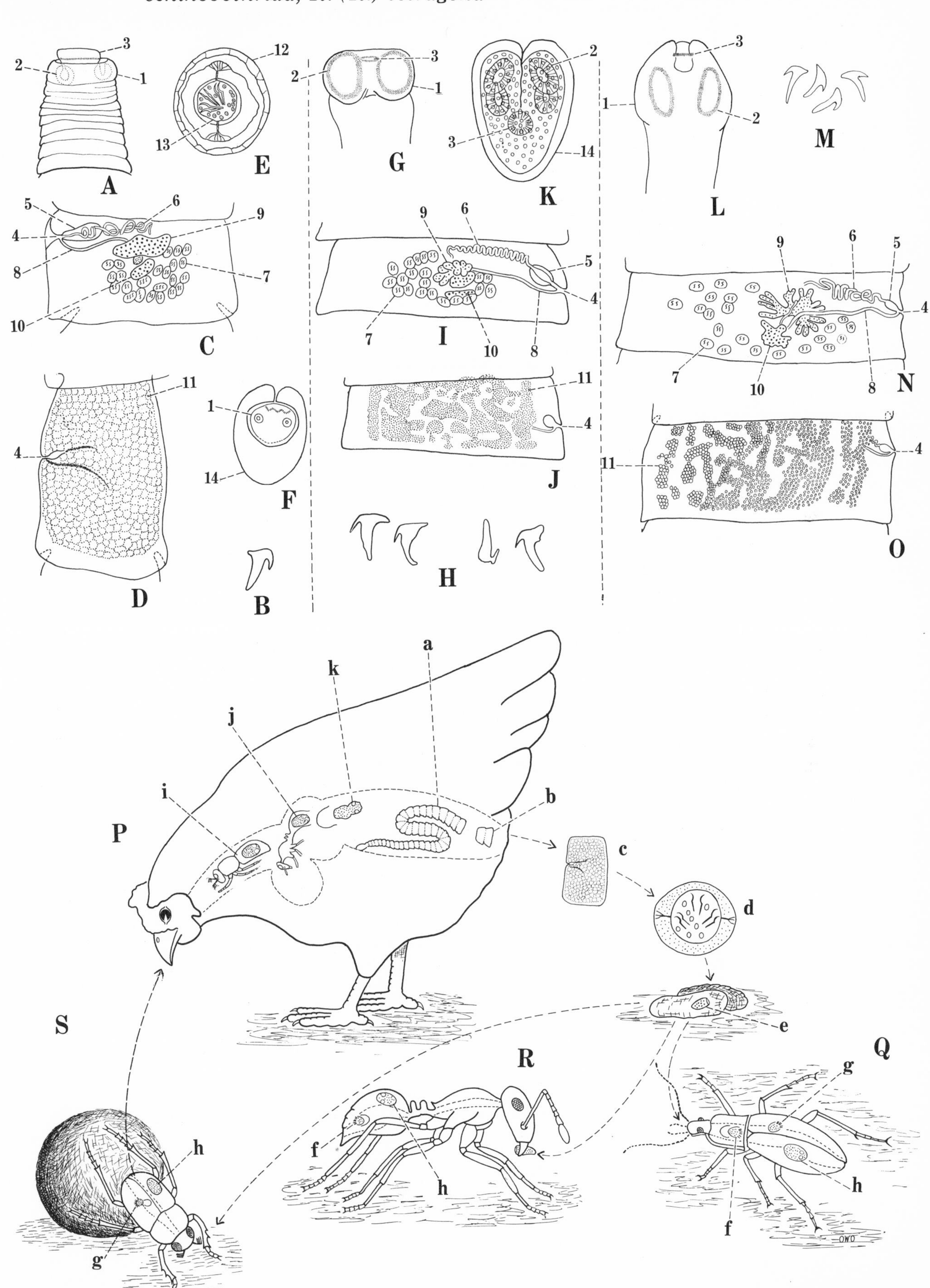

EXPLANATION OF PLATE 97

A. Scolex. **B.** Minute hooks from sucker. **C.** Immature proglottid. **D.** Mature proglottid. **E.** Gravid proglottids. **F.** Egg. **G.** Hook of oncosphere. **H.** Tailed cysticercoid. **I.** Chicken definitive host. **J.** Dung beetle (scarabeid) intermediate host. **K.** Histerid beetle intermediate host. **L.** Carabid beetle intermediary. **M.** Stable fly (larva and adult) reported as intermediate hosts but it is not certain that they are.

1, scolex; **2,** sucker; **3,** unarmed rostellum; **4,** genital pore; **5,** cirrus pouch leading from seminal vesicle; **6,** vas deferens; **7,** testes; **8,** vagina with enlarged seminal receptacle; **9,** ovary; **10,** vitelline gland; **11,** longitudinal excretory canal; **12,** transverse excretory canal; **13,** gravid uterus containing eggs; **14,** egg membranes; **15,** oncosphere with hooks; **16,** body of cysticercoid; **17,** tail; **18,** embryonic hooks.

a, adult cestode in small intestine; **b,** eggs passing out of intestine; **c,** egg; **d,** egg hatching in intestine of beetle intermediary; **e,** hexacanth migrating through intestinal wall; **f,** cysticercoid; **g,** digestion of intermediate host releases cysticercoid; **h,** cysticercoid excysts, evaginates, and attaches to intestinal mucosa where it develops into an adult cestode in about 3 weeks.

Figures A-G adapted from Ransom, 1902, Trans. Amer. Micr. Soc. 23:151; H, from Jones, 1929, J. Agr. Res. 38:629.

---

and the neck very short. There are three testes on the poral side arranged in linear fashion across the proglottid. The ovary is aporal from the testes.

LIFE CYCLE. Eggs passed in the faeces hatch when ingested by several genera of copepods with *Cyclops strenuus* being especially susceptible. The eggs hatch in the intestine and the oncospheres migrate into the haemocoel where development of the tailed cysticercoids takes place. Infection of ducks and geese occurs when the cysticercoid-bearing copepods are eaten.

In the case of other species of hymenolepids occurring in birds and mammals living in an aquatic environment, aquatic invertebrates are most likely to serve as the intermediate hosts, with microcrustacea being predominant in this role.

EXERCISE ON LIFE CYCLE

Adult cestodes may be obtained from the intestine of wild ducks and geese during the hunting season, as well as from domestic birds when available. Feed infective eggs from the posterior proglottids of the tapeworms to copepods; dissect individuals on the day they eat them and examine the intestinal contents for oncospheres, and again at intervals of 2 days thereafter to observe the migration and development of the cysticercoids in the body cavity.

If available, ducklings may be infected by feeding copepods known to contain cysticercoids. Watch for the first occurrence of eggs or proglottids in the faeces in order to determine the prepatent period.

SELECTED REFERENCES

Ransom, B. H. (1904). Hyg. Lab., U. S. Pub. Health Serv. and Marine Hosp., Bull. 18.

Ruszkowski, J. S. (1932). Bull. Internat. Akad. Polo. Sci. Classe Sci., Math., Nat., S. B. Nat. (II), (1-4): 1-8.

Hymenolepis fraterna Stiles, 1906 (Plate 99)

This small cestode is a parasite of rats and mice in many parts of the world. It is so similar morphologically to *H. nana* of humans that some authors consider them to be physiological strains rather than distinct species. It is chosen for discussion because the life cycle deviates markedly in certain aspects from that normally encountered in Cyclophyllidean cestodes.

DESCRIPTION. These small cestodes measure 7 to 80 mm long. The retractable rostellum is armed with 16 to 18 hooks (24 to 26 according to some authors). The genital pores are unilateral and on the left side of the proglottid. The three testes are arranged in a transverse line and separated by the ovary so that one testis is poral and two aporal.

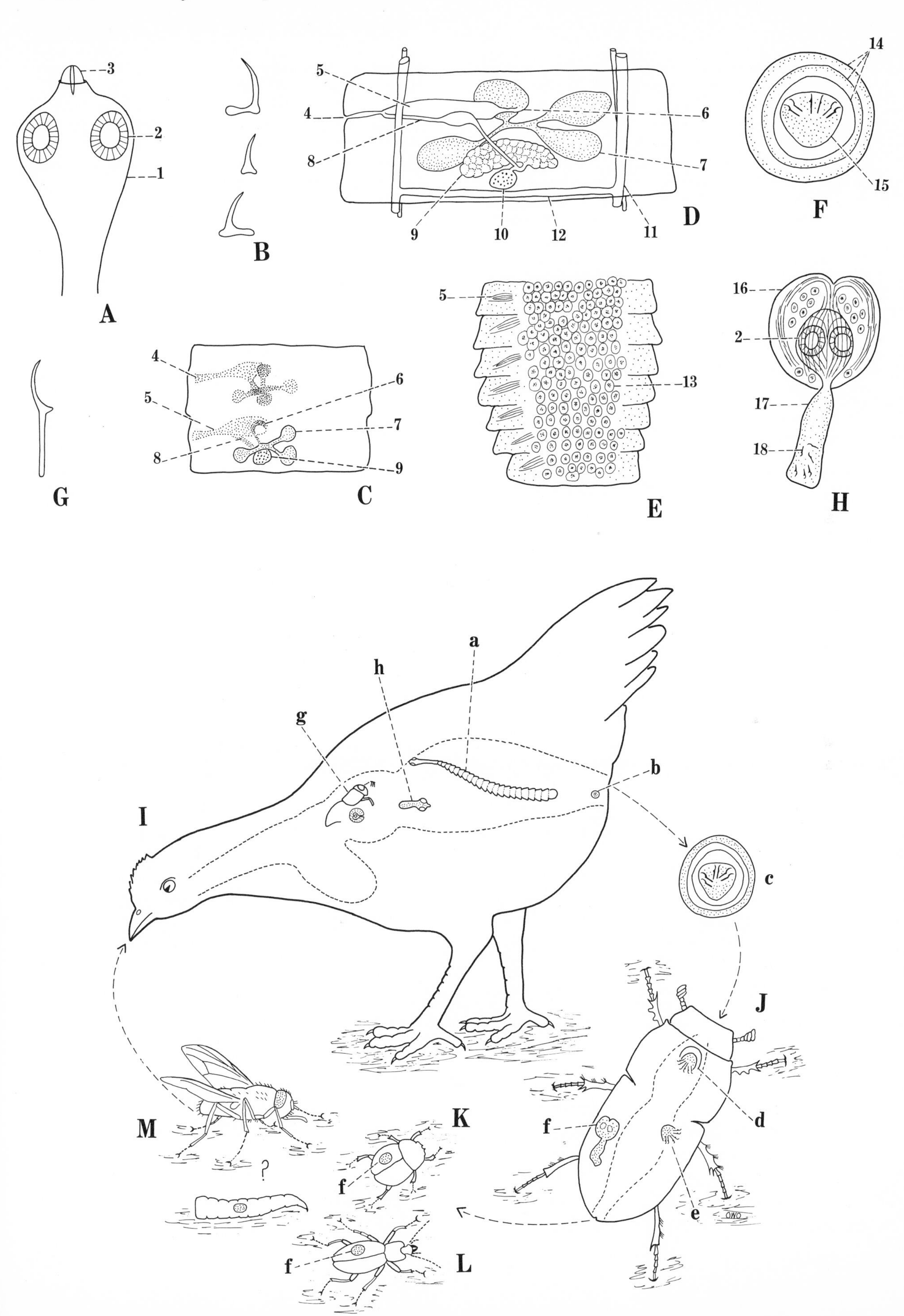
1
2
3
4
5
6
7
8
9
10
11
12
13
14
15
16
17
18
A
B
C
D
E
F
G
H
I
J
K
L
M
a
b
c
d
e
f
g
h
?
ONO

EXPLANATION OF PLATE 98 ⇨

A. Scolex and anterior end of strobilus. **B.** Hook from rostellum. **C.** Mature proglottid. **D.** Gravid proglottid. **E.** Embryonated egg. **F.** Invaginated cysticercoid. **G.** Evaginated cysticercoid. **H.** Duck and goose definitive hosts. **I.** Copepod intermediate host.

1, scolex; **2,** armed rostellum; **3,** sucker; **4,** neck; **5,** anterior proglottids; **6,** handle; **7,** guard; **8,** blade; **9,** protruding cirrus; **10,** cirrus pouch; **11,** seminal vesicle; **12,** testes; **13,** ovary; **14,** oviduct; **15,** vitelline gland; **16,** Mehlis' gland; **17,** seminal receptacle; **18,** vagina; **19,** developing uterus; **20,** dorsal longitudinal excretory canal; **21,** ventral excretory canal; **22,** eggs; **23,** common genital pore; **24,** egg shell; **25,** inner membrane; **26,** oncosphere; **27,** hooks; **28,** body of cysticercoid; **29,** tail; **30,** oncospheral hooks.

a, adult cestode in small intestine; **b,** eggs passing out of gut; **c,** egg in water; **d,** egg hatching in gut of copepod; **e,** oncosphere migrating through intestinal wall; **f,** cysticercoid in haemocoel; **g,** digestion of infected copepod releases invaginated cysticercoid; **h,** evaginated cysticercoid attaches to intestinal wall and grows into a mature cestode.

Adapted from Ruszkowski, 1932, Bull. Internat. Akad. Polo. Sc., Classe Sci. Math., Nat. (II), (1-4):1-8.

LIFE CYCLE. The life cycle may be initiated in one of three ways. They are by 1) swallowing infective eggs by the definitive host, *i.e.*, a direct life cycle; 2) eggs hatching in the intestine of the definitive host without first having left it, *i.e.*, direct infection by internal autoinfection from within the intestine; and 3) eggs developing in fleas or larvae of meal beetles to infective tailed cysticercoids, *i.e.*, an indirect cycle.

When eggs are swallowed by rats or mice, they hatch in the intestine and the oncospheres penetrate the intestinal mucosa of the villi, entering the submucosal tissue. Here they grow into tailless cysticercoids which when fully developed return to the intestinal lumen, evaginate, attach to the mucosa, and grow to maturity.

When eggs hatch in the intestine without leaving the host, the oncospheres penetrate the intestinal wall and development to sexual maturity takes place in the same manner as when eggs are swallowed. This manner of infection from within is designated as internal autoinfection.

Eggs passed in the faeces and eaten by meal beetles or flea larvae hatch in the intestine and the hexacanths migrate to the body cavity where they develop into tailed cysticercoids. When infected beetles or their larvae are eaten by rats and mice, the cysticercoids are released, evaginate, attach to the intestinal wall, and develop to maturity.

Hymenolepis nana of humans in some parts of the world occurs in great numbers in some individuals. It is believed that such heavy infections result from internal autoinfection.

EXERCISE ON LIFE CYCLE

These parasites are sufficiently common in rats and mice in most regions to provide material for life history studies. The direct cycle and that involving an intermediate host are preferred for general studies.

Gravid proglottids fed to flour beetles (*Tribolium confusum*) result in infections. Cysticercoids are developed in 2 to 3 weeks at room temperature. Examine the intestinal contents of beetles 4 to 5 hours after ingestion of eggs for the presence of newly hatched oncospheres and again at intervals of 1 or 2 days thereafter to observe the development of the cysticercoids in the haemocoel.

Infect mice with cysticercoids originating from worms taken from mice, and likewise rats with those from rats. Also try cross-infection of rats with cysticercoids originating from mice and vice versa to determine whether differences of susceptibility occur with the use of different physiological strains of cestodes. Watch for eggs in the faeces to ascertain the prepatent period.

Feed gravid proglottids directly to mice to establish infections. Examine the intestinal contents of a mouse for oncospheres four to five hours after it has eaten eggs. Examine the intestinal mucosa at intervals of two days to observe 1) the development of the cysticercoids, 2) the time they enter the lumen of the intestine, and attach to the mucosa, and 3) the course and rate of development to adults. Sections should be employed for the first two steps.

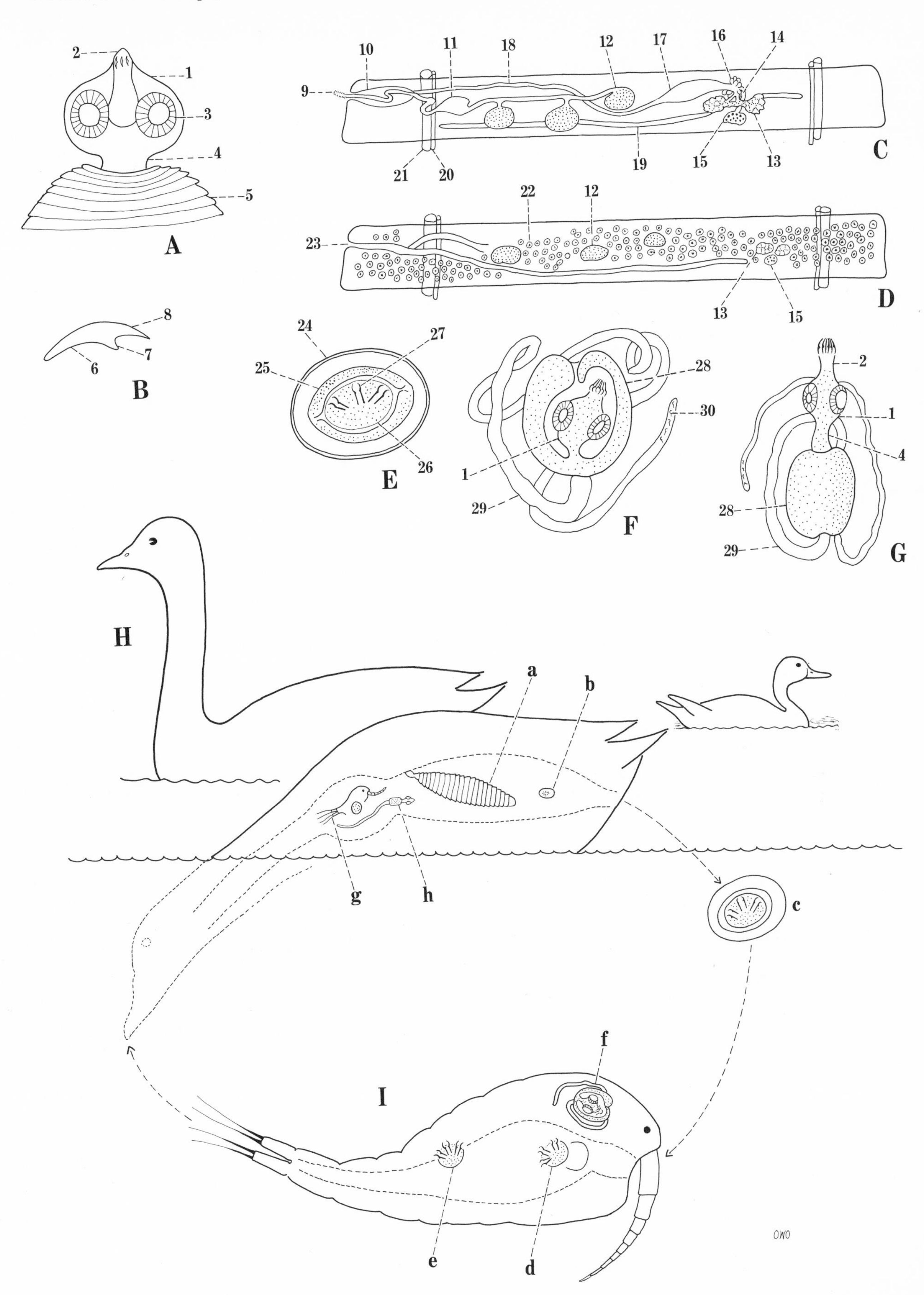
A
B
C
D
E
F
G
H
I
a
b
c
d
e
f
g
h
OWO

EXPLANATION OF PLATE 99 ⇨

A. Scolex. **B.** Rostellar hook. **C.** Mature proglottid. **D.** Gravid proglottid. **E.** Embryonated egg. **F.** Cysticercoid. **G.** Cysticercoid in villus of intestine. **H.** Mouse definitive host. **I.** Larval intermediate beetle host *(Tenebrio molitor, Tribolium confusum.)* **J.** Adult beetles.

1, scolex; **2,** sucker; **3,** armed rostellum; **4,** handle of hook; **5,** guard; **6,** blade; **7,** common genital pore; **8,** cirrus pouch; **9,** testes; **10,** vagina; **11,** seminal receptacle; **12,** ovary; **13,** oviduct; **14,** vitelline gland; **15,** longitudinal excretory canal; **16,** gravid uterus; **17,** shell or outer membrane of egg; **18,** thick inner membrane with terminal filaments; **19,** oncosphere; **20,** tail of cysticercoid; **21,** oncospheral hooks; **22,** intestinal villus; **23,** cysticercoid embedded in villus.

a, adult worm in small intestine; **b,** gravid proglottid detached from strobilus; **c,** egg in faeces passing out of intestine; **d,** egg free; **e,** egg swallowed and returned to small intestine; **f,** egg hatches in small intestine; **g,** oncosphere burrows into intestinal wall; **h,** cysticercoid develops in villus; **i,** cysticercoid breaks out of intestinal wall and evaginates; **j, k, l, a,** cysticercoid attaches to intestinal wall and grows to sexually mature cestode; **m,** some infective eggs do not leave the body, but hatch in the intestine, initiating internal autoinfection in which development proceeds as in e-l; **n,** eggs passed in faeces are infective to arthropod intermediate hosts; **o,** eggs swallowed by larva of beetle or flea hatch in intestine; **p,** oncospheres enter haemocoel and develop into cysticercoids; **q,** eggs swallowed by adult beetles hatch in intestine; **r,** oncospheres migrate from intestine into haemocoel; **s,** tailed cysticercoids develop; **t,** infected beetles swallowed by definitive hosts; **u,** cysticercoids released from beetle; **v,** cysticercoids evaginate and shed tail; **j, k, l, a,** cysticercoids develop to adult worms.

Figures A-E adapted from Stiles, 1903, Hyg. Lab., U. S. Pub. Health Serv. and Marine Hosp. Bull. 25; F, from Voge and Heyneman, 1957, Univ. Calif. Publ. 59:549; G, from Dr. W. S. Bailey, Auburn University, Alabama.

SELECTED REFERENCES

Bailey, W. S. (1947). J. Parasit. 33:433.

Heyneman, D. (1961). J. Infect. Dis. 109:10; (1962). Amer. J. Trop. Med. 11:46.

Hunninen, A. V. (1935). Amer. J. Hyg. 22:414; (1936). J. Parasit. 22:84.

Schiller, E. L. (1959). Exp. Parasit. 8:91.

Voge, M., and D. Heyneman. (1957). Univ. Calif. Publ. Zool. 59:549.

FAMILY ANOPLOCEPHALIDAE

The members of this family are medium-sized to relatively large cestodes with the scolex devoid of a rostellum and hooks. The proglottids have one or two sets of reproductive organs with the genital pores located on the lateral margins. They are parasites of reptiles, birds, and mammals.

Moniezia expansa (Rudolphi, 1810) (Plate 100)

This is one of the largest members of the family and occurs commonly in the small intestine of sheep and cattle in most parts of the world.

DESCRIPTION. The length is up to 600 cm and the width 1.6 cm. Proglottids are wider than long and have a double set of reproductive organs in each one. The testes are numerous and scattered throughout the proglottid. A single transverse row of hollow interproglottid glands lies at the posterior border of each proglottid. The eggs have a pyriform apparatus.

LIFE CYCLE. Chains of gravid proglottids passed in the faeces liberate the embryonated eggs. When these are eaten by oribatid mites known commonly as soil mites, of the genera *Galumna, Scheloribates,* and others, they hatch in the intestine. The oncospheres migrate through the intestinal wall into the haemocoel where they develop into tailed cysticercoids. When infected mites are swallowed by sheep, the cysticercoids are liberated in the intestine where they attach to the mucosa and develop to maturity. The worms persist in the sheep for a period of about 3 months after reaching maturity.

EXERCISE ON LIFE CYCLE

Adult cestodes for experimental studies are available in abundance from abbattoirs where sheep and lambs are slaughtered.

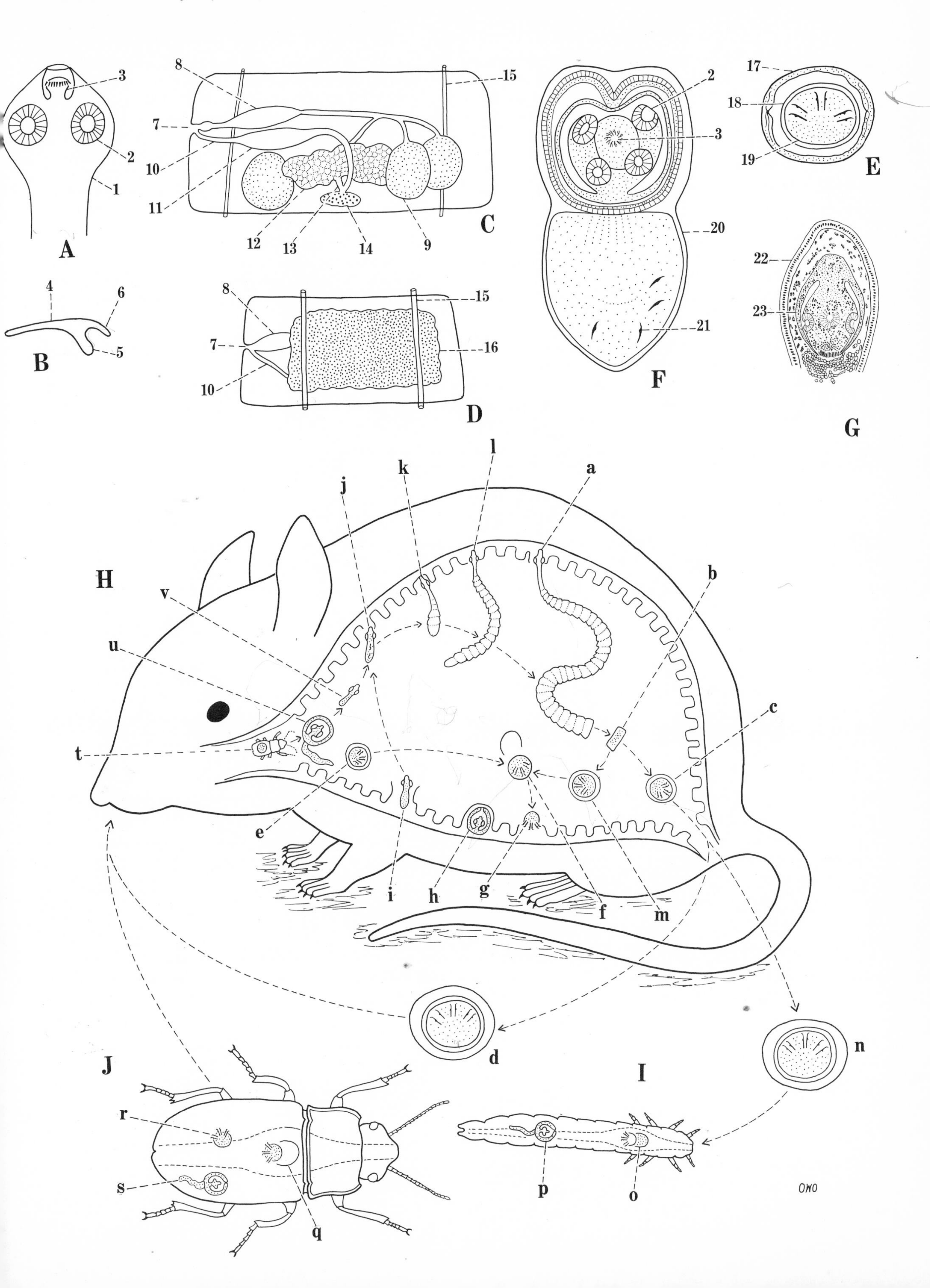
A
B
C
D
E
F
G
H
I
J
1
2
3
4
5
6
7
8
9
10
11
12
13
14
15
16
17
18
19
20
21
22
23
a
b
c
d
e
f
g
h
i
j
k
l
m
n
o
p
q
r
s
t
u
v
OWO

EXPLANATION OF PLATE 100 ▷

A. Scolex. **B.** Gravid proglottid. **C.** Egg. **D.** Suckered cysticercoid. **E.** Segmenting cysticercoid. **F.** Invaginated cysticercoid. **G.** Mature cysticercoid. **H.** Sheep definitive host. **I.** Oribatid mite intermediate host.

1, scolex; **2,** sucker; **3,** immature proglottid; **4,** common genital pore; **5,** cirrus pouch; **6,** vas deferens; **7,** testes; **8,** vagina; **9,** seminal receptacle; **10,** ovary; **11,** vitelline gland; **12,** longitudinal excretory canal; **13,** interproglottid glands; **14,** egg shell (outer membrane); **15,** pyriform apparatus; **16,** oncosphere; **17,** scolex of cysticercoid; **18,** membrane surrounding scolex; **19,** segmenting tissue to form surrounding membrane; **20,** tail.

a, adult cestode in small intestine of sheep; **b,** proglottid passing to outside with faeces; **c,** free proglottids; **d,** egg released from free proglottids; **e,** egg eaten by oribatid mites hatches in intestine and the oncosphere migrates to the body cavity; **f,** cysticercoid encysted in body cavity; **g,** infected mite swallowed by sheep; **h,** cysticercoid escapes from digested mite; **i,** cysticercoid evaginates, loses tail, and attaches to intestinal mucosa where it develops to a mature cestode in about 5 to 6 weeks; adults persist in a sheep for about 3 months after they attain sexual maturity.

Figures A-C original; D-G, adapted from Potemkin, 1948, in Spasskii, 1951, Osnovy tsestodologii (Fundamentals of Cestodology), Vol. 1, Fig. 81.

Soil mites of the genera *Galumna, Scheloribates,* and *Scutovertex* may be obtained from sod placed in a modified Berlese funnel with a 60-watt lamp hanging over it. The heat from the light drives the mites through the soil whence they drop into the funnel and fall into the container below.

Mites placed in a glass container together with eggs of *Moniezia* eat them and become infected. Dissection of the mites and examination of the intestinal contents during the early hours of the experiment will show empty egg shells and free oncospheres. Examination of the haemocoel of mites at intervals of 1 or 2 days will reveal stages of cysticercoids during the course of development.

The life cycles of other anoplocephalids may be examined in a similar manner. Some common ones include *Cittotaenia* from wild rabbits and hares (Stunkard) and *Monoecocoestis* from porcupines (Freeman). Field mice (*Microtus*) harbor a related genus (*Paranoplocephala*) whose life cycle has not been studied.

SELECTED REFERENCES

Edney, J. M., and G. W. Kelley, Jr. (1953). J. Tenn. Acad. Sci. 28:287.

Freeman, R. S. (1949). J. Parasit. 35:605; (1952). Ibid. 38:111.

Krull, W. H. (1939). Proc. Helminth. Soc. Wash. 6:10; (1940). Ibid. 7:68.

Kates, K. C., and C. E. Runkel. (1948). Proc. Helminth. Soc. Wash. 15:19.

Stunkard, H. W. (1932). Z. Parasitenk. 6:481; (1937). Science 86:312; (1938). Parasitology 30:491.

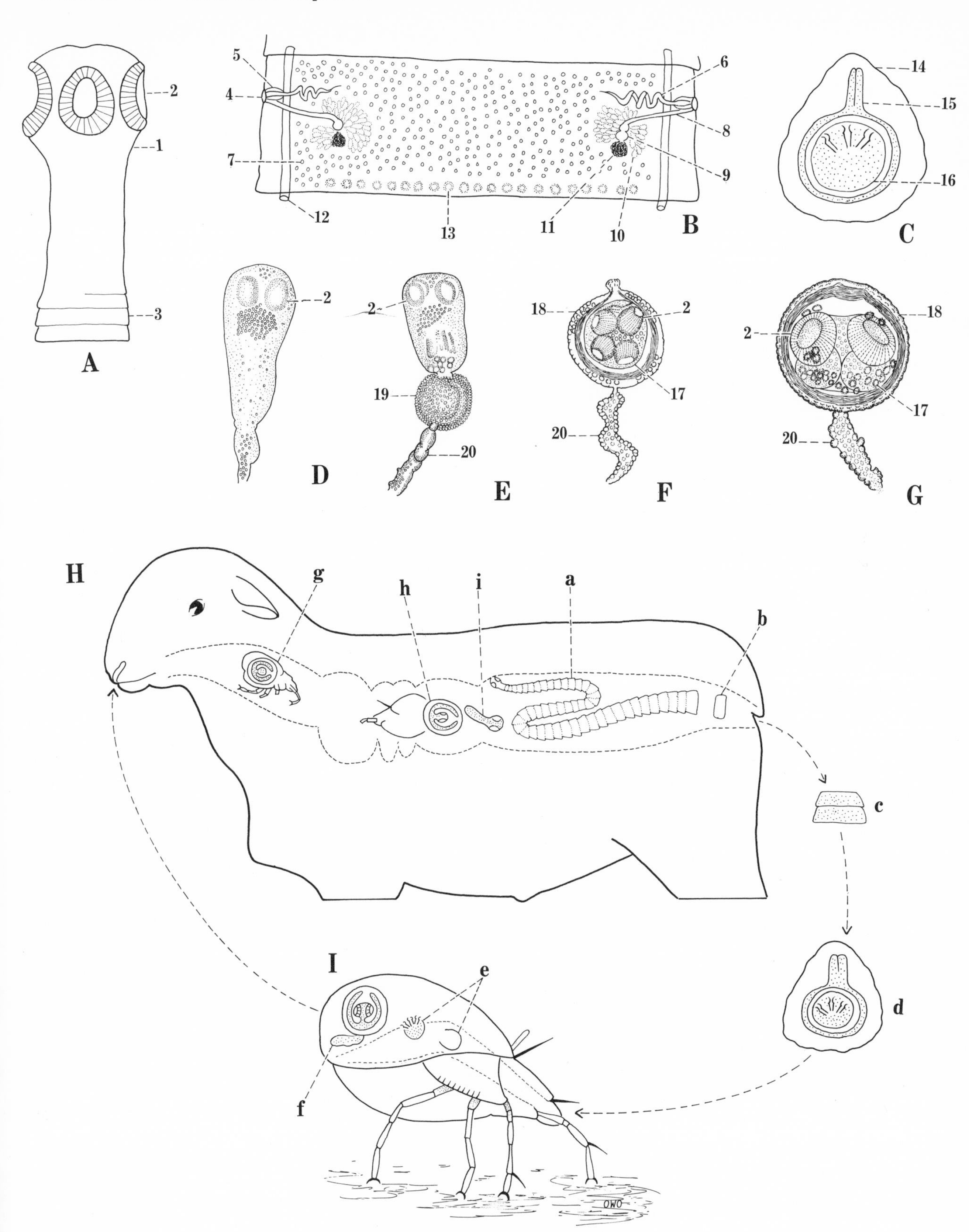
A
B
C
D
E
F
G
H
I
1
2
3
4
5
6
7
8
9
10
11
12
13
14
15
16
17
18
19
20
a
b
c
d
e
f
g
h
i
OWO

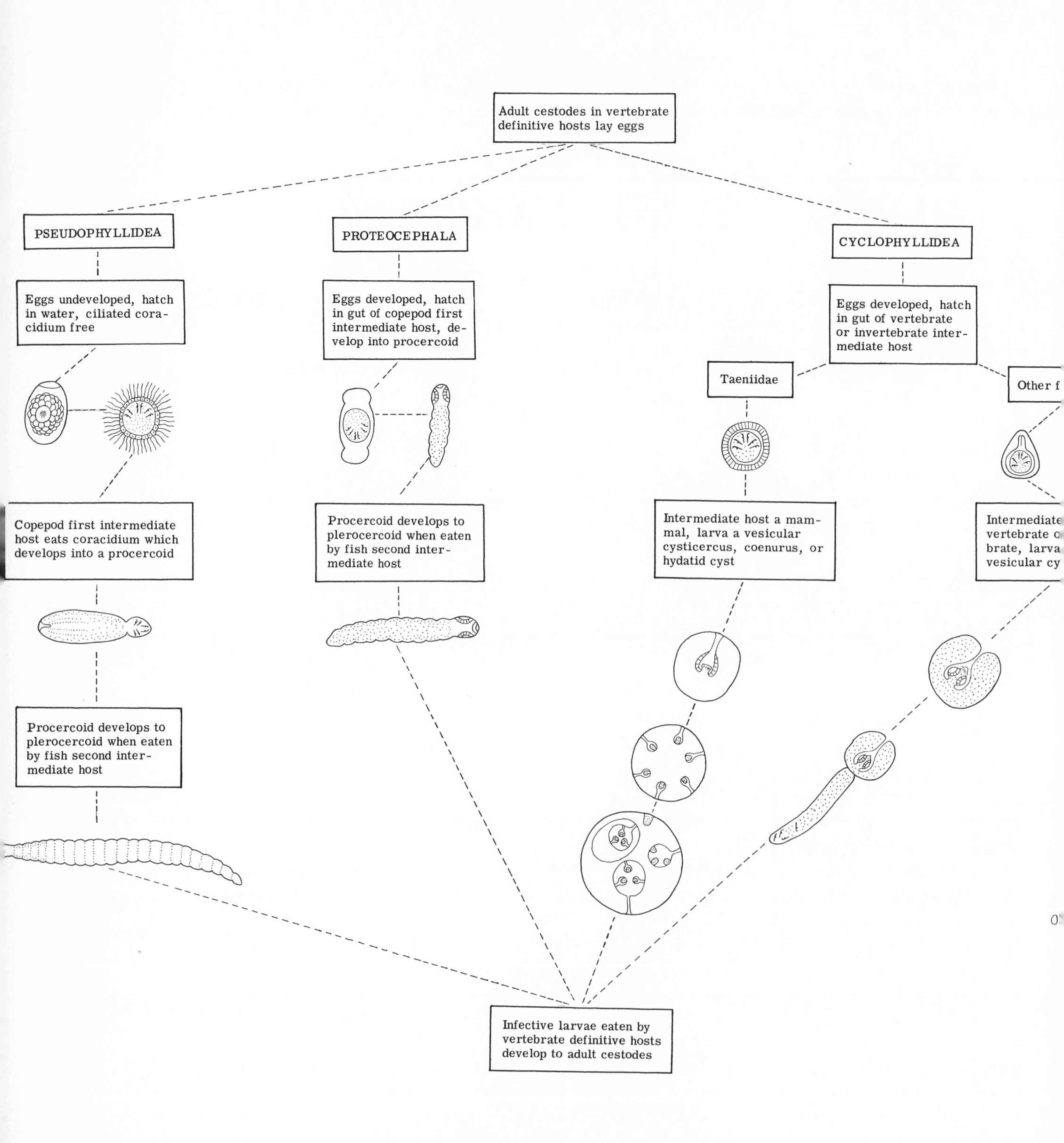
Adult cestodes in vertebrate definitive hosts lay eggs
PSEUDOPHYLLIDEA
PROTEOCEPHALA
CYCLOPHYLLIDEA
Eggs undeveloped, hatch in water, ciliated coracidium free
Eggs developed, hatch in gut of copepod first intermediate host, develop into procercoid
Eggs developed, hatch in gut of vertebrate or invertebrate intermediate host
Taeniidae
Other f
Copepod first intermediate host eats coracidium which develops into a procercoid
Procercoid develops to plerocercoid when eaten by fish second intermediate host
Intermediate host a mammal, larva a vesicular cysticercus, coenurus, or hydatid cyst
Intermediate
vertebrate o
brate, larva
vesicular cy
Procercoid develops to plerocercoid when eaten by fish second intermediate host
Infective larvae eaten by vertebrate definitive hosts develop to adult cestodes

PART IV PHYLUM ACANTHOCEPHALA

This phylum consists of a small group of unique, cylindrical, unsegmented, parasitic worms characterized by a thorny retractable proboscis at the anterior end of the body as the most obvious and distinguishing feature. As adults, they are parasites of vertebrates.

The higher taxa of the Acanthocephala, like that of many groups, are not clearly delimited and several arrangements of classification have resulted. For the purposes of this discussion, three orders are recognized. Members of the order Archiacanthocephala are parasites of terrestrial hosts. The males possess eight separate uninucleate cement glands, and the females have two persistent ligament sacs. Species of the order Paleacanthocephala are mostly parasites of aquatic hosts. They have six multinucleate cement glands in the males and a single ephemeral ligament sac in the females. Individuals of the order Eoacanthocephala parasitize aquatic hosts. The males have a single multinucleate syncytial cement gland with a closely associated cement reservoir and the females have permanent dorsal and ventral ligament sacs.

The body is of two parts, the presoma, consisting of the proboscis and neck, and the hindbody, or trunk. The anterior part of the presoma consists of a globular or cylindrical proboscis that is almost universally covered with hooks. The size of the hooks varies according to their location on the proboscis, those near the base being the smallest. The arrangement of the hooks over the proboscis is in three basic patterns. They are 1) alternating radial rows, 2) radial rows, and 3) horizontal rows. The last arrangement may be interpreted as spiral. In some cases a few inordinately large hooks appear, disrupting the characteristic pattern of distribution in the area around them. In some cases, it is difficult to interpret the pattern of arrangement of the hooks. The posterior part of the presoma, which is usually unarmed, is the neck and connects with the trunk. The entire proboscis is retractable by special muscles into a thick-walled sac, the proboscis receptacle. It is everted hydrostatically by fluids under pressure by body contraction.

The trunk consists of the large part of the body posterior to the presoma. It is essentially a hollow structure containing the reproductive, excretory, and nervous systems, and the pseudocoelomic fluid. The body wall is composed of an outer cuticle and a thick layer consisting of three outer layers of fibrils and an inner plasmatic syncytium containing a few large branched nuclei, and an innermost layer of muscles. A lacunar system of dorsal and ventral, or lateral, canals extend the length of the body and are connected by a network or transverse system of small canals.

An elongated lemniscus attached to the anterior wall of the body at each side of the proboscis receptacle hangs free in the pseudocoel, or body cavity. Extending obliquely and posteriorly from the posterior end of the proboscis receptacle to the body wall where they attach are two ventral and one dorsal retractor muscles. The gonads are suspended in the pseudocoelomic fluid by a ligament arising from the base of the proboscis receptacle. In the early stages of development, it consists of a dorsal and ventral sac. In the Archiacanthocephala and Eoacanthocephala, they persist but are ephemeral in the Paleacanthocephala, remaining only as a remnantal ligament that supports the testes and uterine bell.

The adult male reproductive system consists of two testes followed posteriorly by cement glands, pouches, and genital ducts. The cement glands are of three types, each characteristic of an order. There are eight uninucleate glands in the Archiacanthocephala, six multinucleate ones in the Paleacanthocephala, and a large single multinucleate syncytial one with an enclosed cement reservoir in the Eoacanthocephala. The ducts of the cement glands join posteriorly with the ejaculatory duct. The copulatory apparatus consists of a muscular pouch containing the penis and an eversible copulatory bursa at the posterior extremity of the body. Eversion is probably by means of hydrostatic pressure and inversion by muscular action. The cement glands provide a substance that forms a plug in the vagina following mating to prevent loss of the spermatozoa.

The female reproductive system consists of an ovary, uterine bell, uterus, vagina, and vulva. The ovary develops on the wall of the dorsal ligament sac. As development proceeds, it breaks into ovarial balls, or floating ovaries, that occur in the dorsal ligament sac of the Archiacanthocephala and Eoacanthocephala and in the pseudocoel of the Paleacanthocephala where the ligaments are ephemeral.

The uterine bell is, as the name implies, a bell-shaped structure with its large opening directed anteriorly and its narrow one opening posteriorly by means of a duct into the uterus. Near the posterior end of the bell, lateral pores open into the dorsal ligament sac or into the pseudocoel when the sac is absent.

Immature eggs are being liberated continuously in the dorsal ligament sac or body cavity where embryonation is completed. Hence a mixture of eggs in all stages of development is present at all times. When eggs in various degrees of development enter the uterine bell, it is believed by some to serve as a sorting apparatus by rejecting the immature ones through the lateral pores and allowing the mature ones to pass into the uterus. Since both mature and immature eggs appear in the uterus, the concept of a sorting apparatus appears untenable to others. The idea of its being a mechanism by which the worm may pass eggs, regardless of the stage of development, into the uterus for oviposition or return them to the body at will is more acceptable to them. The uterus is a simple tube, surrounded by a sphincter, that empties through a terminal or subterminal funnel-shaped vagina. Eggs are embryonated when laid and variable in shape, being oval, fusiform, or elliptical. There are three shells of different thickness, the two outer ones being thick and the inner one membranous. The anterior end of the fusiform larva bears hooks and the body is covered with minute spines. Inside is a centrally located mass of small nuclei.

The excretory system consists of a pair of protonephridia located bilaterally. They may be dendritic or of a simple capsular type. Each is provided with a tuft of flickering cilia at the end of the individual dendrites or capsules. A duct from each protonephridium extends medially where they unite to form a common tubule that empties into the ejaculatory duct or uterus.

The basic pattern of the life cycle is similar for all acanthocephalans. Eggs hatch only when ingested by insect or crustacean intermediate hosts. In case of terrestrial definitive hosts, the intermediaries likewise are terrestrial, and when the definitive hosts are aquatic, the intermediate hosts also are aquatic. Infection occurs when invertebrate hosts containing fully developed acanthellas are eaten. In some cases, transport hosts are common. These are vertebrates in which the acanthellas are unable to develop to maturity. Under these circumstances, they migrate from the gut into the body cavity and encyst. A common example is the encysted forms of *Corynosoma* of seals and sea lions that occur in marine fish.

The classification of the Acanthocephala proposed by Meyer and Van Cleave in which the phylum is divided into three orders with families and genera, is given below together with some common hosts.

I. Order Archiacanthocephala: Proboscis hooks arranged in concentric rows; main lacunar canals on dorsal and ventral sides; nuclei of body wall few, large, ramified or elongated; wall of proboscis receptacle consists of a single muscular layer; two persistent ligament sacs in females; eight uninucleate cement glands in males; egg shell thick. Parasites of terrestrial vertebrates. Acanthellas in grubs, cockroaches.

A. Family Gigantorhynchidae
1. *Gigantorhynchus;* anteaters
2. *Mediorhynchus;* birds

B. Family Oligacanthorhynchidae
1. *Oligacanthorhynchus;* birds

2. *Hamanniella;* marsupials
3. *Prosthenorchis;* monkeys
4. *Macracanthorhynchus;* pigs

C. Family Moniliformidae
1. *Moniliformis;* rodents

D. Family Pachysentidae
1. *Oncicola;* dogs

II. Order Paleacanthocephala: Hooks on proboscis in alternating radial rows; main lacunar canals lateral; wall of proboscis receptacle two layers of muscles; nuclei of body wall ramified or fragmented; protonephridia absent; ligament sacs ephemeral in females; cement glands with central cavity, usually six or less and multinucleate; egg shells thin. Parasites of fish, aquatic birds, and mammals. Acanthellas in crustacea.

A. Family Rhadinorhynchidae
1. *Rhadinorhynchus;* fish, mainly marine
2. *Telosentis;* marine fish
3. *Illiosentis;* marine fish
4. *Aspersentis;* marine fish
5. *Leptorhynchoides;* fresh-water and marine fish

B. Family Gorgorhynchidae
1. *Serrasentis;* marine fish
2. *Gorgorhynchus;* marine fish

C. Family Polymorphidae
1. *Polymorphus;* aquatic birds
2. *Corynosoma;* marine birds and mammals
3. *Filicollis;* ducks
4. *Bulbosoma;* marine mammals
5. *Arhythmorhynchus;* fish, batrachians, and reptiles
6. *Centrorhynchus;* birds of prey mainly
7. *Prosthorhynchus;* birds, occasionally mammals

D. Family Echinorhynchidae
1. *Acanthorhynchus;* fish
2. *Echinorhynchus;* fish
3. *Pomphorhynchus;* fish
4. *Acanthocephalus;* fish, amphibians, reptiles

III. Order Eoacanthocephala: Small body, hooks on proboscis arranged radially; main lacunar canals dorsal and ventral; nuclei of body wall few, generally large; protonephridia absent; dorsal and ventral ligament sacs persistent; wall of proboscis receptacle single layer of muscles. A single syncytial cement gland with cement reservoir included. Mainly parasites of fish, rarely in turtles. Acanthellas in crustacea.

A. Family Pallisentidae
1. *Pallisentis;* fresh-water fish

B. Family Quadrigyidae
1. *Quadrigyrus;* fresh-water and marine fish

C. Family Neoechinorhynchidae
1. *Neoechinorhynchus;* marine and fresh-water fish, amphibians, turtles
2. *Octospinifer;* fresh-water fish

EXPLANATION OF PLATE 102 ⇨

A-K. General morphological characteristics of Acanthocephala. **A.** Partial dissection of adult female *Neoechinorhynchus rutili.* **B.** Adult male of *Acanthocephalus ranae.* **C-H.** Six genera of Acanthocephala showing relative development of proboscis and neck. **C.** *Neoechinorhynchus.* **D.** *Acanthocephalus.* **E.** *Polymorphus.* **F.** *Eocollis.* **G.** *Pomphorhynchus.* **H.** *Filicollis.* **I.** Cross-section of body of *Filisoma fidium* in region of double-walled receptacle of proboscis. **J.** Portion of section of body wall of *Centrorhynchus pinguis.* **K.** Portion of surface view of body wall of *Quadrigyrus torquatus,* showing lacunar canals and giant nucleus. **L-N.** Eggs typical of acanthocephalans whose hosts are aquatic animals. **L.** *Corynosoma strumosum* from seals. **M.** *Echinorhynchus gadi* from cod. **N.** *Polymorphus* from ducks. **O-P.** Eggs typical of acanthocephalans whose hosts are terrestrial. **O.** *Moniliformis* from shrew. **P.** *Pachysentis* from fox. **Q-R.** *Corynosoma villosum* (Paleacanthocephala) from Stellar's sea lion, showing the major internal organs. **Q.** Male. **R.** Female. **S-W.** Basic morphological features of the order Archiacanthocephala. **S.** Lacunar system of *Moniliformis,* showing dorsal longitudinal canal and encircling branches that connect dorsal and ventral longitudinal canals. **T.** Proboscis of *Oncicola,* showing concentric rows of hooks. **U.** *Hamanniella,* showing protonephridia of male. **V.** *Oligacanthorhynchus* female reproductive system from left side, showing dorsal and ventral ligament sacs. **W.** Cement glands, showing individual uninucleate glands.

1, proboscis armed with hooks; **2,** neck; **3,** trunk or hindbody; **4,** proboscis sheath; **5,** dorsal retractor muscle of proboscis sheath; **6,** ventral retractor muscles of proboscis sheath; **7,** retractor muscles of anterior end of worm; **8,** lemniscus with nucleus; **9,** dorsal longitudinal lacunar canal with branches; **10,** ventral longitudinal lacunar canal; **11,** lateral longitudinal lacunar canal with branches; **12,** floating ovary; **13,** eggs; **14,** adjacent walls of dorsal and ventral ligaments; **15,** dorsal ligament sac; **16,** ventral ligament sac; **17,** uterine bell; **18,** pockets of uterine bell; **19,** opening from uterine bell into dorsal ligament sac; **20,** duct from uterine bell to uterus; **21,** uterus; **22,** exit from uterine bell to body cavity; **23,** vulva; **24,** vagina; **25,** testis; **26,** vas efferens; **27,** ejaculatory duct; **28,** penis; **29,** copulatory bursa; **30,** cement glands; **31,** cement reservoir; **32,** Saefftigen's pouch; **33,** genital sheath; **34,** suspensory ligament; **35,** giant nucleus of lacunar canal; **36,** cuticle; **37,** subcuticle; **38,** circular canal of lacunar system; **39,** body musculature; **40,** body cavity; **41,** acanthor; **42,** protonephridium; **43,** excretory bladder.

Figures A, B, S, V redrawn from Meyer, 1933, Bronn's Klassen und Ordnung des Tierreichs 4:2; C, D, E, F, G, H, from Van Cleave, 1952, Exp. Parasit. 1:308; L, N, O, P, from Baer, 1961, Traité de Zoologie 4:733; I, from Van Cleave, 1947, J. Parasit. 33:487; K, from Van Cleave, 1920, Proc. U. S. Nat. Mus. 58:455; T, from Van Cleave, 1941, Quart. Rev. Biol. 16:157; W, from Van Cleave, 1949, J. Morph. 48:431; M, from Rauther, 1930, Handbuch der Zoologie (Kükenthal and Krumbach) 2:449; U, from Kilian, 1932, Z. Wschr. Zool. 141:246; Q, R, original.

SELECTED REFERENCES

Baer, J. C. (1961). Embranchement des Acanthocephales. Traité de Zoologie 4:733-782.

Hyman, L. H. (1951). The Invertebrates. Vol. 3: Acanthocephala, Aschelminthes, and Entoprocta. McGraw-Hill Book Co., New York, pp. 1-52.

Meyer, A. (1933). Acanthocephala. Bronn's Klassen und Ordnung Tierreichs 4(2/2):1.

Rauther, Max. (1930). Sechste Klasse des Cladus Nemathelminthes. Acanthocephala = Kratzwurmer. Handb. Zool. (Kükenthal u. Krumbach). Vol. 2, 10. Lief., Teil 4, Bogen 33-37, pp. 449.

Van Cleave, H. J. (1936). J. Parasit. 22:202 (numerous articles by Van Cleave appear in periodicals).

Yamaguti, S. (1963). Systema Helminthum. Vol. 5: Acanthocephala. John Wiley and Sons, New York, 423 pp.

ORDER ARCHIACANTHOCEPHALA

Two common and well-known members of this order are the widely distributed large thorn-headed worm *Macracanthorhynchus hirudinaceus* of the family Oligacanthorhynchidae found in the small intestine of swine and *Moniliformis dubius* of the family Moniliformidae of rats.

FAMILY OLIGACANTHORHYNCHIDAE

The members of this family are long slender worms, having slightly ringed or wrinkled bodies. The relatively small ovoid or globular proboscis bears a few circles of hooks, with those at the apex being larger than those toward the base.

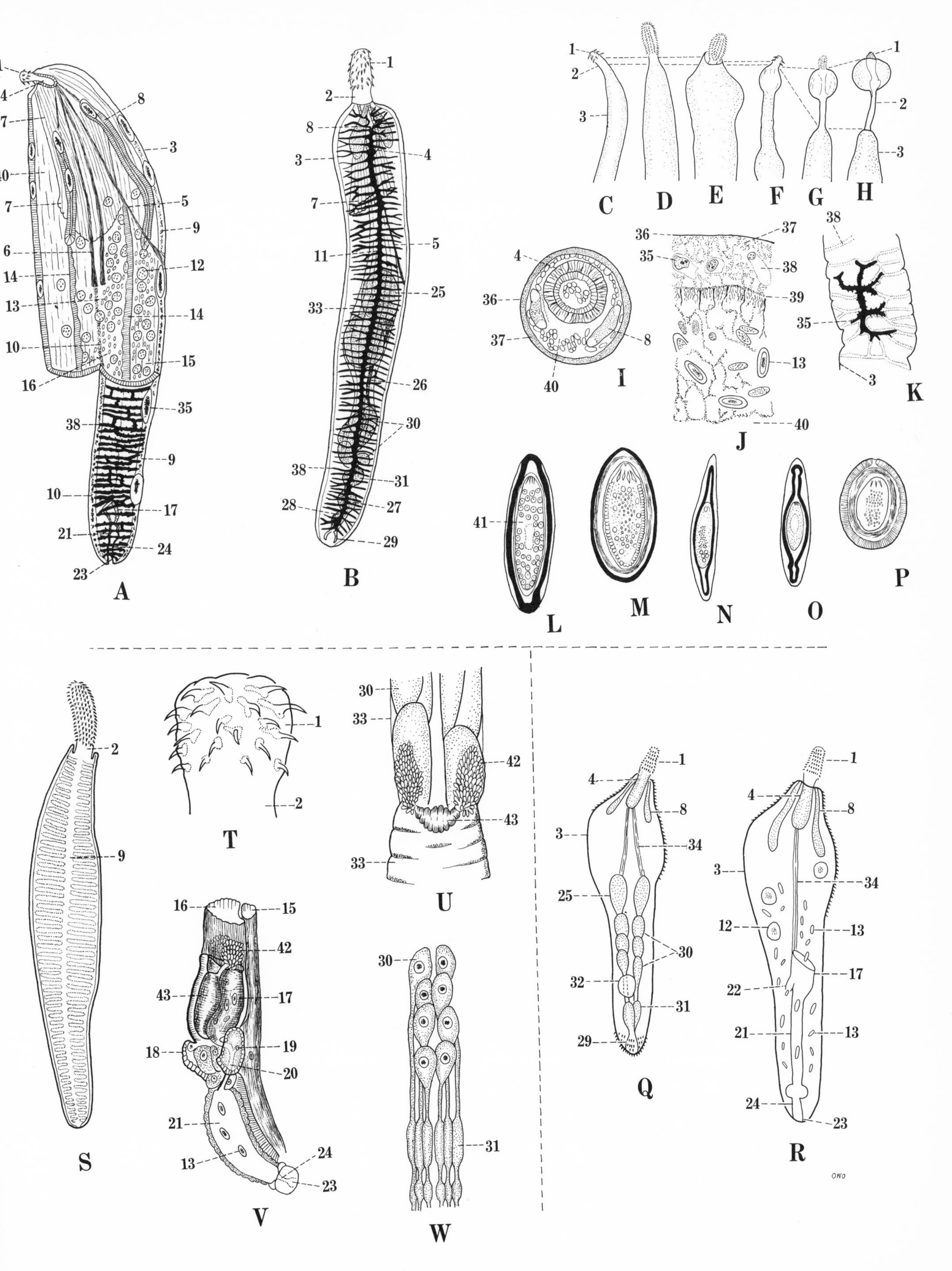
A
B
C
D
E
F
G
H
I
J
K
L
M
N
O
P
Q
R
S
T
U
V
W
OWO

EXPLANATION OF PLATE 103 ▷

A-H. Basic morphological features of the order Paleacanthocephala. **A.** Lacunar system of *Centrorhynchus,* showing netlike branching. **B.** Proboscis of *Corynosoma turbidum,* showing large ventral hooks that disturb symmetrical alternating radial arrangement of hooks. **C.** Proboscis of *Acanthocephalus dirus,* showing typical alternating radial or quincuncial arrangement of hooks. **D.** Male reproductive system of *Illiosentis furcatus.* **E.** Cement glands, showing arrangement, number, and multinucleated characteristic of the Order Paleacanthocephala. **F.** Reproductive system of female *Acanthocephalus lucii,* showing suspensory ligament but no ligament sacs. **G.** Giant nuclei of body wall of *Macracanthorhynchus.* **H.** Cross-section through anterior region of body of paleacanthocephalan, showing remnant of ephemeral ligament and lateral lacunar channels. **I-M.** Basic morphological features of the order Eoacanthocephala. **I.** Proboscis of *Neoechinorhynchus,* showing characteristic number of hooks and radial arrangement of them. **J.** Cross-section of anterior part of body showing dorsal and ventral ligament sacs and dorsal and ventral lacunar channels. **K.** Male reproductive system of *Gracilisentis gracilisentis,* showing syncytial type of cement gland. **L.** Cement gland characteristic of the eoacanthocephalans. **M.** *Neoechinorhynchus emydis* in process of attaching to the intestine of turtle host. **N.** Larval stages of *Macracanthorhynchus hirudinaceus* typically found in the life cycle of Acanthocephala (for description see Plate 104).

1, proboscis armed with hooks; **2,** neck; **3,** trunk or hindbody; **4,** lemniscus; **5,** dorsal longitudinal lacunar canal with branches; **6,** ventral longitudinal lacunar canal; **7,** lateral longitudinal lacunar canal with branches; **8,** egg; **9,** dorsal ligament sac; **10,** ventral ligament sac; **11,** remnant of ligament; **12,** uterine bell; **13,** uterus; **14,** uterine glands; **15,** sphincter of uterine bell; **16,** testis; **17,** vas efferens; **18,** ejaculatory duct; **19,** penis; **20,** copulatory bursa; **21,** cement glands; **22,** cement reservoir; **23,** Saefftigen's pouch; **24,** giant nucleus of lacunar canal; **25,** body cavity; **26,** intestinal wall of host.

A, redrawn from Yamaguti, 1939, Jap. J. Zool. 8: ; F, H, J, from Meyer, 1933, Bronn's Klassen und Ordnung des Tierreichs 4:2; D, K, from Baer, 1961, Traité de Zoologie 4:733; B, C, I, from Van Cleave, 1941, Quart. Rev. Biol. 16:157; E, L, from Van Cleave, 1949, J. Morph. 84:431; G, from Van Cleave, 1951, Trans. Amer. Micr. Soc. 70:37; M, from Van Cleave, 1952, Exp. Parasit. 1:317; K, from Van Cleave, 1947, J. Parasit. 33:118.

Macracanthorhynchus hirudinaceus (Pallas, 1781) (Plate 104)

These large wrinkled worms attach to the wall of the small intestine of swine by forcing the spiny proboscis into the lining of it. They do not remain attached to one spot but move about.

DESCRIPTION. The body is more or less flattened and with numerous transverse wrinkles. The proboscis is small, globular in shape, and bears about six transverse rows of hooks. Adult males measure up to 100 mm long. Females are much larger, reaching 350 mm or more in length. The eggs have a four-layered shell; they measure 80 to 100 μ long by 46 to 65 μ wide. A fully developed and hooked embryo known as an acanthor is present when the eggs are laid.

LIFE CYCLE. Embryonated eggs laid by the females leave the body of the host in its faeces. The spined acanthor is already infective to the grubs of a number of species of May and June beetles of the genera *Cotinus* and *Phyllophaga.* When swallowed by grubs, the eggs hatch within an hour and the acanthors quickly migrate through the gut wall into the haemocoel. They usually remain attached to the outer surface of the midgut for 5 to 20 days, becoming somewhat oval in shape.

As growth continues, the larvae detach from the intestinal wall, becoming free in the body cavity. They go through a period of gradual development. By 35 days, the testes are well developed but the primordia of the "egg-balls" and eggs are present as isolated cells within the ligaments. Cells which are the primordia of various other structures appear. As growth continues, the various organs develop until a fully formed acanthella, which is essentially a juvenile parasite, appears. It has an armed proboscis, a trunk containing all the organs, and skin nuclei. The latter are greatly attenuated and branched at this stage. These juvenile stages appear with the proboscis extended or with it retracted into a proboscis sheath. When in the latter condition, they are referred to as cystacanths. The acanthella is fully developed and infective to swine by 65 to 90 days after entering grubs that are kept under optimal conditions for growth.

Swine eating infected grubs acquire the parasites which develop to sexual maturity in 2 to 3 months. Females lay up to 260,000 eggs per day during the peak of the reproductive period which lasts for about 10 months.

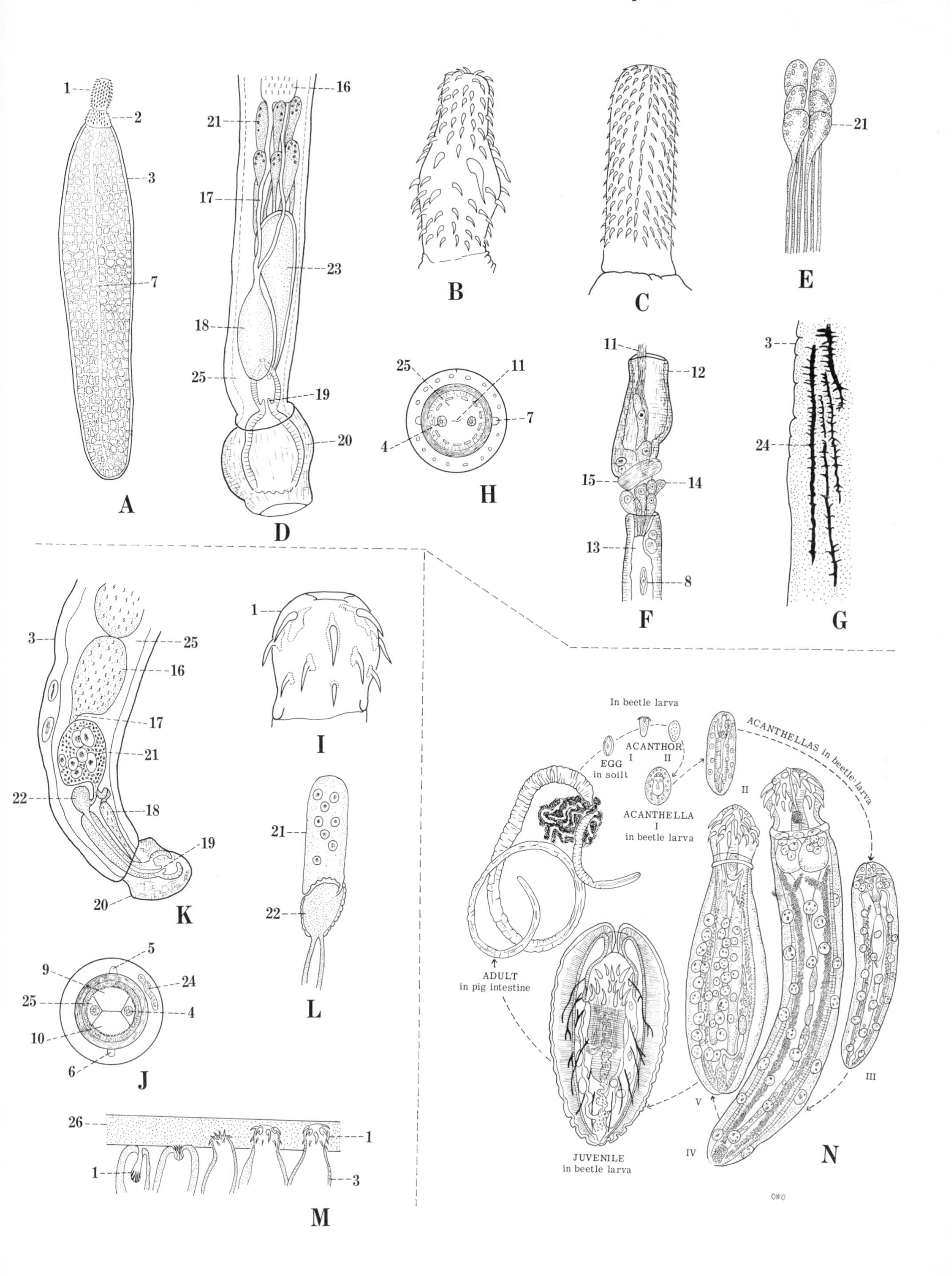

A
B
C
D
E
F
G
H
I
J
K
L
M
N
In beetle larva
EGG
in soil
ACANTHOR
I II
ACANTHELLA
I
in beetle larva
ACANTHELLAS in beetle larva
II
III
IV
V
ADULT
in pig intestine
JUVENILE
in beetle larva
OWO

EXPLANATION OF PLATE 104 ⇨

A. Outline of adult worm. **B.** Presoma and anterior end of trunk. **C.** Egg with part of shell removed to show layers and larva. **D.** Acanthor. **E.** Acanthella with proboscis extended. **F.** Cystacanth with proboscis retracted. **G.** Reproductive system of female. **H.** Cross-section of body of female anterior to uterine bell. **I.** Proboscis. **J.** Swine definitive host. **K.** Beetle grub *(Cotinus* and *Phyllophaga)* intermediate host.

1, proboscis; **2**, spines; **3**, anterior end of trunk; **4**, sculpturing characteristic of eggs of this species; **5**, egg shell and three inner membranes; **6**, raphe of shell; **7**, acanthor; **8**, larval hooks; **9**, skin nuclei; **10**, embryonic nuclear mass; **11**, proboscis sheath; **12**, brain; **13**, lemniscus; **14**, nuclei of lemniscus; **15**, testes; **16**, urinogenital primordium of male; **17**, subcuticula; **18**, ovary; **19**, dorsal ligament; **20**, ventral ligament; **21**, protonephridium; **22**, excretory bladder; **23**, uterine bell; **24**, opening of uterine bell; **25**, uterine duct; **26**, uterus; **27**, vagina; **28**, median canal; **29**, cuticle; **30**, hypodermis; **31**, circular muscles; **32**, longitudinal muscles; **33**, lateral nerve; **34**, pseudocoel; **35**, eggs in various stages of development; **36**, sense organ.

a, adult worm in small intestine; **b**, eggs passing from intestine in faeces; **c**, embryonated egg in soil; **d**, egg swallowed by grub; **e**, egg hatches in midgut; **f**, acanthor migrates through gut wall; **g**, acanthor attaches to wall of intestine; **h**, early acanthella free in haemocoel; **i**, **j**, later stages of acanthellas; **k**, infective acanthella (cystacanth); **l**, grub being swallowed by pig; **m**, digestion of grub and liberation of cystacanth; **n**, young worm ready to attach to intestinal wall and grow to maturity.

Figures A, B, G, H original schematic drawings; C-F, adapted from Kates, 1943, Amer. J. Vet. Res. 4:173.

Prosthorhynchus formosus from robins and flickers use terrestrial isopods, *Armadillidium vulgare*, *Porcellio laevis*, and *P. scaber* as intermediate hosts. Under experimental conditions, the acanthellas develop to adults in chickens and turkeys.

EXERCISE ON LIFE CYCLE

The hatching of the eggs and the development of the acanthors to the acanthella stage can be followed during the season when grubs of May and June beetles are available.

Eggs of the thorn-headed worms may be obtained from adult females collected at packing houses where swine are slaughtered. When the eggs are mixed with soil in which the grubs are kept, the larval insects ingest them. Acanthors may be found in the lumen of the intestine within an hour, and a short time later in the haemocoel. The various stages of development in the haemocoel should be sought at 15, 30, 40, 50, and 60 days after ingestion of the eggs by grubs kept at 70° F during the period of the experiment.

SELECTED REFERENCES

Kates, K. C. (1942). J. Agr. Res. 64:93; (1943). Amer. J. Vet. Res. 4:173.

Schmidt, G. D., and O. W. Olsen. (1964). J. Parasit. 50:721.

FAMILY MONILIFORMIDAE

The body is long and slender with regular constrictions, giving it a somewhat beadlike appearance. The proboscis is cylindrical and armed with small hooks, becoming fewer basally. They are parasites primarily of rodents.

Moniliformis dubius Meyer, 1933 (Plate 105)

This is a common parasite of rats throughout the world, particularly in regions where cockroaches, which serve as intermediate hosts, are present.

DESCRIPTION. The body is divided superficially, except at the extremities, into numerous beadlike pseudosegments. The proboscis is cylindrical and truncate distally; it bears 12 longitudinal rows of hooks, each row with 10 hooks. Each hook has a strongly recurved blade and a simple root directed posteriorly.

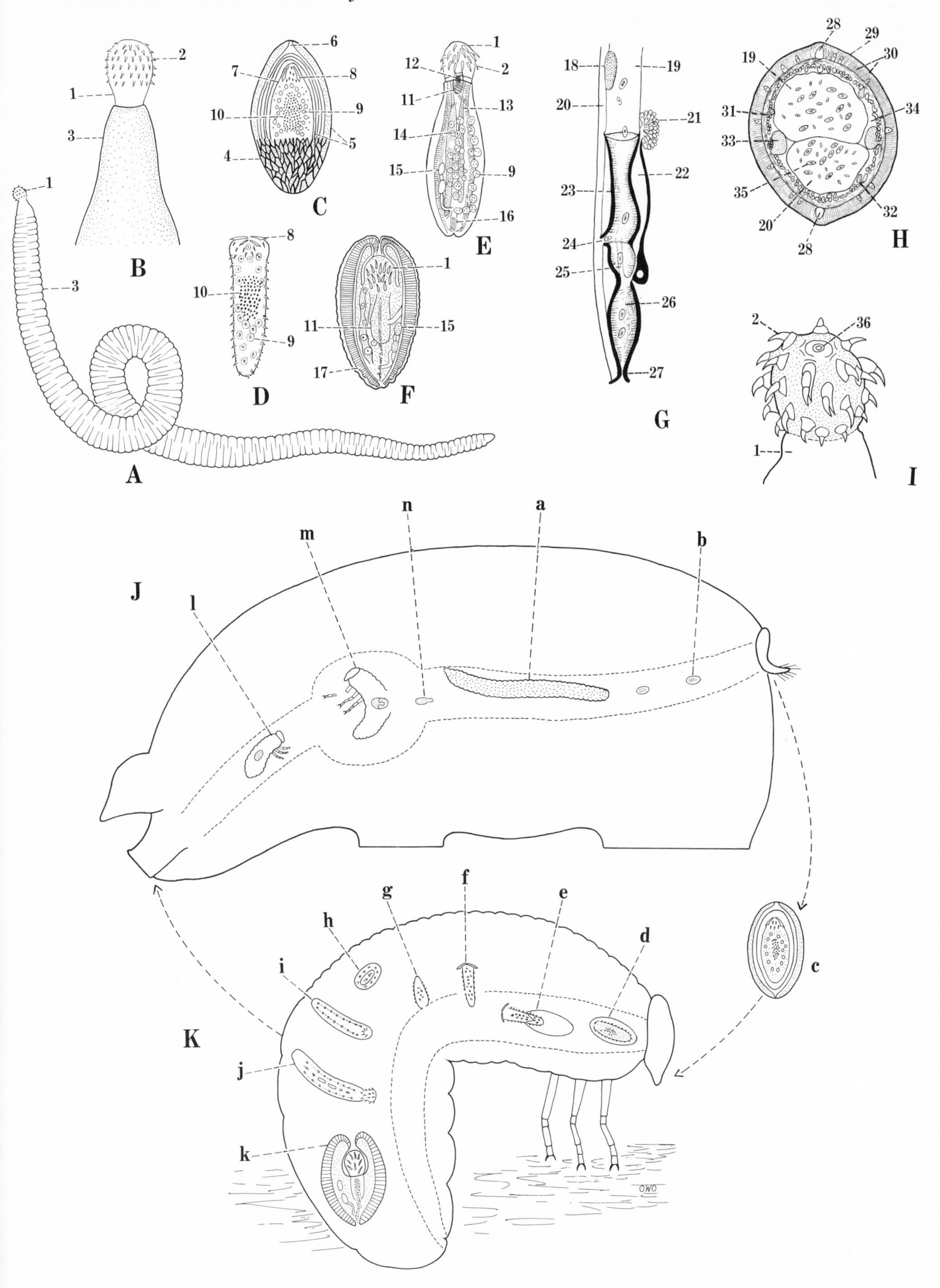
A
B
C
D
E
F
G
H
I
J
K
a
b
c
d
e
f
g
h
i
j
k
l
m
n
OWO

EXPLANATION OF PLATE 105 ⇨

A. Outline of adult worm showing moniliform shape. **B.** Embryonated egg. **C.** Acanthor in process of escaping from egg shell and membranes. **D.** Acanthor dissected from gut wall of cockroach. **E.** Acanthella from haemocoel 46 days after infection. **F.** Encysted acanthella. **G.** Cystacanth free from cyst and with proboscis evaginated. **H.** Proboscis of fully developed acanthella. **I.** Rat *(Rattus)* definitive host. **J.** Cockroach *(Periplaneta americana)* intermediate host.

1, proboscis; **2,** lemniscus; **3,** testes; **4,** cement glands; **5,** cement reservoir; **6,** inverted bursa; **7,** outer egg shell; **8,** inner egg shell; **9,** rostellar hooks; **10,** central nuclear mass of acanthor; **11,** body spines; **12,** retractor muscle; **13,** giant nuclei; **14,** nuclei of nerve ring; **15,** proboscis sheath; **16,** brain; **17,** inverter muscles; **18,** hypodermis; **19,** urinary bladder; **20,** cyst; **21,** suspensory ligament; **22,** nuclei of apical ring; **23,** Saefftigen's pouch.

a, adult worm in small intestine; **b,** egg passing out of body with faeces; **c,** embryonated egg in faeces; **d,** egg swallowed by cockroach; **e,** egg hatches in gut; **f,** acanthor migrates through gut wall; **g,** acanthella in early stages of development; **h,** fully developed and infective acanthella (cystacanth); **i,** infected cockroach being digested in stomach of rat; **j,** cystacanth being released from roach; **k,** acanthella escaping from cyst; **l,** acanthella attaches to gut wall and grows into an adult worm.

Adapted from Moore, 1946, J. Parasit. 32:257.

Males are up to 80 mm long; the testes are elongated. There are six cement glands crowded together immediately anterior to Saefftigen's pouch. The bursal cap has eight short digitiform rays. Females attain a length of 200 mm. The eggs have an outer shell and an inner embryonic membrane; the other measurements are 112 to 130 μ by 54 to 64 μ. A fully developed embryo covered with numerous minute spines is present in the egg when it is laid.

LIFE CYCLE. The females lay fully developed eggs which are passed in the faeces. When ingested by cockroaches (*Periplaneta americana* and probably other species since the parasite is worldwide in distribution), the eggs hatch in the midgut in 24 to 48 hours. The newly hatched acanthors bearing six bladelike hooks work their way through the intestinal wall and appear as minute iridescent specks attached to the outer wall in 10 to 12 days. In about 22 days, the acanthors are nearly spherical after which they begin to elongate and internal development is taking place. Sometime between the 38th and 44th days after infection, the structure, shape, and size have progressed to a stage intermediate between that of the acanthor in the egg and the infective stage. The shape begins to resemble that of an acanthocephalan in which the major organs can be recognized. Between the 44th and 51st days, the larval worms continue to elongate and the organs assume the definitive form. By the 55th day after infection of the cockroaches, the acanthellas complete their development. They are enclosed in cysts with the proboscis withdrawn into the proboscis receptacle and are designated as cystacanths.

Infection of the rats takes place when infected roaches are eaten. Upon digestion of the insect hosts, the cysts are liberated. The acanthellas escape from them, attach to the wall of the intestine, and develop to maturity in 5 to 6 weeks.

EXERCISE ON LIFE CYCLE

In habitats occupied concurrently by cockroaches and rats, both are likely to show a high incidence of infection. Adult worms obtained from rats provide eggs for experimental feeding to roaches. Developing acanthellas can be obtained by dissecting naturally infected roaches.

For experiments on infection of cockroaches, it is necessary to either rear them or obtain them from locations where natural infections do not occur. Dissection of an adequate sample of a population will show whether they are free of natural infection and therefore suitable for experimental purposes.

Cockroaches to be used for experimental purposes may be kept readily in glass jars containing moist sand over which is placed wet paper towels. The latter maintain the moisture and provide a place for the roaches to hide. They thrive on pabulum and are fond of apples.

Acanthocephalan eggs from gravid females placed on bits of pabulum are readily eaten by roaches from which food has been kept for 24 hours. Infect a sufficient number of them so that dissections can be made at intervals of 10 days or less for a period of 2 months. This procedure will reveal all of the stages of development within the intermediate host.

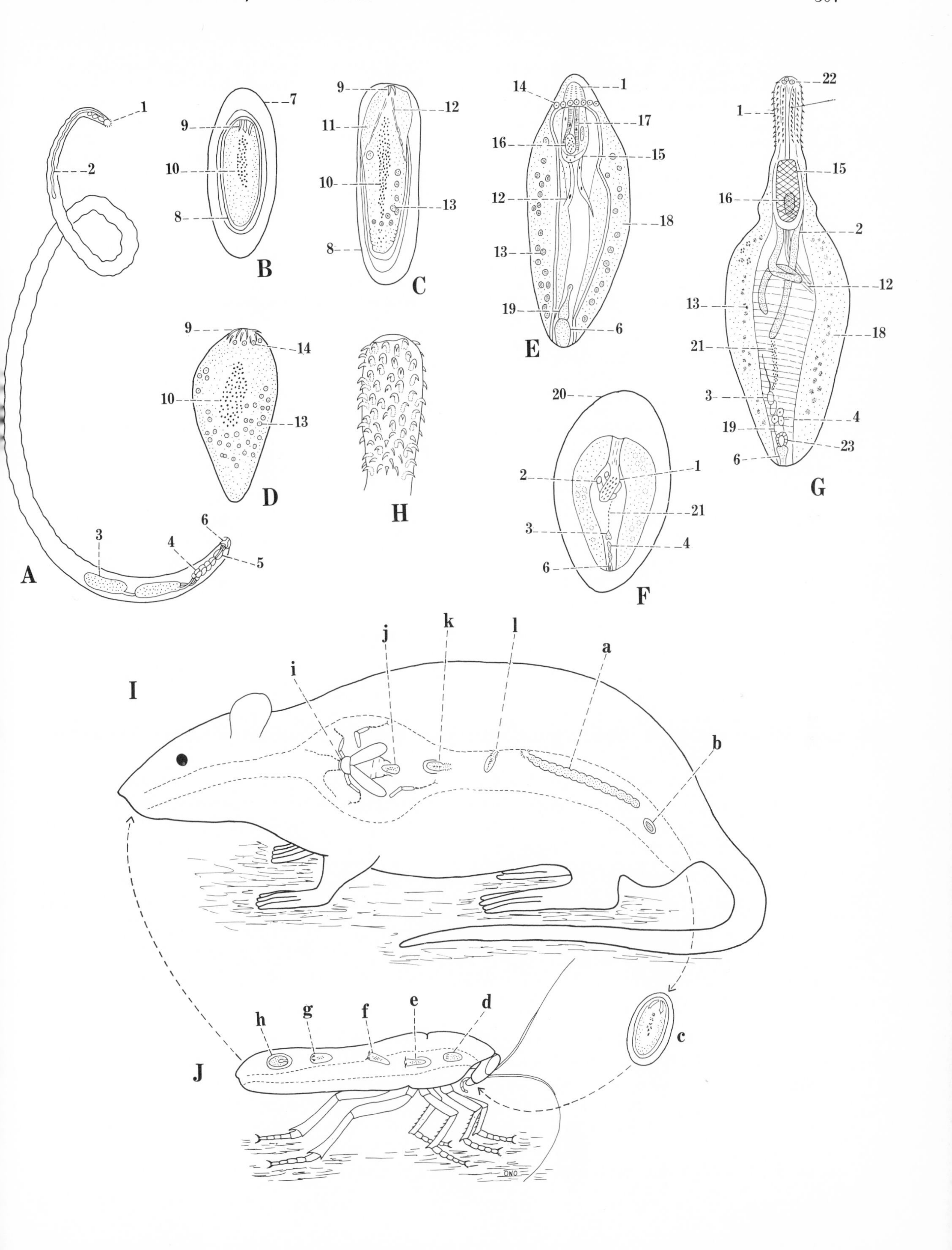
A
B
C
D
E
F
G
H
I
J
a
b
c
d
e
f
g
h
i
j
k
l

EXPLANATION OF PLATE 106 ▷

A. Adult male. **B.** Embryonated egg containing acanthor. **C.** Acanthor just hatched. **D.** Acanthor lying between basement membrane and serosa of intestine of gammarid intermediate host. **E.** Formation of acanthella from acanthor in five days in intestinal wall of gammarid. **F.** Acanthella at 14 days of development, forming a distinct stalk between it and body of acanthor. **G.** Male acanthella at 17 days of development in amphipod. **H.** Male acanthella at 20 days of development. **I.** Male acanthella at 22 days of development. **J.** Female juvenile at 32 days of development in amphipod. **K.** Rock bass *(Ambloplites rupestris)* definitive host. **L.** Amphipod *(Hyalella azteca)* intermediate host.

1, proboscis; **2,** neck; **3,** body or trunk; **4,** proboscis sheath; **5,** lemniscus; **6,** retractor muscle of proboscis; **7,** testes; **8,** cement glands; **9,** Saefftigen's pouch; **10,** muscular cap of bursa; **11,** bursa; **12,** genital pore; **13,** egg shell; **14,** acanthor; **15,** larval spines; **16,** nuclear mass; **17,** giant nuclei; **18,** epithelial cells of intestine of amphipod host; **19,** serosa of intestine; **20,** basement membrane of intestine; **21,** acanthella; **22,** anlagen of lemniscal ring; **23,** anlagen of proboscis sheath; **24,** anlagen of body musculature; **25,** anlagen of genital suspensory ligament; **26,** anlagen of testes; **27,** anlagen of cement glands; **28,** anlagen of penis and bursa; **29,** anlagen of bursa and genital pore; **30,** cells from which proboscis is formed; **31,** giant cells which form division between presoma and trunk; **32,** brain; **33,** genital sheath; **34,** cortical layer; **35,** ovary; **36,** uterine bell; **37,** uterus; **38,** stalk.

a, adult acanthocephalan attached deep in gastric caecum; **b,** embryonated eggs laid in intestine; **c,** eggs passed with faeces into water; **d,** amphipod intermediate host eats eggs; **e,** eggs hatch in intestine of amphipod; **f,** acanthor enters intestinal wall; **g,** acanthella develop from acanthor at five days; **h,** acanthella at 14 days forms a distinct stalk; **i,** male acanthella at 17 days having become detached by rupture of stalk and liberated in haemocoel; **j,** male acanthella at 22 days free in haemocoel; **k,** female juvenile after 32 days of development in amphipod; **l,** fish become parasitized upon swallowing infected amphipods; **m,** juvenile acanthocephala escape when amphipod is digested; **n,** juvenile free in alimentary canal; **o,** juvenile enters gastric caecum and males develop to sexual maturity in four weeks and females begin laying eggs in eight weeks.

Figure A adapted from Van Cleave, 1919, Bull. Ill. State Lab. Nat. Hist. 13:225; other figures from De Guisti, 1949, J. Parasit. 35:437.

Feed mature acanthellas to rats and mice to determine if both become infected and how long after exposure until eggs appear in the faeces.

SELECTED REFERENCES

Burlingame, P. L., and A. C. Chandler. (1941). Amer. J. Hyg. 33(D):1.

Chandler, A. C. (1921). J. Parasit. 7:179; (1941). Ibid. 27:241.

Moore, D. V. (1942). J. Parasit. 28:495; (1946). Ibid. 32:257; (1962). Ibid. 48:76.

Yamaguti, S., and I. Miyata. (1938). Livro Jubilar Prof. Travassos, p. 567.

ORDER PALAEACANTHOCEPHALA

The members of this order are primarily parasites of aquatic vertebrates, including fish, birds, and mammals. A few species occur in birds of prey and terrestrial mammals. Species of the family Rhadinorhynchidae are parasites of marine fishes, with exception of the genus *Leptorhynchoides* which includes forms in both marine and fresh-water fish.

FAMILY RHADINORHYNCHIDAE

The body is of considerable length; the proboscis is very long, club-shaped, bears hooks that show dorsoventral differentiation, and has a double-walled sheath. The lemnisci are as long or longer than the proboscis sheath. There are six short pyriform or elongated cement glands.

Leptorhynchoides thecatus (Linton, 1891) (Plate 106)

This is a common parasite of at least six families of fish in the United States, especially the large-mouthed bass (*Huro salmoides*), small-mouthed bass (*Micropterus dolomieui*), and rock bass (*Ambloplites rupestris*).

DESCRIPTION. The proboscis, when fully extended, forms an angle with the long axis of the body. It is about 1 mm long and armed with 12 longitudinal rows of 12 to 13 hooks each. Individual hooks are surrounded throughout most of their length by an ensheathing cuticular collar. Males are 7 to 12 mm long; there are six cement glands closely compacted at the posterior border of the hind

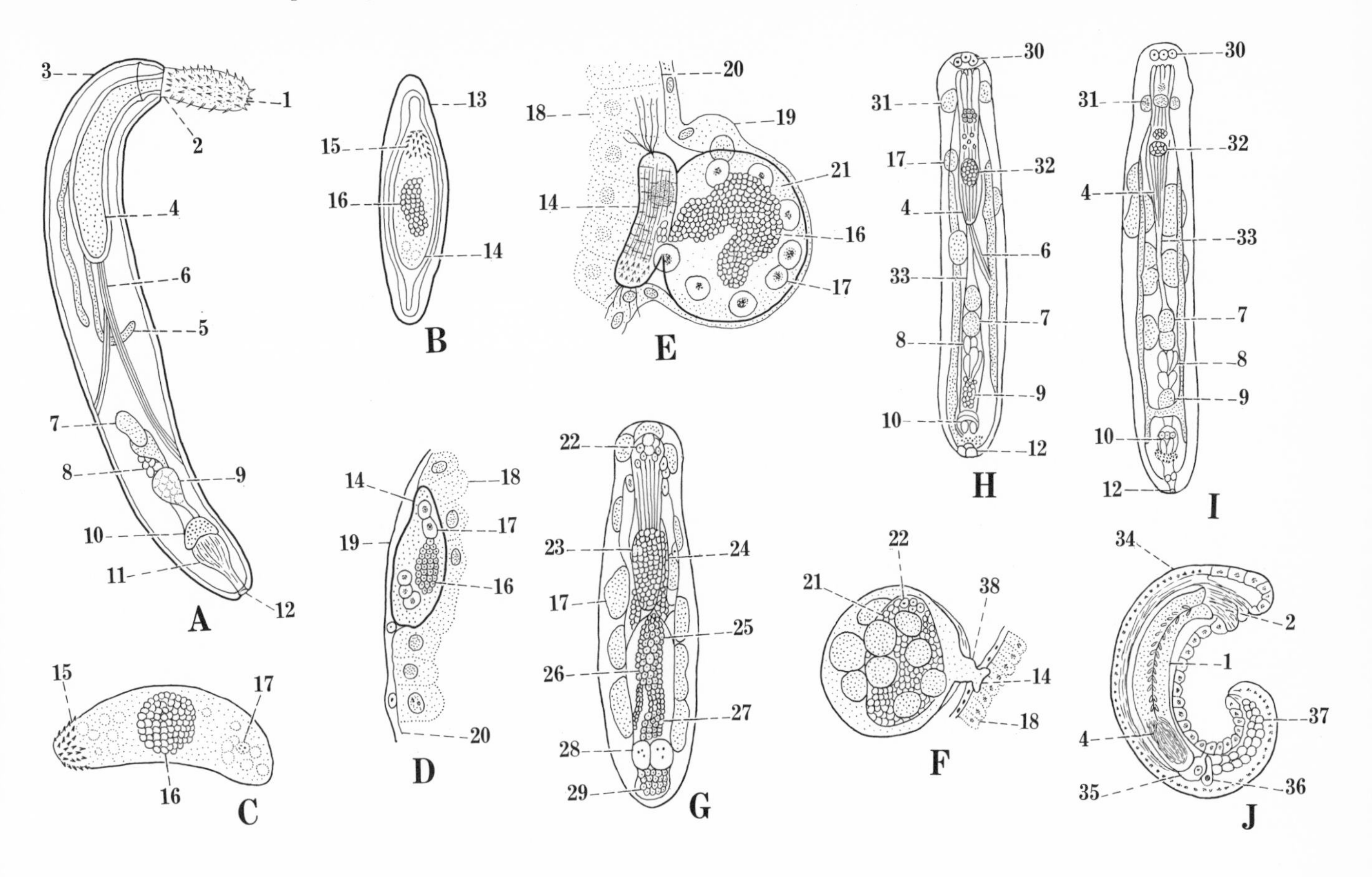
A
B
C
D
E
F
G
H
I
J

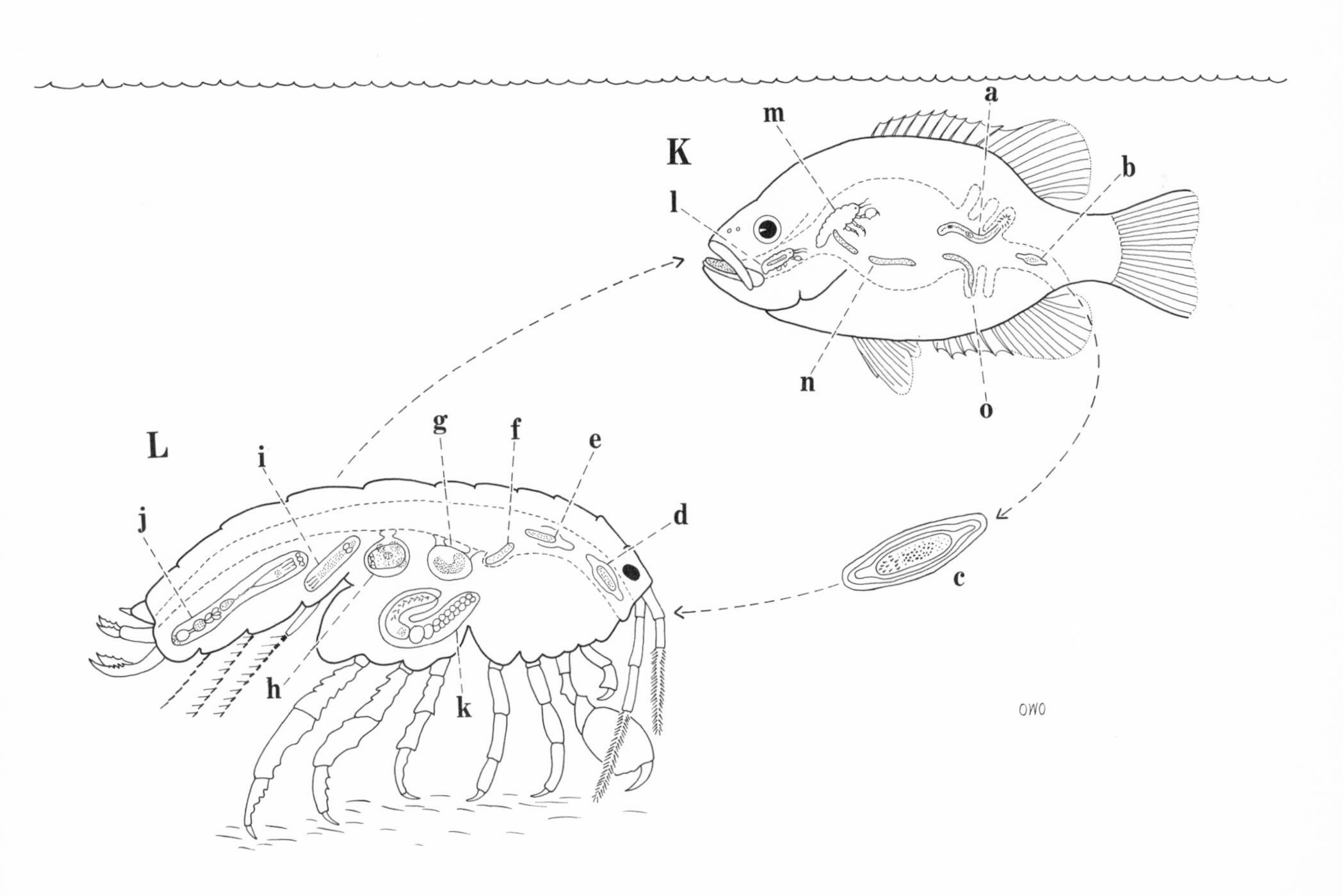
K
L
a
b
c
d
e
f
g
h
i
j
k
l
m
n
o
OWO

testis. Females measure 11 to 26 mm long. The embryonated eggs in the body cavity are 80 to 110 μ long by 24 to 30 μ wide.

LIFE CYCLE. Eggs passed in the faeces of fish are immediately infective to amphipods (*Hyalella azteca*) when ingested by them. Hatching occurs in the intestine within 45 minutes after being swallowed. The acanthors are very active and crawl over the surface of the intestinal epithelium for a short time after emergence from the eggs. They soon attach, however, and bore through the epithelium without the aid of the bladelike hooks which are lacking, coming to rest between the cells and the serosa of the intestine. Motility ceases and the acanthors enter the acanthella stage.

Growth of the acanthella begins as a bulging of the body which develops into a large spherical structure that is attached by the remains of the acanthor. The serosa ruptures and the newly formed acanthella hangs free in the coelom, being anchored by means of the dwindling acanthor. Between the 9th and 14th days after infection, there is extensive growth in size of the acanthella and organization of the central nuclear mass. At the end of this period, the acanthella breaks its stalk and becomes free in the haemocoel. The basic structure of the adult worm is attained by the 25th day, and it becomes a fully developed infective juvenile by the 32nd day in the amphipod.

Infection of fish is accomplished when amphipods harboring juvenile acanthellas are eaten. Digestion of the crustaceans results in release of the parasites in the stomach of the fish. They enter the pyloric caeca and attach by means of the proboscis. The rate of development is controlled somewhat by the temperature of the water. Under favorable conditions, eggs appear in the faeces 8 weeks after the fish eat infected amphipods. The males are sexually mature at the end of 4 weeks.

EXERCISE ON LIFE CYCLE

For experiments, amphipods, fish (rock bass or sunfish are preferred because they are natural hosts and are adaptable to laboratory conditions), and worm eggs are needed.

Amphipods collected from habitats lacking fish hosts are suitable for experimental infections. They may be kept readily in battery jars to which are added a few willow rootlets and duck weed, in addition to bits of yeast from time to time. A stream of air bubbled through the jar will improve the environmental conditions in it.

Rock bass and sunfish live well in aquaria when kept on a diet of earthworms.

Gravid females of *L. thecatus* provide eggs. The worms may be stored in water in a refrigerator for long periods without adverse effects on the viability of the eggs.

Amphipods may be infected by placing 100 of them in a jar with a large number of worm eggs. An hour of exposure is sufficient to allow four or five larvae per individual. After exposure, wash the crustaceans to free them of any eggs that might be adhering and place them in clean jars. Dissect them at frequent intervals over a period of 40 days to observe the progress of development. Examine the intestinal lumen for free newly hatched acanthors and the wall for those that have entered it. Examine the haemocoel for acanthellas.

Since fish are commonly infected naturally, uninfected ones are difficult to obtain from natural habitats. In order to assure having fish suitable for experimental feeding, it is necessary to hold them in aquaria for about 2 months. In this time, any parasites present would have developed to maturity and could be detected by eggs in the faeces. Fish are infected readily by introducing a known number of infected acanthellas into the stomach by means of a glass pipette or by allowing them to eat infected gammarids. Fish should be wrapped in a wet cloth while handling in order to avoid injury. Faecal examinations should begin during the sixth week after infection in order to determine the length of the prepatent period.

SELECTED REFERENCES

De Guisti, D. L. (1939). J. Parasit. 25:180; (1949). Ibid. 35:437.

Van Cleave; H. J. (1934). Roosevelt Wildlife Ann. 3(3-4):314.

ORDER EOACANTHOCEPHALA

Hosts of the members of this order are aquatic, usually fish but occasionally turtles.

FAMILY NEOECHINORHYNCHIDAE

These are small to medium-sized acanthocephala with spines only on the proboscis. The wall of the proboscis receptacle is a single layer of muscle. The nuclei of the lemnisci and body wall are fixed in number, definite in arrangement, and very large, the latter producing pronounced oval elevations on the body surface. The testes are elliptical and usually contiguous. The cement gland is a single syncytial mass.

The Neoechinorhynchidae are common parasites of fish and occasionally of turtles throughout the world.

Neoechinorhynchus cylindricus (Van Cleave, 1913) (Plate 107).

This species occurs in a number of North American fish, including large mouth bass, *Micropterus dolomieui, Stizostedion vitreum, Esox niger, E. lucius, Amia calva, Erimyzon sucetta, Anguilla rostata, A. chrysypa*, and *Carpiodes carpio*. Possibly there are others.

DESCRIPTION. Adult females are 7 to 11.2 mm long by 0.35 to 0.7 mm wide, with greatest diameter between first and second nuclei. The proboscis is globular in shape, measuring 0.1 to 0.14 mm long by 0.16 to 0.19 mm broad. It bears three circles of six hooks each. The uninucleate lemniscus is slightly shorter than the binucleate one, which is 0.95 to 1.4 mm long. Uterine bell, uterus, and vagina total 0.49 to 0.73 mm long. The eggs are ellipsoidal and measure 50 to 60 μ long by 17 to 28 μ wide.

Adult males measure 4.7 to 6.3 mm long by 0.36 to 0.63 mm wide. The proboscis is 0.1 to 0.14 mm long by 0.15 to 0.17 mm wide. The uninucleate lemniscus is slightly shorter than the binucleate one, which is 0.84 to 1.2 mm long. The testes are arranged in tandem, followed by an elongate syncytial cement gland with eight large nuclei. A cement reservoir is incorporated in the posterior part of the cement gland. There is a bell-shaped copulatory bursa.

LIFE CYCLE. Adult females in the intestine of large-mouthed bass lay fully embryonated eggs that are voided with the faeces. Ostracods (*Cypria* (*Physacypria*) *globula*), which are common in ponds, serve as the first intermediate host. Hatching of the eggs occurs when they are eaten by the ostracods. Upon release from the eggs, the acanthors promptly burrow through the intestinal wall, arriving in the body cavity within 24 hours. When too many embryos are eaten, the ostracods die after 10 days. Growth is slow, requiring up to 30 days or more before the larvae have reached the definitive shape of the adult males and females. There is little change in size or structure during the first 6 days. On the tenth day after infection, the larvae have enlarged greatly and show a few large cuticular nuclei. By the end of the third week the size and shape are similar but a primordial body wall is apparent and the interior is filled with dividing cells. On the 28th day, after entering the ostracod, the body has elongated greatly, giving it a vermiform appearance. The large nuclei which will develop into the proboscis and its various parts, such as hooks and receptacle, have appeared by this time. The precise time after the fourth week when the acanthellas become infective is unknown.

Blue gills serve as the second intermediate hosts. They become infected by eating ostracods harboring fully developed acanthellas. In the alimentary canal of the fish, ostracods are digested and the acanthellas freed. Those that have developed to the infective stage burrow through the intestinal wall and penetrate the liver. Inside, the worms coil up and become enclosed in a cyst composed of modified liver cells. A layer of granular material lines the inside of the cyst wall. Encysted worms are similar to adults except in size and degree of development of the reproductive organs. They are infective to bass when encystment is completed.

Bass become infected by eating parasitized blue gills. Little growth occurs during the first 30 days and sexual maturity is not attained until about 5 months after ingestion of encysted acanthellas. Longevity of the adult worms in the fish is unknown.

Studies on the life cycles of *Neoechinorhynchus emydis* from the map turtle and *N. rutili* from many species of fish have been done. Eggs hatch when ingested by the ostracod (*Cypria maculata*). The

EXPLANATION OF PLATE 107 ⇨

A. Adult male *Neoechinorhynchus cylindricus.* **B.** Proboscis, showing arrangement of hooks. **C.** Adult female. **D.** Egg. **E.** Embryo 24 hours after ingestion by ostracod. **F.** Embryo in ostracod 10 days. **G.** Embryo in ostracod 20 days. **H.** Embryo in ostracod 28 days. **I.** Immature male from ostracod. **J.** Encysted immature female from liver of blue gill. **K.** Immature male dissected from cyst from liver of blue gill. **L.** Immature female from cyst. **M.** Large-mouthed bass *(Micropterus salmoides)* definitive host. **N.** Ostracod *(Cypria (Physacypria) globula)* first intermediate host. **O.** Blue gill *(Lepomis pallidus)* second intermediate host.

1, hooked proboscis; **2,** hook of proboscis; **3,** proboscis receptacle; **4,** lemniscus; **5,** retractor muscle of proboscis receptacle; **6,** giant nucleus of body wall; **7,** testes; **8,** syncytial cement gland; **9,** cement reservoir; **10,** seminal vesicle; **11,** copulatory bursa; **12,** ovarial ball or floating ovary; **13,** eggs; **14,** ligament; **15,** uterine bell; **16,** uterus; **17,** vagina; **18,** outer shell of egg; **19,** inner shell of egg; **20,** shellfolds at each end of acanthor; **21,** acanthor; **22,** nuclear mass of acanthor; **23,** anlagen of subcuticula.

a, adult female with smaller male beside her, both attached to intestinal wall; **b,** eggs; **c,** embryonated egg voided with faeces into water; **d,** egg ingested by ostracod; **e,** acanthor hatching from egg; **f,** acanthor burrowing through wall of gut; **g,** acanthor in body cavity; **h,** growing acanthor; **i,** young acanthella; **j,** ostracod in gut of blue gill; **k,** young acanthella escaping from ostracod as latter is digested; **l,** acanthella burrowing through wall of small intestine and into liver of blue gill; **m,** fully developed and encysted infective acanthella in liver of blue gill; **n,** infected blue gill eaten by bass; **o,** acanthella released by digestion in intestine; **p,** young acanthocephalans, larger female and smaller male in intestine, having been released from liver and cysts.

Figures A-L adapted from Ward, 1940, Trans. Amer. Micr. Soc. 59:327; others original.

---

acanthors enter the body cavity and develop into unencysted juveniles in 21 days. When infected ostracods are eaten by the snail *Campeloma rufum,* the juvenile worms encyst in the tissues, especially in the foot. When infected snails are eaten by turtles, development of the worms takes place in the intestine. *N. rutili* has a life cycle different from the other two species in that there is no second intermediate host. In Washington State, the eggs hatch in the intestine of the ostracod *Cypria turneri.* Acanthors are free in the haemocoel of the ostracod after 6 to 12 days and complete their development to the juvenile stage in 48 to 57 days. These juveniles are infective directly to various species of fresh-water fishes.

EXERCISE ON LIFE CYCLE

Infected fish or map turtles provide a source of eggs for experimental infection of ostracods. Eggs may be obtained from the faeces of infected hosts but this can be a laborious task with a low yield. By rupturing the posterior region of the gravid female worms, a mass of eggs escapes into the dish. They are washed by a series of centrifugations and stored in tap water in a refrigerator for future use.

Infect ostracods by placing them in a small dish of water containing a few eggs which they will eat. Care should be taken to avoid too heavy infections lest the ostracods die as a result. Observe the development of the acanthellas in the body cavity of the ostracods by dissecting them at intervals in order to obtain all of the stages. Determine the time of infectivity of the juvenile worms in the ostracods by appearance and by feeding experiments. These should be designed to determine whether infection of the definitive host may be obtained by feeding infected ostracods directly to them. If *N. rutili* is available for experimentation, determine whether the life cycle may also include a second intermediate host such as a snail or some other animal.

SELECTED REFERENCES

Hopp, W. B. (1954). J. Parasit. 40:284.

Merritt, S. V., and I. Pratt (1964). J. Parasit. 58:394.

Ward, H. L. (1940). Trans. Amer. Micr. Soc. 59:327.

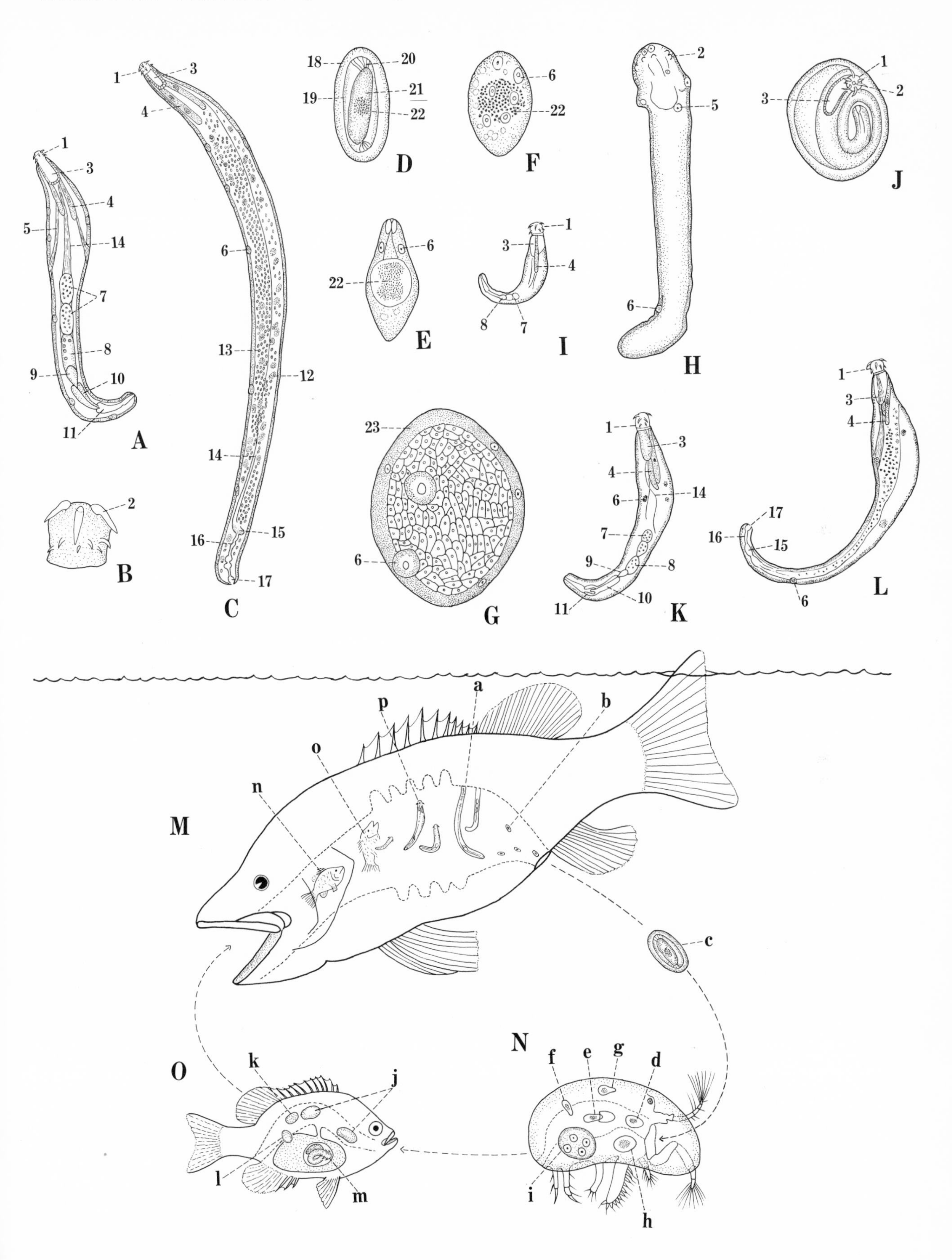
A
B
C
D
E
F
G
H
I
J
K
L
M
N
O
a
b
c
d
e
f
g
h
i
j
k
l
m
n
o
p

RESUME OF ACANTHOCEPHALAN LIFE CYCLES

Acanthocephala appear to utilize only arthropods for the true intermediate hosts in which the infective juveniles develop.

Parasites of terrestrial definitive vertebrate hosts utilize land invertebrates, primarily insects, as intermediate hosts. Those of aquatic definitive hosts similarly employ aquatic invertebrates as intermediaries. These are commonly crustacea, both Entomostraca and Malacostraca, but insects may also serve in this capacity.

Some species parasitize animals that do not normally eat the small invertebrate intermediate hosts. In these cases, a secondary host that serves as a transport to carry the parasite to the definitive host has been included in the life cycle. When the definitive host is a land species, the transport hosts generally are a number of small animals that eat insects. Those in turn are preyed upon by the definitive host and the infection is transferred to them. In the case of species in aquatic definitive hosts, the intermediaries are commonly crustacea but also aquatic insects. Snails and fish are known to act as transport hosts.

Parasites are masters in the art of adaptability, an asset they exploit to great advantage!

PART V PHYLUM NEMATHELMINTHES

GENERAL CONSIDERATIONS

The Phylum Nemathelminthes includes a great assemblage of species. Some of them are free-living and others parasitize either plants or animals.

The nematodes as defined by Chitwood, included the subclasses Phasmidia and the Aphasmidia which were raised later (Chitwood and Chitwood) to classes. Dougherty observed that Phasmidia had been applied much earlier as a name for walking sticks (Orthoptera). In order to correct this situation, he emended and brought forth Secernentea von Linstow, 1905 to replace Phasmidia. Following suit in the same year, Chitwood replaced Aphasmidia with an emendation of Adenophorea von Linstow, 1905. Chitwood and Allen and Thorne used Secernentea and Adenophorea as classes of the Phylum Nemata. While free-living and parasitic species occur in both classes, the great majority of the species parasitic on plants and in animals belong to the Secernentea.

The life cycles of many of the nematodes parasitic in animals have been studied. They range from simple to complex, the latter involving two or three hosts. The degree of complexity does not always follow the sequence of phylogenetic progression and relationship of the worms.

The species selected to illustrate representative cycles are presented in order, according to the classification scheme of Chitwood and Chitwood, as given below. Only the specific representatives discussed in the text are included in the classification. The basic types of life cycles of nematodes are given on Plates 141 and 142.

CLASSIFICATION OF NEMATHELMINTHES INCLUDED IN THIS CHAPTER

Class Secernentea

Order Rhabditida
Suborder Rhabditina
Superfamily Rhabditoidea
Family Strongyloididae
Strongyloides papillosus

Suborder Strongylina
Superfamily Strongyloidea
Family Ancylostomatidae
Ancylostoma caninum
Uncinaria lucasi

Family Strongylidae
Oesophagostomum columbianum

Stephanurus dentatus
Strongylus edentatus
Strongylus equinus
Strongylus vulgaris
Syngamus trachea

Superfamily Trichostrongyloidea
Family Trichostrongylidae
Haemonchus contortus
Ostertagia circumcincta
Trichostrongylus colubriformis

Superfamily Metastrongyloidea
Family Metastrongylidae
Dictyocaulus filaria
Metastrongylus elongatus
Muellerius capillaria
Protostrongylus rufescens

Suborder Ascaridina
Superfamily Oxyuroidea
Family Oxyuridae
Enterobius vermicularis

Superfamily Ascaridoidea
Family Heterakidae
Heterakis gallinae
Ascaridia galli

Family Ascaridae
Ascaris lumbricoides
Toxocara canis
Contracaecum aduncum

Order Spirurida
Suborder Camallinina
Superfamily Dracunculoidea
Family Dracunculidae
Dracunculus medinensis

Suborder Spirurina
Superfamily Spiruroidea
Family Thelaziidae
Oxyspirura mansoni

Family Spiruridae
Habronema megastoma

Family Acuariidae
Tetrameres crami

Family Ascaropidae
Physocephalus sexalata
Ascarops strongylina

Physalopteridae
Physaloptera phrynosoma

Superfamily Filarioidea
Family Diplotriaenidae
Diplotriaenoides translucidus

Family Onchocercidae
Litomosoides carinii
Dirofilaria immitis

Class Adenophorea

Order Enoplida
Suborder Enoplina
Superfamily Trichuroidea
Family Trichuridae
Trichuris ovis
Capillaria annulata
Capillaria hepatica
Capillaria plica

Family Trichinellidae
Trichinella spiralis

Suborder Dioctophymina
Superfamily Dioctophymoidea
Family Dioctophymatidae
Dioctophyma renale

SELECTED REFERENCES

Chitwood, B. G. (1933). J. Parasit. 20:131; (1958). 15th Internat. Congr. Zool., Sect. VIII, Paper 28.

Chitwood, B. G., and M. W. Allen. (1959). Freshwater Biology, 2nd Ed. John Wiley and Sons, Inc., New York, p. 380.

Chitwood, B. G., and M. B. Chitwood. (1950). An Introduction to Nematology, Sec. I. Anatomy, Monumental Publishing Co., Baltimore, p. 2.

Dougherty, E. C. (1958). Bull. Zool. Nomenclat. 15:523, 896.

Thorne, Gerald. (1961). Principles of Nematology. McGraw-Hill Book Co., Inc. New York, p. 88.

MORPHOLOGICAL CHARACTERISTICS OF NEMATODES

Nematodes are cylindrical, nonsegmented animals with a complete digestive tract. The body is covered with a thin cuticle secreted by a noncellular hypodermis. The cuticle may be smooth, with fine transverse striations or with adornments. These include wartlike elevations, longitudinal ridges along the sides, epaulets and cordons at the anterior end, lateral expansions anteriorly and posteriorly, and spines.

The hypodermis consists of a thin layer except for thickened cords located at the dorsal, ventral, and lateral margins that extend the full length of the body, dividing it into quadrants. Bundles of longitudinal muscles in varying numbers lie between the cords. Species with about 12 bundles per quadrant as in the Ascaridoidea are designated as polymyarian, those with two to three large bundles per quadrant are meromyarian and represented by the Oxyuroidea, and forms with uniform musculature are holomyarian and include the Trichuroidea (Plate 108, F-H).

Lacking a peritoneal lining, the body cavity is designated as a pseudocoel. In males, the intestine and the reproductive tract both open into the cloaca. The alimentary canal consists of a muscular oesophagus, and intestine, and a rectum. The oesophagus and rectum are lined with an inflexion of the external cuticle. The mouth may be surrounded by six, three, two, or no lips (Plate 109, A_2, E_3, I_3, J_3). In some species, the mouth is surrounded by a crown of leaflets (Plate 109, B_1).

EXPLANATION OF PLATE 108 ▷

A-E. Systems. **A.** Alimentary canal. **B.** Typical male reproductive system. **C.** Typical female reproductive system as shown by Trichostrongyloidea. **D.** Excretory system of *Rhabditis*. **E.** Excretory system of *Ascaris*. **F-H.** Types of body musculature. **F.** Polymyarian type of musculature of the Ascaridoidea. **G.** Meromyarian type of musculature of the Oxyuroidea. **H.** Holomyarian type of musculature of the Trichuroidea. **I-S.** Developmental stages of nematodes as represented by the hookworm *Ancylostoma duodenale*, except L which is *Strongyloides papillosus*. **I.** First stage rhabditiform larva. **J.** Second stage rhabditiform larva in process of shedding molted cuticle of first stage larva. **K.** Third stage larva enclosed in the shed cuticle of the second stage larva; it has a strongyliform oesophagus characteristic of Strongylina. **L.** Ensheathed third stage larva of *Strongyloides papillosus* showing filariform oesophagus characteristic of most superfamilies. **M-Q.** Development of primitive and definitive buccal capsule in third stage larva. **M.** Bladder-like structures of primitive buccal capsule forming around oral cavity of the third stage larva. **N.** Primitive oral capsule nearly complete together with teeth in base; larval oral cavity persists in center. **O.** Fully developed primitive capsule with teeth and beginning of bladders as forerunners of definitive buccal capsule. **P.** Further development of dorsal and ventral bladders. **Q.** Appearance of definitive buccal capsule; primitive capsule still present and attached to oesophagus prior to being lost. **R-S.** Final or fourth stage. **R.** Male after final molt but still enclosed in shed cuticle of third stage larvae with adherent primitive buccal capsule. **S.** Female in process of undergoing final molt with primitive capsule still attached.

1, oesophagus; **2,** rhabditiform larval oesophagus; **3,** filariform larval oesophagus; **4,** intestine; **5,** spicules; **6,** ejaculatory duct; **7,** seminal vesicle; **8,** vas deferens or sperm duct; **9,** testis; **10,** vulva; **11,** vagina; **12,** ovejector; **13,** uterus; **14,** oviduct; **15,** ovary; **16,** excretory pore; **17,** ducts of H-shaped excretory system with glands of Rhabditoidea; **18,** glands of excretory system; **19,** ducts of H-shaped excretory system without glands of Ascaridoidea; **20,** renette cell; **21,** dorsal cord; **22,** lateral cord; **23,** ventral cord; **24,** longitudinal muscle bundles of body wall; **25,** larval buccal capsule; **26,** shed cuticle from first stage larva; **27,** shed cuticle from second stage larva; **28,** shed cuticle from third stage larva; **29,** early stage of primitive buccal capsule; **30,** later stage of primitive buccal capsule with angular teeth and remnant of larval oral cavity (25); **31,** fully formed primitive buccal capsule with two pairs of well-developed teeth; **32,** appearance of dorsal (on left) and ventral (on right) bladders that are precursors of definitive buccal capsule; **33,** advanced stage of development of dorsal (on right) and ventral (on left) bladders; **34,** early stage of definitive capsule; **35,** definitive capsule; **36,** primitive capsule is shed with cuticle of fourth stage larva; **37,** genital primordium; **38,** bursa with rays.

Figures redrawn and modified from various authors.

REPRODUCTIVE SYSTEMS

The reproductive organs of the male consist of a muscular ejaculatory duct, followed in succession by a seminal vesicle, sperm duct, and a filamentous testis (Plate 108, B, R). In many forms, there are one or two spicules that may be extended from the anus. The gubernaculum, a small sclerotized structure of variable shape, lies dorsal to the spicules and serves as a guide to them. In some species there is a cuticularized thickening of the ventral wall of the cloaca known as the telamon.

The males of the Strongylina have a membranous copulatory bursa supported by a system of fleshy rays (Plate 109, C_4) and those of Dioctophymoidea have a fleshy, bell-shaped, rayless bursa (Plate 109, M_2). In groups in which the males do not have a bursa, there are paired sessile or pedunculate papillae arranged in lateroventral rows on the posterior end of the body (Plate 109, E_2, F_2, G_2, H_2).

The female reproductive system consists of a basic pattern but with variations. The vulva opens into a vagina which gives rise to one or two uteri, occasionally four. These may arise directly from the vagina and extend posteriorly, or there may be an anterior and a posterior uterus followed in each case by an oviduct, and a filamentous ovary. In some species, a muscular ovejector connects each uterus to the vagina (Plate 109, C_3).

Eggs vary in shape, surface markings, and structure of the shell (Plate 109, C, D, E, F, I, L, M). Some are undeveloped when laid, whereas others are embryonated.

The excretory system is basically H-shaped with variations resulting from the loss of parts. Modifications occur in the reduction of one or both anterior limbs, giving h- or ∩-shaped structures. Reduction may include both the anterior and posterior limbs on one side. Other forms include the original H-shape but with one or two oval glands attached to the posterior side of the bar. In some species, only a single gland, known as a renette, appears. There are no flame cells. The minute excretory pore opens ventrally near the middle region of the oesophagus.

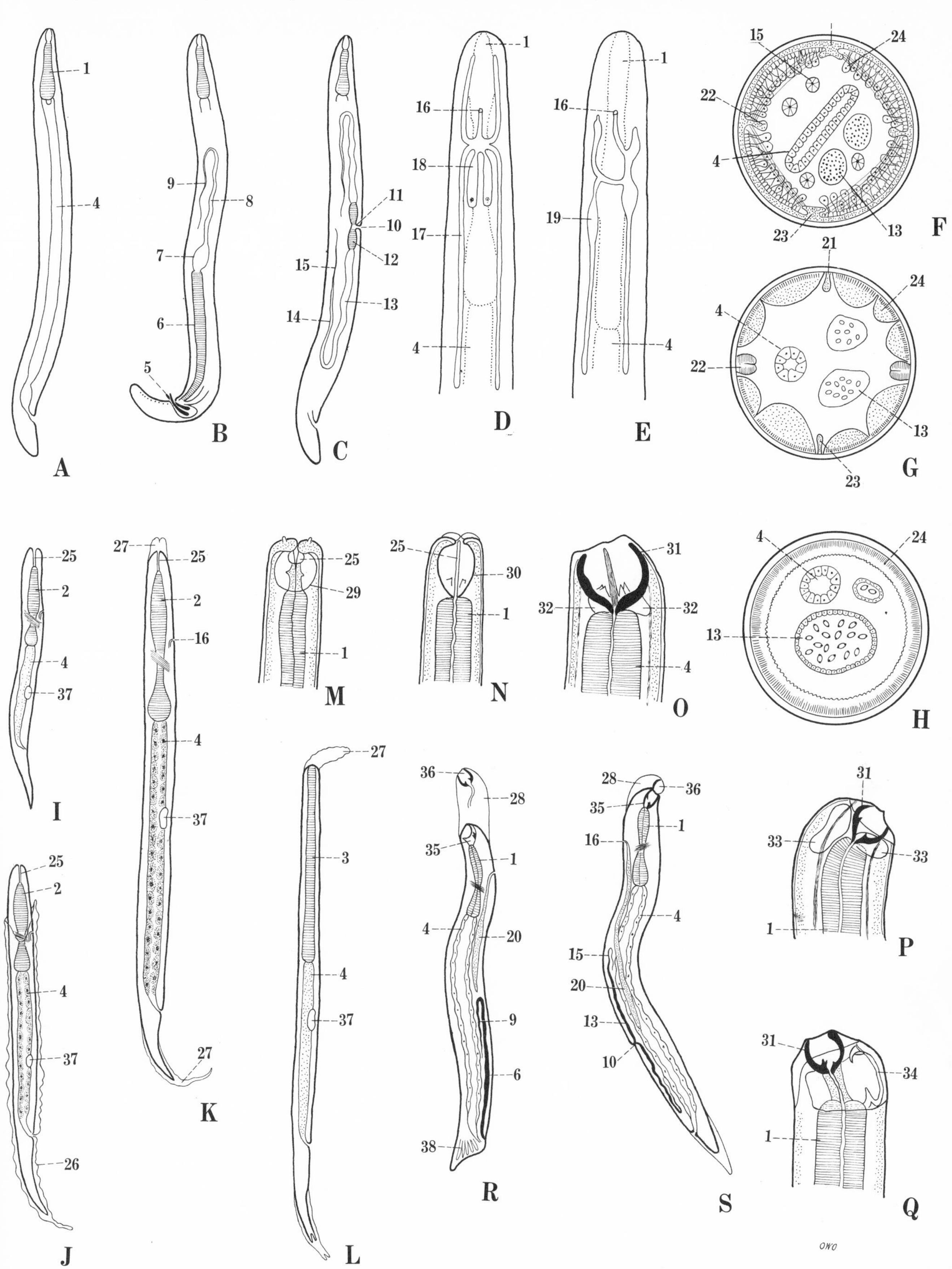
A
B
C
D
E
F
G
H
I
J
K
L
M
N
O
P
Q
R
S
OWO

EXPLANATION OF PLATE 109 ⇨

I. Order Rhabditida
A Suborder Rhabditina
A. Superfamily Rhabditoidea
Rhabditis strongyloides: **1,** anterior end of body; **2,** *en face* view; **3,** right side of caudal end of male; **4,** left side of caudal end of female.
B-D Suborder Strongylina
B. Superfamily Strongyloidea
Strongylus vulgaris: **1,** anterior end, showing large buccal capsule; **2,** caudal end with bursa and supporting rays characteristic of suborder.
C. Superfamily Trichostrongyloidea
Cooperia curticei: **1,** anterior end with rudimentary buccal capsule characteristic of superfamily; **2,** caudal end of female; **3,** vulva and ovejectors; **4,** caudal end of male, showing rayed bursa; **5,** egg in early stage of cleavage, characteristic of Strongyloidea and Trichostrongyloidea.
D. Superfamily Metastrongyloidea
Metastrongylus apri: **1,** anterior end with rudimentary buccal capsule; **2,** bursa with rays reduced in number and size normal for Strongylina; thick-walled embryonated egg (eggs hatch in the uterus in some species.)
E-F Suborder Ascaridina
E. Superfamily Ascaridoidea
Ascaris lumbricoides: **1,** anterior end of body, showing straight oesophagus and three lips; **2,** caudal end of male; **3,** *en face* view, showing three lips characteristic of suborder; **4,** egg showing ridges over surface.
F. Superfamily Oxyuroidea
Syphacea obvelata: **1,** anterior end of body, showing bulb at posterior end of oesophagus, characteristic of the superfamily; **2,** caudal end of male; **3,** caudal end of female; **4,** *en face* view, showing three lips; **5,** asymmetrical egg with flattened side, characteristic of superfamily.

II. Order Spirurida
G-H Suborder Camallanina
G. Superfamily Camallanoidea
Camallanus americanus: **1,** anterior end, showing buccal plate and two-part oesophagus (anterior muscular and posterior glandular portions) characterized by members of the order; **2,** dextral view of tail of male, showing papillae; **3,** *en face* view, showing plates.
H. Superfamily Dracunculoidea
Dracunculus medinensis: **1,** anterior end of body showing swollen anterior and posterior parts of glandular portion of oesophagus; **2,** ventral view of posterior end of male; **3,** *en face* view.
I-J Suborder Spirurina
I. Superfamily Spiruroidea
Physaloptera rara: **1,** anterior end, showing collarette and two-parted oesophagus; **2,** ventral view of posterior end of male, showing pedunculate papillae; **3,** *en face* view showing two lips, each with a tooth-like projection; **4,** thick-shelled embryonated egg of Spiruroidea.
J. Superfamily Filarioidea
Dirofilaria immitis: **1,** anterior end of adult female with vagina in region of oesophagus as is characteristic of this superfamily; **2,** ventral view of caudal end of male, showing spicules of different length, a characteristic of the Suborder Spirurina; **3,** *en face* view of head.

III. Order Enoplida
K. Suborder Dorylaimina
Superfamily Mermithoidea
Paragordius robustus: **1,** anterior end; **2,** ventral view of caudal end of male; **3,** dorsal view of caudal end of female; **4,** egg.
L. Superfamily Trichuroidea
Capillaria hepatica: **1,** anterior end of adult female, showing anterior muscular part of oesophagus and long posterior stichosome portion characteristic of this superfamily; vulva is near end of oesophagus; **2,** caudal end of male, showing single spicule in extruded spicular sheath; **3,** egg characteristic of Trichuroidea.
M. Suborder Dioctophymatoidea
Dioctophyma renale: **1,** anterior end of female; **2,** caudal end of male, showing bell-shaped fleshy bursa with single spicule characteristic of this suborder; **3,** *en face* view; **4,** egg in optical section.

a, lips; **b,** dorsal lip; **c,** ventrolateral lip; **d,** mouth; **e,** labial papillae; **f,** buccal capsule; **g,** excretory pore; **h,** caudal papillae; **i,** phasmid; **j,** amphid; **k,** spicule enclosed in spicular sheath; **l,** bursa; **m,** bursal rays; **n,** buccal plates; **o,** muscular portion of oesophagus; **p,** glandular portion of oesophagus; **q,** bulb of oesophagus; **r,** stichosome; **s,** vagina; **t,** uterus; **u,** ovejector; **v,** eggs.

Figures redrawn from various sources.

The nerve system consists of an oesophageal ring and an anal ring from which nerve fibers extend anteriorly and posteriorly. Six fibers extend from the nerve ring to the lips, where their branches enervate the labial papillae. In addition, one pair leads to each of the amphids, or cephalic pits, one of which lies

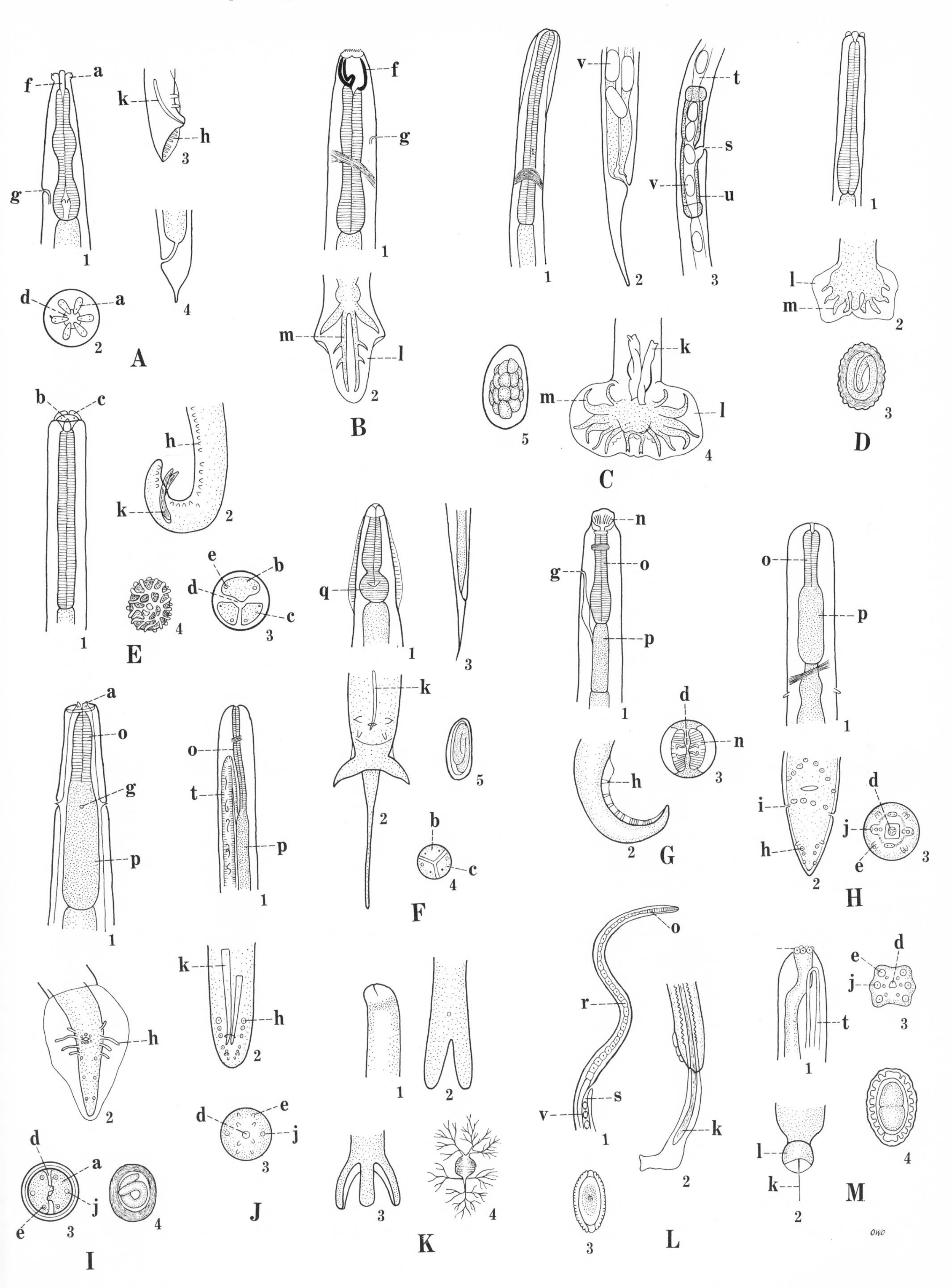
A
B
C
D
E
F
G
H
I
J
K
L
M
owo

on each side of the head. Large commissures extend through the cords, connecting the anterior and posterior parts. The rectal commissure sends nerves to rectal muscles, caudal papillae, and phasmids. The phasmids are minute pits located laterally between the anus and tip of the tail in the Secernentea.

LIFE CYCLES

The life cycle of nematodes may be direct without the need of an intermediate host, or it may be indirect in which case an intermediary is necessary for the development of the larvae to the infective stage. In some nematodes such as *Physaloptera* and *Gnathostoma*, third-stage larvae when eaten by unsuitable hosts migrate from the intestine to the tissues where they continue to exist. If these are fortunate enough to enter a susceptible host at a later time, growth to maturity will occur.

Development in the nematodes follows a simple pattern consisting of four stages, each separated by a molt of the cuticle and a period of growth. This procedure may be expressed by the following formula:

$$Egg \rightarrow L_1 + M \rightarrow L_2 + \boxed{M \rightarrow L_3} + M \rightarrow L_4 + M \rightarrow Adult$$

First and second stage larvae are rhabditoid in that the oesophagus is rhabditiform. The third stage larvae have a slender strongyliform or a filariform oesophagus, depending on the superfamily to which they belong, and are the infective stage. Generally, they are inside the free cuticle of the second stage, which serves as an enclosing sheath (Plate 108, K, L).

Upon entering the definitive host, third stage larvae begin development. In the Strongylina, the larval buccal capsule is replaced by a primitive one suggestive of the definitive stage in the adult. As development proceeds, a dorsal and ventral vesicle called bladders develops at the base of the primitive buccal capsule. These are precursors of the definitive buccal capsule (Plate 108, Q31, P33). As the definitive capsule develops, the primitive one is shed along with the cuticle during the final molt which takes place at the end of the fourth stage. During the parasitic phase of the third stage larva, the genital primordium develops into the definitive male or female reproductive systems (Plate 108, R, S).

Upon maturity, gravid females deposit unembryonated eggs (Strongyloidea, Trichostrongyloidea, Ascaridoidea, Oxyuroidea, Mermithoidea, Trichuroidea), fully embryonated eggs (Spiruroidea, Metastrongyloidea, some Filarioidea), or produce first stage larvae (Camallanoidea, Dracunculoidea, most Filarioidea). Upon embryonation, the eggs may hatch, producing first stage larvae, or development may continue to the third stage before hatching (*Nematodirus, Uncinaria*). In others, first stage larvae hatch when eaten by the intermediate hosts (Spiruroidea) or as second stage larvae upon reaching the intestine of the definitive host (Ascaridoidea).

Hatching of eggs occurs under a variety of conditions in the different groups of nematodes. In most of the Strongyloidea and Trichostrongyloidea, it takes place when the larvae are in the first stage, whereas in the genera *Uncinaria* and *Nematodirus* of the two above superfamilies, respectively, it does not occur before the larvae have developed to the third stage. In the Ascaridina, the larvae develop to the second stage in the eggs but hatch only when swallowed by the definitive host.

First stage larvae are present in the eggs of the Spiruroidea, some Metastrongyloidea, and the Filarioidea of the lungs and air sacs at the time of oviposition. There is no further development until they hatch in the intestine of an intermediate host. In the Camallanoidea, Dracunculoidea and tissue-dwelling Filarioidea, hatching occurs in the uterus of the female and first stage larvae are born.

CLASS SECERNENTEA

Phasmids are present laterally between the anus and tip of tail but they are difficult to see in adult parasitic worms. The terminal portion of the excretory duct is lined with cuticle. Lateral canals are present. The cephalic sensory organs are papilloid. The amphids are two small porelike openings located laterally on the lips.

ORDER RHABDITIDA

Oesophagus of adult worms variable in shape, ranging from clavate (club-shaped) to cylindrical but showing a corpus (elongate anterior enlargement), isthmus, and bulbular posterior portion in the early larval stages.

Suborder Rhabditina

There is no stylet in the mouth and the latter is not surrounded by a corona radiata, *i.e.*, one or two rows of leaflet-like structures. There are 0, 2, 3, or 6 lips.

SUPERFAMILY RHABDITOIDEA

The stoma (mouth) is usually distinct and the oesophagus consists basically of a corpus, isthmus, and valved or nonvalved posterior swelling.

FAMILY STRONGYLOIDIDAE

The members of this family are small and for the most part free-living nematodes. Some of them have adapted to a parasitic life during part of their existence. *Rhabditis strongyloides* is normally free-living but invades sores in the skin of dogs, under which circumstances it is parasitic. Members of the genus *Strongyloides*, on the other hand, have advanced their relationship with the vertebrate host so that in addition to the free-living heterogonic generation of rhabditiform males and females there is a parasitic homogonic one of only parthenogenetic females with greatly elongated filariform oesophagus in the intestine of vertebrates.

Strongyloides papillosus (Wedl, 1856) (Plate 110)

This species is parasitic in the small intestine of domestic and wild ruminants, and rabbits, particularly in warm moist climates.

DESCRIPTION. Parasitic females: These are slender worms 4.78 to 5.85 mm long by 50 to 60 μ in diameter at the vulva. The cuticle is marked with fine striations. There are four lips, four cephalic papillae, and two large amphids. The tail is 32 μ long, tapering finger-like. There are two ovaries, one anterior and one posterior, each containing eggs. The vulva lies between the middle and posterior thirds of the body. The eggs are embryonated when laid and measure 40 to 60 μ by 32 to 40 μ.

Third stage larvae are active and measure 575 to 640 μ long by 16 μ wide; the tip of the tail is trifid. The oesophagus is filariform and about 40 per cent of the total length of the body.

Free-living adults: Females measure 770 to 1,110 μ long by 50 to 90 μ wide. There are two lips, each with two papillae. The oesophagus is rhabditiform and 140 μ long. Ovaries are paired, one anterior and one posterior; the vulva is median. Males are 700 to 825 μ long by 50μ wide with a single testis. The gubernaculum is 20 μ long by 2.5 μ wide and the arcuate spicules are 33 μ long.

Parthenogenetic females in the alimentary canal of the vertebrate host produce eggs with different numbers of chromosomes. They are 1) the 3N type that develops directly into homogonic filariform female larvae; 2) the 1N type that produces heterogonic free-living rhabditiform males; and 3) 2N type that produces heterogonic free-living rhabditiform females. The progeny of the 1N males and 2N females are 3N larvae that develop into parasitic parthenogenetic females upon entering the vertebrate host.

LIFE CYCLE. This parasite has two kinds of life cycles, the heterogonic and the homogonic.

In the homogonic cycle, the parthenogenetic females are parasitic, being partially embedded in the mucosa of the small intestine. The 3N eggs produce first stage rhabditiform larvae that during growth pass through a second rhabditiform stage into filariform infective third stage larvae. These are infective to sheep, entering either by mouth or through the skin. They develop into parthenogenetic females. Parasitic males have not been found.

In the heterogonic cycle, the 1N eggs develop into rhabditiform free-living males and the 2N eggs into similar free-living females. They develop to adults by going through four molts characteristic of all nematodes. Their offspring are 3N larvae which develop into infective filariform larvae, similar to those of the homogonic cycle. The preparasitic larvae molt twice in the soil before reaching the infective filariform stage. Infection of sheep takes place by two routes. Filariform larvae may enter by mouth along with contaminated food or by burrowing through the skin from moist soil. When swallowed, they molt twice in the intestine and grow to maturity. If entrance is by way of the skin, they are carried by the blood through the heart and into the lungs where one molt occurs. Leaving the pulmonary vessels,

EXPLANATION OF PLATE 110 ▷

A. Adult parasitic female (males unknown). **B.** *En face* view of adult parasitic female. **C.** Embryonated egg. **D.** First stage rhabditiform larva. **E.** First molt producing second stage rhabditiform larva. **F.** Second molt with loose cuticle enclosing third stage filariform infective larva. **G.** Tip of tail of third stage larva. **H.** Adult free-living female. **I.** *En face* view of free-living adult. **J.** Adult free-living male. **K.** Spicule. **L.** First stage rhabditiform larva of free-living parents. **M.** Second stage rhabditiform larva with molting cuticle. **N.** Third stage rhabditiform larva with loose cuticle. **O.** Sheep definitive host.

1, filariform oesophagus; **2,** nerve ring; **3,** intestine; **4,** anus; **5,** tail; **6,** anterior ovary; **7,** oviduct; **8,** uterus; **9,** posterior ovary; **10,** oviduct; **11,** egg in uterus; **12,** vulva; **13,** cephalic papilla; **14,** amphid; **15,** mouth; **16,** larva in egg; **17,** genital primordium; **18,** loose cuticle of first stage larva; **19,** cuticle of second stage larva enclosing third stage larva; **20,** trifurcate tip of tail of third stage parasitic filariform larva; **21,** rhabditiform oesophagus; **22,** testis; **23,** seminal vesicle; **24,** spicules.

a, adult parthenogenetic female partially embedded in intestinal mucosa; **b,** eggs deposited in mucosa; **c,** eggs escape from mucosa into intestinal lumen; **d,** eggs passed in faeces; **e,** eggs already embryonated when voided with faeces; **f,** eggs hatch, releasing rhabditiform larva; **g,** free first stage rhabditiform larva of parasitic line in soil; **h,** second stage rhabditiform larva shedding cuticle of first stage larva; **i,** third stage filariform larva shedding cuticle of second stage larva; **j,** third stage infective larva; **k,** infection occurs when fully developed third stage larvae are swallowed; **l,** larvae pass down digestive tract; **m,** third stage larvae molt, producing fourth stage; **n,** fourth stage larvae penetrate mucosa of intestine and mature; **o,** infection of host may occur also through the skin, with larvae entering circulatory system; **p,** larva carried toward heart in veins; **q,** larvae pass through right side of heart toward lungs; **r,** in lungs, larvae pass from blood vessels into alveoli; **s,** larvae molt and migrate up trachea; **t,** larvae enter pharynx, are swallowed, and pass through stomachs; **u,** larvae molt fourth time; **v,** larvae burrow into mucosa; **w,** adult female.

a′, molting first stage larvae of rhabditiform free-living line; **b′,** second stage larva molts (two other molts follow); **c′,** adult free-living male; **d′,** adult free-living female; **e′,** embryonated egg from free-living female; **f′,** egg produces rhabditiform first-stage larva; **g′,** second stage rhabditiform larva; **h′,** filariform third stage parasitic larva infective to sheep by mouth or by skin.

Figures adapted from Basir, 1950, Canad. J. Res. (D) 28:173.

---

the larvae migrate up the trachea into the pharynx, and are swallowed. The fourth and final molt takes place in the small intestine. Maturity is attained in about 1 week.

Unfavorable environmental conditions in the host due to stresses of various kinds may exert a selective influence on the survival of the different kinds of eggs.

Other species of *Strongyloides* with similar life cycles include *S. stercoralis* of humans and dogs, *S. westeri* of horses, *S. cati* of cats, *S. ransomi* and *S. suis* of swine, *S. avium* of chickens and turkeys, and *S. ratti* of rats.

EXERCISE ON LIFE CYCLE

The most suitable species for experimental studies is *Strongyloides ratti* found commonly in wild rats. Freshly voided faeces from infected rats contain eggs. When droppings are kept moist at room temperature for 48 to 72 hours, preferably the latter, infective filariform larvae are present. They are easily isolated by means of a small Baermann apparatus.

Infection of rats may be accomplished 1) by feeding filariform larvae, 2) by placing them on a shaved area of the skin in a drop of water which is permitted to evaporate, 3) or by injecting them subcutaneously. Infection with a single filariform larva is done by placing it on the shaved skin of a rat or injecting it under the skin. If the infection is successful, a single parthenogenetic female will develop in the small intestine and produce eggs in about a week.

Following large doses of infective larvae given by mouth or through the skin, the rats should be sacrificed on the second, third, and fifth days to determine the route followed by the larvae in reaching the intestine. Mince the lungs of each rat and baermannize them to determine when the larvae are migrating through them. Also wash the stomach and intestine separately to ascertain where the larvae are at a given period after infection. Determine whether both third stage filariform and rhabditiform larvae appear in the faeces after incubation for 48 to 72 hours.

PLATE 110 *Strongyloides papillosus*

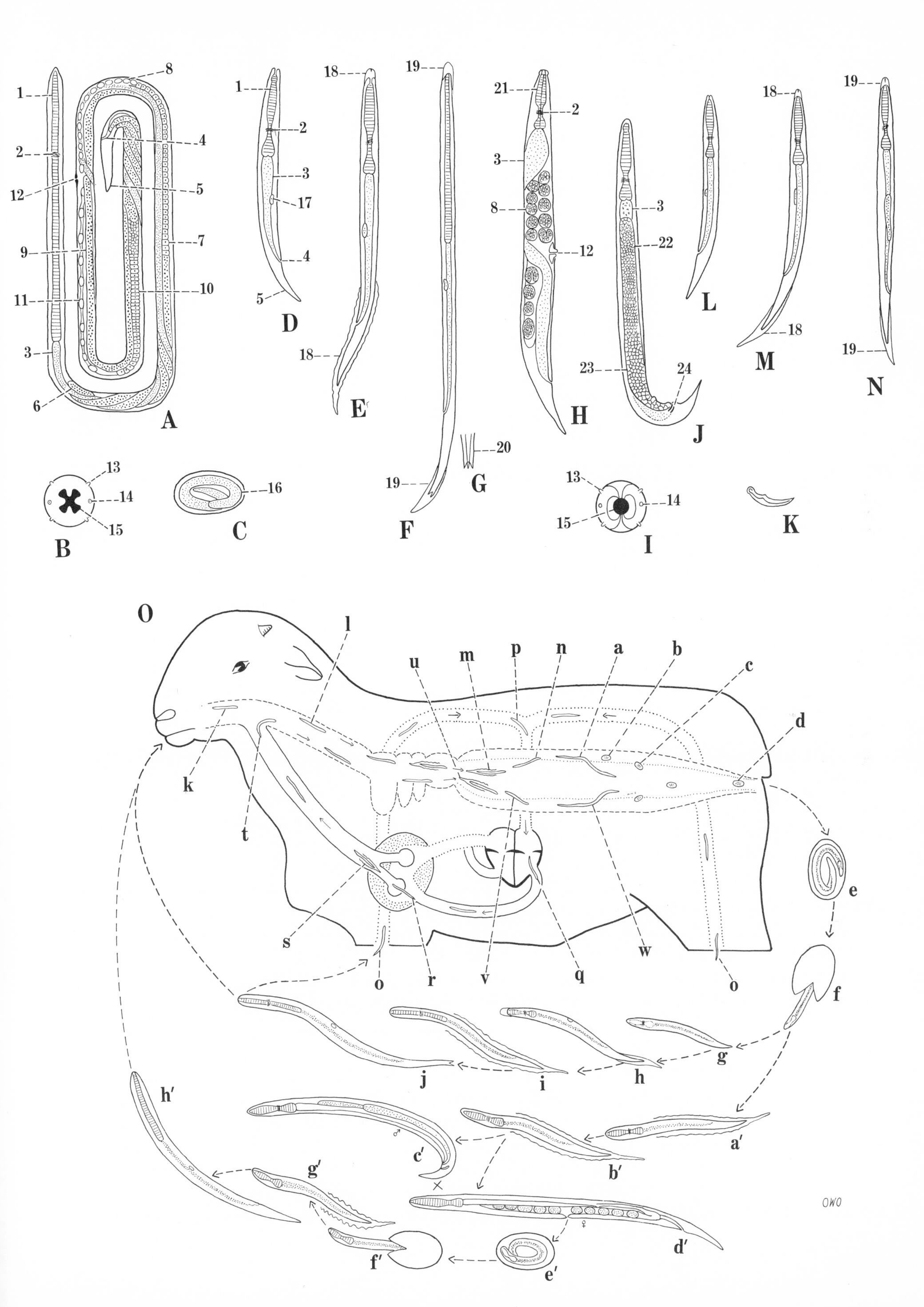

SELECTED REFERENCES

Basir, M. A. (1950). Canad. J. Res. D. 28:173.

Faust, E. C., and P. F. Russell. (1957). Craig and Faust's Clinical Parasitology, 6th Ed. Lea and Febiger, Philadelphia, p. 352.

Graham, G. L. (1936). Amer. J. Hyg. 24:71; (1938). Ibid. 27:221; (1938). J. Parasit. 24:233; (1939). Amer. J. Hyg. D. 30:15; (1939). J. Parasit. 25:365; (1940). Ibid. 26:207.

Lucker, J. L. (1934). U. S. Dept. Agr. Tech. Bull. 437.

Suborder Strongylina

The stoma of this group varies from a well-developed to a rudimentary one but it is never collapsed. There may or may not be a corona radiata surrounding the mouth. The males have a true or strongyloid bursa supported by four groups of well-developed muscular rays. With the exception of the dorsal ray, which is single and median, they are bilateral. These groups are 1) the single dorsal ray; 2) one pair of externodorsal rays; 3) the paired postero-, medio-, and anterolateral rays; and 4) the paired latero- and ventroventral rays.

SUPERFAMILY STRONGYLOIDEA

The mouth may or may not be surrounded by a crown of leaflet-like structures. The stoma is well-developed and has thick walls. Adults occur in the gut, kidney, or respiratory tract of reptiles, birds, and mammals. Two families are considered.

FAMILY ANCYLOSTOMATIDAE

This family includes the hookworms which occur in the gut of humans, dogs, cats, domestic ruminants, swine, and pinnipeds.

In this group there is no corona radiata surrounding the mouth. The oral opening has a well-developed pair of dorsal and ventral cutting plates.

Hookworms are common in the warm, moist climates but may reach abundant proportions in cold areas, as in the fur seals on the Pribilof Islands in the Bering Sea.

Ancylostoma caninum Ercolani, 1859 (Plate 111)

A. caninum is a parasite of dogs, foxes, and cats, inhabiting the small intestine where it sucks blood for nutrition and oxygen. It occurs in warm and temperate climates, especially where there is adequate moisture.

DESCRIPTION. Males are 10 to 12 mm and females 14 to 16 mm long. They usually have blood in the intestine. The anterior end is bent dorsad and the mouth has a pair of dorsal cuticularized plates each with three sharp teeth, the outer being the largest; there is a pair of triangular dorsal and ventrolateral teeth inside the buccal capsule. The male bursa is well developed and the rays are arranged in a manner characteristic of the species. The spicules are 0.9 mm long. The vulva is near the junction of the middle and posterior thirds of the body. Eggs are 56 to 65 μ long by 38 to 43 μ wide and have developed to about the eight-cell stage when laid.

LIFE CYCLE. The partially embryonated eggs develop and hatch into first stage rhabditiform larvae in the soil. They feed on organic matter for a short time and then undergo the first molt, completely shedding the cuticle. After a short period of feeding again, the cuticle of the second stage rhabditiform larva loosens and forms an enclosing sheath for the third stage infective filariform larva. It differs from the two preceding rhabditiform stages in having an elongated strongyliform oesophagus, *i.e.*, one with a weak, flasklike swelling at the posterior end.

Infection of dogs and other hosts occurs when the infective third stage larvae are swallowed or burrow through the skin. Swallowing appears to be the common means of infection due to the eating habits of dogs and to the toughness of the skin which makes burrowing through it difficult. Upon being swallowed, the larvae molt in the stomach and enter the crypts. After a short time, they migrate to the small intestine, molt the fourth and final time, and develop to maturity in about 5 weeks.

If entrance is by burrowing through the skin, the larvae migrate by way of the blood stream to the heart and lungs. In the latter, they enter the alveoli, undergo the third molt, migrate up the trachea, and are swallowed, going directly to the intestine. The final molt occurs in the small intestine and maturity is attained in about 5 weeks.

Some larvae pass through the capillaries of the lungs and are carried back to the heart. These worms circulate throughout the body, finally lodging in various organs where they die and are absorbed or become calcified. In the case of pregnant bitches, however, the larvae may enter the foetuses, thus infecting them prenatally. They usually remain dormant in the liver until the puppies are born, at which time they undertake the pulmonary portion of the migration, reaching the intestine and developing to maturity while the pups are still very young.

The life cycles of the other species of hookworms are basically the same as that described for *A. caninum*. The point on prenatal infection is not so well known for them. In the case of those infecting humans and cattle, penetration of the skin is the more common route of infection.

Ancylostoma braziliense (Plate 111), a parasite of cats and dogs, is of particular interest because the third stage larvae readily penetrate the skin of humans. Being in a foreign host, they are unable to pass through the skin but migrate laterally in it, causing a severe dermatitis known as creeping eruption. Beaches, yards, and playgrounds frequented by dogs and cats become heavily infested with larvae which attack people working or playing in contact with the soil.

EXERCISE ON LIFE CYCLE

Eggs obtained from the faeces of dogs, preferably young ones, may be incubated in a mixture of moist sand and faeces, and the different stages of larvae obtained by baermannizing portions of the material at short intervals. As a precaution, the sand should be heated prior to use in order to destroy free-living nematodes that might be in it, creating complications in identification and experimentation. Likewise, the faeces should not have been in contact with the soil as that might be a means of introducing free-living nematodes. Third stage larvae in the protective sheathlike cuticle of the second stage larvae are easily procured from the culture by means of a Baermann apparatus.

The route of migration in the vertebrate host after entering by way of the mouth or the skin may be followed in mice. After feeding a large number of third stage larvae to each of five or six mice, examine the intestine, liver, and lungs of one at intervals of 24 hours to determine where the larvae are at each period. Place third stage larvae in a drop of water on the shaved skin of an equal number of mice, allowing it to dry and examine them on the same plan presented above. Lungs of these mice but not the liver should be examined by means of a Baermann apparatus and by sections to determine route of larvae. Place a piece of mouse skin over a beaker of warm saline water (37° C) with the flesh side in contact with the water, and pipette a known number of third stage larvae on the haired side. Examine the sediment in the beaker after several hours to determine whether larvae have passed through it. Wash the haired side in another beaker of water to recover those that did not penetrate. Determine what percentage of them burrowed through the skin. Section a portion of this skin to ascertain whether larvae were migrating through it.

SELECTED REFERENCES

Faust, E. C., and P. F. Russell. (1957). Craig and Faust's Clinical Parasitology, 6th Ed. Lea and Febiger, Philadelphia, p. 383.

Foster, A. O. (1932). J. Parasit. 19:112.

Foster, A. O., and S. X. Cross. (1934). Amer. J. Trop. Med. 14:565.

Matsusaki, G. (1951). Yokohama Med. Bull. 2:154.

Morgan, B. B., and P. A. Hawkins. (1949). Veterinary Helminthology. Burgess Publishing Co., Minneapolis, p. 226.

Price, E. W., and P. D. Harwood. (1942). U. S. Dept. Agr. Yrbk., Washington, p. 1157.

Uncinaria lucasi Stiles, 1901 (Plate 112)

U. lucasi is a hookworm parasitic in the lower part of the small intestine of only young pups of the northern fur seal (*Callorhinus ursinus*) and Steller's sea lions (*Eumetopias jubata*). Pups of fur seals beyond 5 months of age rarely remain infected and older seals are not infected. These parasites

EXPLANATION OF PLATE 111 ⇨

A. Anterior end of adult *Ancylostoma caninum.* **B.** Bursa of *A. caninum.* **C.** Anterior end of *A. braziliense.* **D.** Bursa of *A. braziliense.* **E.** Anterior end of rhabditiform second stage larva. **F.** Posterior end of second stage rhabditiform larva. **G.** Anterior end of filariform infective third stage larva. **H.** Posterior end of third stage larva. **I.** Dog definitive host. **J.** Humans susceptible to infection by larvae of *A. braziliense* hatching from eggs passed by dogs and cats.

1, mouth; **2,** dorsal cutting plates; **3,** ventral cutting plates; **4,** wall of buccal capsule; **5,** oesophagus; **6,** intestine; **7,** anus; **8,** copulatory bursa; **9,** dorsal lobe of bursa; **10-11,** ventral rays (**10,** ventroventral rays; **11,** lateroventral rays); **12-14,** lateral rays (**12,** externo- or anterolateral rays, **13,** mediolateral rays; **14,** posterolateral rays); **15-16,** dorsal rays (**15,** externodorsal rays; **16,** dorsal ray); **17,** rhabditiform oesophagus of second stage larva; **18,** nerve ring; **19,** excretory tubule; **20,** filariform (or strongyliform) oesophagus of third stage larva; **21,** retained cuticular sheath of second molt enclosing third stage larva.

a, adult worms in small intestine; **b,** unembryonated eggs laid in intestine; **c,** eggs leave body in faeces; **d,** development of eggs takes place outside of body; **e,** fully developed first stage larva in egg; **f,** hatching of first stage larva; **g,** first stage rhabditiform larva feeds and grows; **h,** molting of first stage larva produces the second stage rhabditiform larva; **i,** molting of second stage larva produces third stage filariform larva enclosed in loose cuticle of second stage; **j,** infection of dogs occurs when infective third stage larvae are swallowed; **k,** larvae molt twice en route through stomach and intestine to final location where they attach and mature **(a)** in about 5 weeks; **l,** infective larvae penetrating skin enter blood vessels or **m,** lymph vessels and are carried to the heart in the circulation; **n,** larvae from blood vessels and lymphatics enter postcaval vein; **o,** larvae in right side of heart; **p,** larvae leave heart via pulmonary artery; **q,** larvae migrate from capillaries of lungs into alveoli of lungs; **r,** larvae migrate up trachea; **s,** larvae enter pharynx and are swallowed; **t,** two molts occur before they grow to maturity in small intestine **(a)**; **u,** some larvae pass through the lungs in the blood vessels; **v,** they enter left side of heart and are carried into the general circulation; **w,** larvae enter dorsal aorta; **x,** larvae in dorsal aorta; **y,** some larvae enter uterine artery; **z,** in cases of pregnancy, larvae pass through the foetal membrane and are carried by the blood into the liver of the foetus where they remain until after birth, at which time migration through the lungs is completed and infection occurs in the intestine of very young pups.

a', in the case of *A. braziliense,* third stage larvae penetrate the skin of humans coming in contact with them and cause a dermatitis known as creeping eruption; the larvae are eventually destroyed in the skin.

Figures A-C adapted from various sources; E-F, schematized stages of hookworm larvae; D, adapted from Biocca, 1951, J. Helminth. 25:1.

---

are known to occur only on the breeding grounds, or rookeries as they are called, of the fur seals on the Pribilof and Kommandorski Islands in the Bering Sea. Probably they occur wherever sea lions breed but this point has not been ascertained. It is the only strongyle parasite of fur seals.

DESCRIPTION. Adult males are 7.4 to 8.7 mm long and the females 12.4 to 16 mm. The lateral rays of the copulatory bursa are almost equal in length. Spicules measure 500 to 560 μ long and have transversely striated flanges along the dorsal side for almost the entire length; the flanges are fused near the distal tips of the spicules but the tips of the latter are free. The tail of the female has a small terminal spikelike tip. Eggs have transparent, three-layered shells, and measure 120 to 140 μ long by 80 to 88 μ wide. They are in the early stages of cleavage when passed in the faeces.

LIFE CYCLE. The life cycle consists of three phases. They are 1) the intestinal; 2) the tissue; and 3) the free-living phases. In the intestinal phase, adult worms occur in the lower extremity of the small intestine of only young fur seal pups from 2 weeks to 4 to 5 months of age; they do not occur in any other age group of fur seals. In the tissue phase, third stage larvae occur in the tissues, especially the blubber of the belly of all age groups of seals. They are in the mammary glands of pregnant cows during the sojourn at sea and in parous cows for a short period after parturition. The free-living phase consists of third stage preparasitic larvae in the soil.

New born pups are infected during the first few days of their lives by means of the milk which contains parasitic third stage larvae. Upon entering the alimentary canal, two molts occur and the worms develop to maturity in the lower portion of the small intentine without migrating through the body.

Sexual maturity is attained in about 2 weeks by all of the worms, since they were acquired at one time through the milk, and large numbers of eggs in the early stages of cleavage are passed in bloody faeces. The eggs continue development during the summer (June to September), reaching the third stage strongyliform larvae. These do not hatch, however, until late in the summer, usually some time

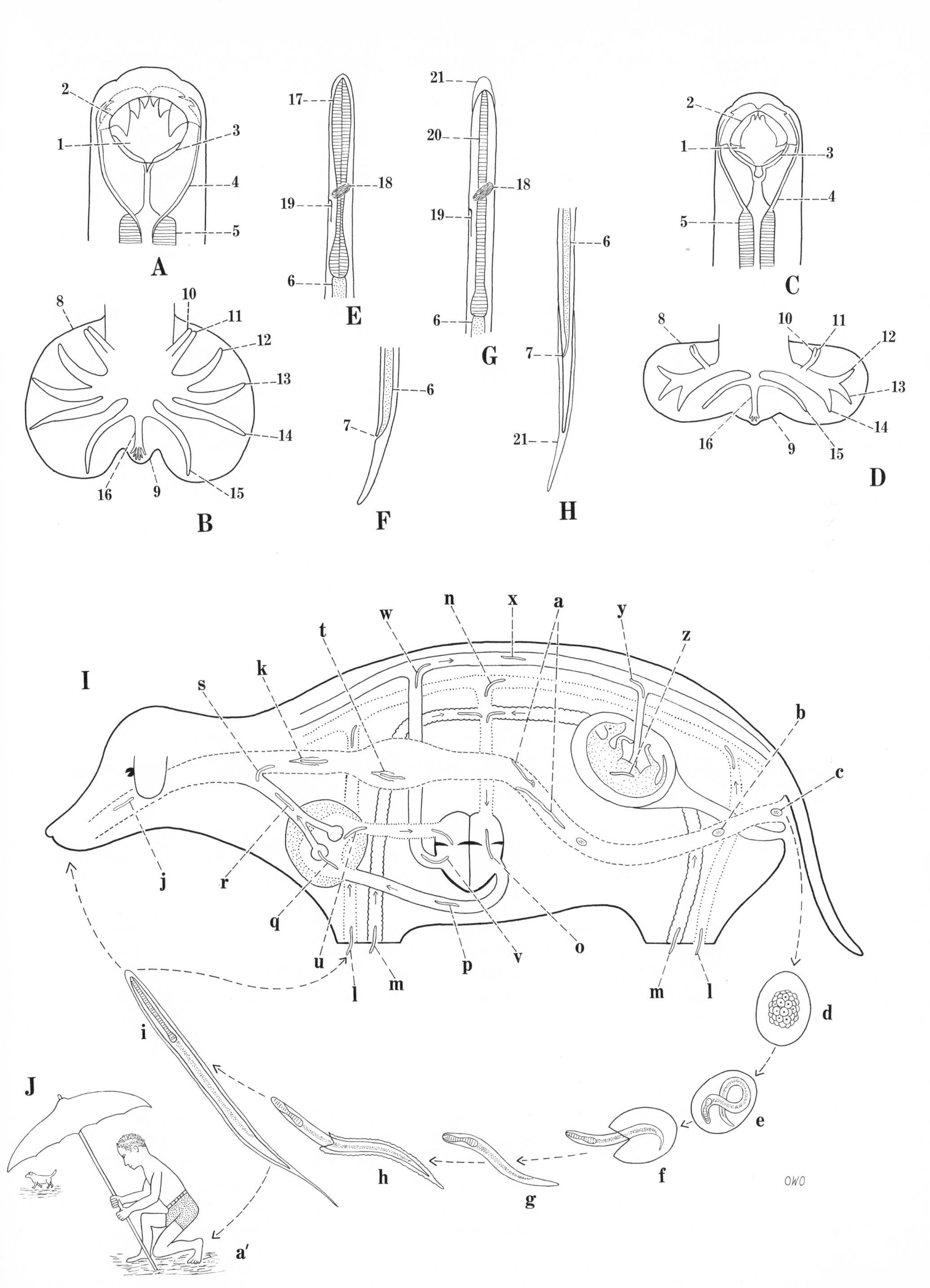
A
B
C
D
E
F
G
H
I
J
1
2
3
4
5
6
7
8
9
10
11
12
13
14
15
16
17
18
19
20
21
a
a′
b
c
d
e
f
g
h
i
j
k
l
m
n
o
p
q
r
s
t
u
v
w
x
y
z
OWO

EXPLANATION OF PLATE 112 ▷

A. Dorsal view of adult showing mouth and cutting plates. **B.** Dextral view showing buccal capsule with pair of spinelike teeth on ventral wall. **C.** Dorsal view of copulatory bursa of adult male. **D.** Sinistral view of tail of adult female. **E.** Ventral view of anterior end of 81-hour-old fourth stage larva. **F.** Sinistral view of tail of 81-hour-old male fourth stage larva. **G.** Egg in early stage of development. **H.** First stage larva. **I.** Second stage larva. **J.** Third stage larva. **K.** Adult cow seal nursing pup. **L.** Newborn pup taking its first meal of milk. **M.** Small group of seals.

1, mouth; **2**, cutting plates; **3**, buccal capsule; **4**, spines in buccal capsule; **5**, oesophagus; **6**, ventroventral ray; **7**, lateroventral ray; **8**, anterolateral ray; **9**, mediolateral ray; **10**, posterolateral ray; **11**, externodorsal ray; **12**, dorsal ray; **13**, membrane of bursa; **14**, anus; **15**, tail; **16**, buccal capsule of fourth stage larva; **17**, vacuole from which buccal capsule of fifth stage will develop; **18**, cuticle surrounding fourth stage larva; **19**, developing bursa of fifth stage; **20**, developing egg; **21**, first stage larva; **22**, second stage larva; **23**, loose cuticle of first stage larva serving as a sheath (remains of buccal capsule inside sheath); **24**, third stage larva; **25**, so-called "spears" which are buccal capsule in optical section; **26**, loosened cuticle of second stage larva serving as a sheath.

a, adult worms in pups (the prepatent period is about 14 days; for convenience of illustrating the life cycle, adult worms are shown in newborn pups); **b**, developing egg; **c**, egg with first stage larva; **d**, egg with second stage larva; **e**, egg with third stage larva; **f**, third stage larva hatching; **g**, free-living third stage larva which shows but one sheath; **h**, free-living third stage larvae penetrate flippers of seals of all ages; **i**, larvae enter veins; **j**, larvae go to vena cava; **k**, larvae pass through heart; **l**, larvae enter capillaries of lungs and continue through them; **m**, larvae in pulmonary artery; **n**, larvae go through left side of heart; **o**, larvae enter dorsal aorta whence they are distributed to all parts of the body; **p**, larvae in blood vessels leading to ventral wall of body; **q**, third stage parasitic larvae accumulate in blubber of belly of all ages and both sexes of seals; **r**, larvae accumulate in mammary glands of pregnant cows; **s**, everted nipple; **t**, third stage parasitic larvae swallowed by newborn pups during their first meal; **u**, fourth stage larvae molt; **v**, fifth stage, which will develop to maturity in about 14 to 15 days; **w**, placenta of newborn pup; **x**, eggs from intestinal phase of adult passed in faeces of only young pups; **y**, eggs hatch in sand of rookeries and third stage infective larvae appear; **z**, larvae penetrate flippers of all ages and both sexes of seals and go to tissues where they remain as third stage parasitic larvae unless ingested with the milk.

Figures E-J adapted from E. T. Lyons, 1961; others original.

---

around the beginning of September, although the time may vary somewhat. The free-living third stage larvae are hardy and may or may not survive the winter months. They may be abundant in the sand in the spring when the breeding seals return to the rookeries following their winter sojourn at sea.

Adult seals returning to the rookeries each season are exposed to the active penetration of the third stage free-living larvae in the sand. Upon entering the tissues, the larvae presumably enter the circulation and are carried to the heart, pass through the lungs, and back to the heart, whence they are distributed to all parts of the body. They accumulate in the blubber of the belly of all seals and in the mammary glands of the females, where they develop to parasitic third stage larvae.

New born pups are exposed to the free-living third stage larvae in the sand and to the parasitic third stage larvae in the milk of their mothers. Larvae entering the skin from the sand go to the belly blubber, remaining in the third stage, whereas those that are swallowed with the milk develop to adults in the small intestine.

Having homing instincts, together with being social and gregarious, the breeding seals assemble in great numbers in compact herds on the rookeries which are used year after year from early June until late August. At the latter time, the social structure of the harems begins to disintegrate and the seals move to the water's edge. The social and homing instincts of the seals favor the perpetuation of the hookworms, assuring a very high incidence of infection of each generation of pups with the intestinal phase and subsequent production of eggs.

While eggs are passed onto the rookeries throughout the summer, hatching does not occur until late August or early September when the harems begin to break up and the seals leave them for the sea and the narrow margin of land along the shore. Presumably the intense contamination of the rookeries with faeces and urine inhibit hatching of the eggs until such a time that the soil begins to freshen in the absence of the seals and under the influence of the weather. These larvae infect seals that return to the harem areas during the remainder of their stay on land and when they return the following year.

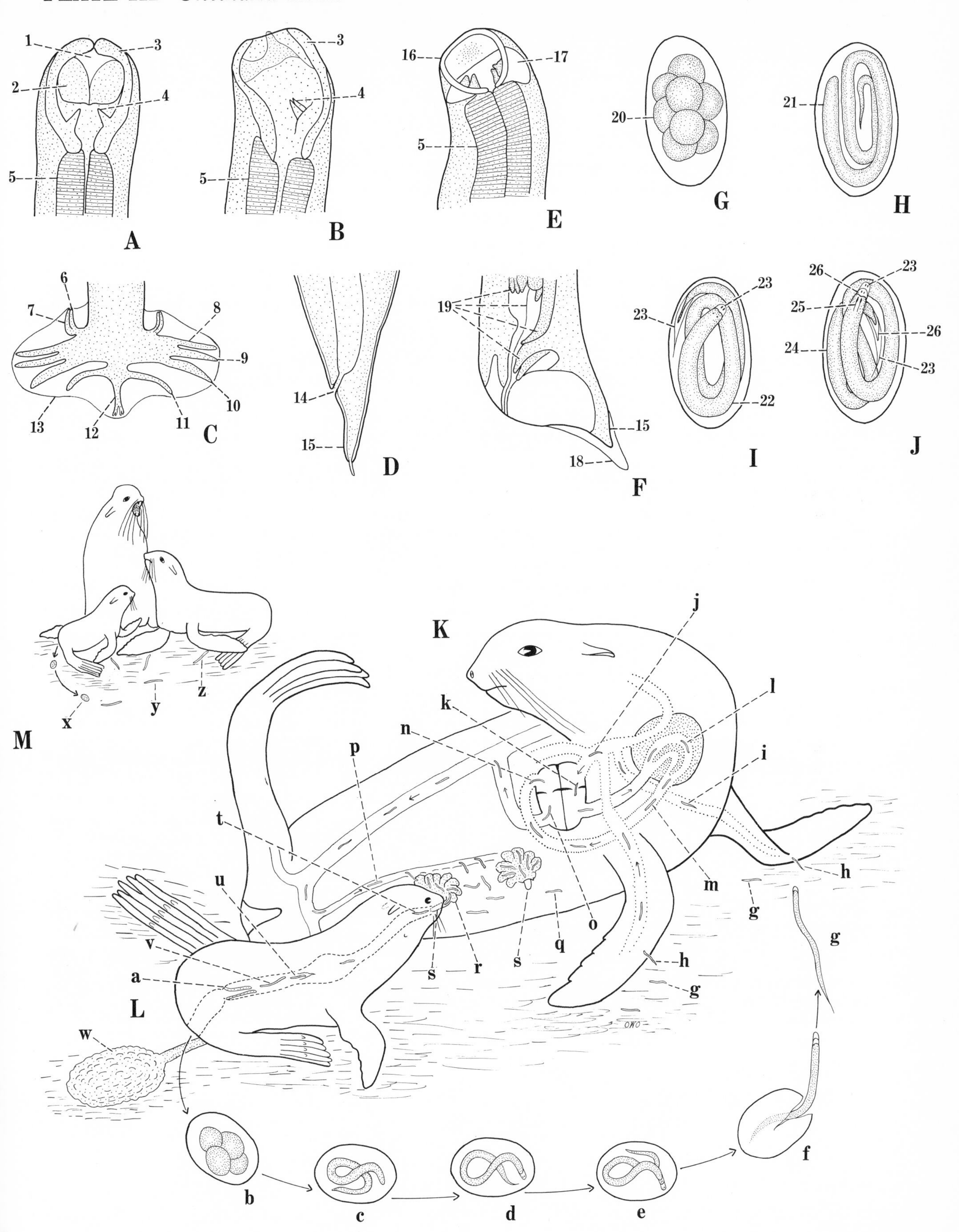

1
2
3
4
5
A
B
E
G
H
16
17
20
21
6
7
8
9
10
11
12
13
C
14
15
D
19
18
F
22
23
I
24
25
26
J
K
L
M
a
b
c
d
e
f
g
h
i
j
k
l
m
n
o
p
q
r
s
t
u
v
w
x
y
z

Breeding animals returning to the harems year after year presumably build up intense infections in the tissue since the larvae survive beyond a year in them.

In summary, the life cycle of *U. lucasi* is as follows: parasitic third stage larvae of the tissue phase in the mammary glands are swallowed by the pups with their first meal of milk. These larvae develop in about 2 weeks to adults which remain in the intestine of the pups until late in the fall, when they are lost completely. Eggs passed onto the rookeries in the faeces during the summer begin hatching at the end of August or thereabouts and infect seals that come in contact with the larvae. These go to the tissues and remain there. Larvae surviving the winter in the soil enter the flippers of the adult seals as soon as they return to the harems from the sea in the spring, and the pups as soon as they are born. Larval infections in the tissues persist for long periods.

The life cycle is unique in that the larvae of the tissue phase are transmitted to the young pups through the milk and develop to the intestinal phase as adults only in the young, never occurring as such in adult animals.

Uncinaria hamiltoni, a hookworm of the southern sea lion, *Otaria byroni,* the California sea lion, *Zalophus californicus,* and the sea elephant, *Mirounga leonina,* may have a life cycle similar to that of *U. lucasi.* Gibbs showed that the life cycle of *U. stenocephala* is similar to that of *Ancylostoma caninum.*

EXERCISE ON LIFE CYCLE

While no life history studies on the hookworms of seals are possible, investigations on the biology of other hookworms should be directed toward learning whether there is a tissue phase with transmission of larvae in the milk. Prenatal infection of pups has been reported for *Ancyostoma caninum.* The possibility of infection through the milk was not ruled out.

Ancylostoma caninum, A. brazilense, and *Uncinaria stenocephala* may be studied in dogs and cats for transmission in the milk. *Uncinaria stenocephala* of canines apparently has a life cycle similar to that of *Ancylostoma caninum.*

SELECTED REFERENCES

Baylis, H. A. (1947). Parasitology 38:160.

Doyle, L. P. (1957). Investigations of the death losses in fur seal pups on St. Paul Island, Alaska, June 28 to August 15, 1957. Fish and Wildlife Serv., U. S. Dept. Int., Seattle; 10 pp.

Gibbs, H. C. (1961). Canad. J. Zool. 39:325.

Lucas, F. A. (1899). The causes of mortality among seals. In: The fur seals and fur seal islands of the North Pacific Ocean. David Starr Jordan Rept., Part 3, pp. 75-98; Govt. Printing Off., Washington, D. C.

Lyons, E. T., and O. W. Olsen. (1960). Report on seventh summer of investigations of hookworms, *Uncinaria lucasi* Stiles, 1901, and hookworm diseases of fur seals, *Callorhinus ursinus* Linn., on the Pribilof Islands, Alaska, from 15 June to 3 October, 1960. Colorado State University, Dept. Zoology. hectograph, 26 pp.; (1961). Report on eighth summer of investigations on hookworms . . . from 7 June to 6 November, 1961. Colorado State University, Dept. Zoology, hectograph, 40 pp.

Olsen, O. W. (1952). Report on investigations of hookworms, *Uncinaria lucasi* Stiles, 1901, and hookworm diseases of fur seals, *Callorhinus ursinus,* on the Pribilof Islands, Alaska, from July 7 to September 2, 1951. Fish and Wildlife Serv., U. S. Dept. Int., Seattle, ozalid, 98 pp.; (1953). Report on second summer of investigations on hookworms. . . , Fish and Wildlife Serv., U. S. Dept. Int., Seattle, ozalid, 92 pp.; (1954). Report on third summer of investigations on hookworms. . . , Fish and Wildlife Serv., Seattle, ozalid, 117 pp.; (1956). Report on fifth summer of investigations on hookworms. . . , Fish and Wildlife Serv., U. S. Dept. Int., Seattle, Ozalid, 81 pp.; (1958). Trans. 23rd North Amer. Wildlife Conf., pp. 152.

Olsen, O. W., and E. T. Lyons. (1962). J. Parasitol. 48 (2/2):42; (1965). Ibid. 51:689.

FAMILY STRONGYLIDAE

The members of this family tend to be stout, varying in size from small to large, being up to 35 mm long. The mouth is surrounded by a double or single leaf crown (corona radiata), is without cutting plates but may have toothlike spines inside capsule which has a groove along the dorsal side. They are parasites of reptiles, birds, and mammals, especially equines.

Four common species, one of sheep and three of equines, are considered.

Oesophagostomum columbianum (Curtice, 1890) (Plate 113)

This is the well-known nodular worm of sheep and goats throughout the world, particularly in warm, moist climates. The adults are in the large intestine. Larvae enter the colonic and caecal epithelium for part of their development. Some of them, however, fail to escape and are surrounded by a caseous material that forms a nodule which gives rise to the popular names of nodular worm or pimply gut.

DESCRIPTION. Stout worms, whose males are 12 to 16 mm and females 14 to 18 mm long. A groovelike ring sets the head off from the body. A ventral cervical groove is present near the level of the cervical papillae which are anterior to the middle of the oesophagus. The external leaf crown has 20 to 24 elements in it and the internal one 40 to 44. The spicules are 750 to 950 μ long and the vulva is near the posterior end of the body. Eggs are 74 to 88 μ long by 45 to 54 μ wide.

LIFE CYCLE. Adults in the colon lay eggs already in the early stages of cleavage. They hatch into first stage rhabditiform larvae in 15 to 20 hours after being voided in the faeces. After feeding for about 24 hours, they molt to form similar second stage larvae. These likewise feed and grow for 3 days when the cuticle loosens and forms a free investing sheath for the third stage infective larvae. Feeding ceases, but the larvae may live several months under favorable conditions. Freezing is lethal to them.

Infection of sheep is by swallowing third stage ensheathed larvae with the forage. In the abomasum, the larvae escape from the loose cuticle and migrate to the intestine where they enter the epithelial mucosa and lie coiled next to the muscularis mucosae. After about 4 days of growth, they undergo the third molt, entering the fourth stage, following which further growth takes place. Within another 3 to 4 days, the larvae migrate from the nodules into the lumen of the intestine where they molt the last time and develop to adults in about 7 weeks after entering the host. When larvae leave the nodules, the latter subside and disappear. Larvae that fail to escape for unknown reasons become enclosed in a caseous mass that forms a permanent nodule.

Other species of *Oesophagostomum* common in this country are *C. venulosum* of sheep, goats, and deer, *O. radiatum* of cattle, and *O. dentatum* of pigs. The life cycles are similar except that *O. venulosum* does not cause nodules.

EXERCISE ON LIFE CYCLE

Adult females obtained from the colon of infected sheep slaughtered at abattoirs provide a source of eggs for hatching. Eggs may be available in faeces obtained from infected flocks.

Eggs should be incubated at room temperature in a moist animal charcoal-faeces mixture or one of sand and faeces. The sand should be heated prior to using it in order to destroy free-living nematodes, because their presence complicates the problem of separating the different species. Larvae are separated from the incubation medium by a Baermann apparatus. Proper timing is necessary to obtain the first and second stages.

If the eggs are obtained from faeces rather than females, there is a great probability that a mixture of species will occur, as sheep generally are host to several species of intestinal worms whose eggs are very similar. In this case, it is feasible to recognize only the third stage larvae of the oesophagostomes. In so doing, one gets excellent experience in critical observations, for the third stage larvae of the various species of nematodes of sheep are recognizable only on rather fine differences.

Known studies on the life cycles of oesophagostomes are limited to the vertebrate hosts of the respective species. No studies appear to have been made on the developmental stages as they might occur when introduced into small mammals such as rabbits, guinea pigs, mice, or rats. Such investigations might yield some interesting and valuable heretofore unknown aspects of the biology of these nematodes.

SELECTED REFERENCES

Anataraman, M. (1942). Ind. J. Vet. Sci. Anim. Husb. 12:87.

Andrews, J. S., and J. F. Maldonado. (1941). Res. Bull. (2) Puerto Rico Agr. Exp. Sta.

EXPLANATION OF PLATE 113

A. Anterior end of adult worm. **B.** *En face* view. **C.** Ventral view of bursa. **D.** Lateral view of posterior end of adult female. **E.** Anterior end of infective third stage larva. **F.** Posterior end of third stage larva. **G.** Sheep host.

1, crown of leaflets (corona radiata); **2,** cephalic papillae; **3,** cervical papillae; **4,** oesophagus; **5,** intestine; **6,** nerve ring; **7,** mouth; **8,** amphids; **9,** ventroventral ray; **10,** lateroventral ray; **11,** externolateral ray (also called anterolateral); **12,** mediolateral ray; **13,** posterolateral ray; **14,** externodorsal ray; **15,** dorsal ray with terminal digitations; **16,** spicules; **17,** anus; **18,** posterior loop of uterus; **19,** ovejector; **20,** vulva; **21,** tail; **22,** loose cuticle of second stage larva enclosing third stage larva; **23,** excretory pore.

a, adult worms in colon; **b,** egg being voided with faeces; **c,** developing egg; **d,** embryonated egg; **e,** first stage larva hatching; **f,** molting first stage larva, giving rise to second stage larva; **g,** infective third stage larva enclosed in free cuticle of second stage larva; **h,** infective larvae on forage; **i,** infective larvae being swallowed; **j,** third stage larvae shed loose cuticle in abomasum (this is not a molt); **k,** larvae entering intestinal mucosa; **l,** nodule containing third stage larva; **m,** third molt in nodule; **n,** fourth stage larvae escape from nodules, leaving cuticle; **o,** fourth and final molt in lumen of intestine, after which larvae develop to adult worms.

Figures A, C, D adapted from Ransom, 1911, U. S. Dept. Agr., Bur. Anim. Ind. Bull. 127, p. 42; B, from Goodey, 1924, J. Helminth. 2:97; E, F, from Dikmans and Andrews, 1933, Trans. Amer. Micr. Soc. 52:1.

Dikmans, G., and J. S. Andrews. (1933). Trans. Amer. Micr. Soc. 52:1.

Fourie, P. J. J. (1936). Onderstepoort J. Vet. Sci. Anim. Husb. 7:277.

Goldberg, A. (1951). Proc. Helminth. Soc. Wash. 18:36.

Morgan, B. B., and P. A. Hawkins. (1949). Veterinary Helminthology. Burgess Publishing Co., Minneapolis, p. 126.

Spindler, L. A. (1933). J. Agr. Res. 46:531.

Veglia, F. (1928). 13th and 14th Rept. Direct. Vet. Ed. and Res., Dept. Agr. Union South Africa, p. 755.

Stephanurus dentatus Diesing, 1839 (Plate 114)

This is the kidney worm of pigs which is prevalent in warm climates throughout most of the world. The adults occur in cysts in the pelvis of the kidneys and the wall of the ureters from which the eggs enter the urinary bladder and are finally voided with the urine. Larvae migrating in the body are found in many places such as the perirenal fat, pancreas, loins, hams, and spinal cord.

DESCRIPTION. The adult worms are stout, with the males 20 to 30 mm long and the females 30 to 45 mm by 2 mm wide. The buccal capsule has thick walls and is cup-shaped, with six teeth at the base. The margin bears a crown of a few small leaflet-like structures and six thickened areas. The copulatory bursa is small and with short rays of which the ventrals, laterals, and digitations of the dorsal ray are fused distally. The spicules are equal or unequal in length and 0.66 to 1 mm long. The vulva is near the anus. Eggs are 100 by 60 μ in size.

LIFE CYCLE. Adult kidney worms normally occur in cysts in the wall of the pelvis of the kidneys or the ureters. These cysts have openings through which the eggs pass into the pelvis of the kidney or lumen of the ureters and are washed into the urinary bladder. Vast numbers of partially developed eggs are voided with the urine at each micturation. In moist, warm but shaded soil, the eggs develop and hatch usually within 48 hours. The first stage rhabditiform larvae feed and soon molt to form foraging second stage rhabditiform ones. In 3 to 5 days the second molt takes place, with retention of the cuticle, to form the infective third stage strongyliform larvae. When embryonated eggs are swallowed by earthworms, they hatch, enter the coelom, and develop to infective larvae.

Infection of swine takes place by mouth or through the skin. When infective larvae free in the soil or in earthworms are swallowed, they enter the gastric epithelium and molt the third time, becoming fourth stage forms. They soon leave the stomach lining, go to the intestine, and enter the hepatic portal vessel. It is thought that they might be carried through the liver, right side of the heart, lungs, left side of the heart, and into the dorsal aorta whence they are scattered throughout the body. Whether larvae going through the hepatic portal vein from the intestine stop en route through the liver and develop or circulate through the heart and lungs and return through the hepatic artery or both is unknown. Larvae entering the skin by-pass the liver in going directly to the heart but may reach the liver through the hepatic artery. Considerable time is spent in this organ where the final molt probably occurs

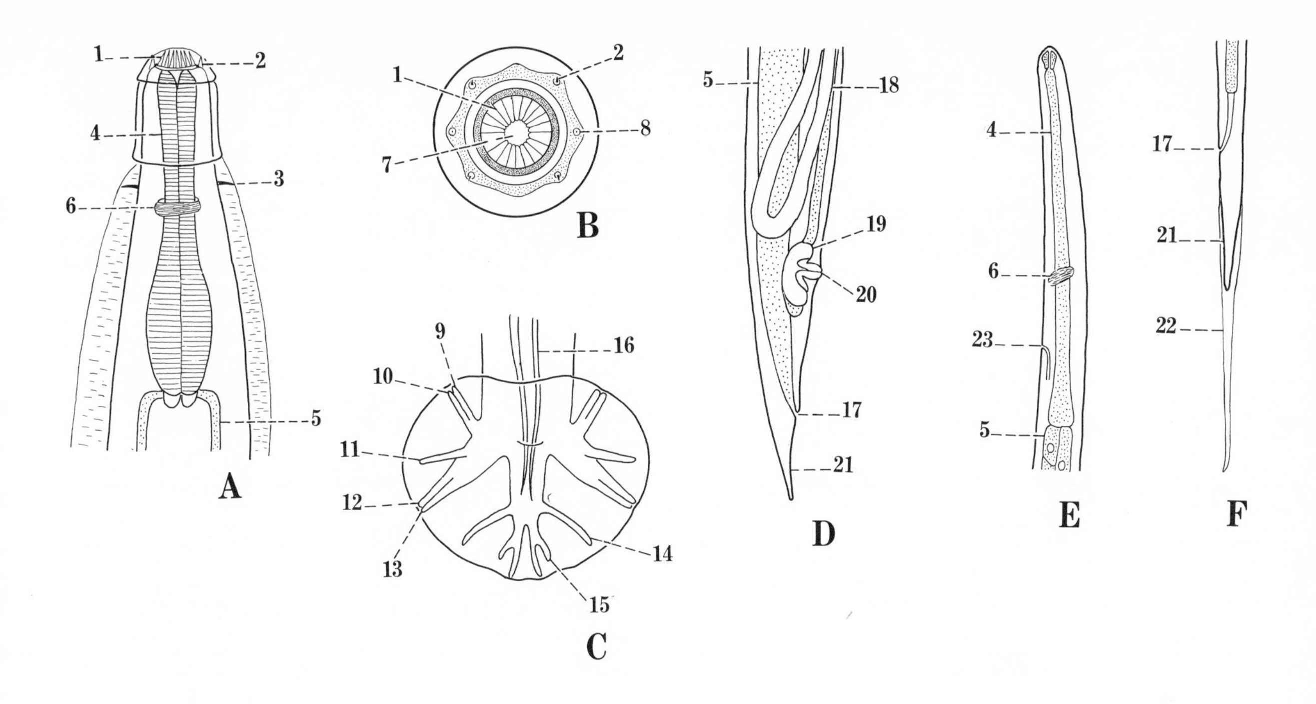
1
2
4
3
6
5
A
1
2
8
7
B
9
16
10
11
12
13
14
15
C
5
18
19
20
17
21
D
4
6
23
5
E
17
21
22
F

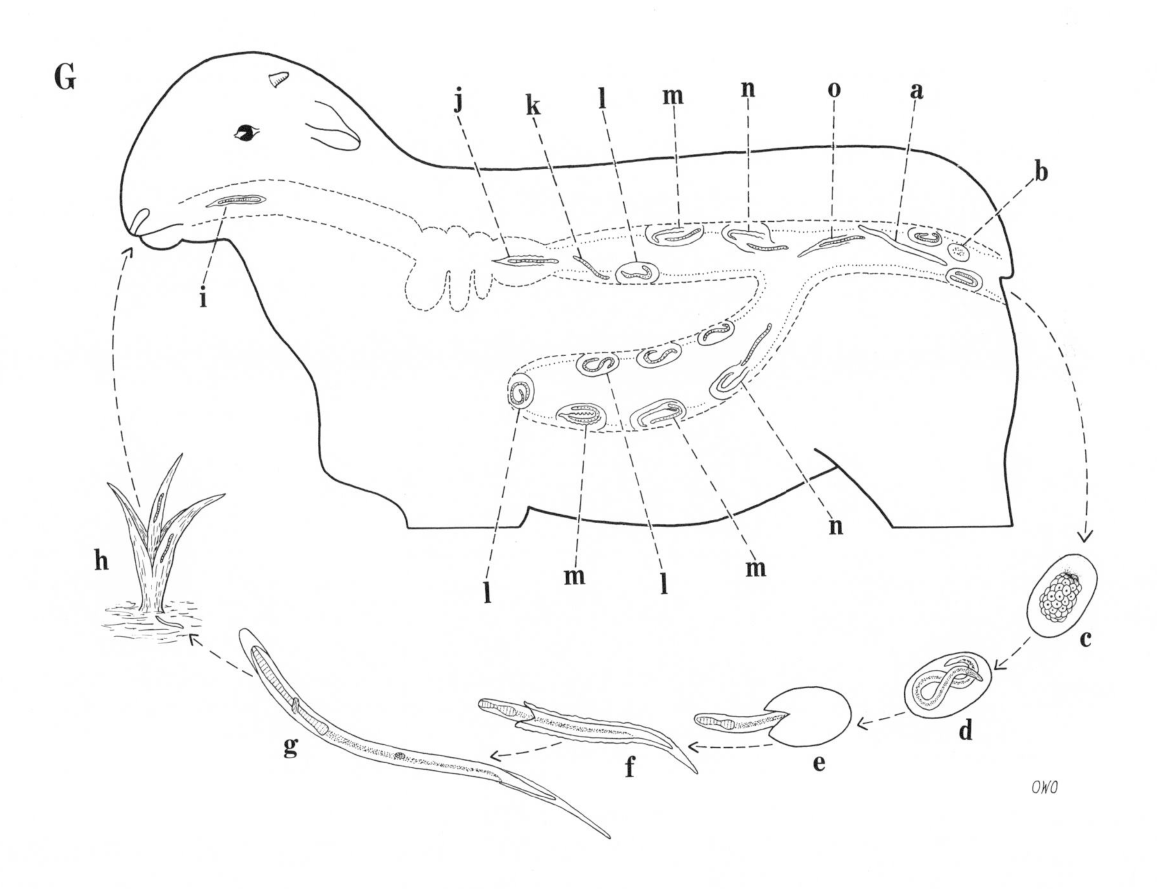
G
j
k
l
m
n
o
a
b
i
l
m
l
m
n
h
c
d
e
f
g
OWO

EXPLANATION OF PLATE 114 ▷

A. Anterior end of adult worm. **B.** Copulatory bursa of male. **C.** Partially embryonated egg. **D.** Anterior end of first stage rhabditiform larva. **E.** Anterior end of second stage rhabditiform larva. **F.** Anterior end of third stage strongyliform larva. **G.** Caudal end of third stage larva enclosed in investing cuticle of second stage larva. **H.** Swine definitive host. **I.** Earthworm (a collector of third stage larvae).

1, buccal capsule; **2,** leaf crown elements; **3,** cuticular thickenings of rim of buccal capsule; **4,** teeth in base of buccal capsule; **5,** pharynx; **6,** intestine; **7,** anus; **8,** tail; **9,** sheath of third stage larva; **10,** nerve ring; **11,** excretory pore; **12,** lateral lobe of bursa; **13,** ventroventral ray; **14,** externoventral ray; **15,** anterolateral ray; **16,** mediolateral ray; **17,** posterolateral ray; **18,** externodorsal ray; **19,** dorsal ray with two bifid branches.

a, adult worm in cyst in pelvis of kidney; **b,** adult worm encysted in wall of ureter; **c,** eggs in urinary bladder, having gone through the ureter; **d,** partially developed egg voided with urine; **e,** embryonated egg; **f,** first stage rhabditiform larvae emerging from egg; **g,** second stage rhabditiform larva shedding cuticle of first stage larva; **h,** third stage infective strongyliform larva enclosed in loose cuticle of second stage larva; **i,** earthworms swallow eggs which hatch, pass through the intestinal wall into the coelom where they develop to infective third stage larvae; **j,** infection of swine by mouth with third stage larvae; **k,** larvae enter mucosa of stomach; **l,** third molt takes place in mucosa; **m,** fourth stage larva leaves mucosa and goes into intestine; **n,** larva enters hepatic portal vein; **o,** larva passes through liver; **p,** larva in right side of heart; **q,** larva in lungs; **r,** larva in left side of heart; **s,** larva in aorta; **t,** larva in hepatic artery; **u,** growth and final molt occurs in liver; **v,** larva migrates from liver into coelom; **w,** larva enters kidneys or ureters from coelom (?) and matures; **x,** larva penetrates skin; **y,** third stage larva molts in blood vessel; **z,** larva goes to right side of heart and follows route to kidneys as described above **(p-w).**

a', some larvae do not find their way to kidneys and ureters but become lost in the hams, loins, and perirenal fat.

Figures A-B from various sources; C-G, adapted from Alicata, 1935, U. S. Dept. Agr. Tech. Bull. 489, p. 73.

---

and much growth takes place. They eventually work their way out of the liver and into the coelom. Such worms presumably migrate through the body cavity. Migrants reaching the kidneys penetrate them and encyst in the wall of the pelvis and ureters. The time required for development from infection to the appearance of eggs in the urine is about 6 months. Third stage larvae may live several months in moist soil protected by shade but die quickly upon exposure to direct sunlight and dryness.

Some larvae appear as "lost" individuals in the pancreas, loins, hams, perirenal fat and spinal cord. Whether these erratic specimens arrive at these points as small larvae by way of the blood stream or as large individuals migrating from the liver is unknown.

EXERCISE ON LIFE CYCLE

Adult females may be obtained from the kidneys and ureters of pigs at abattoirs as a source of eggs for experiments on the life history.

The three stages of free-living larvae may be obtained by incubating eggs in a mixture of animal charcoal and pig faeces or in moist sand and pig faeces. Care must be taken to destroy eggs and nematodes of unwanted species by heating the sand and faeces prior to introducing the eggs of the kidney worms. The different stages of larvae can be procured by baermannizing portions of the medium at appropriate intervals.

Embryonated eggs fed to earthworms hatch and the larvae develop to the infective stage in the annelids. The various stages may be recovered from them.

Guinea pigs are suitable experimental animals. By exposing a series of them to infective larvae by mouth and by the skin, it is possible to follow the intramammalian routes of migration and the major stages of development as they occur in these animals. The liver, lungs, body cavity, and kidneys should be examined at appropriate intervals after exposure to third stage larvae in order to find the different stages.

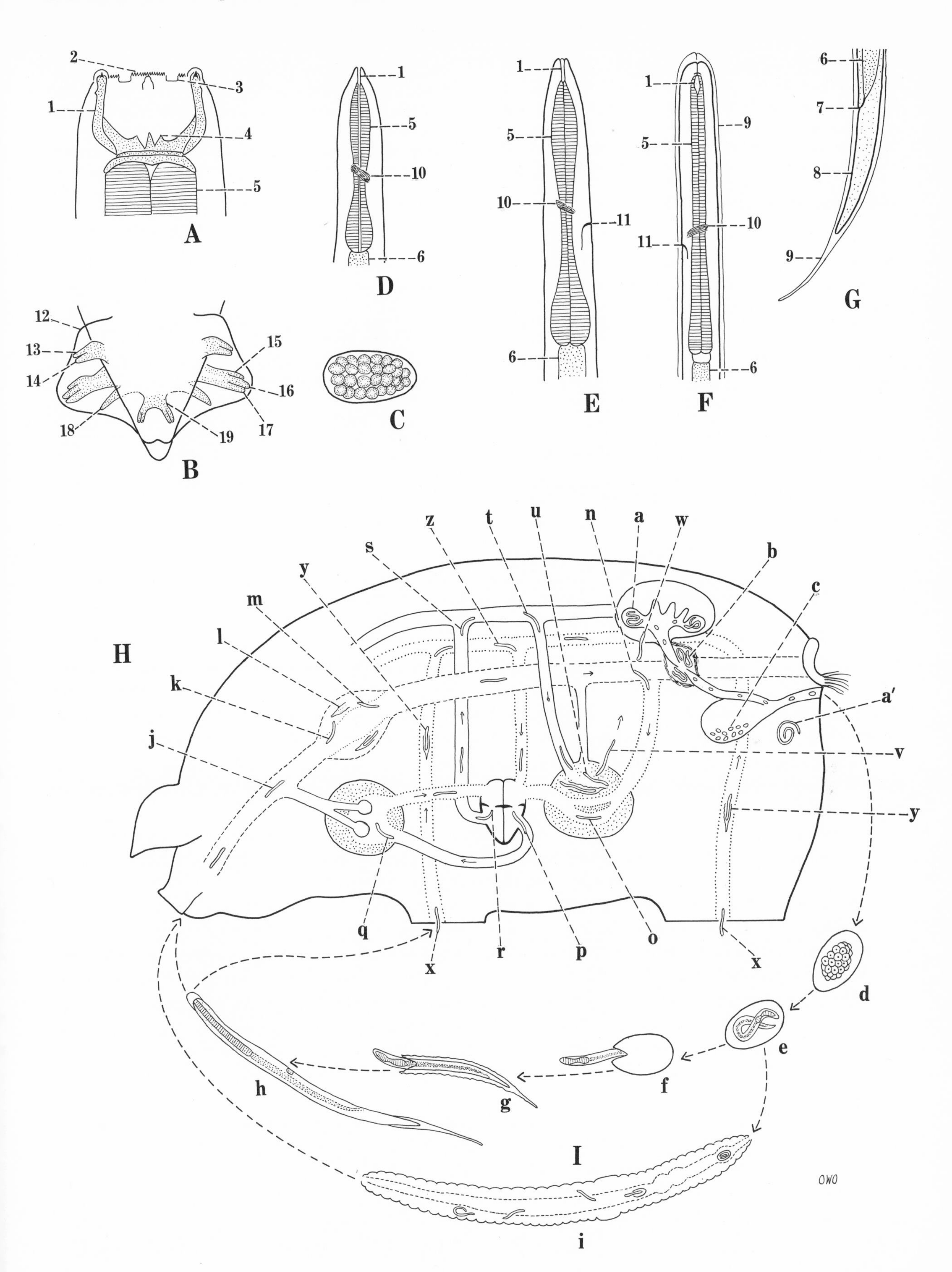
A
B
C
D
E
F
G
H
I
OWO

SELECTED REFERENCES

Alicata, J. E. (1935). U. S. Dept. Agr., Tech. Bull. No. 489, p. 73.

Schwartz, B., and E. W. Price. (1931). J. Amer. Vet. Med. Assoc. 79, N. S. 32:359.

Spindler, L. A. (1934). U. S. Dept. Agr. Tech. Bull. No. 405; (1934). North Amer. Vet. 15:32; (1942). U. S. Dept. Agr. Yrbk., pp. 760, 780.

Spindler, L. A. and J. S. Andrews. (1955). U. S. Livestock Sanit. Assoc. (Nov. 1954) 58th Ann. Meeting, p. 296.

Tromba, F. G. (1955). J. Parasit. 41:157; (1958). Ibid. 44(Suppl.):29.

Genus Strongylus Müller, 1780

Several species of *Strongylus* are common parasites of equines. *Strongylus edentatus, S. equinus,* and *S. vulgaris* of the caecum and colon are the best known. They are referred to variously as large strongyles, red worms, and palisade worms. They are credited with causing untoward effects in horses, particularly *S. vulgaris.*

The mouth is directed anteriorly and surrounded by an external leaf crown. They have a large semiglobular buccal capsule with or without internal toothlike projections and with a thickened longitudinal ridge known as the dorsal gutter. The dorsal ray of the copulatory bursa is double for most of its length and has external projections.

The life cycle of these three species is basically the same for the stages outside the host. They differ inside but there is not general agreement on the details for some of them.

Strongylus edentatus (Looss, 1900) (Plate 115, G)

This is the medium-sized, toothless strongyle. It occurs mainly in the ventral colon and to a lesser extent in the caecum.

DESCRIPTION. The buccal capsule is cone-shaped and devoid of any kind of thickenings resembling teeth. The males measure 23 to 44 mm long by 1.6 to 2.3 mm wide, and the females 33 to 44 mm long by 1.6 to 2.3 mm wide. The vulva is 9 to 10 mm from the caudal end.

LIFE CYCLE. The eggs are in the early stages of cleavage when voided in the faeces. They become fully embryonated and hatch in a day or so under favorable conditions of moisture and temperature. The first stage rhabditiform larvae feed for a short while and then molt, shedding the cuticle and transforming into larger, second stage larvae. When they molt to form the third stage, the cuticle of the second stage merely loosens and forms a protective sheath for the free-moving infective strongyliform larvae on about the fifth day.

The development of the eggs and the larvae to and including the third stage is similar for all of the horse strongyles.

Infection is passive and occurs when third stage larvae ascend blades of grass and are swallowed with the forage by grazing horses, or are otherwise picked up from the ground or stalls. This type of infection is common for all of the species of strongyles of equines.

In the large intestine, the larvae burrow through the intestinal wall to the outer layer of connective tissue where nodules are formed in which they grow for about 3 months. After this time, they return to the intestinal wall and form more nodules in which development is continued. Eventually they leave the nodules, enter the lumen of the large intestine and caecum where maturity is attained in about 11 months. The only migration in this species is in the wall of the large intestine and caecum.

Strongylus equinus Müller, 1780 (Plate 115, H)

This is another of the large strongyles of horses, often called the large-toothed strongyle, occurring primarily in the caecum.

DESCRIPTION. The males measure 26 to 35 mm long by 1.1 to 1.3 mm wide and the females 38 to 47 by 1.8 to 2.2 mm. The buccal capsule is round and has four small toothlike projections at the base; the two ventral ones are somewhat larger and less pointed than the two dorsal ones.

LIFE CYCLE. The infective larvae burrow into the walls of the colon and caecum, shedding the loose cuticle. They continue to the serosa where nodules are formed in which further development takes place. After about 11 days in the nodules, the larvae molt the third time and break through into the coelom, burrow into the liver, and grow there for 6 to 7 weeks. Upon leaving the liver, they go into the coelom and enter the pancreas where the fourth and final molt takes place about 4 months after infection. They are now sexually differentiated but not mature. It is not clear how they get from the pancreas into the colon and caecum, but it is thought that the pancreatic duct might be the route. The migration in this species is much more extensive than in the case of *S. edentatus*.

Strongylus vulgaris (Looss, 1900) (Plate 115, I)

This is the small-toothed strongyle found more commonly in the caecum than in the colon as adults. Fourth stage larvae frequently occur in aneurysms in mesenteric arteries of the colon. It is believed that colic is the result of diminished circulation to the intestine through these damaged mesenteric arteries leading to the colon.

DESCRIPTION. The males are 14 to 16 mm long by 0.75 to 0.95 mm wide and the females 20 to 24 mm by 1 to 1.4 mm. The buccal capsule is goblet-shaped with two large earlike projections inside at the base.

LIFE CYCLE. This species has the most complicated life cycle of the three. There are several opinions as to the nature of the intramammalian development and migrations. Lapage has reviewed the concepts of the different workers. He concluded that probably the larvae follow several routes of migration and therefore each concept of it contains an element of truth. A plausible explanation is the one described and illustrated. Third stage larvae entering the colon or caecum burrow into the venules of the hepatic portal vein and are carried to the lungs by way of the liver and heart. Some of them break out of the blood vessels of the lungs and migrate up the trachea to the pharynx and are swallowed. Development of these is completed in the caecum and colon. Some larvae, on the other hand, fail to escape from the blood vessels in the lungs and are carried back to the heart and into the general circulation. Such larvae reaching the anterior mesenteric artery attach to the intima and grow. Their presence in the artery and the damage done to it cause thrombi and aneurysms. This concept provides a simple, direct explanation of how the larvae may reach the anterior mesenteric artery.

Failure to find migrating larvae in the liver or lungs of experimentally infected animals led some investigators to discredit the concept of tracheal migration and the passage of larvae through the lungs back to the heart and into the general circulation. They believe that the larvae migrate from the lumen of the intestine into the wall whence they burrow into the artery.

The genus *Strongylus* includes the so-called large strongyles. There are, in addition to them, eight genera containing approximately 50 species of lesser size and known collectively as the small strongyles of equines. Little is known of their life cycles except that the free-living phase is similar to that of the large strongyles.

EXERCISE ON LIFE CYCLE

The strongyles of horses provide an abundant supply of eggs for studying the development and hatching of them together with the growth of the first three stages of larvae.

Eggs obtained from the faeces of horses most probably represent a mixture of species. For ease of collecting the eggs, the faeces should be comminuted in water and the coarse material removed by passing the whole mass through a series of graded screens. Further cleaning of the sample can be achieved by sedimenting and decanting until the water is clear, allowing sufficient time for the eggs to settle to the bottom of the container between each decantation.

Eggs may be recovered by placing the cleaned sediment in a cylinder filled with a saturated solution of table salt. After an hour or so, they will have risen to the surface and may be poured into a dish of water and washed free of salt. Incubation may be in a shallow dish with a small amount of water or on a moist filter paper. By examining the material at frequent intervals, the first two stages of rhabditiform larvae may be found.

A method not mentioned heretofore for collecting third stage larvae is by means of two shallow glass dishes of different diameter. In the smaller one, eggs are placed on a moist filter paper or in a mixture of animal charcoal and faeces. It is placed in the second dish which is partially filled with water and

EXPLANATION OF PLATE 115 ⇨

A. Right side of head of *Strongylus edentatus*. **B.** Dorsal view of copulatory bursa of *S. edentatus*. **C.** Right side of head of *S. equinus*. **D.** Dorsal view of bursa of *S. equinus*. **E.** Right side of head of *S. vulgaris*. **F.** Dorsal view of bursa of *S. vulgaris*. **G.** Life cycle of *S. edentatus*. **H.** Life cycle of *S. equinus*. **I.** Life cycle of *S. vulgaris*.

1, external leaf crown; **2**, internal leaf crown; **3**, buccal capsule; **4**, dorsal gutter; **5**, dorsal tooth; **6**, ventral teeth; **7**, oesophagus; **8**, copulatory bursa of male; **9**, dorsal lobe of bursa; **10**, externodorsal ray; **11**, bifurcated dorsal ray.

a, adult worms of *S. edentatus;* **b**, unembryonated eggs passed in faeces; **c**, egg in early stages of cleavage; **d**, fully developed larva; **e**, first stage rhabditiform larva escaping from egg; **f**, first stage larva molting to form second stage rhabditiform larva; **g**, third stage infective filariform or strongyliform larva enclosed in loose, intact cuticle of second stage larva; **h**, infective larvae on grass; **i**, larvae swallowed with forage; **j**, larvae of *S. edentatus* enter intestinal and caecal mucosa where they form nodules and molt; **k**, larvae escape from nodules, enter caecum, and develop to maturity in about 10 to 11 months.

a′, adult worms of *S. equinus* in colon and caecum; **b′**, unembryonated eggs passed in faeces develop in soil similar to *S. edentatus* (c-h); **i′**, infections occur when larvae are swallowed with forage; **j′**, larvae molt enroute through intestine; **k′**, fourth stage larvae penetrate wall of colon; **l′**, nodules formed by larvae on outer surface of intestinal wall; **m′**, larvae break out of nodules into coelom; **n′**, larvae burrow into liver; **o′**, larvae burrow into pancreas; **p′**, larvae emerge from liver or pancreas; **q′**, another molt occurs and larvae enter caecum, presumably by penetration of the wall, or some may go through pancreatic duct.

a″, adult of *S. vulgaris* in colon and caecum; **b″**, unembryonated eggs passed in faeces develop in soil similar to the two species discussed above (c-h); **i″**, infection occurs when infective larvae are swallowed; **j″**, larvae penetrate intestinal wall and enter hepatic portal vein; **k″**, larvae pass through liver; **l″**, larvae pass through right side of heart; **m″**, larvae carried through pulmonary artery; **n″**, larvae leave pulmonary capillaries and enter alveoli of lungs; **o″**, some larvae migrate up trachea; **p″**, upon reaching pharynx, they are swallowed; **q″**, some larvae continue through the lungs in the blood and return via the pulmonary vein to the left side of heart; **r″**, they pass through the aortic arch; **s″**, they enter the dorsal aorta; **t″**, larvae entering mesenteric arteries may lodge in them, causing serious damage that results in aneurysms while those that pass through re-enter the intestine and develop to maturity in the colon.

Original figures.

---

the whole covered to prevent evaporation and to maintain a film of moisture on the side of the dish. The third stage larvae creep up the sides of the small dish and into the water of the second one where they are trapped.

SELECTED REFERENCES

Enigk, K. (1950). Z. Trop. Med. Parasitenk. 1:124; 2:287; (1951). Ibid. 2:523.

Farelly, B. T. (1954). Vet. Rec. 66:53.

Foster, A. O. (1942). U. S. Dept. Agr. Yrbk., p. 463.

Lapage, G. (1957). Veterinary Parasitology. Oliver and Boyd, London, p. 89.

Schwartz, B., M. Imes, and A. O. Foster. (1948). U. S. Dept. Agr. Circ. 148.

Theiler, G. (1923). Thesè, Faculté Sci. Univ. Neuchâtel, 175 pp.

Wetzel, R. (1940). Arch. Wschr. Prakt. Tierheilk. 76:81.

Wetzel, R., and K. Enigk. (1938). Arch. Wschr. Prakt. Tierheilk. 73:83.

Syngamus trachea (Montagu, 1811) (Plate 116)

Syngamus trachea is the gapeworm of poultry, occurring in the trachea of chickens, turkeys, pheasants, and others including some wild birds. It is widespread in many parts of the world. Young chickens and pheasants show symptoms of "gapes" by labored breathing due to the worms occluding the trachea. Turkeys are more resistant than chickens to the worms.

DESCRIPTION. Living adults are red due to the blood in the intestine. Males are 2 to 6 mm long and the females 5 to 20 mm. The male is permanently attached in copula with the female, thus giving a Y-shaped appearance to the pair. The mouth is wide and devoid of leaf crowns; the buccal capsule is thick, cup-shaped, and shallow, with 6 to 10 small teeth in the bottom. The bursa and rays of the male are short; the dorsal ray is split to the base, with each branch thick and tridigitate distally.

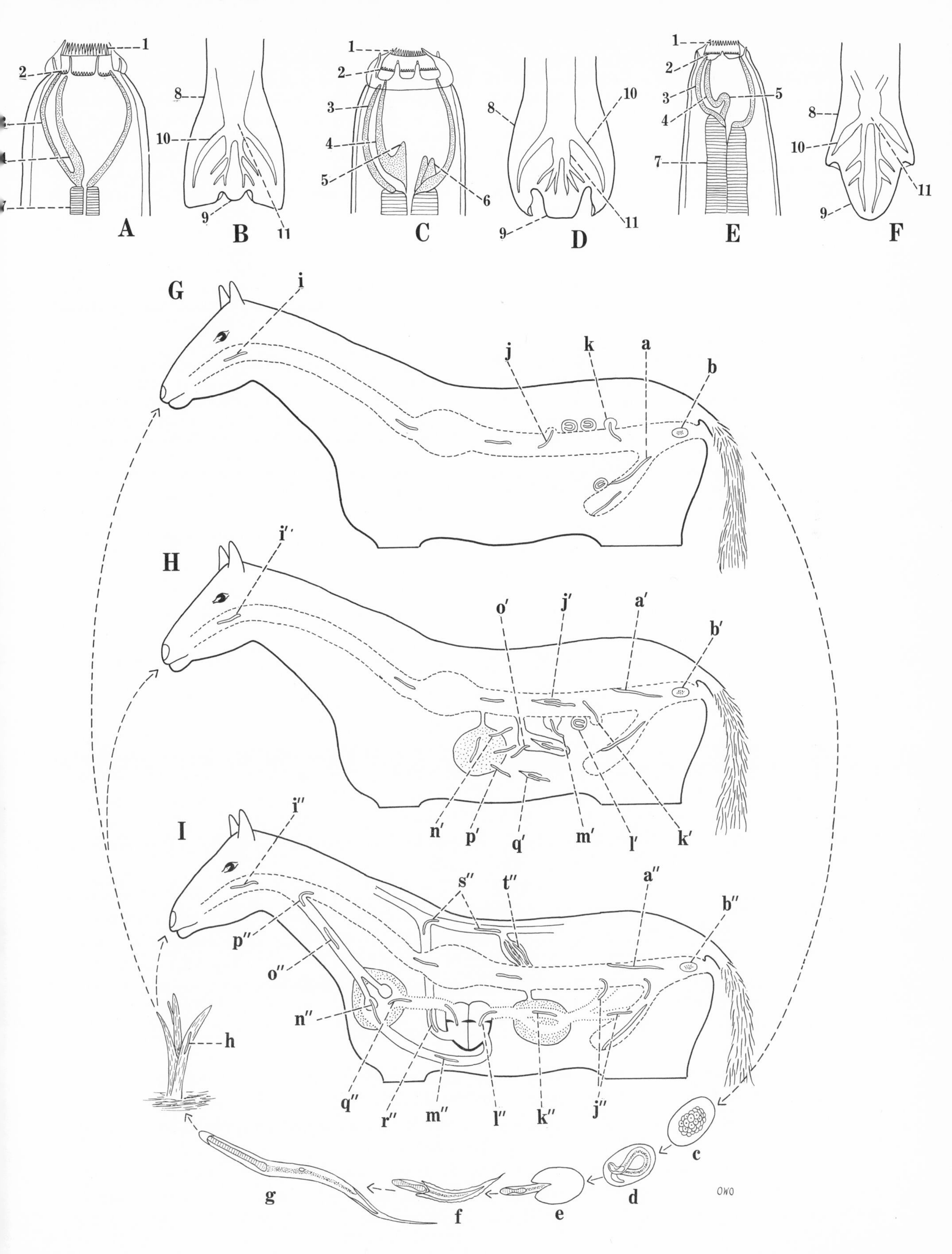
1
2
8
10
9
11
A
B
3
4
5
6
C
D
7
E
F
G
i
j
k
a
b
H
i′
o′
j′
a′
b′
n′
p′
q′
m′
l′
k′
I
i″
s″
t″
a″
b″
p″
o″
n″
h
q″
r″
m″
l″
k″
j″
c
d
e
f
g

EXPLANATION OF PLATE 116

A. Adult male and female worms in copula. **B.** Anterior end of young male. **C.** Copulatory bursa of young male. **D.** Anterior end of adult male. **E.** Bursa of adult male. **F.** Embryonated egg containing third stage larva. **G.** Anterior end of rhabditiform second stage larva. **H.** Third stage filariform or strongyliform infective larva. **I.** Chicken definitive host. **J.** Starling definitive host as a representative of wild birds that serve as hosts. **K-M.** Earthworms **(K)**, house flies **(L)**, and slugs **(M)** serve as transport hosts.

1, adult male attached to female; **2,** gravid adult female; **3,** uterine coils; **4,** buccal capsule; **5,** teeth of buccal capsule; **6,** oesophagus; **7,** anterior end of intestine; **8,** copulatory bursa; **9-10,** ventral rays (**9,** ventroventral; **10,** lateroventral); **11-13,** lateral rays (**11,** externo- or anterolateral; **12,** mediolateral; **13,** posterolateral); **14-15,** dorsal rays (**14,** externodorsal; **15,** dorsal ray with bifurcated branches); **16,** thick shell of egg; **17,** mucoid plug at each end of shell; **18,** third stage infective larva; **19,** cuticle of first molt; **20,** cuticle of second molt, both being retained as sheaths; **21,** rhabditiform type of oesophagus in first and second stage larvae; **22,** filariform or strongyliform oesophagus of infective third stage larva; **23,** oesophageal nuclei; **24,** excretory duct.

a, adult worms attached to the tracheal wall; **b,** unembryonated eggs laid in trachea; **c,** eggs carried up trachea and into pharynx are swallowed; **d,** eggs pass from body in faeces; **e,** undeveloped egg on ground; **f,** developing egg; **g,** egg containing second stage larva with sheath; **h,** fully developed third stage filariform larva encased in two cuticles resulting from previous molts; **i,** egg hatching with release of third stage larva; **j,** infection of chickens takes place when hatched or unhatched third stage larvae are swallowed; **k,** larvae and embryonated eggs pass down digestive tract where the latter hatch; **l,** larvae molt to fourth stage in small intestine; **m,** larvae penetrate intestinal wall and enter hepatic portal vein; **n,** larvae carried by blood through liver to heart; **o,** larvae pass through right side of heart into pulmonary artery; **p,** larvae migrate from blood vessels into alveoli and up trachea; **q,** final (fourth) molt occurs in the trachea; **r,** young worms attach to wall of trachea and grow to maturity; **s,** embryonated eggs are eaten by earthworms, house flies, or slugs which serve as transport hosts; **t,** eggs hatch in intestine; **u,** larvae migrate through intestinal wall; **v,** larvae encyst; **w,** digestion of transport hosts harboring encysted larvae transfers the infection to chickens.

Figure A adapted from Wehr, 1941, U. S. Dept. Agr. Leaflet 207; B, C, F, G, H, from Wehr, 1937, Trans. Amer. Micr. Soc. 56:72; D, from York and Maplestone, 1962, Nematode Parasites of Vertebrates, Hafner Publishing Co., New York, p. 156; E, from Chapin, 1925, J. Agr. Res. 30:557.

The vulva is in the anterior third of the body. The eggs are 78 to 110 μ long by 43 to 46 μ wide, with a thickened mucoid plug at each end.

LIFE CYCLE. The adult worms are attached to the tracheal wall. Eggs in the early stages of cleavage are deposited under the bursa of the male, whence they escape. They are carried up the trachea, swallowed, and voided with the faeces. In the soil where conditions are favorable, development proceeds to the third stage larva within the egg prior to hatching. The first two stages are rhabditiform and the third strongyliform. It is enclosed in the sheaths of the first and second molts. Third stage larvae swallowed by house flies, slugs, or earthworms burrow through the intestinal wall into the body tissues and encyst. Fully embryonated eggs eaten by these animals hatch and the larvae encyst in them. They remain viable and infective for long periods.

Infection of birds takes place when third stage larvae, whether hatched, unhatched, or encysted in invertebrates, are swallowed. In the intestine, they shed the two loose cuticles, molt once, burrow into the venules of the hepatic portal vein, and are carried to the lungs via the liver and heart. Having reached the lungs in about 6 hours after entering the host, they break out of the blood vessels, enter the air sacs and bronchioles. After about 9 days in the lungs, they migrate into the trachea and mature in 17 to 20 days after entering the bird.

Infected wild birds, such as starlings, serve as ambulatory hosts, carrying the infection to poultry yards over a wide area.

Earthworms serve as biological reservoirs where third stage larvae are protected against unfavorable conditions to which exposed eggs and larvae are subjected. They are not intermediate hosts because no development takes place in them. Passage of the larvae through earthworms makes them more infective, which enables strains from wild birds to infect chickens.

Other species of *Syngamus* occur in crows, cormorants, nutcrackers, cattle, deer, and mountain lions. The closely related genus *Cyathostoma* infects swans, geese, gulls, owls, and cassowaries. Their life cycles are unknown.

PLATE 116 *Syngamus trachea*

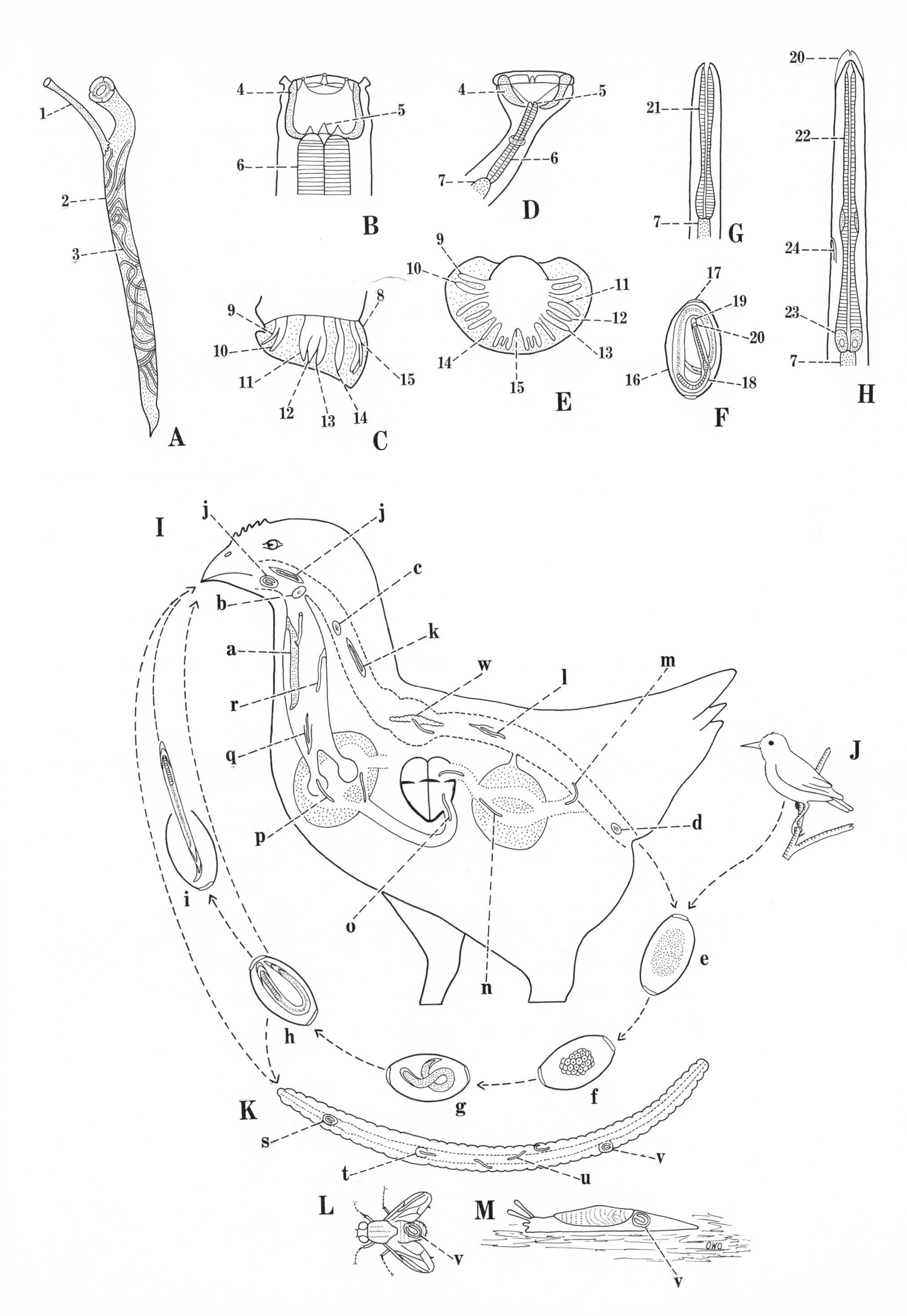

EXERCISE ON LIFE CYCLE

In areas where gapeworms occur, a plentiful supply may be obtained from poultry-dressing plants when farm-raised chickens and turkeys are processed.

The significant thing in a study of the parasite is to see the three stages of larvae develop within the egg before hatching. In this respect, they differ from most other Strongylidae. A similar type of development occurs in *Nematodirus*, a common Trichostrongylidae parasite of sheep, in some Amidostomidae from the gizzards of ducks, and in *Uncinaria*, an Ancylostomatidae, from fur seals.

When embryonated eggs or hatched larvae are fed to house flies, earthworms, or slugs, the larvae may be traced through the intestine and body tissues or cavities to the point of encystment.

Young chicks may be infected by feeding them embryonated eggs, hatched third stage larvae, or infected reservoir hosts such as house flies, slugs, or earthworms. Infect a sufficient number of chicks to be able to sacrifice one each day for the first week to follow the course of migration and rate of development. Hold a few of the infected chicks until eggs of the gapeworms appear in the faeces in order to determine the length of time required for them to reach sexual maturity.

SELECTED REFERENCES

Chapin, E. A. (1925). J. Agr. Res. 30:557.

Clapham, P. A. (1934). Proc. Roy. Soc. Ser. B. 115:18; (1939). J. Helminth. 17:61.

Hall, W. J., and E. E. Wehr. (1953). U. S. Dept. Agr. Farmers' Bull. 1652, p. 64.

Morgan, D. O., and P. A. Clapham. (1934). J. Helminth. 12:63.

Wehr, E. E. (1937). Trans. Amer. Micr. Soc. 56:72; (1939). Proc. World's Poultry Congr., p. 267; (1941). U. S. Dept. Agr. Leaflet 207.

SUPERFAMILY TRICHOSTRONGYLOIDEA

The members of this superfamily are relatively small, threadlike nematodes of the intestine of amphibians, reptiles, birds, and mammals. They are among the commonest and most abundant parasites of sheep, goats, cattle, and wild ruminants. Likewise, they are the most pathogenic notwithstanding the smallness of size.

DESCRIPTION. They are small to minute worms with the buccal capsule very small or absent and with no leaf crowns; male bursa is strongyloid, well developed, and supported by a full complement of rays similar to the Strongyloidea.

FAMILY TRICHOSTRONGYLIDAE

Only a single family is recognized but at least 14 subfamilies have been described. Of the many genera, *Haemonchus*, *Ostertagia*, and *Trichostrongylus* are well known and common representatives in sheep and cattle throughout the temperate and tropical regions of the world.

The external phase of the life cycle of the species of these three genera is similar to that of strongyles of horses. Infection of the host is passive, i.e., by swallowing the infective third stage larvae with forage.

Haemonchus contortus (Rudolphi, 1830) (Plate 117, A–D)

These are the so-called twisted or barber-pole stomach worms of the abomasum of sheep chiefly but commonly of goats and cattle, as well as many wild ruminants. They are more prevalent in warm, moist regions than in cold, dry ones. They are among the most pathogenic nematode parasites of sheep, being voracious blood suckers.

DESCRIPTION. The males are 10 to 20 mm and the females 18 to 30 mm long. The white uteri and ovaries winding around the red blood-filled intestine give a twisted or barber-pole appearance. The small buccal capsule bears a curved dorsal tooth. There are two prominent lateral spikelike cervical papillae near the junction of the first and second quarters of the oesophagus. The male bursa has long lateral lobes and slender rays with a flaplike dorsal lobe located asymmetrically near the base of the left lateral lobe. The spicules are 450 to 500 μ long, each with a terminal barb; the gubernaculum is navicular. Usually, the vulva is covered by an anterior thumblike flap which may be reduced to a mere knob in some individuals. The oval eggs are 70 to 85 μ long by 41 to 44 μ wide and in the early stages of cleavage when laid. They are somewhat yellowish.

LIFE CYCLE. Eggs passed in the faeces complete their development in moist situations. The first stage rhabditiform larvae hatch, feed, and molt, forming second stage rhabditiform individuals. After a short period of feeding they molt, forming third stage strongyliform larvae that are enclosed in the cuticle of the second stage larva. The loose-fitting sheath protects these infective larvae against desiccation. They are active climbers, ascending blades of grass during the dim light of mornings and evenings, and on overcast days. Infection of the sheep occurs when the larvae are ingested with forage.

While the third stage larvae are passing through the fore stomachs, the cuticle enclosing them is lost. Upon reaching the abomasum, they undertake a minor migration in the mucosa for a short period. Twelve hours after being swallowed the larvae appear on the surface of the mucosa. Migration into it begins, and by the end of the first day nearly all of them are in the mucosa, mostly at the level of the gastric pits. The third molt takes place in the tissue, following which the fourth stage larvae return to the surface of the mucosa where nearly all of them are located by 40 hours after entering the host. Very few remain embedded in the tissue at this time. The final molt occurs and the worms develop to sexual maturity in about 14 days following entrance into the host (Plate 117, a-o). Veglia believed there was no mucosal migration but merely attachment and feeding followed by the fourth molt and development to maturity.

Since the worms appear not to feed on blood while in the tissue, the migration may be a requirement for molting under conditions of lowered oxygen tension in the lumen of the abomasum.

If the host animals survive the infection, there is a gradual loss of the parasites as the sheep acquire an immunity and undergo a "self cure." Being blood suckers, the parasites cause a severe anemia due to their feeding and from bleeding from the wounds made by them. The degree of anemia depends upon the number of parasites present.

SELECTED REFERENCES

Andrews, J. S. (1942). J. Agr. Res. 65:1.

Dikmans, G., and J. S. Andrews. (1933). Trans. Amer. Micr. Soc. 52:1.

Dinaburg, A. G. (1944). J. Agr. Res. 69:421.

Lapage, G. (1956). Veterinary Parasitology. Oliver and Boyd, London, p. 49.

Morgan, B. B., and P. A. Hawkins. (1949). Veterinary Helminthology. Burgess Publishing Co., Minneapolis, p. 138.

Ransom, B. H. (1911). U. S. Dept. Agr., Bur. Anim. Ind. Bull. 127, p. 50.

Shorb, D. A. (1944). J. Agr. Res. 68:317; (1944). Ibid. 69:279.

Stoll, N. R. (1943). J. Parasit. 29:407.

Veglia, F. (1915). 3rd and 4th Rep. Direct. Vet. Res. Dept. Agr., Union South Africa, p. 347.

Ostertagia circumcincta (Stadelmann, 1894) (Plate 117, E–H)

The species of *Ostertagia* are parasites of the abomasum of sheep, goats, cattle, and other ruminants. Because of their color, they are known collectively as the brown stomach worm. They are smaller than the twisted stomach worm and different in structure. While *Ostertagia* is widespread, it tends to reach into the colder climates beyond the optimal range of *Haemonchus*. *O. circumcincta* is one of the most common members of the genus occurring in sheep.

DESCRIPTION. The males measure 7.5 to 8.5 mm and the females 9.8 to 12.2 mm long. The buccal capsule is rudimentary. Cervical papillae are located toward the posterior end of the oesophagus. Spicules are slender; the distal end is bifurcated, with the branches parallel and subequal; the longer outer one has a knob and the shorter one is acute. The vulva is usually in the posterior fifth of the body and generally covered by a flap. Several thickened cuticular rings occur near the tip of the tail of the female. Eggs are 80 to 100 μ by 40 to 50 μ in size.

LIFE CYCLE. The life cycle is similar to that of *Haemonchus contortus*. Sexual maturity is attained in about 17 days. The cycle is presented in Plate 117, a′, b–j, k′–q′.

EXPLANATION OF PLATE 117

A-D. *Haemonchus contortus.* **A.** Anterior end of adult. **B.** Anterior extremity of adult showing small buccal capsule and dorsal tooth. **C.** Copulatory bursa. **D.** Caudal end of female showing vulvular flap. **E-H.** *Ostertagia circumcincta.* **E.** Anterior end of adult. **F.** Copulatory bursa of male. **G.** Tail of adult female. **H.** Caudal end of female showing vulvular flap. **I-M.** *Trichostrongylus colubriformis.* **I.** Anterior end of adult. **J.** Copulatory bursa. **K.** Spicule. **L.** Gubernaculum. **M.** Caudal end of female. **N.** Sheep definitive host.

1, circumoral papillae; **2**, cervical papillae; **3**, buccal capsule; **4**, buccal spine; **5**, oesophagus; **6**, intestine; **7**, anus; **8**, tail; **9**, lateral lobe of copulatory bursa; **10**, dorsal lobe of bursa; **11**, ventrolateral ray; **12**, lateroventral ray; **13**, antero- or externolateral ray; **14**, mediolateral ray; **15**, posterolateral ray; **16**, externodorsal ray; **17**, dorsal ray; **18**, spicule; **19**, gubernaculum; **20**, vulvular flap; **21**, vulva; **22**, ovejector; **23**, uterus; **24**, egg in uterus; **25**, ovary.

Haemonchus contortus. **a**, adult worms attached to abomasal mucosa; **b**, eggs passed in faeces; **c**, egg in early stage of cleavage; **d**, embryonated egg; **e**, hatching of egg; **f**, first stage rhabditiform larva; **g**, molting and appearance of second stage rhabditiform larva; **h**, ensheathed third stage infective, filariform larva; **i**, infection of sheep takes place when third stage larvae are swallowed; **j**, third stage larva shedding loose cuticular sheath; **k**, third stage larva penetrating abomasal mucosa; **l**, larva in mucosa; **m**, larva molts; **n**, fourth stage larva in mucosa; **o**, fourth stage larva emerges from mucosa, molts to young adult stage, and develops to maturity in abomasum.

Ostertagia circumcincta. **a'**, adults attached to abomasal mucosa where females lay eggs; **b-j**, life cycle outside of host is similar to that of *Haemonchus contortus;* **k'**, larvae penetrate abomasal mucosa; **l'**, larvae molt third time to form fourth stage larvae; **m'**, larvae grow; **n'**, larvae escape from mucosa into abomasum but remain in contact with epithelium; **o'**, larvae undergo fourth and final molt; **p'**, **q'**, larvae grow to sexual maturity.

Trichostrongylus colubriformis. **a"**, adult worms attached to mucosa of small intestine; **b-j**, similar to *Haemonchus contortus;* **k"**, larvae pass through four stomachs and enter intestine, burrowing into the mucosa; **l"**, larvae molt third time to form fourth stage in mucosa; **m"**, larvae leave mucosa; **n"**, larvae in lumen and in contact with epithelium; **o"**, fourth and final molt producing last stage; **p"**, young nematodes grow into adults.

Figures adapted from Ransom, 1911, U. S. Dept. Agr., Bur. Anim. Ind. Bull. 127.

Other common species are *Ostertagia ostertagi* primarily of cattle but also in sheep, and *O. trifurcata* of sheep and goats. Both of them are parasites of the abomasum.

SELECTED REFERENCES

Furman, D. P. (1944). Amer. J. Vet. Res. 5:79.

Groceclose, N. P. (1935). Unpublished. (See Threlkeld, W. L. (1958). Some Nematode Parasites of Domestic Animals. Economy Printing Co., Roanoke, Va., p. 91.

Morgan, B. B., and P. A. Hawkins. (1949). Veterinary Helminthology. Burgess Publishing Co., Minneapolis, p. 143.

Sommerville, R. I. (1954). Aust. J. Agr. Res. 5:130.

Threlkeld, W. L. (1934). Va. Agr. Exp. Sta. Tech. Bull. 52.

Threlkeld, W. L., and M. E. Henderson. (1936). J. Parasit. 22:187.

Trichostrongylus colubriformis (Giles, 1892) (Plate 117, I–M)

The trichostrongyles as a group are the smallest members of the family, being tiny hairlike nematodes. They are parasites of the small intestine of sheep, goats, cattle and other ruminants, together with rodents and birds. One species, *Trichostrongylus axei,* occurs in the abomasum of ruminants, in the stomach of horses, pigs, and sometimes in humans. The species of the genus have a wide geographic distribution. *T. colubriformis* is a common parasite of sheep and its life cycle is well known. It serves as representative of the genus.

DESCRIPTION. Males are 4.5 to 5 mm and the females 5 to 7 mm long. The buccal capsule is absent. There are no cervical papillae, and a vulvular flap is lacking. Spicules are stout, consisting of a single piece with a distal enlargement; the length is 0.135 to 0.156 mm; the gubernaculum is arcuate. Eggs are 75 to 85 μ long by 34 to 35 μ wide.

LIFE CYCLE. Being inhabitants of the small intestine, the third stage larvae pass through the abomasum without any development. In the small intestine, they penetrate the mucosa, undergo the

PLATE 117 *Haemonchus contortus, Ostertagia circumcincta, Trichostrongylus colubriformis*

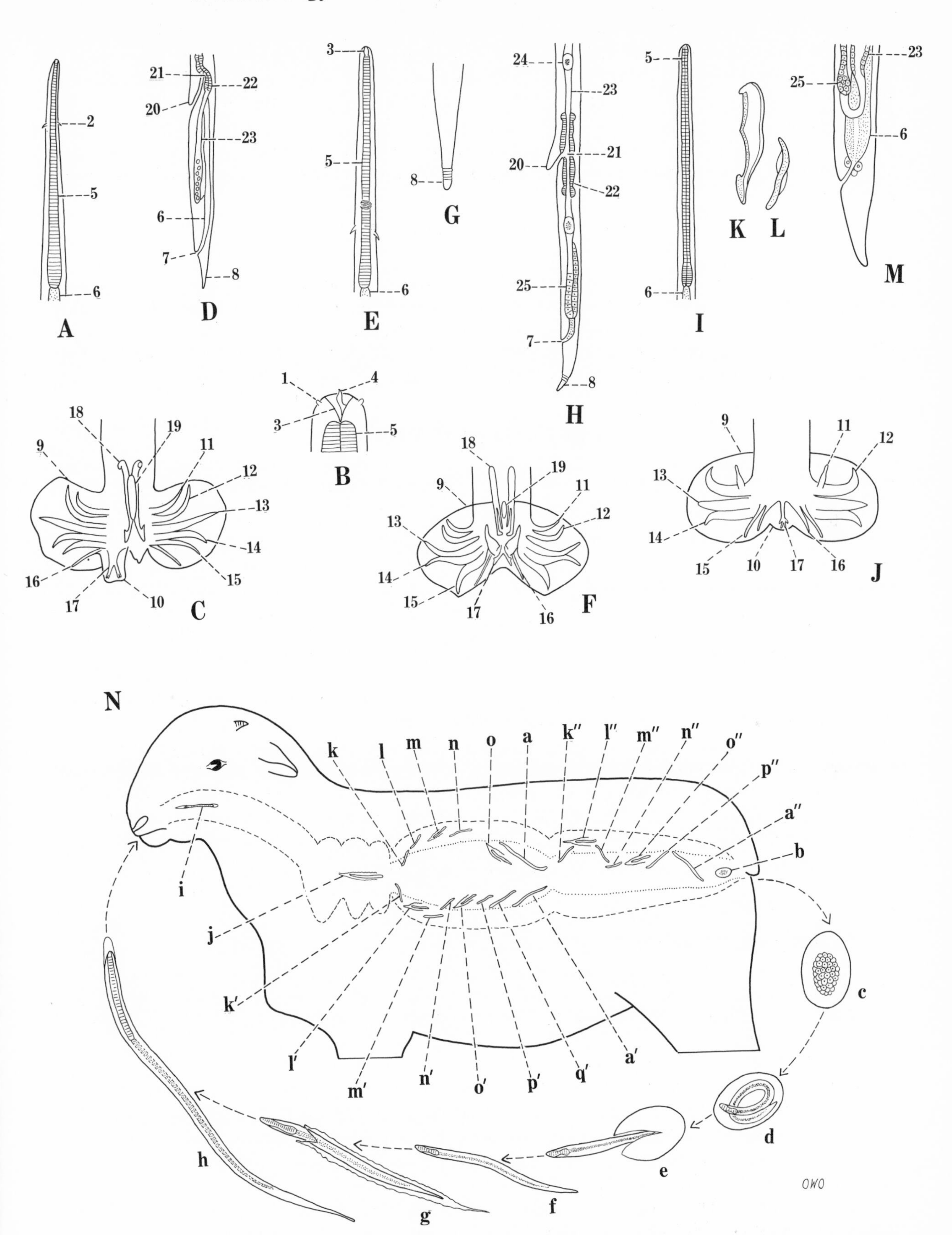

third molt, becoming fourth stage larvae, and remain there a short time. They return to the lumen of the intestine and molt for the last time. Sexual maturity is reached in about 17 days after entering the host. The cycle is represented in Plate 117 by a″, b–j, k″–p.″

Other common species of the genus are *T. falcatus, T. vitrinus, T. capricola, T. rugatus* of ruminants; *T. tenuis* of chickens and turkeys; and *T. calcaratus, T. ransomi,* and *T. affinis* of rabbits. Their life cycles are similar to that described for *T. colubriformis.*

Differences in the three life cycles are slight. *Haemonchus* and *Ostertagia* are similar in having a migration in the abomasal mucosa. *Trichostrongylus* differs in having the tissue migration in the intestinal mucosa.

EXERCISE ON LIFE CYCLE

Nippostrongylus brasiliensis, a common trichostrongyle nematode of rats and mice, is an excellent species for experimental studies on the developmental stages of larvae, mode of infection, and migration inside the host. The species infecting sheep are excellent for study of the larvae in their various stages. Infection of small mammals such as rats and mice with them should be undertaken. Species occurring in rabbits provide good material for study. Follow instructions outlined for *Strongylus.*

SELECTED REFERENCES

Andrews, J. S. (1939). J. Agr. Res. 58:761.

Mönnig, H. O. (1926). 11th and 12th Rept. Diret. Vet. Educ. Res., Dept. Agr., Union South Africa, p. 231.

Morgan, B. B. and P. A. Hawkins. (1949). Veterinary Helminthology. Burgess Publishing Co., Minneapolis, p. 134.

Seghetti, L. (1948). Amer. J. Vet. Res. 9:52.

SUPERFAMILY METASTRONGYLOIDEA

The Metastrongyloidea are lungworms of land and marine mammals. The four genera considered represent the basic types of life cycles known for over a dozen species. The life cycle of species of *Dictyocaulus* is direct, whereas those of all of the others are indirect. Species of *Metastrongylus* and *Choerostrongylus* of swine utilize earthworms as intermediate hosts, and the remaining genera, insofar as known, develop in slugs and land snails. Some species utilize collector or storage (paratenic) hosts such as water snakes for *Crenosoma mephitidis* of skunks, and mice for *Aelurostrongylus abstrusus* of cats. The paratenic hosts acquire the parasites by swallowing infected snails or slugs. The larvae migrate to the tissues where they accumulate without further development. The definitive hosts become infected upon eating the paratenic hosts. None of the life cycles of the lungworms of marine mammals is known.

DESCRIPTION. Strongyloid nematodes with small, rudimentary, or no buccal capsule. The copulatory bursa is usually asymmetrical, except in *Dictyocaulus.*

FAMILY METASTRONGYLIDAE

Only one family is recognized.

Dictyocaulus filaria (Rudolphi, 1809) (Plate 118, A–D)

This is the common thread lungworm of sheep and goats in all parts of the world. The adults occur in the bronchi.

DESCRIPTION. These are white threadlike worms. Males are 30 to 80 mm long. The bursa is short, symmetrical, with the medio- and posterolateral rays fused except at the tip, and the dorsal ray is split from the base to the tip. The spicules are reticulated, dark brown, boot-shaped structures 500 μ long. Females are 50 to 100 mm long, have a pointed tail, and the vulva is near the middle of the body. The uterus has an anterior and a posterior branch. First stage larvae passed in the faeces are characterized by a small knob on the anterior end of the body.

LIFE CYCLE. The adults lay fully embryonated eggs which hatch en route up the trachea and through the intestine. The first stage larvae appear in the faeces. They molt twice, retaining both cuticles, to form third stage infective larvae. Infection of the sheep occurs when these larvae are swallowed with contaminated food, water, and soil.

In the stomach or intestine, the cuticles are shed and the third molt occurs, producing the fourth stage larvae. They penetrate the lacteals of the small intestine and are carried through the lymph nodes and vessels to the blood stream, through the right side of the heart, and into lungs. In the lungs, the larvae enter the alveoli, migrate to the bronchi, and develop to maturity.

Dictyocaulus viviparus of cattle and *D. arnfieldi* of horses have similar life cycles.

Dictyocaulus shows morphological and biological affinities to the Trichostrongylidae and is considered by some authors as belonging to that family rather than to the Metastrongylidae.

SELECTED REFERENCES

Kauzal, G. (1933). Aust. Vet. J. 9:20.

Shaw, J. N. (1934). Oreg. Agr. Exp. Sta. Bull. 327, p. 5 (technique).

Soliman, K. N. (1953). J. Comp. Path. Ther. 63:75.

Protostrongylus rufescens (Leuckart, 1865) (Plate 118, E–G)

This is the brown lungworm of sheep, goats, and deer of North America, Europe, Africa, Australia, and possibly other areas of the world. The adults are in the bronchioles.

DESCRIPTION. The adults are thread-like brown worms. The males are 16 to 28 mm long, and have a short bursa that is strengthened dorsally by a cuticularized bar; the dorsal ray of the bursa is thick, the tubular spicules are 260 μ long, and a gubernaculum and telamon are present. Females are 25 to 35 mm long, with the vulva near the anus. First stage larvae have a characteristic undulating, pointed tail.

LIFE CYCLE. Eggs laid in the lungs hatch en route through the trachea and intestine and the characteristic first stage larvae are passed in the faeces. Development of the larvae to the third stage takes place in land snails of the genus *Helicella,* snails with flat, coiled shells. Larvae enter the snails either by being swallowed or by penetrating them. Two molts occur to form third stage larvae which retain both cuticles. Infection takes place when the definitive hosts swallow infected snails. Upon being released from the snails in the stomach or intestine, the larvae migrate to the lungs via the lymphatics as does *Dictyocaulus.*

SELECTED REFERENCES

Mapes, C. R., and D. W. Baker. (1950). J. Amer. Vet. Med. Assoc. 116:433.

Muellerius capillaris (Müller, 1889) (Plate 118, H–J)

These worms, known as the hair lungworms, live in the parenchyma of the lungs of sheep and goats in the United States, Europe, Australia, South Africa, and possibly other parts of the world.

DESCRIPTION. These are delicate, white, hairlike worms. The males are 12 to 14 mm long with the pointed, nonbursate posterior end spirally coiled. The spicules are 150 μ long, curved, and with sharp points. The females are 19 to 23 mm long. The vulva has a small swelling at the posterior margin and is located near the anus. First stage larvae with a distinct spinelike process on the dorsal side of the tail and are passed in the faeces.

LIFE CYCLE. The parasites live in grayish nodules in the parenchyma of the lungs. Eggs laid in them hatch there and the larvae migrate up the trachea to the pharynx, are swallowed, and passed in the faeces. Development to the third stage continues when the larvae enter land snails of the genera *Helix* and *Succinea,* both having shells with spires, or in slugs belonging to the genera *Arion, Limax,* and *Agriolimax.* Russian workers claim development takes place in fresh-water snails as well as land forms, with natural infections being as high as 0.3 per cent. Like the preceding species, the larvae molt twice to become third stage individuals which retain both cuticles. Infection of the sheep occurs when infected

EXPLANATION OF PLATE 118 ⇨

A-D. *Dictyocaulus filaria.* **A.** Anterior end of adult. **B.** Sinistral view of copulatory bursa of male. **C.** Anterior end of first stage larva. **D.** Caudal end of first stage larva. **E-G.** *Protostrongylus rufescens.* **E.** Ventral view of copulatory bursa. **F.** Anterior end of first stage larva. **G.** Caudal end of first stage larva. **H-J.** *Muellerius capillaris.* **H.** Sinistral view of caudal end of male. **I.** Anterior end of first stage larva. **J.** Caudal end of first stage larva. **K.** Sheep definitive host. **L.** Snail intermediate host of *Protostrongylus rufescens.* **M.** Snail intermediate host of *Muellerius capillaris.*

1, cephalic knob; **2,** oesophagus; **3,** intestine; **4,** anus; **5,** tail; **6,** nerve ring; **7,** copulatory bursa; **8,** ventroventral ray; **9,** lateroventral ray; **10,** antero- or externolateral ray; **11,** mediolateral ray; **12,** posterolateral ray; **13,** externodorsal ray; **14,** dorsal ray; **15,** spicules; **16,** gubernaculum; **17,** cuticularized bar.

a, adult worm of all three species (*Dictyocaulus* and *Protostrongylus* in bronchioles and bronchi, and *Muellerius* in nodules in lung parenchyma); **b,** eggs; **c,** eggs hatching; **d,** larvae pass to outside in faeces. *Dictyocaulus:* **e,** first stage larvae with characteristic cephalic knob; **f,** second stage larvae with retained cuticle; **g,** third stage larvae with two retained cuticles; **h,** third stage larvae when swallowed infect sheep; **i,** larvae molt to form fourth stage; **j,** larvae enter intestine; **k,** larvae penetrate intestinal wall, enter lacteals; **l,** larvae undergo final molt in lymph nodes; **m,** larvae enter lymph vessels and go to heart; **n,** larvae pass through right side of heart and go to lungs; **o,** larvae migrate from blood vessels of lungs into alveoli, bronchioles, and bronchi; **p,** some larvae go through blood vessels of lungs, pulmonary vein, and left side of heart; **q,** larvae enter dorsal aorta, are carried through general circulation; **r,** in case of pregnant ewes, some larvae enter uterine artery and foetal circulation, producing prenatal infection of lambs.

Muellerius. **a′,** first stage larvae free in faeces and soil; **b′,** larvae penetrate land snails or slugs; **c′,** second stage larvae; **d′,** third stage larvae; **e′,** infection of definitive host by swallowing infected mollusks; migration in host same as in *Dictyocaulus.*

Protostrongylus. **a″,** first stage larvae; **b″,** larvae enter molluscan host; **c″,** second stage larvae; **d″,** third stage larvae; **e′,** infection of host and further development similar to that in *Muellerius.*

Figures adapted from various sources.

---

mollusks containing third stage larvae are swallowed with the forage. Larvae released by digestion of the snails go to the intestine, migrate to the lungs via the same route as *Dictyocaulus* and *Protostrongylus,* and mature.

SELECTED REFERENCES

Egorov, Y. G. (1960). Trudi Nauchno-Issledovatelskogo Vet. Inst. Minsk. 1:160 (Helm. Abst. 31:319. 1962).

Hobmaier, A., and M. Hobmaier. (1930). München Tierärztl. Wschr. 81:285.

Rose, J. H. (1957). J. Helminth. 31:17.

Williams, D. W. (1942). J. Animal Ecol. 11:1.

EXERCISE ON LIFE CYCLE

Life history studies on the lungworms of sheep may be conducted in the laboratory. Examine faeces of sheep for larvae by placing freshly passed pellets in a Baermann funnel for not longer than 3 hours. It is important that the faeces be fresh and uncontaminated with soil. In faeces allowed to stand longer than 3 hours, eggs of intestinal nematodes hatch and those coming in contact with soil may show free-living soil nematodes. Larvae of the three species of lungworms can be identified by the morphological characters described above.

Interesting experiments may be performed to demonstrate the life cycle of *Dictyocaulus filaria.* Having obtained first stage larvae from the faeces, keep them in water long enough to develop to the infective third stage characterized by the two loose cuticles.

Third stage larvae fed to mice undertake the characteristic migration through the lymphatics, arriving in the lungs in about 5 days. By killing infected mice at intervals of 24 hours over a period of 5 to 6 days, the course of migration through the lymphatics may be followed. Ascertain whether some larvae migrate by the way of the hepatic portal vessel and liver.

When larvae of *Protostrongylus* or *Muellerius* are procurable in the faeces of sheep, experiments using land snails and white mice may be conducted to follow the details of their life cycles. Snails

PLATE 118 *Dictyocaulus filaria, Protostrongylus rufescens, Muellerius capillaria*

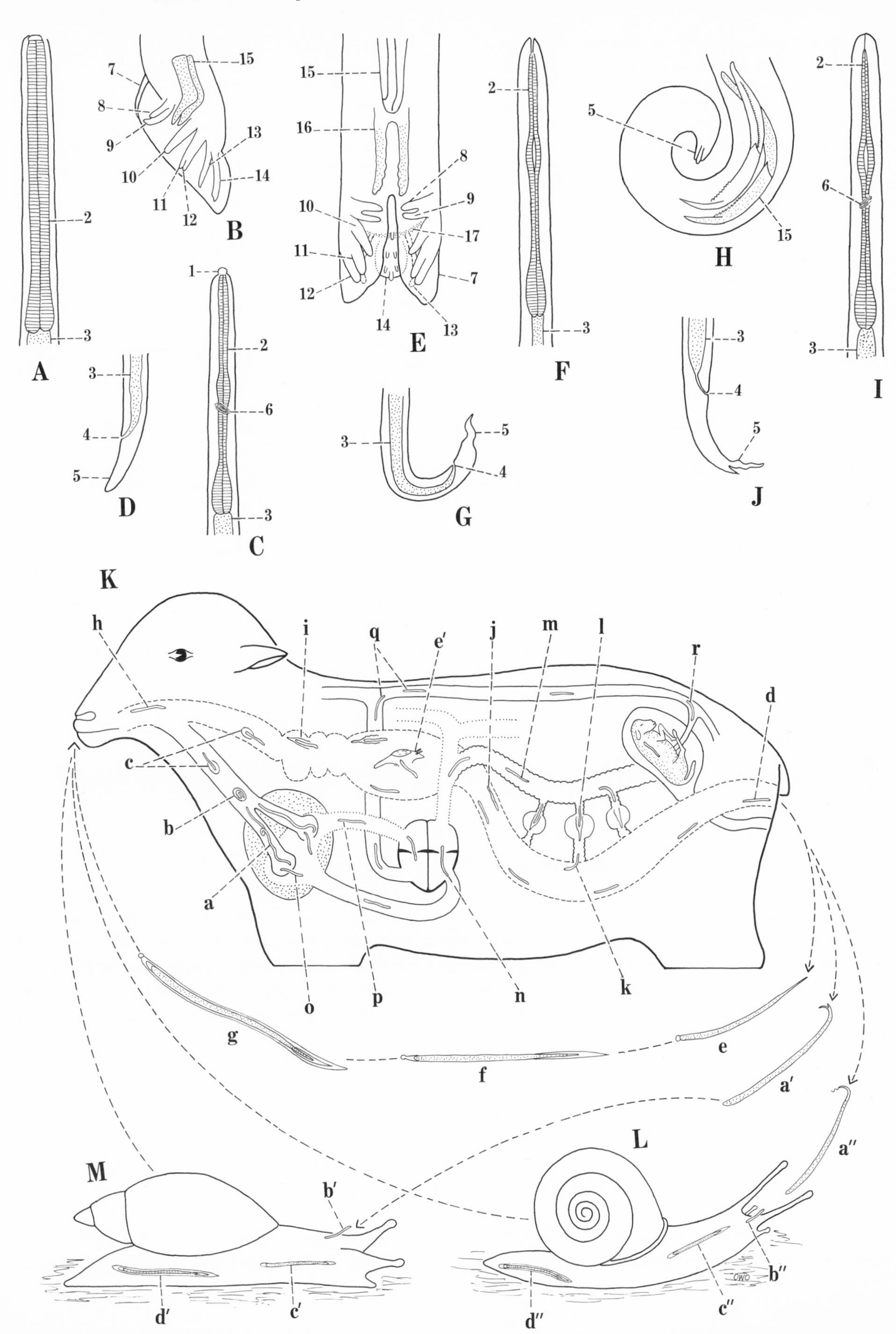

EXPLANATION OF PLATE 119 ⇨

A-H. *Metastrongylus apri.* **A.** Anterior end of adult. **B.** Lateral view of posterior end of mature male. **C.** Dorsal view of caudal end of male. **D.** Tip of spicule. **E.** Lateral view of posterior end of adult female. **F.** Embryonated egg. **G.** Caudal end of newly hatched first stage larva. **H.** Caudal end of third stage larva. **I-J.** *Choerostrongylus pudentotectus.* **I.** Dorsal view of caudal end of adult male. **J.** Tip of spicule. **K.** *Metastrongylus salmi.* Dorsal view of bursa. **L.** Pig host. **M.** Earthworm intermediate host.

1, mouth; **2**, copulatory bursa; **3**, dorsal ray; **4**, externodorsal ray; **5**, anterolateral ray; **6**, mediolateral ray; **7**, posterolateral ray; **8**, externoventral ray; **9**, ventroventral ray; **10**, spicules; **11**, tip of spicule with barb; **12**, tail; **13**, intestine; **14**, vagina uterina with embryonated eggs; **15**, vulva.

a, adult worms in air tubes of lungs; **b**, embryonated eggs pass up trachea and are swallowed; **c**, embryonated eggs pass out of body in faeces; **d**, embryonated eggs free in soil or faeces; **e**, eggs swallowed by earthworms; **f**, eggs hatch in pharynx and oesophagus; **g**, larvae migrate into wall of alimentary canal; **h**, second molt in intestine; **i**, larvae enter hearts; **j**, third stage larvae in wall of oesophagus; **k**, swine become infected by swallowing earthworms; **l**, larvae released from annelid intermediary in stomach; **m**, larvae enter intestine; **n**, larvae penetrate intestinal wall and enter lacteals; **o**, larvae enter lymph nodes and molt; **p**, larvae enter lymph vessels; **q**, larvae pass through the right side of heart; **r**, larvae carried in blood to capillaries of lungs; **s**, larvae leave capillaries and enter alveoli, maturing as early as 24 days after being swallowed.

Figures A-E, I-K, adapted from Gedoelst, 1922, Bull. Soc. Path. Exot. 16:622; F-H, from Alicata, 1935, U. S. Dept. Agr. Tech. Bull. 489, p. 37.

---

known to serve as intermediate hosts collected from pastures should be examined for larvae either by crushing or digesting them. It is important to keep in mind that protostrongyline lungworms of rabbits and hares may be present and that they also infect mollusks. Snails collected from areas where sheep and lagomorphs do not occur should be uninfected. However, the preferred procedure is to rear them in laboratory terrariums.

Infect parasite-free snails with first stage larvae and examine them over a period of 4 to 6 weeks in order to follow the development of the larvae. When infective third stage larvae appear, mice may be infected by feeding snails to them. Follow the course of migration as described for *Dictyocaulus.*

Metastrongylus apri (Gmelin, 1790) (Plate 119)

The adults are slender, white worms in the bronchi and bronchioles of swine throughout the world.

DESCRIPTION. Males are up to 25 mm long, with a small bursa in which the mediolateral and posterolateral rays are fused; the spicules are slender and 4 to 4.2 mm long, with a terminal harpoon-like barb. Females are up to 85 mm long, with the posterior end flexed ventrally upon itself; the vulva and anus open near the posterior end of the body. Eggs are 45 to 57 μ long by 38 to 41 μ wide, have thick shells, and contain first stage larvae when deposited.

LIFE CYCLE. Adults lay eggs in the lungs from where they pass up the trachea, are swallowed, and voided with the faeces. When swallowed by earthworms (*Helodrilus caliginous, H. foetidus,* and others), the eggs hatch in the anterior portion of the alimentary canal and the larvae migrate into the oesophageal wall, having a tendency to accumulate in the hearts. They molt twice and the third stage larvae generally encyst in the wall of the oesophagus. Infection of swine takes place when earthworms harboring infective third stage larvae are swallowed. Upon being freed from the annelids by the digestive processes of the stomach, the larvae enter the intestine, migrate into the lymphatics, through the lymph glands and vessels, vena cava, heart, and into the lungs. In the latter, they enter the air tubes and develop to maturity as soon as 24 days after entering the body. The last two molts occur in the lymphatics and lungs.

The virus of swine influenza may gain entrance into larval lungworms in the bronchi of infected pigs and be carried by these larvae to the lungs of uninfected pigs in which the disease appears.

EXERCISE ON LIFE CYCLE

Adult lungworms may be obtained from the bronchioles of swine slaughtered in abattoirs in many sections of the country. Dissect the uterus from gravid females and note the thick-shelled embryonated

PLATE 119 *Metastrongylus apri*

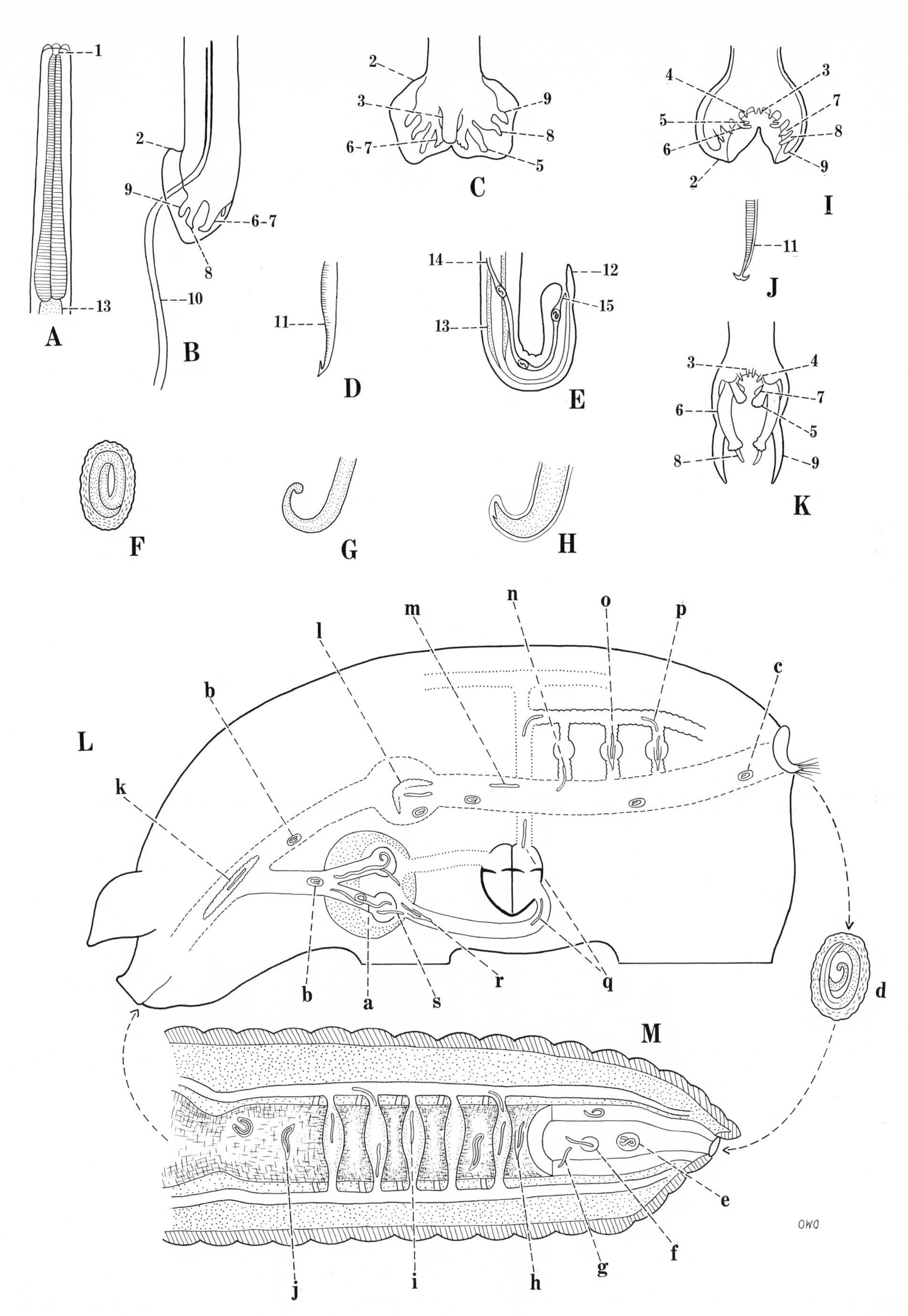

eggs, containing first stage larvae. Mix the eggs with moist soil in a glass container and place earthworms of the genera *Helodrilus, Lumbricus, Dendrobaena,* or *Eisenia* in it. Keep the cultures at room temperature. Both soil and earthworms should be obtained from places where swine have not been kept to avoid having naturally infected annelids. Examine the pharynx, oesophagus, and hearts over a period of a month for larvae and note the stages of development. Also obtain earthworms from hog lots and examine them for natural infections of lungworms.

Feed infected earthworms to six white mice, white rats, or guinea pigs. Kill five of them at intervals of 24 hours after infection and examine the intestinal contents, lymph nodes, and lungs for larvae. Note the stages of development of the larvae in the different locations and correlate them with the time elapsed since infection. Leave one animal for 4 weeks or longer and examine its lungs for worms.

SELECTED REFERENCES

Alicata, J. E. (1935). U. S. Dept. Agr. Tech. Bull. 489, p. 33.

Kates, K. C. (1941). J. Parasit. 27:265.

Schwartz, B., and J. E. Alicata. (1934). U. S. Dept. Agr. Tech. Bull. 456.

Shope, R. E. (1941). J. Exp. Med. 74:41, 49; (1943). Ibid. 77:111, 127.

Suborder Ascaridina

The members of this suborder are parasites of the alimentary canal of all classes of vertebrates and some terrestrial arthropods. The oesophagus may have a terminal bulb or be straight; the mouth is surrounded by three, two, or no lips. The males usually have two spicules but there may be only one, the tail curves ventrally, and caudal alae may be present. Two superfamilies, Oxyuroidea and Ascaridoidea, are recognized.

SUPERFAMILY OXYUROIDEA

In the oxyurids, the oesophagus is terminated posteriorly by a distinct valved bulb. The stoma is cylindroid but not surrounded by oesophageal tissue. There are four double or eight single papillae in the external circle and six minute ones in the internal circle. They are parasites of terrestrial arthropods, and all classes of vertebrates.

FAMILY OXYURIDAE

This family contains common parasites of amphibians, reptiles, and mammals, usually in the large intestine. The tail of the female is long and slender. *Enterobius vermicularis,* a common species infecting humans, will be used to illustrate the typical life cycle of this group.

Enterobius vermicularis (Linnaeus, 1785) (Plate 120)

Enterobius vermicularis is the ubiquitous pinworm or seatworm of humans throughout the northern hemisphere. Strangely enough, it is uncommon, but not unknown, in the southern part of the world. Upwards of 60 per cent of the white children in some of the cities in the United States are infected. It is especially prevalent in families, orphanages, and mental hospitals where personal hygiene is not maintained at a high level.

DESCRIPTION. They are small white worms. The males measure 2 to 5 mm and the females 8 to 13 mm long. The males have a single spicule 70 μ long and the caudal end of the body is curved ventrally. The tail of the female is long and pointed, equal to about one-third the total length of the body. The vulva is near the union of the anterior and middle thirds of the body and the long vagina extends caudad. When gravid, the female assumes a slight spindle shape due to the great number of eggs, which are 50 to 60 μ long by 20 to 30 μ wide, flattened somewhat on one side, and contain an embryo in the tadpole stage when laid.

LIFE CYCLE. The adult worms are in the large intestine where mating occurs, after which the males tend to disappear. As the females approach gravidity, they move toward the posterior end of the colon. When ready to oviposit, they crawl out of the anus and creep over the sensitive perianal region, leaving a trail of eggs numbering in the thousands, and at the same time causing intense itching.

Attempts on the part of the host to alleviate the discomfort results in scratching and the transfer of eggs to the fingers. Eggs may also get on underpants, pajamas, in the beds, and throughout the dwellings of infected groups.

Infection may occur in three ways. They are 1) transferring the eggs from the anus or soiled clothing to the mouth by means of the fingers; 2) inhaling eggs that become airborne by currents created in bed when the person raises and lowers the covers, or by sweeping and dusting in houses where infected people reside; and 3) by eggs hatching in the perianal region about 6 hours after deposition and the larvae crawling through the anus into the intestine where sexual maturity is attained. This is called retrofection, meaning infection from behind.

Normally, infective eggs containing fully developed first stage larvae hatch in the duodenum. They molt three times en route to the large intestine where they mature, mate, and reproduce. Eggs appear on the skin around the anus, rarely in the faeces, in 15 to 43 days.

A few other common and well-known species of oxyurids include *Passalurus ambiguus* and *Dermatoxys veliger* of rabbits, *Syphacia obvelata* and *Aspicularis tetraptera* of rats and mice, *Skrjabinema ovis* of sheep, and *Oxyuris equi* of equines. Their life cycles are basically the same as that of *Enterobius vermicularis*. It appears doubtful on the basis of experimental evidence available that retrofection occurs in these species.

EXERCISE ON LIFE CYCLE

An excellent species for exercises on life cycles is *Syphacia obvelata* because of its prevalence and the ease of obtaining and handling the definitive hosts.

Like *E. vermicularis*, eggs are laid in the perianal region where they may be collected by dabbing the area with bits of scotch tape or by washing. By collecting at appropriate time intervals, the stages of development in them may be observed. The scotch tape method is especially good for this observation. If embryonated eggs are fed to a series of mice, the various stages of development and their location may be ascertained by killing the hosts and examining the alimentary canal at intervals of 8 to 10 hours, or even at shorter periods for the first 48 hours, and thereafter at 12 to 24 hours. Determine whether males and females have similar longevity in the gut. Try experiments to ascertain whether retroinfection occurs.

SUPERFAMILY ASCARIDOIDEA

The Ascaridoidea are parasites of the various classes of vertebrates. They range from relatively small to large nematodes of the alimentary canal and are characterized by an oesophagus that is straight or one that terminates in a bulb. The stoma is usually collapsed and surrounded by oesophageal tissue. There are four large double papillae in the external circle on the lips.

FAMILY HETERAKIDAE

These are common parasites of reptiles, birds, and mammals. The oesophagus may or may not have a posterior bulb. The males possess a distinct perianal sucker. The eggs are smooth, unembryonated when laid, and have thick shells.

Heterakis gallinae (Gmelin, 1790) (Plate 121)

This is the caecal worm of chickens, turkeys, pheasants, quails, and related upland game birds. It is extremely common and widely distributed. It is associated with the spread among birds of the flagellate *Histomonas meleagridis*, the causative organism of enterohepatitis of turkeys (Plate 1).

DESCRIPTION. The males are 7 to 13 mm and the females 10 to 15 mm long; each sex has a pointed tail. Alae, or expansions of the cuticle, extend along the lateral sides of the body. The oesophagus terminates posteriorly as a distinct valved bulb. The tail of the male has wide alae, a prominent

EXPLANATION OF PLATE 120

A. Adult female. **B.** Adult male. **C.** Ventral view of caudal end of male. **D.** Embryonated egg. **E.** Human host. **F.** Hand contaminated with eggs from anus. **G.** Hands contaminated from soiled underclothing. **H.** Bedding and sleeping garments contaminated with eggs. **I.** Eggs air-borne as result of sweeping, dusting, and movement of bedding.

1, cephalic alae; **2,** oesophageal bulb; **3,** intestine; **4,** anus; **5,** tail; **6,** vulva; **7,** vagina; **8,** anterior ovary; **9,** anterior uterus; **10,** posterior ovary; **11,** posterior uterus; **12,** spicule; **13,** caudal ala; **14,** caudal papillae; **15,** ejaculatory duct; **16,** seminal vesicle; **17,** sperm duct; **18, 19,** testis; **20,** egg shell; **21,** first stage larvae.

a, adult female in ascending colon; **b,** adult male in ascending colon; **c,** adult females in transverse and ascending colon; **d,** gravid female making her way through rectum to anus; **e,** gravid female outside in perianal region to oviposit; **f,** eggs in perianal region; **g,** embryonated egg with first stage larva; **h,** eggs on fingers and under nails being transferred to mouth; **i,** embryonated egg from fingers; **j,** infection by swallowing eggs; **k,** eggs pass through stomach; **l,** eggs hatch in duodenum; **m, n, o,** first, second, and third molts, respectively, after which larvae continue growth to maturity; **p,** underwear soiled with eggs that get on hands when clothing is handled; **q,** eggs accumulate in bed and are stirred into air with movement of occupant or when bedding is shaken; **r,** eggs become air-borne by sweeping and dusting; **s,** air-borne embryonated eggs inhaled and infection results; **t,** eggs in perianal region hatch and larvae enter anus, producing infection by retrofection; **u,** larvae migrate up descending colon and develop to maturity.

Original drawings.

---

precloacal sucker, and 12 pairs of papillae. The right spicule is 2 mm and the left 0.65 to 0.7 mm long. The vulva opens directly behind the middle of the body and the eggs are 65 to 80 μ by 35 to 46 μ in size, have smooth shells, and are unembryonated when laid.

LIFE CYCLE. The life cycle is direct. Earthworms, however, harbor infective stages and are capable of transmitting infections when eaten by chickens. After being passed in the faeces, the eggs develop to first stage larvae. By the end of 2 weeks at room temperature, they have molted and transformed into the second stage without further development until entering the host. Hatching occurs to some extent in the crop, but mostly in the gizzard and duodenum. No development takes place as the larvae migrate down the intestine.

They reach the mouth of the caeca about 24 hours after ingestion of the eggs, and by the end of 48 hours all of them are in the caeca. No trace of larvae entering the caecal mucosa was found by Clapham who made careful studies from sections taken from birds fed large numbers of eggs, the claims of other workers to the contrary. Three molts occur in the caeca, requiring about 9 to 10 days. Sexual maturity is attained about 24 days after the eggs have been swallowed.

EXERCISE ON LIFE CYCLE

These parasites are readily available from plants where farm-raised chickens are processed.

Observe the development of the eggs to the second stage larvae enclosed in the sheath of the first molt.

By feeding embryonated eggs to a series of 10 chicks and examining one postmortem each day, the movement of the larvae toward and into the caeca, and the molts that occur in the latter, may be observed. Sections of the caeca or digestion of them after the larvae have entered will provide information on whether there is migration into the epithelium.

SELECTED REFERENCES

Baker, A. D. (1933). Sci. Agr. 13:356.

Clapham, P. A. (1933). J. Helminth. 11:67.

Lund, E. E., E. E. Wehr, and D. J. Ellis. (1963). J. Parasit. 49(5/2):122.

Morgan, B. B., and P. A. Hawkins. (1949). Veterinary Parasitology. Burgess Publishing Company, Minneapolis, p. 286.

Uribe, C. (1922). J. Parasit. 8:167.

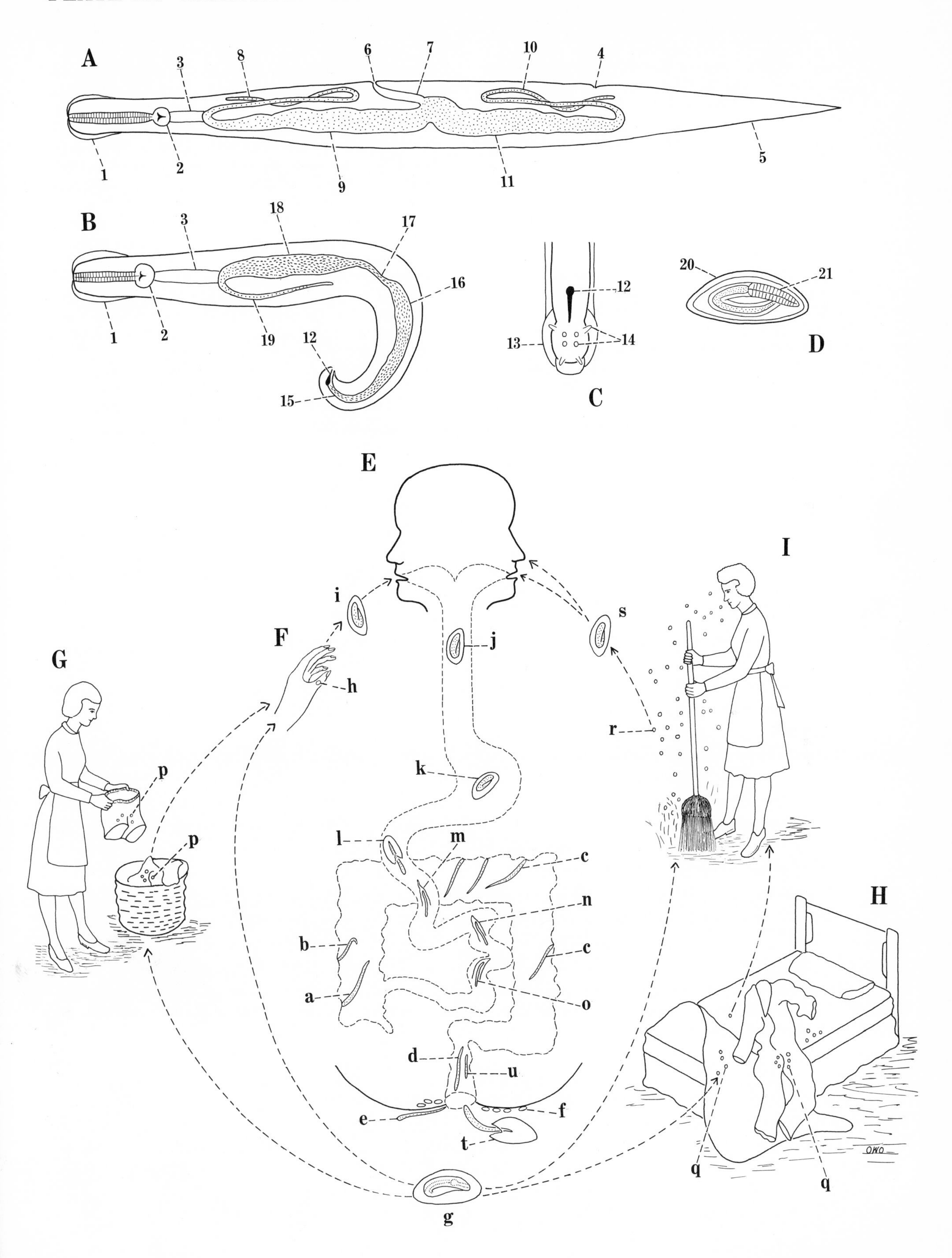
A
1
2
3
4
5
6
7
8
9
10
11
B
1
2
3
12
15
16
17
18
19
C
12
13
14
D
20
21
E
F
G
H
I
a
b
c
d
e
f
g
h
i
j
k
l
m
n
o
p
q
r
s
t
u
OWO

EXPLANATION OF PLATE 121 ▷

A-C. *Ascaridia galli:* **A.** *En face* view of adult. **B.** Anterior end of adult. **C.** Ventral view of posterior end of adult male. **D-F.** *Heterakis gallinae:* **D.** Dorsal view of anterior end of adult. **E.** *En face* view of adult. **F.** Ventral view of posterior end of adult male. **G.** Unembryonated egg. **H.** Chicken definitive host of *A. galli* and *H. gallinae.*

1, dorsal lip; **2,** lateroventral lip; **3,** ventrolateral cephalic papillae; **4,** dorsolateral cephalic papillae; **5,** cervical papillae; **6,** cervical alae; **7,** precloacal sucker; **8,** papilla in precloacal sucker; **9,** preanal papillae; **10,** postanal papillae; **11,** caudal alae; **12,** spicules (markedly unequal in length in *Heterakis*); **13,** buccal capsule; **14,** oesophagus; **15,** valved bulb of oesophagus; **16,** intestine; **17,** anus; **18,** thick shell of egg.

a, adult *Ascaridia galli* in small intestine; **b,** eggs in faeces passing from intestine; **c,** unembryonated egg outside host; **d,** developing egg; **e,** egg containing first stage larva; **f,** egg containing second stage ensheathed infective larva; **g,** infection of chicken by swallowing infective egg; **h-j,** egg hatching in crop, gizzard, and intestine; **k-n,** development in lumen of intestine; **k,** newly hatched second stage larva; **l,** second molt producing third stage larva; **m,** third molt producing fourth stage larva attached to bottom of mucosal crypt; **n,** fourth molt producing final stage that matures to adult; **o-r,** stages with development in mucosa; **o,** third stage larva entering mucosa; **p,** third molt in mucosa forming fourth stage larva; **q,** fourth stage larva leaves mucosa for lumen; **r,** after returning to lumen, it molts fourth time, attaches to mucosa, and matures.

a′, adult *Heterakis gallinae* in caeca; **b′,** eggs laid in caeca; **b-j,** development of eggs of *Heterakis* is similar to that of *Ascaridia;* **c′,** newly hatched second stage larva in small intestine; **d′,** second stage larva entering caeca; **e′,** second molt (which is the first to occur in the caeca); **f′,** third stage larva; **g′,** third molt; **h′,** fourth stage larva; **i′,** fourth and final molt after which the parasite develops to adulthood **(a′).**

Figures A, B, D, E adapted from various sources; C, F, from Boughton, 1937, Minn. Agr. Exp. St. Tech. Bull. 121 (spicules added in F); G, original.

Ascaridia galli (Schrank, 1788) (Plate 121)

These parasites occur in the small intestine of chickens, turkeys, quails, pheasants, ducks, geese, and a number of species of wild birds in most parts of the world. Unlike *Heterakis gallinae,* which has no migration in the tissue, *A. galli* has a limited one by a small percentage of the larvae which enter the intestinal epithelium for a short period.

DESCRIPTION. These are the largest nematodes in poultry. The males are 50 to 76 mm long and females 72 to 116 mm. The oesophagus is straight, being devoid of a terminal bulb. The tail of the male bears a precloacal sucker and 10 pairs of papillae, three pairs precloacal on the ventral side, and seven pairs postcloacal and lateral.

LIFE CYCLE. After being passed in the faeces, the eggs develop under favorable conditions to the second stage larva. Hatching occurs *in vitro* to a limited extent, which indicates that it may likewise happen in the soil. Normally, it takes place in the duodenum of the host birds. Chickens fed hatched larvae became infected with few worms, indicating that ingestion of hatched larvae under natural conditions in the feed or soil may be one means, though limited, of infection. Normally, however, infection results from swallowing embryonated eggs.

According to Ackert, the larvae remain in the lumen and intervillar spaces of the small intestine for the first 9 days where they molt once between the sixth and eighth days. On the 10th, they begin to penetrate the intestinal mucosa, molt once in it, and leave as fourth stage larvae by the 18th day. The final molt occurs in the lumen between the 18th and 20th days, after which they grow to adults.

Todd and Crowdus, on the other hand, pointed out that on the basis of Ackert's report it was generally assumed that all of the larvae enter the mucosa as a normal course of development. However, their experiments showed that on the seventh day after infection only a very small percentage (5.67 per cent) of 1,059 worms in 54 chicks were in the mucosa; the others were free in the lumen. At 14 days after infection, 94 (11.5 per cent) of 817 worms in 54 chicks were in the mucosa. The remaining 723 were free in the lumen. From these observations, it appears that the great majority of the nematodes undergo their development free in the intestinal lumen where all three molts occur. A few, however, penetrate the mucosa where they remain for about a week, molting once during that time. Thus in *Ascaridia,* there is a limited migration on the part of a few larvae. The few that do enter the epithelium appear to be the ones that cause the most serious damage to the development of the host. The worms become sexually mature and produce eggs in 5 to 8 weeks.

PLATE 121 *Heterakis gallinae, Ascaridia galli*

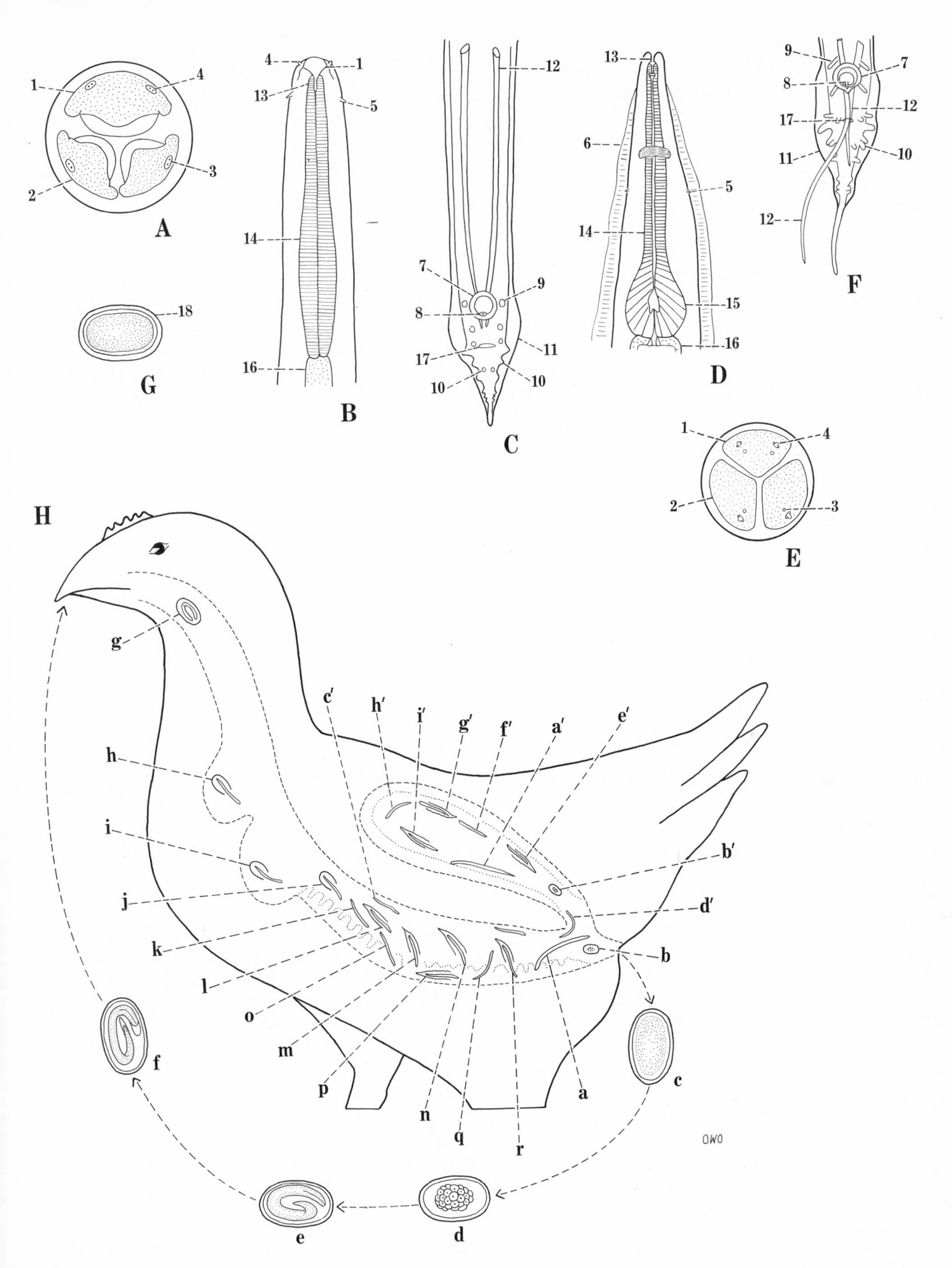

Other common species of *Ascaridia* are *A. columbae* of pigeons and *A. numidiae* of guinea fowls. Their life cycles are basically the same as that described for *A. galli.*

In *Ascaridia columbae,* some of the larvae penetrate the intestinal mucosa, enter the hepatic portal vein, and go to the liver. No development takes place in the liver and migrating larvae do not appear in the lungs and trachea. Experimental evidence indicates that this migration is not essential to development, since all stages of worms occur in the small intestine.

EXERCISE ON LIFE CYCLE

Since the life cycle of this parasite is similar to that of *Heterakis gallinae,* most of the same procedures may be followed. One difference, however, exists. Since most of the larvae do not enter the intestinal mucosa, special efforts may be directed toward determining more about this phase of the cycle.

Feed each of about a dozen or more chicks 50 fully embryonated eggs. Beginning on about the sixth day after infection, sacrifice one bird daily. Wash all larvae from the intestine, count them, and ascertain the stage of development. After having removed all of the worms from the lumen and those attached to the mucosa, scrape it from the intestinal wall and digest it in a standard preparation of pepsin. Collect all of the worms, ascertain the stage of development, and the percentage of the total that entered the mucosa.

Examine the liver, lungs, and trachea to determine whether some of them may reach the intestine by migrating through these organs.

SELECTED REFERENCES

Ackert, J. E. (1931). Parasitology 23:360.

Morgan, B. B., and P. A. Hawkins. (1949). Veterinary Helminthology. Burgess Publishing Co., Minneapolis, p. 283.

Todd, A. C., and D. H. Crowdus. (1952). Trans. Amer. Micr. Soc. 71:282.

Wehr, E. E., and J. C. Huang. (1964). J. Parasit. 50:131.

FAMILY ASCARIDAE

The Ascaridae are large nematodes of the alimentary tract of all classes of vertebrates throughout the world.

They have three well-developed lips. The oesophagus is more or less straight and without a distinct terminal enlargement. The tail of the male bears numerous ventral papillae, bends ventrad, and is without alae; there is a pair of small spicules. The vulva is cephalad from the middle of the body. The eggs are oval and have a shell that is thick and covered with distinct ridges or pits.

Ascaris lumbricoides (Linnaeus, 1758) (Plate 122)

This is the large nematode parasitic in the small intestine of humans and swine, and is present almost wherever its hosts occur. It is probably represented by different physiological strains in the two hosts.

DESCRIPTION. The males are 15 to 25 cm long by 3 mm wide and the females up to 41 cm long and 5 mm in diameter. There are three lips, a large dorsal one and two smaller lateroventral ones. The tail of the male bends strongly ventrad and bears a large number of preanal papillae and fewer postanal ones. The female is straight, with a rather blunt tail. The vulva is located near the posterior end of the first third of the body and joins two parallel uteri that extend posteriorly. Eggs are 50 to 75 μ long by 40 to 50 μ wide with thick shells whose surface is covered by a reticulation of ridges.

LIFE CYCLE. The life cycle is direct. Eggs laid in the intestine reach the outside with the faeces in an undeveloped stage. Development to the second stage infective larvae takes place within the egg in approximately 10 days under optimal conditions of temperature and moisture. They exhibit great resistance to unfavorable conditions in both the unembryonated and embryonated stages.

Infection of the host occurs when infective eggs are swallowed. Hatching is in the duodenum and the larvae migrate through the intestinal mucosa into the hepatic portal venules. Upon reaching the lungs via the liver and heart, the majority of them enter the air sacs, remaining there about 16 days. During this time, they molt the second time on about the sixth day, becoming third stage forms, and again about 10 days later for the third time to become fourth stage larvae. At this time, they migrate up the bronchioles and trachea into the pharynx and are swallowed. In the intestine, the fourth and final molt takes place about 3 weeks after the eggs have been swallowed. Sexual maturity is attained about 2 months after ingestion of the eggs.

As indicated above, some of the larvae do not remain in the lungs but continue through them to the left side of the heart and into the arterial circulation. They are distributed to the tissues and organs, including the spleen and kidneys. In the case of pregnant animals, they have a tendency to accumulate in the liver of the foetuses, resulting in prenatal infection. When the young animals are born, the migration through the lungs and trachea is completed. This accounts for the early appearance of adult worms in very young animals.

It is seen from this life cycle that *Ascaris lumbricoides* has an extended hepato-pulmonary migration in the host. Only the first step of such a migration appeared in *Ascaridia galli* where but a small minority of the larvae migrated into the intestinal mucosa for a short time after which they returned to the lumen of the intestine for final development.

Other common species of this group include *Ascaris vitulorum* of bovines, *A. columnaris* of mustelids, and *Parascaris equorum* of equines. Their life cycles are basically the same as that of *A. lumbricoides*. While prenatal infection is possible in these species due to their migrations, it has not been observed.

EXERCISE ON LIFE CYCLE

Eggs are readily obtained from female worms available at abattoirs where swine are slaughtered. They are easily incubated and may be kept for long periods of time in that stage, even in a solution of 10 per cent formalin. Verify that the larvae in fully developed eggs are in the second stage by observing the sheath of the first stage.

The migration route through the host can be determined by feeding large numbers of embryonated eggs to a group of about a dozen mice. One of these should be sacrificed each day for the first 6 days and one every other day thereafter. Wash out the contents of the intestine and examine them for larvae. Make sections of the intestine, liver, and lungs to ascertain when larvae are migrating through them. The trachea should be washed thoroughly and the sediment examined to determine whether larvae continue their migrations beyond the lungs.

SELECTED REFERENCES

Alicata, J. E. (1935). U. S. Dept. Agr., Tech. Bull. 489, p. 44.

Ransom, B. H., and E. B. Cram. (1921). Amer. J. Trop. Med. 1:129.

Ransom, B. H., and W. D. Foster. (1920). U. S. Dept. Agr. Bull. 817.

Roberts, F. H. S. (1934). Queensland Dept. Agr. and Stock, Anim. Health Sta., Yeerongpilly, Bull. 1.

Schwartz, B. (1960). Smithsonian Rept. for 1959. p. 465.

Sprent, J. F. A. (1952). J. Infect. Dis. 90:165; (1954). J. Parasit. 40:608.

Toxocara canis (Werner, 1782) (Plate 123)

Toxocara canis is a parasite of the small intestine of dogs and foxes throughout the world. It is the largest of the ascarids occurring in canines.

While these worms are parasites of canines, the larvae may occur in the visceral organs and tissues of humans with serious effects, causing a condition known as larval visceral migrans.

DESCRIPTION. The males measure up to 10 cm long and the females up to 18 cm. Broad cervical alae are present but caudal alae are absent. The tail of the male is abruptly reduced in diameter

EXPLANATION OF PLATE 122

A. *En face* view of adult. **B.** Dorsal view of anterior end of adult. **C.** Lateral view of posterior end of adult male. **D.** Undeveloped fertilized egg. **E.** Embryonated egg with first stage larva. **F.** Egg with second stage or infective larvae. **G.** Second stage larva freed from egg. **H.** Anterior and posterior ends of second stage larva. **I.** Pig definitive host.

1, dorsal lip; **2**, lateroventral lip; **3**, labial papillae; **4**, mouth; **5**, preanal papillae; **6**, postanal papillae; **7**, spicules; **8**, oesophagus; **9**, intestine; **10**, anus; **11**, free cuticle on second stage larva; **12**, shell in optical section, showing roughened surface; **13**, undeveloped stage of egg; **14**, first stage larva; **15**, second stage larva.

a, adult male and female worms in small intestine; **b**, eggs passing out of intestine with faeces; **c**, unembryonated egg; **d**, egg in morula stage; **e**, egg with first stage larva; **f**, infective egg with second stage larva enclosed in cuticle of first stage larva; **g**, infection of host by swallowing infective eggs; **h**, **i**, eggs hatch in stomach and small intestine; **j**, larvae free in intestine; **k**, larvae enter venules of hepatic portal system; **l**, larvae migrate through liver; **m**, larvae pass through right side of heart; **n**, second molt occurs in veins of lungs to form third stage larva; **o**, third stage larvae; **p**, second molt to form fourth stage larva; **q**, fourth stage larvae enter alveoli and migrate up trachea; **r**, larvae enter pharynx and are swallowed; **s**, final molt occurs in small intestine and worms develop to adults **(a)**; **t**, larvae pass through lungs, left side of heart, and into general circulation; **u**, larvae carried to various parts of the body, including kidneys and other organs, as well as to foetuses in pregnant sows.

Figures A, B, C adapted from various sources; D-H, from Alicata, 1935, U. S. Dept. Agr. Tech. Bull. 489, p. 46.

---

and bears five papillae on each side, with about 20 pairs of preanal papillae. The vulva is in the anterior fourth of the body; the eggs measure 90 by 75 μ and are covered with thick, finely pitted shells.

LIFE CYCLE. The eggs are unembryonated when voided with the faeces but develop to the infective stage as soon as 5 to 6 days under optimal conditions. The second stage larva in the egg is infective, as in the case of *Ascaris*. Infection of the host begins when the fully embryonated eggs are swallowed. They hatch in the small intestine and the larvae enter the hepatic venules, migrating to the lungs as in the case of *Ascaris*.

From this point, the life cycle varies, depending on the host and its age. It includes three phases. They are 1) a tissue phase, 2) an intestinal phase, and 3) a prenatal phase.

The tissue phase occurs in older dogs, rodents, and humans, especially children, when infective eggs are swallowed. Upon hatching, the larvae enter the hepatic portal vein and are carried via the liver and heart to the lungs. Some of the larvae migrate into the liver and lung parenchyma where they remain. Others continue through the pulmonary veins and heart into the arterial circulation. Upon reaching the capillaries of the skeletal muscles, kidneys, or central nervous system, they enter the tissues, remaining in an inactive stage in them (H, J, K).

The intestinal phase occurs in young pups when they swallow infective eggs. The eggs hatch in the small intestine and the larvae migrate into the venules of the hepatic portal vein and are carried via the liver and heart to the lungs. Here they escape from the blood vessels and enter the alveoli. Their migration takes them up the trachea, into the pharynx, and finally to the small intestine, as in the case of *Ascaris*, where development to maturity is attained (I). Pups and dogs eating rodents harboring larvae in their tissues, acquire intestinal infections. The larvae, upon being released by the digestion of the rodent reservoir host, undertake the normal hepato-pulmono-tracheal migration, as seen in *Ascaris*, to the intestine where they develop to maturity (H, I).

Prenatal infection apparently results from larvae in the tissue of pregnant animals being activated by the hormones of pregnancy and re-entering the blood stream. Of those that make their way into the uterine circulation, some enter the umbilical artery and reach the bodies of the developing foetuses. Third stage larvae are in the heart and lungs of full term but unborn foetuses, also in the lungs at birth and during the first week of life. Fourth stage larvae appear in the intestine 3 days after birth and are molting by the beginning of the second week (H). Eggs appear in the faeces 21 to 22 days after birth.

Other closely related and common species include *Toxocara mystax* of felines and *Toxascaris leonina* of canines and felines.

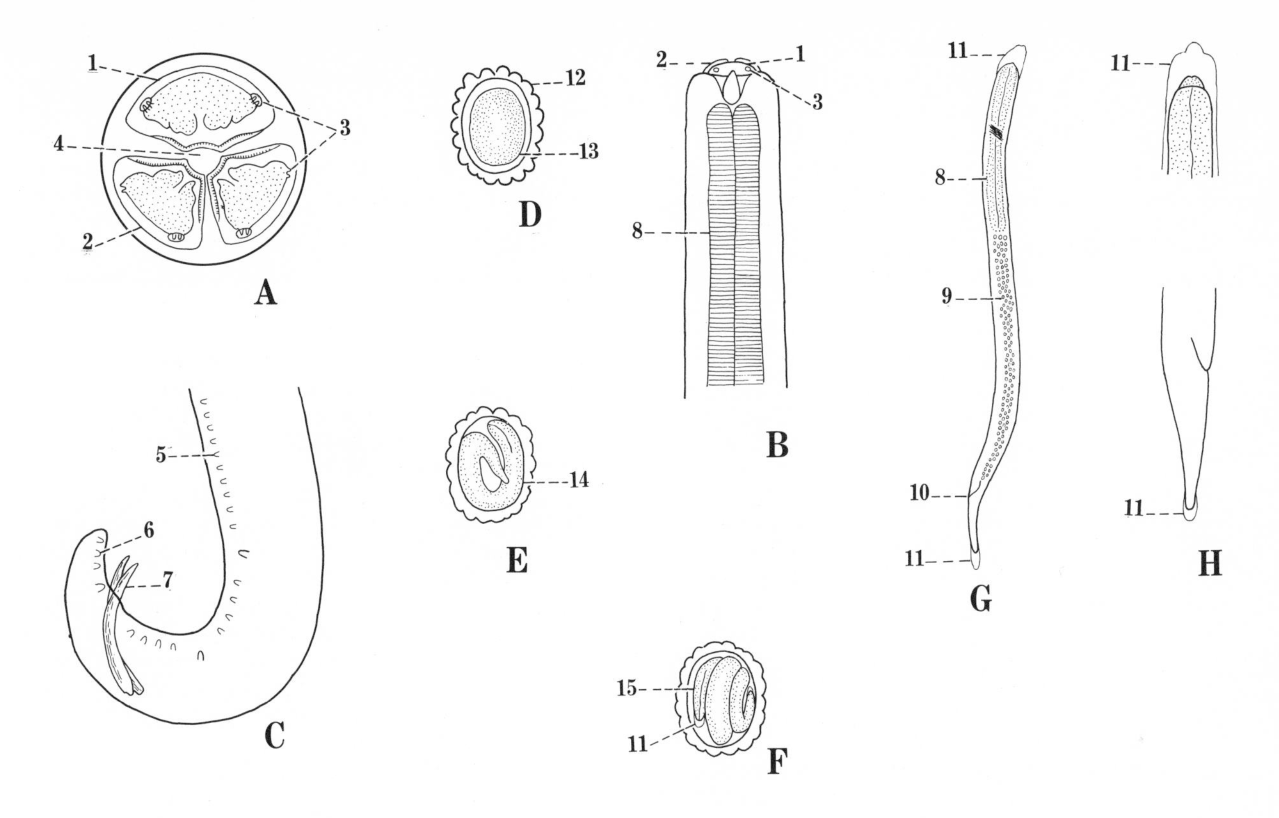
1
2
3
4
A
12
13
D
2
1
3
8
B
11
8
9
10
11
G
11
11
H
5
6
7
C
14
E
15
11
F

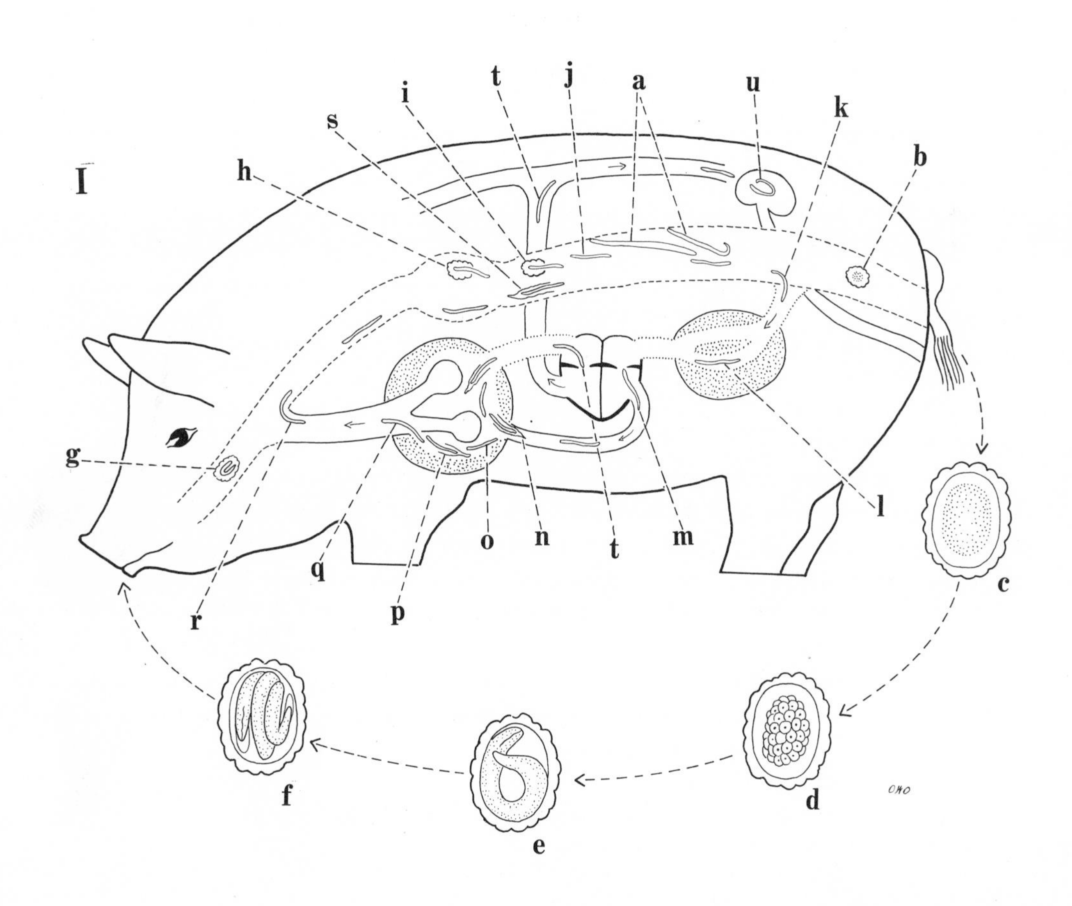
I
t
j
a
u
k
i
s
h
b
g
r
q
p
o
n
t
m
l
c
d
e
f

EXPLANATION OF PLATE 123

A. *En face* view of adult. **B.** Dorsal view of anterior end of adult. **C.** Lateral view of anterior end of adult. **D.** Lateral view of posterior end of adult male. **E.** Ventral view of tail of adult male. **F.** Lateral view of tail of adult female. **G.** Embryonated egg. **H.** Dog definitive host. **I.** Pup definitive host. **J.** Mouse host. **K.** Human in which larval visceral migrans occurs, as in mice.

1, dorsal lip; **2**, lateroventral lip; **3**, labial papillae; **4**, mouth; **5**, cervical alae; **6**, preanal papillae; **7**, anus; **8**, spicules; **9**, postanal papillae; **10**, oesophagus; **11**, ventriculus; **12**, intestine; **13**, anus; **14**, excretory pore; **15**, excretory gland; **16**, nerve ring.

a, adult worms relatively rare in intestine of adult dogs but common in young ones (**i'**); **b**, eggs are voided with faeces; **c**, eggs undeveloped when passed in faeces; **d**, egg in morula stage; **e**, first stage larva in egg; **f**, second stage infective larva in egg; **g**, infective egg being swallowed by adult dog; **h**, eggs hatch in stomach; **i**, larvae (stippled) go into small intestine; **j**, larvae penetrate intestinal wall and enter hepatic portal vein; **k**, larvae leave capillaries in liver; **l**, some larvae accumulate in liver parenchyma; **m**, some larvae continue in blood stream through right side of heart; **n**, larvae enter lungs; **o**, larvae enter lung parenchyma; **p**, larvae in lung parenchyma; **q**, some larvae pass through lungs to left side of heart; **r**, larvae enter general circulation; **s**, larvae enter umbilical artery and eventually go into foetus; **t**, larvae in liver, heart, and lungs of foetus; **u**, larvae in kidneys; **v**, larvae in skeletal muscles.

a, mouse with larvae in tissues being swallowed; **b**, larvae (unstippled) freed from mouse by digestive processes in stomach; **c**, larvae enter hepatic portal vein; **d**, **e**, larvae migrate to lungs via heart; **f**, larvae enter bronchioles from blood vessels; **g**, larvae migrate up trachea, are swallowed, and develop to adults, but infrequently in grown dogs.

a', embryonated eggs swallowed by puppy; **b'**, eggs hatch in stomach; **c'**, **d'**, **e'**, larvae (stippled) enter hepatic portal vein and migrate through liver, heart, and into lungs; **f'**, larvae enter alveoli and migrate up trachea; **g'**, larvae in pharynx; **h'**, larvae in oesophagus are swallowed; **i'**, larvae develop readily to adults and lay eggs (when infected mice are eaten, the larvae (unstippled) migrate and develop in the same manner as those from eggs).

a'', embryonated eggs swallowed by mice and other rodents; **b''**, eggs hatch in intestine; **c''**, larvae enter hepatic portal vein; **d''**, some larvae enter liver parenchyma; **e''**, larvae remain in liver; **f''**, **g''**, some larvae migrate through liver and heart; **h''**, some larvae enter lung parenchyma; **i''**, larvae remain in lung parenchyma; **j''**, **k''**, other larvae pass though heart and into arterial circulation; **l''**, **m''**, larvae enter central nervous system and kidneys where they remain inactive and without further development until released in stomach of dogs.

Figures A, D, E, F adapted from Mozgovi, 1953, Osnovi Nematodologii, Vol. 2, pp. 449-452; B, from Yorke and Maplestone, 1962, Nematode Parasites of Vertebrates, Hafner Publishing Co., New York, Fig. 176 A; C from Sprent, 1958, Parasitology 48:184; G, original.

When dogs and cats ingest embryonated eggs of *Toxascaris leonina,* the second stage larvae hatching from them burrow into the intestinal wall where they undergo the second and third molts. The resulting fourth stage larvae return to the lumen of the intestine and complete their development. Eggs swallowed by mice hatch and the larvae migrate to the somatic tissues, where they undergo the second molt to form third stage larvae, but further development does not take place in this location. When infected mice are eaten by dogs and cats, the larvae develop in the intestine to adults.

EXERCISE ON LIFE CYCLE

Obtain adult female *Toxocara canis* from a veterinary hospital where dogs are treated for worms. Dissect eggs from the proximal portions of the uteri near the vagina and incubate them in tap water or normal saline at room temperature. Note the stages of developing larvae and the time when each occurs. Recognize the second stage larva by the presence of the loose cuticle around it.

Feed eggs containing second stage infective larvae to mice. Kill the mice at intervals and examine the intestinal contents, the liver, heart, lungs, kidneys, and central nervous system to determine the course of movement of the larvae in the body and the time required for them to reach the various locations. Ascertain whether the larvae develop beyond the second stage in the mice by comparing them with larvae pressed from fully embryonated eggs.

SELECTED REFERENCES

Sprent, J. F. A. (1958). Parasitology 48:184; (1958). Ibid. 44(4/2):27; (1958). Aust. Vet. J. 34:161.

Webster, G. A. (1958). Canad. J. Zool. 36:435.

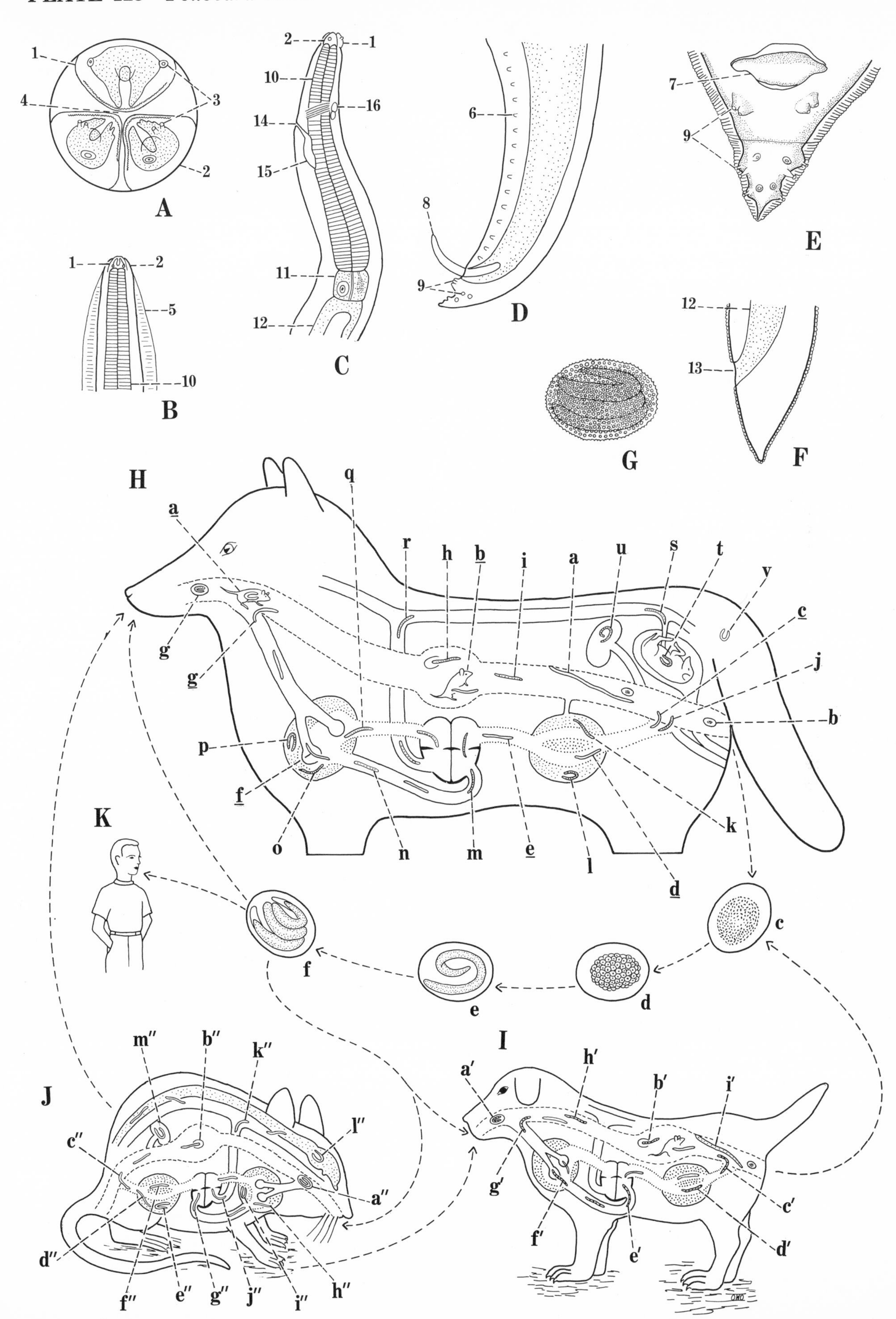
A
B
C
D
E
F
G
H
I
J
K

EXPLANATION OF PLATE 124 ⇨

A. *En face* view of adult. **B.** Sinistral view of caudal end of adult male. **C.** Dorsal lip. **D.** Caudal end of female. **E.** Ventral view of caudal end of male. **F.** Oesophago-intestinal junction, showing caeca. **G.** Egg in early stage of cleavage. **H.** Tadpole stage of larva. **I.** Fully developed first stage larva. **J.** Second stage larva. **K.** Third stage larva from intestine of copepod. **L.** Eelpout *(Zoarces)*. **M.** Marine copepod *(Eurytemmora)* intermediate host. **N.** Herring *(Clupea)*.

1, dorsal lip; **2**, lateroventral lip; **3**, papillae; **4**, pulp of lip; **5**, mouth; **6**, caudal papillae; **7**, spicular sheath; **8**, spicule; **9**, spines; **10**, anal opening; **11**, oesophagus; **12**, ventriculus; **13**, anterior intestinal caecum; **14**, posterior oesophageal or ventricular caecum; **15**, intestine; **16**, rough egg shell; **17**, cells of developing embryo; **18**, embryonic membrane; **19**, tadpole stage of larva; **20**, first stage larva; **21**, nerve ring; **22**, cuticle of first stage larva surrounding second stage larva; **23**, second stage larva; **24**, third stage larva; **25**, spine; **26**, genital primordia.

a, adult worm in eelpout; **b**, egg laid by worm; **c**, egg in first stage of cleavage passed in faeces; **d**, egg in early stages of cleavage; **e**, larva developed to tadpole stage; **f**, fully developed second stage larvae; **g**, ensheathed second stage larva hatching from egg eaten by copepod; **h**, second stage larva escaping from sheath and passing through intestinal wall; **i**, second stage larva in haemocoel; **j**, second stage larva presumably is released from copepod by digestive processes in alimentary canal of plankton-feeding herring; **k**, larva molts (?) to third stage and burrows through wall of intestine; **l**, third stage larva (?) encysts in mesenteries; **m**, larva released from tissues of herring by digestive processes of the predacious eelpout; **n**, larva molts (?) fourth time, attaches to intestinal wall and matures.

Figures A, B, C, D, E, F, G adapted from Skrjabin *et al*, 1951, Opredeliteli Parasiticheski Nematod Vol. 3, Plates 205, 206; H-K, from Markowski, 1937, Bull. Internat. Acad. Polo. Sci. Lett., Cl. Sci. Math. et Nat. Ser. B, Sci. 2:227.

Contracaecum (Railliet and Henry, 1912)

Contracaecum contains many species infecting piscivorous fish, birds, and mammals, both fresh-water and marine. The genus is ascaridoid, characterized by having lips without dentigerous ridges and two caecum-like projections at the junction of the oesophagus and intestine. The oesophageal caecum is the smaller, solid, and pointed posteriorly; the intestinal caecum is almost twice as long as the other one and extends anteriorly. (*Porrocaecum* Railliet and Henry, 1912 has similar caeca but the lips have dentigerous ridges).

Three species of this genus, one each in fish, birds, and mammals, are of interest. Their life cycles include at least one intermediate host and possibly two, but on this latter point definite information is not available.

Contracaecum aduncum (Rudolphi, 1802) (Plate 124)

This species is parasitic in the intestine of the European eelpout (*Zoarces viviparus*), perch (*Perca fluviatilis*) and others, including food fishes. Numerous plankton-feeding fish serve as intermediate hosts. *C. aduncum* was chosen to illustrate the life cycle because more details concerning its stages are known, as presented by Markowski.

DESCRIPTION. Males measure 18 to 20.5 mm long by 0.434 to 0.511 mm wide. Cervical alae are 4.21 mm long. The ventriculus is 0.154 to 0.170 mm long with a ventricular caecum 0.540 to 0.528 mm long; the intestinal caecum is 0.648 to 0.930 mm long. There are 23 pairs of preanal and seven to eight pairs of postanal papillae. The spicules are 2.01 to 2.94 mm long.

The females are 24 to 36 mm long with the vulva near the junction of the anterior and middle thirds of the body; the vagina divides into two uteri. Eggs are 62 to 70 μ long by 46 to 47 μ wide.

LIFE CYCLE. *Contracaecum aduncum* is especially abundant in the eelpouts during the summer, virtually filling the intestine, and occurring in approximately half of the population. During the winter months, infections are relatively few and light.

The eggs are in the first cleavage when passed in the faeces. At room temperature, they contain a fully developed second stage larva at the end of the third or fourth day.

Hatching apparently does not occur until the embryonated eggs are ingested by appropriate invertebrates such as the copepods *Acartia bifilosa* and *Eurytemora affinis* in which it has been shown to occur under experimental conditions. Naturally infected Chaetognatha have been found.

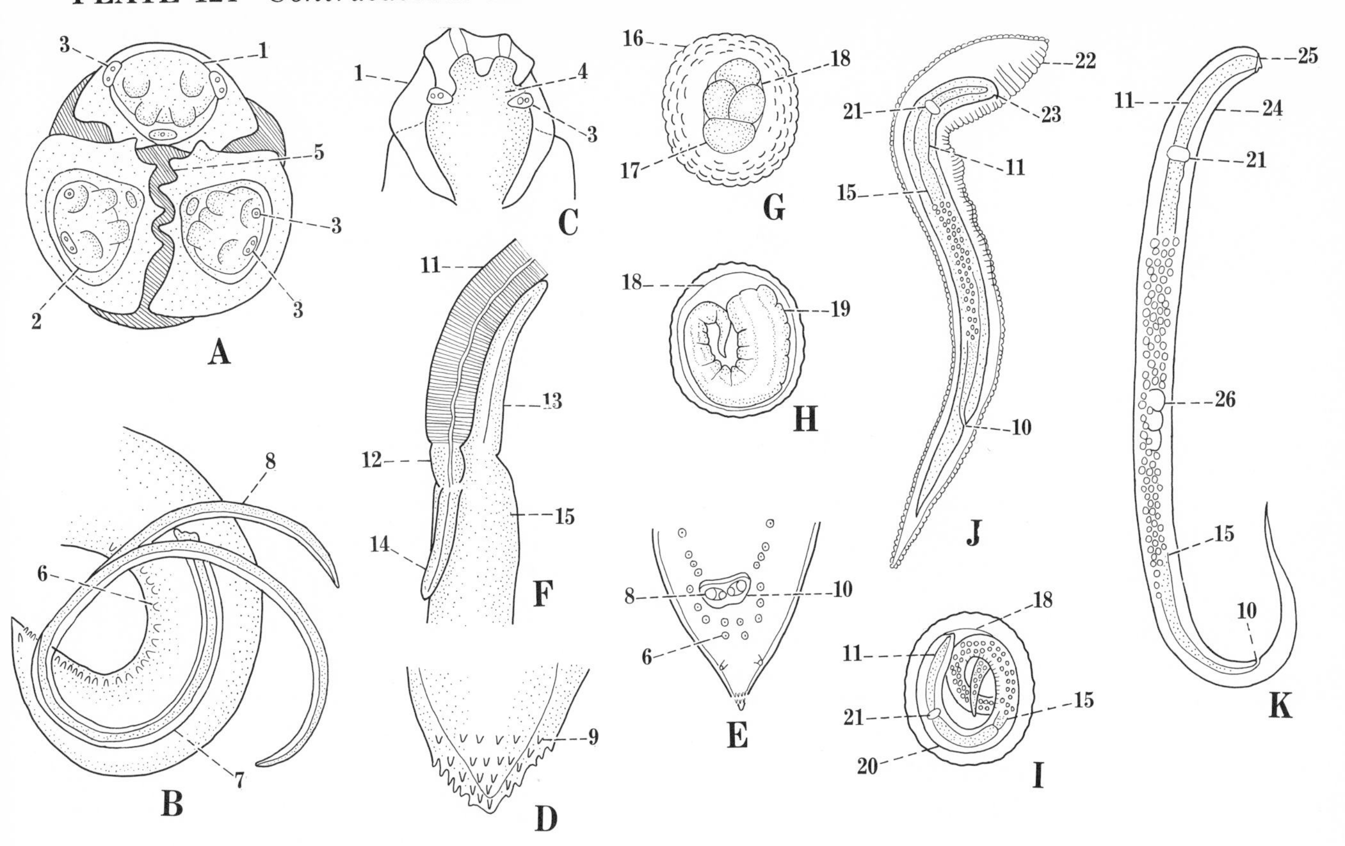

A
1
2
3
5
B
6
7
8
C
4
D
9
E
10
F
11
12
13
14
15
G
16
17
18
H
19
I
20
21
J
22
23
K
24
25
26

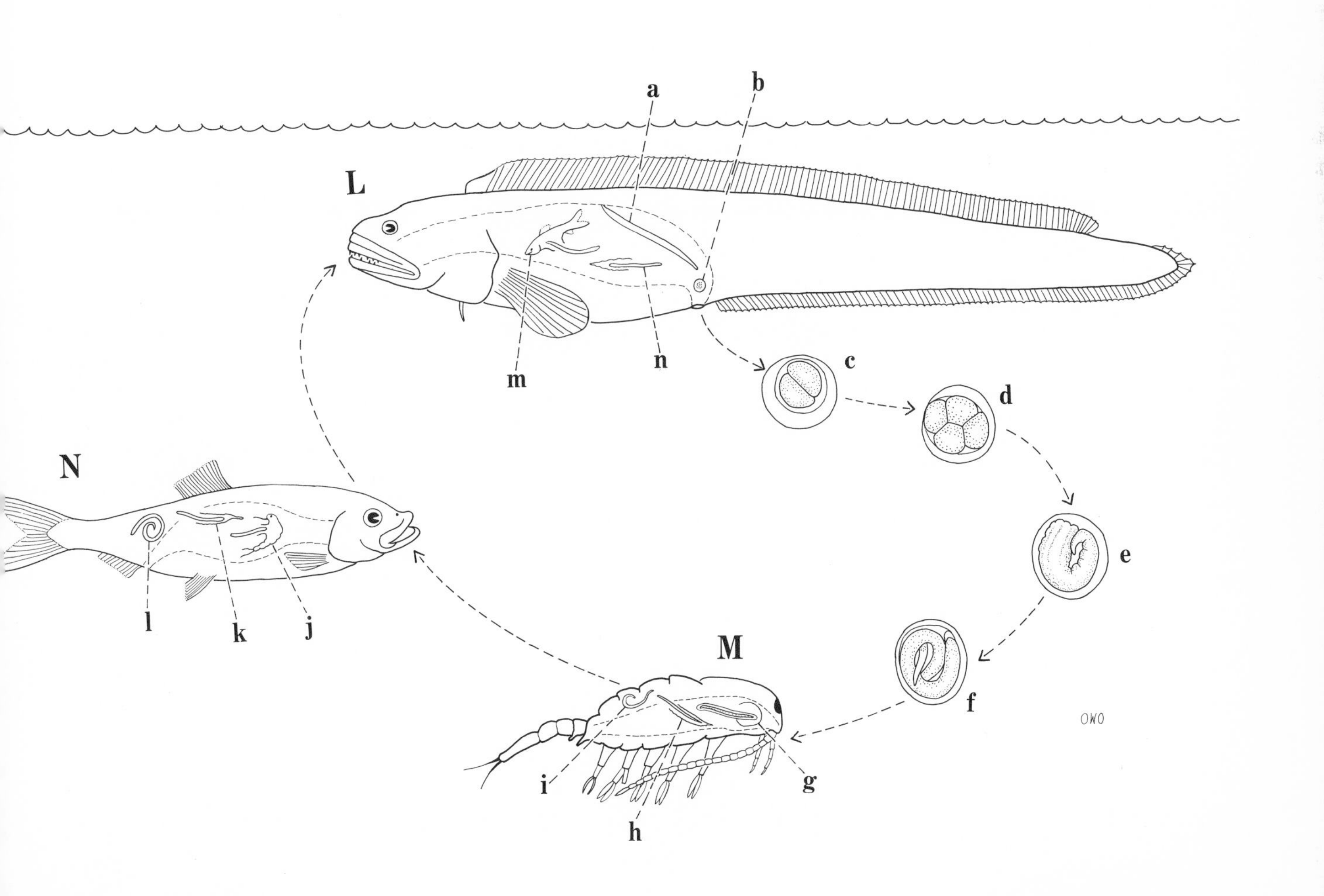

L
a
b
m
n
c
d
e
f
N
l
k
j
M
i
h
g
OWO

Upon being ingested by the copepods, the larvae shed the cuticle of the first molt in the intestine and migrate to the haemocoel. From this point, there is no experimental evidence that these crustaceans serve as intermediaries in nature. The abundance of fourth stage larvae in the body of plankton-feeding fish such as herring leads to the conclusion that some common invertebrate serves as the first intermediate host.

While not demonstrated experimentally, it is likely that eelpouts become infected by eating the infected plankton feeders since the larvae in them and the young parasites in the intestine of the definitive host are similar.

Contracaecum spiculigerum (Rudolphi, 1809) is common in cormorants (*Phalocrocorax auritus auritus*) in the United States, and occurs in ducks, gulls, grebes, pelicans, and other fish-eating birds. The life cycle of specimens from cormorants was studied by Thomas in the United States. He found that two molts occur within the egg by the end of the fifth day at room temperature, and hatching takes place the same day. The third stage larvae were very active, swimming about in the water and coiling and uncoiling within the enclosing sheaths. When eaten by guppies (*Lebistes reticulatus*), the first two enclosing cuticles were shed in the intestine and some of the larvae migrated to the body cavity and encysted on the mesenteries. Attempts to infect large-mouthed bass (*Huro salmoides*), chicks, and ducklings were unsuccessful, presumably because they are unfavorable hosts. Natural infections with larvae occur in bluegills (*Lepomis macrochira*), warmouth bass (*Chaenobryttus gulosus*), and large-mouthed bass. It is concluded without experimental evidence that small fish become infected by eating larvae, piscivorous fish by eating small infected fish, and cormorants by eating either size that contains sufficiently developed and encysted larvae.

Contracaecum osculum (Rudolphi, 1802) is common in pinnipeds. Larvae identical with the adults occur encysted in marine and certain fresh-water fish.

Larvae in the body cavity, stomach, intestine, and liver of a Miller's-thumb-like fish of Lake Baikal in Siberia are so similar to the adult worms in the fresh-water Baikal seal that their identity is assumed. An amphipod is believed to be the first intermediate host (Sudarikov and Rizhikov; Mozgovoi).

EXERCISE ON LIFE CYCLE

There is not agreement on the number of molts that occur in the eggs prior to hatching. In *C. aduncum* there is said to be one but in *C. spiculigerum* two are reported. This should be re-examined for *C spiculigerum* which is available to most students of parasitology.

Copepods should be checked to determine whether they serve as an intermediate host for *C. spiculigerum.*

Cormorants should be used to check the final step in the life cycle. This can be done only by hatching and rearing the birds in the laboratory where they will not be exposed to infection through natural food.

SELECTED REFERENCES

Markowski, S. (1937). Bull. Internat. Acad. Polo. Sci. Lett., Classe Sci. Math. et Nat. Ser. B. Sci. 2:227.

Mozgovi, A. A. (1953). Osnovi Nematodologii, II, p. 169.

Sudarikov, V. E., and K. M. Rizhikov. (1951). Trud. Gelminth. Lab. Akad. Nauk SSR 5:59 (Helminth. Abst).

Thomas, L. J. (1937). J. Parasit. 23:429; (1940). Internat. Congr. (3rd) Microbiol. Rept. Proc. N. Y., p. 458; (1944). Trans. Ill. State Acad. Sci. 37:7.

ORDER SPIRURIDA

The members of this order are parasites of the alimentary canal, coelom, subcutaneous tissues, and blood and lymph vessels of vertebrates. They are characterized by a cylindrical oesophagus that basically is composed of an anterior muscular and a posterior glandular part. The mouth may be surrounded by six weak lips, a cuticular circumoral elevation, or paired lateral pseudolabia. The spicules of the males usually are unequal. The life cycle is indirect, requiring an intermediate host, usually an arthropod.

Representatives from the suborders Camallanina and Spirurina are discussed.

Suborder Camallanina

In this suborder, the oesophageal glands are uninucleate and the larvae are without cephalic hooks but have large pocket-like phasmids. The intermediate hosts are copepods.

SUPERFAMILY DRACUNCULOIDEA

The mouth is porelike and surrounded by an inner circle of four to six papillae and an outer one of four double papillae. The amphids are lateral and posterior from the lateral papillae. The vulva is near the middle of the body; it atrophies before sexual maturity. The females are ovoviparous, with the larvae developing in copepods.

FAMILY DRACUNCULIDAE

The oesophagus consists of a short cylindrical anterior muscular portion followed by a larger and longer part that has a marked median constriction at the level of the nerve ring.

The only representative of this group discussed is the guinea worm *Dracunculus medinensis* whose life cycle is known better than any of the others.

Dracunculus medinensis (Linnaeus, 1758) (Plate 125)

This is a parasite of the subcutaneous tissues of man in many parts of the tropical sections of the world, particularly in Africa and Asia. It has been reported from foxes, mink, and raccoons in North America. Chandler considers *Dracunculus insigne* from raccoons as the North American representative of this genus and not *D. medinensis.*

DESCRIPTION. The adult worms are in the subcutaneous tissue. The males are up to 40 mm and the females from 60 to 120 mm long by a maximum of 1.7 mm wide. There are eight well-developed papillae in the outer and six in the inner cephalic circles; the amphids are well developed. The posterior end of the male is coiled and bears four pairs of preanal and six pairs of postanal papillae; the spicules are 490 and 730 μ long and the gubernaculum 200 μ long. The glandular portion of the oesophagus has a marked constriction at the level of the nerve ring and cephalic papillae.

LIFE CYCLE. Gravid females lie in the subcutaneous tissue with the anterior end pressing outward against the under surface of the skin. The pressure and possibly secretions produce first a papule that develops into a blister and finally into an ulcer-like sore. When the sore is wetted with water, the female is stimulated and thrusts her anterior end outward through it. Internal pressure, possibly due to water entering the pseudocoel of the worm through the membranes, causes the body wall to rupture, allowing the gravid uterus to prolapse. Rents appear in it and a mass of first stage larvae escape into the water. The female withdraws into the subcutaneous region to repeat the process upon subsequent wetting of the area until her entire brood of larvae has been expelled, following which she dies.

Larvae wriggling free in the water are captured and ingested by common copepods of the genera *Cyclops, Eucyclops, Mesocyclops, Macrocyclops,* and several others. The larvae migrate from the intestine into the haemocoel, where two molts take place. Infected cyclops become inactive and move relatively little, usually sinking to the bottom.

Infection of the host occurs when copepods containing third stage larvae are swallowed with drinking water. Upon digestion of the copepods, the larvae are freed in the gut. They penetrate the intestinal mucosa, enter the lymphatics, and travel via the heart, lungs, and heart into the arterial circulation. Upon reaching the capillaries, they leave the blood vessels and migrate to the subcutaneous tissue, undergoing further molts. The sexes are of about equal numbers. After mating takes place, the males disappear and the females continue to move toward the skin. Maturity is reached in 8 to 9 months or longer.

The dracunculids occurring in North American raccoons are thought by Chandler to represent a different but very similar species which he named *D. insigne.* They occur in the subcutaneous tissue of the hind limbs.

Another species, *D. ophidensis* Brackett, 1938, in garter snakes has a life cycle apparently similar to

EXPLANATION OF PLATE 125 ⇨

A. *En face* view of adult female. **B.** Anterior end of adult. **C.** Ventral view of posterior end of adult male. **D.** Anterior end of first stage larva. **E.** Posterior end of first stage larva. **F.** Posterior end of second stage larva. **G.** Posterior end of third stage larva. **H.** Mammalian definitive host. **I.** *Cyclops* intermediate host.

1, mouth; **2,** inner circular circumoral elevation; **3,** quadrangular elevation; **4,** inner circle of six papillae; **5,** outer circle of four double papillae; **6,** amphid; **7,** cervical papillae; **8,** caudal papillae of male; **9,** phasmid; **10,** buccal capsule; **11,** muscular portion of oesophagus; **12-14,** glandular portion of oesophagus; **12,** precorpus of glandular portion of oesophagus; **13,** isthmus; **14,** postcorpus of oesophagus; **15,** nerve ring; **16,** denticle; **17,** oesophagus of first larva; **18,** intestine; **19,** rectum; **20,** phasmid cell; **21,** tail of first stage larva; **22,** cuticle of first stage larva; **23,** tail of second stage larva; **24,** freed cuticle of second stage larva; **25,** tail of third stage larva; **26,** anus.

a, adult worms found first in connective tissue of oesophagus; **b,** adult worms appear later in subcutaneous tissue; **c,** adult female extends anterior portion of body to skin, causing it to vesiculate; **d,** ulcer-like sore forms and ruptures so that the female may extend a portion of her body through the skin to the outside; **e,** when skin is wetted, the female is stimulated to extend the anterior end through the hole in it, at which time a rent occurs in her body wall, the uterus protrudes, ruptures, and releases a mass of first stage larvae; **f,** wriggling larvae attract cyclops which eat them; **g,** larvae migrate through intestinal wall into haemocoel; **h,** larvae molt first time; **i,** second stage larva; **j,** larvae molt second time; **k,** third stage filariform larvae infective to vertebrate host; **l,** vertebrate host infected by swallowing parasitized crustaceans; **m,** larvae freed when cyclops is digested; **n, o,** larvae penetrate intestinal mucosa and enter lacteals and lymph vessels; **p,** larvae enter postcaval vein; **q, r, s,** larvae are carried through right side of heart, lungs, and left side of heart; **t,** larvae in general arterial circulation; **u,** larvae leave blood vessels to enter subcutaneous connective tissue; **v,** partially grown worm in subcutaneous connective tissue (number of molts in body of definitive host unknown but there probably are two).

Figures A, B, C adapted from Moorthy, 1937, J. Parasit. 23:220; D-G, from Moorthy, 1938, Amer. J. Hyg. 27:437.

---

that of *D. medinensis* but it has been studied incompletely. A tadpole has been interpolated into the life cycle of this species.

The Philometridae in the tissue of catastomid fishes have life cycles apparently quite similar to those of the Dracunculidae.

EXERCISE ON LIFE CYCLE

Dracunculus ophidensis of garter snakes and *Philometra nodulosa* of catastomid fishes provide excellent material for studying the life cycles. In areas where infected raccoons occur, *D. insigne* should be studied.

Infected animals provide a source of larvae that may be used for infecting cyclops. Ascertain the development of the larvae in the crustacean hosts. Determine whether tadpoles are essential for infection of garter snakes or whether they provide only an ecological expediency for transferring the larvae to the final host. The phases of the life cycle of *D. ophidensis* and *P. nodulosa* in the definitive hosts are inadequately known.

SELECTED REFERENCES

Brackett, S. (1938). J. Parasit. 24:353.

Chandler, A. C., and C. P. Read. (1961). Introduction to Parasitology, 10th Ed. John Wiley and Sons, New York, p. 503.

Faust, E. C., and P. F. Russell. (1957). Craig and Faust's Clinical Parasitology, 6th Ed. Lea and Febiger, Philadelphia, p. 480.

Moorthy, V. N. (1937). J. Parasit. 23:220; (1938). Amer. J. Hyg. 24:437.

Onabamiro, S. D. (1954). West African Med. J. 3:180; (1956). Ann. Trop. Med. Parasit. 50:157.

Thomas, L. J. (1944). Trans. Ill. State Acad. Sci. 37:7.

Suborder Spirurina

This group of the order Spirurida is characterized by multinucleate oesophageal glands, larvae commonly with cephalic hooks, and phasmidia that are porelike. The intermediate hosts are arthropods but rarely copepods. The Spirurina consists of the superfamilies Spiruroidea and Filarioidea.

PLATE 125 *Dracunculus medinensis*

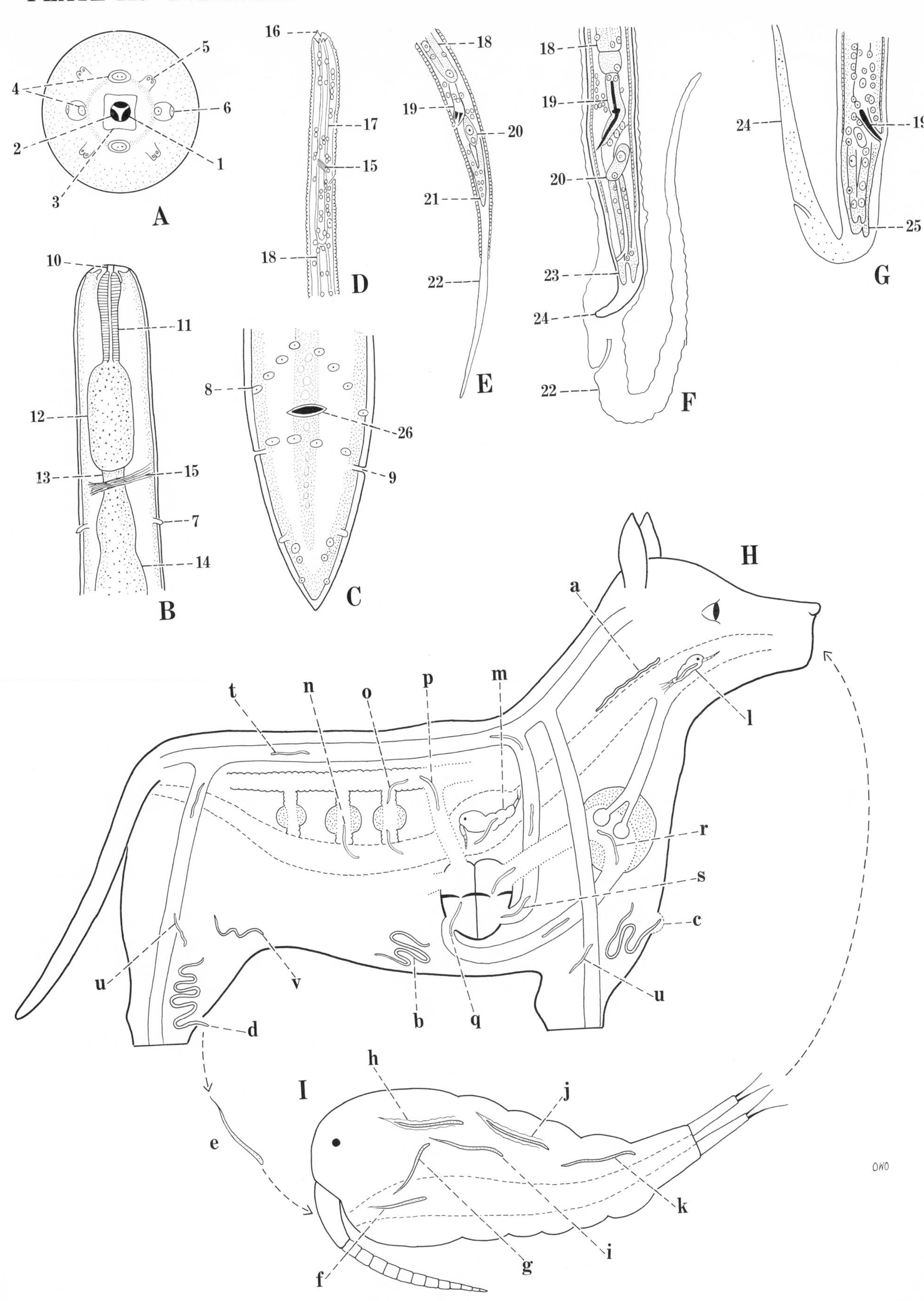

EXPLANATION OF PLATE 126 ▷

A. Anterior end of mature nematode. **B.** *En face* view of adult worm. **C.** Lateral view of posterior end of adult male worm. **D.** Ventral view of adult male worm. **E.** Lateral view of posterior end of adult female. **F.** First stage larva. **G.** Anterior and posterior ends of second stage larva, showing trifurcate tip of tail. **H.** Third stage larva. **I.** Fourth stage larva. **J.** Chicken definitive host. **K.** Cockroach *(Pycnoscelus surinamensis)* intermediate host.

1, outer circle of cephalic papillae; **2**, inner circle of cephalic papillae; **3**, amphid; **4**, mouth surrounded by six-lobed cuticularized ring; **5**, buccal capsule; **6**, oesophagus; **7**, oesophagointestinal valve; **8**, intestine; **9**, nerve ring; **10**, excretory pore; **11**, seminal vesicle; **12**, ejaculatory duct; **13**, preanal papillae; **14**, postanal papillae; **15**, short spicule; **16**, long spicule; **17**, tail; **18**, anus; **19**, ovary; **20**, uterus containing eggs; **21**, vulva; **22**, digitation at tip of tail of second stage larva.

a, adult worm under eyelids of chickens and other birds; **b**, embryonated eggs laid in eyes enter alimentary canal by way of tear duct; **c**, eggs pass down oesophagus into stomach; **d**, eggs pass through intestine; **e**, eggs escape from intestine in faeces; **f**, embryonated eggs do not hatch in soil or faeces; **g**, eggs eaten by woods cockroach; **h**, eggs hatch in intestine and first stage larvae pass through intestinal wall into haemocoel; **i**, first stage larvae molt, producing second stage larvae; **j**, second stage larvae molt into third stage larvae; **k**, third stage larvae encyst in cockroach, producing the infective stage; **l**, infection of birds occurs when cockroaches containing encysted larvae are swallowed; **m**, digestion of cockroaches releases larvae from cysts or body cavity; **n**, larvae escape from body of cockroach; **o**, larvae migrate up oesophagus; **p**, larvae enter tear ducts and migrate into eyes where the two final molts take place, after which maturity is attained.

Figures A, B, C, D, E adapted from Ransom, 1904, U. S. Dept. Agr., Bur. Animal Ind. Bull. 60; F, G, H, I, from Schwabe, 1951, Pacific Sci. 5:18.

SUPERFAMILY SPIRUROIDEA

In this superfamily, the stoma is well developed and there may or may not be two large, lateral, liplike structures. The vulva is near the middle or posterior part of the body and the eggs are fully embryonated when laid.

FAMILY THELAZIIDAE

These nematodes occur under the eyelids of birds and mammals in many parts of the world. They lack lips and have a small buccal capsule without thickenings in the wall.

Oxyspirura mansoni (Cobbold, 1879) (Plate 126)

This is the eyeworm of chickens, turkeys, and a number of wild birds, including English Sparrows, in many of the warm parts of the world, including the southeastern United States. The adults are under the nictitating membrane.

DESCRIPTION. The males are 8.2 to 16 mm long with ventrally curved tail bearing four pairs of preanal and two pairs of postanal papillae. The spicules are markedly unequal in length, one being 0.2 to 0.25 mm long and the other 3.0 to 3.5 mm. The females measure 12 to 20 mm long with the vulva 1 to 1.4 mm from the posterior end of the body. The eggs measure 50 to 65 μ long by 40 to 45 μ wide and contain a first stage larva when laid.

LIFE CYCLE. Adult female worms under the nictitating membrane lay their eggs. These are washed through the nasolacrimal ducts into the pharynx, swallowed, and voided with the faeces. Upon leaving the body, the eggs remain unhatched and without further development of the larvae until eaten by the woods or burrowing cockroach, *Pycnoscellus surinamensis*, an insect of the warmer parts of the world.

Upon reaching the gut of the cockroach, the eggs begin hatching in about 48 hours, and continue for several days. First stage larvae appear in the body cavity by the eighth day. They are surrounded by a cystlike structure of host origin. About 3 weeks later, the second and final molt in the roach occurs. The third stage larvae may be free or encysted in the body cavity. They are infective to birds.

When roaches harboring infective larvae are swallowed by the birds, the parasites are liberated in the crop. They quickly make their way up the oesophagus, into the pharynx, and through the naso-

PLATE 126 *Oxyspirura mansoni*

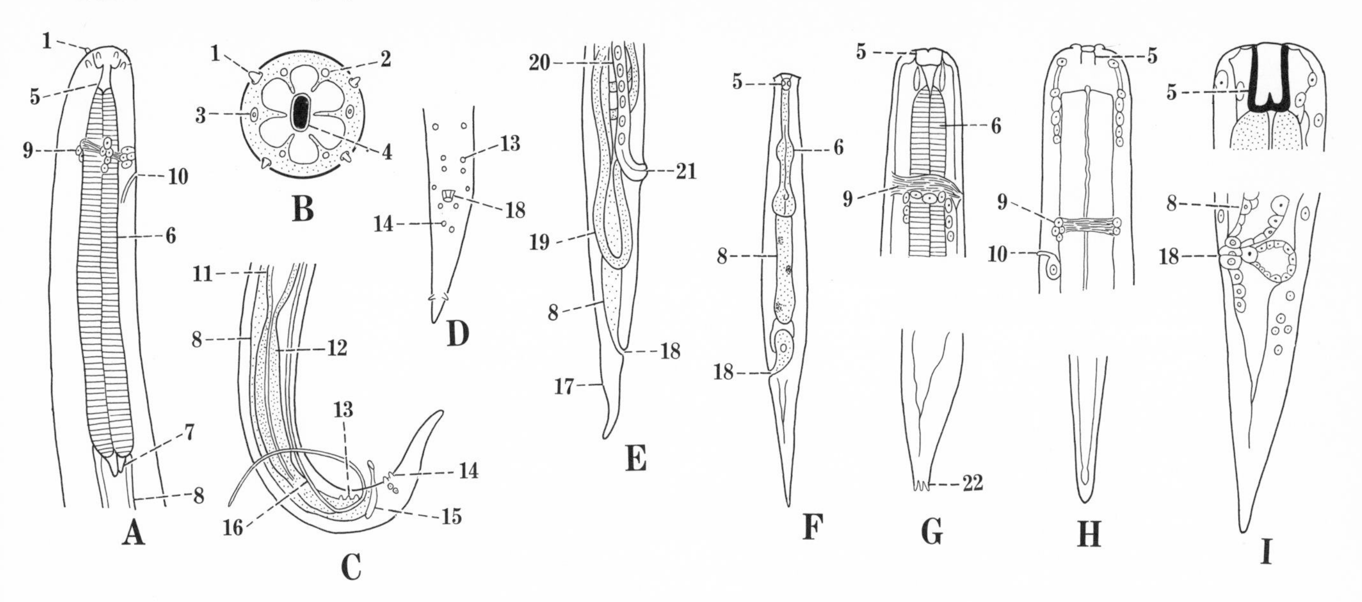

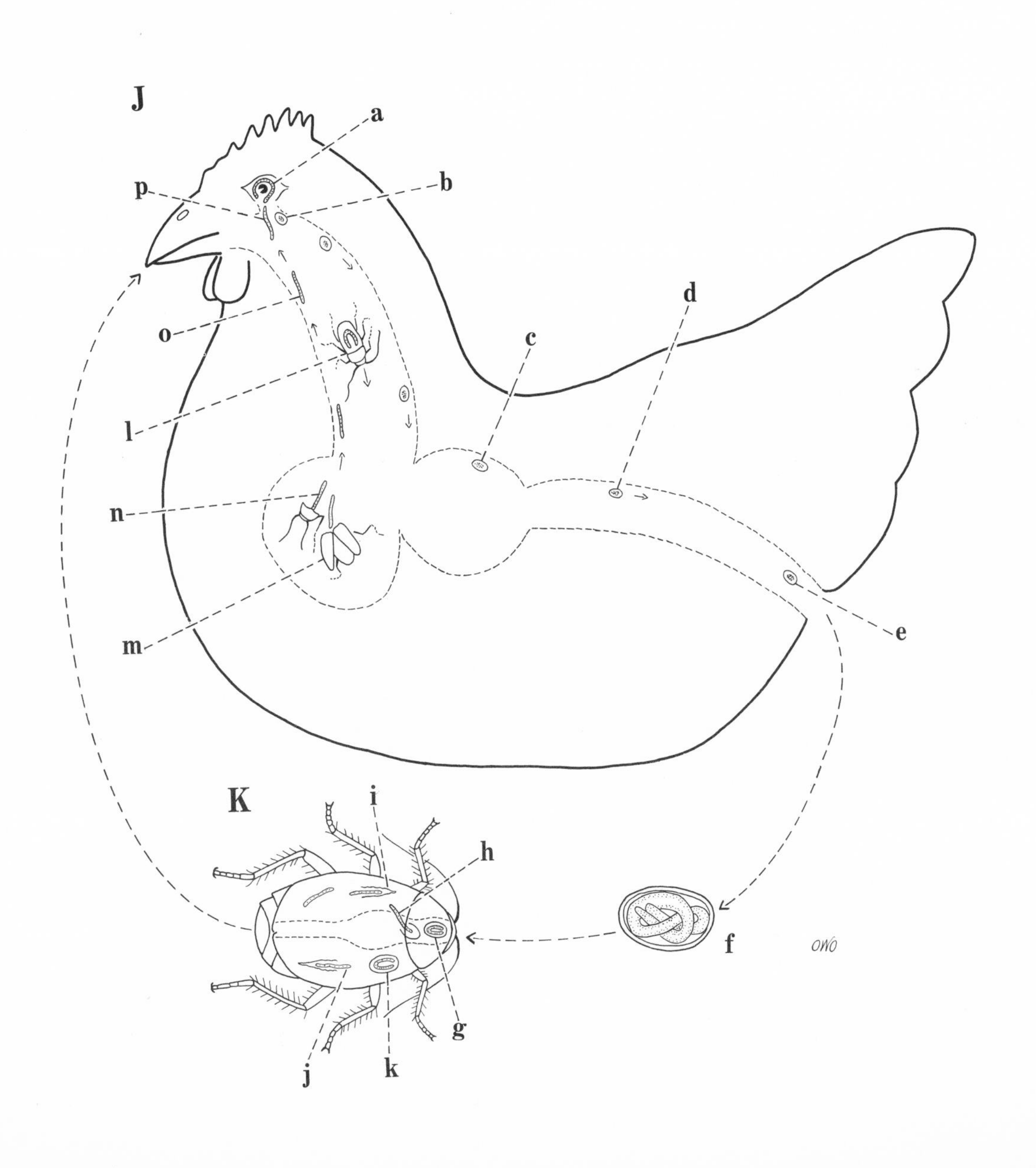

lacrimal ducts into the eyes. The third molt takes place in about 2 days and the fourth and final one about 3 weeks later. Sexual maturity is attained in about 30 days after infection.

A number of species of *Thelazia*, a related genus, occur in the eyes of sheep, goats, cattle, and other animals. *T. californiensis* in sheep, deer, horses, cats, dogs, coyotes, bears, and humans in California showed development in the lesser house fly *Fannia canicularis*, a relative of *Musca*. In Russia, the flies *Musca larvipara* and *M. autumnalis* serve as intermediate hosts of *Thelazia rhodesii* in cattle. *Stomoxys calcitrans*, other bloodsucking flies, and the common house fly (*Musca domestica*) are of no importance in transmitting this parasite.

EXERCISE ON LIFE CYCLE

In regions where eyeworms of chickens occur, interesting experiments can be performed. A colony of uninfected roaches for experimental purposes may be obtained from adult females kept in small dishes, fed brown bread, and provided with water.

Embryonated eggs obtained by macerating gravid females from the eyes of chickens are suitable for infecting laboratory-reared cockroaches.

After feeding a large series of roaches embryonated eggs, examine some daily for the first 10 days and at 2 to 3 day intervals for the next 40 days. Hatching in the gut, migration of the larvae into the body cavity, and the development of the second and third stage larvae will be observed.

Upon obtaining third stage larvae, introduce some of them, freed from the roaches, into the oesophagus of young unexposed chicks by means of a pipette. Check the eyes within 5 minutes by rinsing with a saline solution and at similar intervals to ascertain how quickly the larvae reach them from the oesophagus. Feed a dozen chicks infected roaches and examine the eyes at 2-day intervals to trace the development to adults.

SELECTED REFERENCES

Burnett, H. S., W. C. Parmelee, R. D. Lee, and E. D. Wagner. (1957). J. Parasit. 43:433.

Klesov, M. D. (1949). Dokladi Nauk USSR 66:309.

Lapage, G. (1956). Mönnig's Veterinary Helminthology and Entomology, 4th Ed. Williams and Wilkins Co., Baltimore, p. 27.

Ransom, B. H. (1904). U. S. Dept. Agr., B. A. I. Bull. 60.

Sanders, D. A., and M. W. Emmel. (1938). Univ. Florida Agr. Exp. Sta. Press Bull. 511.

Schwabe, C. W. (1949). Proc. Hawaii Ent. Soc. 13:433; (1951). Pacific Sci. 5:18.

FAMILY SPIRURIDAE

The members of this family are parasites of the oesophagus, stomach, and intestine of vertebrates. The eggs are embryonated when laid, or they may even hatch in the uterus of the female. There are two well-developed bilobed lateral lips; small interlabia, one dorsal and one ventral, may be present.

Habronema megastoma (Rudolphi, 1819) (Plate 127)

This is one of the three species of related stomach worms in equines. It is the cause of stomach ulcers and granulomatous summer sores originating from wounds in the skin that are infected with larvae from the probosci of house flies feeding on them.

The life cycle of *Habronema* in flies is very similar to that of Filarioidea in mosquitoes. It is thought that this may be a connecting link between the superfamilies Spiruroidea and Filarioidea.

DESCRIPTION. The head is separated from the body by a constriction. The males are 7 to 10 mm long. There are three pairs of preanal and one pair of postanal papillae on the ventrally curved tail. The left spicule is cylindrical and 460 μ long and the right one is flattened and 280 μ long.

The females measure 10 to 13 mm long with the vulva about median. The eggs are embryonated when passed in the faeces and are 40 to 50 μ long by 9 to 11 μ wide normally but they may stretch far beyond this length.

LIFE CYCLE. The elongated eggs contain a first stage larva folded upon itself when laid in the stomach. These are voided with the faeces, where survival may be up to 2 weeks without further development.

When eaten by the larvae of house flies (*Musca domestica*), the eggs hatch soon and first stage larvae 105 to 110 μ long are present in the intestine. They bear a small, inverted, V-shaped movable stylet similar to the larvae of filarioid worms. No growth takes place in the intestine of flies. The larvae enter the Malpighian tubules on the third day where they molt and differentiate into short and thick (90 μ by 8 to 10 μ) sausage-shaped second stage larvae similar to those of the filarioids. Outlines of the oesophagus, intestine, and rectum appear by the fourth day when most of the larvae have entered the Malpighian tubules. The sausage stage persists into the pupal stage of the flies. As growth of the larval worms continues, the epithelial cells of the Malpighian tubules are destroyed, leaving the larvae encased in the membranes. They have grown to 500 μ long and 30 to 35 μ wide, which appears to be the only change.

On the sixth day, they molt the second time and transform from the sausage to the vermiform stage which is 600 to 900 μ long and enclosed in the loose cuticle of the sausage stage. By the seventh day, they are 1.3 to 2 mm long. The third stage larvae begin to migrate from the Malpighian tubules into the body cavity on the eighth day. They are in the thorax, head, and proboscis by the ninth to eleventh days, being infective to the horses at this time.

Infection of horses takes place when third stage larvae escaping from the labella of flies feeding on the moist mucuous membranes of the lips are swallowed. Chilled or dead infected flies swallowed with forage also result in infections. Upon reaching the stomach, the larvae presumably enter the glands of the mucosa and molt twice, but there is no experimental evidence to verify this. As growth continues, ulcers are formed in the wall of the stomach, where adult worms occur.

When infected flies feed on the moist surfaces of wounds in the skin of horses, the larvae escape from the mouth parts and enter them. Irritation caused by the larvae prevents healing, and a large pulpy mass of tissue appears that may persist throughout the summer. Since the etiology of these granulomas is larvae from infected flies, they occur during the warm season when these insects are active, hence the name summer sores. The larvae do not develop to maturity in the skin but die toward the end of the summer.

The intermediate host of *Habronema muscae* is house flies but that of *H. microstoma* is stable flies. The life cycles of these two species are basically the same as that of *H. megastoma*. In *H. microstoma*, the eggs hatch in the uterus of the parent worm, whereas those of *H. muscae* hatch in the intestine of the flies. The larvae of *H. muscae* and *H. microstoma* develop in the fat bodies of the flies instead of in the Malpighian tubules.

Some species of *Habronema* may utilize transport hosts such as appears to be the case with *H. mansioni* of falcons (*Gypaetus barbatus*) in northern China. About 60 per cent of the toads (*Bufo b. asiaticus*) of the area harbor encapsulated larvae in the stomach wall. When the infected toads were fed to falcons, the larvae developed into *H. mansioni* such as occur naturally in the raptors. It might be assumed that the toads acquired the infections from insects and that the amphibians constitute an ecological necessity in the biology of the parasite which has associated itself with the food chain of the falcons.

EXERCISE ON LIFE CYCLE

If an abattoir where horses are slaughtered is accessible, adult female worms may be obtained from the stomach ulcers for a supply of eggs for experimental infections. Embryonated eggs dissected from the uterus and mixed with sterilized horse faeces serve as a medium for infecting larval house flies. These should be reared in horse faeces previously sterilized by heat. Dissection of larval flies each day for 2 weeks after feeding them eggs will show the developmental stages and the time required for each to develop.

SELECTED REFERENCES

Hsü, H. F., and C. Y. Chow. (1938). Chinese Med. J. Suppl. No. 2, p. 419.

Ransom, B. H. (1913). U. S. Dept. Agr. Bull. 163.

Roubaud, E., and J. Descazeaux. (1921). Bull. Soc. Path. Exot. 14:471; (1922). Ibid. 15:572, 978.

Theiler, G. (1923). Thèse, Faculté des Sci., Univ. Neuchâtel. Govt. Print. and Stat. Off., Pretoria.

EXPLANATION OF PLATE 127

A. Lateral view of anterior end of *Habronema megastoma.* **B.** Lateral view of anterior end of *Habronema microstoma.* **C.** Lateral view of anterior end of *Habronema muscae.* **D.** Embryonated egg. **E.** Egg hatching. **F, G.** First stage larva. **H.** Second stage sausage-shaped larva. **I.** Third stage larva. **J.** Anterior end of third stage larva. **K.** Caudal end of third stage larva. **L.** Horse definitive host. **M.** Larval stage of house fly *(Musca domestica).* **N.** Pupal stage of house fly. **O.** Adult house fly.

1, head; **2,** neck; **3,** buccal capsule; **4,** muscular portion of oesophagus; **5,** intestine; **6,** rectum; **7,** anus; **8,** tail; **9,** spiny, knob-shaped tail of third stage larva; **10,** nerve ring; **11,** cervical papilla; **12,** egg shell; **13,** first stage larva; **14,** V-shaped structure at anterior end of first stage larva; **15,** cast cuticle of second stage larva; **16,** portion of Malpighian tubule, surrounding third stage larva.

a, adult worms in gastric ulcers of stomach where eggs are laid; **b, c,** embryonated eggs free in stomach and being passed in faeces; **d,** embryonated egg free in faeces; **e,** eggs swallowed by larvae of fly hatch in intestine; **f,** larvae free in intestine; **g,** larvae enter Malpighian tubules; **h,** first molt occurs in Malpighian tubules of larval fly; **i,** second stage sausage-shaped larvae; **j,** sausage stage larvae in pupa; **k,** elongation of sausage stage; **l,** second molt in pupa or adult fly forming third stage filariform larvae; **m,** ensheathed third stage larvae; **n,** larvae leave Malpighian tubules, entering thorax; **o,** larvae in thorax and proboscis; **p,** larvae escape from labellum in response to warmth of skin when flies feed on moist mucous membranes of mouth; **q, r,** larvae deposited on lips enter mouth and are swallowed; **s,** larvae molt, probably twice, and enter glandular crypts of stomach; **t, u,** infected flies are swallowed with food; **v,** digestion of flies releases larvae; **w,** larvae from flies enter stomach wall; **x,** some larvae encyst in lungs of horse; **y,** flies feeding on open wounds deposit larvae which cause granulomatous growths known as summer sores.

Figures A-C adapted from Theiler, 1923, Thèse Faculté Sci. Univ. Neuchatel, Govt. Print. and Stat. Off., Pretoria; E-K, from Roubaud and Descazeaux, 1921, Bull. Soc. Path. Exot. 14:471.

FAMILY TETRAMERIDAE

These nematodes occur in the crypts of Lieberkühn of the proventriculus of chickens, turkeys, pigeons, ducks, and many wild birds. The males are small and vermiform, whereas gravid females become greatly distended with eggs, assuming a markedly fusiform shape. In some species, the females are somewhat coiled. The anterior end of the worms is without raised looping ridges known as cordons.

Tetrameres crami (Swales, 1933) (Plate 128)

T. crami is a parasite of the proventriculus of domestic and wild ducks of North America.

DESCRIPTION. The males are 2.9 to 4.1 mm long by 70 to 92 μ wide. There is a double row of spinelike sensory organs extending the full length of the body, together with one pair of cervical spines. The lateral pseudolabia are trilobed with interlabia. The right spicule is 136 to 185 μ and the left 272 to 350 μ long. The gravid females are globular to spindle-shaped, 1.5 to 3.25 mm long by 1.2 to 2.2 mm wide, and are blood red. The vulva is near the posterior end of the body. Eggs are 42 to 57 μ long by 26 to 34 μ wide.

LIFE CYCLE. The eggs contain fully developed first stage larvae when laid. They hatch when eaten by fresh-water gammarids (*Hyallela knickerbockeri* and *Gammarus fasciatus*). The larvae migrate into the coelom and molt for the first time. Second stage larvae appear in 7 to 11 days after the eggs are eaten. They migrate to various parts of the body and generally encyst in thin-walled vesicles, commonly in the coxae, on the inner surface of the dorsal shield, and occasionally in the muscles of the walking legs.

The second molt usually occurs in the cyst with subsequent development of the third stage larvae continuing inside it. These encysted larvae acquire great length, up to 1.4 mm in 20 to 65 days. Infection of ducks occurs when gammarids containing third stage larvae are eaten. They escape from the crustacea in the crop and make their way to the proventriculus. The third molt takes place and the fourth stage larvae are found in the crypts of Lieberkühn. While a fourth molt is indicated, it has not been observed. Male worms develop to maturity in about one month and females sometime between one and two months.

Tetrameres americanus of poultry and quail in North America utilizes grasshoppers (*Melanoplus femurrubrum* and *M. differentialis*) and cockroaches (*Blatella germanica*) as intermediate hosts.

PLATE 127 *Habronema megastoma, H. microstoma, H. muscosae*

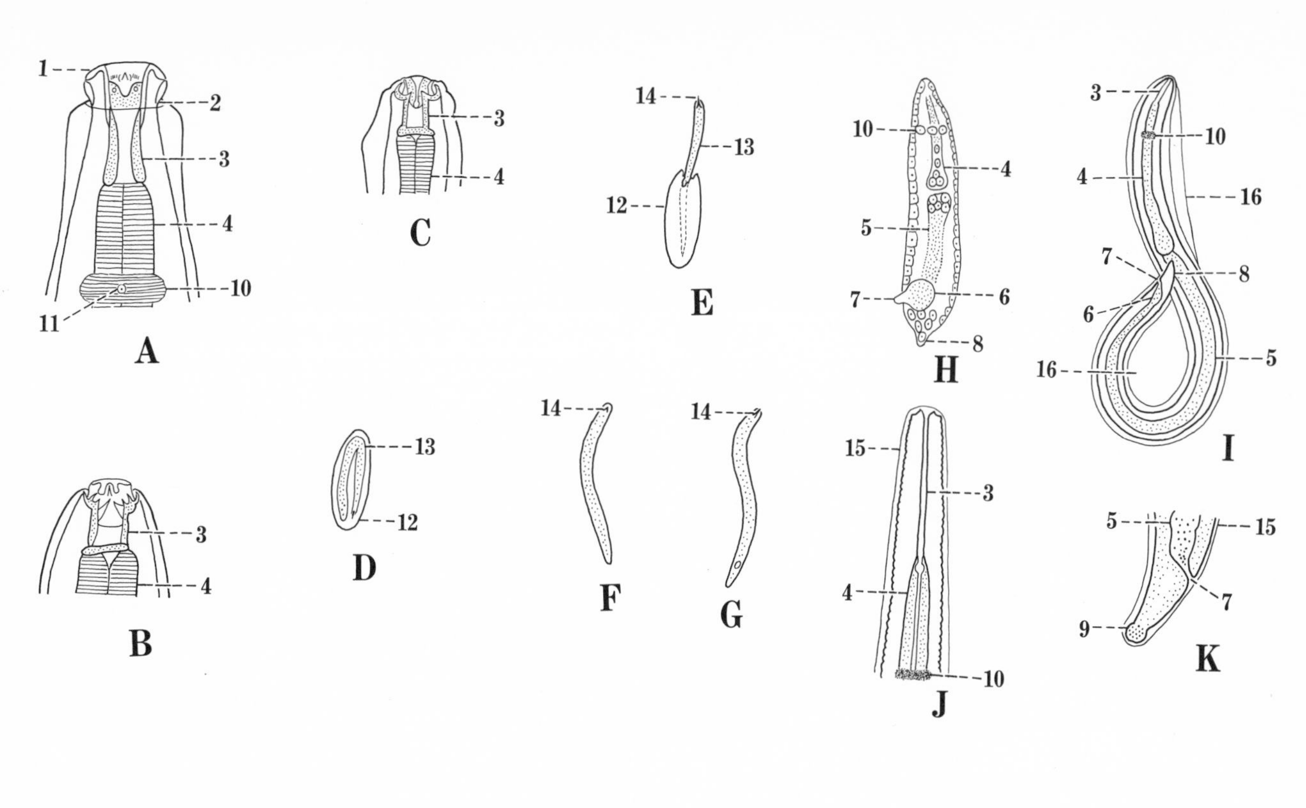

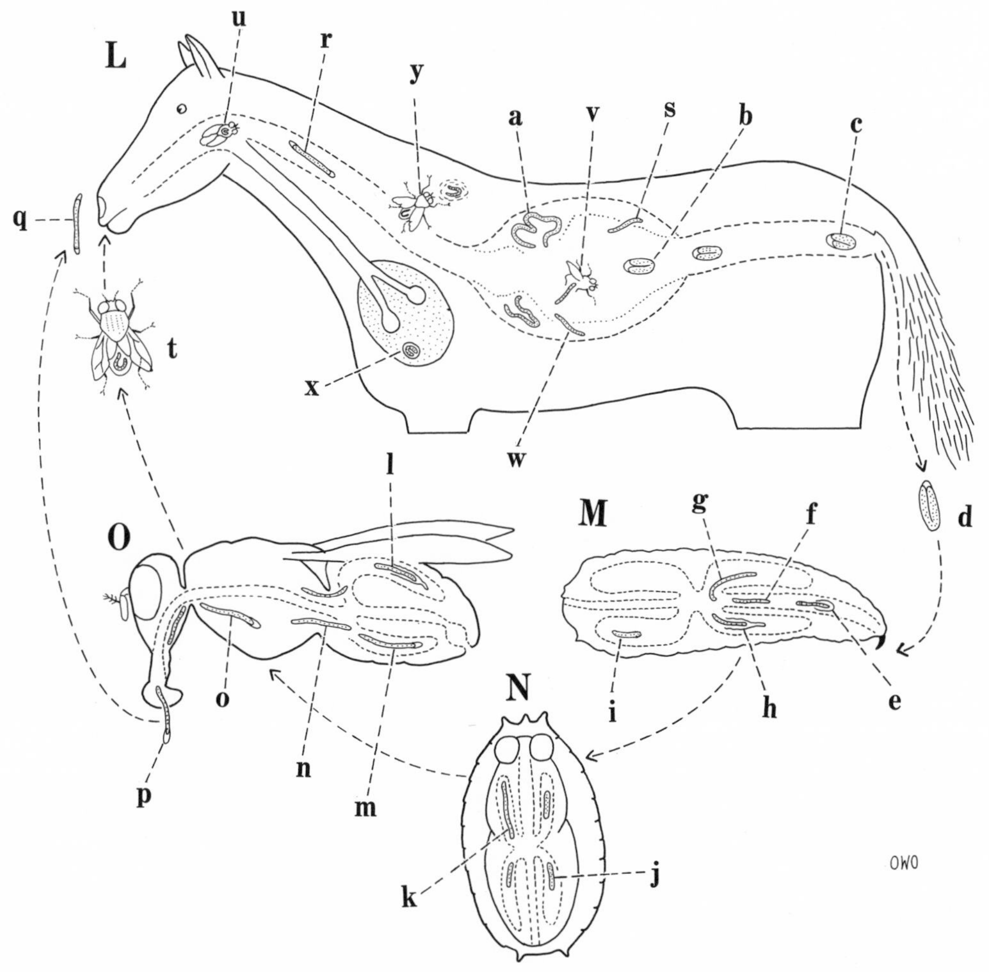

EXPLANATION OF PLATE 128 ⇨

A. Anterior end of adult male. **B.** Posterior end of adult male. **C.** Gravid female. **D.** Embryonated egg containing first stage larva. **E.** Caudal end of second stage larva taken from intestine of gammarid. **F.** Caudal end of third stage larva from body cavity of gammarid 60 days after infection. **G.** Caudal end of fourth stage male from proventriculus of duck. **H.** Fourth stage female larva from proventriculus of duck. **I.** Definitive host (duck). **J.** Intermediate gammarid host *(Gammarus* and *Hyalella)*.

1, cephalic papilla; **2,** anterior spinelike sensory organs; **3,** cervical papilla; **4,** buccal capsule; **5,** muscular portion of oesophagus; **6,** glandular portion of oesophagus; **7,** nerve ring; **8,** posterior spinelike sensory papillae; **9,** genital papillae; **10,** intestine; **11,** anus; **12,** ejaculatory duct; **13,** left spicule; **14,** right spicule; **15,** cuticular caudal cone; **16,** uterus of gravid female; **17,** vulva; **18,** thick shell of egg; **19,** first stage larva in egg; **20,** genital primordium; **21,** sensory organs; **22,** caudal sensory papillae; **23,** primordium of male reproductive organs; **24,** primordium of female reproductive organs.

a, gravid female in crypts of Leiberkühn of proventriculus; **b,** embryonated eggs containing first stage larva when laid; **c,** eggs mixed with faeces; **d,** embryonated eggs in water; **e,** gammarid intermediate host eating embryonated eggs; **f,** eggs hatching in intestine and liberation of first stage larvae; **g,** larvae pass through intestinal wall into haemocoel; **h,** first stage larvae molt; **i,** second stage larvae encyst; **j,** second molt takes place in cysts and third stage larvae grow; **k,** gammarids partially digested in crop; **l,** cysts released from body of crustaceans; **m,** larvae escape from cyst; **n,** loose cuticle of second molt discarded (not a molt); **o,** third molt; **p,** fourth stage larvae enter proventricular crypts; **q,** fourth molt not seen but presumed to take place after which development proceeds to the adult stage.

Adapted from Swales, 1936, Canad. J. Res. 14:151.

It may be generalized that species of *Tetrameres* infecting terrestrial birds utilize land arthropods, namely Orthoptera, as intermediate hosts, whereas those infecting waterfowl are in aquatic crustacea, gammarids primarily.

EXERCISE ON LIFE CYCLE

Place eggs dissected from gravid females in small containers of water together with *Gammarus fasciatus* or *Hyalella knickerbockeri,* common gammarids in streams, lakes and ponds of North America. Dissection of some of the crustacea at daily intervals for 3 to 4 weeks will show the stages of development of the second and third stages of larvae.

Adult worms can be obtained by feeding infected gammarids to ducklings, and at the same time the prepatent period can be determined.

Eggs of *Tetrameres* from chickens should be fed to grasshoppers, preferably young ones but not necessarily only immature individuals. Dissect a series of grasshoppers at intervals after eating infective eggs in order to follow the stages of development of the larvae.

Feed grasshoppers containing infective third stage larvae to a series of chicks. Sacrifice the birds at intervals to follow the development of the worms. Check the faeces for the appearance of eggs to ascertain how long it takes for the nematodes to reach sexual maturity.

SELECTED REFERENCES

Cram, E. B. (1931). U. S. Dept. Agr., Tech. Bull. 227, p. 3.

Swales, W. E. (1933). Canad. J. Res. 8:334; (1936). Ibid. D. 14:151.

FAMILY ASCAROPIDAE

Members of this family parasitize the anterior portion of the alimentary canal. They occur in the stomach of swine, rats, and mice, in the rumen, intertwined in the mucosa and submucosa of the oesophagus of ruminants, and in the crop of chickens. They are thick-bodied or filiform worms with small lips. The wall of the pharynx is provided with distinct spiral or annular thickenings (*Ascarops, Physocephalus*), or the anterior end of the body is covered with distinct cuticular plaques (*Gongylonema*). Irregular caudal alae are present on the males.

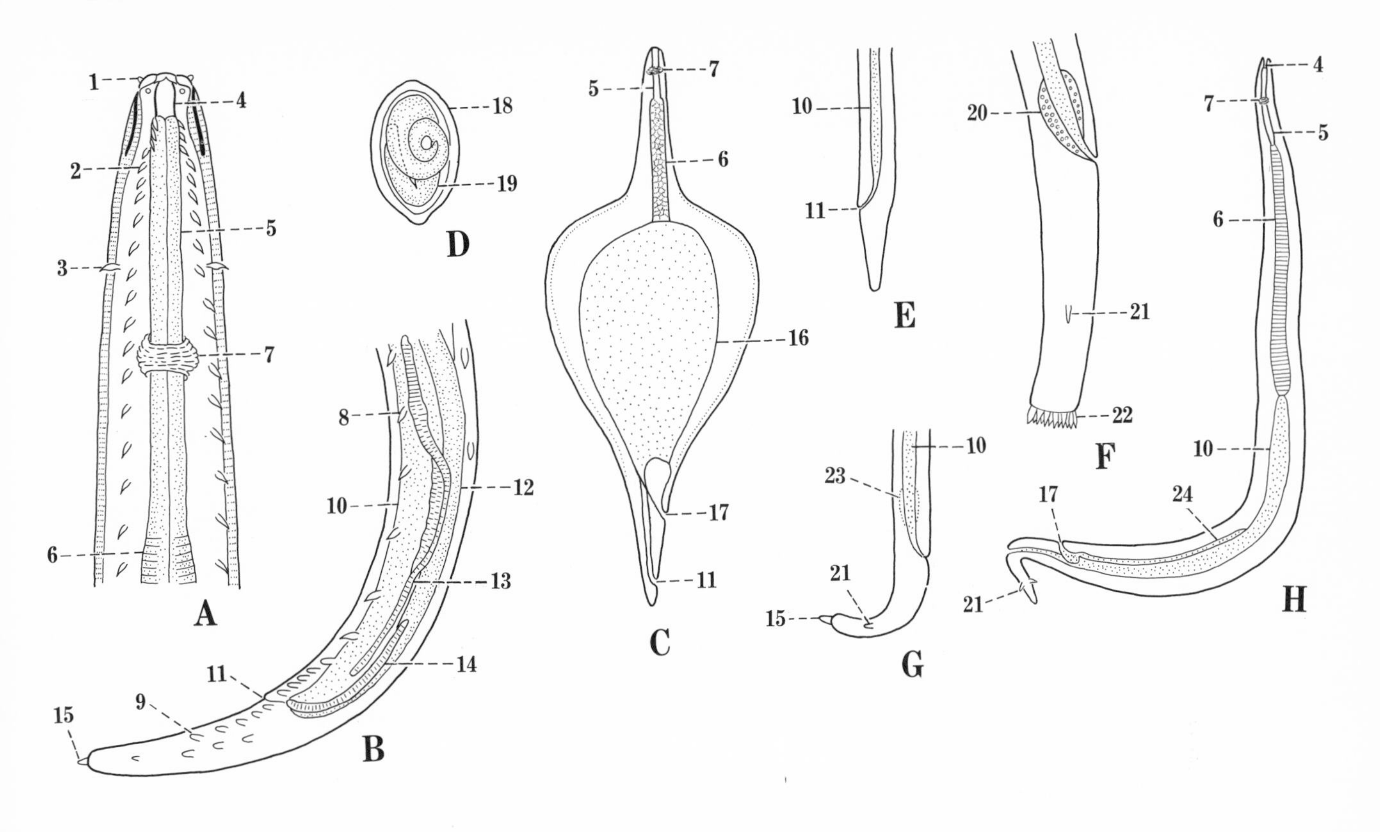
1
2
3
4
5
6
7
A
8
9
10
11
12
13
14
15
B
18
19
D
5
6
7
16
17
11
C
10
11
E
10
23
21
15
G
20
21
22
F
4
7
5
6
10
17
24
21
H

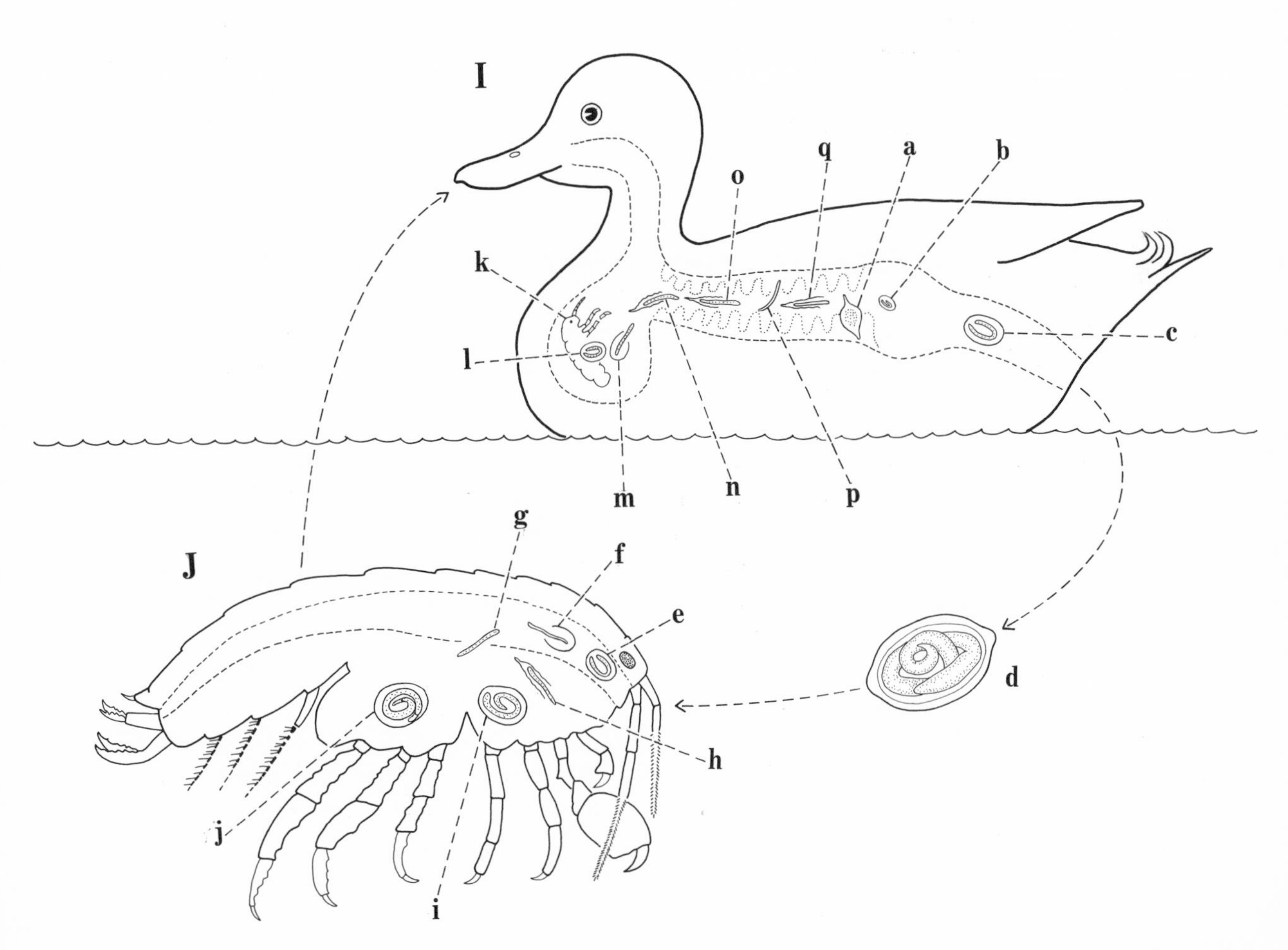
I
o
q
a
b
k
l
c
m
n
p
g
J
f
e
h
d
j
i

EXPLANATION OF PLATE 129 ⇨

A. Anterior end of adult *Ascarops strongylina.* **B-D.** First stage larva of *A. strongylina* (relatively similar for *P. sexalatus*). **B.** Sinistral view of anterior end. **C.** Ventral view. **D.** Tail. **E.** Tail of second stage larva. **F.** Tail of third stage larva. **G.** Encysted third stage larva. **H.** Anterior end of adult *Physocephalus sexalatus.* **I.** Tail of third stage larva of *P. sexalatus,* showing morphological characteristic. **J.** Swine definitive host. **K.** Dung beetle *(Ataenius cognatus* and *Aphodius granarius)* intermediate host.

1, inner circle of cephalic papillae; **2,** outer circle of cephalic papillae; **3,** buccal capsule; **4,** spiral pharynx; **5,** muscular portion of oesophagus; **6,** cervical papillae; **7,** cervical alae; **8-18,** *Ascarops strongylina;* 8, cephalic hooks; **9,** rows of spines; **10,** tail showing terminal spine; **11,** anus; **12,** characteristic knoblike tip of tail of second stage larva; **13,** free cuticle from first stage larva; **14,** rectal glands; **15,** intestine; **16,** characteristic knoblike tip of tail of third stage larva; **17,** third stage larva encysted in beetle host; **18,** cyst wall of beetle origin; **19,** spiny tip of tail of third stage larva of *P. sexalatus.*

a, adult worm in stomach; **b,** embryonated eggs passed in faeces; **c,** egg with characteristic thick shell, having striations at each end; **d,** eggs are eaten by dung beetles *(Ataenius* and *Aphodius);* **e,** eggs hatch in intestine; **f,** first stage larvae migrate through intestinal wall into haemocoel; **g,** larvae encyst and undergo first molt within cyst; **h,** second stage larvae with free cuticle; **i,** second molt in cyst with two cuticles free; **j,** fully developed third stage larvae in thick-walled cysts; **k,** pigs become infected by swallowing infected dung beetles; **l,** beetles digested so that cysts and larvae are liberated; **m,** third stage larvae penetrating gastric mucosa; **n,** third molt presumably takes place in mucosa; **o,** fourth stage larvae leave mucosa; **p,** fourth and final molt in stomach.

Figures A and H adapted from various sources; B-G, I, from Alicata, 1935, U. S. Dept. Agr. Tech. Bull. 489.

Ascarops strongylina (Rudolphi 1819) (Plate 129)

A. strongylina, together with *Physocephalus sexalatus* (Molin, 1860), a closely related species, are known as the thick stomach worms of swine. They are common in many parts of the United States.

DESCRIPTION. The pharynx appears as a spiralled rod and is 83 to 98 μ long. Males measure 10 to 15 mm long with a cervical ala on the left side; the right caudal ala is about twice the length of the left. There are four pairs of preanal and one of postanal papillae, all arranged asymmetrically. The left spicule is 2.24 to 2.95 mm long and the right 0.46 to 0.62 mm. Females are 16 to 22 mm long with the vulva slightly anterior to the middle of the body. Eggs measure 34 to 39 μ long by 20 μ wide, have thick shells with a striated plug at each end, and are embryonated when passed.

LIFE CYCLE. When ingested by dung beetles (*Aphodius granarius* and others) the eggs hatch in the midgut and the first stage larvae migrate through the intestinal wall into the haemocoel where they remain free for a short time. After about 2 weeks, most of the first stage larvae are in thin cysts in the walls of Malpighian tubules. Two to 3 days later they undergo the first molt in the cyst. Following a week of growth they go through the second molt, which is about a month after infection of the beetles. Both the second and third stage larvae completely shed the cuticle inside the cyst. Fully developed cysts containing third stage larvae usually become free in the haemocoel.

Infection of swine takes place when infected dung beetles are swallowed and digested. Third stage larvae freed from the beetles enter the gastric mucosa where the third molt occurs. When the fourth stage larvae return to the lumen of the stomach, they molt for the final time and develop to maturity in about 1 month.

The life cycle of *Physocephalus sexalatus* is similar in general to that of *A. strongylina.* This parasite develops in a large number of species of dung beetles. When infected beetles harboring third stage larvae are eaten by chickens and bats, as well as other animals, the larvae migrate from the alimentary canal to the coelom and encyst on the wall of the gut. These larvae are capable of development when eaten by pigs, thus chickens and bats become paratenic hosts and can be a source of infection to pigs.

Species of *Gongylonema* develop in dung beetles in a manner similar to that of *A. strongylina.* In the case of those species embedded in the oesophageal wall, the route of migration from the point where the larvae are liberated to the final site is unknown.

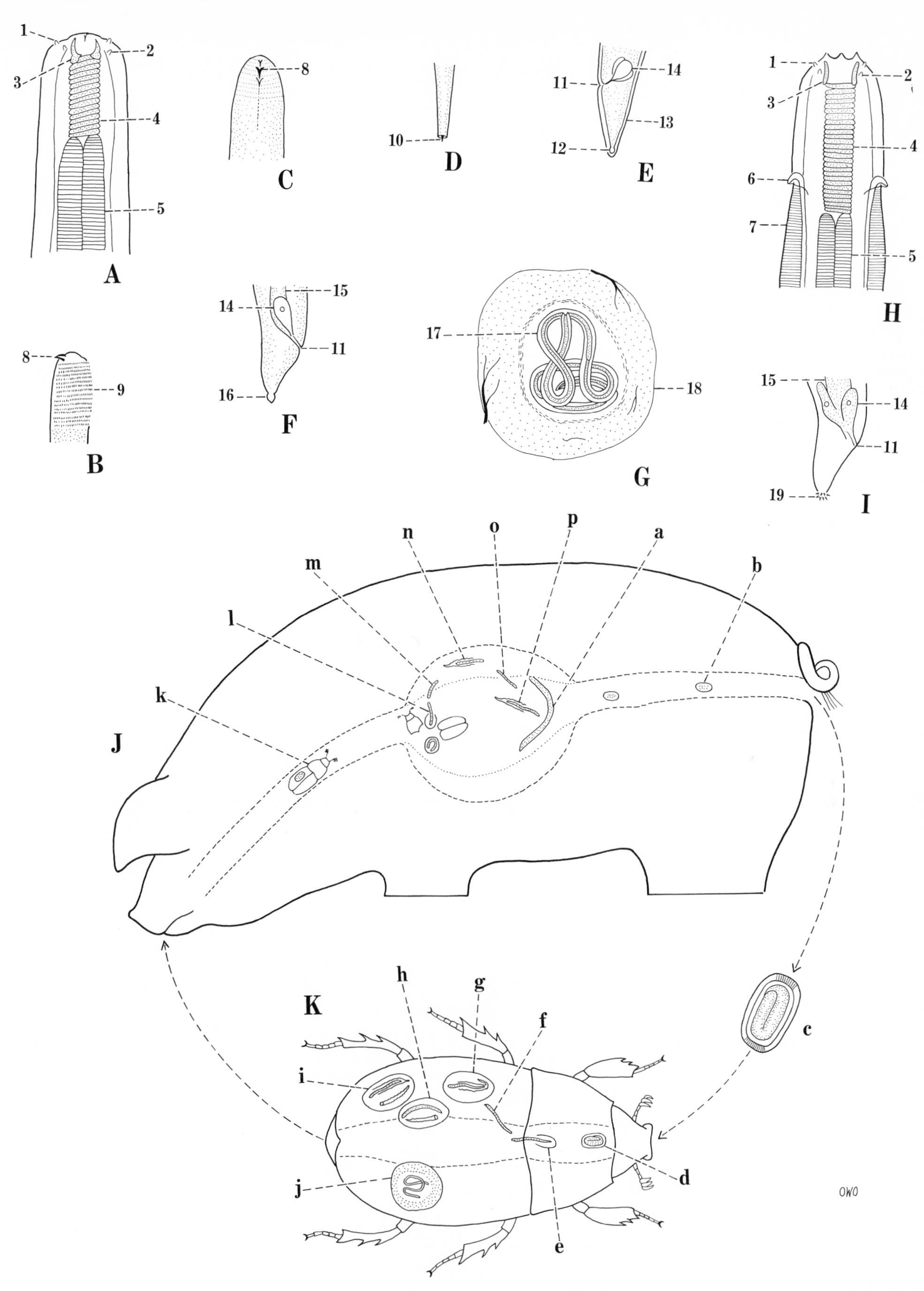
1
2
3
4
5
A
8
C
10
D
11
14
13
12
E
6
7
H
9
B
15
16
F
17
18
G
19
I
n
o
p
a
m
b
l
k
J
K
h
g
f
c
i
d
j
e
OWO

EXPLANATION OF PLATE 130

A. Lateral view of anterior end of adult worm. **B.** Ventral view of anterior end of adult. **C.** *En face* view (somewhat diagrammatic). **D.** Ventral view of posterior end of adult male. **E.** Amphidelphis uterus. **F.** Egg capsule containing eggs. **G.** Cyst from larval *Pogonomyrmex barbatus.* **H.** Cyst with larva from pupal ant. **I.** Cyst from gaster of callow. **J.** Cyst from gaster of adult ant. **K.** First stage larva. **L.** Second stage larva. **M.** Third stage larva. **N.** Horned lizard *(Phrynosoma cornutum)* definitive host. **O.** Worker ants *(P. barbatus)* carry gravid female worms into nest. **P.** Larval ant. **Q.** Pupal ant. **R.** Adult ant intermediate host.

1, tooth; **2**, amphid; **3**, external row of papillae; **4**, mouth; **5**, anus; **6**, sessile preanal papillae; **7**, sessile postanal papillae; **8**, stalked lateral papillae; **9**, lateral ala; **10**, oesophagus; **11**, intestine; **12**, rectum; **13**, vulva; **14**, vagina; **15**, branch of amphidelphis uterus; **16**, egg capsule; **17**, embryonated eggs; **18**, cyst wall; **19**, fat droplets in trophocytes inside cyst; **20**, larva; **21**, excretory organ; **22**, genital primordium; **23**, female reproductive primordium; **24**, nerve ring.

a, adult worms in stomach; **b**, gravid female passing through intestine to outside; **c**, gravid female outside lizard; **d**, gravid females carried into nest of ants by workers; **e**, embryonated egg; **f**, eggs hatch in intestine; **g**, larval nematodes pass through intestinal wall into haemocoel; **h**, cyst containing larva and fat droplets; **i**, cyst in pupa; **j**, cyst in gaster of adult worker; **k**, infected worker being digested in stomach of lizard; **l**, cyst being liberated from ant; **m**, larval nematodes escape from cysts; **n**, larvae molt and develop to maturity (a).

Figures A-E adapted from Morgan, 1942, Lloydia 5:314; F-M, from Lee, 1957, J. Parasit. 43:66.

EXERCISE ON LIFE CYCLE

Adult female worms procured from abattoirs where swine are slaughtered provide a source of eggs for experimental infection of dung beetles. Eggs may be obtained by chopping up gravid worms in a few drops of water and transferring the material to pieces of blotting paper which are placed in small dishes containing five or six dung beetles. Dissect some of the beetles at 12 and 24 hours after they have eaten the eggs to ascertain the location of the first stage larvae. Continue dissections at 2- and 3-day intervals to follow the development of them.

If working with *P. sexalatus,* feed beetles containing third stage larvae to young chicks to obtain larvae encysted on the wall of the alimentary canal. In the event *P. sexalatus* is not available, third stage larvae of *A. strongylina* should be fed to chicks to determine if they encyst on the viscera.

SELECTED REFERENCES

Alicata, J. E. (1934). Proc. Helminth. Soc. Wash. 1:13.

Allen, R. W., and L. A. Spindler. (1949). Proc. Helminth. Soc. Wash. 16:1.

Porter, D. A. (1939). Proc. Helminth. Soc. Wash. 6:79.

Spindler, L. A. (1942). U. S. Dept. Agr. Yrbk., p. 751.

FAMILY PHYSALOPTERIDAE

This family contains a large number of species which occur commonly in reptiles, birds, and mammals, but only rarely in amphibians. They are relatively large worms with thick bodies and attach to the mucosa of the stomach or intestine. The cuticle of the anterior end of the body is reflected forward over the pseudolabia, forming a collarette. The caudal alae are supported by long slender papillae.

Physaloptera phrynosoma Ortlepp, 1922 (Plate 130)

P. phrynosoma is a common parasite of the stomach of horned lizards (*Phrynosoma cornutum*) from the arid regions of the southwestern part of the United States and similar areas of Mexico.

DESCRIPTION. Adult males are 8 to 10 mm long by 0.526 mm in diameter with a single lobed pseudolabium. The left spicule is 482 to 754 μ long and the right one 180 to 200 μ. The arrangement of the ventral and lateral papillae are shown in Figure D. Females are 12 to 24 mm long by 0.634 mm in diameter with two uteri (Fig. E). Eggs are 52 by 34 μ in size and contained in capsules.

LIFE CYCLE. Gravid females leave the lizards in the faeces, die, and become dried. The eggs are contained in capsules within the uterus, where they develop and are able to survive desiccation for at least 2 years, a desirable property for living in arid regions. There are 5 to 69 eggs per capsule which is composed of five layers. Eggs become infective when second stage larvae appear in them.

PLATE 130 *Physaloptera phrynosoma*

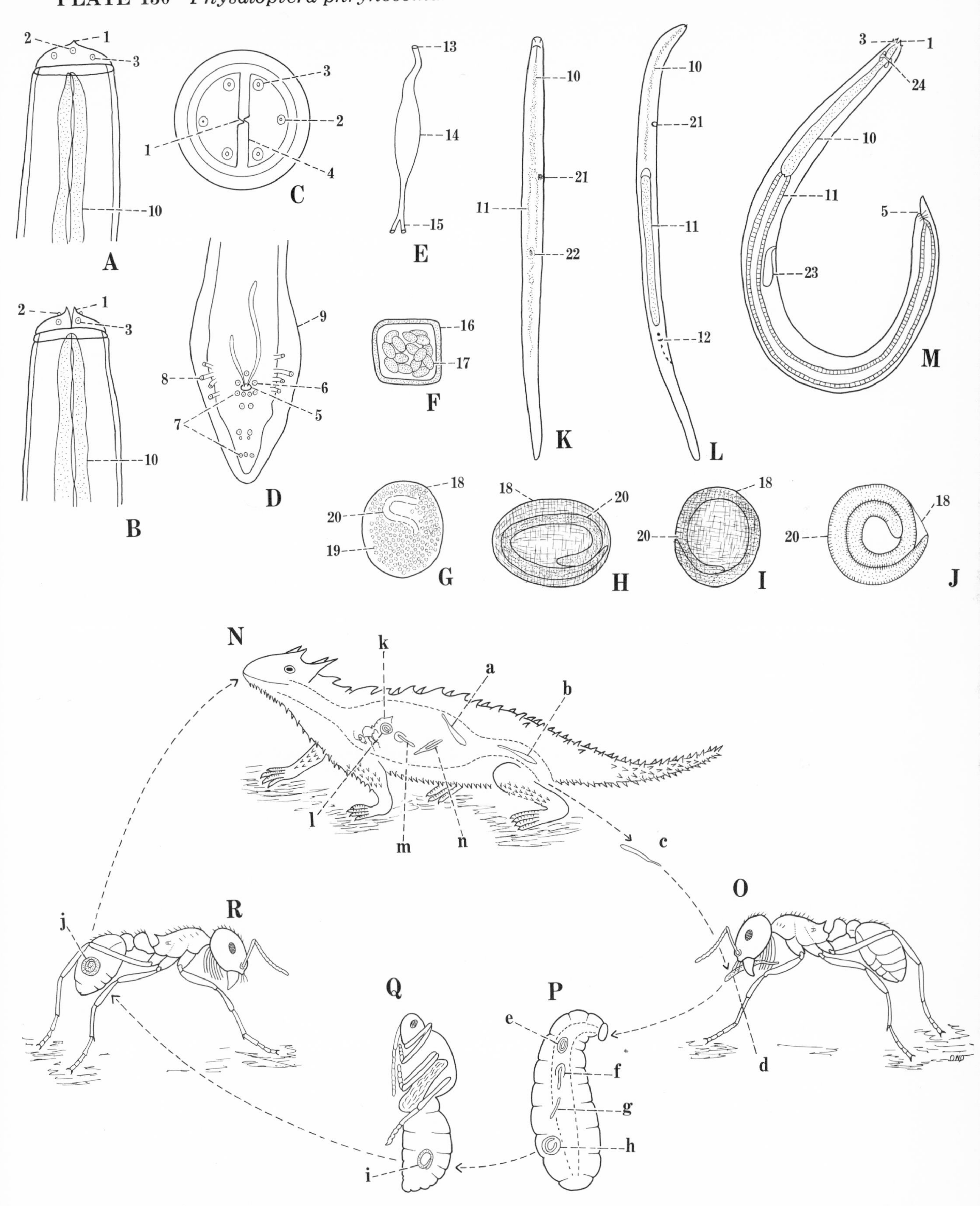

Workers of agricultural ants (*Pogonomyrmex barbatus* var. *molefaciens* and possibly other species of the genus) find and carry the desiccated females of *P. phrynosoma* into the nests where they are fed to the larvae. Mature ants as such are not susceptible to infection. The eggs hatch in the intestine and the second stage larvae burrow through the wall into the haemocoel where they enter the fat body trophocytes. Cysts produced by the larval ants enclose the trophocyte and the larval nematode. As the parasite consumes the fat, it grows and molts a second time. By the time the ant has completed its metamorphosis through the pupal stage and to the callow, the parasite has consumed all of the fat together with the two molted cuticles contained in the cyst.

Adult ants harboring third stage larvae are the source of infection of the horned lizards. Upon digestion of the infected ants in the stomachs of the myrmecophagous lizards, the larvae are released and grow to adults, presumably after two more molts, making a total of four, one of which occurred in the egg, one in the ants, and two in the lizards. Sexual maturity is reached by the males in 19 days and by the females in 65 days.

Life histories of several species of the genus *Physaloptera* have been solved. Like all spirurids, they have arthropod intermediate hosts but not the unique method of egg disposal and protection of *Physaloptera phrynosoma*. Some of the commoner ones include *P. rara and P. praeputialis* of dogs in which German cockroaches (*Blatella germanica*), flour beetles (*Tribolium confusum*), field crickets (*Gryllus assimilus*), and ground beetles (*Harpulus* spp.) serve as intermediate hosts.

Physaloptera hispida of the cotton rat develops in German cockroaches, ground beetles, and European earwigs (*Forficula auricularia*).

Physaloptera turgida of opossums develops to third stage larvae in the German cockroach. Attempts to infect dogs, cats, guinea pigs, rats, and chickens were unsuccessful. However, larvae become encapsulated in the stomach of rats, indicating that perhaps they may be passed to the definitive host through an intermediary. Larval *Physaloptera* are common in the tissues of rattlesnakes and white-footed mice in Colorado. They develop to *P. rara* in cats (Widmer).

EXERCISE ON LIFE CYCLE

If unavailable naturally in a region, horned lizards may be purchased from biological supply houses in the southwest as a source of eggs of the parasite. Infective eggs are available only in gravid females that have been passed in the faeces of lizards and allowed to desiccate. When lizards are kept in shoe boxes, the dried females are easily collected from the faeces. The first and second stage larvae may be seen inside the eggs.

Infection of larval ants in the laboratory has not been reported and may not be possible at all. It should be approached by first establishing a colony of ants consisting of workers and larvae in an artificial nest. Provide dried female worms for the workers to carry into the nest to feed to the larvae. If an artificial nest cannot be established, small natural colonies away from where lizards occur might be used by placing dried female worms for the workers to find and carry into the nests. Adult ants, being resistant, possibly due to age, do not become infected. After a week or more, pupae or callows obtained from the nest may be infected. Other genera of ants should be tried to ascertain whether they are capable of acting as intermediate hosts.

Horned lizards under 50 mm long from snout to vent do not eat large agricultural ants and therefore are not infected with *P. phrynosoma*. They are useful for feeding experiments to determine the phases of development in the vertebrate host.

SELECTED REFERENCES

Alicata, J. E. (1937). Papers on Helminth. 30th Jubl. K. I. Skrjabin and 15th Anniv. All-Union Inst. Helminth. Moscow, p. 11.

Lee, S. H. (1955). J. Parasit. 41:70; (1957). Ibid. 43:66.

Morgan, B. B. (1942). Lloydia 5:314.

Petri, L. H. (1950). Trans. Kansas Acad. Sci. 53:331.

Schell, S. C. (1952). Trans. Amer. Micr. Soc. 71:293.

Widmer, E. A. (1961). Unpublished dissertation, Colorado State University.

SUPERFAMILY FILARIOIDEA

These are threadlike nematodes which occur in the blood or lymphatic systems, connective tissues, nerve tissues, skin, lungs, air sacs, eye sockets, and body and nasal cavities of all classes of vertebrates except fishes.

In addition to the filariform bodies and the habitats, the group is characterized further by a mouth without lips and the buccal capsule poorly developed or absent. The tail of the male is usually but not always spirally coiled, has ventral papillae, and may be with or without alae. The spicules are distinctly unequal in length. The tail of the female is straight and the vulva is near the anterior end of the body. They are ovoviviparous in most cases with the young (microfilaria) in the body fluids or tissues. Some species are oviparous and the embryonated eggs leave the host through natural openings. Arthropods, insects and acarines serve as intermediate hosts. They become infected by ingesting the microfilariae or eggs.

In some species, the microfilariae are present in the peripheral blood only during certain definite periods of the day or night. They are said to show periodicity.

FAMILY DIPLOTRIAENIDAE

The Diplotriaenidae are parasites of the air sacs and subcutaneous tissues of reptiles and birds. The family is characterized morphologically by a small mouth with a vertical opening but without lips. There are lateral cephalic cuticularized thickenings ("epaulettes"), or two projecting denticulate embossments, or two internal tridents. They are oviparous with thick, smooth-shelled eggs containing well-developed first stage larvae when laid.

Diplotriaenoides translucidus Anderson, 1956 (Plate 131)

This filarioid is a parasite of the air sacs of ovenbirds (*Seiurus aurocapillus*) examined in eastern Canada.

DESCRIPTION. Males are 26 to 50 mm long by 0.43 to 0.53 mm wide. The tail is straight and blunt with a subterminal circular anus. Spicules are dissimilar; the left is lance-shaped and 0.9 to 1.3 mm long, the right is twisted twice and 0.53 to 0.71 mm long; each terminates in a membranous hooklike tip. Females are 66 to 108 mm long by 0.71 to 0.81 mm in diameter. The rectum is atrophied and the anus may not be visible. The vulva opens slightly behind the junction of the muscular and glandular portions of the oesophagus. There is a long vagina divided into two uteri that are packed with eggs 34 by 50 μ in size, containing short thick embryoes.

LIFE CYCLE. Embryonated eggs laid in the air sacs and lungs are conveyed up the trachea into the pharynx, swallowed, and voided from the body with the faeces. Further development does not take place until they are eaten by arthropods. Eggs hatch in the intestine of young grasshoppers (*Camnula pellucida*) but not in ants (*Formica*), ground beetles (Carabidae), tenebrionids (Tenebrionidae), camel crickets (Rhaphidophorinae), field crickets (Gryllidae), and land snails (*Zonotoides* and *Discus*). The young grasshoppers used in the study were collected at random. On the basis of the absence of natural infection in the ones examined, it is highly probable that the 21 infections in the 31 grasshoppers fed eggs resulted from the ingestion of them.

Newly hatched first stage larvae are very active in the intestine, burrowing through the wall into the haemocoel. The first molt occurs 24 days after the eggs are eaten by grasshoppers. Molting second stage larvae are present on the 27th day, and third stage larvae, both free and encysted, on the 31st day. When fed to white-crowned sparrows in the absence of ovenbirds, they failed to develop.

Diplotrianea bargusinca of the willow thrush (*Hylocichla fuscesens*) has a similar life cycle. Eggs hatch in grasshoppers (*Melanoplus bilituratus, M. fasciatus*, and *Camnula pellucida*). Development of larvae takes place in the fat bodies with the first molt on the 9th day and the second on the 14th to 16th days at 30° C. Most third stage larvae become encapsulated. Subadult worms occurred in willow and russet-backed thrushes 55 to 301 days after eating infected grasshoppers. Late fourth stage larvae were found in the heart and aorta of a naturally infected nestling russet-backed thrush.

On the basis of this evidence, the life cycle is postulated to follow the pattern outlined below and

EXPLANATION OF PLATE 131

A. Anterior end of adult female. **B.** Posterior end of adult male. **C.** *En face* view of adult female. **D.** Distal end of spicules from dorsal side. **E.** Thick-shelled egg containing embryo. **F.** First stage larva just hatched from egg in intestine of grasshopper. **G.** *En face* view of first stage larva showing dorsal tooth and rows of spines around anterior end of body. **H.** Second stage larva in process of molting. **I.** Third stage larva in characteristic horseshoe shape when fixed. **J.** Tail of first stage larva, showing serrated tip. **K.** Ovenbird *(Seiurus aurocapillus)* definitive host. **L.** Experimental arthropod intermediate host *(Camnulla pellucida)*.

1, anterior muscular portion of oesophagus; **2,** posterior glandular part of oesophagus; **3,** vulva; **4,** vagina; **5,** uterus with eggs; **6,** short right and long left spicules; **7,** anus; **8,** anal papillae; **9,** outer and inner cephalic papillae; **10,** trident; **11,** amphid; **12,** mouth; **13,** thick, smooth shell of egg; **14,** embryo; **15,** nerve ring; **16,** larval oesophagus; **17,** excretory cell; **18,** intestine; **19,** rectal plug; **20,** tail; **21,** rectum; **22,** anus.

a, adults in alveoli of lungs; **b,** adults in abdominal air sacs; **c,** eggs moving up trachea; **d,** eggs entering oesophagus to pass through intestine; **e,** embryonated eggs with first stage larvae passed in faeces; **f,** eggs eaten by grasshoppers; **g,** eggs hatch in intestine; **h,** larvae migrate from intestine into haemocoel; **i,** larvae molt first time to form second stage; **j,** third stage larva with loose cuticle; **k,** infection of definitive host occurs when infected intermediate hosts are eaten (probably grasshoppers are not natural hosts of *D. translucidus* since they are not an important food item of ovenbirds); **l,** larvae freed when arthropod intermediate host is digested; **m-p,** not demonstrated experimentally but it may be presumed that the hepatic portal vein or the lymphatics would be the likely route by which to reach the lungs and air sacs; **m,** larvae molt in intestine, burrow through wall into hepatic portal vein; **n,** larvae pass through liver; **o,** fourth stage larvae pass through right side of heart and enter pulmonary artery and lungs; **p,** larvae leave capillaries and enter alveoli or air sacs where they develop to maturity.

Adapted from Anderson, 1956, Canad. J. Zool. 34:213; (1957). Ibid. 35:15.

---

shown in Plate 131. It is chosen to illustrate the probable course of the life cycle of the egg-laying filarioids. Embryonated eggs eaten by arthropods (probably some insect other than grasshoppers in the case of *D. translucidus,* since these insects are not a regular part of the diet of ovenbirds) hatch in the intestine. After migration to the haemocoel, the first stage larvae shorten and molt twice. The third stage larvae are either free or encysted. This life cycle has points in common with that of *Habronema megastoma* (Plate 127), thus affirming a relationship between the two superfamilies of worms.

Infection of the vertebrate host occurs when arthropods harboring third stage larvae are ingested. Since the adult worms are in the air sacs, it is probable that the larvae migrate from the intestine via the hepatic portal vein or lymphatics to the heart and lungs.

Anderson regards it likely that all species of egg-laying filarioids of reptiles and birds occur in the air sacs of these hosts at some time and that they have life cycles similar to that of *Diplotriaenoides translucidus.* The following genera occur in the air sacs of birds: *Dicheilonema, Serratospiculum, Haematospiculum, Monopetalonema, Pseudoprocta, Lissonema,* and *Tetracheilonema. Hastospiculum* of reptiles probably occurs in the air sacs.

EXERCISE ON LIFE CYCLE

Diplotriaenidae occurs in a number of birds, including such common ones as grackles, red-winged blackbirds, and corvids.

Eggs obtained from female worms should be fed to insects that figure prominently in the food of the vertebrate host. Use an adequate number of each species of insect to provide enough specimens for dissection over a sufficiently long period to make the necessary observations on the development in them. Recall that in *D. translucidus* third stage larvae were found on the 31st day after the grasshoppers had ingested eggs.

When laboratory-reared insects are not available for feeding experiments, checks must be made on the wild ones to determine the percentage of the sample population that is naturally infected in order to give validity to the experimental results when such animals are fed infective eggs.

SELECTED REFERENCES

Anderson, R. C. (1956). Canad. J. Zool. 34:213; (1957). Ibid. 35:15; (1962). Ibid. 40:1175.

Chabaud, A. G., and R. C. Anderson. (1956). Ann. Parasit. Hum. Comp. 34:64.

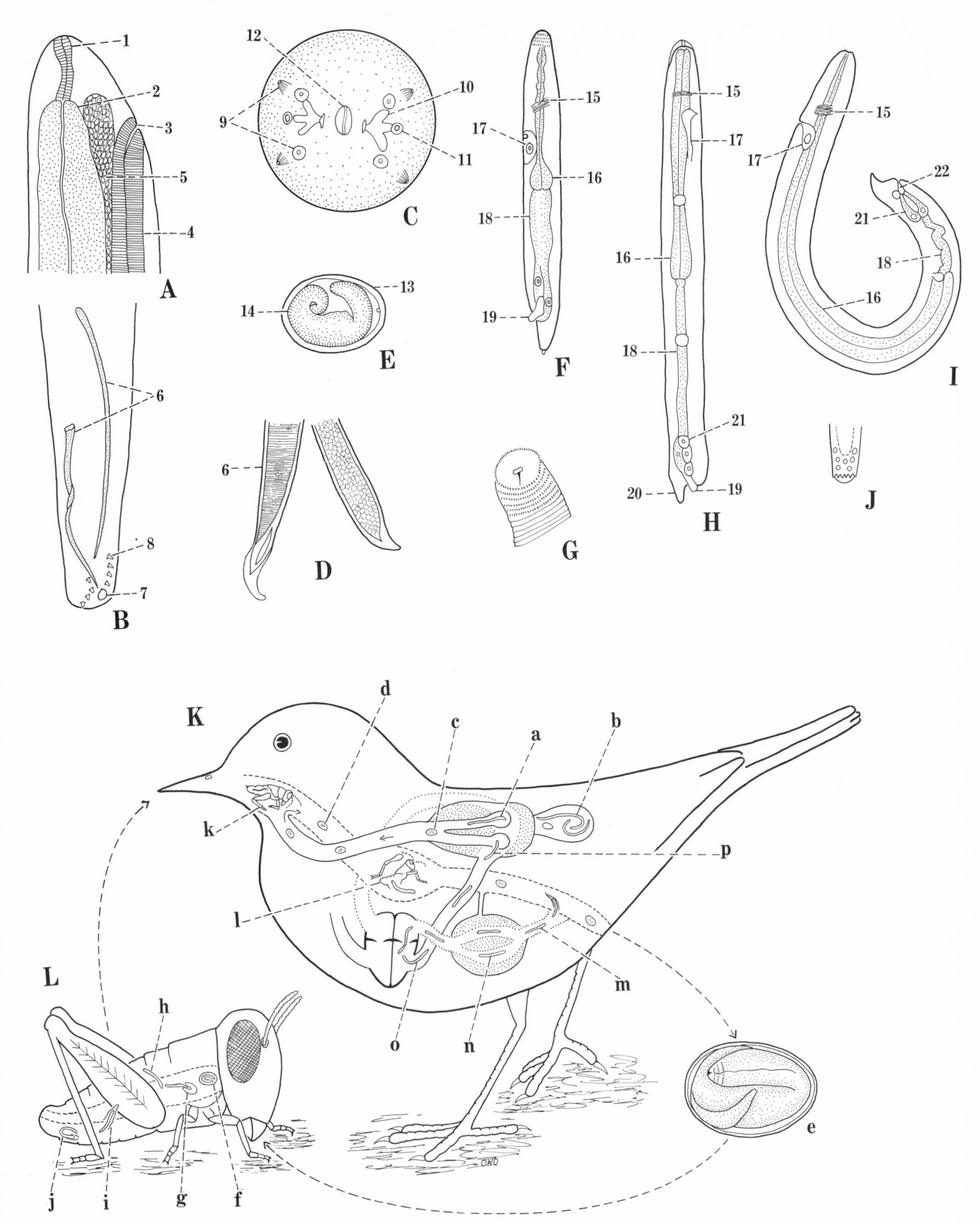
1
2
3
4
5
A
6
8
7
B
12
9
10
11
C
6
D
14
13
E
17
15
16
18
19
F
G
15
17
16
18
21
20
19
H
15
17
22
21
18
16
I
J
K
d
c
a
b
k
p
l
m
o
n
e
L
h
j
i
g
f

EXPLANATION OF PLATE 132 ⇨

A. Anterior end of mature female. **B.** Posterior end of mature male. **C.** Right spicule of mature male. **D.** Posterior end of mature female. **E.** Vulvular region with vagina containing oviform embryoes. **F.** Larva in embryonic sheath. **G.** First stage larva from intestine of mite. **H.** Second stage larva from haemocoel of mite. **I.** Third stage larva from haemocoel of mite. **J.** Anterior end of fourth stage larva from rat, showing development and cast cuticle. **K.** Posterior end of fourth stage larva, showing development and cast cuticle. **L.** Cotton rat *(Sigmodon hispidis)*. **M.** Tropical rat mite *(Bdellonyssus bacoti)*.

1, mouth; **2**, stoma of adult; **3**, oesophagus; **4**, cephalic (?) glands; **5**, intestine; **6**, testis; **7**, left spicule; **8**, right spicule; **9**, anus; **10**, postanal papillae (three to five in number); **11**, tail; **12**, ovaries; **13**, vulva; **14**, vagina vera; **15**, vagina uterina; **16**, stoma of first stage larva; **17**, stoma of second stage larva; **18**, loose cuticle; **19**, stoma of third stage larva; **20**, stoma of fourth stage larva after it has been shed; **21**, detailed view of stoma of fourth stage larva; **22**, embryo; **23**, embryonic sheath (egg shell(?)).

a, adult worms in pleural cavity; **b**, sheathed larvae being born; **c**, first stage larva entering blood capillaries of lung; **d**, first stage larva in pulmonary vein; **e**, first stage larva passing through left side of heart; **f**, first stage larva leaving heart through aortic arch; **g**, first stage larva in dorsal aorta; **h**, first stage larva in peripheral vein of foot; **i**, first stage larva being ingested by mite; **j**, first stage larva in gut of mite; **k**, first stage larvae passing through intestinal wall of mite into haemocoel; **l**, molting first stage larvae; **m**, second stage larva; **n**, molting of second stage larva; **o**, third stage larva; **p**, third stage larvae being injected into tissues of cotton rat from where they enter veins; **q**, third stage larva in vein going to heart; **r-s**, third stage larva entering right side of heart and passing through it; **t**, third stage larvae in pulmonary artery on their way to lungs; **u**, fourth stage larvae probably enter pleural cavity from capillaries of lungs; **v**, peritoneal cavity.

Figures A-F adapted from Cross and Scott, 1947, Trans. Amer. Micr. Soc. 66:1; G-J, from Scott, MacDonald, and Terman, 1951, J. Parasit. 37:425.

FAMILY ONCHOCERCIDAE

The Onchocercidae are parasites of the tissues and cavities of all classes of vertebrates except the fishes.

They are characterized by a head that is smooth and round, an oesophagus that may or may not be divided, and spicules that are unequal in length. Sometimes the tail of the male is weakly alate. The vulva is median or anterior but not near the mouth; the egg shells are very thin, and the microfilariae accumulate in the tissues or blood where they are ingested by bloodsucking arthropods.

Litomosoides carinii (Travassos, 1919) (Plate 132)

This is a common parasite of the thoracic cavity of cotton rats (*Sigmodon hispidus*) of the southern United States and countries to the south.

DESCRIPTION. Males are 24 to 28 mm long and 0.13 to 0.14 mm in diameter. The tail is corkscrew-like and bears three to five postanal papillae; the right spicule measures 100 to 105 μ and the left 185 to 295 μ, each with a filamentous tip. Females are 50 to 65 mm long and 0.3 to 0.32 mm wide. The vulva is about 1.25 mm from the mouth, or a distance equal to about twice the length of the oesophagus. It opens into a thick muscular vagina. The uterus is filled with embryos about 94 μ long.

LIFE CYCLE. Adult females in the thoracic cavity give birth to sheathed microfilariae that average 94 μ in length. They are active burrowers, going into muscles, connective tissue, and the lungs. The lungs probably constitute the most important route by which they enter the blood stream. There is no periodicity of larvae in the blood as they are present at all times. Microfilariae circulating in the peripheral blood are ingested by rat mites (*Bdellonyssus bacoti*) feeding on infected rats. Only those swallowed by adult mites develop. The microfilariae remain in the stomach of the mites a few hours, but have left it by the end of the first day when they appear in the haemocoel.

During the first week, the larvae thicken in the middle region of the body and attain the sausage stage typical of late first stage filarioid larvae. By the end of the first week they begin the initial molt and most of them have completed it by the 13th day. After the molt, they elongate, attaining a length of 450 μ as fully developed second stage larvae.

Beginning on the ninth day, the second molt commences and the majority of them have completed it by the 15th day. The third stage larvae grow rapidly during the first 2 days after molting, reaching

PLATE 132 *Litomosoides carinii*

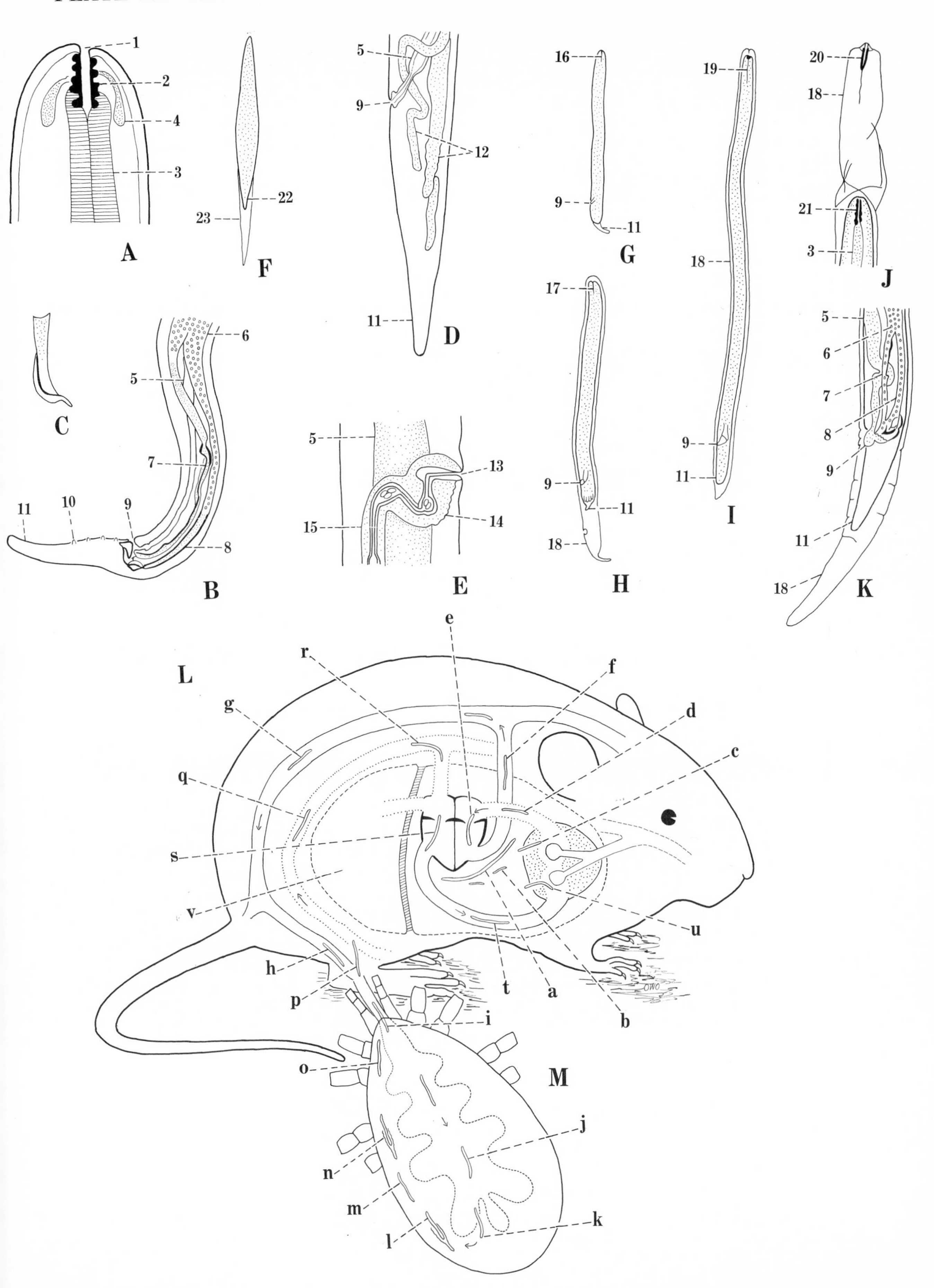

an average length of 853 μ. They are infective to cotton rats and white rats about 15 days after having been ingested by the mites. They migrate to the mouth parts and escape while the mites are feeding. Entry is through the wound in the skin made by the chelae of the mites.

Once inside the skin, the third stage larvae make their way to the thoracic cavity. The route taken by them is unknown, although some workers imply that they migrate through the tissues. It seems more logical that they enter the lymph and blood vessels at the point of invasion and are carried through them to the lungs via the right side of the heart. Once in the lungs, it would be an easy matter for them to migrate into the thoracic cavity.

Two molts occur after the third stage larvae enter the rat host. While these have been described, the place where they occur has not been given. Presumably it is in the pleural cavity. Fourth stage larvae average 1.2 mm long when the cuticle is shed by the 15th day. They attain an average length of 6.4 mm in the males and 8.7 in the females when fully formed. The fourth and final molt takes place on the 23rd to 24th days in the males and a day or two later in the females. They grow 1 to 2 mm in length during the molt.

Sexual maturity may be attained as early as 50 days after the mites have infected the rats but the prepatent period is usually 70 to 80 days. The peak of the microfilarial population in the blood occurs in 4 to 5 months and the larvae usually disappear in about 9 months. The majority of the adult worms die by the end of the first year but some may live up to about 3 years.

EXERCISE ON LIFE CYCLE

Infected cotton rats infested with tropical rat mites captured in their natural habitat or purchased from dealers provide a source of microfilariae for study. The rats should be kept in cages containing grass and placed over sawdust. This arrangement provides places for both the rats and mites to hide and for the latter to breed.

A colony of uninfected mites should be maintained on uninfected white rats for experimental purposes. Precautions should be taken to prevent infected mites from wandering and exposing all of the experimental rats. Infected mites can be detected by examining them with the aid of a dissecting microscope and transmitted light.

Adult mites allowed to feed on infected rats provide a source of material for studying the development of the larvae through the third stage. By dissecting them in half strength Tyrode's solution at close intervals up to 15 days after feeding, development through the third stage can be followed in detail.

The migration and development of the fourth stage larvae and development of the adults can be followed in rats. Determine whether the third stage larvae migrate to the pleural cavity via the tissues or the blood. Examination of the blood of exsanguinated rats and the lungs at appropriate times after infected mites have fed on them should provide the answer to the question.

SELECTED REFERENCES

Bertran, D. S. (1947). Ann. Trop. Med. Parasit. 41:253.

Cross, J. B., and J. A. Scott. (1947). Trans. Amer. Micr. Soc. 66:1.

Hughes, T. E. (1950). Ann. Trop. Med. Parasit. 44:285.

Kershaw, W. E. (1948). Ann. Trop. Med. Parasit. 42:377; (1949). Ibid. 43:238; (1949). Trans. Roy. Soc. Trop. Med. Hyg. 42:318.

Scott, J. A., and J. B. Cross. (1946). Amer. Trop. Med. 26:849.

Scott, J. A., E. M. MacDonald, and B. Terman. (1951). J. Parasit. 37:425.

Williams, R. W. (1948). J. Parasit. 34:24.

Dirofilaria immitis (Leidy, 1856) (Plate 133)

The adults of this filarioid are parasites mainly of the chambers of the right side of the heart and pulmonary artery of dogs, foxes, wolves, coyotes, and cats. The long, sheathless microfilariae are in the blood stream. The worms are worldwide in distribution, being most common in mild and warm climates.

DESCRIPTION. Adults are long, white, threadlike worms. Males measure 12 to 16 cm long with the tail spirally coiled. It bears narrow alae and three pairs of large caudal papillae, one of which is postanal and three pairs of small ones near the tip of the tail. The left spicule is 324 to 375 μ long and the right 190 to 229 μ. Females are ovoviparous, 25 to 30 cm long, and with the vulva opening just behind the posterior end of the oesophagus. The sheathless microfilariae are 218 to 329 μ long and have a long pointed tail.

LIFE CYCLE. The microfilariae are deposited by the females in the blood of the heart and pulmonary artery and distributed to all parts of the body. There appears to be a slight nocturnal periodicity at which time they are more abundant in the blood than during the day.

Mosquitoes (*Aedes, Culex, Anopheles, Myzorhynchus*) serve as intermediate hosts in which the larvae are capable of development. Microfilariae ingested by mosquitoes migrate from the intestine to the Malpighian tubules. In their development, they shorten and thicken in shape, becoming the sausage stage which molts to the second stage larvae. As growth continues, they elongate and molt the second time, forming third stage filariform larvae.

In the process of larval growth, the cells of the Malpighian tubules are destroyed. Eventually the larvae escape from them and migrate through the thoracic haemocoel to the labium and labellum. While the mosquito is feeding, the larvae are stimulated to activity, possibly by the warmth of the vertebrate body, and migrate through the labellum onto the skin which they enter through natural pores or the wound made by the mosquito. Once inside the body, they go first to the subcutaneous adipose and muscle tissues. From these locations, they enter the blood veins about 85 to 120 days after infection and are carried to the heart where development continues to the adult stage which is attained 8 to 9 months after infection. Two molts in the vertebrate host must be accounted for but where they occur is unknown. It seems likely that the third might take place in the tissues just after entering the host and the fourth in the blood vessels or heart.

A second filiarioid worm, *Dipetalonema reconditum,* occurs in the subcutaneous tissue of dogs in North America. The adults are about one-tenth the size of the heart worms. Microfilariae fixed with the blood in 2 per cent formalin have a sharply bent tail shaped like a buttonhook, as opposed to the straight one of the heart worms. Both species occur simultaneously in dogs. The microfilariae of *Dipetalonema* are believed to develop only in dog and cat fleas (*Ctenophalides canis* and *C. felis*), whereas those of *D. immitis* develop only in mosquitoes.

Birds are common hosts of onchocercid filarioids. The American black-billed magpie (*Pica pica hudsonia*) harbors at least four species. Midges of the genus *Culicoides* are the intermediate hosts of at least three of them. *Splendidofilaria picacardina* Hibler from the myocardium behind the aortic and pulmonary semilunar valves develops in the abdominal fat bodies of *Culicoides crepuscularis; Chandlerella striatospicula* Hibler from the connective tissue surrounding the splenic artery develops in the thoracic muscles of *Culicoides haematopotus;* and *Eufilaria longicaudata* Hibler from the connective tissue surrounding the oesophagus develops in the thoracic muscles of *Culicoides crepuscularis* and *C. haematopotus.*

The life cycles of other onchocercid filarioids, where known, are similar basically to *D. immitis.* In addition to mosquitoes and fleas, other intermediate hosts for them include tabanids, simuliids, *Culicoides,* and *Stomoxys.*

An exhaustive list of filarial worms known to develop in arthropods together with both vertebrate and invertebrate hosts and references is given by Hawking and Worms.

EXERCISE ON LIFE CYCLE

Numerous species of wild birds and mammals, also some reptiles and amphibians, are infected with filarioids, as can be ascertained first hand by looking for the microfilariae in fresh and stained blood smears.

By means of a series of blood smears taken at all hours of the day and night, determine whether there is a time when the number of microfilariae in the blood is greatest. The periodicity, if it occurs, should be established as a preliminary step to feeding experiments with the intermediate hosts.

Permit insects to feed when the microfilariae are at their maximal number in the blood. Dissection

EXPLANATION OF PLATE 133 ⇨

A. Anterior end of adult of female worm. **B.** *En face* view of head of adult worm. **C.** Caudal end of adult male worm. **D.** Ventral view of caudal end of male. **E.** Sinistral view of caudal end of adult female. **F.** Microfilaria from blood (other stages of larvae similar to those of species infecting man). **G.** Dog definitive host. **H.** Mosquito (*Aedes* spp.) intermediate host in feeding position on dog.

1, inner circle of cephalic papillae; **2,** outer circle of cephalic papillae; **3,** amphid; **4,** mouth without lips; **5,** muscular portion of oesophagus; **6,** glandular portion of oesophagus; **7,** intestine; **8,** anus; **9,** nerve ring; **10,** uterus containing unsheathed microfilariae; **11,** preanal papillae; **12,** adanal papillae; **13,** postanal papillae; **14,** long spicule; **15,** short spicule; **16,** nerve ring of microfilaria; **17,** excretory cell; **18,** G_1 cell; **19,** anal space; **20,** tail cells.

a, adult worms in heart and pulmonary artery; **b, c, d,** microfilariae borne in and circulating through blood stream; **e,** microfilariae in peripheral blood and available to feeding mosquitoes; **f,** section of skin of dog; **g,** microfilaria being sucked up from peripheral blood vessel; **h,** microfilaria in stomach of mosquito; **i,** microfilaria entering Malpighian tubules; **j,** microfilaria changes to sausage stage and prepares to undergo first molt; **k,** second stage larva; **l,** sausage stage elongating and preparing for second molt; **m,** third stage filariform larva in Malpighian tubule; **n,** infective third stage larva having escaped from Malpighian tubule; **o,** larva migrating through thorax; **p, q,** larva entering and migrating down labium; **r,** larva escaping from labellum onto the skin; **s,** larva entering skin; **t,** larvae in subcutaneous tissue (also muscle and adipose tissues); **u,** larva entering peripheral vessels from tissues 85 to 129 days after infection; **v,** larva entering general circulation; **w,** larva entering heart.

Figures A, F, adapted from various sources; B, from Chitwood and Chitwood, Rev. 1950, Introduction to Nematology, Sec. I, Anatomy. Monumental Printing Co., Baltimore, p. 64, Fig. A; C, D, from Ortlepp, 1924, J. Helminth. 2:15; E, from Petrow, 1931, in Skrjabin, Shikhobalowa, and Sobolew, 1949, Opredeliteli Parasiticheskikh Nematod, Vol. 2, Plate 20.

---

of them must be made at frequent intervals after feeding to determine the fate of the microfilariae ingested with the blood. Microfilariae might be found in the intestine of all dipterons that feed, but the clue to the relationship of any particular insect to the biology of the worm will be in the larvae that undergo changes leading to the sausage and filariform stages.

Having found an infected vertebrate as a source of microfilariae, attempts should be made to find the arthropod host. The choice of insect should be made on the basis of the species that feed most commonly on the vertebrate host at the time when the microfilariae are most abundant in the blood, but there is no way of determining before hand which of these might be the intermediate host. Mosquitoes, black flies, *Culicoides,* tabanids, or stable flies and horn flies should be tested as intermediate hosts.

SELECTED REFERENCES

Hawking, F., and M. Worms. (1961). Ann. Rev. Ent. 6:413.

Hibler, C. P. (1963). Dissert. Abst. 24:4322; (1964). J. Parasit. 50:667.

Kartman, L. (1953). J. Parasit. 39:572; (1956). Ibid. 42(4/2):19; (1953). Amer. J. Trop. Med. 2:1062.

Kume, S., and S. Itagaki. (1955). Brit. Vet. J. 3:16.

Newton, W. L., and W. H. Wright. (1956). J. Parasit. 42:246; (1957). Vet. Med. 52:75.

Orihel, T. C. (1961). J. Parasit. 47:251.

Otto, G. F., and P. M. Bauman. (1959). Vet. Med. 54:87.

Steuben, E. B. (1954). J. Parasit. 40:580; (1954). J. Amer. Vet. Med. Assoc. 125:57.

Summers, W. A. (1940). Proc. Soc. Exp. Biol. Med. 43:448; (1943). Amer. J. Hyg. 37:173.

Wallenstein, W. L., and B. J. Tibola. (1960). J. Amer. Vet. Med. Assoc. 137:712.

FAMILY DIPETALONEMATIDAE

Members of this family are ovoviparous parasites of the body tissues, cavities, and blood of vertebrates. The microfilariae are long and slender, and devoid of spines on the anterior end.

Genus Foleyella Seurat, 1917

Species of this genus are parasites of the subcutaneous connective and muscular tissues of saurians

PLATE 133 *Ditrofilaria immitis*

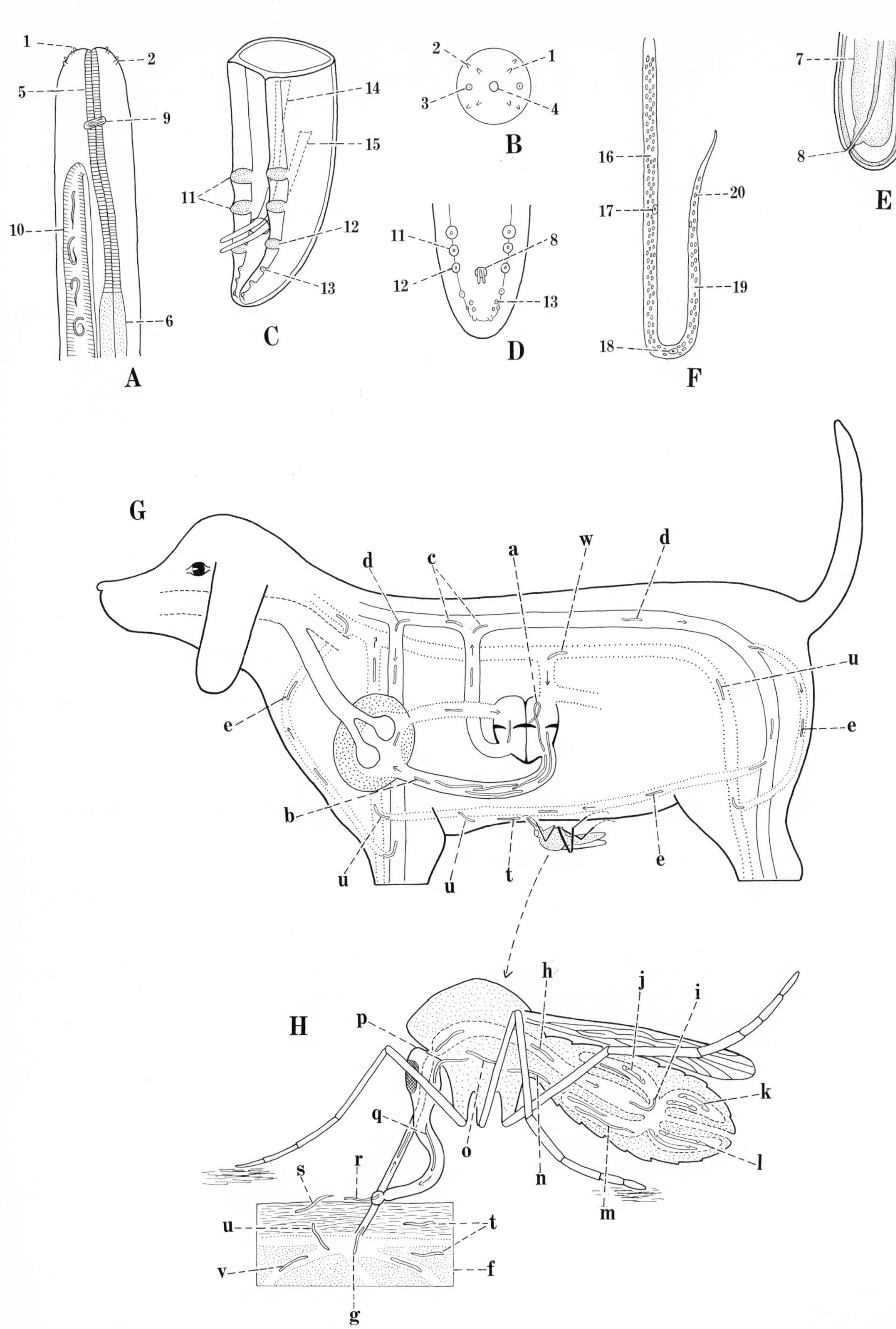

EXPLANATION OF PLATE 134 ⇨

A. Anterior end of adult female of *Foleyella brachyoptera*. **B.** Right lateral view of posterior end of adult female. **C.** Ventral view of adult male. **D.** Embryo coiled in egg membrane. **E.** Microfilaria partially coiled and stretching egg membrane. **F.** Microfilaria extended with loose-fitting membrane. **G.** Fully developed sheathed microfilaria in blood stream which is stage ingested by mosquitoes. **H.** First stage larvae in sausage stage on sixth day after ingestion by mosquito host. **I.** Sausage stage on eighth day after infection of mosquito. **J-K.** Second stage larvae on 11th and 13th days, respectively, after infection of mosquito. **L.** Third stage infective larva on 18th day after infection of mosquito. **M.** Infective larva emerging from labellum of mosquito. **N.** Frog *(Rana sphenocephala)* definitive host. **O.** Mosquito *(Aedes, Culex)* intermediate host.

1, toothlike cuticular projections from mouth; **2,** anterior muscular portion of oesophagus; **3,** posterior glandular position of oesophagus; **4,** oesophagointestinal valve; **5,** intestine; **6,** rectum; **7,** anus; **8,** vulva; **9,** vagina; **10;** uterus; **11,** right spicule; **12,** caudal papillae; **13,** caudal alae; **14,** anal plug; **15,** nerve ring; **16,** egg membrane; **17,** unhatched coiled microfilaria; **18,** unhatched extended microfilaria; **19,** sheath (elongated egg membrane) of microfilaria circulating in blood; **20,** microfilaria with rows of body cells and anlage of certain organs; **21,** cells of nuclear column; **22,** space of nerve ring; **23,** excretory pore; **24,** excretory cell; **25,** inner body; **26,** genital primordium; **27-30,** G-cells (G_1, G_2, G_3, G_4); **31,** anal cell; **32,** labellum; **33,** third stage larva (G) escaping from mosquito proboscis.

a, adult worm on intestinal mesentery; **b,** mesentery; **c,** microfilariae in capillaries and subcutaneous connective tissue; **d,** feeding mosquito *(Aedes, Culex)*; **e,** epidermis of frog skin; **f,** subcutaneous connective tissue; **g,** microfilaria in capillary; **h,** microfilaria being sucked up by feeding mosquito; **i,** microfilaria in foregut; **j,** microfilaria passing through gut wall of ventriculus into haemocoel; **k,** egg membrane of microfilaria; **l,** actively coiling microfilaria; **m,** microfilaria shortening in pre-sausage stage, showing anus and excretory pore; **n,** musculature of abdominal body wall; **o,** pre-sausage stage entering musculature of body wall; **p,** sausage stage (end of first stage); **q,** newly molted second stage larva; **r,** cuticle of first stage larva (sausage stage); **s,** full grown second stage larva; **t,** recently molted third stage larva; **u,** cuticle of second stage larva; **v,** infective third stage larvae in musculature of thorax; **w,** infective larva entering hollow proboscis sheath; **x,** larva passing down proboscis sheath; **y,** larva through its activities ruptures thin membrane of labellum and escapes onto skin of frog during feeding activities of infected mosquitoes; **z,** third stage larva on skin of frog, whose fate from this point is unknown.

Figs. A-C adapted from Wehr and Causey, 1939, Amer. J. Hyg. 39(D):65; D-M from Kotcher, 1941, Amer. J. Hyg. 34:36; N-O original.

---

and amphibians. They produce sheathed microfilariae which circulate in the blood. Mosquitoes are the intermediate hosts.

Adults have lateral alae extending almost the full length of the body. The spicules are unequal in length and the vulva is near the posterior end of the oesophagus.

Foleyella brachyoptera Wehr and Causey, 1939 (Plate 134)

These filarioids are parasites of the body cavity, chiefly on the mesenteries, of the southern leopard frog (*Rana sphenocephala*) in Florida.

DESCRIPTION. The oral opening has a toothlike projection on each side and the oesophagus consists of a short narrow anterior muscular portion and long wider posterior glandular portion. Males are 15 to 18 mm long by 0.3 mm wide. Lateral alae extend from the anterior extremity to the level of the anus. There are six and possibly seven pairs of sessile postanal papillae, diminishing in size posteriorly. The long spicule is 420 to 460 μ in length, alate, and with a pointed tip; the short one is 168 to 180 μ long, alate, and with the tip bluntly rounded. Females are 60 to 70 mm long by 0.7 mm wide. The vulva is near the posterior end of the oesophagus. The rectum is relatively short. Microfilariae are sheathed and about 125 μ long.

The location of anatomical structures used in the classification of microfilariae are given in percentage of body length for *F. brachyoptera* as follows: 1) nerve ring, 30; 2) excretory cell, 33; 3) beginning of inner body, 64; 4) G_1 cell, 74; and 5) anal pore, 87. The other G-cells ($G_{2,\,3,\,4}$) and anal pore are difficult to make out.

LIFE CYCLE. Adult worms occur on the mesenteries of the alimentary canal. Upon fertilization, the eggs appear as uncleaved spherical bodies enclosed in a thick shell or membrane. As development of the larvae progresses, they are first coiled and later appear to be in three or four folds within

PLATE 134 *Foleyella brachyoptera*

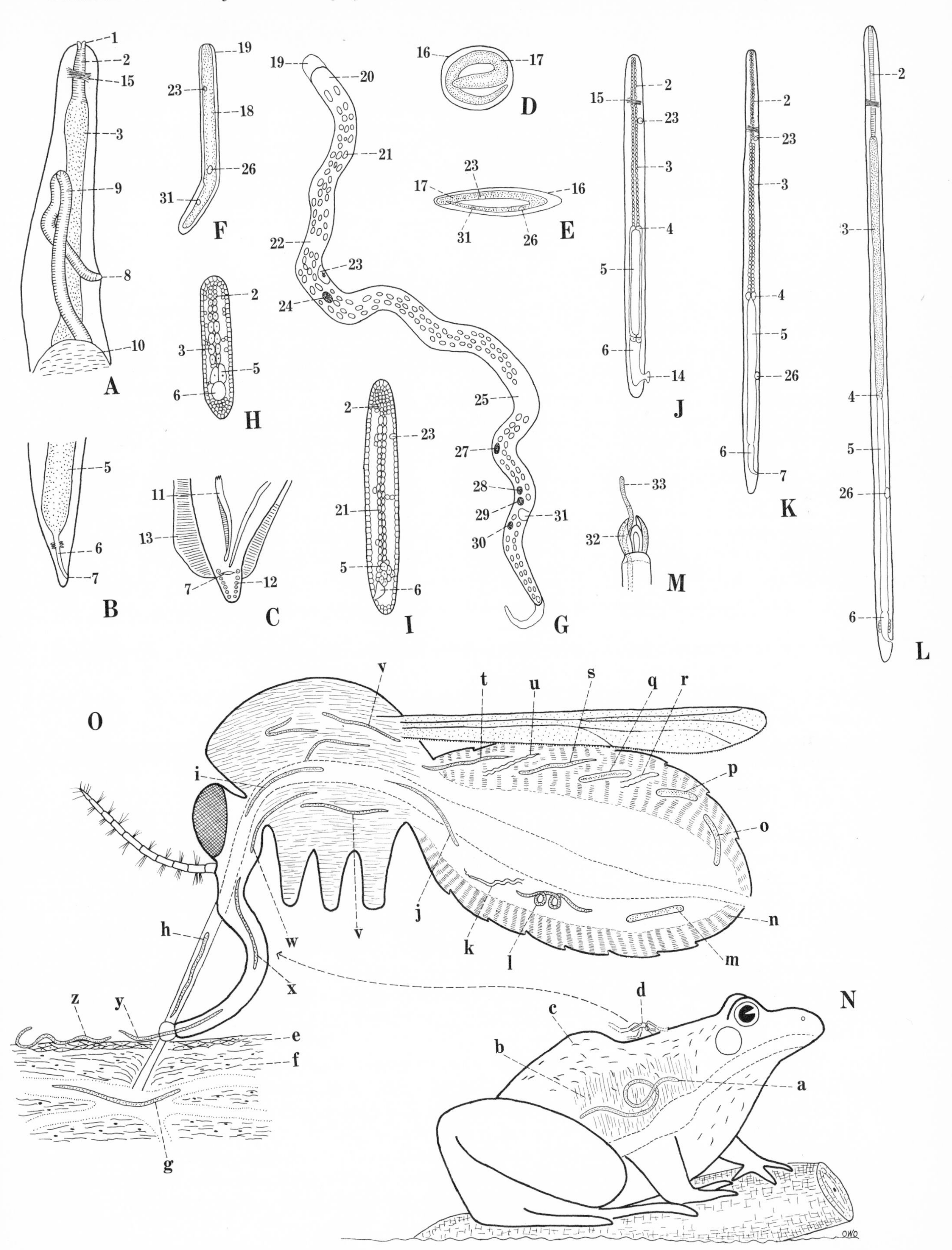

the eggs in the vaginal portion of the uterus. As the larvae approach the size of microfilariae, the membrane stretches, becoming progressively thinner, eventually forming a thin, single-layered hyaline sheath. In fully developed microfilariae, the sheath conforms to the body shape, but extends somewhat beyond each end. Upon birth, the microfilariae penetrate tissue, finding their way into the blood vessels in which they circulate.

Upon being swallowed by the mosquitoes, the microfilariae migrate through the gut wall into the haemocoel by the end of the first day. They are active, coiling and uncoiling. During this time, the only change is the loss of the sheath. By the third day, internal changes take place and the body becomes shortened to form the pre-sausage stage which is 107 μ by 7 μ in size. They are inactive at this time. By the fifth day, they have migrated into musculature of the abdominal wall and shortened still more to form the sausage stage, which is 89 by 9 μ to 14 μ in size.

During the next 3 days internal development of the sausage stage continues, with the formation of the hypodermis and basic parts of the alimentary canal. This completes the development of the first stage larva which measures 158 by 23 μ. The first molt occurs on about the ninth day in mosquitoes kept at 23° C. Second stage larvae are 456 by 26 μ in size. The oesophagus consists of large cuboidal cells and is about one-half the length of the body. An anal plug projects from the anus. The second molt occurs between the 13th and 16th days, at which time the larvae begin the third stage. By the 18th day, third stage larvae have migrated from the musculature of the abdominal wall to that of the thorax. They are 88 μ long by 13 to 17 μ wide, and active. Larvae live up to 43 days after ingestion by the mosquitoes.

Infection of the frogs is presumed to take place while infected mosquitoes are feeding on them. This point, however, has not been demonstrated experimentally. Mosquitoes show reluctance to bite cold frogs. After the frogs are warmed to about 38° C, however, hungry mosquitoes feed readily. During the time of feeding, larvae escape from the labellum onto the skin of the frogs, but they are unable to penetrate. Whether infection is through the skin by penetrating larvae is unknown. Infection may take place through the intestine from parasitized mosquitoes that are swallowed by frogs.

Other species of *Foleyella* occurring in American frogs include *F. ranae* Walton, 1929 with three pairs of preanal and four pairs of postanal papillae from *Rana catesbeiana; F. americana* Walton, 1929 with four pairs of preanal and three pairs of postanal papillae from *Rana pipiens;* and *F. dolichoptera* Wehr and Causey, 1939 with four pairs of postanal papillae from *Rana sphenocephala.*

Development of *F. dolichoptera, F. americana, F. ranae* from frogs in the United States, *F. duboisi* from frogs in Palestine, and *F. furcata* from chameleons in Madagascar in mosquitoes is basically similar to that of *F. brachyoptera.*

In addition to serving as intermediaries for *Foleyella* in amphibians and reptiles, mosquitoes also function in a similar capacity for *Dipetalonema arbuta* in porcupines. Other arthropod intermediate hosts for dipetalonematids include *Culicoides* for *Dipetalonema streptocara* in humans; fleas for *D. reconditum* in dogs in the United States and *D. manson-bahri* of spring hares in Kenya; hippoboscid flies for *D. dracunculoides* of dogs in Kenya; and ticks for *D. blanci* of meriones in Iran.

EXERCISE ON LIFE CYCLE

In addition to observing the developmental stages in mosquitoes, efforts should be made to learn how infection of the frogs takes place. In laboratory studies, mosquitoes are reluctant to bite cold frogs. After frogs are warmed to about 38° C, hungry mosquitoes will feed on them. Since the temperature of frogs under natural conditions remains far below that at which mosquitoes will feed in the laboratory, there must be circumstances under which they do feed. These conditions should be investigated.

While larvae, presumably third stage ones, emerge from the labellum of feeding mosquitoes onto the skin of frogs, they fail to penetrate. Inasmuch as the usual route of infection in the Dipetalonematidae is the skin, it would be expected to be the case for species of *Foleyella.* Experiments should be conducted to clarify the problems of mosquitoes feeding on the frogs and how infection takes place. The possibility of infection of the frogs through ingestion of parasitized mosquitoes should not be overlooked.

SELECTED REFERENCES

Anderson, R. C. (1957). J. Helminth. 21:203.

Blatazard, M., A. G. Chabaud, and A. Minou. (1952). C. R. Acad. Sci. Paris 234:2115.

Brygoo, E. R. (1960). Arch. Inst. Pasteur Madagascar 28:129.

Causey, O. R. (1939). Amer. J. Hyg. 29(D): 79, 131; 30(D):69, 117.

Chabaud, A. G. (1952). Ann. Parasit. Hum. Comp. 27:250.

Chardome, M., and E. Peel. (1949). Ann. Soc. Belge Med. Trop. 29:85.

Hawking, F., and M. Worms. (1961). Ann. Rev. Ent. 6:413.

Highby, P. R. (1943). J. Parasit. 29:243.

Kotcher, E. (1941). Amer. J. Hyg. 34:36.

Nelson, G. S. (1961). J. Helminth. 35:143; (1962). 36:235, 297.

Newton, W. L., and W. H. Wright. (1957). Vet. Med. 52:75.

Walton, A. C. (1929). J. Parasit. 15:227.

Wehr, E. E., and O. R. Causey. (1939). Amer. J. Hyg. 30(D):65.

Witenberg, G., and C. Gerichter. (1944). J. Parasit. 30:245.

Worms, M. J., R. J. Terry, and A. Terry. (1961). J. Parasit. 47:963.

CLASS ADENOPHOREA

Phasmids are absent but the caudal and hypodermal glands usually are present. The terminal excretory duct generally is not lined with cuticle. The cephalic sensory organs are setose (in free-living forms) or papilloid (in parasitic forms). Amphids are circular, spiral, shepherd's crook, pocket-like shapes (free-living forms), or sometimes porelike (parasitic forms).

ORDER ENOPLIDA

Amphids are pocket- to porelike, or tuboid. The oesophagus may be multinucleate.

Suborder Enoplina

The amphids usually are pocket-like. The oesophagus is grossly cylindrical and the glands are uninucleate, followed by a functional intestine.

SUPERFAMILY TRICHUROIDEA

In this superfamily, the anterior end of the worms is slender. The oesophageal glands are free in the body cavity, forming a long chain, known as the stichosome, with the capillary-like oesophagus embedded in the cells. Males have one or no spicules. The females have a single ovary and the unembryonated eggs, when present, have a clear mucoid plug in each end. They are parasites of vertebrates.

FAMILY TRICHURIDAE

The members of this family are characterized by females that are oviparous and by males that have but one spicule. They are parasites of the intestine primarily but occur in the liver and urinary bladder.

The life cycles of the species of this family present a series of patterns. There is the direct cycle in *Trichuris ovis* and *Capillaria columbae* where the eggs hatch in the intestine after being ingested and develop without migration into the tissues. In *Capillaria annulata*, the eggs hatch when ingested by oligochaete annelids and the larvae migrate to the tissues. When freed from the earthworms in the crops of chickens, the larvae penetrate its wall and develop to maturity. A somewhat similar situation occurs with *Capillaria plica* in which case the eggs hatch when swallowed by earthworms. Larvae released in the gut of the vertebrate host migrate via the blood stream to the kidneys, and through the ureters to the urinary bladder where maturity is attained. *Capillaria hepatica* deposits its eggs in the liver parenchyma from which they are freed when the host decomposes after death, or is eaten and digested by another animal and they are passed in the faeces. Development to the infective stage takes place only after the eggs have been freed from the liver and exposed to the air. Upon ingestion of infective eggs by rodents, they hatch and the larvae migrate to the liver via the hepatic portal vein and develop to maturity.

EXPLANATION OF PLATE 135 ⇨

A. Gravid female. **B.** Caudal end of male with spicular sheath extended. **C.** First stage larvae pressed from egg. **D.** Second stage larva from intestine of rabbit. **E.** Third stage larva from intestine. **F.** Posterior end of fourth stage male larva. **G.** Posterior end of fourth stage female larva. **H.** Vulvar region of fourth stage larva. **I.** Sheep definitive host.

1, slender anterior end of body; **2**, broad posterior end of body; **3**, mouth; **4**, muscular portion of oesophagus; **5**, stichosome, or oesophageal cells; **6**, intestine; **7**, anus; **8**, ovary; **9**, beginning of oviduct; **10**, uterus; **11**, vagina; **12**, vulva; **13**, spicular sheath; **14**, spicule; **15**, spear of first stage larva; **16**, developing spicule; **17**, developing spicular sheath; **18**, developing ovary.

a, adult female in caecum; **b**, unembryonated eggs laid in caecum; **c**, unembryonated eggs mingle with faeces and pass outside of body; **d**, unembryonated egg on ground; **e**, egg in two-cell stage; **f**, egg in four-cell stage; **g**, egg in six-cell stage; **h**, fully developed first stage larva in egg on ground; **i**, infection occurs when embryonated egg is swallowed; **j**, larva escapes from egg; **k**, larva enters caecum; **l**, first stage larva with anterior end embedded in mucosa of caecum; **m**, first stage larva molts; **n**, second stage larva attaches to mucosa, feeding and growing; **o**, second stage larva molts, producing third stage; **p**, third stage larva; **q**, third stage larva molts to produce fourth stage larva that is said to develop to adulthood, but an additional molt should be expected.

Figure A adapted from various sources; B-H, from Thapar and Singh, 1954, Proc. Indian Acad. Sci., Ser. B. 40:69.

Trichuris ovis (Abildgaard, 1795) (Plate 135)

This is one of the several whipworms from the caecum of sheep, cattle, and other ruminants in many parts of the world. They feed on blood.

DESCRIPTION. The anterior part of the body is much thinner than the posterior portion. Males are 50 to 80 mm long with the slender anterior part forming three-fourths of the body. The spicule is 5 to 6 mm long and the spicular sheath has an oblong spinose enlargement near the caudal end. The females are 35 to 70 mm long with the anterior end forming two-thirds or more of the body. The unembryonated brown eggs have a transparent plug in each end and measure 70 to 80 μ long by 30 to 42μ wide.

LIFE CYCLE. Unembryonated eggs are passed in the faeces. Development of them is slow, taking about 3 weeks in optimal temperature for the first stage larvae to appear but longer under less favorable circumstances. They are highly resistant, surviving up to 6 months in the soil. When swallowed with contaminated food and water by sheep and other ruminants, the mucoid plugs are dissolved by the digestive juices of the duodenum and the first stage larvae escape. They migrate to the caecum via the intestine and attach to the mucosa by forcing the anterior end of the body into it. Three molts only are reported. The first one produces the second stage larva and occurs about 4 weeks after ingestion of the infective egg. Second stage larvae attach to the mucosa and continue growth for a period of 3 weeks; the second molt takes place 7 weeks after infection, and the third stage larvae appear. Further growth results in the third molt and the appearance of fourth stage larvae. A fourth molt has not been reported but it should be expected. Sexual maturity is attained in 12 weeks.

Capillaria columbae of pigeons has a life cycle similar to that of *Trichuris ovis*. Being direct, both of them are completed without the aid of an intermediate host. Suggestions for studies on the life cycle of *T. ovis* apply to *C. columbae* except that chickens or pigeons should be used as experimental animals instead of mammals.

EXERCISE ON LIFE CYCLE

Adult females as a source of eggs may be obtained from abattoirs where sheep are slaughtered. Eggs dissected from gravid females should be washed several times to free them of tissue and then incubated in shallow water in glass dishes. Frequent changes of the water will prevent extensive growth of deleterious bacteria and fungi. Progress of embryonation should be observed by making daily examinations of the eggs.

When the first stage larvae have appeared, infection experiments may be conducted by feeding them to rabbits, or to mice and guinea pigs. Development of the larvae to the fourth stage may be observed

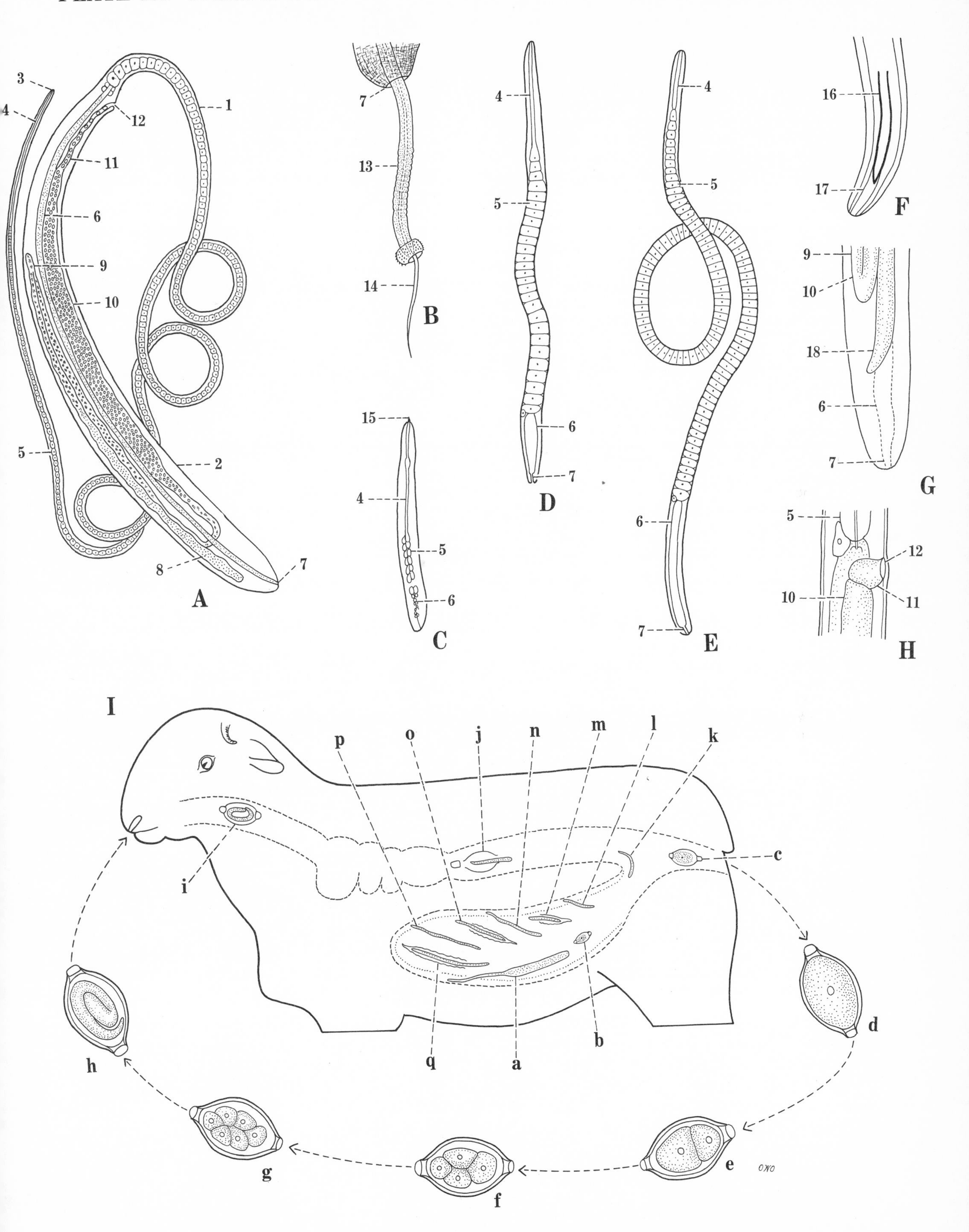
3
4
1
12
11
6
9
10
5
2
8
7
A
7
13
14
B
15
4
5
6
C
4
5
6
7
D
4
5
6
7
E
16
17
F
9
10
18
6
7
G
5
12
10
11
H
I
p
o
j
n
m
l
k
c
i
d
q
a
b
h
g
f
e

EXPLANATION OF PLATE 136 ⇨

A. Anterior end of adult worm. **B.** Posterior end of adult male; **C.** Adult female. **D.** Adult male. **E.** Section of crop of chicken with adult worm embedded in it. **F.** Early stage larva from experimentally infected earthworm. **G.** Details of anterior end of larva shown in **F.**

1, mouth with spearlike structure; **2,** bulbous swelling of cuticle; **3,** anterior muscular portion of oesophagus; **4,** spiny spicular sheath; **5,** stichosome; **6,** vulva; **7,** uterus filled with eggs; **8,** ovary; **9,** testis; **10,** portion of wall of crop; **11,** adult worm embedded in mucosa; **12,** egg in mucosa; **13,** cephalic spine; **14,** vacuolated areas; **15,** intestine; **16,** rectum.

a, adult worm embedded in wall of crop; **b,** eggs in wall of crop; **c,** mucosa of crop sloughing due to damage by worms and eggs which releases trapped eggs; **d,** eggs passing through gizzard; **e,** eggs pass through intestine; **f,** unembryonated eggs voided in faeces; **g,** embryonated egg; **h,** eggs swallowed by earthworm; **i,** mucoid plugs dissolved by digestive juices; **j,** larvae escape from eggs into intestine; **k,** larvae free in intestine where they may molt (but this and subsequent molts have not been seen, only assumed); **l,** larvae migrate through intestinal wall; **m,** larvae probably molt second time to form third stage; **n,** larvae encyst in tissues of body, becoming infective to chickens; **o,** earthworms disintegrate in crop of chicken; **p,** larvae escape from earthworms; **q,** larvae probably molt third time; **r,** fourth stage larvae (?) penetrate wall of crop; **s,** larvae probably molt fourth and final time, after which they grow to adulthood.

Figures A, B adapted from Ciurea, 1914, Z. Infektionsk. Hyg. Haustiere 15:49; C, D, E, from various sources; F, G, from Wehr, 1936, North Amer. Vet. 17:18.

---

by sacrificing experimentally infected animals at 4, 7, 8, 9, and 10 weeks after having fed them infective eggs. Only three molts have been reported but four should be expected on the basis of what occurs in other nematodes.

Ascertain how long embryonated eggs will survive at room temperature when kept moist and when kept dry.

SELECTED REFERENCES

Ransom, B. H. (1911). U. S. Dept. Agr., Bur. An. Ind. Bull. 127, p. 112.

Thapar, G. S., and K. S. Singh. (1954). Proc. Indian Acad. Sci. Ser. B. 40:69.

Capillaria annulata (Molin, 1858) (Plate 136)

C. annulata embeds in the mucosa of the oesophagus and crop of chickens, turkeys and a number of other galliform birds throughout the world. In addition to domestic birds in North America, they parasitize ruffed grouse, Hungarian partridges, ring-necked pheasants, and bobwhite quail.

DESCRIPTION. The body is of about equal diameter throughout its entire length. A bulbous bladder-like enlargement is located just behind the head. Bacillary bands occur dorsally and ventrally. Males are 10 to 25 mm long by 0.05 to 0.08 mm in diameter; the tail has two lateral inconspicuous flaps. The spicular sheath is spined and usually withdrawn, and the spicule is lacking. Females are 25 to 60 mm long by 0.07 to 0.12 mm in diameter. The vulva is located near the posterior end of the stichosome. Eggs measure 60 to 66 μ long by 26 to 28 μ wide, and have a mucoid plug in each end.

LIFE CYCLE. The eggs are unembryonated when voided in the faeces, and development is slow. Infective larvae appear by the 18th day under optimal conditions in cultures free from heavy infestations of bacteria which retard development. Hatching occurs readily in the gut of earthworms (*Eisena foetida, Allolobophora caliginosa, Lumbricus terrestris*), but not *in vitro*. Development of the larvae in earthworms and in the vertebrates has not been described. Two molts might be expected in earthworms and two in the birds. After hatching, the larvae migrate through the intestinal wall and encyst in the muscles of the body wall. These are probably third stage larvae, since they are infective to birds. When infected earthworms are eaten by the birds, the larvae are liberated, probably in the crop.

Doubtless two molts occur somewhere in the crop or oesophagus. The parasites penetrate the mucosa of the crop, becoming completely embedded. Sexual maturity is attained in chickens in 19 to 26 days after infection when eggs appear in the faeces.

PLATE 136 *Capillaria annulata*

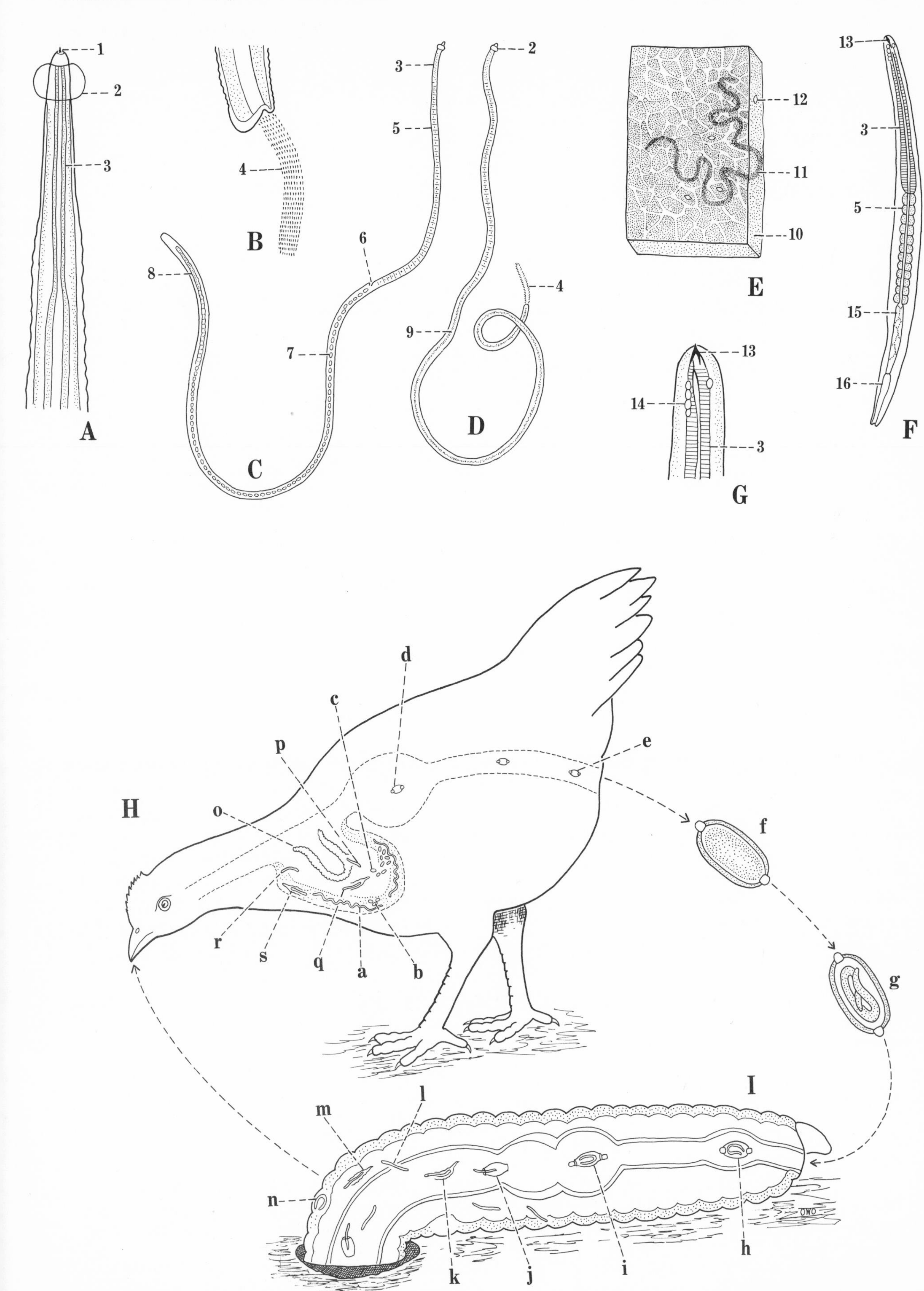

EXPLANATION OF PLATE 137 ⇨

A. Anterior end of adult female. **B.** *En face* view of adult female. **C.** Vulvular region. **D.** Ventral view of posterior end of male, with spicule withdrawn. **E.** Lateral view of posterior end of male with spicule and spicular sheath extended. **F.** Early first stage larva squeezed from egg. **G.** Late first stage larva from liver of mouse 2 days after infection. **H.** Anterior end of first stage larva. **I.** Stichosome of molting first stage larva from liver of mouse 3 days after infection. **J.** Second stage larva from liver of mouse 3 days after infection. **K.** Detail of stichosome of second stage larva. **L.** Third stage larva from liver of mouse 7 days after infection. **M.** Detail of stichosome of third stage larva. **N.** Stichosome of fourth stage larva from mouse 9 days after infection. **O.** Mouse definitive host. **P.** Carnivore in whose alimentary canal the definitive host is digested, the eggs released from the liver, and voided with the faeces where development to the infective stage takes place. **Q.** Dead mouse host decomposes, releasing eggs from liver with subsequent development.

1, muscular portion of oesophagus; **2,** stichosome, or glandular portion of oesophagus; **3,** intestine; **4,** vulva; **5,** evaginated portion of vagina; **6,** vagina; **7,** unembryonated egg; **8,** mouth; **9,** amphid; **10,** outer circle of cephalic papillae; **11,** inner circle of papillae; **12,** anus of male; **13,** caudal papilla; **14,** spicular pouch; **15,** spicule; **16,** spicular sheath; **17,** early stage of oesophagus, with nerve ring; **18,** early stage of intestine; **19,** undifferentiated oesophagus; **20,** beginning of buccal capsule; **21,** differentiating stichosome; **22,** undifferentiated muscular portion of oesophagus of second stage larvae; **23,** differentiating stichosomal portion of oesophagus; **24,** coelomocytes; **25,** ventral cell; **26,** binucleate genital primordium; **27,** gonad; **28,** nerve ring.

a, adult worm embedded in liver parenchyma of mouse; **b,** mass of undeveloped eggs in liver parenchyma; **c,** definitive host about to be eaten by carnivore; **d,** definitive host digested; **e,** eggs released from liver in alimentary tract; **f,** eggs travel through digestive tract without further development; **g,** eggs voided with faeces; **h,** embryonated egg containing first stage larva; **i,** infection takes place when embryonated eggs are swallowed by mouse or other definitive host; **j,** mucoid plugs released from egg by digestive juices; **k,** larvae escape from eggs; **l,** first stage larvae penetrate wall of intestine or caecum, entering hepatic portal vein; **m,** some larvae enter coelom; **n,** larvae escape from capillaries of liver to enter hepatic tissue; **o,** molt of first stage larvae; **p,** second stage larvae; **q,** molt of second stage larvae; **r,** third stage larvae which molt and continue development, finally reaching adult stage after fourth molt (not shown).

Figure A adapted from various sources; B, F-N, redrawn from Wright, 1961, Canad. J. Zool. 38:167; C, from Pavlov in Skrjabin *et al.*, 1954, Opredelitel Paraziticheskikh Nematod, Vol. 4, Plate 143, Fig. B; D-E, from Baylis, 1931, Parasitology 23:533.

EXERCISE ON LIFE CYCLE

Specimens of *C. annulata* for experimental studies may be obtained from poultry-processing plants handling farm birds. Dissect eggs from gravid females and after washing them several times, incubate them in shallow water in dishes at room temperature. Changing water daily will prevent the growth of large numbers of bacteria which retard development of the eggs.

When first stage larvae have appeared, the eggs should be fed to earthworms for development of the second and third stage larvae. Examination of infected annelids at daily intervals after ingestion of eggs will show the different stages of larvae, their location in the body, and time of their development.

Earthworms containing third stage larvae fed to 10 chicks which are examined at intervals of 2 days will enable the investigator to follow the development of the parasite in the vertebrate host.

SELECTED REFERENCES

Allen, R. W. (1949). J. Parasit. 35(6/2):35; (1950). Proc. Helminth. Soc. Wash. 17:58.

Cram, E. B. (1936). U. S. Dept. Agr. Tech. Bull. 516, p. 4.

Wehr, E. E. (1936). North Amer. Vet. 17:18.

Zucchero, P. J. (1942). Proc. W. Virginia Acad. Sci. 15:96.

Capillaria hepatica (Bancroft, 1893) (Plate 137)

Capillaria hepatica is a common parasite of rats, mice, and other rodents, together with a number of other mammals. It has been reported from humans in a few instances. The adult worms are embedded deep in the liver parenchyma. Eggs laid in the liver appear as yellow patches that are retained there

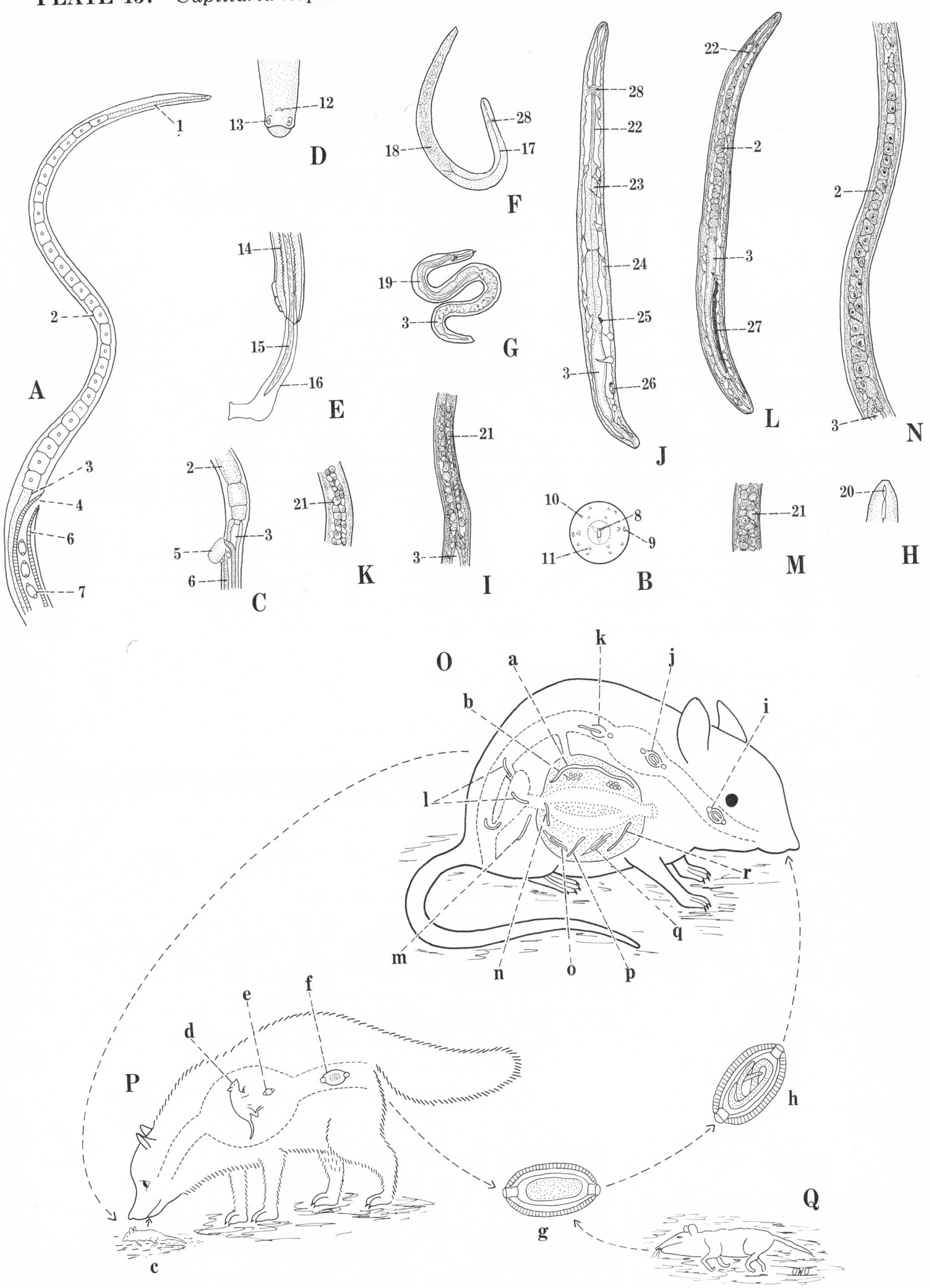

A
B
C
D
E
F
G
H
I
J
K
L
M
N
O
P
Q
a
b
c
d
e
f
g
h
i
j
k
l
m
n
o
p
q
r

during the life of the host. Development takes place only when they are freed from the liver and exposed to air with its oxygen.

DESCRIPTION. Males are 17 to 32 mm long by 0.04 to 0.08 mm in diameter. The muscular oesophagus is 0.32 mm long and the glandular portion 6.2 to 7.5 mm. The posterior end is blunt and bears a pair of subventral lobes. There is a well-developed though lightly cuticularized spicule 425 to 500 μ long and a membranous protrusible spicular sheath that expands distally into a funnel-shaped dilatation. Adult females attain a length of 98 mm and a diameter of 0.19 mm. The vulva is located slightly posterior to the end of the oesophagus and has a protrusible membranous structure. The surface layer of the shell is traversed by rodlike structures, each with a knoblike enlargement on the end. Measurements of eggs as given by various authors range in size from 48 to 62 μ long by 29 to 37 μ wide.

LIFE CYCLE. With the females embedded deeply in the liver parenchyma, the eggs are retained in clumps when deposited. They are uncleaved when laid in the liver parenchyma and do not develop beyond the eight-cell stage while still in it. Development continues only after they are freed from the liver by death and disintegration of the host or digestion of it by some animal. The eggs are extremely resistant, being able to survive for 750 days in livers kept unfrozen in a refrigerator. Also, they remain viable when exposed to the elements during the winter. Under favorable environmental conditions, first stage larvae are fully developed in 6 weeks when kept at 20 to 24° C, but do not hatch until eaten by rodents.

Upon hatching, the first stage larvae begin to leave the caecum about 48 hours later via the hepatic portal vein and some have reached the liver by 52 hours. Considerable growth in size and of organs, particularly the alimentary canal, takes place in the first stage.

Second stage larvae appear as early as 3 days after infection and continue until the seventh day. The first stage cuticle remains closely adherent to the body. Considerable growth and internal differentiation takes place, especially in the oesophageal region. The oesophagus and intestine are clearly differentiated. The binucleate genital primordium appears about midway between the oesophago-intestinal junction and the posterior extremity.

Third stage larvae first appear by the fifth day after infection. The intestine has increased greatly in length as has the genital primordium. The sexes are not recognizable at this time. Much growth and differentiation has occurred in the stichosome and the lateral bacillary bands have appeared.

Fourth stage larvae are present by the ninth day after infection, with both the males and females ensheathed in the cuticle of the third stage. In addition to greatly increased size of the body, the alimentary canal and reproductive organs are much advanced in development. The spicule is recognizable 12 days after infection. When the cuticle is shed after about 18 days for the males and 20 days for the females, they have reached adulthood. Eggs are present in the uterus by the 21st day. Females live as long as 59 days and males 40.

EXERCISE ON LIFE CYCLE

When infected livers are fed to rats or mice, the eggs are freed and passed undeveloped in the faeces, from which they may be retrieved by standard methods. Artificial digestion of the liver would also free them, but it is not known whether eggs freed by this method would develop and hatch. Infective larvae appear after about 6 weeks of incubation under warm, moist conditions.

Feed fully embryonated eggs to a series of mice and examine some of them at close intervals for a period of 60 days. Determine the date of hatching, migration through the wall of the caecum, entry into the liver, time and number of molts, length of the prepatent period, and longevity of the males and females in the liver.

SELECTED REFERENCES

Baylis, H. A. (1931). Parasitology 23:533.

Fülleborn, F. (1924). Arch. Schiffs- u. Trop. Hyg. 28:48.

Luttermoser, G. W. (1938). Amer. J. Hyg. 27:275; (1938). Ibid. 27:321.

Shorb, D. A. (1931). J. Parasit. 17:151.

Wright, K. A. (1961). Canad. J. Zool. 38:167.

Capillaria plica (Rudolphi, 1819) (Plate 138)

This species is a common parasite of the urinary bladder of dogs, wolves, and foxes, particularly the last species. Martens, badgers, and cats also are reported as hosts. Occasionally the worms occur in the pelvis of the kidney. Typical capillarid eggs in an undeveloped stage are passed in the urine.

DESCRIPTION. Males are 13 to 30 mm long, with the thin anterior part of the body only slightly shorter than the thicker posterior portion. There is a small bursa-like structure at the caudal end of the body. The spicular sheath is long and thin, with a punctate appearance due to the crossing of the transverse and longitudinal striae. The spicule is threadlike, rounded terminally, and 4.49 mm long.

Females are 30 to 60 mm long, with the slender portion of the body consisting of two-thirds of the total length. The caudal end is blunt and the anus is terminal. The vulva is at the end of a cylindrical appendage. Eggs measure 60 by 30 μ and are unembryonated when laid.

LIFE CYCLE. Adult females in the urinary bladder deposit their eggs which are voided with the urine. Under favorable conditions of moisture and temperature, the first stage larvae develop in 30 to 36 days. Further growth and hatching do not occur until the embryonated eggs are swallowed by earthworms (*Lumbricus terrestris, L. rubellus, Dendrobaena subrubicunda*). Shortly after reaching the posterior two-thirds of the intestine, the eggs hatch and the larvae soon burrow through the intestinal wall into the connective tissue where the first stage larvae become infective to the final host in about 24 hours.

Infection of the vertebrate host takes place when earthworms harboring first stage larvae are eaten. Upon escaping from the annelids, the larvae molt again and burrow into the wall of the small intestine where the second molt occurs within 7 days. The third stage larvae enter the hepatic portal vein sometime before the 20th day, going to the lungs via the liver and heart. They pass through the pulmonary capillaries, return to the heart, and enter the general circulation.

It is believed that larvae enter the kidneys by way of the renal arteries and follow the blood vessels to the glomeruli. Here they migrate into Bowman's capsule, go through the tubular portion of the nephron, and enter the pelvis of the kidney, going down the ureter to the urinary bladder. Third and fourth stage larvae are present in the bladder on or about the 33rd day after infection. Sexually mature worms appear 58 to 63 days after infection, as indicated by the appearance of eggs in the urine.

EXERCISE ON LIFE CYCLE

Eggs collected from gravid females obtained from the urinary bladder or from the urine of infected dogs should be incubated in a 2 per cent solution of potassium bichromate. When the first stage larvae have developed, they may be released from the eggs for purposes of study by gently applying pressure on the cover slip.

Earthworms may be infected by mixing embryonated eggs with the soil in which they are kept. Examine the intestinal contents and the connective tissue surrounding the gut for first stage larvae. This may be done effectively by digesting them in artificial media *in vitro*. Determine the hatching time and how soon thereafter they migrate into the coelom. Ascertain in what part of the gut migration from it into the body cavity takes place.

If a dog is available for feeding experiments, introduce infected earthworms into its food and determine the prepatent period of the nematodes by observing the date when eggs appear in the urine. These parasites are not especially pathogenic when present in small numbers.

SELECTED REFERENCES

Chitwood, M. B., and F. D. Enzie. (1953). Proc. Helminth. Soc. Wash. 20:27.

Enigk, K. (1950). Zeitschr. Tropenmed. Parasit. 1:560.

Enzie, F. D. (1951). J. Amer. Vet. Med. Assoc. 119:210.

Teixeira de Freitas, J. F., and H. Lent. (1936). Mem. Inst. Oswaldo Cruz. 31:85.

EXPLANATION OF PLATE 138 ▷

A. Caudal end of adult male with spicule and spicular sheath extended. **B.** Caudal end of body of adult male showing lobes. **C.** Vulvar region of adult female. **D.** Cross section of body showing lateral bacillary bands. **E.** Unembryonated egg. **F.** First stage larva. **G.** Second stage larva from intestine of earthworm. **H.** Fox definitive host. **I.** Earthworm intermediate host.

1, basal portion of spicule; **2,** spicular pouch; **3,** distal portion of spicule; **4,** caudal lobe; **5,** stichosome; **6,** capillary tube of oesophagus; **7,** intestine; **8,** bacillary band; **9,** vulva; **10,** vagina; **11,** spear; **12,** nerve ring; **13,** anterior portion of oesophagus; **14,** rectum; **15,** reproductive primordium.

a, adult worm in urinary bladder; **b,** eggs laid in urinary bladder; **c,** eggs pass from body through urethra in urine; **d,** eggs undeveloped when voided with urine; **e,** fully developed egg; **f,** embryonated eggs swallowed by earthworms; **g,** embryonated eggs hatch in middle third of intestine; **h,** newly hatched larvae molt and as second stage larvae migrate through intestinal wall into coelom; **i,** larvae encyst in loose connective tissue of coelom; **j,** earthworms eaten by foxes; **k,** digestion of infected earthworms, releasing second stage larvae; (**l-t** not demonstrated experimentally but postulated to occur); **l,** second stage larvae molt to third stage; **m,** third stage larvae enter hepatic portal vein; **n,** larvae pass through capillaries of liver; **o,** larvae pass through right side of heart; **p,** larvae pass through capillaries of lungs; **q,** larvae pass through left side of heart; **r,** larvae enter dorsal aorta; **s,** larvae enter renal artery; **t,** larvae leave glomeruli in kidneys, entering Bowman's capsule and travel through renal tubules to pelvis of kidneys; **u,** larvae in pelvis of kidney; **v,** larvae travel down ureter, enter urinary bladder, and develop to maturity.

Figures A-E adapted from de Freitas and Lent, 1936, Mem. Inst. Oswaldo Cruz. 31:85; F, G, from Enigk, 1950, Zeitschr. Tropenmed. Parasit. 1:560.

FAMILY TRICHINELLIDAE

This family consists of a single species. The adults occur in the lumen and mucosal lining of the small intestine of mammals. Gravid females give birth to hatched larvae which make their way via the blood and lymph vessels to the skeletal muscles where they encyst. This parasite is prevalent in the northern hemisphere and parts of South America, but rare in the tropics and other areas of the southern hemisphere. Humans are commonly infected with it.

Trichinella spiralis (Owen, 1835) (Plate 139)

T. spiralis is a common parasite of many species of carnivorous and omnivorous mammals, including humans. On the basis of surveys in the United States, it is estimated that approximately 16 per cent of the human population and about 1.5 per cent of the swine are infected. The principal source of infection for humans in the United States is pork. In the arctic regions, polar bears, walruses, and seals constitute the primary sources. Extremely high incidences of infection occurs in the wild rats on community garbage dumps.

Among domestic animals other than swine, dogs and cats commonly are infected. Wild mammals such as foxes, coyotes, bobcats, mink, opossums, raccoons, bears, walruses, hair seals, squirrels, mice, muskrats, and others serve as natural hosts.

DESCRIPTION. These are nematodes of small size with the posterior portion of the body only slightly greater in diameter than the anterior. The oesophagus consists of a short anterior muscular part and a long posterior stichosome, or row of cells.

Males measure 1.4 to 1.6 mm long by 40 μ in diameter. A pair of lobes is located at the posterior extremity with one pair of papillae between them. There is no spicule or spicular sheath. Females are 3 to 4 mm long by 60 μ in diameter with the vulva near the middle of the stichosome. They are ovoviparous.

LIFE CYCLE. Transmission of the parasite from host to host is by ingesting flesh containing encysted larvae or by swallowing viable cysts passed in faeces resulting from meals of trichinous meat.

Upon reaching the stomach, the larvae escape quickly from the cysts and are carried to the small intestine where they penetrate the mucosa within 5 hours after arriving. There are probably four molts. The first one occurs within 8 hours after the first stage larvae have entered the mucosa. The second stage larvae undergo the second molt 12 to 16 hours later while still in the mucosa. They are sexually differentiated by the end of the second day, when they return to the lumen of the intestine where the

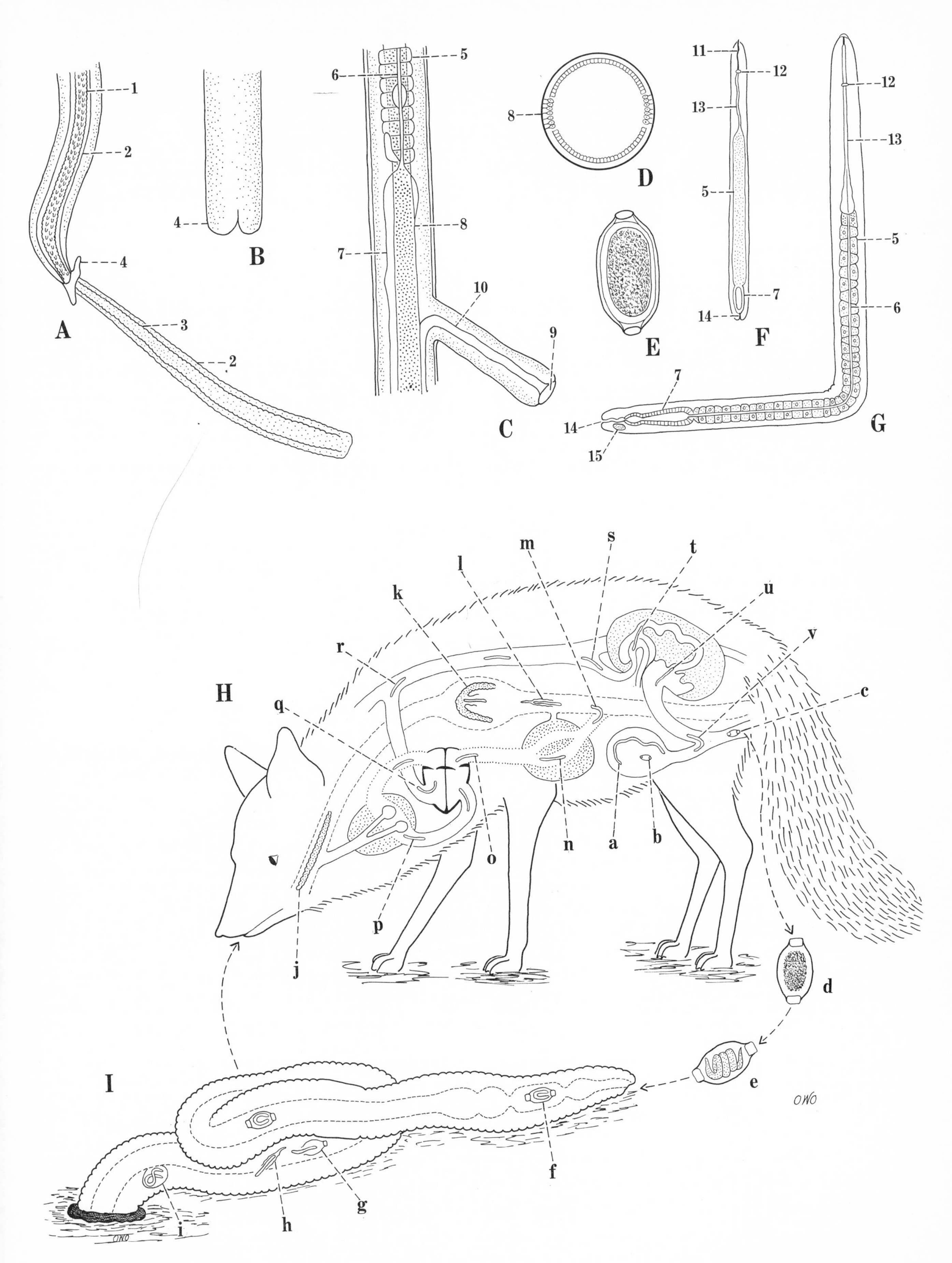
1
2
4
3
2
A
4
B
5
6
8
7
10
9
C
8
D
E
11
12
13
5
7
14
F
12
13
5
6
7
14
15
G
m
s
l
t
k
u
r
v
c
H
q
o
n
a
b
p
j
d
e
I
f
g
h
i
OWO

EXPLANATION OF PLATE 139 ⇨

A. Adult female. **B.** Adult male. **C.** Ventral view of posterior end of male. **D.** Unencysted and fully developed larva. **E.** Unencysted young larvae in skeletal muscles. **F.** Encysted larvae in skeletal muscles. **G.** Swine host. **H.** Sylvatic cycle with carnivores, scavengers, and carrion as sources of infection of swine and other animals that eat them. **I.** Marine cycle. **J.** Rat cycle. **K.** Urban cycle with garbage containing scraps of infected pork or bodies of infected animals fed to swine.

1, mouth; **2**, anus; **3**, copulatory appendages; **4**, genital papillae; **5**, muscular portion of oesophagus; **6**, glandular portion of oesophagus, or stichosome; **7**, intestine; **8**, ovary; **9**, uterus; **10**, vulva; **11**, testis; **12**, sperm duct; **13**, ejaculatory duct; **14**, cloaca; **15**, nerve ring; **16**, skeletal muscle; **17**, unencysted young larvae in skeletal muscle; **18**, older larvae with cyst forming from host material; **19**, cyst formed by reaction of host tissues.

a, flesh containing infective cysts being swallowed by pig; **b**, cysts being freed from flesh and larvae from them in stomach; **c**, first stage larvae free in duodenum; **d**, larvae entering intestinal mucosa; **e**, first molt; **f**, second stage larvae; **g**, second molt; **h**, third stage larvae migrate from mucosa to lumen of intestine; **i**, third molt; **j**, fourth stage males and females mate in intestinal lumen; **k**, inseminated fourth stage females return to mucosa and molt; **l**, adult females in mucosa give birth to larvae; **m**, larvae enter lacteals and pass through lymph nodes; **n**, larvae in lymph vessel; **o**, larvae enter postcaval vein; **p**, larvae enter hepatic portal vein; **q**, larvae pass through liver; **r**, larvae from lymph and blood vessels enter right side of heart; **s**, **t**, larvae pass through capillaries of lungs and return to left side of heart; **u**, larvae entering dorsal aorta and general circulation; **v**, larvae entering capillaries of skeletal muscles; **w**, unencysted larvae in muscle; **x**, encysted larvae; **y**, intact cyst which failed to open while passing through stomach being voided in faeces; **z**, adult males are passed out of body after mating; **aa**, viable cyst passed in faeces is infective to swine and other animals, course of development same as **a-x**.

a' (H section), rodents as scavengers of carrion or faeces of large animals become infected; **b'**, predators eat parasitized rodents and become infected; **c'**, carcasses of predators (and rodents) become available to rodents; **d'**, swine eat rodents and carcasses of predators, becoming infected; offal from slaughtered swine is left for carnivores, scavengers (including swine).

a" (I section), polar bears; **b"**, whales; **c"**, hair seals; **d"**, walruses are infected with trichina.

a (J section), rats transmit infection among themselves through cannibalism; **b**, rat faeces containing viable cysts infective to rats, swine, and any mammal that might ingest them; **c** (K section), scraps of pork, or carcasses of small mammals, containing viable cysts are a source of infection to swine that are fed garbage and to mammals (rats, cats, dogs, etc.) that eat them.

Figures A, B adapted from Faust and Russell, 1957, Craig and Faust's Clinical Parasitology, 6th Ed., Lea and Febiger, Philadelphia, p. 330; C, from Wu, 1955, J. Parasit. 41:40; D, from Skrjabin, Shikobalova, Paramonov, and Sudarikov, 1954, Opredelitel Paraziticheskikh Nematod, Vol. 4, Plate 147, Fig. B; E, F, G, H, I, J, K, original.

---

third molt takes place. At this time, the fourth stage larvae are believed to mate, following which the majority of the males are expelled from the intestine. Probably the males molt only three times. The first and second molts take place in the mucosa and the third after they return to the intestinal lumen and prior to mating.

The inseminated females re-enter the mucosa and undergo the final molt when 3 days old. They are sexually mature 1 day later, or about 96 hours after entering the host, and larvae are being born in the mucosa.

The newly born larvae make their way through the tissues to the venules of the hepatic portal vein or to the lacteals. They are carried through the right side of the heart, the capillaries of the lungs, back to the left side of the heart, and into the general circulation of the body. From the capillaries of the skeletal muscles, especially active ones such as those of the tongue, diaphragm, and thorax which have a rich supply of blood, they enter the muscle cells, migrating along the fibers, leaving a hyaline trail. A capsule of host origin eventually forms around each larva. The larvae become infective at 17 or 18 days of age, which is about 2 weeks before encapsulation. Development of the parasite constitutes three critical periods for the host. They are 1) development of the larvae in the mucosa of the intestine, 2) larviposition and larval migration in the intestinal wall, and 3) migration and encystation of the larvae in the skeletal muscles.

Three ecological types of life cycles are recognized. They are 1) the urban cycle in which rats and swine serve as reservoirs from which each may be infected, and humans are infected by eating parasitized pork that is insufficiently cooked to kill the infective larvae; 2) the sylvatic cycle in which predators and

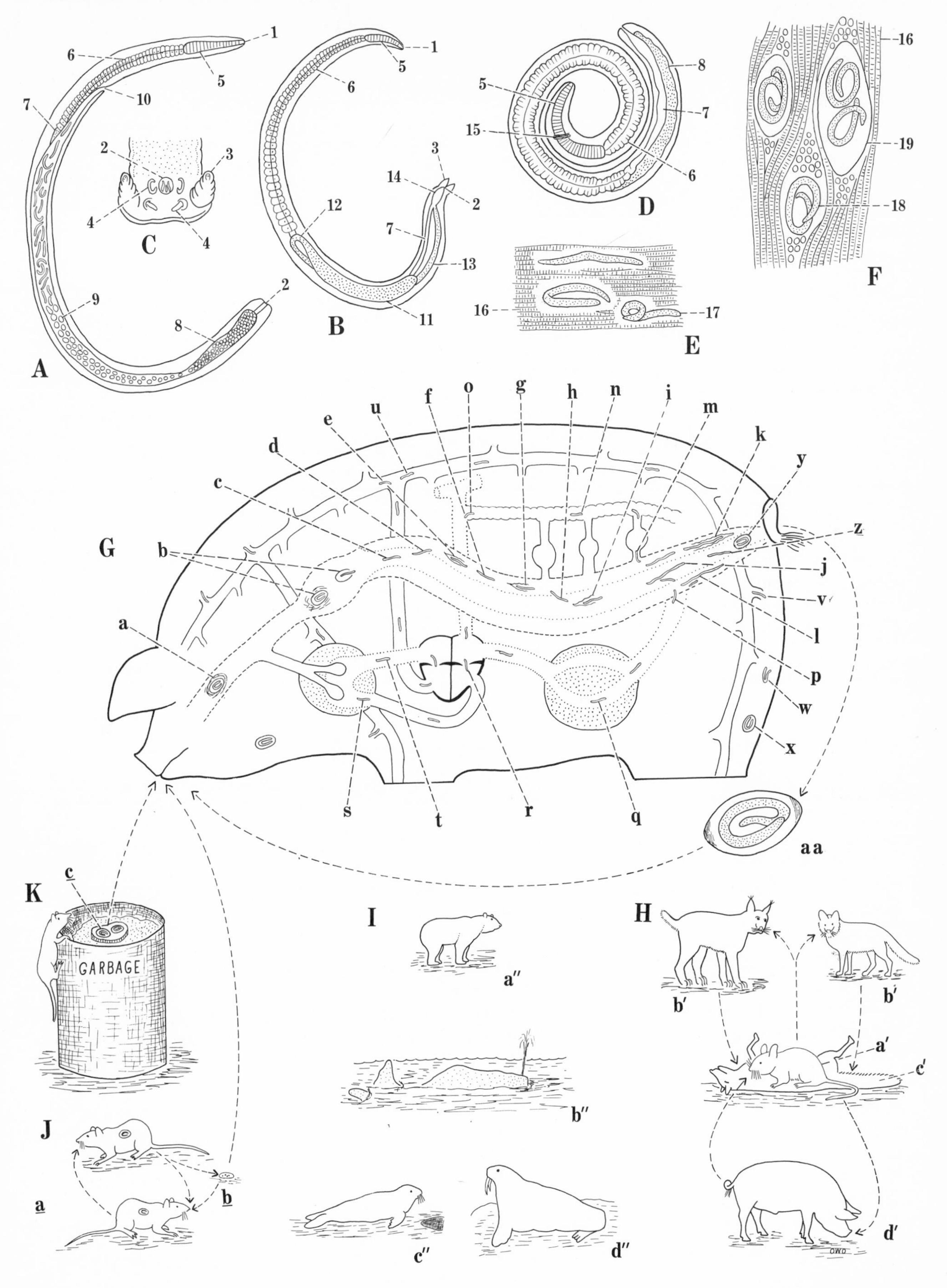

1
2
3
4
5
6
7
8
9
10
11
12
13
14
15
16
17
18
19
A
B
C
D
E
F
G
H
I
J
K
a
b
c
d
e
f
g
h
i
j
k
l
m
n
o
p
q
r
s
t
u
v
w
x
y
z
aa
a′
b′
c′
d′
a″
b″
c″
d″
GARBAGE

scavengers serve as hosts; and 3) the marine cycle in which hair seals, walruses, whales, and polar bears are the hosts. Each of these types is related to infection of humans.

Necrophagous insects commonly ingest encysted larvae of trichina which are able to survive for several days in them. Such arthropods serve as short term reservoir hosts for transferring cysts from infected carcasses to any mammals that might eat them.

The occurrence of trichina in marine mammals may be explained in a similar manner. Bodies of infected mammals entering the sea are fed upon by crustacea which could ingest the cycts and harbor them in the intestine. Plankton-feeding fish eating such crustacea would in turn serve as a second reservoir. Mammals such as whales feeding on the crustacea or seals on fish containing infected crustacean could become infected.

EXERCISE ON LIFE CYCLE

Rats living on municipal dumps usually provide a plentiful source of trichina larvae for experimental purposes. The presence of larvae in them may be determined by examining with the aid of a dissecting microscope bits of muscle tissue pressed between two plates of glass.

Feed infected flesh to a few white rats to obtain heavily infected muscles for further experiments. The larvae become infective in 17 to 18 days, which is before encapsulation. Muscle tissue in equal amounts from a heavily infected rat should be fed to 10 white rats on the same day. Kill a rat on the 1st, 2nd, 3rd, 4th, 5th, 6th, 8th, 12th, 16th, and 20th days. Examine the intestine of each rat by slitting it open and washing the contents into a dish of normal saline, and the mesenteric lymph nodes and striated muscle by pressing bits of them between glass plates. Sections of intestine and lymph nodes are useful for showing developmental stages in them. Note when and where each stage in the life cycle occurs. Make permanent mounts of each stage, using the glycerin method.

To determine the extent to which cysts and larvae are passed in the faeces, feed a rat a fairly large number of cysts (1,000 to 2,000 by counting them) and examine the pellets passed during the first 24 hours afterward to determine the percentage of larvae that was retained. About 3 to 4 weeks later, feed it a similar number of cysts and ascertain whether more or fewer larvae appear in the faeces. Test the larvae and cysts passed in the faeces for infectivity be feeding them to separate uninfected rats.

SELECTED REFERENCES

Berezancev, J. A. (1960). Polski Towarzystwo Paraszytologizne 6:315.

Gould, S. D. (1945). Trichinosis. Charles C Thomas, Springfield, Ill., 366 pp.

Kreis, H. A. (1937). Zbl. Bakt. (Orig.) 138:290.

Rausch, R. L. (1960). Polski Towarzystwo Paraszytologizne 6:305.

Rausch, R. L., B. B. Babero, R. V. Rausch, and E. L. Schiller. (1956). J. Parasit. 42:259.

Robinson, H. A., and O. W. Olsen. (1960). J. Parasit. 46:589.

Zimmerman, W. J., E. D. Hubbard, and J. Mathews. (1959). J. Parasit. 45:441.

Suborder Dioctophymatina

These nematodes lack a stylet, at least in the adult stage. The oesophageal glands are highly polynucleate and inside the wall of the cylindrical oesophagus. The eggs are operculate and covered with deep pits.

SUPERFAMILY DIOCTOPHYMOIDEA

These nematodes are medium to very large in size. The males are characterized by a muscular bell-shaped bursa without supporting rays and a single bristle-like spicule. The eggs have a thick pitted shell that is lighter in color at the poles.

There are two families: Dioctophymatidae without and Soboliphymatidae with a muscular cephalic sucker. They are parasites of mammals and birds.

FAMILY DIOCTOPHYMATIDAE

The family consists of the genera *Dioctophyma, Eustrongylides,* and *Hystrichis. Dioctophyma* occurs in the kidneys and abdominal cavity of mammals. The other two are in the proventriculus of aquatic birds.

Dioctophyma renale (Goeze, 1782) (Plate 140)

This is the giant kidney worm found in the kidneys and peritoneal cavity of mammals, particularly in mink and dogs, with the former probably the natural host. It occurs fairly commonly in North America. Nearly 8 per cent of 388 wild mink from one locality in Michigan were infected.

DESCRIPTION. Living worms are red in color. Males measure 140 to 200 mm long by 4 to 6 mm in diameter. The copulatory bursa is a fleshy bell-shaped structure without supporting rays, as occur in the Strongylina. There is a single bristle-like spicule. Females attain a length of 200 to 1,000 mm and a diameter of 5 to 12 mm. The vulva is located in the anterior part of the body. Eggs are in the two-cell stage when laid; the shell is thick, deeply pitted, and lighter in color at each end; the average size is 74.3 by 46.7 μ.

LIFE CYCLE. Eggs laid in the kidneys pass to the urinary bladder and are voided with the urine. Motile larvae appear after 21 days of incubation at room temperature but hatching does not occur until they are ingested by branchiobdellid annelids (*Cambarincola philddelphica*), a genus of worldwide distribution. Just when the eggs become infective to the annelids is not known but they are still infective after being kept in glass dishes at room temperature for nearly one year.

Branchiobdellids feeding on the bottom of ponds frequented by infected mink and other hosts ingest the infective eggs. Hatching takes place in the intestine, and the first stage larvae soon migrate into the coelom. The first molt occurs 2 days later by larvae hatching from eggs that have incubated 9 months, and in 7 days in those that have incubated 7 months. The second stage larvae soon develop six long pointed papillae on the head. Encystment takes place after the larvae cease their migration in the coelom. The cyst is formed from secretions extruded from the head. No noticeable development takes place in the cyst.

The annelids commonly attach to the gills of crayfish after a period of living free in the water. When crayfish bearing annelids on their gills are eaten by bullheads, cysts freed from the tissues by the action of the digestive juices rupture, releasing the second stage larvae. They migrate through the intestinal wall of the fish into the coelom where the second molt takes place. The third stage larvae attach to the mesenteries and encyst. They continue to grow, eventually molting to the fourth stage, as evidenced by the presence of the cast cuticle in the cyst. If they remain long periods in the cyst, development continues with the formation of pre-adults.

Infection of the vertebrate host occurs when bullheads containing fourth stage larvae or pre-adults are eaten. The cysts are freed from the fish in the stomach and the larvae from the cysts in either the stomach or duodenum. Migration from the intestine is through the wall of the duodenum. In mink, this portion of the intestine is in contact with the right kidney, so the parasite continues its progress directly into that renal organ. In dogs, the kidney is separated from the duodenum a short distance which probably accounts for the high percentage of worms being in the peritoneal cavity of these hosts. Sexual maturity is attained in about 3 months or more after the worms reach the kidneys. Evidence indicates a longevity of 1 to 3 years, after which the worms die and degenerate and the remaining shell of the infected kidney shrivels. A total of about 2 years is required to complete the cycle.

Karmanova's studies in Russia showed that eggs eaten by oligochaetes hatch and the larvae enter the vascular system where they undergo three molts, becoming infective to the final host. If the larvae pass from an oligochaete to a fish, the latter serves as a reservoir only. According to these studies, fish do not appear to be a biological necessity for completion of the life cycle of *D. renale.* However, they do serve an important ecological function in bringing the parasite more directly into the food chain of the final host.

It is Karmanova's opinion that Woodhead was dealing with the larvae of one of the Gordiacea instead of *Dioctophyma.*

EXPLANATION OF PLATE 140 ⇨

A. Lateral view of anterior end of adult male. **B.** *En face* view of adult. **C.** Caudal end of adult male showing bursa and spicule. **D.** Egg in early stage of cleavage. **E.** First stage larva 227 days old. **F.** Penetration glands of first stage larva. **G.** Second stage larva penetrating tissue of annelid. **H.** Second stage larva encysted in annelid. **I.** Third stage larva migrating in tissue of bullhead. **J.** Third stage larva encysted in bullhead. **K.** Fourth stage larva migrating from intestine of ferret to kidney. **L.** Mink, the common natural definitive host. **M.** Annelid *(Cambarincola philadelphica)* first intermediate host. **N.** Crayfish to which annelids habitually attach. **O.** Bullhead *(Ameiurus melas)* second intermediate host.

1, papillae on anterior end of adult male; **2**, oesophagus; **3**, anterior loop of testis; **4**, outer ring of cephalic papillae; **5**, inner ring of cephalic papillae; **6**, mouth; **7**, fleshy rayless copulatory bursa; **8**, spicule; **9**, terminal plug; **10**, embryo in first cleavage; **11**, stylet; **12**, penetration glands; **13**, excretory reservoir; **14**, excretory cell; **15**, elongated papilla; **16**, pharyngeal rods; **17**, anterior portion of body designated as a reservoir; **18**, tissue of annelid host; **19**, second stage larvae encysted in annelid; **20**, cyst; **21**, small intestine of ferret; **22**, fourth stage larva migrating through intestinal wall toward kidney.

a, adult male giant kidney worm in kidney of mink; **b**, eggs laid by females in kidneys escape by way of ureters; **c**, eggs in urinary bladder; **d**, undeveloped eggs voided with urine into water where embryonation occurs; **e**, embryonated eggs eaten by branchiobdellids; **f**, eggs hatch in intestine of annelid; **g**, first stage larvae migrate through intestinal wall into coelom; **h**, molting of first stage larvae occurs in tissues; **i**, second stage larvae encyst in annelids; **j**, annelids attach to gills of crayfish, especially during the winter (newly laid coccoons appear in March and by the end of May many young annelids can be found free in water); **k**, crayfish carrying infected annelids eaten by bullheads serve as a means of introducing cysts into second intermediate host; **l**, second stage larvae are released from cysts in intestine of bullheads; **m**, larvae migrate through intestinal wall into coelom; **n**, in bullheads, larvae molt second time to form third stage larvae; **o**, third stage larvae encyst in viscera of bullheads and molt for third time, this time in the cyst, and become fourth stage larvae; **p**, cast cuticle from third molt; **q**, cysts containing larvae freed from fish by action of digestive juices; **r**, larvae escape through rupture in cyst wall into digestive tract; **s**, larvae penetrate wall of duodenum at point where it makes contact with right kidney in mink, thus affecting entrance into kidney at that point.

Adapted from Woodhead, 1950, Trans. Amer. Micr. Soc. 69:21.

The life cycle of *Hystrichus tricolor* of the proventricular glands of ducks involves only earthworms as intermediate hosts. The first stage larva develops in the egg as in *D. renale.* Hatching takes place in the intestine of oligocheates and the larvae develop to the fourth stage in the blood vessels. When the earthworms are eaten by ducks, the larvae bore into the proventricular wall, molt the fourth time, and develop to maturity in a month.

In both *Dioctophyme renale* and *Hystrichus tricolor,* annelids serve as intermediate hosts.

EXERCISE ON LIFE CYCLE

Since this life cycle does not lend itself to a general study, no instructions are given for it. These are available in the papers by Woodhead and Hallberg for *D. renale* and Karmanova for *H. tricolor.*

SELECTED REFERENCES

Hallberg, C. W. (1953). Trans. Amer. Micr. Soc. 72:351.

Karmanova, E. M. (1956). Dokladi Akad. Nauk. SSSR 111:245; (1959). Ibid. 127:1317; (1961). Trudi Gelmintol. Lab. Akad. Nauk. SSSR 11:118; (1963). Med. Parasitol. i Parazitar. Bolezoi, Moscow, 32:331.

Woodhead, A. E. (1945). J. Parasit. 31(Suppl.):12; (1946). Ibid. 32(Suppl.):16; (1950). Trans. Amer. Micr. Soc. 69:21.

PLATE 140 *Dicotophyma renale*

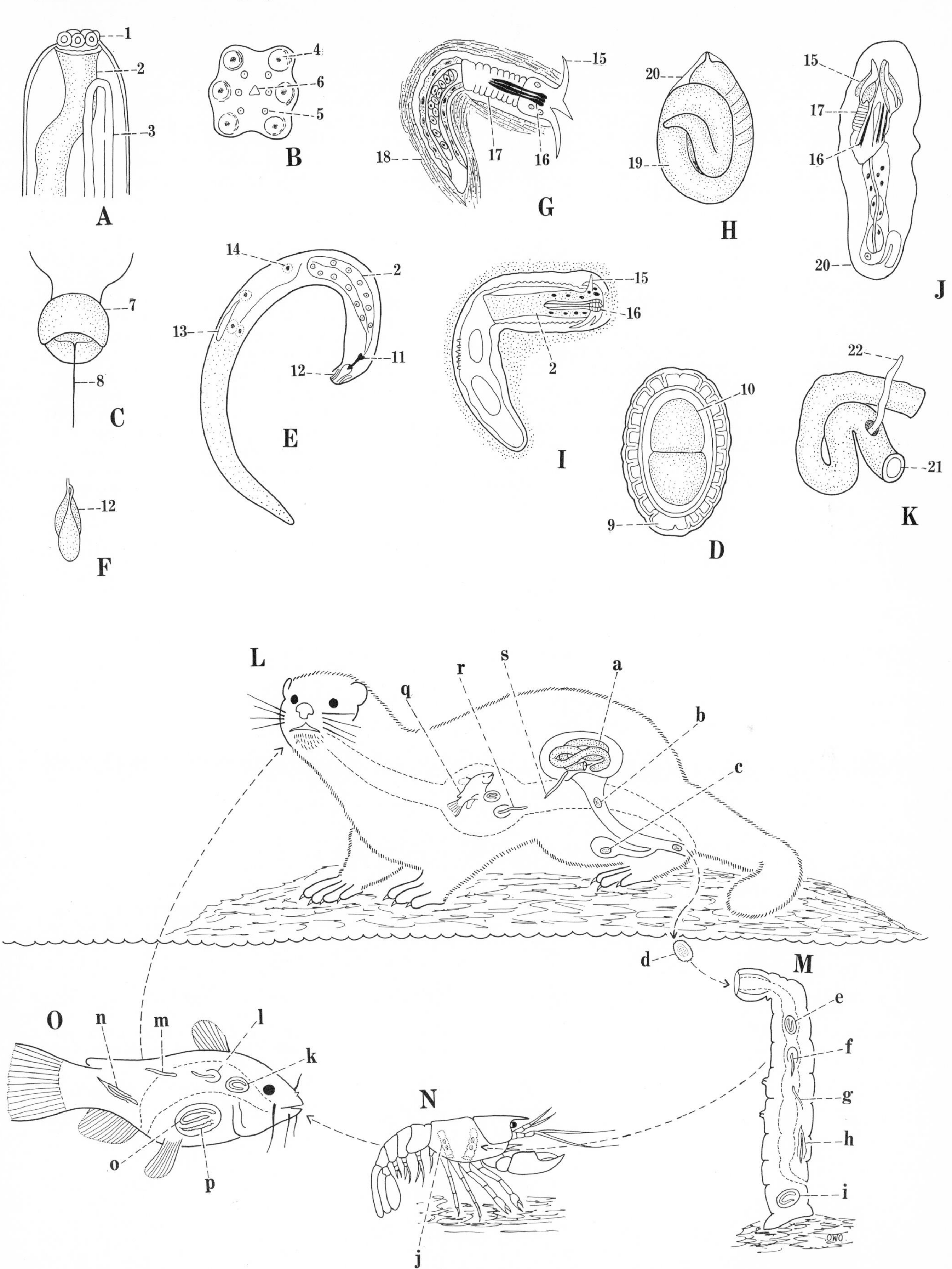

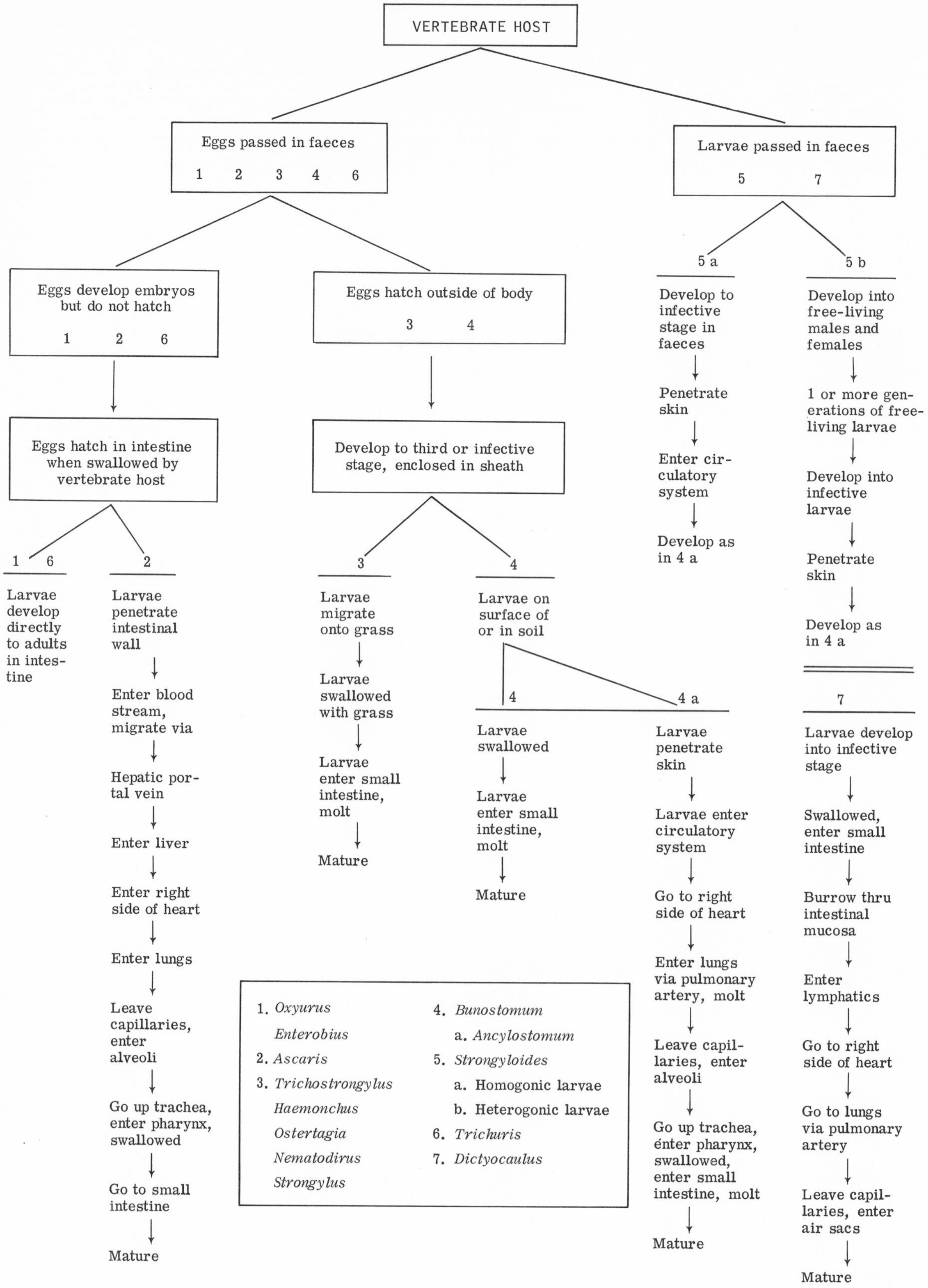

VERTEBRATE HOST

Eggs passed in faeces — 1 2 3 4 6

- **Eggs develop embryos but do not hatch** — 1 2 6
  - Eggs hatch in intestine when swallowed by vertebrate host
    - **1 6**: Larvae develop directly to adults in intestine
    - **2**: Larvae penetrate intestinal wall → Enter blood stream, migrate via → Hepatic portal vein → Enter liver → Enter right side of heart → Enter lungs → Leave capillaries, enter alveoli → Go up trachea, enter pharynx, swallowed → Go to small intestine → Mature
- **Eggs hatch outside of body** — 3 4
  - Develop to third or infective stage, enclosed in sheath
    - **3**: Larvae migrate onto grass → Larvae swallowed with grass → Larvae enter small intestine, molt → Mature
    - **4**: Larvae on surface of or in soil
      - **4**: Larvae swallowed → Larvae enter small intestine, molt → Mature
      - **4 a**: Larvae penetrate skin → Larvae enter circulatory system → Go to right side of heart → Enter lungs via pulmonary artery, molt → Leave capillaries, enter alveoli → Go up trachea, enter pharynx, swallowed, enter small intestine, molt → Mature

Larvae passed in faeces — 5 7

- **5 a**: Develop to infective stage in faeces → Penetrate skin → Enter circulatory system → Develop as in 4 a
- **5 b**: Develop into free-living males and females → 1 or more generations of free-living larvae → Develop into infective larvae → Penetrate skin → Develop as in 4 a
- **7**: Larvae develop into infective stage → Swallowed, enter small intestine → Burrow thru intestinal mucosa → Enter lymphatics → Go to right side of heart → Go to lungs via pulmonary artery → Leave capillaries, enter air sacs → Mature

1. *Oxyurus*
   Enterobius
2. *Ascaris*
3. *Trichostrongylus*
   Haemonchus
   Ostertagia
   Nematodirus
   Strongylus
4. *Bunostomum*
   a. *Ancylostomum*
5. *Strongyloides*
   a. Homogonic larvae
   b. Heterogonic larvae
6. *Trichuris*
7. *Dictyocaulus*

PLATE 142 *Summary of Indirect Life Cycles of Some Nematodes*

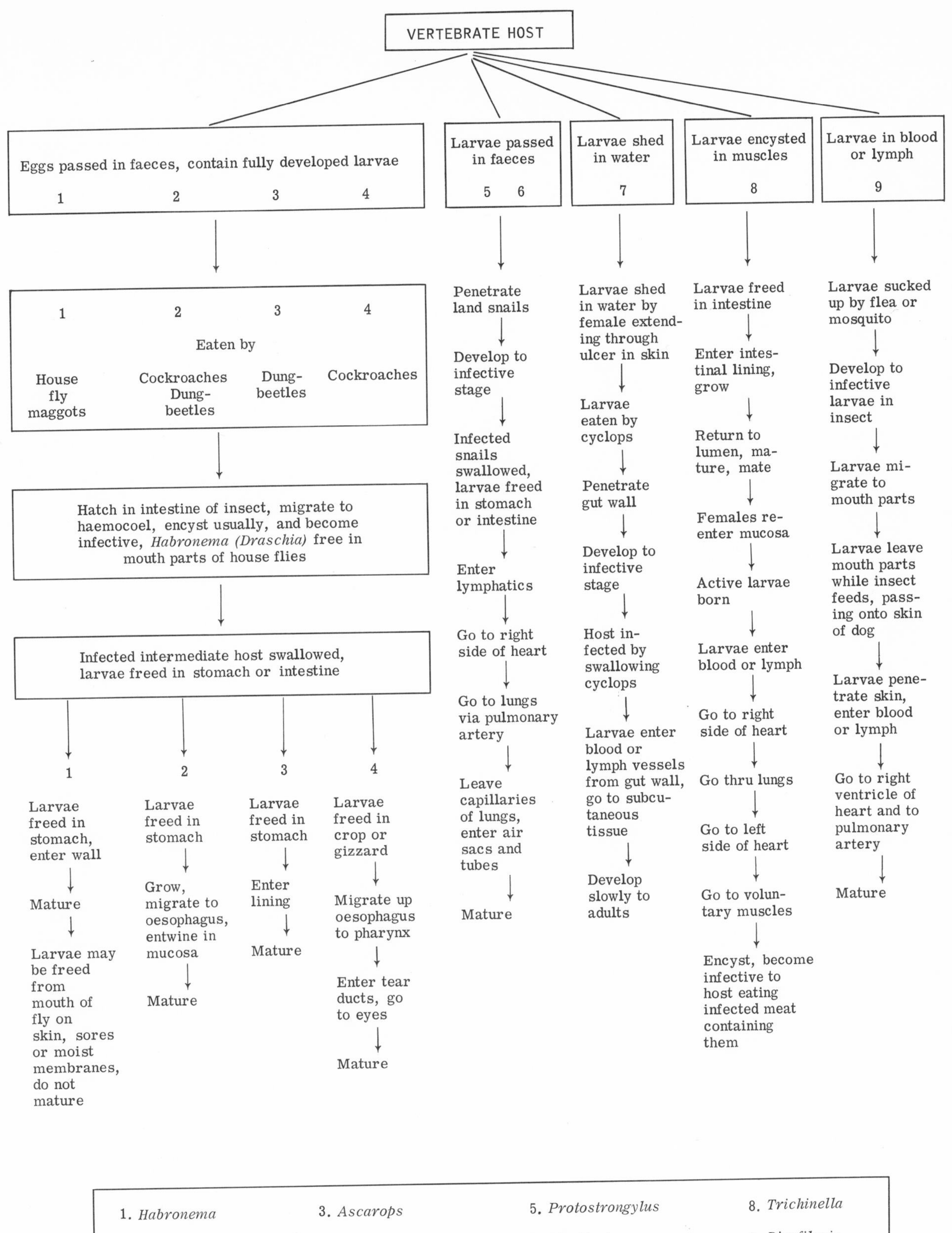

1. *Habronema*
2. *Gongylonema*
3. *Ascarops*, *Physocephalus*
4. *Oxyspirura*
5. *Protostrongylus*
6. *Muellerius*
7. *Dracunculus*
8. *Trichinella*
9. *Dirofilaria*, *Dipetalonema*

INDEX

A

Abcess
  brain, 52
  intestinal, 50
  liver, 50
  lung, 50
Acanthella, 7, 298, 306, 308
Acanthocephala, 297, 300
Acanthocephalus, 299
  dirus, 302
  lucii, 302
  ranae, 300
Acanthocotyle minima, 140
Acanthodactylus vulgaris, 76, 77, 78
Acanthor, 7, 302, 304, 306
Acanthorhynchus, 299
Acartea bifilosa, 366
Acella, 164
Acephalina, tribe, 54
Acnidosporidia, 114
Actinomyxidia, 122
Actitis macularia, 220
Acuariidae, 316
Adaptation, 3
  evolutionary, 5
  hallmark, 3
  parasitic life, 3, 4
Adelea
  mesnili, 82
  ovata, 82
Adeleidae, 77, 78
Adeleidea, 68, 77
Adeleina, 77
Adelina, 78, 82
  cryptocerci, 78
    description, 78
    life cycle, 80, pl. 25
  triboli, 82
Adenophorea, 315, 317, 397
Adhesive gland, 174
Aedes, 60, 391, 392, 394
Aelurostrongylus abstrusus, 348
African sleeping sickness, 9
Aggregata, 56, pl. 16, 68
  eberthi, 74
    description, 76
    life cycle, 76, pl. 23
Aggregatidae, 74
Agriolimax, 166, 283, 284, 348
  agrestis, 195
Air
  borne eggs, 356
  sac, 385, 386
Akeridae, 159
  Haminoae, 159
Ala, 378
  body, 378
  caudal, 380
  cervical, 364, 382
Alaria, 154
  canis, 154, 160, 176
    description, 176
    life cycle, 176, pl. 56
Allassotomoides parvum, 212
Allocreadiidae, 152, 154, 234
Allocreadium, 156, 235
  angusticolle, 235
  ictoluri, 235
  isosporum, 156
Allocreadoidea, 156, 234
Alloglossidium corti, 160
Allolobophora caliginosa, 400
Ambloplites, 270
  rupestris, 198, 308
Ambystoma maculatum, 240, 242
Ameiurus melas, 130, 247, 250, 412
Amia calva, 268, 270, 311
Amnicola, 159, 162, pl. 51
  limnosa, 232, 252, 254
Amnicolidae, 159, pl. 51, 162, 164
  Amnicola, 162
  Bulimus (=*Bithinia*), 162
  Cincinnatia, 162
  Flumnicola, 162
  Oncomelania, 164
  Pomatiopsis, 162
Amphibians, 26, 39, 49, 128, 129, 142, 240, 258, 375, 394, 396
Amphid, 322, 323, 324, 372, 397
Amphinucleus, 134
Amphipod, 235, 238, 308, 310, 368, 397
Amphistome, 154
Ampullaria, 162, 164, pl. 57
Ampullaridae, 164, pl. 51
  Ampullaria, 164
  Pomacea, 164
Anadonta grandis, 150
Anchor, 140, 144
Ancylidae, 162, 164, pl. 51
  Ancylus, 162
  Ferrissia, 162
Ancylostoma, 413
  braziliense, 327, 328
  caninum, 315, 326, 328
    description, 326
    life cycle, 326, pl. 111
Ancylostomatidae, 315, 326
Ancylus, 162, 164, pl. 51
Ancyrocephalus aculeatus, 140
Anemone, sea, 1
Anepitheliocystida, 150, 160, 167
Anguilla
  chrysypa, 311
  rostata, 311
Anguispira, 29, 162, 166
  alternata, 164, pl. 52, 195, 196
Anisogamete, 68
Anisotarsus, 286
Annelids, 53, 122, 258, 262, 354, 411, 412
Anopheles, 391
  crucians, 124
  quadrimaculatus, 94
Anoplocephala, 260
Anoplocephalidae, 292
Anoplura, 3
Ant, 217, 218, 283, 286, 382, 384, 385
Anteater, 298
Antibodies, 4, 6, 112
Apatemon gracilis, 170
  life cycle, 170
Aphodius granarius, 380
Aphryngostrigea pipientis, 170
Apical
  gland, 180
  papilla, 186
  ring, 112
Apis mellifera, 124
Aplexa, 164
Aplodinotus, 120
  grunniens, 140
Apodius, 286
Apophallus, 171, 248
  brevis, 171
  imperator, 171
  venustus, 248
    description, 248
    life cycle, 248, pl. 81
Aporocotylidae, 192
Apple, 306
Archiacanthocephala, 297, 298, 300
Archigetes, 258, 262
  sieboldi, 260, 262
    description, 262
    life cycle, 262, pl. 86
Ardea herodias, 180, 250
Argia, 224, 242
Arhythmorhynchus, 299
Arion, 283, 284, 349
Arionidae, 162
  Arion, 162
Armadillidium, 218
  quadrifrons, 218
  vulgare, 304
Armadillos, 18, 20
Arthropod, 11, 129, 370, 378, 386, 396, 401
  blood sucking, 3, 388
  hosts, 294
Ascaridae, 316, 360
Ascaridia, 316, 358
  columbae, 360
  galli, 316, 358, 361
    description, 358
    life cycle, 358, pl. 121
  numidiae, 360
Ascaridina, 316, 320, 354
Ascaris, 316, 362, 413
  columnaris, 361
  lumbricoides, 316, 320, pl. 109, 360
    description, 360
    life cycle, 360, pl. 122
  vitulorum, 361
Ascaroidoidea, 316, 322, 354
Ascaropidae, 316, 378
Ascarops, 316, 378, 380, 414
  strongylina, 316, 380
    description, 380
    life cycle, 380, pl. 129
Ascelepias syrica, 14
Asellus aquaticus, 235
Aspersentis, 299
Aspicularis tetraptera, 355
Aspidobothrea, 6, 139, 148
Aspidogaster, 148
  conchicola, 148
    description, 148
    life cycle, 148, pl. 47
Aspidogastridae, 148
Ataenius cognatus, 380

Australorbis, 164
Autoinfection, 272, 290
Axolotl, 33
Axoneme, 12, 14, 18, 20, 26, 29
Axostyle, 10, 34, 40
Azygiidae, 154

B

Babesia, 104
  annulata, 104
  bigemina, 104
    description, 104
    life cycle, 104, pl. 33
  bovis, 104
  caballi, 104
  canis, 104
  equi, 104
  felis, 104
  gibsoni, 104
  motasi, 104
  trautmani, 104
Babesiidae, 90, 104
Bacillary band, 400
Bacteria, 130
Badger, 405
Baermann apparatus, 324, 327
Balantidiidae, 129
Balantidium, 129
  coli, 130, 133, 134
  entozoon, 134
  praenucleatum, 133, 134
Basommatophora, 159
Bats, 15, 18, 20
Bdellonyssus bacoti, 388
Bear, 266, 374, 406, 410
Beaver, 207, 210
Bed, 355
Bedding, 356
Bee, honey, 123
Beef tapeworm, 272
Beetles
  carabid, 284
  chrysomelid, 218
  dung, 283, 284, 286, 288, 380
  flour, 384
  ground, 283, 384, 385, 386
  histerid, 286
  June, 302, 304
  May, 302, 304
  meal, 283
  tenebrionid, 385
Behavioral activities, 4
Benedenia girellae, 140
Berlese funnel, 294
Bile duct, 217
Bilharziella, 186
Bilharziellinae, 182, 186
Biotic potential, 4
Birds, 5, 49, 89, 90, 95, 114, 171, 180, 182, 194, 201, 217, 230, 243, 250, 258, 282, 283, 292, 298, 299, 308, 324, 340, 355, 366, 372, 376, 378, 385, 386, 391, 410, 411
  fish-eating, 366, 368
  frog-eating, 179
Birth pore, 240
Bithinia, 159, 162, pl. 51
Bithynia tentaculata, 207, 222
Bittern, 179, 250
Blackbirds, 386
Black disease, 202
Black spot disease, 171
Bladder, urinary, 120, 334, 405
Blatella germanica, 64, 376, 384
Blatta orientalis, 64
Blepharoplast, 12, 14, 18, 20, 26, 29, 40, 128
Blood
  fluke, 185, 189
  leucocyte, 28
  reticuloendothelial cell, 20
  sucking arthropod, 3
Blubber, 330
Blue gill, 368
Boattail grackle, 218
Bobcat, 406
Bodonidae, 33
Bonasa umbellus, 100
Bone marrow, 18, 86
Boophilus (Margaropus)
  annulatus, 104
  microplus, 105
Botflies, 3
Bothrium, 258
Bowfin, 250, 268, 270
Bowman's capsule, 405
Brachylaemata, 152, 194
Brachylaemidae, 152, 194
Brachylaemoidea, 152, 194
Brachylaemus virginianus, 195
Brachylecithum americanum, 218
Bradybaena, 160
Bradybaenidae, 160
  Bradybaena, 160
Brain, 24, 52, 172, 174
  hydatid, 276
  ulcer, 52
Branchial
  basket, 223
  fluke, 146
Branchiobdellid annelid, 411
Brood capsule, 276
Buccal capsule, 328, 330, 336, 340, 378
Bucephalidae, 152, 194, 196
Bucephaloidea, 196
Bucephalus, 154
  elegans, 154, 160, 196
    description, 196
    life cycle, 198, pl. 63
  papillosa, 198
Bufo, 128
  americanus, 170, 176, 178, 223
  asiaticus, 375
  bufo, 128
Bug, 16
  boxelder, 14
  Oncopeltis fasciatus, 14
  reduviid, 16, 17, 20, 83
Bulimnea, 162, 164
  megasoma, pl. 51
Bulimulidae, 162, pl. 52, 164
Bulimulus, 162, 164
  alternatus mariae, 218
Bulimus, 164
  dealbatus, pl. 52
Bull, 40
Bullfrog, 224
Bullhead, 200, 412
  (see fish)
Bunostomum, 413
Bursa
  copulatory, 318, 334, 350, 352, 410, 412
  Fabricii, 234
Bursal
  cap, 306
  rays, 330, 334, 340, 342, 346, 350
Buttonhook tail, 391

C

Caecal worm, 355
Caecum
  intestinal, 10, 207, 214, 333, 355
  oesophageal, 366
Calcium alginate, 166
California sea lion, 332
Callorhinus ursinus, 327
Callow, 384
Camallinina, 316, 320, 368, 369
Camallanoidea, 322
Camallanus, 320
  americanus, 320, pl. 109
Cambarincola philadelphica, 411, 412
Cambarus, 240, 242, 244
  diogenes, 244
  propinquis, 244
  robustus, 244
  rusticus, 244
  virilis, 244
Camnula pellucida, 385, 386
Campeloma, 151, 162, pl. 51
  decisum, 195
  rufum, 247, 312
Canachites canadensis, 100
Canals, 297, 300
Canary, 94, 95
Canidae, 171, 361
Cannabilism, 408
Capillaria, 317, 397
  annulata, 397, 400
    description, 400
    life cycle, 400, pl. 136
  columbae, 398
  hepatica, 3, 397, 402
    description, 404
    life cycle, 404, pl. 137
  plica, 397, 405
    description, 405
    life cycle, 405, pl. 138
Capitulum, 40
Capsule, 116
Carabidae, 283, 286, 288, 385
Cardicola, 192
  davisi, 192
    description, 192
    life cycle, 192, pl. 61
  klamathensis, 194
Caretta caretta, 149
Carnivore, 406, 408
Carpiodes carpio, 311
Carrion, 408
Cartilage, 120
Carychium, 166
  exiguum, pl. 52
Caryophyllaeidae, 262
Caryophyllaeus, 258, 264
Caryophyllidea, 258, 260, 262
Cassowary, 342
Castor canadensis, 210
Cat, 20, 39, 72, 108, 114, 243, 250, 252, 276, pl. 93, 280, 324, 326, 327, 348, 374, 384, 390, 405, 406
Catastomus, 31
  commersoni, 31, 119, 140, 238, 250, 254, 264
Catbird, 95
Caterpillar, 123
Catfish, 120, 200

Cattle, 20, 22, 39, 40, 48, 104, 110, 114, 201, 204, 206, 217, 218, 270, 272, 292, 327, 333, 342, 344, 345, 346, 349, 361, 398
Cautolatilus princeps, 140
Cement
gland, 297, 298, 300, 302, 306, 312
reservoir, 297
Centipede, 82
Centrorhynchus, 299, 302,
pinguis, 300
Cepaea, 283
Cepedea, 128
cantabrigensis, 126
Cephalic glands, 5
Cephalina, tribe, 63
Ceratomyxidae, 122
Ceratomyxon blennius, 120, pl. 37, D, 122
Ceratopogon solstitialis, 63
Ceratopogonidae, 95
Cercarial types, 150
characteristics, 153
amphistome, 153, pl. 49A
Diplocotylea, 153
Pigmenta, 153
cercariaea, 156, pl. 49R
Helicis, 156
Mutabale, 156
cotylocercous, 154, pl. 49, P
cystophorous, 154, pl. 49, E
cystophorous, 255
cysticercaria, 154
macrocercous, 154
echinostome, 154, pl. 49, G
furcocercous, 156, pl. 49, K-O
apharyngeate, 156
ocellate, 156
monostome, 156
suckerless, 156
gasterostome, 156
pharyngeate, 156
gymnocephalus, 154, pl. 49, C, D
parapleurocercous, 154
pleurocercous, 154
microcercous, 154, pl. 49, H
monostome, 154, pl. 49, B
Ephemera, 154
Urbanensis, 154
rat-king, 156, pl. 49, S
rhopalocercous, 156, 49, Q
trichocercous, 154, pl. 49, F
no eyes, 154
two eyes, 154
xiphidiocercous, 154, pl. 49, I, J, 226
Armate, 154
Ornate, 154
Microcotylae, 154
Virgulae, 154
Cercaria marilli, 216
precocious, 222
Cercomer, 264
Cerebrospinal fluid, 26
Cerophyl, 166
Cervical groove, 333
Cervidae, 204, pl. 93
Cestoda, 258
Chaenobryttus gulosus, 368
Chaetognatha, 366
Chandlerella striatospicula, 391
Cheese skipper, 3, see *Piophila casei*
Chemotropic, 4
Chicken, 10, 39, 43, 69, 72, 116, 195, 201, 216, 232, 282, 283, 284, 288, 304, 324, 340, 348, 355, 358, 368, 372, 376, 384, 398, 400
Children, 3
Chilomastigidae, 38
Chilomastix
bettencourti, rats, 38
caprae, goats, 38
caulleryi, frogs, 38
cuniculi, rabbits, 38
gallinarum, poultry, 38
intestinalis, guinea pigs, 38
mesnili, humans, 31, 38
description, 38
life cycle, 38, pl. 8
Chipmunks, 195
Chironomidae, 220, 222
Chloromyxon trijugum, 120, pl. 37, J
Choeridium, 286
Choerostrongylus, 348
pudentotectus, 352
Chordeiles minor, 220
Chorioretinitis, 114
Chromagrion conditum, 224
Chromatin ring, 34, 44
Chromatoidal bodies, 50, 54
Chrysemys picta, 189, 190
Ciliata, 128
Ciliophora, 128
Cincinnatia, 159, 162, pl. 51
Cionella, 162, 164
lubrica, pl. 52, 217, 218
Cionellidae, 162, pl. 52, 166
cionella, 162
Cittotaenia, 294
Civet, 108
Clams, 148, 149, 198, 201, 235
fingernail, 201
Musculium partumeium, 235, 240, 243
transversum, 235
Pisidium adbitum, 235, 242
compressum, 235
llijeborgi, 235
nitidum, 235
subtruncatum, 235
Sphaerium solidum, 242
Classification
Acanthocephala, 297, 298
Cestoda, 258
Nematoda, 315
Protozoa, 9
Trematoda, 140, 150
Clinostomatidae, 152, 156, 179
Clinostomatoidea, 152, 179
Clinostomum
attenuatum, 179
complanatum, 179
description, 179
life cycle, 179, pl. 57
Cloacal sucker, 358
Clonorchis sinensis, 5, 254
Clostridium novji, 5, 202
Clothing, 355, 356
Clupea, 366
Cnidosporidia, 116
Coccidia, 56, 66
Coccidiosis, 72
Cocconema, 124
Coccosporidae, 123
Cochlicella, 160
Cochlicopidae, 166
Cockroach, 49, 64, 80, 133, 134, 298, 304, 306, 372, 376, 384
burrowing, 372
woods, 372
Coelozoic, 9, 53
Coenurus, 7, 260, 270, 278
Collarette, 382
Collector host, 348
Columella, 166
Commensal, 34, 130
Commensalism, 1
Conch, 149
Conjugation, 134, 136
Conoid, 110, 115, 116
Conspicuum
icteridorum, 218
macrorchis, 218
Contracaecum, 316
aduncum, 316, 366
description, 366
life cycle, 366, pl. 124
osculum, 368
spiculigerum, 368
Cooperia curticei, 320, pl. 109
Copepod, 266, 269, 290, 366, 368, 369, 370
Copulatory appendage, 408
Coracidium, 258, 266
Corallobothrium parvum, 269
Cordon, 317, 376
Cormorant, 250, 342, 368
Corona radiata, 323, 326, 332, 334
Corpus, 322
Corvid, 386
Corynosoma, 298, 299
strumosum, 300
turbidum, 302
villosum, 300
Costa, 34, 36, 40
Costia necatrix, 36
description, 36
life cycle, 36, pl. 10
pyriformis, 38
Cotinus, 302, 304
Cottontail, 218
Cotylaspis, 148
Cotylogaster, 148
Cotylurus, 168
flabelliformis, 168
description, 168
life cycle, 168, pl. 53
Coyote, 272, 374, 390, 406
Crab, 56, 68, 74, 76
Crassiphiala bulboglossa, 171
Crayfish, 240, 412
Creeping eruption, 327
Crenosoma mephitidis, 348
Crepidostomum, 234
cooperi, 234
description, 234
life cycle, 235, pl. 76
cornutum, 235
farionis, 235
Crickets, 384, 385
camel, 385
field, 385
Crithidia gerridis, 12, 14
life cycle, pl. 2
Crithidial type, 12
Crocodile, 83
Crow, 218, 232, 342
Crustacea, 129, 222, 258, 369, 378, 410
Cryptobia helicis, 29, 31
description, 29

life cycle, 31
Cryptobiidae, 29
Cryptobothrius, 264
Cryptocercus punctulatus, 78, 80
Cryptocotyle lingua, 250
Cryptozoite, 92
Ctenocephalides, 280
canis, 14, 280, 391
cati, 280, 391
Ctenodactylus gondi, 108
Cucumber seed, 280
Culex, 391, 392
fatigans, 83
pipiens, 94
Culicoides, 100, 391, 396
crepuscularis, 391
haematopotus, 391
Cultures, flagellate, 16
Cutting plates, 328, 330
Cuttlefish, 56, 68, 74
Cyathostoma, 342
Cyclic development, 22
Cyclocoelium, 154
Cyclophyllidea, 258, 260, 270
non-taenioid, 280
Cyclops, 256, 268, 269, 270, 369, 370
serrulatus, 256
strenuus, 288
vernalis, 256
viridus, 256
vulgaris, 255
Cypria
maculata, 311
(*Physacypria*) *globula*, 311, 312
Cypridopsis, 256
vidua, 256
Cyprinid, 236
Cyprinidae, 171
Cyprinodontidae, 171
Cyprinus, 31
carpio, 124, 142
Cystacanth, 7, 304, 306
Cysticercoid, 7, 260, 286, 290
Cysticercus, 7, 260, 270, 272
fasciolaris, 5
Cystogenous glands, 200
Cytomere, 74, 98, 102
Cytopharynx, 133, 134, 136
Cytopyge, 129, 134, 136
Cytostome, 10, 31, 129, 130, 132, 134
Cytozoic, 9

D

Dactylogyridae, 139
Dactylogyrus, 139
anchoratus, 140
extensus, 140
macracanthus, 140
vastator, 139, 140
description, 139
life cycle, 140, pl. 44
Damsel fly, 224
Argia, 224
Chromagrion conditum, 224
Enallagma divagons, 224
Lestes vigilax, 224
D'Antoni's standardized iodine solution, 52
Dosymetra villicaeca, 229
Daughter cell (toxoplasm), 112
Davainea, 282
proglottina, 282
description, 282
life cycle, 282, pl. 95
Davaineidae, 282
Deer, 206, 217, 218, 270, 272, 274, pl. 93, 342, 349, 374
Deer mouse, 182, 384
Defense against parasites, 6
Delivery tube, 256
Dendrobaena, 354
subrubicunda, 405
Dendrobilharzia, 186
Dermacentor reticulatus, 105
Dermal plates, 182, 210
Dermanyssus gallinae, 26
Dermatitis, 36
cercarial, 182, 186
nematodal, 327
Dermatoxys veliger, 355
Derocercas, 166, 195
agreste, pl. 52
gracile, pl. 52
Desmognathus fuscus, 242
Deutomerite, 64, 66
Diaphragm, 185, 408
Diaptomus, 268
Diarrhea, 69
Dibothriocephalidae, 266
Dibothriocephalus, 5, 260
latus, 260, 262, 266
description, 266
life cycle, 268, pl. 88
Dicheilonema, 386
Diclidophora caulolatili, 140
Diclidophoridae, 140
Dicnidina, 123, 126
Dicrocoelidae, 152, 217
Dicrocoelium
dendriticum, 217
description, 217
life cycle, 217, pl. 70
Dictyocaulus, 316, 348, 350, 352, 413
arnfieldi, 349,
filaria, 316, 348, 350
description, 348
life cycle, 348, pl. 118
viviparous, 349
Dientamoeba, 49, pl. 14 E
Digenea, 6, 139, 148, 149
characteristics, 153
morphology, 158, pl. 50
Dilepididae, 280
Dioctophyma, 317
renale, 317, 320, 411, pl. 109
description, 411
life cycle, 411, pl. 140
Dioctophymatidae, 317, 411
Dioctophymina, 317, 410
Dioecious flukes, 180
Dipetalonema, 391, 396, 414
arbuta, 396
blanci, 396
dracunculoides, 396
manson-bahri, 396
reconditum, 391, 396
streptocara, 396
Dipetalonematidiae, 392
Diplocystidae, 60
Diplodiscidae, 152, 208
Diplodiscus temperatus, 208
Diplomonadina, 36, 43
Diplostomatidae, 152, 156, 170
Diplostomulum, 156, 158, pl. 50, 160, 172, 174, 178
Diplostomum
baeri eucaliae, 172
description, 172
life cycle, 172, pl. 55
Diplotriaenidae, 317, 385
Diplotriaenoides, 317, 385
bargusinca, 385
translucidus, 317, 385, 386
description, 385
life cycle, 385, pl. 131
Dipylidium, 260, 280
caninum, 280
description, 280
life cycle, 280, pl. 94
Dirofilaria, 317, 390, 414
immitis, 317, 320, pl. 109, 390
description, 391
life cycle, 391, pl. 133
Discocotylidae, 140
Discus, 385
Disporous, 120, 122
Distome, 154
Distribution
geographic, 95
parasites in host, 5
Dithyridium, 7
Ditrichomonas, 39
Dog, 3, 20, 39, 48, 72, 108, 114, 220, 243, 250, 252, 266, 276, pl. 93, 280, 299, 323, 324, 326, 327, 328, 361, 362, 364, 374, 384, 390, 391, 396, 405, 406
Dorylaimina, 320
Dourine, 24
Doves, 43
Dracunculidae, 316, 369
Dracunculoidea, 316, 320, 322, 369
Dracunculus, 316, 414
insigne, 369
ophidensis, 369
medinensis, 316, 320, pl. 109, 369, 370
description, 369
life cycle, 369, pl. 125
Dragon fly, 223, 224, 232, 234, 242, 256
Drepanidotaenia, 286
lanceolata, 286
description, 286
life cycle, 288, pl. 98
Duboscquia, 123
Duck, 39, 90, 102, 114, 170, 174, 186, 188, 195, 201, 216, 232, 286, 290, 299, 368, 376, 378, 412
Dysentery, amoebic, 9

E

Earthworms, 10, 53, 58, 60, 62, 348, 397, 400, 406, 412
Earwigs, 384
Echinococcus, 4, 260, 270, 274
granulosus, 274, pl. 93
description, 274
life cycle, 274, pl. 92
multilocularis, 274
Echinoparyphium recurvatum, 201
Echinorhynchidae, 299
Echinorhynchus, 299, 300
gadi, 300
Echinostoma, 154
revolutum, 160, 200
description, 200
life cycle, 201, pl. 64
Echinostomata, 200
Echinostomatidae, 152, 154, 200
Echinostomatoidea, 200
Echinostome, 154
Echinostomida, 200

Ecology, 2
Eel, 235, 311
Eelpout, 366, 368
Eggs, types
 Acanthocephala
  aquatic hosts, 300, 312
  terrestrial hosts, 300, 304
 Cestoda
  normal, 260, 292
  packet, 260
  pyriform, 260
  striated, 274
 Nematode
  asymmetrical, 356
  plugged, 320, 398
  rough shell, 360, 362, 366
  smooth shell, 330, 338
 Trematode
  filamentous, 214
  operculate, 150, 204
  non-operculate, 184, 186, 190
Eimeria, 2, 56, pl. 16, 68, 89
 stiedae, 66
 tenella, 69
  description, 69
  life cycle, 70, pl. 22
Eimeridia, 68, 77
Eimeriidae, 69
Eisenia, 60, 354
 foetida, 60, 400
Electron microscope, 94, 110
Elephant, 108
Elk, 217, 272
Elliptio, 198
Ellobiidae, 164, 166, pl. 52
 Carychium, 164
Emys orbicularis, 84, 86
En face, 320, 324, 334, 358, 362, 364, 366, 370, 372, 382, 386, 392, 402, 412
Enallagma divagans, 224
Encapsulation, 408
Endamoeba, 49, pl. 14 A
 blattae, 49
Endamoebidae, 49
Endaxostylar chromidia, 40
Endodontidae, 162, 164, pl. 52, 166
 Anguispira, 162
 Goniodiscus, 166
 Helicodiscus, 162
 Punctum, 166
Endodyogeny, 110, 112
Endolimax, 49, pl. 14 D
Endosome, 49
Endotoxin, 116
Enoplida, 317, 397
Enoplina, 317, 397
Entamoeba, pl. 14 B
 coli, 52
 gingivalis, 52
 histolytica, 9, 49, 130
  description, 50
  life cycle, 50, pl. 15
 invadens, 49
 muris, 52
 ranarum, 49
Enterobius, 316, 354, 413
 vermicularis, 316
  description, 354
  life cycle, 354, pl. 120
Enterohepatitis, 10
Entomostraca, 258, 268, 314
Environment
 biotic, 2
 physical, 2
Eoacanthocephala, 297, 302, 311
Eocollis, 300
Epaulette, 385
Ephemera, 126, 235
Ephestia kuehniella, 82
Epicordulia, 232
Epidermal plate, 212
Epidermis, 132
Epimerite, 60, 64
Epitheliocystida, 150, 152, 160, 216
Erimyzon sucetta, 311
Erythrocytes
 Babesia, 104
 Entamoeba, 50
 Haemogregarina, 86
 Haemoproteus, 98
 Plasmodium, 90
Esocidae, 171
Esox, 120
 lucius, 311
 niger, 311
Etheostomidae, 171
Eucalia inconstans, 172
Euciliata, 132
Euconolus, 164
Eucyclops, 269, 270, 369
Eufilaria longicaudata, 391
Eugregarinina, 53
  life cycle, 53
Eulota similaris, 195
Eumetopias jubata, 327
Euphorbia, 14
Eurynia iris, 198
Eurytemmora affinis, 366
Eurytrema procyonis, 218
Eustachean tube, 255, 256
Eustrongylides, 411
Euthyneura, 159
Euthynnus alletteratus, 140
Evolution of parasites, 5, 6
Excretory
 appendage, 256
 gland, 364
 pore, 190, 318, 334
 system, 226, 318
Exflagellation, 92
Exo-erythrocytic, 92
Exuvia, 110
Eye, 172, 372, 385

F

Faecal extractor, 136
Falcon, 375
Fannia canicularis, 374
Fasciola
 gigantica, 204
 hepatica, 5, 202
  description, 202
  life cycle, 202, pl. 65
Fasciolaria gigas, 149
Fasciolidae, 152, 154, 201
Fascioloides magna, 6, 204
Fasciolopsis buski, 204
Fellodistomatidae, 152
Ferrissia, 162, 164, pl. 51
Fever
 African East Coast, 108
 Texas cattle, 104
Filariform larva, 324
Filarioidea, 317, 320, 322, 370, 374, 385
Filicollis, 299, 300
 fidium, 300
Fin, 192
Fish, 26, 128, 129, 132, 179, 201, 240, 248, 258, 268, 269, 299, 311, 312, 366, 411
 angler, 124
 bass, 171, 179, 194, 234, 268, 270, 308, 311, 368
 bluegill, 368
 bowfin, 268, 270
 bullhead, 130, 200, 234, 247, 250, 412
 carp, 130, 142, 194
 catastomid, 236, 238, 258
 catfish, 120, 200, 234, 235
 cod, 140
 crappie, 120
 cyprinid, 31, 236, 254
 eel, 235
 eelpout, 366
 fathead, 120
 garpike, 250
 goldfish, 28
 guppy, 368
 herring, 366, 368
 mackerel, 140
 minnow, 120, 238
 perch, 179, 180, 229, 268, 366
 pickerel, 120, 198
 pike, wall-eyed, 140, 194, 198, 266, 268
 rudd, 31
 salmonid, 118, 268
 sheepshead, 120
 shiner, 120
 skate, 140
 smelt, 124, 126
 stickleback, 124, 126, 172, 174
 sucker, 119, 254
 sunfish, 119, 171, 179, 229, 234
 trout, 44, 171, 234, 235, 236, 248, 268, 269
Fish-eating, 120, 179, 266, 366, 368
Fission, binary, 17, 29
Fixative, stain, 52
Flagellum, 11, 18, 26, 27, 31, 40
Flea, 3, 14, 16, 18, 83, 280, 391, 396
 cat, 391
 dog, 280, 391
  adult, 280
  larva, 280
  pupa, 280
 rat, 18
Flicker, 304
Flipper, 332
Flotation, technique, 52
 Entamoeba, 52
 Giardia, 48
Flukes, adult types, 153, pl. 48
 amphistome, D
 distome, H
 echinostome, F
 gasterostome, A
 monostome, C
 schistosome, G
 strigeids or holostomes, B
Flumnicola, 159, 162, pl. 51
 seminalis, 194
Fly
 black, 56, 96, 101, 102
 blow, 3, 14
 bot, 3, 6
 horn, 392
 hippoboscid, 96, 396
 house, 14, 40, 283, 374, 375, 376

ked, 16, 17
maggot, 3
nose bot, 6
pigeon, 56, 98, 100
sand, 28, 29
simuliid, 391
stable, 286, 288, 375
tabanid, 16, 22, 391
tsetse, 23
Foleyella, 392, 394
americana, 396
brachyoptera, 394
description, 394
life cycle, 394, pl. 134
dolicoptera, 396
duboisi, 396
furcata, 396
ranae, 396
Forebody, 174
Forficula auricularia, 384
Formalin, 39
Formica fusca, 217, 218, 385
fusca, 217, 218
Fossaria, 160, 162, 164
modicella, pl. 51, 202, 204
parva, 207, 210
Fox, 252, 272, 280, 326, 361, 369, 390, 405, 406
Frog, 38, 42, 48, 49, 52, 120, 129, 133, 134, 136, 138, 179, 208, 212, 223, 224, 228, 229, 242, 255, 256, 298, 394
Frog-eating, 179

G

Gadus callaris, 140
Galba, 160, 164
Gall bladder, 120, 217, 218, 236
Galliform, 400
Gallinaceous birds, 282
Galumna, 292, 294
Gamasidae, 88
Gamete, 70, 72, 129
Gametoblast, 78, 80
Gametocyte, 53, 70, 72, 92, 98, 102, 126, 128
Gametogony, 51, 53, 70
Gammaridae, 235
Gammarus, 235, 376, 378
fasciatus, 376
pulex, 235
Gapes, 340
Gapeworm, 340, 344
Garbage, 408, pl. 139
Garments, 356
Gasterosteus, 124
Gasterostome, 154
Gastrocopta, 164, 166
procera, pl. 52
Gastrointestinal canal, 142, 144, 146
Gastrophryne, 128
Gastropods, 148, 149, 159, pls. 51, 52
fresh-water, 159, pl. 51
land, 159, pl. 52
Gecko, 34, 83, 114, 116
Genital tract, 22, 39
Genotype, 6
Geotropic, 4
Geotrupes, 286
Gerbil, 83
Germ cells, 150, 158, pl. 50
Germinal layer, 276
Giant
cell, 12
kidney worm, 411
nucleus, 312
Giardia, 43
agilis, 46, 48
bovis, 48
canis, 48
cati, 48
caviae, 48
duodenalis, 48
equi, 48
lamblia, 46, 48, 49
description, 48
life cycle, 48, pl. 13
muris, 46, 49
ondatrae, 49
simoni, 49
Gigantobilharzia, 186
Gigantorhynchidae, 298
Gigantorhynchus, 298
Gill, 223
filament, 192
Girella nigricans, 140
Gland
apical, 174, 180
cephalic, 388
interproglottid, 294
oesophageal, 182
penetration, 182, 186
ventral, 214
vitelline, 182
Glaridacris, 260, 262, 264
catastomus, 260
description, 264
life cycle, 264, pl. 87
Glomerulis, 405
Glossina, 16, 17, 22
palpalis, 83
Glugea
anomala, 124, 126
hertwigi, 124, 126
Glycogen mass, 52
Glypthelmins pennsylvaniensis, 228
Gnathostoma, 322
Goat, 20, 38, 104, 206, 217, 333, 344, 345, 346, 348, 349
Goblet cells, 5
Golgi complex, 112
Gomphus, 232
Gondi, 109
Gongylonema, 378, 380, 414
Goniobasis, 159, 162, 164, pl. 51
livescens, 236, 238, 248, 250
Goniodiscus, 166
Gonotyl, 248
Goose, 39, 286, 290, 342
Gordiacea, 411
Gorgodera, 240
amplicava, 240
description, 240
life cycle, 242, pl. 78
Gorgoderidae, 240, 252
Gorgoderina attenuata, 242
Gorgorhynchidae, 299
Gorgorhynchus, 299
Gracilisentis gracilisentis, 302
Grackle, 218, 386
Grasshopper, 376, 385
Grebe, 201, 250, 368
Gregarina
blattarum, 64
description, 64
life cycle, 64, pl. 20
Gregarine, 60, 69
Gregarinida, 53, 56, 68
Gregarinidae, 64
Grouse
ruffed, 10, 100, 400
spruce, 100
Grubs, 298, 302, 304
black, 171
yellow, 179
Gryllidae, 385
Gryllus assimilus, 384
Gubernaculum, 318, 346
Guinea fowl, 283, 360
Guinea pigs, 38, 48, 78, 250, 336, 354, 384
Gulls, 171, 186, 201, 207, 220, 250, 342, 368
Gurleyia, 123
Gynaecophoric groove, 182, 188
Gypaetus barbatus, 375
Gyraulus, 162, 164
circumstriatus, pl. 51, 162
parvus, 170, 214, 224
Gyrodactylidae, 140
Gyrodactyloid larva, 146
Gyrodactylus cylindriformis, 140

H

Habitats
Protozoa, 9
Habronema, 316, 414
mansioni, 375
megastoma, 316, 375, 376, 386
description, 375
life cycle, 375, pl. 127
microstoma, 375, 376
muscae, 375, 376
Haematoloechus, 223
complexus, 223
longiplexus, 224
medioplexus, 223
description, 223
life cycle, 223, pl. 72
parviplexus, 224
Haematophagus, 76
Haematopinus stepheni, 83
Haematospiculum, 386
Haemoglobin, 94, 104
Haemoglobinuria, 104
Haemogregarina, 68
stepanowi, 84, 89
description, 84
life cycle, 86, pl. 27
Haemogregarine, 68
Haemogregarinidae, 77, 84
Haemonchus, 344, 413
contortus, 316, 344, 345, 346
description, 344
life cycle, 345, pl. 117
Haemophysalis, 104
Haemoproteidae, 90, 96
Haemoproteus, 56, pl. 16, 96
canachites, 100
columbae, 98
description, 98
life cycle, 98, pl. 31
lophortyx, 100
nettionis, 100
Haemorrhage, 70
Haemosporidia, 56, 68, 77, 89
Halipegidae, 153, 154, 255
Halipegus, 255
amherstensis, 256
eccentricus, 255
description, 255
life cycle, 255, pl. 83
occidualis, 256

Halteridia, 100
Hamaniella, 299, 300
Hamster, 83
Haplometra cylindricea, 160
Haplometrana, 226
intestinalis, 226, 227
utahensis, 160, 226
description, 226
life cycle, 226, pl. 73
Haplotrema, 164, 166
concavum, pl. 52
Haplotrematidae, 164, 166, pl. 52
Haplotrema, 166
Haptor
opistohaptor, 140, 142, 144, 146
prohaptor, 140, 142, 144, 146
Hare, 104, 108, 202, 270, 272, pl. 93, 352
Harem, 33
Harpulus, 384
Hastospiculum, 386
Hawaiia, 164
Hawks, 43
Helicella, 160, 349
Helicellidae, 160
Cochlicella, 160
Helicella, 160
Helicidae, 160, 164
Helix, 160
Oreohelix, 166
Helicina, 159, 164
Helicinidae, 159, pl. 52, 164
Helicina, 164
Hendersonia, 164
Helicodiscus, 162, 166
Helisoma, 160, 162, pl. 51, 168, 200, 201, 204, 240
anceps, 171
antrosa, 170, 179, 180, 242, 256
campanulata, 171, 176, 179, 180, 189, 190, 210
duryi, 176
trivolvis, 171, 176, 189, 190, 201, 202, 210, 212, 242, 255
Helix, 31, 82, 160, 349
asper, 29
Helodrilus, 60, 354
caliginosus, 60
Hemiclepsis, 31
Hemiurata, 153, 255
Hemiuroidea, 153, 255
Hendersonia, 159, 164
occulata, pl. 52
Henneguyia, 120
exilis, 120, pl. 37, H
Hepatozoidae, 82
Hepatozoon, 56, pl. 16, 68, 77, 78
balfouri, 83
canis, 83
criceti, 83
gerbilli, 83
mauritanicum, 83
mesnili, 83
muris, 83
description, 83
life cycle, 83, pl. 26
pettiti, 83
triatomae, 83
Herbivore, 1, 201, 206, 272
Herons, 171, 179, 180, 186, 250
Herpetomonas muscarum, 12, 14
life cycle, pl. 2
Herpobdella
atomaria, 82
punctata, 170
Herring, 366, 368
Heterakidae, 316, 355
Heterakis, 10, 11, 316
gallinae, 12, 316, 355, 358
description, 355
life cycle, 356, pl. 121
Heterocotyle minima, 140
Heterodon, 229
Heterogonic cycle, 323, 414
Heterophyes heterophyes, 250
Heterophyidae, 153, 154, 171, 248
Heterotricha, 129
Hexacanth, 258
Hexagenia, 236
limbata, 235
recurvata, 235
Hexamita, 43, 46
life cycle, 44, pl. 12
batrachorum, 44
intestinalis, 44
meleagridis, 44
ovatus, 44
muris, 44
salmonis, 44
Hexamitidae, 43
Hexastomatidae, 140
Himasthla quissetensis, 201
Hindbody, 174
Hippoboscidae, 56, 96, 396
Hister, 286, 288
Histomonas, 10
gallinae, 11
meleagridis, 10, 12, 355
description, 10
life cycle, 10, pl. 1
Histozoic, 9
Holdfast organ, 176
Holomyarian, 317
Holophryidae, 132
Holostome, 154
Holotricha, 132
Homogonic cycle, 323, 414
Honey bee, 124
Hooks
acanthocephala, 3, 300, 304, 312
cestode, 272, 288
trematode, 3, 140
Hookworm, 5, 326
Horses, 24, 39, 48, 104, 114, 324, 338, 349, 355, 361, 374
Hosts
definitive, 6
intermediate, 6, 7, 266, 284
paratenic, 176, 178
reservoir, 202
transport, 375
House fly, see fly
Human, 5, 9, 20, 38, 54, 90, 114, 129, 180, 184, 200, 204, 252, 254, 266, 270, 272, 274, pl. 93, 280, 284, 288, 324, 326, 327, 328, 354, 360, 362, 364, 374, 396, 410
Huro, 119
salmoides, 268, 308, 368
Hyalella, 238, 308, 376, 378
azteca, 308, 310
knickerbockeri, 238, 376
Hyalomma aegyptium, 83
Hydatid, 7, 260, 270, 276, 278
Hydatigera, 260, 270, 272, 276, pl. 93
Hydra, 49
Hydramoeba, 49, pl. 14F
Hydrocephalus, 114
Hydrostatic pressure, 298
Hyena, 108
Hyla, 128
cinerea, 146
versicolor, 144, 146
Hylocichla fuscens, 385
Hymenolepidiidae, 284
Hymenolepis, 260, 284
carioca, 284
description, 284
life cycle, 284, pl. 97
fraterna, 288
description, 288
life cycle, 290, pl. 99
nana, 288
Hyperparasite, 168
Hypoderaem conoideum, 201
Hypodermis, 317
Hypopharynx, 22, 24
Hystrichis, 411
tricolor, 412

I

Ichthyophthirius, 132
multifiliis, 130, 132
Illiosentis, 299
furcatus, 302
Immunology, 4
Infection
active, 4
contact, 24
inoculative, 4
mechanical, 24
passive, 4, 344
Inflammatory response, 6
Influenza, swine, 352
Injury by parasites, 5
chemical, 5
inflammatory, 5
introduction of pathogens, 5
loss of vitamins, 5
mechanical, 5, 48
Insect, 49, 82, 129
(see beetle, bug, flea, fly, may fly, midge, mosquito, necrophagus)
Insectivores, 104
Invasion of host, 4, 5
Io, 164
Iodamoeba, 49, pl. 14C
Iodine solutions, 52
Iodinophilous vacuole, 118, 119, 120
Ischnura verticalis, 242
Isopod, 218, 304
Isospora, 72
Isthmus, 322

J

Jackrabbit, 283
Jaculus jaculus, 83
Jay, blue, 218

K

Kala azar, 9
Kangaroo, 274
Karyolysis, 88
lacertae, 88
description, 88
life cycle, 88, pl. 28
Ked, sheep, 16, 17
Kidney, 405
worm, 334, 411
Kinetic activities, 4
Kingfisher, 171, 172

Kittiwake, 250
Klossia helicina, 82
Koch's blue body, 109, 110

L

Labella, 375
Labellum, 391
Labium, 391
Labium-epipharynx, 24
Lacerta, 33
    muralis, 88
Lacteal, 408
Lacunar system, 297, 300
Laelaps echidninus, 84
Lagomorph, 276, 278, 352
Lampropeltis, 229
Lankesterellidae, 76
Lankesteria, 56, pl. 16
    culicis, 60
        description, 62
        life cycle, 62, pl. 18
Larus argentatus, 220
Larval acanthocephala
    acanthella, 7
    acanthor, 7
    cysticanth, 7
Larval cestodes
    coenurus, 7
    cysticercus, 7
    dithyridium, 7
    hydatid, 7
    plerocercoid, 7
    procercoid, 7
    tetrathyridium, 168, pl. 53
Larval flukes
    cercaria, 6
    miracidium, 6
    mesocercaria, 158
    metacercaria, 6
    redia, 6
    sporocyst, 6
Larval nematodes, 322
    filariform, 324
    microfilaria
    rhabditiform, 324
    stages, 322, 330, 342
    strongyliform, 322
"Larval" sporozoa
    gametocytes, 6
    merozoites, 6
    sporozoites, 6
    trophozoites, 6
Latex, 14
Laurer's canal, 168, pl. 53
Leaf crown, 340
Leaves, tree, 166
Lebistes reticulatus, 238, 368
Lechriorchis, 229
    primus, 229
        description, 229
        life cycle, 229, pl. 74
    tygarti, 229
Lecithodendriidae, 160
Leech, 2, 11, 16, 23, 26, 31, 56, 82, 84, 86
Leishmania, 2, 14, 28, 29
    braziliensis, 26
    donovani, 9, 14
        description, 28
        life cycle, 14, pl. 2, 7
    tropica, 26
Leishmanial type, 11, 12, 29
Leishmaniasis
    cutaneous, 28
    cutaneous-mucocutaenous, 28
    visceral, 28
Lemniscus, 297
Lepomis
    cyanellus, 119
    macrochirus, 119, 198, 368
    pallidus, 312
Leptomonad type, 11, 12, 14, 29
Leptomonas, 29
    ctenocephali, 12, 14
        life cycle, pl. 2
Leptorhynchoides, 299, 308
    thecatus, 308
        description, 308
        life cycle, 310, pl. 106
Lesion, 12, 120
Lestes vigilax, 224
Lettuce, 166
Leuciscus, 31
Leucochloridiomorpha constantiae, 195
Leucochloridium, 154
Leucocyte, 84, 102
Leucocytozoon, 56, pl. 16, 77, 96, 101
    simondi, 90, 101
        description, 101
        life cycle, 101, pl. 32
Leucorrhina, 232
Libellula, 242
    incesta, 256
Lieberkühn, 376
Lice, 2
    biting, 280
Life cycle
    direct, 3, 6, 7, 139, 258, 322, 397
    indirect, 3, 6, 7
    Acanthocephala, 298, 314
    Cestoda, pl. 93, pl. 101
    Leishmania, 28
    Nematoda, pls. 141, 142; 322
    Trematoda, pl. 84, 150, 170
    Trypanosoma, 16
    Sporozoa, text fig. 1, 6, pl. 16, 53
Ligament, 304
    sac, 297, 298
    suspensory, 297, 308
Limacidae, 162, 164, pl. 52, 166
    Agriolimax, 166
    Derocercus, 166
    Limax, 162
Limax, 162, 182, 283, 348
Limnaea, 154, 201
    auricularia, 194
    lessoni, 222
    ovata, 207
    pereger, 222
    stagnalis, 194
Limnodrilus
    hoffmeisteri, 262
    udekemianus, 264
Lip, 358, 362, 364, 366
Liponyssus
    arcuatus, 76
    saurarum, 78, 83, 88
Lissonema, 386
Lithobius forficatus, 82
Litomosoides, 317, 388
    carinii, 317, 388
        description, 388
        life cycle, 388, pl. 132
Littorina, littorea, 250
Littorinidae, 159
    Littorina, 159
Liver fluke, 202, 217, 218, 229, 236, 252
Lizard, 33, 34, 56, 68, 76, 77, 78, 83, 84, 88, 89, 90, 134, 382, 384
    mite, 56, 68, 76, 77, 78, 84, 90
Lobster, 68, 70
Loons, 171, 250
Lophotaspis vallei, 149
Lophuris piscatoris, 124
Louse, 83
Lugol's iodine solution, 52
Lumbricus, 58, 354
    rubellus, 405
    terrestris, 54, 58, 60, 400, 405
Lung fluke, 223, 243
Lungworm, 348, 349, 352
    brown, 349
    hair, 349
    swine, 352
    thread, 348
Lymnaea, 160, 162, 164, 168, 201
    auricularia, pl. 51, 222
    emarginata, 168, 220, 222
    exilis, 184
    haldmani, pl. 51
    palustris, 185
    reflexa, 184
    traskii, 240
    stagnalis, pl. 51, 168, 184, 222
Lymnaeidae, 160, pl. 51, 164
    Acella, 164
    Bulimnea, 164
    Fossaria, 160, 164
    Galba, 160
    Lymnaea, 160, 164
    Pseudosuccinea, 164
    Stagnicola, 160, 164
Lymphadenopathy, 114
Lynchia hirsuta, 100
Lynx, 246
Lyperosomum, 218
    monenteron, 218

M

Macracanthorhynchus, 299, 300, 302
    hirudinaceus, 300
        description, 302
        life cycle, 302, pl. 104
Macrocyclops, 270, 369
Macroderoides typicus, 160
Macroderoididae, 228
Macrogamete, 64, 70, 72, 92, 94
Macrogametoblast, 80, 82
Macrogametocyte, 70, 72, 78, 86, 90, 98, 102
Macrophage, 20, 102
Macroschizont, 84
Magpie, 391
Mal de Caderas, 24
Malacostraca, 314
Malaria
    benign tertian, 390
Mallophaga, 5, 280
Malpighian tubule, 60, 62, 105, 106, 315, 375, 376, 380
Mammals, 49, 89, 90, 104, 114, 129, 142, 180, 194, 201, 206, 217, 243, 250, 258, 266, 270, 272, 282, 283, 292, 299, 308, 324, 348, 355, 366, 370, 372, 402, 410, 411
    fish-eating, 171, 179
    frog-eating, 179
    land, 348
    marine, 142, 348
Mammary gland, 328, 330

Marine cycle, 408
Marmots, 217, 218
Marrow, bone, 18, 86
Marsupial, 299
Martin, 405
Mastigamoebidae, 10
Mastigophora, 10, 49
May fly, 235
Mazocraeidae, 140
Mazocraes macracanthum, 140
Meadowlark, 218
Meal worm, 283
Measles, 274
Mediorhynchus, 298
Megalodiscus, 154
    temperatus, 154, 208
        description, 208
        life cycle, 208, pl. 68
Megalogonia ictaluri, 235
Megaloschizont, 101, 102
Melanoplus, 376
    bilituratus, 385
    differentialis, 376
    fasciatus, 385
    femurrubrum, 376
Melophagus ovinus, 17
Membrane, undulating, 14, 18, 20, 26, 40
Membranelle, 129, 132, 133, 136
Menetus, 162
    exacuous, pl. 51
Merganser, 171, 216
Merione, 396
Mermithid nematodes, 3
Mermithoidea, 3, 322
Meromyarian, 317
Meront, 123, 124
Merozoite, 53, 64, 70, 72, 78, 80, 84, 90, 98
Merthiolate-iodine, formaldehyde fixative stain, 52
Mesocercaria, 158, pl. 50, 176, 178
Mesocestoides, 260
Mesocestoididae, 262, 280
Mesocyclops obsoletus, 255, 369
Mesodon thyroides, 164, pl. 52, 218
Mesomphix, 164
Mesothemis, 232
Metacercaria, 158, pl. 50
Metacryptozoite, 92
Metacyclic trypanosome, 16, 17
Metacystic amoeba, 50
Metastrongylidae, 316, 348
Metastrongyloidea, 315, 320, 322, 348
Metastrongylus, 320, 348, 352
    apri, 320, pl. 109, 352
        description, 352
        life cycle, 352, pl. 119
    elongatus, 316
Metorchis, 252
    conjunctus, 252
        description, 252
        life cycle, 254, pl. 82
    intermedius, 254
    orientalis, 254
    taiwanensis, 254
    xanthosoma, 254
Microbothrium apiculatum, 140
Microcotyle spinicirrus, 140
Microcotylidae, 140
Microcrustacea, 288
Microfilaria, 3, 385, 390
    sheathed, 388, 392, 394
    unsheathed, 391
Microgamete, 64, 70, 78, 92, 94
Microgametoblast, 78, 80
Microgametocyte, 70, 72, 78, 86, 90, 92, 98, 102
Microhabitat, 4
Micropterus
    dolomieui, 171, 268, 270, 308, 311, 312, 368
Microschizont, 86
Microsporidia, 122, 126
Microtine, 274, 278
Microtus pennsylvanica, 182, 212, 214, 294
Midge, 63, 100, 391
Midgut, 23, 24
Miescher's tubes, 114
MIF fixative stain, 52
Milax, 283, 284
Milk, 328
Milkweed, 14
    bug, 14
Miller's Thumb, 235, 368
Mink, 243, 244, 247, 252, 369, 406, 411, 412
Miracidium, 150, 174, 210
Mirounga leonina, 332
Mite, 83, 84, 89, 390
    lizard, 76, 77, 90
    rat, 83, 84, 388, 390
Mollusk, 29, 352
Molt, 7
Monadenia fidelis, 29
Moniezia, 292
    expansa, 124, 292
        description, 292
        life cycle, 292, pl. 100
Moniliformidae, 299, 300, 304
Moniliformis, 298, 300
    dubius, 304
        description, 304
        life cycle, 306, pl. 105
Monkey, 299
Monocnidina, 123
Monocystidae, 54, 60
Monocystis, 58, 62
    lumbrici, 54
        description, 54
        life cycle, 54, pl. 17
Monoecious fluke, 192
Monoecocoestis, 294
Monoflagellate, 11
Monogenea, 6, 139, 144
Monomonadina, 36
Monomorphic trypanosomes, 14, 22
Monopetalonema, 386
Monopisthocotylea, 139
Monostome, 150
Monozoic, 139, 258
Moose, 274
Morphology
    Acanthocephala, 297
    Cestoda, 258, pl. 85
    Digenea, 158, pl. 50
    Monogenea, pl. 43
    Nematoda, 317, pls. 108, 109
Mosquito, 16, 56, 60, 96, 124, 392
    anopheline, 92, 94, 391
    culicine, 26, 83, 94, 391, 392, 396
Mother sperm cell, 58
Mountain lion, 342
Mouse, 38, 44, 48, 49, 78, 83, 108, 114, 115, 182, 276, 284, 288, 292, 308, 348, 354, 355, 364, 402, 406
Mrazekia argoisi, 124
Mrazekiidae, 123
Muellerius, 316, 349, 350, 414
    capillaria, 316, 349, 350
        description, 349
        life cycle, 349, pl. 118
Mullet, 250
Multiceps, 4, 260, 270, 276
    multiceps, 276, pl. 93
    serialis, 276, pl. 93
Murre, 250
Musca, 374
    autumnalis, 374
    domestica, 283, 375, 376
    larvipara, 374
Muscidae, 283
Muscle, 20
Musculature
    holomyarian, 317
    meromyarian, 317
    polymyarian, 317
Musculium, 236
    partumeium, 240, 242
    transversum, 235
Muskrat, 48, 182, 214, 216, 243, 252, 406
Mussel, 150
Mustela vison, 244
Mustelid, 361
Mutualism, 1
Mya, 201
Myliobatis californicus, 140
Myoneme, 26
Myriopod, 134
Myxididae, 118, 120
Myxidium
    aplodinoti, 120, pl. 37, M
    lieberkühnii, 120, pl. 37, L
    serotinum, 120
Myxobolidae, 119
Myxobolus
    notemigoni, 119
        description, 119
        life cycle, 119, pl. 37 K
Myxosoma, 118
    cartilaginis, 119
    catastomi, 119, 120
    cerebralis, 118, 120
        description, 118
        life cycle, 118, pl. 37
Myxosomatidae, 118
Myxosporidia, 118
Myzorhynchus, 391

N

Nagana, 22
Naiad, 223, 224
Nanophyetus, 246
    salmincola, 246
        description, 246
        life cycle, 247, pl. 80
    schikhobalowi, 246
Nassa, 201
Nassariidae, 159
    Nassarius, 159
Natrix, 229
Natural selection, 6
Neascus, 156, 158, pl. 50, 160, 172
Necrophagous insects, 410
Necturus maculosus, 142, 144
Nemathelminthes, 315
Nematode, free living, 315, 327
Nematodirus, 322, 413
Neoechinorhynchidae, 299, 311

Neoechinorhynchus, 299, 300, 302
cylindricus, 311, 312
description, 311
life cycle, 311, pl. 107
emydis, 302, 311
rutili, 300, 311, 312
Neohexastoma euthynni, 140
Neorickettsia helminthoeca, 246
Neotenic, 262
Nephron, 405
Neritidae, 159
Neritina, 159
Neritina, 159
fluviatalis, 235
Newt, 33, 242
Nighthawk, 220
Nippostrongylus brasiliensis, 348
Nocomis biguttatus, 238
Nodular worm, 333
Nodule, 333
Nosema, 123
apis, 123, 124
description, 123
life cycle, 123, pl. 38
bombycis, 124
helminthorum, 124
locustae, 124
lophurii, 124
morii, 124
Nosematidae, 123
Nosophyllus fasciatus, 18
Notocotylidae, 152, 214
Notocotyloidea, 152, 214
Notocotylus
stagnicolae, 216
urbanensis, 216
Notropus, 238
cornutus, 238
delicious, 254
Nucleus, 20, 26
macronucleus, 128, 130, 132, 134, 136
micronucleus, 128, 132, 134, 136
Nudacotyle novicia, 216
Nutcracker, 342
Nutrition, 5
Nyctotherus, 133, 138
cordiformis, 133, 136
ovalis, 134
velox, 134
woodi, 134

O

Ochetosoma aniurum, 229
Octomacrum lanceatum, 140
Octomitus, 43, 46
pulcher, 44, 46
Octospinifer, 299
Odonata, 224, 242
Oesophageal caecum, 366
Oesophagostomum, 333
dentatum, 333
columbianum, 315, 333
description, 333
life cycle, 333, pl. 113
radiatum, 333
venulosum, 333
Oesophagus, 312
bulbed, 354, 356
filariform, 318, 323
glandular, 368, 369, 370, 378
rhabditiform, 318, 323
sheep, 116
stichosome, 397, 398, 400, 402
strongyliform, 326, 328
Olfactory lobe, 174
Oligacanthorhynchidae, 298, 300
Oligacanthorhynchus, 298, 300
Oligochaete, 78, 122, 258, 397, 411, 412
Omnivore, 406
Onchocercidae, 317, 388
Onchorhynchus, 248
Oncicola, 299, 300
Oncomelania, 164
nosophora, 243
Oncopeltis fasciatus, 14
Oncosphere, 270, 286
Ondatra zibethica, 182, 214
Oniscus asellus, 218
Ontophagus, 286
Oocyst, 53, 64, 72, 78, 80, 84
Ookinete, 53, 84, 92, 94, 100
Opalina
obtrigonoidea, 128
ranarum, 126, 128
Opalinidae, 126
Operculum, 204, 264
Orphanage, 354
Ophrycystidae, 63
Ophthalmoxiphidiocercaria, 235
Opisthaptor, 139, 142, 144
Opisthobranchiata, 159
Opisthorchiata, 153, 248
Opisthorchiida, 153, 247
Opisthorchiidae, 153, 154, 252
Opisthorchioidea, 153, 248
Opisthorchis sinensis, 254
Opossums, 15, 18, 20, 195, 384, 406
Optic
lobe, 172
nerve, 172
Orcheobius herpobdellae, 82
Organelles, 10
Oribatid mite, 292, 294
Orthoptera, 315, 378
Osmerus, 124, 126
Ostertagia, 344, 345, 413
circumcincta, 315, 345, 346
description, 345
life cycle, 345, pl. 117
ostertagi, 346
trifurcata, 346
Ostracod, 256, 311, 312
Otaria byroni, 332
Ovenbird, 385, 386
Ovoviparous, 140
Owl, 342
african, 95
great horned, 170
screech, 95
snowy, 170
Oxyspirura, 372, 414
mansoni, 316, 372
description, 372
life cycle, 372, pl. 126
Oxytrema (*Goniobasis*)
circumlineata, 192
silicula, 247, 248
Oxyuridae, 316, 354
Oxyuris, 413
equi, 355
Oxyuroidea, 316, 320, 322, 354

P

Pabulum, 306
Pachysentidae, 299
Pajamas, 355
Paleacanthacephala, 297, 302, 308
Palisade worm, 338
Pallifera, 166
Pallisentidae, 299
Pallisentis, 299
Pancreas, 217, 218
Panopistus pricei, 195
Pansporoblast, 122
Panstrongylus megistis, 20
Papilla
caudal, 358, 360, 362, 382
cephalic, 324, 334, 372, 378, 380, 392, 412
cervical, 333, 334, 346, 376, 378
lateral, 190
Parabasal body, 10, 12, 14, 18, 20, 26, 29, 40
Paradesmose, 40
Paragonimus
kellicotti, 160, 243
description, 243
life cycle, 243, pl. 79
westermani, 246
Paragordius robusta, 320, pl. 109
Paramphistomata, 152, 206
Paramphistomatidae, 206
Paramphistomatoidea, 206
Paramphistomum
cervi, 206
description, 206
life cycle, 206, pl. 66
Paranoplocephala, 294
Parascaris equi, 361
Parasite
aberrant, 3
ectoparasite, 2
endoparasite, 2
erratic, 336
facultative, 3
incidental, 3
obligate, 3
periodic, 3
permanent, 3
stationary, 2
temporary, 2
Parasitism, 1, 2
defensive, 5
effect on host, 5
evolution of, 5, 6
evolutionary effect of, 6
hallmark of, 3
injurious, 5
origin, 1
properties, 3
Parasitology, 1
Paratenic host, 176, 178, 348
Paravitrea, 164
Parorchis acanthus, 207
Parthenogenetic 323, 324
Partridge, 10, 44, 400
Paruterine organ, 260
Paruterinidae, 262, 280
Passalurus ambiguus, 355
Passer domesticus, 72
Pathogens transmitted
Clostridium oedematiens, 5
Histomonas meleagridis, 5
Neorickettsia helminthoeca, 5
Pathology, 120
gills, 192
haemorrhage, 172
popeye, 171
liver, 218
Pea fowl, 10
Pelicans, 186, 368

Pelta, 10, 39
Pentatrichomonas, 39
Pentatrichomonoides, 39
Perca flavescens, 180, 268, 366
Perezia, 120
Pericardial cavity, 150
Periplaneta americana, 64, 66, 306
Peristome, 129, 133, 136
Peritoneal exudate, 112
Peritrophic membrane, 23, 24, 123
Peromyscus, 182, 195, 196
Petasiger chandleri, 201
Phagocytes, 28
Phalocrocorax auritus, 368
Phanerozoite, 92
Pharynx, 23, 24
Phasmid, 322, 369, 370, 397
Phasmidia, 315
Pheasant, 10, 44, 232, 340, 355, 400
Pheidole, 283
 bicarinata, 283
 sitarches, 283
Philometra nodulosa, 370
Philometridae, 370
Philomycidae, 162, pl. 52
 Pallifera, 166
 Philomycis, 162
 carolinianus, pl. 52
Phlebotomus, 14, 28, 29
 argentipes, 28
 papatasii, 28
 sergenti, 28
Phototropic, 176, 188, 190, 210
Phrynosoma cornutum, 382
Phyllodistomum solidum, 242
Phyllophaga, 302, 304
Physa, 160, 162, 164, 168, 200, 202, 204, 255
 ampullacea, 226, 240
 ancillaria, 184
 gyrina, pl. 51, 184, 186, 187, 200, 226, 229, 230, 255, 256
 halei, 229, 242
 integra, pl. 51
 parkeri, 216, 229, 230, 242, 255
 sayi, pl. 51, 255
 utahensis, 226
Physoloptera, 316, 382
 hispida, 384
 phrynosoma, 316, 384
  description, 382
  life cycle, 382, pl. 130
 praeputialis, 384
 rara, 320, pl. 109; 384
 turgida, 380
Physalopteridae, 316, 382
Physidae, 160, pl. 51, 164
 Aplexa, 164
 Physa, 160, 164
Physocephalus, 322, 380, 414
 sexalata, 316, 380
Phytomonas
 davidi, 14
  life cycle, pl. 2
 elmassiani, 14
Pica pica hudsona, 391
Pig, see swine
Pigeon, 39, 43, 94, 98, 282, 283, 360, 376, 398
Pigment granules, 92, 94
Pimply gut, 333
Pinniped, 326, 368
Pinocytosis, 94
Pinworm, 354
 horses, 355
 humans, 354
 mice, 355
 rabbits, 355
 rats, 355
 sheep, 355
Piophila casei, 3
Pirenella, 159
Piscicola, 26, 31
Pisidium, 236
 adbitum, 235, 242
 compressum, 235
 llijeborgi, 235
 nitidum, 235
 subtruncatum, 235
Placobdella catenigra, 84, 86
Plagioporus, 236
 lepomis, 238
 sinitsini, 236
  description, 236
  life cycle, 236, pl. 77
Plagiorchiata, 152, 216
Plagiorchiidae, 152, 154
Plagiorchiida, 152, 216
Plagiorchioidea, 152, 216
Plagiorchis, 154, 160
 arcuatus, 222
 jaenschi, 222
 maculosus, 222
 megalorchis, 222
 micranthus, 222
 muris, 5, 220
  description, 220
  life cycle, 220, pl. 71
 parorchis, 222
 proxmis, 222
Plankton-feeding, 366, 368, 410
Planont, 123
Planorbidae, 160, pl. 51, 162
 Australorbis, 164
 Gyraulus, 164
 Helisoma, 160, 162, 164
 Planorbis, 154, 160, 164
 Planorbula, 164
 Segmentina, 164
 Tropicorbis, 164
Planorbis, 154, 160, 162, 164, pl. 51, 201, 212
 planorbis, 222
 vortex, 207
Planorbula, 162, 164, pl. 51
 armigera, 170, 223, 224
Plasmodiidae, 90
Plasmodium, 2, 56, pl. 16, 78, 96
 birds, 95
 cathemerium, 95, 96, pl. 30
 circumflexum, 95, 96, pl. 30
 elongatum, 95, 96, pl. 30
 fallax, 95
 gallinaceum, 95, 96, pl. 30
 hexamerium, 95, 96, pl. 30
 lophurae, 95, 96, pl. 30
 nucleophilum, 95, 96, pl. 30
 oti, 95, 96, pl. 30
 paddae, 95
 praecox, 95
 polare, 95, 96, pl. 30
 relictum, 94, 96, pl. 30
 rouxi, 95, 96, pl. 30
 vaughani, 95, 96, pl. 30
 vivax, 90
  description, 90
  life cycle, 92, pl. 29
Plasmodroma, 10
Platyhelminthes, 139
Pleurocerca, 159, 162, 164, pl. 51
 acuta, 235
Pleuroceridae, 162
Plerocercoid, 7, 268
 neotenic, 264
 type larva, 280
Pleuroceridae, 159, pl. 51, 164
 Goniobasis, 159
 Io, 164
 Pleurocera, 159
 Semisulcospira, 164
Plistophora, 123
Pogonomyrmyx barbatus, 382, 384
Polar
 capsule, 53, 116, 119
 filament, 53, 116, 120, 122, 126
 ring, 110
Polychaete, 149
Polygyra, 162, 164, 166, 195, 283
 albolabris, 164, pl. 52
 texasiana, 218
 thyroides, 195
Polygyridae, 162, pl. 52, 166
 Polygyra, 162
Polymastigina, 34
Polymitarcys, 235
Polymorphic trypanosomes, 23
Polymorphidae
Polymorphus, 299, 300
 gadi, 300
Polymyarian, 317
Polyopisthocotylea, 142
Polysporous, 120
Polystoma, 144
 integerrimum, 144, 146
 integerrimum nearcticum, 144
 nearcticum, 144
  description, 144
  life cycle, 146, pl. 46
Polystomidae, 142
Polystomoides cornutum, 140
Polyzoic, 258
Pomacea, 164
Pomatiopsis, 159, 162, pl. 51
 cincinnatiensis, 243
 lapidaria, 216, 243, 244
Pomoxis, 120
Pomphorhynchus, 299, 300
Populations of parasites, 6
Porcellio, 304
 laevis, 304
 scaber, 304
Porcupine, 396
Pork tapeworm, 270
Porpoise, 76
Porrocaecum, 366
Portunus depurator, 74, 76
Postharmostomum, 195
 gallinum, 195
 helicis, 160, 195
  description, 195
  life cycle, 195, pl. 62
Potamidae, 159
 Pirenella, 159
Potassium dichromate, 72
Poultry, 38, 283, 284, 376
Praticolella, 164
 berlandierana, 218
 mobiliana, pl. 52
Pre-adult, 411
Pre-erythrocytic, 92
Prenatal infection, 326, 327, 348, 350, 361, 362
Prepharynx, 252
Presoma, 297

Primate, 39, 104, 108
Primite, 64
Proboscis, 20, 297
    receptacle, 297
    sheath, 308
Probstmyria viviparus, 7
Procercoid, 7, 262
    neotenic, 262, 264
Progenetic, 158
    metacercaria, 222
    miracidium, 207
Prohaptor, 142
Pronucleus, 134
Prosobranchiata, 159
Prosthenorchis, 299
Prosthogonimidae, 230
Prosthogonimus, 232
    macrorchis, 232
        description, 232
        life cycle, 232, pl. 75
Prosthorhynchus, 299
    formosus, 304
Proteocephala, 258, 260, 268
Proteocephalidae, 268
Proteocephalus, 260
    ambloplitis, 260, 268
        description, 269
        life cycle, 269, pl. 89
    pinguis, 269
    tumidicollis, 269
Proteromonas lacertae
        description, 33
        life cycle, 33, pl. 9
Protociliata, 128
Protomerite, 64, 66
Protomomonadina, 11
Protonephridium, 196, 298, 300
Protoopalina, 128
    mitotica, 126
Protostrongylus, 316, 349, 350, 414
    rufescens, 316, 349, 350
        description, 349
        life cycle, 349, pl. 118
Protozoa, phylum, 9
    habitats, 9
Proventriculus, 23, 24
Psammodromus hispanicus, 76, 77, 78
Pseudacris nigrita, 178
Pseudocoel, 297
Pseudolabium, 382
Pseudolynchia maura, 98
Pseudophyllidea, 258, 260, 266
Pseudoprocta, 386
Pseudosuccinea, 162, 164, 200
    columella, pl. 51, 224, 242
Pseudosucker, 174, 176
Pseudotrypanosoma, 39
Pulex cleopatra, 83
Pulmonata, 159
Punctum, 166
Pup
    dog, 364
    fur seal, 328
Pupilla, 166
Pupillidae, 164, 166, pl. 52
    Columella, 166
    Gastrocopta, 166
    Pupilla, 166
    Pupisoma, 166
    Pupoides, 166
    Vertigo, 166
Pupisoma, 166
Pupoides, 166
Pustule, 132, 133
Pycnoscelus surinamensis, 372
Pyriform apparatus, 260
Pyrometra, 40

Q

Quadrigyrus, 299
    torquatus, 300
Quail, 10, 44, 355, 376
    California valley, 100
    bobwhite, 400
Quinqueserialis, 154
    quinqueserialis, 154, 214, 216
        description, 214
        life cycle, 214, pl. 69

R

Rabbits, 38, 48, 116, 182, 202, 204, 217, 270, 272, pl. 93, 348, 352, 355
Raccoon, 20, 218, 252, 369, 406
Radinorhynchus, 299
Radix auricularia, 222
    see *Lymnaea*
Raillietina, 283
    cesticillus, 283, 286
        description, 283
        life cycle, 283, pl. 96
    echinobothrida, 283, 286
        description, 283
        life cycle, 283, pl. 96
    loeweni, 283
    tetragona, 283, 286
        description, 283
        life cycle, 283, pl. 96
Raja clavata, 140
Rajonchocotyloides emarginata, 140
Rana, 128, 340, 342
    catesbiana, 224, 256, 396
    clamitans, 170, 224, 230, 256
    pipiens, 170, 178, 223, 224, 230, 396
    pretiosa, 226
    sylvatica, 170, 178
    sphenocephala, 394, 396
    temporaria, 128, 144
Raptor, 375
Rat, 5, 18, 38, 42, 48, 83, 84, 108, 220, 243, 250, 270, 276, pl. 93, 288, 300, 304, 306, 308, 324, 348, 354, 355, 384, 388, 390, 402, 406
    cycle, 408
Rattenkönig, 156
Rattlesnake, 384
Rattus, 306
Receptacle, 84
Red worms, 338
Redia, 150, 158, pl. 50, 202
Reduviidae, 20
Renette cell, 318
Reproductive system
    trematode, 318
Reptiles, 26, 39, 49, 89, 90, 114, 128, 142, 149, 217, 240, 258, 290, 292, 298, 324, 355, 386, 396
    lizards, 56, 68, 88
    snakes, 49, 52, 170, 176, 229, 230, 384
    tortoise, 84
    turtle, 148, 149, 150
Requirements
    biological, 6
    physical, 6
Reservoir host, 20, 342, 362, 411
Response
    chemotropic, 4, 5
    geotropic, 4
    thermotropic, 4
Reticuloendothelial cells, 18, 28
Retinella, 164
Retrofection, 355
Rhabditida, 315, 320
Rhabditiform larva, 324
Rhabditina, 315, 320, 323
Rhabditis, 3
    strongyloides, 320, pl. 109, 323
Rhabditoidea, 315, 323
Rhabdocoel, 139
Rhadinorhynchidae, 299, 308
Rhaphidophorinae, 385
Rhipicephalus
    appendiculatus, 108
    sanguineus, 83
Rhizoblast, 34
Ribonucleic acid, 115
Ring stage, 92, 98
Ringer's solution, 130, 136
RNA, 115
Robin, 95, 218, 304
Rodent, 299, 304, 362, 397, 402
Rookery, 330
Rosette, 18, 266
Rostellum, 272, 284, 286
Ruminants, 1, 204, 278, 324, 344, 346, 348, 398

S

Saefftigen's pouch, 304, 306
Salamander, 33, 42, 128, 133, 144, 240, 242
Salientia, 128
Salivary gland, 24, 94, 101, 106, 110
Salmon, 44
    poisoning fluke, 5, 246
Salvelinus salmo, 248
Sand, 327
Sandfly, 28
Sandpiper, 220
Sanguinicola, 192
    huronis, 194
    inermis, 194
    occidentalis, 194
Sanguinicolidae, 152, 192
Saprophitic, 38
Sarcocyst, 114, 116
Sarcocystin, 116
Sarcocystis, 114, pl. 36
    miescherina, 114, 116
    muris, 114, 116
    platydactyli, 114, 116
    rileyi, 114
    tenella, 114, 116
        description, general, 114
        life cycle, general, 115
Sarcodina, 49
Sarconeme, 116
Sarcosporidia, 114
Sarcosporidian cell, 116
Satellite, 64
Sausage stage, 391, 396
Scarabaeidae, 283, 286, 288
Scavenger, 3, 408
Schellackia, 56, pl. 16, 68
    bolivari, 76
        description, 76
        life cycle, 77, pl. 24
Scheloribates, 292, 294
Schistosoma

haematobium, 185
japonicum, 185
mansoni, 185
Schistosomatidae, 152, 156, 158, 180
Schistosomatinae, 182
Schistosomatium
douthitti, 182
description, 182
life cycle, 184, pl. 58
Schistosomatoidea, 152, 180
Schistosomatula, 182
Schistosome, 154
Schizocystidae, 63
Schizocystis, 56, pl. 16, 68
gregarinoides, 63
description, 63
life cycle, 63, pl. 19
Schizogony, 53
Schizogregarinina, 62
Schizont, 53, 64, 72, 78, 80, 84 90, 92
Schüffner's dots, 92, 94
Scolex, 258
Scotch tape, 355
Scutovertex, 294
Sea elephant, 332
Sea lion, 298
California, 332
southern, 332
Steller's, 300, 327, 332
Seal, 406, 410
Baikal, 368
fur, 298, 326, 327, 330
Seatworm, 354
Secernentea, 315
Segmenter, 51, 72, 92, 94
Segmentina, 162, 164, pl. 51
Seiurus aurocapillus, 385, 386
Selachian, 258
Selenococcididae, 68
Selenococcidium, 56, 68
intermedium, 68, 69
description, 68
life cycle, 69, pl. 21
Self-cure, 345
Sellacotyle mustelae, 247
Seminal vesicle, 54
Semisulcospira, 164
Sepia officinalis, 74
Serrasentis, 299
Serratospiculum, 386
Sheep, 20, 104, 114, 124, 202, 204, 206, 217, 218, 272, 274, 276, pl. 93, 292, 294, 323, 334, 344, 345, 346, 348, 349, 350, 352, 355, 374, 398
Shrew, 195, 300
Shrimp, 222
Sigmodon hispidis, 388
Silkworm, 122, 124
Simuliidae, 96, 102
Simulium
croxtoni, 101
euryadminiculum, 101
venustum, 101
Skin, 120
Skrjabinema ovis, 355
Skunk, 348
Sleeping sickness, 23
Slimeball, 217
Slugs, 82, 162, 283, 348
Snails, 29, 82, 159, pls. 51, 52; 348, 385
rearing, 166
Snakes, 49, 52, 229, 230, 348, 369, 384, 392
garter, 229, 369
rattle, 384
water, 229
Soboliphymatidae, 410
Somatic migration, 178
Sore, summer, 375
Southern sea lion, 332
Sparganum, 268
Sparrows
Algerian, 95
English, 72, 94, 95, 116, 232, 372
Java, 95
white crowned, 385
Spear, 328
Specificity
host, 4, 95
host-parasite, 4
organ, 4
tissue, 4
Sperm morula, 54
Spermatigonium, 58
Sphaerium, 154
occidentalis, 242
Sphaeromyxa, 120
Sphyranura, 142
oligorchis, 142
description, 142
life cycle, 144, pl. 45
Spicule, 334, 346, 350, 352, 368, 372, 385, 392, 400, 410
Spinal cord, 24
Spirorchiidae, 152, 189
Spirorchis
elephantis, 190
parvus, 189
description, 189
life cycle, 189, pl. 60
Spirostomidae, 133
Spirotricha, 129
Spirurida, 316, 368
Spiruridae, 316, 374
Spirurina, 316, 320, 368, 370
Spiruroidea, 316, 322, 370, 372, 374
Spleen, 29
Splendidofilaria picardina, 391
Sporadin, 53, 60, 62, 64, 66
Spore, 53, 120, 126
chain, 66
duct, 64
Sporoblast, 53, 72, 74, 116
Sporocyst, 150
Sporozoa, 72, 80, 84, 90, 116
Trematoda, 150
daughter, 158, pl. 50
mother, 158, pl. 50, 174
Sporogony, 53
Sporokinete, 88, 90
Sporont, 53, 120
Sporoplasm, 53, 118, 120
Sporozoa, 6, 52
Sporozoite, 53, 66, 74, 78, 84, 90, 98, 102
Spring hares, 396
Squalus acanthias, 140
Squirrel, 406
Stable fly, see fly
Stagnicola, 160, 162, 164, 168, 182, 200
bulimoides, 202, 204, 208
caperata, pl. 51
emarginata, 216
palustris, 172
Stain, merthiolate-iodine-formaldehyde, 52
Starling, 342, pl. 116
Station
anterior, 22
posterior, 17
Steller's sea lion, 327, 328
Stempellia, 123
Stenocephalus agilis, 14
Stephanurus, 334
dentatus, 316
description, 334
life cycle, 334, pl. 114
Stichocotylidae, 148
Stichorchis
subtriquetrus, 160, 207
description, 207
life cycle, 207, pl. 67
Stichosome, 400, 402, 406
Stickleback, see Fish
Stizostedion vitreum, 140, 226, 311
Stoma, 323
Stomachworm
barber-pole, 344
brown, 345
swine, 378
thick, 378
twisted, 344, 345
Stomoxys calcitrans, 374, 391
Storage host, 348
Stratum corneum, 208, 228
Streptaneura, 159
Striatura, 164
Striders, water, 14
Streptoceryle alcyon, 172
Strigea elegans, 170
Strigeata, 150, 167
Strigeatida, 150, 167
Strigeidae, 150, 156, 167
Strigeoidea, 150, 167
Strobilocercus, 7, 260, 270
Strobilops, 164, 166
affinis, pl. 52
Strobilopsidae, 164, 166, pl. 52
Strobilops, 164
Strobilus, 258
Strongyle, 338
common, 339
large, 338
large-toothed, 339
medium-sized, 338
small, 339
small-toothed, 339
toothless, 338
Strongylidae, 315, 332
Strongyliform, 328
Strongylina, 315, 320, 322, 326
Strongyloidea, 315, 320, 322, 326
Strongyloides, 413
avium, 324
cati, 320
papillosus, 315, 323
description, 323
life cycle, 323, pl. 110
ransomi, 324
ratti, 324
stercoralis, 324
suis, 324
westeri, 324
Strongyloididae, 323
Strongylus, 338, 348, 413
edentatus, 316, 338, 340
description, 338
life cycle, 338, pl. 115
equinus, 316, 338, 340
description, 338
life cycle, 338, pl. 115

vulgaris, 316, 320, pl. 109, 339, 340
description, 339
life cycle, 339, pl. 115
Stylet, 216, 220, 412
Stylommatophora, 160
Styphlodorinae, 160
Subulina octoma, 195
Succinea, 162, 166, 349
putris, 207
retusa, 164, pl. 52
Succineidae, 162, 164, pl. 52, 166
Succinea, 162
Sucker, see fish
Suctoria, 128
Sunfish, see fish
Surra, 24
Survival, means of, 4
Suture, 120
Swallow, 95
Swan, 342
Swarmer, 130, 132
Swimmer's itch, 182 (see dermatitis)
Swine, 49, 104, 114, 129, 130, 134, 204, 217, 243, 272, 274, pl. 93, 300, 301, 304, 324, 326, 333, 334, 336, 348, 352, 360, 362, 380, 406, 408
Sylvatic cycle, 408
Symbiont, 1
Symbiosis, 1
Symbiotic, 9
Sympetrum
obtrusum, 223, 224
rubicundum, 224
Syncytial mass, 311
Syngamus, 340
trachea, 316, 340
description, 340
life cycle, 340, pl. 116
Syphacea obvelata, 320, pl. 109, 354
Systellommatophora, 162
Syzygy, 66

T

Tabanids, 16, 24, 315, 316
Tadpoles, 52, 126, 129, 134, 136, 138, 144, 170, 178, 200, 201, 202, 208, 222, 229, 240, 242, 255
frog, 52, 170, 178, 201, 202, 210, 212, 222, 255, 256
tree toad, 144, 146
salamander, 240, 242
Taenia, 260
hydatigera, 272, 276, pl. 93
krabbei, 272, 276, pl. 93
ovis, 272, 276, pl. 93
pisiformis, 272, 276, pl. 93
solium, 270
description, 272
life cycle, 272, pl. 90
Taeniidae, 270
Taeniarhynchus, 260, 270, 272
saginatus, 272
description, 274
life cycle, 274, pl. 91
Taenioid cestode life cycles, 276, pl. 93
Tarentola, 33, 34
Technique, *Entamoeba*, 52
Telamon, 349
Telomyxa glugeiformis, 124, 126
Telomyxidae, 126
Telosentis, 299
Tenebrio
confusum, 290, 292
molitor, 292
Tenebrionidae, 283, 385
Teneral, 224
Termite, 1
Tern, 250
Testudo mauritanica, 83
Tetracheilonema, 386
Tetracotyle, 156, 158, pl. 50, 160, 168, pl. 53
Tetragoneuria, 232
cynosura, 224
Tetrameres, 316, 376, 378
americanus, 376
crami, 316, 376
description, 376
life cycle, 376, pl. 128
Tetrameridae, 316, 376
Tetramitidae, 36
Tetramorium, 283
Tetrathyridium, 280
Thamnophis, 229
sirtalis, 230
Theileria, 108
parva, 108
description, 108
life cycle, 108, pl. 34
Thelazia
californiensis, 374
rhodesii, 374
Thelaziidae, 316, 372
Thelohanellus, 120
notatus, 120, pl. 37, F
Thelohania, 123
legeri, 124
Thermotropic, 4
Thorax, 408
Thrush, 385
russet-backed, 385
willow, 385
Thysanosoma, 260
Tick, 83, 104, 105, 106, 108, 110
Boophilus (Margaropus) annulatus, 104
Boophilus microplus, 105
Dermacentor reticulatus, 105
Haemaphysalis, 104
Rhipicephalus, 104
Tineola bieseliella, 82
Tissues, 2
Toad, 42, 120, 146, 223, 375
Bufo americanus, 170, 176, 178, 223
B. b. asiaticus, 375
Tree
Hyla cinerea, 146
H. versicolor, 144, 146
Tongue, 408
Tooth, 344, 382, 394
Tortoise, 84, 86
Toxocara, 316, 361, 413
canis, 316, 361
description, 361
life cycle, 362, pl. 123
leonina, 362, 364
mystax, 362
Toxoneme, 110, 112
Toxoplasma, 2
gondii, 90, 109, 112, 114
description, 109
life cycle, 110, pl. 34
Tracheoles, 224
Transmission of parasites
active, 4
contaminative, 17, 20, 32
inoculative, 4, 22
mechanical, 16, 22
passive, 4
venereal, 40
Transovarial, 106
Transport host, 68, 314, 342
Trematoda, 6
aspidogastrid, 6, 139
digenetic, 6, 139
monogenetic, 3, 6, 139
Triactinomyxon ignotum, 122
Triatoma rubrovaria, 83
Tribocytic organ, 154
Tribolium, 82, 292
confusum, 292, 384
ferrugineum, 82
Tricercomitus, 39
Trichinella, 317, 406, 414
cycles
marine, 410
sylvatic, 408
urban, 408
spiralis, 317, 406
description, 406
life cycle, 406, pl. 139
Trichinellidae, 317, 406
Trichobilharzia
adamsi, 188
cameroni, 160, 182, 186
description, 186
life cycle, 188, pl. 59
ocellata, 188
oregonensis, 188
physellae, 188
stagnicolae, 188
Trichodectes canis, 280
Trichomonadidae, 34, 39
Trichomonas
hominis, 43
gallinae, 43
vaginalis, 40, 43
tenax, 43
Trichostomida, 127
Trichostrongylidae, 316, 322
Trichostrongyloidea, 316, 320, 344
Trichostrongylus, 344, 346, 413
affinis, 348
calcaratus, 348
capricola, 348
colubriformis, 316, 346
description, 346
life cycle, 346, pl. 117
falcatus, 348
ransomi, 348
rugatus, 348
tenuis, 348
vitrinus, 348
Trichuridae, 317, 397
Trichuroidea, 317, 322, 397
Trichuris, 317, 397, 413
ovis, 317, 397, 398
description, 398
life cycle, 398, pl. 135
Trident, 385
Triodopsis albolabris, 29
Tritrichomonas
augusta, 40, 42
batrachorum, 42
foetus, 39, 40
description, 39
life cycle, 40, pl. 11
muris, 42

Tritrichomoniasis, 42
Triturus, 229
viridiscens, 242
Troglotrematidae, 152, 154
Trophozoite, 50, 51, 54, 66, 72, 74, 80, 86, 92, 116, 130, 134, 136
Tropicorbis, 164
Trout, 44, 171, 192, 234, 235, 248
Trunk, 297
Trypanoplasma borreli
description, 31
life cycle, 31, pl. 8
Trypanosoma, 14, 16
brucei, 23
brucei-evansi group, 17, 23, 24
brucei subgroup, 17, 23, pl. 5
congolense group, 17, 22
description, 22
life cycle, 20, pl. 4
cruzi, 14, 16, 18
description, 20
life cycle, 20, pl. 4
danilewskyi, 26
duttoni, 17
equinum, 14, 16, 22, 24
equiperdum, 14, 16, 22, 24
evansi, 16, 22
subgroup, 24
gambiense, 9
description, 23
life cycle, 23, pl. 5
granulosum, 26
lewisi, 14, 16, 17
lewisi-group, 17
description, 16
life cycle, 16, pl. 3
melophagium, 16, 17
metacyclic, 18
percae, 26
life cycle, 26, pl. 6
rhodesiense, 23, 24
vivax, 17, 22
vivax-group, 22
description, 22
life cycle, 22, pl. 5
Trypanosomal type, 12
Trypanosomatidae, 11
classification, 12
morphology, 12
Trypanosome, 12
of birds, reptiles, amphibians, and fish, 26
of mammals, 17
metacyclic, 16, 17, 18, 20, 22, 23, 24, 27
slender, 23
stumpy, 23
Tsetse fly, 16, 22, 24
Tubifex tubifex, 122, 262
Tumor, 124
Tunicate, 62
Tupinambus teguizin, 83
Turbotrix, 3
Turdus migratorius, 218
Turkey, 10, 12, 43, 44, 304, 324, 340, 348, 355, 372, 376, 400
Turtle, 83, 86, 87, 128, 140, 148, 149, 150, 189, 190, 212, 311, 312
loggerhead, 149
painted, 89, 190, 191, 212
snapping, 212
Typhlocoelium cymbium, 207

U

Udonella caligorum, 140
Ulcer
brain, 54
intestinal, 54
liver, 54
lung, 54
stomach, 375, 376
Umbra limi, 140
Umbridae, 171
Uncinaria, 315, 322
hamiltoni, 332
lucasi, 315, 322, 327
description, 328
life cycle, 328, pl. 112
stenocephala, 332
Underpants, 355
Unionidae, 148
Urban cycle, 408
Ureter, 196
Urinary bladder, 120, 146, 334, 406
Uterine bell, 298, 304, 308
Uvilifer
ambloplitis, 171
description, 171
life cycle, 171, pl. 54

V

Vacuoles, 132
contractile, 49, 129, 136
food, 129
pulsating, 132
Vagina
uterina, 352, 388
vera, 388
Vallonia, 164, 166
costata, pl. 52
Vallonidae, 164, 166, pl. 52
Vallonia, 166
Valvata, 151, 162, pl. 51
Valvatidae, 159, pl. 51
Valve, 119, 120
Vector, 14
Vegetative form, 11
Ventrides, 164
ligerus, pl. 52, 195
Vermicule, 104, 105, 106
Vermiform, 106
Veronicella, 162
Veronicellidae, 162
Veronicella, 162
Vertigo, 166
Virgula, 154
Virus, 10, 352
Vitamin B_{12}
Vitellovaginal duct, 146
Vitrina, 82
Viviparidae, 159, pl. 51, 162
Campeloma, 162
Viviparus, 162
Viviparus, 159, 162, pl. 51
Voles, 182, 184, 212, 214, 216
Vulvar flap, 346

W

Walking stick, 315
Walrus, 406, 410
Water striders, 14, pl. 2
Whale, 410
Whipworm, 398
Wildcat, 243
Willet, 216
Wolf, 272, 390, 405
Woman, 43

X-Y-Z

Xantusia vigilis, 134
Zalophus californicus, 332
Zapus hudsonius, 214
Zelleriella, 126
elliptica, 128
Zeugorchis eurinus, 229
Zinc sulphate, flotation, 48, 52
Zoarces viviparus, 366
Zoomastigina, 10
Zonitidae, 162, pl. 52, 164
Euconulus, 164
Hawaiia, 164
Mesomphix, 164
Paravitrea, 164
Retinella, 164
Striatura, 164
Ventridens, 164
Zonitoides, 162, 164
Zonitoides, 162, 164, 283, 385
arboreus, 195, 218
Zygocotyle lunata, 212
Zygocystidae, 60
Zygocystis, 62
Zygote, 53, 72, 84, 120, 129